The Good Food Guide 1990

CW00421307

# The Good Food Guide *1990*

Edited by Tom Jaine

Published by Consumers' Association
and Hodder & Stoughton

*Which? Books* are commissioned and researched by
The Association for Consumer Research and published by
Consumers' Association,
2 Marylebone Road, London NW1 4DX and
Hodder and Stoughton,
47 Bedford Square, London WC1B 3DP

Special thanks for this year's *Guide* to John Crawford Fraser for
the cover illustration, Mon Mohan for the cover design, Tim Higgins
for the typography. The maps are by Cartographic Services
(Cirencester) Ltd and GEOprojects (UK) Ltd

**British Library Cataloguing in Publication Data**
Jaine, Tom
   The good food guide
   1990
I. Restaurants, lunch rooms, etc.–
   Great Britain – Directories
   I. Title      II. Consumers' Association
   647'.9541'05      TX 10.G7
ISBN 0-340-51141-9

Photoset in Linotron Meridien Medium
by Tradespools Ltd, Frome, Somerset
Printed and bound in The Netherlands
by Rotatie Boekendruk B.V., Krommenie

# Contents

# An appeal to readers

*The Good Food Guide* survives on a diet of reports sent to it by its readers: good meals, bad meals; joy and disaster; discoveries of new cooks and new places; reaffirmation of the old and established.

Every letter counts, without them we starve. The post is free, we acknowledge all communications. Please think of writing to us after any meal out. Just tear off a report form at the back of this book, or write a letter. In either event it will cost you nothing but time; and it will earn you our gratitude. Please write to The Editor, *The Good Food Guide*, FREEPOST, 2 Marylebone Road, London NW1 1YN.

## A new service to keep readers up to date

From December 1989 *The Good Food Guide* will offer a recorded telephone message giving details of restaurant sales, closures, chef changes and so on, since this edition was published. Telephone 01-224 4597 (from 6 May 1990, 071-224 4597) to hear the latest information. All letters to the *Guide* will also be acknowledged with an account of significant changes to *Guide* entries.

## *The Vegetarian Good Food Guide*

We plan to publish this new guide, edited by Annabel Whittet, in spring 1990. Our aim is to list restaurants, hotels, cafés and pubs where vegetarians are assured of a main course that is more than just an omelette or a salad. Many entries will be purely vegetarian eating places, but equally, many will not. Please send reports to *The Vegetarian Good Food Guide*, FREEPOST, 2 Marylebone Road, London NW1 1YN.

# Introduction

Post arrives at *The Good Food Guide* four times a day. I had not realised this when I accepted the job of editing the *Guide*, despite appreciating that it would be my task to read all reports and letters from readers. Current input is running at some 10,000 items per year. To one who for years has thrust brown envelopes to the bottom of an ever-increasing pile, the ceaseless waves of correspondence came as a shock. So began my continuing course in letter reading. What could not fail to impress a new editor is how eager readers are to find good food, how keen to report on pleasure, surprise and delight, or to relay accounts of dismay and disillusionment. Discovering this wealth of feedback has indeed been a major delight of my first months of editing. So much is going on, so much needs to be broadcast to the world beyond. Individuals, couples, small firms, even large corporations are cooking and serving good food in Britain today. While the *Guide* is always weighing up, testing and questioning, it is at heart a celebration of enterprise, a gathering of much that is good about a simple, and not so insignificant, corner of British life.

Since taking up the editorship I have, however, been struck by how few outsiders understand how the *Guide* operates. Long-standing readers will forgive me if I spell out afresh how we work, for the system is at the heart of what we hope to achieve. Everyone who buys this *Guide* becomes, automatically, a member of the Good Food Club, an army of people concerned about what and how they eat. A computer database holds a mass of information derived from the letters and reports sent in annually by this army, many referring to several different meals and different restaurants. The *Guide*'s activities depend on this postbag. New enterprises need to be investigated, old ones revisited as chefs change or partnerships dissolve. Also, any variation in a restaurant's standards becomes apparent as reports accumulate. Checking on restaurants is done in part by the editor and editorial team, but mostly by inspectors of the Good Food Club, volunteers of long service and like minds. They eat at our instigation and we pay their expenses. A restaurant first appears in the *Guide* as a result of a positive inspection; continued presence in the book will activate periodic reinspection – as indeed would a flurry of mixed reports. All inspectors' visits are made anonymously. Not every restaurant appearing in the Guide is inspected formally every year, but no restaurant continues to appear unless there has been positive feedback from members or inspectors eating at their own expense. This is perhaps the most complete reporting system of any publication in this field. It is remarkably sensitive to nuance and variation. What is more, it is independent of *any* sponsorship and *any* business interest. The only corner it fights is yours – the consumer's.

## Frustrating the customer

It has to be said that the *Guide*, as a pointer to good eating experiences, charts the exceptions. It could be argued that, as a nation, the British have failed to develop the right means for delivering good food to customers, when the customers want it. I have in front of me a letter from an inspector who was looking for something to eat in Devon on a Sunday afternoon in June:

*First port of call was A. They proved to cater almost exclusively for large parties (were closed during most of the week to recover) and were fully booked for the next two months. So on to B where there was a pub open for Sunday dinner. When I looked, there was no menu displayed on the outside so I knocked on the door to ask for one. They laughed sarcastically and provided a list along the lines of prawn cocktail, grilled steak and blackberry pie.*

*I felt sure at least of a meal in the neighbouring town because the Guide had said a place there was open seven days a week. I drove there on spec. Nothing doing, they had had a large party the evening before and 'were flat out on their backs'. So, flat out behind the steering wheel, to C, the temperature now soaring to 27 degrees C. This place, although a pub, only cooked meals five days a week and, when they did, it was a no-choice-until-the-sweet-stage six-course table d'hôte – whatever the weather. The other pub in the village had a notice stating they were open for lunch and dinner Tuesday to Sunday. At 6.50, they neither answered the telephone nor showed any sign of life on the other side of windows or door.*

*It was a long way to the one hotel I knew to offer proper food but the relief at knowing I would not have to subsist on mineral water and cherry tomatoes was very great as I turned into the drive. I ended up leaving an idiotically large tip.*

Why are the possibilities for eating good food so limited? It seems an idiocy, when there have always been several types of catering outlet in the UK: cafés, pubs, restaurants, hotels, not to mention the sub-groups of brasseries, wine bars, milk- and coffee-bars and fast-food outlets. All these are not only more discrete than in other countries, having fewer points of contact and comparison, they are also more exclusive: children cannot go into a great number of pubs; men not wearing ties cannot enter many restaurants. Each outlet, too, has its own unwritten rules about payment, hours, holidays and what-have-you. There is in truth an apparent lack of a 'restaurant culture' in large parts of Britain: the exceptions of central London and, for example, the 'café society' of Glasgow only point up, as you reach the suburbs of Teddington or Bearsden, its widespread absence. Restaurant societies – one thinks of Italy or France – thrive in great cities with high technology, or in countries with fine weather. It is not easy to promenade on a Sunday morning in the teeth of a force 10 gale, as sleet drifts across the horizon. The English, particularly, have always loved enclosure and prefer eating and drinking to be done in private, behind net curtains or frosted glass. And today much of it is done in stuffy surroundings, commencing between 7.30 and 8.30pm and costing at least £30 a head. This, it must be admitted, may be partly the fault of customers: there's small point in a restaurant opening up for no one, and considerable difficulties in offering a cheap menu, or a facility for cheapness, especially as so many customers perceive low cost as equalling low quality.

What is frustrating for all those people who genuinely want to eat out – from necessity, not just for joy – is that the places that are open all day, every day, cook by and large such diabolical food. The exceptions are the gamut of oriental restaurants. Sometimes it seems that, almost unaided, they keep British dining out alive. However, just as one does not normally want fish and chips three times a week, an undiluted diet of Indian or Chinese cooking may begin to pall.

## The possibilities of the pub

There is, of course, one catering resource in existence that, suitably managed, could convert us to fun-loving, socially minded caters out: the pub. As alcohol ceased to be consumed as part of the normal round of eating, so the pub – originally the tavern rather than the inn – was left as a one-armed provider, and one that pandered to a vice, in the eyes of many. It took many years for publicans to wake up to the possibilities of serving food. It has taken them still longer to realise the potential of *good* food. While our sister publication *The Good Pub Guide* this year lists some three thousand pubs where customers need not be afraid to eat, that still accounts for only one pub in 20. What happens in the other 19? There is little point in waxing too eloquent against their spongiform sandwiches, slimy sausages and woven shepherd's pies, served merrily and with clear conscience. They, like so many cafés, fast-food outlets, motorway service stations and chain hotels, are devoted to poor food because: a) they think their customers like it; and b) many of their customers do like it. The notion that each side could be weaned from its prejudice does not occur. Yet as social habits change, and the licensing laws unbend, so the capacity for pubs to expand into full provisioning is growing. Before the licensed trade relaxes, however, thinking itself well on the way to successfully fulfilling a new role, it should consider some aggravating shortcomings. For one, surroundings. Why is 'pub' so often synonymous with counterfeit nostalgia, a refusal to have tables of normal height, dreadful music, gaming machines and an urge to enclose the drinker/customer in some lurid womb of the brewer's imagination? For a second, standards. Good wine, good beer, fresh orange juice, fresh food and decent coffee are still rare finds. Third, company. Many pubs still do not allow, want, or would be suitable for the presence of children. Habits of mind and constraints of law need to be loosened and proper thought given to the reabsorption of pubs into our social fabric. All reports sent to the *Guide* on pubs showing the way with good food are most welcome.

## A contract with the consumer

Let us not forget that a meal in a restaurant is a contract between customer and provider. Is the contract, as generally understood, fair? One aspect of the contract is that of admission. Not often does one find a notice on the lawn of a country-house hotel reading 'Football coaches by arrangement only'. The owners reason that ambience and price will put off the soccer fans. Nor are there notices stating 'Ties only' or 'Children not admitted'. Perhaps the restaurateurs reckon that such notices would do nothing for their image. A parent, indeed, might biff them on the nose. Although it goes against the grain to seem to support such restaurateurs, the *Guide* does give details of any limitations on age or dress in the factual details under each restaurant entry, for information. Heartening this year, however, is the number of restaurants that have abandoned their insistence on jackets and ties – though this should not be read as an incitement to walk in wearing singlet and shorts. Why anyone should think a tieless drunk more dangerous than a besuited one – and there are plenty of those – is difficult to grasp, save that in their strange way restaurants sometimes preserve patterns of behaviour much older than, for instance, their technology for accepting payment. In this small matter of clothing, as in the welcome extended to children, success is reserved for those proprietors who radiate calm and hospitality, who do much better than the irritable and unwelcoming. That children of any age are excluded, saved from sights that may deprave them (does this include their parents eating and drinking?), is an unnatural feature of British society that may be likened to the most pernicious forms of discrimination. Children, and their parents, can be a terrible pain and it behoves a restaurant's staff and owner to discipline them when necessary – but never to exclude them on principle.

## Service snatch

Another aspect of the customer/restaurant contract is that of payment.
It is fair to agree that the one time the proprietor of a restaurant has
absolute rights (save over bad behaviour) is when time comes to
settle the bill. If he or she wants payment in US dollars, so be it, so
long as the customer is told first. But what a proprietor should not do
is post a price on a menu and then add a percentage surcharge – even
having given a warning that it will be levied. There are a very few
restaurants whose published prices still exclude VAT. This is close to
sharp practice and certainly unhelpful. The most frequent annoyance
is the dreaded service charge. For some years the *Guide*, and even more
its sister publication, *The Good Hotel Guide*, has pointed out the
illogicalities surrounding tips, service charge, call it what you will.
What's more, the degree to which Britain is now out of step with
countries on the mainland of Europe makes the matter more
worrisome, not to say demeaning, for the customer.

In 1989 the Consumer Protection Act recommended a code of
practice for the expression of non-optional service charges on menus.
It says that they should be included in all prices displayed, 'wherever
practicable'. The so-called 'optional' percentage charge is
discouraged. There are two flaws in these provisions. On the one
hand they do not concentrate on the single recommendation that
prices be wholly inclusive. In that they allow the notional existence
of a service addition, the original intention – to rationalise the service
charge out of separate existence – is lost. The second is that the
recommendations do not have the force of law. In consequence, many
restaurants have ignored them completely and will continue to do so.
In the light of recognition by trade and government that all is not well
in the land of service charges and tipping, what should we, as
consumers, do?

The first step is to define the meanings of 'service charge', 'tips' and
'gratuities'. Some outrageous establishments claim that the service
charge is distinct from the tip. In other words, the first is a surcharge
levied to pay for the service – to pay the wages – and the second is a
freewill offering direct to the staff. This is a scandalous hijacking of a
substantial amount of money that rightfully belongs to the staff and a
blatant ploy for increasing the bill. In short, we have been gulled by
rapacious gangsters. Think back even 15 years. There was no 'service
charge'. You might tip, and the head waiter might keep most of it, but
no surcharge was levied by the management. Along came the 10 per
cent addition. Its intention was to help the customer to tip fairly, to
remove doubt. It was also a means of ensuring that everyone *did* leave
a tip. It was, no bones about it, a *substitute* for the tip. Then, little by
little, as the Inland Revenue has insisted it be shown on the tax

returns and as proprietors became loath to give up all that lovely money, it has been converted (not everywhere, but in too many places for comfort) into a payment towards service. In a flash, another 10 per cent was added to the restaurant's revenue with no extra expenditure incurred (nor service rendered). The transformation of 'tip' into 'service' complete, consumers started to worry all over again about tipping. 'Should we leave a bit extra?' they would whisper. And hundreds of restaurants began leaving open the bottom line of the credit card slip – soliciting for a tip even though the phrase 'service included' appeared on the bill.

The latest government intervention will have its repercussions. Owners will see that the service charge is out of favour and delete all reference to it. On an increasing number of menus, and of course on bills, the message 'Gratuities are at the discretion of the customer' or 'Service not included' is rammed home – rubber stamps are bought to make it even clearer. The unsuspecting might see this as helpful elucidation. The cynic might think it a heavy-handed hint. From the point of view of management, it is the only answer. 'The staff have to be paid, the wages must be kept low, so let's ask the customer to help,' runs the argument.

I do not wish to outlaw tipping. If you, the customer, wants to distribute money in free gift, then go ahead. The government recommendation, however, could have been expressed more forcefully and to greater effect. The *Guide* suggestion would have been as follows: *Restaurants should impose no percentage surcharges, for any reason. The prices displayed on their menus should be net. All bills and menus should display, for the next five years at least, and in type at least as prominent as other information, the message that all prices are inclusive and no further payment is necessary. No bill or menu should display any other information about tipping. Management should not collude with staff in soliciting tips.* In five years that might change restaurant habits and staff wages might increase to more realistic levels. No doubt this would give cause for another rise in the cost of eating, but the justification would be flimsier than owners would make out. On the one hand, there are many owners who already operate such policies, bearing the apparent financial loss themselves, and those restaurants appearing in the *Guide* who have told us of it, are identified. On the other hand, just remember that original 10 per cent surcharge swallowed before our very eyes.

## Moderation matters

Another clause in the customer/restaurateur contract is that cooks should not kill us, whether by kindness, misjudgement or bad practice. The bad practice we must leave to others, particularly the environmental health departments. Central government has a part in this issue, witness the salmonella, listeria and botulism scandals, but here is not a good forum for their discussion, save to observe that food is not a good area in which to practise *laissez-faire*. As the public becomes more and more reliant on foodstuffs, in and out of restaurants, that have undergone storage, processing or mutation by human agency, so all those stages must be stringently controlled. *The Good Food Guide* can urge the consumption of food that is freshest and has been least tampered with – much the most likely to be healthy and whole – and it can promote those cooks who appear to treat their raw materials most sympathetically. It can, however, enforce no general rules. In like fashion, it cannot take on the function of health officer and courts of law. It cannot inspect kitchens or condemn them, though it should react to official condemnation, when proven.

Where the *Guide* can act usefully, however, is in the encouragement of opinion. There is a feature at the end of this year's edition on the serious difficulties of eating healthily in restaurants. Chefs do not give enough thought to this. Most do not eat their own meals. They often eat very little, or enjoy simple, non-messed-about food. It does not strike the majority of them that there is a dissonance here. Yet if there arises a disjunction between cooking and nourishment, if cooking becomes an art form rather than a means of providing a reasonable diet for life, then surely something is wrong. The stock retort that customers demand grotesque blow-outs of outrageous mountains of fats and proteins is dodging the issue. There is no need for excess. At the same time, one diner's sufficiency may be another's death warrant, and menus should attempt – and staff should know how to suggest – a proper modulation of quantity and content.

## Smoke signals

A constant topic in the *Guide* postbag is smoking. The campaigning work against smoking in restaurants by previous *Guide* editor Christopher Driver did not always fall on receptive ears. It is timely, therefore, to restate the position. Most people, a majority of adults, do not smoke. The slight majority becomes a large one if the profile is restricted to likely customers of restaurants in the *Guide*. It is surprising that, given the swell of feeling against smoking, restaurant areas are still designated 'non-smoking'. The opposite should obtain. In Victorian days, before smoking cigarettes became either universal or smart, smoking was restricted to billiard room, conservatory or verandah. Surtees' Facey Romford may have puffed the odd cigar in his bedroom, but he was careful to smoke it up the chimney.

Today, smoking is unacceptable in a number of public places, among them theatres, some cinemas and shops, some aeroplanes, tube trains, coaches and many taxi cabs. Many restaurants have also seen the light and we urge others to follow suit. It is, of course, quite simple for a hotel or country house with bags of space to introduce a no-smoking policy in the dining-room: those who wish can retreat to a lounge and puff away. It is not so easy for the small, town-centre restaurant. There are more compromises open to such places than often they will admit. Owners could, for instance, arrange tables further apart and instal air-conditioning or extraction (not just a fan in the window). Then they could consider altering the geometry of the place, to create relatively pollution-free zones; there's little point placing a non-smoking table next to a smoker. Another compromise is that of time: smoking could be – and in some *Guide* restaurants is – forbidden before a certain point, say 2pm at lunch and 10pm at dinner. Cigars and pipes generate too great and too pungent a smoke to be permitted at meals: banning them from dining-rooms is the only answer.

## The new marking system

When the *Guide* was first written by Raymond Postgate in 1951, its object was simple: to tell people of places where a passable meal could be obtained. As time passed so the message took on more levels: not only identification but also some sort of assessment was desirable; more facts were supplied, too, as readers became more curious. Drew Smith, editor of the editions from 1983 to 1989, had the courage to add a figure to his text assessment, marking each restaurant out of 20, thus providing rapid guidance and a national league table. Such marking systems are always open to criticism but they are none the less useful. We have continued this principle, although in simplified form.

Each entry is given a mark out of five for the standard of its cooking, without reference to elegance, service or even ambience. Reducing the total from 20 to five intentionally broadens the bounds of each mark. Attempting too fine a judgement, encouraging too much of a talent contest is neither helpful to the reader nor unfailingly accurate. Performances vary and our perception of them is highly subjective. We reckon that the reader needs straightforward guidance that is not based too much on nit-picking and reading of the entrails. This new marking system affords it. Its principles are clearly laid out on the inside front cover and at intervals throughout the text.

## Price indications

Prices in annual publications are vexatious things. There is no denying their usefulness, but restaurants, and inflation, have an unnerving habit of increasing charges soon after the *Guide* arrives in the shops. No fault can be laid at anyone's door, yet every year readers complain that the prices we give are often no longer applicable and that they have had to pay substantially more in *Guide* restaurants than they expected. This year, therefore, in quoting prices for three-course meals at the top of each entry (by the word 'Cost'), *we have put a more pessimistic complexion on the upper price by inflating it by 20 per cent*. This, we trust, will soften the financial blow, accommodating inflation during the life of the *Guide* and also reflecting the price of a meal taken without constant attention to the likely size of the bill. The prices quoted in smaller print below the text remain, as in previous editions, strict computer calculations of an average three-course meal, the price in brackets reflecting an average meal with coffee, service and half a bottle of house wine per person. See also 'How to use this *Guide*'.

The point of putting the mark for cooking next to a financial notation is to help readers make their own assessment of whether the place is worth going to. A luxury hotel charging £100 for dinner for two, where we mark the cooking only 1 out of 5, i.e. competent, is evidently a poor bargain. You may wish to pay for it none the less; we hope the text will help you make that judgement.

## Awards for wine

An area of undoubted improvement in restaurants over the last five or so years is the standard of wine, as in retail shops (though not yet to any major degree in pubs). Not only has wine-making extended into new territories, but it has got better in areas once good for only the meanest table wine. It may be argued that in classic regions it has not improved so much as changed, not necessarily for the better. But new techniques of viticulture and vinification have evened out the effects of bad seasons, thus allowing us fair drinking in years that once would have yielded hard, depressing wines.

Simultaneously, there has been an explosion of wine retailing in the British Isles. Never has so much been available at once. Restaurants have no business running uninteresting lists; a little curiosity and a small effort are all that is required. The general standard has improved so much that we have reconsidered the *Guide*'s bottle award for outstanding wine cellars, and reverting to a two-tiered notation now seems useful – if only to preserve the value of the chief prize. The glass symbol therefore signifies a good list, a list well above the ordinary, worth travelling for if that sort of thing takes your fancy. The prices should be fair, the range may not be. It could be awarded to a place that stocked only Bulgarian wines, or bottles from New Zealand. Such specialisation may reduce overall stature, but the collection can still be special. The glass may also be awarded to what may be called 'intelligent' lists, even though short. Length is never a virtue in itself, although for a restaurant attempting to build a truly great list it is difficult to avoid. But a short list, where each wine is a winner, where each part balances another, can be a work of art and certainly the product of much thought. There has been a welcome growth in the number of restaurants achieving this, seemingly in direct proportion to the rise in the number of able merchants at the end of a telephone line. Such lists are often 'instant'; thought, not capital, is the commodity expended. The wines are often young, the cellar affording storage for no more than a few months, but they repay investigation.

The bottle symbol is reserved for the truly outstanding wine lists. Often these are of great length, though the rule is made to be broken. Certainly the vintages offered need to be good ones; a cellarful of 1963 clarets will delight nobody. And the properties or growers selected will alter, over time, in accordance with the fortunes of each region. Change is as endemic to Bordeaux as it is to California or Washington State. The 1855 classification may seem cast in stone but châteaux decline, improve, change hands and more. The cycle is a slow one but wine lists can still reflect the ups and downs. A great list will usually have good territorial spread. It is no longer acceptable to dismiss the New World, Italy or Spain as beyond the pale. They provide good wine, for one, and they offer value. Once more, such rules are made to be broken, for the true enthusiast – and enthusiast a bottle winner may be – will be a person of strong opinions, perhaps refusing to stray outside a chosen patch.

Another quality of a great list, however highly priced or marked-up, is that it makes an effort to supply the bottom price brackets as imaginatively as the upper. Mark-ups are indeed a contentious matter. It is very easy to observe a bottle of Muscadet at £3 in the supermarket and at £7 in the restaurant and bear some grudge at profiteering against the latter. Easy, but not wholly fair. The restaurant will usually have some idea how much gross revenue it must earn from each customer. It is then at liberty to apportion this charge in whatever manner it chooses: half on food, half on wine, for instance. This is merely a statement of reality. It is, however, unfortunate that one section of diners may be hit harder than another. Why, for instance, should wine drinkers subsidise those who consume only mineral water? Why should those who drink Ch. Latour pay so much more over the odds (absolutely, if not proportionately) than the buyer of Sancerre? A restaurant should operate fairly. Customers are therefore entitled to object to excessive mark-ups on wine and high percentage mark-ups on good wine. It is not so much that it is robbery, more that the proprietor should manage the restaurant's affairs more efficiently and equitably. Some wine awards may therefore be affected by consideration of price, while cookery marks are not. Wine assessments and comment, also 'What to drink in 1990', have been undertaken with the help and guidance of Aileen Hall, joint editor of *Which? Wine Monthly*.

## Routing the bogus guides

In last year's *Guide* we published a lengthy warning on the subject of bogus 'good food guide' promoters and certificate pedlars who were busily taking money from unsuspecting restaurateurs for worthless bits of paper. We're pleased to say that all the operations using names similar to ours have now ceased, as a result of proceedings Consumers' Association has brought or threatened against them. However, it is proving exceedingly difficult to weed out the crop of certificates they left behind them in the windows and on the walls of restaurants the length and breadth of the country. Those who display such certificates are usually in contempt of court. The claims they make are false and deceptive and it is in everyone's interests that they be eradicated. Scattered among the 'fillers' at the foot of the pages of entries you will find the names of the offending 'guides': please tell us if you see on display a certificate from one of them so that we can take the appropriate action.

## And finally ...

*The Good Food Guide* had three distinguished editors before I succeeded Drew Smith at the onset of 1989. Each was a writer or journalist. I have been a writer a relatively short while but have spent much of my life involved, through family or profession, in restaurants. Some might suggest that I cannot speak wholeheartedly for the customer, that my views will be coloured by sympathy for the poor cook, the roguish waiter or the downtrodden waitress. Yes and no. The sympathy certainly exists, but at sufficient distance to be controllable. Also, it may not always be misplaced. It may in any case usefully be harnessed to the interests of the diner-out. Pity the poor cook, yes; but pour vitriol on those who do the trade a discredit. I have no financial interest in any restaurant. Those that I used to own in partnership, I no longer own. I have taken part in no other ones. Friendships, it's true, I have. But not, I hope, so fond that they affect my ability to discern quality or imperfection. Because I was a partner of the Carved Angel in Dartmouth, all of the Dartmouth entries have been written by others.

May this *Guide* lead you to good experiences. Do write and tell us.

*Tom Jaine*

# The top-rated restaurants

## Mark 5 for cooking

### London
L'Arlequin, SW8
Chez Nico, W1
Le Gavroche, W1
Tante Claire, SW3

### England
Le Manoir aux Quat'Saisons,
    Great Milton
L'Ortolan, Shinfield

### Scotland
Peat Inn, Peat Inn

## Mark 4 for cooking

### London
Alastair Little, W1
Bibendum, SW3
Capital Hotel, SW3
Clarke's, W8
Connaught, W1
Four Seasons, Inn on the Park, W1
Harvey's, SW17
Oak Room, Meridien Piccadilly
    Hotel, W1
Sutherlands, W1
Turner's, SW3

### England
Adlard's, Norwich
Box Tree, Ilkley
Carved Angel, Dartmouth
Castle Hotel, Taunton
Chez Nous, Plymouth
Croque-en-Bouche, Malvern Wells
Gidleigh Park, Chagford
Gravetye Manor, East Grinstead
Hambleton Hall, Hambleton
Miller Howe, Windermere
Morels, Haslemere
Oakes, Stroud
Old Vicarage, Ridgeway
Poussin, Brockenhurst
Seafood Restaurant, Padstow
Waterside Inn, Bray
White Moss House, Grasmere
Whites, Cricklade
Winteringham Fields,
    Winteringham

### Scotland
Altnaharrie Inn, Ullapool
Cromlix House, Kinbuck
Inverlochy Castle, Fort William
Murrayshall Hotel, Scone
The Oaks, Craigendarroch Hotel
    and Country Club, Ballater
La Potinière, Gullane

### Wales
Walnut Tree Inn, Llandewi Skirrid
Plas Bodegroes, Pwllheli

# Restaurants with outstanding wine cellars
## marked in the text with a ▮

**London**

Capital Hotel, SW3
Gilbert's, SW7
Mijanou, SW1
Oak Room, Le Meridien Piccadilly
  Hotel, W1
Sutherlands, W1

**England**

Adlard's, Norwich
Bell, Aston Clinton
Brookdale House, North Huish
Carved Angel, Dartmouth
Castle Hotel, Taunton
Chedington Court, Chedington
Corse Lawn House Hotel, Corse
  Lawn
Croque-en-Bouche, Malvern Wells
Crown, Southwold
Dundas Arms, Kintbury
Epworth Tap, Epworth
Fountain House, East Bergholt
French Partridge, Horton
George, Stamford
Gidleigh Park, Chagford
Gravetye Manor, East Grinstead
Hambleton Hall, Hambleton
Harvey's Cathedral Restaurant/
  Troffs, Lincoln
Hintlesham Hall, Hintlesham
Hope End, Ledbury

Kenwards, Lewes
Lake Isle, Uppingham
Old Manor House, Romsey
Old Vicarage, Ridgeway
Pebbles, Aylesbury
Porthole Eating House, Bowness-
  on-Windermere
Sir Charles Napier Inn, Chinnor
Starr, Great Dunmow
Le Talbooth, Dedham
The Manor, Chadlington
Thornbury Castle, Thornbury
The Three Lions, Stuckton
Village Restaurant, Ramsbottom
White Moss House, Grasmere

**Scotland**

Airds Hotel, Port Appin
Champany at the Horseshoe Inn,
  Eddleston
Champany Inn, Linlithgow
Knipoch Hotel, Oban
Peat Inn, Peat Inn
La Potinière, Gullane
Summer Isles Hotel, Achiltibuie
Ubiquitous Chip, Glasgow

**Wales**

Meadowsweet Hotel, Llanrwst
Walnut Tree Inn, Llandewi Skirrid

Please see Introduction for a full explanation of the criteria for awarding
the bottle symbol.

# County restaurants of the year

Our indulgence. The restaurants listed below are not invariably the best (highest rated) in their respective counties, but they are the ones that have caught the eye this year, engendered most excitement, or generally seemed laudable enterprises. Not all counties have an award winner.

**England**
**Avon** Markwick & Hunt, Bristol
**Bedfordshire** Paris House, Woburn
**Berkshire** L'Ortolan, Shinfield
**Buckinghamshire** Hartwell House, Aylesbury
**Cambridgeshire** Old Fire Engine House, Ely
**Cheshire** Abbey Green, Chester
**Cornwall** Long's, Blackwater
**Cumbria** Uplands, Cartmel
**Derbyshire** Old Vicarage, Ridgeway
**Devon** Whitechapel Manor, South Molton
**Dorset** Stock Hill House, Gillingham
**East Sussex** Kenwards, Lewes
**Essex** Warehouse Brasserie, Colchester
**Gloucestershire** Redmond's at the Malvern View, Cleeve Hill
**Greater Manchester** Village Restaurant, Ramsbottom
**Hampshire** Provence, Lymington
**Hereford & Worcester** Croque-en-Bouche, Malvern Wells
**Humberside** Winteringham Fields, Winteringham
**Kent** Thackeray's House, Tunbridge Wells

**Lancashire** River House, Thornton-le-Fylde
**Leicestershire** Hambleton Hall, Hambleton
**Lincolnshire** Wig & Mitre, Lincoln
**Norfolk** Adlard's, Norwich
**North Yorkshire** Floodlite Restaurant, Masham
**Northamptonshire** Vine House, Paulerspury
**Northumberland** John Blackmore's, Alnwick
**Nottinghamshire** Perkins Bar Bistro, Plumtree
**Oxfordshire** Stonor Arms, Stonor
**Shropshire** Park Cottage, Hopton Castle
**Somerset** White House Hotel, Williton
**Suffolk** Mr Underhill's, Stonham
**Surrey** Chez Max, Richmond
**Tyne & Wear** 21 Queen Street, Newcastle upon Tyne
**Warwickshire** Mallory Court, Bishop's Tachbrook
**West Midlands** New Hall, Sutton Coldfield
**West Sussex** Jeremy's at the King's Head, Cuckfield
**West Yorkshire** Restaurant 19, Belvedere Hotel, Bradford
**Wiltshire** Whites, Cricklade

## Scotland

**Borders** Champany at the
  Horseshoe Inn, Eddleston
**Central** Cromlix House,
  Kinbuck
**Dumfries & Galloway**
  Knockinaam Lodge,
  Portpatrick
**Fife** Cellar, Anstruther
**Grampian** The Oaks,
  Craigendarroch Hotel and
  Country Club, Ballater
**Highland** The Cross, Kingussie
**Lothian** Pierre Victoire,
  Edinburgh
**Strathclyde** Airds Hotel, Port
  Appin
**Tayside** Atkins at Farleyer
  House, Aberfeldy

## Wales

**Clwyd** Tyddyn Llan, Llandrillo
**Dyfed** Ann FitzGerald's
  Farmhouse Kitchen, Mathry
**Gwent** Walnut Tree Inn,
  Llandewi Skirrid
**Gwynedd** Cemlyn, Harlech
**South Glamorgan** Armless
  Dragon, Cardiff
**West Glamorgan** Fairyhill,
  Reynoldston

# How to use this *Guide*

All the entries in this year's *Guide* have been rewritten between April and August. The information on which they are based is from reports sent in by readers over the last year and confirmed by anonymous inspection. No entry is based on a single nomination. In every case readers and inspectors have been prepared to endorse the quality of the cooking, the dining-room and the value for money.

This year there are two changes to the way entries are presented. A new rating system grades restaurants, on the basis of their cooking only, from 1 to 5. This takes no account of elegance, ambience, service or value. The marks take into account the perception of the *Guide* and its reporters, and signify the following:

1 **Competent cooking**  Restaurants that achieve a satisfactory standard, endorsed by readers as worthy of the *Guide*.

2 **Good cooking**  Restaurants that produce good food in most departments, though some inconsistencies may have been noted. They please most readers much of the time.

3 **Very good cooking**  The kitchen achieves consistent quality, rarely disappointing in any department. Seldom faulted by *Guide* reporters.

4 **Excellent cooking**  Restaurants with a high level of ambition and achievement. Generally, they delight.

5 **The best**  These may excite debate, not as to whether the cooking is good, but whether it is better than their peers'.

We have also reviewed the prices given above and below entries, in the light of persistent comment from readers that they are too low and that it is very hard to eat a three-course meal for the amount the *Guide* says.

The *Guide* office is reliant on proprietors for price information. Each year owners are asked to mark on a questionnaire the cost, for autumn of that year, of any set meals, and also the lowest and highest à la carte prices for each course. Our computer then adds the quoted price for coffee, service, and half a bottle of house wine per head. For à la carte prices it calculates the strict average cost. In practice, however, most people do not eat an 'average' meal, but may have drinks before the meal, drink a more expensive wine, and choose at least some top-flight dishes. The result can be a bill much higher than expected. Also, prices are likely to rise during the currency of the *Guide*.

To try and satisfy everyone, the *Guide* continues, in the prices below the entry, to give the average cost of three-course meals as calculated by computer and double-checked. However, above the entry, the cost quoted gives the lowest such price, and the highest such price *inflated by 20 per cent* to bring some realism to bear on the likely upper limit. Random checks against actual bills received in the office as we go to press have confirmed that we are not overstating the cost.

Last year's County Round-ups, listing additional eating places that might prove useful for the reader to know about, were popular and this year are extended. They now appear together, after the main entries. All feedback is most welcome.

# How to read a *Guide* entry

---

CANTERBURY Kent **1**                                                                 map 3 **2**

## ▲ *Mary's Kitchen* **3** ▮   ♟ **4**

16 Elwood Avenue, Canterbury CT41 4RX **5**
CANTERBURY (0227) 7770666 **6**                                              COOKING  2 **8**
behind Scala Cinema **7**                                                        COST  £19–£24 **9**

(main text) **10**          CELLARMAN'S CHOICE  **11**

CHEF: Mary Smith    PROPRIETORS: Mary and David Smith **12**
OPEN: Mon to Sat **13**
CLOSED: Aug **14**
MEALS: 12 to 2, 7 to 9 **15**
PRICES: £13 (£19), Set D £15 (£20), Snacks from £1.50. **16**  Service 10% **17**
CARDS: Access, Amex, Diners, Visa **18**
SEATS: 72. 4 tables outside. Private parties: 26 main room, 10 private room. **19**  Car-park, 40 places. Vegetarian meals. **20**  Children's helpings. No children under 10. **21**  Jacket and tie preferred. **22**  No-smoking area. **23**  Wheelchair access (2 steps; also WC). **24**  Music. **25**  One sitting **26**
ACCOMMODATION: 14 rooms, all with bath/shower. B&B £20 to £40. **27**  No pets. **28**  Afternoon teas. **29**  Garden. Swimming-pool. Tennis [GHG] **30**

---

1  The town and county (in the London section, restaurants are listed alphabetically by name rather than geographically).

2  The map number. The maps are at the end of the *Guide*.

3  The name of the restaurant. ▲ by the name denotes that it offers accommodation too.

**4**  ♟ denotes a wine list that is good, well above the ordinary. The symbol ▐ indicates a truly outstanding wine list.

**5**  The restaurant's address, with post code whenever possible.

**6**  The restaurant's telephone number, including its STD code.

**7**  Any special directions in case the restaurant is difficult to find.

**8**  The *Guide*'s mark, out of five, for cooking quality, ranging from 1 for competent cooking to 5 for the best. See page 24 or the inside of the front cover for a full explanation.

**9**  This is the price range for three-course meals, based on our computer's calculation of an average three-course meal, including coffee, wine and service, according to prices provided by the proprietor. The top figure, however, has been inflated by 20 per cent to reflect (i) that many readers do not eat an 'average' meal and are therefore shocked when, with extra drinks and some top-range dishes, the bill rises well beyond the average price, and (ii) likely price rises that will come into play during the life of the *Guide*.

**10**  The text is based on reports sent in by readers during the last *Guide* year, confirmed by commissioned, anonymous inspections.

**11**  Most entries conclude with a CELLARMAN'S CHOICE . This is a wine, usually more expensive than the house wine, that the restaurateur assures us will be in stock during 1990, and recommends as suitable for the kind of food served, if you do not want to order the house wine.

**12**  The names of the chef and the owner, so that any change in management will be instantly detectable.

**13**  The days of the week the restaurant is open.

**14**  Annual closures.

**15**  The times of first and last orders for meals. It is always advisable to book before going to a restaurant. If you book and then cannot go, please remember to phone the restaurant to cancel.

**16**  These are average prices for three-course meals, giving the à la carte price and variations for set lunch (L) and dinner (D) where applicable. The initial price represents the prices on the main menu; the second price, in brackets, is the real cost when the extras of house wine, coffee and service (at 10% unless otherwise specified) have been added.

**17**  This indicates that a fixed service charge will be added to the bill. Where service is included in the menu prices this is specified. When service is not mentioned, it is at the discretion of the customer.

**18**  The credit cards accepted by the restaurant.

**19**  Not all restaurants will take private parties. The maximum number of people in a party is given.

**20** Many restaurants claim to cater for vegetarians but do not include suitable dishes on their menus as a matter of course. It is always advisable to explain, when booking, if you do not eat meat.

**21** Some restaurants and hotels are not keen on children. Where it says children welcome or children's helpings, this indicates that they don't mind. Any limitations on age are specified.

**22** Jackets and ties are compulsory in very few restaurants and this is specified; otherwise it means the proprietor prefers smart dress.

**23** Any no-smoking arrangements as given to us by the restaurants.

**24** Wheelchair access means that the proprietor has confirmed that the entrance is 33 inches wide and passages four feet across. Where there are steps it will say so. If it says 'also WC', then the owner has told us that the toilet facilities are suitable for disabled people. The *Guide* relies on proprietors giving accurate information on wheelchair access. If you find the details in the *Guide* are inaccurate, please tell us.

**25** If a restaurant plays music, this is specified.

**26** The restaurant serves a single sitting at a specific time.

**27** The price for rooms as given to us by the hotels. The first price is for one person in a single room, the second is the upper price for two people in a double room.

**28** Some hotels will not take pets; others prefer to be asked. It is best to check.

**29** Teas are served to non-residents.

**30** [GHG ] denotes that this establishment is also listed in the 1990 edition of our sister guide, *The Good Hotel Guide.*

# New London telephone codes from May 1990

On 6 May 1990 all London telephone numbers will change, the 01- code being replaced by either 071- or 081-. Which code a telephone number takes will depend on the first three digits of the number. For example, 01-434 000 will become 071-434 0000, and 01-666 0000 will become 081-666 0000. As a service to readers telephoning London restaurants after 6 May, we give below and on the next two pages a list of numbers and code.

| 1st 3 digits of no. | The new code | 1st 3 digits of no. | The new code | 1st 3 digits of no. | The new code | 1st 3 digits of no. | The new code | 1st 3 digits of no. | The new code | 1st 3 digits of no. | The new code |
|---|---|---|---|---|---|---|---|---|---|---|---|
| 200 | 081 | 235 | 071 | 265 | 071 | 299 | 081 | 332 | 081 | 366 | 081 |
| 202 | 081 | 236 | 071 | 266 | 071 | 300 | 081 | 335 | 081 | 367 | 081 |
| 203 | 081 | 237 | 071 | 267 | 071 | 301 | 081 | 336 | 081 | 368 | 081 |
| 204 | 081 | 238 | 071 | 268 | 071 | 302 | 081 | 337 | 081 | 370 | 071 |
| 205 | 081 | 239 | 071 | 269 | 071 | 303 | 081 | 339 | 081 | 371 | 071 |
| 206 | 081 | 240 | 071 | 270 | 071 | 304 | 081 | 340 | 081 | 372 | 071 |
| 207 | 081 | 241 | 071 | 271 | 071 | 305 | 081 | 341 | 081 | 373 | 071 |
| 208 | 081 | 242 | 071 | 272 | 071 | 308 | 081 | 342 | 081 | 374 | 071 |
| 209 | 081 | 243 | 071 | 273 | 071 | 309 | 081 | 343 | 081 | 375 | 071 |
| 210 | 071 | 244 | 071 | 274 | 071 | 310 | 081 | 345 | 081 | 376 | 071 |
| 214 | 071 | 245 | 071 | 276 | 071 | 311 | 081 | 346 | 081 | 377 | 071 |
| 215 | 071 | 246 | 071 | 277 | 071 | 312 | 081 | 347 | 081 | 378 | 071 |
| 217 | 071 | 247 | 071 | 278 | 071 | 313 | 081 | 348 | 081 | 379 | 071 |
| 218 | 071 | 248 | 071 | 279 | 071 | 314 | 081 | 349 | 081 | 380 | 071 |
| 219 | 071 | 249 | 071 | 280 | 071 | 316 | 081 | 350 | 071 | 381 | 071 |
| 220 | 071 | 250 | 071 | 281 | 071 | 317 | 081 | 351 | 071 | 382 | 071 |
| 221 | 071 | 251 | 071 | 283 | 071 | 318 | 081 | 352 | 071 | 383 | 071 |
| 222 | 071 | 252 | 071 | 284 | 071 | 319 | 081 | 353 | 071 | 384 | 071 |
| 223 | 071 | 253 | 071 | 286 | 071 | 320 | 071 | 354 | 071 | 385 | 071 |
| 224 | 071 | 254 | 071 | 287 | 071 | 321 | 071 | 355 | 071 | 386 | 071 |
| 225 | 071 | 255 | 071 | 288 | 071 | 322 | 071 | 356 | 071 | 387 | 071 |
| 226 | 071 | 256 | 071 | 289 | 071 | 323 | 071 | 357 | 071 | 388 | 071 |
| 227 | 071 | 257 | 071 | 290 | 081 | 324 | 071 | 358 | 071 | 389 | 071 |
| 228 | 071 | 258 | 071 | 291 | 081 | 325 | 071 | 359 | 071 | 390 | 081 |
| 229 | 071 | 259 | 071 | 293 | 081 | 326 | 071 | 360 | 081 | 391 | 081 |
| 230 | 071 | 260 | 071 | 294 | 081 | 327 | 071 | 361 | 081 | 392 | 081 |
| 231 | 071 | 261 | 071 | 295 | 081 | 328 | 071 | 363 | 081 | 393 | 081 |
| 232 | 071 | 262 | 071 | 297 | 081 | 329 | 071 | 364 | 081 | 394 | 081 |
| 233 | 071 | 263 | 071 | 298 | 081 | 330 | 081 | 365 | 081 | 397 | 081 |
| 234 | 071 | | | | | | | | | | |

| 1st 3 digits of no. | The new code | 1st 3 digits of no. | The new code | 1st 3 digits of no. | The new code | 1st 3 digits of no. | The new code | 1st 3 digits of no. | The new code | 1st 3 digits of no. | The new code |
|---|---|---|---|---|---|---|---|---|---|---|---|
| 398 | 081 | 449 | 081 | 494 | 071 | 543 | 081 | 586 | 071 | 636 | 071 |
| 399 | 081 | 450 | 081 | 495 | 071 | 544 | 081 | 587 | 071 | 637 | 071 |
| 400 | 071 | 451 | 081 | 496 | 071 | 545 | 081 | 588 | 071 | 638 | 071 |
| 401 | 071 | 452 | 081 | 497 | 071 | 546 | 081 | 589 | 071 | 639 | 071 |
| 402 | 071 | 453 | 081 | 498 | 071 | 547 | 081 | 590 | 081 | 640 | 081 |
| 403 | 071 | 455 | 081 | 499 | 071 | 549 | 081 | 591 | 081 | 641 | 081 |
| 404 | 071 | 456 | 081 | 500 | 081 | 550 | 081 | 592 | 081 | 642 | 081 |
| 405 | 071 | 458 | 081 | 501 | 081 | 551 | 081 | 593 | 081 | 643 | 081 |
| 406 | 071 | 459 | 081 | 502 | 081 | 552 | 081 | 594 | 081 | 644 | 081 |
| 407 | 071 | 460 | 081 | 504 | 081 | 553 | 081 | 595 | 081 | 645 | 081 |
| 408 | 071 | 461 | 081 | 505 | 081 | 554 | 081 | 597 | 081 | 646 | 081 |
| 409 | 071 | 462 | 081 | 506 | 081 | 555 | 081 | 598 | 081 | 647 | 081 |
| 420 | 081 | 463 | 081 | 507 | 081 | 556 | 081 | 599 | 081 | 648 | 081 |
| 421 | 081 | 464 | 081 | 508 | 081 | 558 | 081 | 600 | 071 | 650 | 081 |
| 422 | 081 | 466 | 081 | 509 | 081 | 559 | 081 | 601 | 071 | 651 | 081 |
| 423 | 081 | 467 | 081 | 511 | 071 | 560 | 081 | 602 | 071 | 653 | 081 |
| 424 | 081 | 468 | 081 | 512 | 071 | 561 | 081 | 603 | 071 | 654 | 081 |
| 426 | 081 | 469 | 081 | 514 | 081 | 562 | 081 | 604 | 071 | 655 | 081 |
| 427 | 081 | 470 | 081 | 515 | 071 | 563 | 081 | 605 | 071 | 656 | 081 |
| 428 | 081 | 471 | 081 | 517 | 081 | 564 | 081 | 606 | 071 | 657 | 081 |
| 429 | 081 | 472 | 081 | 518 | 081 | 566 | 081 | 607 | 071 | 658 | 081 |
| 430 | 071 | 473 | 071 | 519 | 081 | 567 | 081 | 608 | 071 | 659 | 081 |
| 431 | 071 | 474 | 071 | 520 | 081 | 568 | 081 | 609 | 071 | 660 | 081 |
| 432 | 071 | 475 | 081 | 521 | 081 | 569 | 081 | 618 | 071 | 661 | 081 |
| 433 | 071 | 476 | 071 | 523 | 081 | 570 | 081 | 620 | 071 | 663 | 081 |
| 434 | 071 | 478 | 081 | 524 | 081 | 571 | 081 | 621 | 071 | 664 | 081 |
| 435 | 071 | 480 | 071 | 526 | 081 | 572 | 081 | 622 | 071 | 665 | 081 |
| 436 | 071 | 481 | 071 | 527 | 081 | 573 | 081 | 623 | 071 | 666 | 081 |
| 437 | 071 | 482 | 071 | 529 | 081 | 574 | 081 | 624 | 071 | 667 | 081 |
| 438 | 071 | 483 | 071 | 530 | 081 | 575 | 081 | 625 | 071 | 668 | 081 |
| 439 | 071 | 484 | 071 | 531 | 081 | 576 | 081 | 626 | 071 | 669 | 081 |
| 440 | 081 | 485 | 071 | 532 | 081 | 577 | 081 | 627 | 071 | 670 | 081 |
| 441 | 081 | 486 | 071 | 533 | 081 | 578 | 081 | 628 | 071 | 671 | 081 |
| 442 | 081 | 487 | 071 | 534 | 081 | 579 | 081 | 629 | 071 | 672 | 081 |
| 443 | 081 | 488 | 071 | 536 | 081 | 580 | 071 | 630 | 071 | 673 | 081 |
| 444 | 081 | 489 | 071 | 537 | 071 | 581 | 071 | 631 | 071 | 674 | 081 |
| 445 | 081 | 490 | 071 | 538 | 071 | 582 | 071 | 632 | 071 | 675 | 081 |
| 446 | 081 | 491 | 071 | 539 | 081 | 583 | 071 | 633 | 071 | 676 | 081 |
| 447 | 081 | 492 | 071 | 540 | 081 | 584 | 071 | 634 | 071 | 677 | 081 |
| 448 | 081 | 493 | 071 | 541 | 081 | 585 | 071 | 635 | 071 | 678 | 081 |
|  |  |  |  | 542 | 081 |  |  |  |  |  |  |

| 1st 3 digits of no. | The new code | 1st 3 digits of no. | The new code | 1st 3 digits of no. | The new code | 1st 3 digits of no. | The new code | 1st 3 digits of no. | The new code | 1st 3 digits of no. | The new code |
|---|---|---|---|---|---|---|---|---|---|---|---|
| 679 | 081 | 731 | 071 | 778 | 081 | 839 | 071 | 888 | 081 | 944 | 081 |
| 680 | 081 | 732 | 071 | 780 | 081 | 840 | 081 | 889 | 081 | 946 | 081 |
| 681 | 081 | 733 | 071 | 783 | 081 | 841 | 081 | 890 | 081 | 947 | 081 |
| 682 | 081 | 734 | 071 | 785 | 081 | 842 | 081 | 891 | 081 | 948 | 081 |
| 683 | 081 | 735 | 071 | 786 | 081 | 843 | 081 | 892 | 081 | 949 | 081 |
| 684 | 081 | 736 | 071 | 788 | 081 | 844 | 081 | 893 | 081 | 950 | 081 |
| 685 | 081 | 737 | 071 | 789 | 081 | 845 | 081 | 894 | 081 | 951 | 081 |
| 686 | 081 | 738 | 071 | 790 | 071 | 846 | 081 | 897 | 081 | 952 | 081 |
| 687 | 081 | 739 | 071 | 791 | 071 | 847 | 081 | 898 | 081 | 953 | 081 |
| 688 | 081 | 740 | 081 | 792 | 071 | 848 | 081 | 900 | 081 | 954 | 081 |
| 689 | 081 | 741 | 081 | 793 | 071 | 850 | 081 | 902 | 081 | 958 | 081 |
| 690 | 081 | 742 | 081 | 794 | 071 | 851 | 081 | 903 | 081 | 959 | 081 |
| 691 | 081 | 743 | 081 | 796 | 071 | 852 | 081 | 904 | 081 | 960 | 081 |
| 692 | 081 | 744 | 081 | 798 | 071 | 853 | 081 | 905 | 081 | 961 | 081 |
| 693 | 081 | 745 | 081 | 799 | 071 | 854 | 081 | 906 | 081 | 963 | 081 |
| 694 | 081 | 746 | 081 | 800 | 081 | 855 | 081 | 907 | 081 | 964 | 081 |
| 695 | 081 | 747 | 081 | 801 | 081 | 856 | 081 | 908 | 081 | 965 | 081 |
| 697 | 081 | 748 | 081 | 802 | 081 | 857 | 081 | 909 | 081 | 968 | 081 |
| 698 | 081 | 749 | 081 | 803 | 081 | 858 | 081 | 920 | 071 | 969 | 081 |
| 699 | 081 | 750 | 081 | 804 | 081 | 859 | 081 | 921 | 071 | 974 | 081 |
| 700 | 071 | 751 | 081 | 805 | 081 | 861 | 081 | 922 | 071 | 976 | 071 |
| 701 | 071 | 752 | 081 | 806 | 081 | 863 | 081 | 923 | 071 | 977 | 081 |
| 702 | 071 | 754 | 081 | 807 | 081 | 864 | 081 | 924 | 071 | 978 | 071 |
| 703 | 071 | 755 | 081 | 808 | 081 | 866 | 081 | 925 | 071 | 979 | 081 |
| 704 | 071 | 756 | 081 | 809 | 081 | 868 | 081 | 927 | 071 | 980 | 081 |
| 706 | 071 | 758 | 081 | 820 | 071 | 869 | 081 | 928 | 071 | 981 | 081 |
| 707 | 071 | 759 | 081 | 821 | 071 | 870 | 081 | 929 | 071 | 983 | 081 |
| 708 | 071 | 760 | 081 | 822 | 071 | 871 | 081 | 930 | 071 | 984 | 081 |
| 709 | 071 | 761 | 081 | 823 | 071 | 874 | 081 | 931 | 071 | 985 | 081 |
| 720 | 071 | 763 | 081 | 824 | 071 | 875 | 081 | 932 | 071 | 986 | 081 |
| 721 | 071 | 764 | 081 | 826 | 071 | 876 | 081 | 933 | 071 | 987 | 071 |
| 722 | 071 | 766 | 081 | 828 | 071 | 877 | 081 | 934 | 071 | 988 | 081 |
| 723 | 071 | 767 | 081 | 829 | 071 | 878 | 081 | 935 | 071 | 989 | 081 |
| 724 | 071 | 768 | 081 | 831 | 071 | 879 | 081 | 936 | 071 | 991 | 081 |
| 725 | 071 | 769 | 081 | 832 | 071 | 881 | 081 | 937 | 071 | 992 | 081 |
| 726 | 071 | 770 | 081 | 833 | 071 | 882 | 081 | 938 | 071 | 993 | 081 |
| 727 | 071 | 771 | 081 | 834 | 071 | 883 | 081 | 940 | 081 | 994 | 081 |
| 728 | 071 | 773 | 081 | 835 | 071 | 884 | 081 | 941 | 081 | 995 | 081 |
| 729 | 071 | 776 | 081 | 836 | 071 | 885 | 081 | 942 | 081 | 997 | 081 |
| 730 | 071 | 777 | 081 | 837 | 071 | 886 | 081 | 943 | 081 | 998 | 081 |

# London

## Alastair Little

map 14

49 Frith Street, W1V 5TE
01-734 5183

COOKING **4**
COST £38

For many this is the best, most pleasant eating-house in London. Disregard the columnising and enjoy it for what it is. Were a real enthusiast, with a sense of the multivalence of various cooking traditions, to devote a long weekend to the elaboration of a good meal, food as you find it at Little's would be the result: high on flavour, high on thought and inspiration, witty, wide ranging. It would not depend on a large brigade, each member performing some discrete task, on long-simmered stocks, on manual dexterity practised over months. It would not, in that sense, be refined. It would not depend on a system. Nouvelle cuisine was the imposition of invention on the systematic base of haute cuisine. Alastair Little forswears that. In consequence, his food is supremely edible: you can eat there three days in succession and feel no harm. Try that with haute cuisine; you will need much preliminary training. It means too that the flavours are more direct, less evened-out by submission to careful elaboration. The lack of system is anathema to a certain breed, hence the disparagement of Alastair Little's craft in some quarters. The restaurant itself proclaims his approach. It is a small, venetian-blinded shop front. Within, the room is without softness: neither linen, carpet nor curtains. Napkins are paper, tables black oak veneer, chairs modern constructs. Beyond is the kitchen – stainless steel seen through a service-way. Only the hidebound would find this offensive. You go to eat. Paper napkins apart, the fittings are seemly – though there are bowls of sea-salt, not mills. Service is relaxed, without gush, often impeccable and invariably pleasant; again, you come to eat, not to be scraped at.

The menu changes, in rolling fashion, at each meal. There is a large choice of up to a dozen first courses and half as many for succeeding stages. The inspiration is the same as modern food journalism: eclectic, with Japanese and exotic touches, and full of references to European (especially Italian) peasantry and to good bourgeois cooking that might once have been regional but has now spread the continent over. Because Little's system is not the old one, his repertoire is apparently infinite, showing willingness to try anything – just as the aware home cook turns with pleasure to an unfamiliar book or new piece of writing on cookery. A meal that drew on some of his more constant dishes began with a 'bourride' of turbot and salt cod, a fine gutsy, rusty fish soup with a central mound of exquisite turbot and cod. Parmesan and the croûtons were excellent, the rouille mayonnaise pretty good. To follow came breast of chicken wrapped in pancetta and cabbage leaf, the sauce for this slightly cheesed. A slice that incorporated all elements was an intriguing succession of flavours, the envelope imparting zest and extra dimension to the monotone of the chicken. The sauce was sufficiently rich but had the right degree of edge to allow the next mouthful to be approached with glee, not foreboding. The vegetables, as too often here, were dreadful. Mr Little should stick to green salad and smarten up his approach to potatoes. A cheeseboard which always offers interest and good condition was by-passed for a trifle (a verbal joke) of rhubarb and pistachio. In the centre of a large soup plate was a good compote of rhubarb topped with thick cream. In a surrounding moat of brandied custard were floating cubes of soaked sponge. Over the whole was sprinkled candied pistachios, giving welcome texture to what otherwise would have been a mush. Coffee was super-bitter espresso, with no petits fours.

A catalogue of dishes that have pleased readers would read long. A hint of their flavour comes from these: warm salad of zampone and lentils; fine and generous carpaccio; sashimi of bonito and tuna with mustard and greens; grilled sea bass with a mint pesto; calf's liver with shallots in a red wine sauce; bollito misto; roast John Dory with spring onions and button mushrooms; pear in red wine with a cinnamon ice-cream; chocolate truffle cake and ginger sauce, and a very successful blackcurrant sponge of perfect balance. There is always something interesting going on in the kitchen and luxury items are not scattered through the cooking to aimlessly lend class; rather they are used for themselves. Cooking at this level of enthusiasm will inevitably have faults and inconsistencies. Vegetables have been mentioned, bread is not as it should be, and there is a certain blandness when invention runs out. Complaints are too many to discount, but in themselves do not detract from the qualities of this place when it is running to form. It is also unfortunate that the present climate of hyperbole gives rise to unfulfillable expectations. If only people wanted to go out just to eat and to enjoy each others' company! Deep in the bowels of the property is a new small bar offering an aperitif, coffee or a light meal of sashimi and other first courses from the menu upstairs. It lends a welcome adaptability to a small restaurant that is often booked out. It is not cosy, but you don't expect a snug at Alastair Little. The evident brilliance and directness shown in the menu and the food carries through to the wine list. A short and fluid selection, though refusing any truck with half-bottles, it generally has something interesting from the best of the small wine merchants, not just of London, and prices are not impossible. The house wine, French at £8, does not live up to the food. CELLARMAN'S CHOICE : Pouilly Fumé, Les Berthiers 1987, £16; Ronco di Monpiano 1985, Pasolini, £13.

CHEFS: Alastair Little and Julie Peston   PROPRIETORS: Mercedes Andre-Vega, Kirsten Pedersen and Alastair Little
OPEN: Mon to Sat, exc Sat L
CLOSED: bank hols, last 3 weeks Aug
MEALS: 12.30 to 2.30, 7.30 to 11.30
PRICES: £24 (£32). Snacks from £3
SEATS: 35. Children's helpings

*Report forms are at the back of the book; write a letter if you prefer.*

## *Al Hamra* map 13

31–33 Shepherd Market, W1Y 7RJ      COOKING **3**
01-493 1954 and 6934      COST £24–£34

Super-cool Lebanese restaurant in an ultra-smart district of London: sit and look out at the passers-by. The tables are close packed and the Lebanese smoke a lot. Go there to eat meze, originally a creation of the mountain resort restaurants of Lebanon. The range is great, including lambs' testicles if fancied, which, tasting like soft roes, 'would be excellent on toast'. People have applauded the meze and the products of the charcoal grill. The breads are good too. Service seems to veer from the grim and rude to affable and welcoming. One reader, dining speedily before going to the theatre, reported, 'We got good advice on what would be quick to prepare and good service. We will go back.' Maybe it depends on the day of the week. French house wine, £8.50.

CHEF: Hassan Mardini   PROPRIETORS: R. Nabulsi and H. Fansa
OPEN: all week
CLOSED: 25 Dec, 1 Jan
MEALS: noon to midnight
PRICES: £12 (£24), Set L and D £15 (£25) to £18 (£28). Cover £1.75. Minimum £12
CARDS: Access, Amex, Diners, Visa
SEATS: 73. 4 tables outside. Private parties: 80 main room. Vegetarian meals. Children's helpings. Wheelchair access. Music

## *Andrew Edmunds* map 13

46 Lexington Street, W1R 3LH      COOKING **1**
01-437 5708      COST £22

The piquancy of contrast between this insouciant and atmospheric restaurant (more enjoyable upstairs) and the considered poise of Sutherlands opposite (see entry) is nice. There will be many who prefer the sense of relaxation, the smaller bill and the generally wholesome food, here. No criticism, of course, is intended. Menus often involve not too much cooking, first courses may be no more than materials (cold) in proximity on a plate, but soups are good, casseroles make the mind wander back to the pleasures of old English bistros, there is often a pasta dish and the selection of wine is very intelligent. Service is always cheerful. At lunch it can be crowded and noisy. House wines from £6. CELLARMAN'S CHOICE : Ch. Musar, Lebanon, 1979/80/81, all at £8; Pinot Grigio, 1988, Lungarotti, £8.50.

CHEF: John Quigley   PROPRIETORS: Andrew and Bryony Edmunds
OPEN: Mon to Fri
MEALS: 12.30 to 3, 5.30 to 10.45
PRICES: £12 (£18). Cover 35p L
CARDS: Access, Visa
SEATS: 48. 2 tables outside. Private parties: 30 main room. Vegetarian meals. Children welcome. No pipes in dining-room

## Anna's Place

map 11

90 Mildmay Park, N1 4PR
01-249 9379

COOKING 2
COST £24

'We, as everyone, like Anna's. Food tasty, reliable, remarkably inexpensive; it is the sort of neighbourhood restaurant we'd all love to have.' Tables are packed tight, made to feel closer by the busyness of the business and the decoration − 'just enough space for one person to move at a time, like a hand-held game with sliding pieces.' The food is Swedish, with occasional harking back to outlandish combinations of yesteryear involving cheese and fruit. Gravlax still gets most mention, but Scandophiles should also remark the marinated herring; biff Strindberg − which sounds like a wife's revenge − beef marinated in Swedish mustard and onions served with spiced potatoes and cucumber salad; and desserts that come with Scandinavian fruit − blueberries, lingonberries and cloudberries. Sauces tend to be piquant and relishes abound. Though quality is still applauded, it can descend to the bistro level. The wine list is short and sweet and not expensive. Swedish beer and schnapps are available. Would that everyone's prices were so realistic. House French and Californian are £5.95. CELLARMAN'S CHOICE : Rothbury Chardonnay 1988, £9.90; Mercurey 1984, Michel Juillot, £15.95.

CHEFS: James McCarthy and Roz Mason   PROPRIETOR: Anna Hegarty
OPEN: Tue to Sat
CLOSED: 2 weeks at Christmas and Easter; Aug
MEALS: 12.30 to 2.30, 7.15 to 10.45
PRICES: £14 (£20). Service 10%
SEATS: 52. 5 tables outside. Private parties: 10 main room. Children's helpings. Wheelchair access. Music

## L'Arlequin

map 10

123 Queenstown Road, SW8 3RH
01-622 0555

COOKING 5
COST £24−£53

L'Arlequin usually figures in conversation between enthusiasts. As the latest visit to some rip-off is detailed, the latest antic of some unshaven chef, so is dropped the name Delteil. 'Ah yes, it's all right there.' Quality and skill are presumed. And so it proves: no fireworks, little publicity (though much recognition from his peers), but an even commitment to quality. The understatement and decorum run from the calm rooms, with adequate space between tables to unleash further confidences, to the precise, well-mannered and amiable staff, headed by Mme Delteil but seconded by a fine team and a first-rate sommelier. The food can be matchless. It once was almost boring but has now achieved a balance between delicacy and flavour that's hard to beat. Take the bread. Good bread is interesting because it crops up in unlikely places. Here, the cooking is refined, but the rolls might have been cooked by a peasant: a Granary-style flour (though malt was hardly perceptible); an unglazed crust that is deep, chewy and flavourful; a dough of good texture and tasting as if it had been made with a leaven rather than only yeast. Purists would have said it is too rough for so fine a setting, but what taste, what enjoyment of basics! The crust was a little too thick, but why cavil? If cavil there be, it is on the serving of hot rolls in restaurants. There is nothing worse than hot bread: it ruins the butter and it spoils the dough texture. True, the crust may be improved, but who wants to eat little balls of stodge – the ineluctable effect of compressing hot dough? Return, now, to a meal taken earlier this year. Amuse-gueule were a tiny salmon and halibut skewer with a butter sauce and a diminutive quiche: this has been a recurrent offering for some years. Indeed, one criticism that may be levelled is that the repertoire here shifts slowly, if at all. First course was a dish of scallops with mushroom and fennel ravioli, so fine it passed nearly without remark. The scallops were palpably fresh, the ravioli tender with a filling that added roundness and had real flavour (not invariable with ravioli fillings, however exalted the chef). The sauce seemed to have a meat base – light, but again adding body to what could so easily have been insipid. This was followed, north-country style, by an asparagus soup that avoided the pitfall of too strong a stock base, thus allowing it to taste as it should. Although it would have been difficult to follow the scallops, the saddle of young rabbit arranged round a central mound of cabbage and sauced with a red wine reduction was just as good. For so light, yet inexpressibly tender a meat as the rabbit, a strong sauce might seem suicide, but join it to cabbage, which broadened its impact, and the alchemy was complete. Vegetables on a side plate, a mélange of broad beans, mange-tout and carrots, were fine; dauphinois was tedious. Such amazing quality had to have a qualification and the desserts were that. There were some sorbets of great texture but too sweet, and the chocolate marquise was too soft and mousse-like for the impact one demands of the dish. Coffee from a cafetière was as eloquent as if it were espresso. The wine list is long and pricey with a boring set of half-bottles. It is difficult to get excited by it, as there is so much that is so good which remains unexplored. Lunch remains a bargain, well worth the No. 137 bus-ride from Sloane Street.

CHEFS/PROPRIETORS: Mr and Mrs Christian Delteil
OPEN: Mon to Fri
CLOSED: 1 week in winter, 3 weeks Aug
MEALS: 12.30 to 2, 7.30 to 10.30
PRICES: £34 (£44), Set L £16.50 (£24). Cover £1. Service inc
CARDS: Access, Amex, Diners, Visa
SEATS: 45. Children welcome. Smart dress preferred. No pipes in dining-room. Wheelchair access (also WC). Air-conditioned

## *Auberge* 

map 10

44 Forest Hill Road, SE22 0RR
01-299 2211

COOKING 2
COST £12–£28

Not far from Camberwell cemetery. Sami Youssef's bistro in a row of shops offers food that locals find the best in the area. The atmosphere is family, the service acute, the cooking relaxed. The spelling of the menu belies any Gallic authenticity but there are Franglais standards like mussels marinière (zapped up with Pernod) and crème caramel as well as decidedly Youssevian affairs like calf's liver cooked in thin strips with 'exotic herbs', garlic and lime juice. The menu develops rarely; vegetables, bread and desserts are not as happy as the atmosphere, although that may alter if recent price rises reduce the number of children of a Sunday. A French wine list of 30 bottles; house French is £6.

CHEF/PROPRIETOR: Sami Youssef
OPEN: Tue to Sat D, and Sun L
CLOSED: 3 weeks end Aug
MEALS: 12 to 3, 7 to 10.30
PRICES: Set L £8 (£12), Set D £18 (£23). Service 10%
CARDS: Access, Visa
SEATS: 38. Private parties: 30 main room. Children's helpings (L only). Wheelchair access (1 step; also WC). Music

## ▲ Auberge de Provence, St James's Court Hotel

map 11

51 Buckingham Gate, SW1E 6AF
01-821 1899

COOKING 3
COST £26−£55

When this moved from the left to the right of the entrance of the St James's Court, the caravanserai of a hotel that is its host, there was little perceptible change in the ambience, even though a new chef reputedly brought better notices for the cooking. The decoration is still irresistibly authentic Provençal, that is, just as unattractive as the Artexed, false-vaulted, tiled and wrought-ironed places in Provence itself. The distinction is that, in London, it rains and the illusion is harder to maintain. There is quite a strong lobby for the French (very French, try asking for a grapefruit from a non-English speaker) service, French feel and southern French cooking of this place. Young guinea-fowl on a bed of leeks; monkfish studded with peppers in a cream and basil sauce; a Christmas lunch which had a marvellous wild duck with olives; red mullet with rosemary cream sauce; a lattice of asparagus tips and smoked salmon, have all been well received. From the menu some slight southward leaning may be detected, if not in everything. This comes from the avowed intent of the place and the active consultancy of the Oustaù de Baumanière, a *Michelin* laureate in Provence itself. An inspection meal revealed no southerning at all but a preoccupation with butter so excessive that the diner lost equilibrium for a week. The kitchen showed strengths, such as good purchasing of simple shellfish; quite a pleasant though dryish sea bream sandwiching a layer of tapénade and a distinguished classical veal stock sauce to go with the fish; wonderful cheeses on a great trolley. It also showed weaknesses: an excess of salt coating the fried slices of foie gras − coated also with hazelnuts; a vegetarian ravioli devoid of flavour in the filling even if the simple sauce was pleasant; a tedious dessert trolley. The service can be first-rate, reception particularly − 'all young French people, keen as mustard' − but some reports of disappointments persist. The wine list, drawn largely from the supplies of the Oustaù, is strong on Provence and big on money. House wine is £8.50. For some totally incredible reason, children under 10 are refused entry. Imagine that in Provence.

▲ *This symbol means accommodation is available.*

CHEF: Yves Gravelier   PROPRIETORS: TAJ International Hotels
OPEN: Mon to Sat, exc Sat L
MEALS: 12.30 to 2.30, 7.30 to 11
PRICES: £32 (£46), Set L £17.50 (£27) to £25 (£35), Set D £25 (£35) to £40 (£51)
CARDS: Access, Amex, Diners, Visa
SEATS: 80. Private parties: 40 main room. No children under 10. Smart dress preferred.
Music. Air-conditioned
ACCOMMODATION: 390 rooms, all with bath/shower. Rooms for disabled. Lift. B&B £140 to
£166. Afternoon teas. Sauna. Air-conditioning. TV. Phone. Confirm by 6

## Au Bois St Jean                    map 11

| 122 St John's Wood High Street, NW8 7SG | COOKING 1 |
| 01-722 0400 | COST £12–£31 |

1989 was the 21st year of operation for this basement restaurant that expands
into a bright ground-floor room at lunchtimes and on busy nights. It aims to be
a *restaurant du quartier* and keeps its prices accordingly (ignore the fact that
London cheap equals North Wales luxury). Many have been pleased by the
good ingredients and the amiable Gallic service – offering dishes such as
mushroom mousse with tarragon sauce; avocado pâté with smoked salmon;
sole with lime or sorrel; lamb as a rack or in noisettes; petit pot au chocolat and
a quartet of daily extras. It's a long menu to keep alive. The vegetables are often
criticised. The wine list is short and French (of course) but at fair prices. House
French is £6.50. CELLARMAN'S CHOICE : Ch. Cazelles 1985, Côtes de Bourg,
£11.20; Bourgogne Aligoté 1987, Claude Larousse, £10.50.

CHEF: Jean Claude Broussely   PROPRIETORS: H. A. Saux
OPEN: all week, exc Sat L
MEALS: 12 to 2.30, 7 to 11.30
PRICES: Set L £8 (£12) to £19 (£26), Set D £16 (£23) to £19 (£26). Minimum £8
CARDS: Access, Amex, Diners, Visa
SEATS: 65. Private parties: 20 main room, 25 private room. Vegetarian meals. Children's
helpings (L only). Smart dress preferred. Music

## L'Aventure                        map 11

| 3 Blenheim Terrace, NW8 4JS | COOKING 1 |
| 01-624 6232 | COST £31 |

The pavement terrace and tree-planted tubs outside the front door of this small
St John's Wood restaurant aim for a Parisian feel, almost convincing on warm
summer nights. The staff and food are French, too, with a confident menu that
keeps to half a dozen or so classic dishes. Smoked salmon crêpes, crab omelette,
fillet of sole stuffed with spinach and pink rack of lamb, tarte Tatin and sablé à
la truffe au chocolat have been recommended again this year, but there have
been new additions, such as a tourte au canard with light pastry and a warm
salad of chicken livers. Service is attentively polite and to the point, but slows
when Catherine Parisot is not in evidence. Tables are fairly crammed together
and, and as tables spill into the open air on a fine night, so may speed and
efficacy of delivery decline. House wine is £7.95. CELLARMAN'S CHOICE :
Mâcon-Lugny, Les Charmes 1987, £11.25.

CHEF: Christian Breteche   PROPRIETORS: Catherine Parisot and Chris Mitas
OPEN: all week, exc Sat L
CLOSED: 1 week at Christmas, 1 week at Easter
MEALS: 12.30 to 2.30, 7.30 to 11 (10 Sun)
PRICES: Set L and D £19.50 (£26)
CARDS: Amex, Visa
SEATS: 38. 5 tables outside. Private parties: 38 main room. Children's helpings. No pipes in
dining-room. Music

## Bahn Thai
map 14

21A Frith Street, W1V 5TS
01-437 8504

COOKING 2
COST £36

'In recent months it has gone from strength to strength,' writes one who has
visited eight times in the last year. 'On a visit to Thailand, it was excelled only
by the Bussaracum in Bangkok. Dishes that have been particularly good have
been the satay, chicken curry with coconut cream, Thai spicy fish cakes and the
noodles.' Service is excellent, say many. This rather scruffy, cramped Soho
restaurant (downstairs more serried than up), where it can be so dark as to
make visual distinction of chilli and spring onion excruciating, does appear to
deliver a subtle cuisine, yet hard-hitting when necessary. Other recommended
dishes have included the dim-sum dumplings of pork, bamboo shoots and
water-chestnuts; stuffed chicken wings, first steamed, then fried and served
with a plum sauce. Not all would agree, some finding ingredients lacklustre,
sauces unoriginal, flavours remarkably un-fresh given the style of cooking.
Once more came the story that a special meal, pre-arranged, was superlative
but that members of the same party eating in the ordinary way did less well.
Thai cooking depends more than most on uncloudy flavours, distinct
contributions from each component of a dish. When they give less than their
due, results are the more disappointing. The management of Bahn Thai is of the
hectoring variety. The menu is prefaced by written guidance for ordering,
which may have the novice's best interest at heart but which reads gratingly. It
also includes a justification of the suggested gratuity which may cause blood to
boil: 'Remember that the staff rely on the gratuity for a large percentage of their
income. Those customers who do not pay just because they want a cheaper
meal are not appreciated.' This seems reason enough not to patronise the place.
It used to be employers who paid their staff, not customers. The wine list is
quite serious in attempting to enhance or match the food's flavour, listing
mainly by grape: there is an especially good range of Gewürztraminers from
around the world. If beer is desired, there is Thai beer but no other, cheaper,
alternative. House Chagny, £6.45.

CHEF: Penn Squires   PROPRIETORS: Bahn Thai plc
OPEN: all week
CLOSED: some bank hols, Christmas and Easter
MEALS: 12 to 2.45, 6 to 11.15 (12.30 to 2.30, 6.30 to 10.30 Sun)
PRICES: £19 (£30). Cover 75p (D only). Service 12.5%
CARDS: Access, Amex, Visa
SEATS: 100. Private parties: 25 main room, 35 and 50 private rooms. Vegetarian meals.
Children welcome. No cigars/pipes in dining-room. Wheelchair access (also WC). Music.
Air-conditioned

## La Bastide ♟

map 14

50 Greek Street, W1V 5LQ
01-734 3300

COOKING 1
COST £24–£37

In this handsomely restored Soho house, the kitchen produces French
provincial dishes with an almost apostolic fervour but a somewhat heretical
accuracy. The restaurant offers a tri-une menu: a monthly choice composed of
dishes from a single region of France, consumable at a set price; a short *carte* of
French food; and a Soho regional menu of quasi-brasserie food, ranging from
avocado to foie gras. The cooking is self-advertised as 'honnête'. The intentions
are high: London needs casserole cookery badly. Diners-out must also approve
the prices, which are conservative. However, the cooking does get very mixed
reports, even though the service is appreciated for its willingness. The wine
stocks sometimes get short but, when complete, the list is a good French one at
acceptable prices. Bemusingly, one page of white burgundies has been
transposed to red, and vice-versa. Do not be fooled into thinking Romanée-St-
Vivant a nice light dry white. House wine is £7.50; CELLARMAN'S CHOICE :
Pacherenc du Vic Bilh, Domaine de Bouscasse £9.20; Ch. Gazin 1977, £17.50.

CHEF: Nicolas Blacklock   PROPRIETORS: Nicolas Blacklock and Susan Warwick
OPEN: Mon to Sat, exc Sat L
CLOSED: bank hols
MEALS: 12.30 to 2.30, 6 to 11.30
PRICES: £21 (£31), Set L and D £16.50 (£24) to £18.50 (£26)
CARDS: Access, Amex, Diners, Visa
SEATS: 45. 3 tables outside. Private parties: 60 main room, 75 private room. No children
under 11. Air-conditioned

## Bedlington Café

map 10

24 Fauconberg Road, W4 3JY
01-994 1965

COOKING 1
COST £13

The outside is red and the frosted glass windows bear the legend 'Breakfasts,
Dinners, Snacks' with the telephone number 'Chiswick 1965'. Inside is not
much more up to date: Formica tables, a fridge full of Coke, a lino-tiled floor.
By day a café, by night a Thai restaurant serving good food cooked by Mrs
Priyanu and her relations. And what food it can be: 'I could happily live on this
nectar.' 'Every time a dish goes by, you get a heady waft.' The menu boasts 60
items, cooked fresh and with a sure hand for seasoning. Best dishes reported
have been chicken and coconut cream soup fragrant with lemon-grass, good
chunks of chicken, 'rich, creamy and scented'; red chicken curry, very hot and
full of coconut flavours; and very fine squid with garlic, the squid perfectly
tender. The meal, refreshingly, was not permeated by sweetness, although
fresh spring rolls with a tamarind dipping sauce will satisfy the most douce of
palates. Unlicensed, but the corkage charge is small and there is an off-licence
on the corner. No credit cards are accepted.

*See the back of the* Guide *for an index of restaurants listed.*

CHEF: Mrs Priyanu and family   PROPRIETORS: Mr and Mrs Priyanu
OPEN: Mon to Sat
MEALS: 12 to 2, 6.30 to 9.30
PRICES: £7 (£11). Unlicensed, but bring your own: corkage 50p
SEATS: 30. Private parties: 30 main room. Vegetarian meals. Children's helpings.
No-smoking area. Wheelchair access (1 step)

## Beotys

map 14

| 79 St Martin's Lane, WC2N 4AA | COOKING 1 |
|---|---|
| 01-836 8768 and 8548 | COST £38 |

This long-stayer has been smartened up, 'redecorated, redesigned and
refurnished,' re-everything – but the cooking stays the same and the warmth
and friendliness seems to overcome regulars: 'as good as native Greece'. 'Good
kleftiko, good stifado, short on the dolmadakia.' Good for meals either side of
the theatre and good for birthdays, too: 'after kalamarakia, souvlakia and
baklava came an unexpected cake to round off the evening.' This is an old-
school Greek restaurant that has not sold out. There are two pages of Greek and
Cypriot wines, incuding the CELLARMAN'S CHOICE : Cambas, Cava Grand Vin
red, £11.20 or white, £10.70. House French is £8.

CHEFS: Stelius Sparsis and El Gallant   PROPRIETORS: Frangos family
OPEN: all week
MEALS: 12.15 to 2.30, 5.30 to 11.30
PRICES: £22 (£32). Cover £1. Service 12.5%
CARDS: Access, Amex, Diners, Visa
SEATS: 80. Private parties: 14 main room, 40 private room. Children's helpings. No children
under 9. Smart dress preferred. No pipes in dining-room. Wheelchair access (also WC). Air-
conditioned

## Bibendum ▼

map 12

| Michelin House, 81 Fulham Road, SW3 6RD | COOKING 4 |
|---|---|
| 01-581 5817 | COST £29–£50 |

An aristocrat in blue jeans, Bibendum attempts the marriage of five-star luxury,
a (rich) oenophile's wine list and demotic cooking. As there may be an urge to
tweak the noble's nose, so there is irritation about the performance of this
restaurant. Surroundings are certainly luxurious. Few tables are too small
(except the serried rank of twos), few chairs uncomfortable, however weird
they look or feel. The sense of light and space is enlivening – and better at
lunch than dinner. The service has improved in the last year and begins to
approach the well-drilled brigades it emulates. Maxwell Clarke's welcome is
genuine and the young English staff are amiable. The French, doubtless
suffering from linguistic repression, tend to a less open style. The wine service
is *too* efficient, aver readers who have watched their glasses disappear before
due time. Simon Hopkinson continues to cook a superlative version of western
European domestic cooking with the odd touch of the oriental (chillies, for
example). The understated menu promises what it delivers, never more. If two
ingredients were elected as symbols, they would be saffron and olive oil. The

first (expensive, mark you) because Hopkinson uses it full-bloodedly, no stinting. The second because he only uses the best extra-virgin, copiously. To a business-world clientele, for instance, brought up on the refined luxuries of expense-account lunching, the approach must come as a shock. The vibrant effect may be seen in these descriptions of two dishes. 'The grilled rabbit was served as a whole leg laid beside a generous portion of deep golden risotto. The rice perfectly judged, still nutty to the bite and full of flavour; the rabbit was tender, criss-crossed from the grill. I wished the joints had been separated, as it skidded around the plate a bit and I had to resort to fingers in the end. I was gratified to observe a finger bowl heading our way without having to ask.' 'The baked fillet of cod with leeks and saffron was another winner. The cooking was judged to the second: slightly undercooked, the flesh pure white and almost like curds, really fresh and firm. The saffron sauce was pungent. Here was a simple dish, plain really, but sublime in texture and flavour.' Star dishes for some are the risotto with wild mushrooms, saffron and Parmesan; the Piedmont peppers; a truffle omelette; leek and truffle tart; grilled rabbit on purée potatoes with olive oil; grilled aubergine with pesto; roast beef and Yorkshire pudding; lemon tart; poached pear with cinnamon cream; chocolate Pithiviers. That omits the tête de veau and onglet that people high on nostalgia for Gauloises and baguettes cross town for.

Not all is acclaim, by virtue of the robust style. It may offend by overstatement. The place seems to work better at lunchtime, perhaps because the short (and sometimes less adventurous) menu is such palpable value. Regrets at poor service occur more frequently at dinner. Incidentals are pleasing: nice oily black olives, wonderful orange juice, good coffee, great butter, fair bread (bought in), decent cutlery and glassware. Last word, on the food, to a visitor from the country: 'The public will hopefully see the skill involved in refined simplicity, rather than the bodged artifice they get and like out here.' The wine list is the symbol of wealth that may irritate the most; not much is under £15. A severe critic could reasonably say that the duty of this restaurant is not to flash blank cheques at wine merchants but to go out and find good but inexpensive bottles to match the cooking. French office workers lunching on tête de veau would hardly flick their fingers for a bottle of Ch. La Fleur Pétrus at nigh on £100. The very dissonance of the two forms leaves an ugly scar on the brain. Thus, while the claret list is long, while there are half a dozen Corton Charlemagnes and Montrachets, there are no more than four Beaujolais, and not very interesting ones at that. However, the Italians are fine ones, some of them colour-supplement stuff, but a maker like Jermann is rare and exciting. Equally the Alsaces are well chosen and good value. The most disconcerting development at Bibendum is a marked fluctuation in standards. This seems a recent problem, perhaps associated with seven-day opening and the need for Simon Hopkinson to have at least two of those days away from the stove, if not to take holidays. The message is clear, too many meals have been unsatisfactory, suffering from a crudeness of execution that Hopkinson would not countenance.

CHEF: Simon Hopkinson   PROPRIETORS: Paul Hamlyn, Sir Terence Conran and
Simon Hopkinson
OPEN: all week
MEALS: 12.30 to 2.30 (3 Sun), 7 to 11.30 (10.30 Sun)
PRICES: £29 (£42), Set L £19.50 (£29) to £21.50 (£31). Minimum £19.50. Service 15%
CARDS: Access, Visa
SEATS: 74. Children's helpings. No children under 5. No pipes in dining-room. Wheelchair
access. Air-conditioned

## *Le Bistro*                                                          map 10

13 St Hilda's Road, SW13 9JE                              COOKING 2
01-748 7282                                                       COST £24

Le Bistro is a dead ringer for Christian Gustin's other restaurant, Christian's, in
Chiswick (see entry): the menu is identical; the atmosphere is just as cosily
familiar; the layout is open-plan with the chef in full view. The L-shaped
dining-room, in a hut-like building next door to Lonsdale's Garage, manages to
create a very French ambience, helped no end by the charming Parisienne who
fronts the house while her husband, the chef, keeps to his kitchen. The short
*carte* of affordable dishes changes weekly, and on Saturdays the place is packed
to the gunwhales. A reporter's meal took in a basic and simple tomato and red
pepper soup; lamb 'cooked in the Provençal manner', which was in fact a clever
updating of navarin, the meat consisting of a fan of thinly sliced pieces in a rich
sauce of tomato, garlic and onions – pleasant rather than exciting, but a
triumph as a meeting of old and new. Vegetables were good, the portions more
substantial than one has grown used to in London. Desserts, usually three in
number, are recited at the table by madame. 'Bitter chocolate terrine was made
from good-quality chocolate and came with a few well-judged slices of fruit.' A
list of a dozen wines is supplemented by house French at £5.95.

CHEF: Olivier Bazile   PROPRIETOR: Christian Gustin
OPEN: Tue to Sat, D only
MEALS: 7.30 to 10.45
PRICES: £16 (£20). Service inc
SEATS: 25. Private parties: 10 main room. Vegetarian meals. Children welcome. No cigars/
pipes in dining-room

## *Bloom's*                                                          map 11

90 Whitechapel High Street, E1 7RA                        COOKING 1
01-247 6001                                                       COST £18

An inspector, now living in the wilds of Essex, sent this report. 'Some of my
fondest memories as a child involve sitting at the same tables, looking at the
same view of Petticoat Lane on the walls, being served by the same waiters and
eating myself sideways. On a recent visit, despite too much pepper, the
chopped liver was the best I've had for years. The salt beef sang with flavour, a
real taste of fat in the beef. Exemplary latkes, proper tsimmas – little
dumplings – and overcooked kishka, a shame because it's my favourite.'
Further observations were confined to the staff and their characters: 'frustrated
cabbies at heart'. A place of piquant memories where, although portions are

now smaller, 'the food is as tasty and unquestionably lighter, though it is still a struggle to finish'. House wine, £6.50.

CHEF: Peter Nicholas   PROPRIETORS: The Bloom family
OPEN: Sun to Fri, exc Fri D
CLOSED: Jewish hols and Christmas Day
MEALS: 11.30am to 9.30pm (3pm Fri, 2pm Fri in winter)
PRICES: £9 (£15)
CARDS: Access, Amex, Visa
SEATS: 160. Private parties: 140 main room. Car-park, 100 places. Children's helpings. Wheelchair access. Air-conditioned

## Blue Elephant                                                          map 10

4–5 Fulham Broadway, SW6 1AA                              COOKING 1
01-385 6595                                               COST £18–£41

Through thickets and fronds may tables be discerned, and bevies of meeters, greeters, smilers and servers. The progression of eating areas rises away into a blue and misty beyond. It might be a set for an Indiana Jones adventure film. The joke has always been that this canny set-up knows how to cook Thai food; that although owned by Belgians, with a sister establishment in Brussels, it has taken care to recruit good Thai cooks and to fly fresh foods straight from Thailand. The experience of correspondents and inspectors has not been that it works to any great effect. The experience of others might lead the cynic to believe that initiates and friends of the management will do very well but casual visitors, hoping to have their eyes opened, may run the risk of being gulled. Never, though, will it be the fault of the waiting staff: they are well trained and pleasant. The vice of the kitchen is a peculiarly unsubtle approach to spicing: the food is either so sweet or so harshly hot that pleasure flies through the overhanging palms and might, one imagines, be snatched by a passing monkey. Nor is the food self-evidently fresh, a seafood salad of dubious origin and what appeared to be reheated slices of lamb with ginger and garlic were witness of that. These are two serious impediments to enjoyment. To counter that, some readers have enjoyed the food greatly, though questioning the portion size and the prices. House French, £6.95.
CELLARMAN'S CHOICE : from a good list, including Bruno Paillard's Champagne, which may reconcile anyone to the cooking, are Cheverny 1988, Guy Saget, £8.95; Chinon, Domaine les Milliarges 1987, £9.85.

CHEFS: Thaviseuth Phouthavong and Rungsan Mulijan   PROPRIETORS: Blue Elephant Ltd
OPEN: all week, exc Sat L
CLOSED: 24 to 26 Dec
MEALS: 12 to 2.30, 7 to 11.30
PRICES: £19 (£33), Set L £12.95 (£18), Set D £22 (£31) to £25 (£34). Service 15%
CARDS: Access, Amex, Diners, Visa
SEATS: 150. Private parties: 150 main room. Vegetarian meals. Children welcome. Smart dress preferred. Wheelchair access (2 steps; also WC). Music. Air-conditioned

*See the inside of the front cover for an explanation of the new 1 to 5 rating system recognising cooking standards.*

# Blue Nile

map 11

| | |
|---|---|
| 341A Harrow Road, W9 3RA | COOKING 1 |
| 01-286 5129 | COST £17—£20 |

An Ethiopian restaurant is rare and this one, frequented by ex-patriates, is reckoned authentic by one returning traveller – even if its blue-coloured setting with posters and pictures is not a circular *tukul* with thatched roof. The uninitiated may well prefer to stick with the set menus, though there is a range of a dozen or more chicken, lamb, beef or vegetarian dishes and a promise of more vegetarian ones to come. These are for two people, served on a large platter and eaten with the fingers – helped by the sour unleavened Ethiopian bread (you can have pitta if you prefer). Some of the food is spicy, though one newcomer thought it more pallid and bland than she expected. The spiciness can be controlled by planned ordering. There are wines to drink, teas, and an Ethiopian honey ferment called *tej*. Beers include Jamaican Crucial Brew. Service is relaxed. House Bulgarian, £5.50.

CHEF/PROPRIETOR: Elsa Wubneh
OPEN: all week, D only
MEALS: 7 to 11.30
PRICES: £12 (£17), Set D (for 2) £25 (£33)
CARDS: Access, Visa
SEATS: 50. 2 tables outside. Private parties: 70 main room, 70 private room. Vegetarian meals. Children's helpings. Wheelchair access. Music

# Bombay Brasserie

map 12

| | |
|---|---|
| 140 Gloucester Road, SW7 4QH | COOKING 1 |
| 01-370 4040 | COST £17—£35 |

For some years this has been London's most famous Indian restaurant, offering a range of regional dishes of subtle spicing and exciting ingredients in a setting that reminds people (who never knew it) of how the Raj really was (a concept produced by long television series and longer films). 'We visited after a gap of some six years. The resulting meal was splendid and thoroughly enjoyed by all concerned and now I can't imagine what kept us away so long.' There is a contrary view. The Brasserie, far from being elegant, is dowdy. It resembles nothing so much as a gimcrack modern restaurant plugged into an ageing vessel of tawdry Edwardian classicism: redolent, indeed, of a seaside bingo-hall dropped into once-elegant civic assembly rooms. The service, almost without exception, is effective and pleasant, as well as informed. This is its great quality. There is disjunction, sometimes, between arrival and actually sitting down and getting at it. The lunchtime session, pioneered here, is a self-help buffet. This is better on Sunday than any other day. At night, there is a long and florid menu, whose descriptions help towards decision. There is also a pianist. Opinions may vary as to the value of that: Billy Joel and curry is a funny mixture. Two inspections were launched in the same season. Both reported the same problems. Much of the food was tired, much was overcooked, some was unacceptable. Here was a restaurant coasting on its reputation. Crab malibar had its flavour of crab drowned in too hot, too sweet and too oniony a vehicle; fish with mint chutney, a Parsi speciality steamed in a banana leaf, was dry and tough and the mint purée was too sweet; chicken pista korma was too small, and the chicken too dry; finally, Sali Boti, another Parsi dish of lamb with red masala sauce, dried apricots and straw potatoes, was simply not adequate: dry, gristly, tough meat with little detectable spicing. Even banana ices seem beyond repair. There are cycles, and perhaps a rising curve will resume. House French, £7.25.

CHEFS: S. Rao and Udit Sarkhel   PROPRIETORS: TAJ International Hotels
OPEN: all week
MEALS: 12.30 to 3, 7.30 to 12
PRICES: £17 (£29), Set L £11.50 (£17). Service 12.5%
CARDS: Access, Amex, Diners, Visa
SEATS: 175. 25 tables outside. Vegetarian meals. Children's helpings. Music

## *Boulestin* ♥

map 14

1A Henrietta Street, WC2E 8PS
01-836 7061

COOKING 3
COST £22–£48

Inflation on the menu is running at 17.5 per cent, the Prime Minister notwithstanding, in this grandiose basement restaurant of long heritage and fine pictures. Its founder, a wonderful Frenchman, did more for English cooking than this ossified place will ever do, so locked is it in servile deference to all things Gallic. What's more, M. Boulestin did it with wit and charm. Visitors recently have been underwhelmed, struck mainly by adequate, not great, craftsmanship – although they may have been hampered by non-English-speaking and slow waiting staff. Although the restaurant caters for a large constituency which sets little store by the odd £100 for petty cash, price is often a stumbling block to appreciation. A terrine de foie gras de canard was 'competent, but two microscopic slices looking as though they had been cut by a microtome are not an adequate portion', especially at £14.50. Some consolation should be found in a reasonably priced luncheon *prix fixe*, but not much from the wine list that has a house Sauvignon de St-Bris from Luc Sorin at £12 but for the most part takes £14.50 as its base point. Anyone who thinks it's worth paying £460 for a Ch. Haut-Brion 1961 that might be purchased retail for around £200 must be rich indeed, and value the cooking more highly than our readers. Most of the younger wines seem marked up at a higher rate than this, so they are never bargains. The Champagnes, clarets and burgundies are virtually the only sections that show intensive thought, though there is a run of Torres Penedès reds and a mature 1974 Heitz Cabernet Sauvignon, at a price.

CHEF: Kevin Kennedy   PROPRIETORS: London Clubs Ltd
OPEN: Mon to Sat, exc Sat L
CLOSED: last 3 weeks Aug, 1 week at Christmas
MEALS: 12.30 to 2.30, 7.30 to 11.15
PRICES: £32 (£40), Set L £17.25 (£22) to £22.75 (£30). Minimum £35. Service inc
CARDS: Access, Amex, Diners, Visa
SEATS: 70. Private parties: 25 main room. No children under 5. Smart dress preferred. No cigars/pipes in dining-room

*Preliminary test of a good restaurant: order fresh orange juice and see what you get.*

## Boyd's ▼

map 11

135 Kensington Church Street, W8 7LP      COOKING **3**
01-727 5452      COST £17−£43

The coolth of Boyd's is refreshing, as is its easy approach to customers and the business of eating. The glass garden may have disappeared from the name (another sign of personality cult?) but it is still there in fact, adding an extra dimension to the furthest parts of the restaurant. The use of white from floor to ceiling is handsomely softened by lots of greenery. The apparent cool was not, however, a reality in the heatwave of 1989. Menus are commendably short: a choice of three at lunch, twice that at night. Daily specials may increase the set price somewhat: a £4 supplement for lamb on a menu already offering calf's liver, salmon and turbot seems quixotic, unless Mr Gilmour buys those three commodities more cheaply than he should. The style of cooking is 'London current'; favourable reports have come of a warm salad of quail and mushroom; breast of slightly too fatty duck pan-fried, then served on a julienne of vegetables; apple and almond tart and a fine marquise au chocolat. Pastry, sauces and use of herbs have been mentioned with honour. There are good intentions here which are sometimes not achieved through too many ancillaries not having the impact designed for them. The main wine list numbers some 40 bottles; then there is a score of more expensive items, none of them old, and a very decent number of halves: all credit for providing them in such a place. There are one or two Australian and Californian bottles, but largely the offering is French. House Torres Coronas and Sauvignon de Touraine, £7.95.
CELLARMAN'S CHOICE : Rully, Les Cloux, Duvernay, 1987, £19; Ch. Vieux Chevrol 1982, Lalande de Pomerol, £19.50.

CHEF/PROPRIETOR: Boyd Gilmour
OPEN: Mon to Fri
CLOSED: bank hols, 1 week at Christmas
MEALS: 12.30 to 2.30, 7.30 to 10.30
PRICES: Set L £12.50 (£17) to £14.75 (£19), Set D £27.50 (£32) to £31.50 (£36). Service inc
CARDS: Access, Amex, Visa
SEATS: 40. Private parties: 40 main room. Children welcome

## Le Braconnier

map 10

467 Upper Richmond Road, SW14 7PU      COOKING **3**
01-878 2853      COST £17−£35

Braconnier means poacher. The only poaching that has gone on is that Terence Speers comes from La Bastide in Greek Street (see entry) where a similar formula of French provincial cooking, with monthly regional menus, is pursued. This new enterprise is very small, seating a score of customers, on a street that witnesses a never-ending flow of traffic − supplemented from the car showroom opposite. Inside is pinkly pastel, subdued, with well-dressed tables; 'one almost forgives the piped music because it is so unmemorable.' Reports of the cooking have been very positive. Terence Speers imparts good strong flavours without overloading the palate or the plate, even to unlikely ingredients. Thus a Provençal menu had as a first course shoulder of lamb stuffed with tuna, egg and olives. Shoulder of lamb, as one remarked, 'could hardly qualify for the appetiser stakes', yet it was well handled. Similarly, sardines stuffed with spinach and garlic sound modern but in fact are traditional (see Reboul's *La Cuisinière Provençale*), and were delicious. That flavours are brought out is seen in a pair of boned quail cooked with olives and thyme where the accompaniment and herb excited what spark of taste there was in the little birds. Desserts have also been received enthusiastically: for instance a dense white and dark chocolate truffle with a coffee cream sauce and prune beignets with a hot caramel sauce. The wine list is exclusively French, with some decent bottles at none too high a price. The house wine is cheap, but doubts have been expressed as to its quality. We do know that wines from other countries can often supply as much power or finesse at much lower prices. House Bergerac, £6.80. CELLARMAN'S CHOICE : Ch. Franc-Grace-Dieu 1981, St-Emilion, £13.65; Ch. du Clos Renon 1982, £10.30.

CHEF: Terence Speers   PROPRIETORS: Terence and Maeve Speers
OPEN: Tue to Sat D and Sun L
MEALS: 12 to 3, 7 to 10.30 (11 Fri and Sat)
PRICES: £16 (£25), Set L £10.95 (£17), Set D £16.50 (£23) to £19.50 (£29)
CARDS: Access, Amex, Visa
SEATS: 24. Private parties: 30 main room. Children's helpings. Smart dress preferred.
Wheelchair access (also WC). Music

## Brewer Street Buttery                                             map 13

56 Brewer Street, W1R 3FA                                    COOKING 1
01-437 7695                                                  COST £4–£10

The warm atmosphere and low prices of this friendly, clean café set it apart from most lunchtime places in ever-more fashionable Soho. Soup of the day and main courses, which always include a vegetarian dish, change every day. Among them are Ania Czeremski's Polish dishes like bigos, a rich stew with sauerkraut and, of course, goulash and piroshki, but there are also roundly British roast sausages. There are liqueur ice-creams and pastries, plus fresh fruit juices and good coffee. Unlicensed, but bring your own alcohol if you can face paying the corkage.

CHEF/PROPRIETOR: Ania Czeremski
OPEN: Mon to Fri, L only
MEALS: noon to 3.30
PRICES: £7 (£8), Set L £3.80 (£4) to £5 (£6), Snacks from £2.50. Unlicensed, but bring your own: corkage £2
SEATS: 32. Private parties: 10 main room. Vegetarian meals. Children's helpings. Separate smoking area. Wheelchair access (1 step). Music

## Bua Luang                                                         map 10

26 Upper Richmond Road West, SW15 2RF                        COOKING 2
01-877 1700                                                  COST £23

Once customers have found the restaurant, crouching between a launderette and health-food shop, they are invariably won over by the combination of understated orientalism – silk prints, brass gongs, burning incense and Chiengmai blue tableware – freshly cooked Thai food and discreet family service. Dishes live up to the full descriptions on the menu, with flavours which are clearly differentiated from dish to dish: in gai tomkhar, the lemongrass adds the right fragrance to the coconut cream broth; in neua phat bai, basil and garlic give subtlety to stir-fried beef. Kiew grob – very crisp wun-tun with the merest touch of minced pork served with plum sauce – shows excellent deep frying, and fried noodles, generously covered with egg, pork and shrimp, have been recommended. For those with a sweet tooth, there is golden banana cooked in coconut. Tea complements the food better than wine or beer. House wine £5.95.

CHEF: Mrs Pissamai   PROPRIETOR: Mr Parayuth
OPEN: Tue to Sun, D only
CLOSED: 25 and 26 Dec
MEALS: 6.30 to 11
PRICES: £11 (£19). Service 12.5%
CARDS: Access, Amex, Diners, Visa
SEATS: 35. Private parties: 35 main room. Children welcome. Music

## Burt's ♥                                                    map 14

| 42 Dean Street, W1V 5AP | COOKING 3 |
| 01-734 3339 and 439 0972 | COST £26–£42 |

This year's London openings have eschewed plush and flounce with a vengeance, in favour of hard surfaces and colour at a minimum, or certainly a monotone. Burt's, owned by the partnership which operates Inigo Jones, is named after a composer of musical comedies: quite why is never revealed. It is crisp, it is cool, it is mostly angular, with softenings from the furniture, the carpet and the tables themselves. The bar and reception area is the ultimate in sloping-shouldered svelte, giving way to a light, almost cold, dining-room in blues with monochrome (of course) photographs on the walls. A touch of simplicity, over-riding the style, is given by blue and white china. The pictorial shirts of the waiting staff seem almost camp-*paysan* but are quite fun. The food, however, is anything but simple. Capitalising on Inigo Jones's great success with vegetarian cookery developed by Paul Gayler (chief reviver of its fortunes), the team here have created a menu split equally between vegetarian and fish dishes. For carnivores, there are four meats, which do not read so interestingly as the other sections, tucked behind a flap in the menu. The slight archness of the headings: 'From the Earth' and 'From the Sea' may give rise to concern but this does not carry through to the food itself which, though pretty to a degree, is meant to be full flavoured. Early meals have produced some recommendations: a watercress soup, creamy yet with bite; lightly poached oysters cooled in a jelly with black and red caviare; a risotto of wild rice and asparagus; mousseline of smoked eel; a sablé of polenta with wild mushrooms and a blue cheese sauce; bavarois of chocolate and mint; pear and ginger crème brûlée. Comments have mentioned the quality of flavours in the polenta and wild mushroom dish – intense mushrooms, for once justifying their use, well balanced by a strong sauce but not enhanced by a poor polenta; fine though simple meat cookery in a fillet steak with confit of garlic; good dauphinois potatoes. There have also been occasional errors of tasting, which count in cooking as precise as this: vegetables inadequately glazed and so tasting of caster sugar, not caramel; too much salt here, too light a hand with chocolate there, and a failure to top properly a burnt cream. Breads include London's version of *schwarzbrot*: this is a soft, sweet, spongiform affair that should not be made. The wine list is worth exploration, especially because the producers are first rate and not everything is impossibly dear. One reader wrote of the unexpected pleasure in finding a Clos Fourtet 1960 in halves at under £14. It drank perfectly, though the year may be unpropitious. House wines start at £8.50; the food is not as cheap. It does not outface with quantity, a plus mark. Many will still be hungry when desserts are reached. Those who value according to weight may nonetheless be shocked, for the menu steers refreshingly away from the hackneyed luxuries. 'Suggested' service is a steep 15 per cent.

CHEFS: Andrew Magson and Phil Mears   PROPRIETORS: Peter Ward and Jean-Jacques Kaeser
OPEN: Mon to Sat, exc Sat L
MEALS: 12.15 to 2, 5.30 to 11.30
PRICES: £24 (£35), Set L and D (until 7pm) £16.85 (£26). Service 15%
CARDS: Access, Amex, Diners, Visa
SEATS: 60. Private parties: 100 main room, 40 private room. Vegetarian meals. Children welcome. Wheelchair access (also WC). Music. Air-conditioned

## Le Cadre
map 10

10 Priory Road, N8 7RD
01-348 0606

COOKING 2
COST £20–£31

The blue awning, the tables on the pavement, the general tone of decoration, pictures and menu, not to mention the chef, announce this firmly as a French restaurant, albeit in Crouch End. Much of the cooking is handled in the French way too, though a blue cheese and red onion sauce with a lamb steak and a tart of banana and chocolate with a raspberry sauce – 'such things, unlike prison sentences, are best served consecutively, not concurrently' – may be more to the English taste. There is also a vein of sweetness revealed by dishes such as hare pâté in puff pastry with a honey sauce and prunes, and a mousse of John Dory with blackcurrants with a red wine sauce. Daniel Delagarde's cooking has impressed reporters for accuracy of seasoning – a smoked salmon mousse with dill and cucumber sauce did not offend by over-salting – and for delicacy of technique, so that a roast pigeon breast served with turnips and a mousse of its liver on a port sauce was praised most extravagantly for its mousse. Vegetables seem often to include sauté potatoes and a little mixture of green this and that: the potatoes have been tired but the this and that cooked accurately. Cheeses are often a good selection and rhubarb or blueberry sorbets please by their novelty as well as their flavour. The service is amiable and informed. The wine list is commendably short, only French, and priced very generously. Travellers might think themselves in Scotland, the mark-ups seem so reasonable. House wine is £6.50.

*The* Guide *always appreciates hearing about changes of chef or owner.*

CHEF: Daniel Delagarde    PROPRIETORS: David Misselbrook and Marie Fedyk
OPEN: Mon to Sat, D only
CLOSED: 2 weeks Aug, 25 to 30 Dec, bank hols
MEALS: 7 to 10.30
PRICES: £18 (£26), Set D £12.50 (£20). Cover £1. Service 10%
CARDS: Access, Amex, Visa
SEATS: 40. 12 tables outside. Private parties: 50 main room. Children welcome. Wheelchair access. Music

## Café Bistro

map 10

| 107 Humber Road, SE3 7LW | COOKING 1 |
| 01-858 7577 | COST £26 |

Don't be deceived by the French-bistro look of the place; behind the awnings is a popular local Italian restaurant. Go for the good stock-based soups, authentic, well-flavoured tomato sauces, and plate-filling portions: a whole breast of chicken with peppers, olives and tomatoes; three heaped halves of stuffed peppers with risotto. Vegetables and desserts can be high points. It's worth knowing about in an area with precious little competition, but take note that it can end up being pricey. The wine list is basic. House Italian at £6.

CHEF: Sarah Lo Vecchio    PROPRIETORS: Domenico and Sarah Lo Vecchio
OPEN: Tue to Sat, D only
CLOSED: last week Aug, first week Sept, Christmas
MEALS: 7 to 11
PRICES: £14 (£22)
SEATS: 38. 2 tables outside. Private parties: 20 main room, 12 private room. Vegetarian meals. Children welcome. Music

## Le Café du Marché

map 11

| 22 Charterhouse Square | |
| Smithfield Market, EC1M 6AH | COOKING 2 |
| 01-608 1609 | COST £17−£29 |

Properly speaking a restaurant, the café is, happily, of quite a different breed to most others in the City: open in the evening as well as at lunchtime, it is neither overly smart nor meant primarily for business entertaining. The ground-floor dining-room, with brick and white walls hung with various French posters and a huge mirror at the back, has a bustling atmosphere, but is spacious enough that you can hold a conversation without shouting. Most dishes are regional French – moules, brandade de morue, lapin à la genièvre, beignets de cervelle and duck terrine are among those recommended this year – but there's an oriental streak of stir-fries, satay and so on. Portions are generous, as are the servings of old-fashioned vegetables. Cooking is competent. Service, skilled but sometimes slow when over-extended, is as French as the food. The upstairs dining-room, serving mainly charcoal grills with frites, is now open in the evening as well as at lunchtime and follows the reasonable prices downstairs. House French Merlot and Chilean Sauvignon Blanc, £6.50.

CHEF: Rupert Pitt, Stephen Bullock and Ewan Yapp   PROPRIETOR: C. K. Graham-Wood
OPEN: Mon to Sat, exc Sat L
MEALS: 12 to 2.30, 6 to 10
PRICES: Set L and D £10 (£17) to £16.50 (£24). Service 15%
CARDS: Access, Visa
SEATS: 50. Private parties: 50 main room. Vegetarian meals. Children's helpings. No
children under 2. No pipes in dining-room. Music

## Café Flo

map 11

205 Haverstock Hill, NW3 4QG
01-435 6744

COOKING 1
COST £10—£20

A handy, local bistro, and now the parent of Flo's Bar and Grill, opposite (as
well as a less impressive offspring in St Martin's Lane), Flo's is more popular
and crowded than ever. The atmosphere remains relaxed, with jazz and blues
in the background, and the formula is unchanged. There is a *carte* with various
plats du jour plus set menus. The style tends towards French provincial,
although moussaka des légumes and grilled lemon sole are found along with
not-so-French soups, salads and pastas. There are also more ambitious dishes,
such as poached salmon in a lime and chive sauce or grilled rib of beef served
with a béarnaise sauce and red cabbage. Reports are mixed and suggest that the
kitchen seems to be getting hurried and so the cooking is consequently losing
its edge. First courses, such as the soup of the day, and puddings, such as the
apple tart, seem to impress more than main courses. Meals end on a high note
with powerful coffee. Service is brisk, though prone to panic, and there is some
hustling in a business-like style. House French £7.25; CELLARMAN'S CHOICE :
Lost Hills, California White, £9.25.

CHEF: Philip Unwin   PROPRIETOR: Russel Joffe
OPEN: all week
MEALS: 12 to 3 (3.30 Sat, 3.45 Sun), 6 (6.30 Sat, 6.45 Sun) to 11.30 (11 Sun)
PRICES: £12 (£17), Set L and D £6.50 (£10) to £8.35 (£12). Snacks from £3.40. Minimum £5.
Service inc
CARDS: Access, Visa
SEATS: 38. 6 tables outside. Private parties: 8 main room. Vegetarian meals. Children
welcome. Wheelchair access. Music

## Canal Brasserie

map 11

Canalot Studios,
222 Kensal Road, W10 5BN
01-960 2732

COOKING 1
COST £25

What the River Café is to Hammersmith, the Canal Brasserie aspires to be to
Kensal Rise. They have in common a watery setting reached with difficulty (the
easiest approach here is off Ladbroke Grove, just south of the Grand Union
Canal). Both serve as a daytime canteen for the neighbours who share their
premises, in this case the media types of Canalot Studios. Where Café and
Brasserie part company is over style: less assured and incisive in Kensal Road,
though the Victorian chocolate factory has its appeal, with open lift, porthole
views of the canal, dramatic sculptures in the foyer, and even a DJ'd watchdog

to supervise nocturnal comings and goings. The mood is relaxed and the service amiable, whether for breakfast at 9am Monday to Friday, a drink in the bar, a light meal at odd hours, or a regular lunch or dinner, under a changing display of paintings 'mainly by unknowns'. The menu is eclectic and rather overwritten, in the 'duo of sauces' and 'wrapped in a blanket of spinach' mode, but it serves its purpose of providing mostly fresh and interesting food: soups, salads and little parcels of this and that to begin with, then fish, fowl and enterprising game in season, with more than lip-service paid to vegetarians. On a good day you might meet the brioche of duck foie gras, the monkfish collops with tarragon, the hot avocado strudel, or the steamed pudding with plums. At other times there might be bland mousses, too many fruit garnishes, and some negligent dishes (out-of-season asparagus soup, undressed langoustine salad). But Nicholas Anderson, whose name has appeared on the menu as chef since the Harrises opened in 1987, has simplified and strengthened many of his ideas, a direction worth pursuing. The wine list is short, well chosen and cheap. House French is £5.70. CELLARMAN'S CHOICE : Hardy's Nottage Hill Shiraz 1986, £8.95; New Zealand Coopers Creek Dry White 1987, £8.45.

CHEF: Nicholas Anderson   PROPRIETORS: Antony and Alexandra Harris
OPEN: all week, exc Sat L and Sun D
MEALS: 12 to 3.30, 6 to 10.30
PRICES: £13 (£21). Snacks from £1.80
CARDS: Access, Visa
SEATS: 60. 6 tables outside. Private parties: 150 main room. Vegetarian meals. Children's helpings. Music. Air-conditioned

## Candlewick Room                                                    map 11

45 Old Broad Street, EC2N 1HT                                    COOKING  3
01-628 7929                                                         COST  £36

A sort of ship on dry land: you mount stairs and gangway to the floor above Mr Pontac's Wine Bar in a modern block. Once inside you can sit looking out of a vast (dusty) window on to a not very exciting street scene. This is a wholly French restaurant catering for the City. The standards are higher than this implies. The short menu is well supplemented by changing specials according to the market. A lunch (this is not a place for casual dining) of red pepper and Florence fennel soup, fillet of beef with horseradish and chive sauce and a cold bread-and-butter pudding with an orange sauce was fairly purchased and competently cooked. Flavours, for instance in the horseradish sauce, were not as bold as they might have been. Why City folk need their menu in French when chef and owners are anything but must be a monument to the importance of 1992. House French, from £7.50. CELLARMAN'S CHOICE : Chablis, 1986 Bernard de Monceny, £12.95; Ch. La Tour du Moulin, Fronsac 1979, £10.50.

*The text of entries is based on unsolicited reports sent in by readers, backed up by inspections conducted anonymously. The factual details under the text are from questionnaires the* Guide *sends to all restaurants that feature in the book.*

CHEF: Mark Hix  PROPRIETORS: Philip and Sarah Isles
OPEN: Mon to Fri, L only
CLOSED: between Christmas and New Year
MEALS: 11.45 to 2.30
PRICES: Set L £21 (£30). Cover £1.50. Service 12.5%
CARDS: Access, Amex, Diners, Visa
SEATS: 40. Private parties: 40 main room, 14 private room. Vegetarian meals. Children welcome. Smart dress preferred. Air-conditioned

---

## ▲ *Capital Hotel* ▮                                                    map 12

Basil Street, SW3 1AT                                                  COOKING 4
01-589 5171                                                         COST £25−£51

This select hotel in a street that leads to Harrods continues its remarkable career. It must feel strange to create an institution in one's own lifetime, yet that − in a few short years, to English people and foreign visitors alike − is what David Levin's Capital has become. Refurbishment has gone on apace and the restaurant was closed early in 1989 only to reopen in a blush of elegant pinks. It is nearly box-like, so high is its ceiling, so small the room for a West End hotel. This scale, however, enabled it to be treated as a real restaurant long before other hotels, the Dorchester or Le Meridien Piccadilly for instance, pulled themselves together, gastronomically speaking. Since taking over the kitchen in 1988, Phillip Britten has continued his mission of simplification − gone the silly French menu − and of refinement, which depends on great skill and is apparent from the flavours imparted to the food, but not heedlessly displayed in visual or linguistic fireworks. There is a *carte*, changing every couple of months, of eight beginning courses, four fish, seven meats and a like number of desserts. Then at lunchtime there are two short menus at set prices, with two choices at each stage. These prices really do seem to include everything except alcoholic beverage. An inspection earlier this year revealed a lightness bordering on a wish to avoid offence in a fish soup and a salad of artichoke and rabbit, which formed a pleasing introduction to a small fillet steak on a bed of ceps 'of greater flavour than any eaten in England this year'. The sauce − beef, wine and ceps − was not so strong as to mask the taste of the meat itself. Spinach and salsify came as vegetables, cooked properly. This was yet another place that didn't serve potatoes. To finish, a chocolate mousse without fuss, made of the best chocolate, with the egg just breaking the bitterness to create luxury and sophistication. If that was a simple lunch, the meal that began with mousseline of duck and continued with breast of pheasant served with dauphinois potatoes must have been, as its reporter felt, close to paradise. The details of the meal − free mineral water, fair (though not really good) bread, coffee and petits fours − are of the standard expected. Service is older fashioned than the menu; 'a raised eyebrow is all that is needed to gain attention.' Some will love it, others may feel abashed. Tips are not expected. The wine list is more expensive than the food (which is not cheap, save at lunch). There is one wine, a Pinot d'Alsace, under £10. The selection is entirely French, with particularly sonorous clarets. The house red, Les Bruliers de Beychevelle 1983 is excellent, as it should be: it must pan out as the dearest house wine in London, at £16.50. CELLARMAN'S CHOICE : Bourgogne Aligoté

1987, £12.50; Ch. Meyney 1980, £25. The best value comes from 'Capital Choice' at the front of the list.

CHEF: Phillip Britten   PROPRIETOR: David Levin
OPEN: all week
MEALS: 12.30 to 2.30, 6.30 to 10.30 (10 Sun)
PRICES: £34 (£43), Set L £16.50 (£25) and £18.50 (£29). Minimum £25 at D. Service inc
CARDS: Access, Amex, Carte Blanche, Diners, Visa
SEATS: 35. Private parties: 10 main room, 4 and 24 private rooms. Car-park, 12 places.
Children's helpings. No children under 4. Smart dress preferred. No pipes in dining-room.
Wheelchair access (3 steps; also WC). Air-conditioned
ACCOMMODATION: 54 rooms, all with bath/shower. Rooms for disabled. Lift. B&B £141.50
to £173. Baby facilities. Pets welcome. Afternoon teas. Air- conditioning. TV. Phone.
Confirm the day before [GHG]

## Caprice                                                                    map 13

Arlington House
Arlington Street, SW1A 1RT                                          COOKING 3
01-629 2239                                                          COST £29

Coolly elegant behind its black canopy, the Caprice is one of the few places that manages to be fashionable ('always full'), serve decent food and be personally directed. As one happy customer put it, 'it's a good café for café society.' For the glitterati, there is the attraction of knowing that they are safe from the eyes of the papparazzi; for everybody else, there is the food and plenty of action during gaps between courses. The streamlined grey decoration and extravagant flower arrangements still look good and the room feels spacious even when full. On the menu there are some 30 dishes, an urbane mix of international with an Italian bent – scallops with spinach noodles or grilled polenta – as well as good daily soups and fish, notably warm-water exotics. Salmon fishcakes have been popular and steamed turbot, split-pea soup and fresh tuna have all been recommended. A-visit-a-fortnight-for-the-last-two-years reporter singled out crudités, grilled aubergines and tomatoes, fresh tuna steak, super chips, good apple and lemon tarts, ice-creams and the invariably first-class fresh fruit as reasons for contentment. The current chef – new since the last *Guide* – has reinforced the skills of this kitchen. The wine list, in ascending price order by arbitrary section, repays study in, for example, the middle French reaches. House French and Italian, £5.75.

CHEF: Tony Howorth   PROPRIETORS: C.J. Corbin and J.R.B. King
OPEN: all week
MEALS: 12 to 3, 6 to 12
PRICES: £16 (£24). Cover £1
CARDS: Access, Amex, Diners, Visa
SEATS: 70. No children under 5. Wheelchair access. Music. Air-conditioned

*The 1991* Guide *will be published before Christmas 1990. Reports on meals are most welcome at any time of the year, but are extremely valuable in the spring. Send them to* The Good Food Guide, FREEPOST, *2 Marylebone Road, London NW1 1YN. No stamp is needed if posted in the UK.*

## Carraro's

map 10

32 Queenstown Road, SW8 3RX
01-720 5986

COOKING 3
COST £16–£31

Carraro's has now got well into its stride as one of the promising new-wave Italian restaurants outside central London. Subdued walls, divided between rough grey brickwork and part mock-classical *trompe-l'oeil* frescos in a sequence of three rooms, set the tone for the character of the clientele: part business, part smart residents. The owner, Gian Franco Carraro, who ran Rugantino in Soho for over 20 years, moved here to concentrate on regional dishes at reasonable prices. His northern Italian origins are reflected in the menu's rustic soups, fine risottos – seafood or vegetables like leek and wild mushroom – and Venetian dishes like salt cod, squid in ink or calf's liver in red wine served with polenta. These are indeed good value, although there are also showier items, such as carpaccio of salmon and grilled scampi flamed with grappa, and more expensive seasonal dishes. Home-made pasta has been excellent, as in ravioli from Belluno, tinted pink by the beetroot and mascarpone stuffing and properly dressed with melted butter flavoured with poppy seeds and grated Parmesan, and delicious gnocchi. Careful buying shows in the bresaola, prosciutto and northern Italian cheeses. Unusual puddings have included crespelle filled with crème pâtissière flavoured with a hazelnut liqueur, as well as a vanilla semifreddo. Espresso coffee is good. Service, by young Italian waiters, is courteous, quick and knowledgeable. The wine list gives a good range, though not cheap, of Italian districts, with growers such as Antinori, Jermann, Bolla and Biondi Santi to the fore. House wines are £6.90 for a Soave and £8.25 for a Valpolicella. CELLARMAN'S CHOICE : Pinot Grigio Collio 1988, Comini, £12.90; Montepulciano d'Abruzzo 1987, Umani Ronchi, £7.25.

CHEF: Jairo Carvajal   PROPRIETOR: Gian Franco Carraro
OPEN: Mon to Sat, exc Sat L
MEALS: 12 to 2.30, 7 to 11.30
PRICES: £16 (£26), Set L and D £10.95 (£16). Cover £1.50
CARDS: Access, Amex, Visa
SEATS: 90. Private parties: 100 main room, 20 private room. Vegetarian meals. Children's helpings. No-smoking area. Music. Air-conditioned

## Cavaliers ♥

map 10

129 Queenstown Road, SW8 3RH
01-720 6960

COOKING 3
COST £23–£43

'The cooking shows an abundance of flair and technique; the starters are superb. The lobster ravioli comprises a fat claw wrapped in an al dente envelope accompanied by a lovely seafoody sauce, covered with slightly spicy tomatoes.' So wrote one enthusiastic reader. The Cavaliers have settled into this corner space in the Queenstown Road strip of smartness. You enter, after ringing, by a side door: the dining-room is unexpectedly spacious and handsome (though wear is apparent here and there), the table settings are generous and seemly. David Cavalier cooks his heart out while Susan controls the dining-room. At times there is still a sense of embattlement among the heathen: this is a self-consciously British restaurant (foreign staff notwithstanding) poaching on French preserves. More strength to their efforts, many would say. The actual manner of cooking is British only in its blend of modernity with local materials (viz the board of English cheeses that many praise). In recipes and technique it leans on classical France and its latter-day interpreters. The preoccupation with appearance and status works against the skills shown by David Cavalier. Presentation is complex. A main course of quail roasted in honey came out with a central disc of rösti potatoes topped by a quartered quail, in its turn surmounted by a second, whole, bird. This had the air of a suttee pyre. Around about was the sauce and a succession of vegetable items: a mould of spinach topped by cross-bones of asparagus, a couple of turnips, a potato gratin on top of beetroot, and a super-rich tartlet of mushroom mixed with hollandaise sauce. This succession of little ingredients was overpowered by too sweet a sauce and too much nutmeg in the spinach. The quail had very little inherent flavour. Misplaced priorities are seen, too, in a handsome bourride where seasoning was quite forgotten and the aïoli promised on the menu was barely perceptible. At the dessert stage the menu announces a 'wild tuile' that is filled with apricot ice-cream and decorated with fruit. The dish can be seen in Nico Ladenis' book of recipes (a number of other dishes are borrowed from modern masters). The tuile was good, wild in shape not composition; the ice-cream was fair; the fruit was a mélange of the tasteless sort available in London in March. The effect looked as pretty as a picture, but the eating was tortured by tedium. Were the kitchen to resist photo-finishes, it might be as good as any in London. The wine list has lengthened since the last *Guide*, especially in clarets. There are some decent wines at under £14, a gesture not often encountered at restaurants operating at this price level, and the Loires (supplied 'from a friend's wine cellar in the heart of the Loire valley') are exceptional for old Vouvray and Chinon. Beware the orange juice: it has come from a bottle, when fresh was requested. House Bordeaux £9.50. CELLARMAN'S CHOICE : Taltarni Shiraz 1983, £12.80; Savennières, Ch. de Chamboureau 1987, £11.95.

CHEF: David Cavalier   PROPRIETORS: David and Susan Cavalier
OPEN: Tue to Sat
MEALS: 12.15 to 2, 7.15 to 10.30 (11 Sat if busy)
PRICES: Set L £16.50 (£23), Set D £25 (£36)
CARDS: Access, Amex, Diners, Visa
SEATS: 50. Private parties: 50 main room. No children under 10. Smart dress preferred.
Air-conditioned

## Chanterelle                                                             map 12

| 119 Old Brompton Road, SW7 3RN | COOKING 1 |
|---|---|
| 01-373 5522 and 7390 | COST £13–£24 |

Goes on from year to year, having first appeared in the *Guide*, approved by the good and the great, in 1959. That was under its first owner, Walter Baxter, with the interior design by a young Terence Conran. It continues, now with Fergus Provan as chef/proprietor, to offer a *bistro du quartier* service to residents of Kensington: a fair price for fair food, usually served amiably. The style of the cooking is more adventurous than bistro, at least in first courses, but what draws people back is the bedrock of soup, poached egg tart with pipérade, calf's liver and green bacon, navarin of lamb, salmon in pastry with cream and dill. That and the price – almost halved at lunchtime. 'Reasonable, but not outstanding,' was one summing-up. The wine list is short, French and acceptable. House French, £5.90. CELLARMAN'S CHOICE : Gewürztraminer, Traber 1985, £9; Côte de Beaune Villages, Jaboulet-Vercherre 1985, £11.50.

CHEF/PROPRIETOR: Fergus Provan
OPEN: all week
CLOSED: 4 days at Christmas
MEALS: 12 to 2.30, 7 to 11.30
PRICES: Set L £8 (£13), Set D £14.50 (£20). Service 12% for parties of 6 or more
CARDS: Access, Amex, Diners, Visa
SEATS: 45. 3 tables outside. Private parties: 15 main room. Children welcome. Wheelchair access

## Le Chef
map 11

41 Connaught Street, W2 2BB
01-262 5945

COOKING 2
COST £21–£26

'Very much a French-style bistro, but none the worse for that, although perhaps a coat of paint would improve the ambience.' 'It maintains a splendidly high standard of authentic bourgeois French cuisine.' These are typical of comments received about Alan King's stalwart family-run establishment. Soupe de poisson with croûtons and rouille gets special mentions. Ordinary weekday menus include such dishes as duck with olives, navarin of lamb, kidneys in port wine, skate with black butter, tarte aux fruits, and on Saturday nights there is a set menu of four courses plus cheese and coffee for £19 which has recently included smoked salmon pancakes and monkfish in leek and white wine sauce. All is carefully and correctly prepared to order and briskly served by white-aproned waiters. 'I'd like to see it in the *Guide* for another ten years, they give value for money.' House Bergerac, £6.25. CELLARMAN'S CHOICE : Ch. Millet, Graves 1982, £15.75; Pouilly Fuissé 1987, Javillier, £17.75.

CHEF/PROPRIETOR: Alan King
OPEN: Mon to Sat, exc Sat L
CLOSED: last 2 weeks Aug
MEALS: 12.30 to 2.30, 7 to 11.30
PRICES: £15 (£21), Set Sat D £19 (£22). Cover 50p. Service inc
CARDS: Access, Amex, Diners, Visa
SEATS: 45. 3 tables outside. Private parties: 20 main room, 20 private room. Children's helpings on request. Wheelchair access (2 steps). Music

## Cherry Orchard
map 10

241–245 Globe Road, E2 0JD
01-980 6678

COOKING 1
COST £11

The Orchard continues to flower with smart décor and ever-changing menus. Unlicensed, it has the advantage for the price-conscious that you can bring your own wine to complement such dishes as ravioli with cheese and tamari sauce or creamy coconut beans and rice. An abundance of children at lunchtime may give indigestion to some not so encumbered, but the garden attracts those out to enjoy a reasonably priced family meal – and who, anyway, should object to unformed versions of themselves? Vegans are catered for.

CHEFS: Sheena Marsh and Margie Wood Elsner   PROPRIETORS: Pure Land Co-operative
OPEN: Tue to Sat
CLOSED: 1 week at Christmas
MEALS: 12 to 3, 6 to 10.30
PRICES: £6 (£9), Snacks from 95p. Service of 10% for parties of 6 or more. Unlicensed, but bring your own: corkage 95p
CARDS: Access, Visa
SEATS: 54. 6 tables outside. Private parties: 25 main room. Vegetarian meals. Children's helpings. No smoking. Wheelchair access (1 step)

## Chez Liline
map 10

| | |
|---|---|
| 101 Stroud Green Road, N4 3PX | COOKING 2 |
| 01-263 6550 | COST £28 |

The surroundings and the furnishings of Chez Liline will surprise some but delight or amuse those who recognise that value lurks in unexpected corners. This is a fish restaurant: Mediterranean and tropical mainly, but its salmon dishes are highly rated too. A reporter whom the *Guide* respects contributed this comment: 'vastly under-rated, a very serious fish restaurant. They have a "hand" with spices and herbs (especially green coriander and various peppercorns) much lighter and more adept than many famous Frenchmen. Examples are scallops with oyster mushrooms, calamari sauté with green coriander, moules marinière, bouillabaisse. Six people paid £125 including one bottle of Côtes de Buzet. Vast quantities of prime fish.' Whether everyone is as happy as this may depend on their attitude to externals. Coffee is good. The wine list is an exercise in taciturnity, 'Pouilly-sur-Loire, £8.75' not exactly helping towards a decision, but it is a finely chosen short French selection at very fair prices. House French, £5.25. As we go to press, a new branch, La Gaulette, has opened at 53 Cleveland Street, W1 (01-580 7608). Sylvain Ho-Wing-Cheong, who was originally at Chez Liline, is doing the cooking. Very first reports are optimistic: fresh fish, chosen raw, cooked there and then.

CHEF: Mario Ho-Wing-Cheong   PROPRIETOR: Liline Ng-Yu-Tin
OPEN: all week, exc Sun L
MEALS: 12 to 2.30, 6.30 to 11
PRICES: £16 (£23). Minimum £8.50
SEATS: 44. 2 tables outside. Private parties: 40 main room. Vegetarian meals. Children's helpings. Music

## Chez Moi
map 10

| | |
|---|---|
| 1 Addison Avenue, W11 4QS | COOKING 3 |
| 01-603 8267 | COST £19–£31 |

The best thing about 'old-fashioned' restaurants is the pleasure of belonging, the knowledge of reliability and the relaxed acceptance of a tried system. Chez Moi appears to go from strength to strength: so old (yet a mere two decades) that customers liken it to the Connaught; enough on its toes to keep interest awake. The decoration is of warm red, with mirrors bouncing light, and good linen; solid. The clientele, leavened by BBC, is loyal and substantial. The waiters, at times sardonic, are competent. The menu is reminiscent of a French city restaurant: old-style printing, a longstanding repertoire most famous for its lamb, saddle of hare, tartare of salmon and ceviche. Set lunch (fair value) and daily specials show a wider (and wilder) range: deep-fried prawn balls with a lobster and ginger sauce; a mixture of sweetbreads and monkfish with two sauces; and Thai chicken and pojarski of lamb, to draw on two different cultures. Puddings are old-fashioned, well made and rich. The quality of this place, besides standards that are mostly high, is in the affection it retains in the eyes of its customers: a precious attribute. The wine list is French, French and French with about 60 bins. The best thing is to look at the 'Sélection du Mois'. Prices are medium. House French is £6. CELLARMAN'S CHOICE : Ch. Lyonnat 1981, Lussac St-Emilion, £12.50; Mercurey Clos de L'Evêque 1985, Suremain, £16.50.

CHEF: Richard Walton  PROPRIETORS: Richard Walton and Colin Smith
OPEN: Mon to Sat, exc Sat L
CLOSED: bank hols, Christmas to New Year
MEALS: 12.30 to 2, 7 to 11
PRICES: £18 (£26), Set L £12.50 (£19)
CARDS: Access, Amex, Diners, Visa
SEATS: 45. Children's helpings. No pipes in dining-room. Wheelchair access. Air-conditioned

## Chez Nico ♥                                              map 13

35 Great Portland Street, W1N 5DD          COOKING 5
01-436 8846                                COST £37−£70

Nico Ladenis and his wife Dinah-Jane have moved to new premises just north of Oxford Street in the garment district, bordering on the broadcasting zone − certainly well away from government and society (and coach station), among whom they camped in Victoria. The new restaurant is larger; a simple space, in the shape of an L, light, clean and handsome. Mirrors open it still further, including a mirrored dado rail to amuse the solitary diner with perspective and angles on eavesdropped conversations. More amusement may be had from the pictures, which are good. *Lebensraum* is still at a premium and a few tables are awkwardly placed, given their rental per square inch. Cutlery, china and glass is as good and as fresh as might be expected. Service is by a large and proficient team. Eating a meal cooked by Nico Ladenis is memorable: that is his strength. Flavours are pronounced, sometimes assertive, techniques are sure, complexity is usually masked so that simplicity remains the lasting impression. He appears prepared to pursue a single flavour to its end and present it on a plate. Whereas some cooks, working perhaps in the tradition of refined French cuisine, will impress by a sweet harmony of several notes, his style is more forceful. Miscalculation may make it a bludgeon but that seems a rare event as he resumes full activity in the kitchen. An example of this power is a consommé of langoustines so deep coloured it might have been yeast extract, yet it did not stick the lips together and it tasted superlatively of langoustines, sweet and beguiling. A surprising addition to this was a sprig of leaf coriander. This almost over-toppled the edifice. Another instance is an escalope of salmon lightly browned with a chive cream sauce that seemed to rely more on stock than cream, 'the depth of flavour did not detract from the taste of the fish: the combination had great intensity.' Harmony has been cited as the result of a fricassee of artichoke and calf's sweetbreads flanked by a pile of wild mushrooms sauced with their own essence. The bludgeon can be discerned in reports of, for example, a leg of chicken stuffed with liver and sage, wrapped in caul and roasted; the sauce is slightly sweet and the chicken is placed atop a fine layer of potato and sauerkraut. The dryness of the liver and the strength of the sage vitiate the success of the dish, which should have full marks for bravery. The catalogue of excellence might continue. Nor would it stop at dessert, where are found the virtues that have come before: lemon tart is the best in London (save the pastry has been seen as too thick) for balance of sugar and acid and for the supreme egginess of the filling; a marquise au chocolat with green marzipan wrapping has a deep coffee sauce to slice through the richness; apple tart comes warm, with cinnamon ice-cream to ease its passage. Coffee and petits fours, also amuse-gueule, are up to the mark. Bread is excellent. There is a way of making a very light crumb using characterful flour. This may lack the definition enthusiasts desire but is ideal with food that needs a foil not a competitor. The little light loaflets have excellent crisp, thin crusts and yet some taste; perfect restaurant bread. Butter is Echiré. The wine list is very fine. It has 10 bottles (out of just under 200 bins) priced under £20; 14 come at more than £100; more than 50 are between £50 and £100. It is a pity it has to be so. Choice in half-bottles is generous and thoroughbred. The clarets and burgundies come from the finest makers though there is a feeling of the Rolls-Royce rather than the nervy hand-built sports car about the names; Alsace and Rhône likewise, with too little variety given the wealth of skills in those regions. It may be objected by supporters of the restaurant that its greatest drawback is not of its choosing: exclusivity. This comes also, however, from little things within its power: a menu entirely in French which leaves non-French speakers (why should all English eaters speak that language?) dependent on orotund and boring explication; a certain reputation for ferocity, as often as not quite belied in the event, yet apparently encouraged even now. And then, the prices. One can only regret them, certainly not accusing Nico Ladenis of meanness in materials or effort. It should also be noted that the set-price three-course lunch is worth every penny. Tipping is not encouraged. Vegetarians are discouraged. Mr Ladenis regrets that it is not a suitable place for children.

CHEFS: Nico Ladenis and Paul Flynn   PROPRIETORS: Nico and Dinah-Jane Ladenis
OPEN: Mon to Fri
CLOSED: 10 days at Christmas, 3 weeks in summer
MEALS: 12.15 to 2, 7 to 11
PRICES: Set L £25 (£37), Set D £34 (£58). Service 15% L only
CARDS: Access, Diners, Visa
SEATS: 48. Private parties: 48 main room, 12 private room. Children restricted. Smart dress preferred. No pipes in dining-room. Wheelchair access (1 step). Air-conditioned

♠ *denotes an outstanding wine cellar;* ♟ *denotes a good wine list, worth travelling for. See the Introduction for a fuller explanation.*

# Chiang Mai

map 14

48 Frith Street, W1V 5TE
01-437 7444

COOKING 1
COST £15−£25

Now one of the oldest of the huddle of restaurants in Frith Street, one of the
only ones specialising in northern Thai cuisine and successfully sticking with
its original formula. The clean lines of the interior, with white walls and
wooden pillars, have worn well. On the menu of a hundred savoury dishes
there are the usual salads, soups and curries, all well made, and unusual
northern Thai spicy sausages. Imported exotic fish are good on the days of
delivery and hot-and-sour seafood salad in a spicy chilli sauce always draws
praise. Service could be better, as could the coffee, but the house Blanc de
Blancs is acceptable at £6.50. An introduction to Thai cooking may be found in
the proprietor's own book on the subject.

CHEF/PROPRIETOR: Vatcharin Bhumichitr
OPEN: Mon to Sat
MEALS: 12 to 3, 6 to 11.30
PRICES: £10 (£15), Set L and D for 2 £28.70 (£35) to £33.90 (£41). Service 10%
CARDS: Access, Amex, Visa
SEATS: 60. Private parties: 12 main room, 20 and 25 private rooms. Vegetarian meals.
Children welcome. Music

# China China

map 14

3 Gerrard Street, W1V 7LJ
01-439 7511

COOKING 2
COST £19

We said 'newest is often best' in last year's *Guide* for this busy, three-storey
restaurant on the corner of Gerrard Place. Happily, our expert still thinks it the
best Chinese snack place in the area. Go with the grain, therefore, and choose
such Cantonese one-plate dishes as char siu or roast duck with rice, variously
augmented noodles and stir-fries. We have heard little about more elaborate
dishes recently: are the crab with ginger and the fresh scallops as good as
before? House French is £5.50.

CHEFS: S.K. Tang and Mr Man   PROPRIETORS: Tang Express Ltd
OPEN: all week
MEALS: noon to midnight (1am Fri and Sat)
PRICES: £9 (£16). Service inc
CARDS: Access, Amex, Diners, Visa
SEATS: 150. Private parties: 60 main room. Children welcome. Music. Air-conditioned

# Chinon

map 10

25 Richmond Way, W14 0AS
01-602 4082

COOKING 2
COST £38

Tucked away in a shopping street off Shepherd's Bush Green, in an area that
was once a gastronomic desert, the Chinon has to be searched out. In this sense,
it has had to work hard for its clientele. Reports suggest that, after two years,
the cooking is still evolving and the ambitious ideas behind dishes stretch the

kitchen team, but that when things work there is good eating to be had at reasonable prices. An early summer meal of salmon with an artichoke heart encased in lettuce, followed by chicken in a mildly curried sauce served with lightly cooked baby sweetcorn, runner beans and potatoes, then a rich butterscotch meringue slice, was not faulted. Other similarly modern, imaginative ideas have been clam soup with coriander, saddle of hare on baked blood oranges with madeira sauce and quenelles of beetroot, and an almond shortcrust tartlet with cape gooseberries and lychees. The restaurant obviously enjoys the game season, if only because it gives meat of pronounced taste: another reason for the espousal of goose for party bookings in winter. Puddings have won high praise. Service is efficient and knowledgeable. The wine list is a model of conciseness, here and there too telescoped, but the quality of the choices will reassure the wondering. House wine is Duboeuf.

CHEFS/PROPRIETORS: Barbara Deane and Jonathon Hayes
OPEN: Tue to Sat, exc Sat L
CLOSED: most bank hols
MEALS: 12 to 2, 7 to 10 (11 Fri and Sat)
PRICES: £21 (£32). Minimum £11. Service 12%
CARDS: Access, Amex, Visa
SEATS: 24. Private parties: 30 main room. Smart dress preferred

## Christian's
map 10

1 Station Parade
Burlington Lane, W4 3HD          COOKING 1
01-995 0382 and 0208            COST £26

This dark green place is opposite Chiswick railway station. It is another spot to help remind the residents of W4 of their summer holidays in France, although it is hoped that the addition of Le Bistro (see entry) to Christian Gustin's kingdom does not mean a diminution in his presence here. The atmosphere is casual, conversation from the kitchen sometimes obtruding – it is on full view to the dining-room – but the cooking of soufflés and classics like salmon quenelles with a hollandaise is accurate; the saucing, for instance, of a breast of chicken with a herb and garlic sauce, is light yet sufficiently flavoured, and the vegetables, a rich dauphinois and generous quantities, give pleasure. Sometimes, an ingredient announced on the menu is hardly detectable by the tongue: orange in a ginger and orange sauce with salmon (hollandaise again), almond in an apricot and almond tart. Prices for a simple neighbourhood place are not low. There is a very short French wine list with house wine at £6.35. Coffee refills are offered.

CHEF/PROPRIETOR: Christian Gustin
OPEN: Tue to Sat, D only
CLOSED: bank hols
MEALS: 7.30 to 10.30
PRICES: £18 (£22). Service inc
SEATS: 40. 4 tables outside. Private parties: 8 main room. Vegetarian meals. Children welcome. No cigars/pipes in dining-room. Wheelchair access (2 steps). Music

# *Chuen Cheng Ku*  map 14

17 Wardour Street, W1V 3HD                                    COOKING 2
01-437 1398                                                  COST £9–£24

The trolleys come trundling round the labrynthine series of rooms, each in the hands of a co-operative waitress happy to pass over whatever you request. Unless an adept, it is probable you will be unsure of the contents of each basket until bitten into – even if you have asked for explanations. The hungry will pile them up, the table will groan. Be warned, a little dim-sum goes further than first thought. An economical mode of eating. Drink strong tea to render the food more digestible. Maintaining its place among the better dim-sum establishments of the area, Chuen Cheng Ku is at its best during the lunchtime rush. Once the dim-sum are finished, after 6pm, there's a wide menu ranging through the sweet-and-sour sauced and crispy duck to the less mainstream steamed eel, baked pig's liver and fried lettuce with crabmeat sauce. Drink tea.

CHEF: Yat Au   PROPRIETORS: Choi and Kam Au
OPEN: all week
MEALS: 11 to midnight (11.30pm Sun)
PRICES: £11 (£20), Set L £5.50 (£9) to £10 (£14), Set D from £10 (£14). Service inc
CARDS: Access, Amex, Diners, Visa
SEATS: 400. Private parties: 150 main room, 50 and 80 private rooms. Vegetarian meals. Children welcome. Wheelchair access. Music

# *Ciboure*  map 11

21 Eccleston Street, SW1 9LX                                 COOKING 2
01-730 2505                                                  COST £21–£36

This impeccably cool dining-room, announced by its black awning, may serve as neighbourhood restaurant, if not for all the locals, then at least for their daytime professional neighbours. Of late the style, particularly the fixed-price lunch offering, has moved towards nouvelle cuisine paysanne with black pudding and cabbage stuffed with chicken livers appearing on the menu. Continuity with the last regime is strong, though Melanie Dixon matches specific vegetables with specific dishes rather than providing the same for all. The wine list is less expensive than might be expected for the location and is short and to the point. House Rhône, £7.90. CELLARMAN'S CHOICE : Moulin-à-Vent 1986, Paul Janin, £12.75; Reuilly 1986, Didier Martin, £12.75.

CHEF: Melanie Dixon   PROPRIETOR: Jean Louis Journade
OPEN: Mon to Fri
CLOSED: 3 weeks Aug
MEALS: 12 to 2.30, 7 to 11.15
PRICES: £18 (£27), Set L £14.50 (£21), Set D £17.50 (£26) to £20.50 (£30). Service 15%
CARDS: Access, Amex, Diners, Visa
SEATS: 36. Children welcome. No cigars/pipes in dining-room. Wheelchair access. Air-conditioned

*The* Guide *always appreciates hearing about changes of chef or owner.*

## Clarke's ♥ map 11

124 Kensington Church Street, W8 4BH         COOKING **4**
01-221 9225         COST £20−£38

This short stretch at the top of Kensington Church Street is home to two particular leaders in up-to-the-minute London restaurants as, decades ago, the Ark round the corner drew all the young fashionables. Sally Clarke has continued to attract plaudits for one of the few no-choice dinners in the capital and a style of cookery usually typed as Californian but which may be described as sophisticated-natural − that is, not natural at all. The restaurant is on two floors: a small room with a shop window at pavement level, with a tiny dispense bar at the back and a potential draught from the front door, then downstairs to a cool, light basement, deceptively large, with an open kitchen giving out on to one corner. The atmosphere is wonderfully fresh − striking a chord, perhaps, with the food and cooking. Next door is Clarke's shop. Every small restaurateur dreams of a retail outlet where the surplus energies (and dead time) of the kitchen may be turned to profit; few achieve the reality. Clarke's has done, largely through bread. Every midnight, the baking shift begins. The loaves, in many varieties, are some of the best (and most expensive) in London, sold along with truffles, pizza, tarts, cakes and cheese supplied by Neal's Yard, and served in the restaurant (not much left by 2pm).

Sally Clarke has not deviated from her initial schema: lunch is a good-value but short menu of three dishes in each course (fewer if you come late), while dinner is a no-choice four-course affair. Each is at an all-in price, though 'supper' is offered later in the evening, as an abbreviated dinner. Menus for evenings are planned a week in advance, thus allowing for allergies and violent dislikes to be coped with if warning is given. Sally Clarke cooks lunch herself but normally comes front-of-house at dinner. The char-grill dominates the style of cooking, olive oil the palette of flavour. Clarke's must use more olive oil than all the trattoria of old Soho put together. There are times when the cooking seems little more than assembly: cubes of marinated salmon, for instance, may arrive with cubes of cucumber, an unseasoned yoghurt dressing, some smart red leaves, smarter oil and a wedge of toasted rye bread. By contrast, a grilled breast of guinea-fowl of superlative flavour with crisp charred skin came with an intensely garlicked red pepper and parsley relish and a fine thin juice. This showed judgement in timing and balance of flavours. The simple approach is a tight-rope strung between the quality of the ingredients and the skill of balancing them by the right accompaniment. A spring lunch had a chicken with insufficient taste set next to an inert and gutless pesto, the whole swamped by too much olive oil. But the general voice is that there are few slip-ups. Though unwilling to be thrust into a Californian ghetto, Sally Clarke uses Alice Waters' recipes more than almost anyone else's − Girardet and Wolfgang Puck also enter her pantheon of sources. The Alice Waters' rich chocolate cake that can often be found on the menu (and in the shop) is nigh-on the best chocolate cake made in Britain today: a masterpiece of rich understatement. The wine list is in keeping with the cooking: not too long, wisely chosen, well served. Although there is a French presence (good at that), the Californians are first class. Clarke's is one of the small number of restaurants that succeed in feeding and nourishing without overload. It has been remarked that women chefs are often gentler on the digestions of their customers than are men. Whether this is the natural economy of their gender or the subtlety of their judgement is not settled. A conservative diner commented on leaving that he appeared to have been served nothing at all (and *no* potatoes), yet felt in perfect equilibrium.

CHEFS: Sally Clarke and Elizabeth Payne   PROPRIETOR: Sally Clarke
OPEN: Mon to Fri
CLOSED: 2 weeks Aug, 10 days Christmas, 4 days Easter, bank hols
MEALS: 12.30 to 2, 7.30 to 11
PRICES: Set L £16 (£20) to £18 (£22), Set D £28 (£32). Service inc
CARDS: Access, Visa
SEATS: 90. Private parties: 10 main room. Children welcome. Wheelchair access.
Air-conditioned

---

## ▲ *Connaught* ♀          map 13

Carlos Place, W1Y 6AZ        COOKING 4
01-499 7070        COST £30−£73

Young Members of Parliament are advised by their betters to observe the ways of the House for some time before speaking. Much the same might be said of the Connaught. Only the classiest hotel in this country could have the note, 'The price of the meal THREE COURSE is indicated next to the main dish' printed bold on its menu without a blush for illiteracy. However, with concentration and humility you will learn to love this place. Lots of people do. Lots swear by it as the most consistent, most genuine, most polite and handsomest restaurant in the capital. 'I have not really got the time to write you this letter, but when you come across such excellence, particularly in London, it's worth taking time out.' It needs an initiate to read the menu, about the most runic document in British catering. The waiters rarely elucidate it comprehensibly. When you do happen on a dish, as likely as not it takes too long to cook for you. Surprised by this, you may order something you never desired in the first place. 'I was taken to lunch and asked for guinea-fowl. I was promptly told it would take 45 minutes, so I hastily ordered roast beef from the trolley that was flaccid and overdone.' Persevere; as you learn, so you will adore. If you break the code, the cooking is indeed good. The service never fails to amaze. 'The bread was offered me. I pointed at the roll I wanted. The waiter picked it up with his fingers and placed it on my plate.' It is old-fashioned. Everything comes on flats from the distant kitchen and is put on the flame while a team of two or three deliver it bit by bit to the table. This ritual is performed for kidney and bacon as well as for a game-bird. The Connaught can, of course, be a monument of tact and solicitude, but tarry not too long in the evening: your bill will be brought to you before the last train. The remarkable thing about this restaurant is its ability to be all things to all people. 'Classic and classy with great luxury at every turn. You get the quality you pay for. One was made to feel a very welcome guest. Duc de crêpes de Connaught were liberally filled with lobster and topped with a generous amount of black and white truffles; grilled calf's liver is an excellent speciality; three cuts off the roast lamb was a treat; delicious rice pudding and freshly prepared mille-feuille aux fraises were quite perfect.' This sort of perfect traditional cooking, brought to a high point during the game season, is matched by the coeval heritage of haute cuisine – foie gras, galette Connaught aux 'Diamants Noirs', salmi of guinea-fowl with morels and mushrooms in a cream sauce. Yet there are signs of newer fashions: rendezvous des pêcheurs with lobster, sole, monkfish and scallops or salmon with sorrel and Champagne. Whichever it is, you can guarantee that it will be done with thoroughness but rarely with imagination. Thus kidney and bacon are just that – and people who order it would be shocked if it were otherwise. Coq au vin, too, seemed identical to that in a good bourgeois restaurant in France, or in a good home, yet it had a better stock, a slightly better chicken. Another sign of thoroughness is their bread: the best rolls in London. By contrast to the menu, the wine list is all clarity. The prices are high. There are nearly as many Champagnes as clarets. The clarets are well chosen from good vintages and are deftly served, even if in too small glasses. Many of the red burgundies are from boring sources – Bouchard, Chanson, Latour. There are no old burgundies, white or red, and the whites are similarly unconsidered. The only excitements that remain are nice Italian and German selections and a range of vintage ports that offers nothing younger than 1958. This must be the only place that you can buy three vintages (1934, 1948 and 1955) of Tuke Holdsworth, a shipper of Dartmouth origin long since swallowed by bigger fish.

CHEF: Michel Bourdin   PROPRIETORS: Savoy Hotel Plc
OPEN: all week
CLOSED: weekends and bank hols (Grill Room)
MEALS: 12.30 to 2, 6 to 10.15
PRICES: £40 (£60), Set L and D £19.60 (£30) to £45.50 (£61). Service 15%
CARD: Access
SEATS: 115. Private parties: 20 private room. No children under 6. Smart dress preferred. No pipes in dining-room. Wheelchair access (also WC). Air-conditioned
ACCOMMODATION: 90 rooms, all with bath/shower. Rooms for disabled. Lift. Rooms £145 to £200. Afternoon teas (priority to residents). TV. Phone [GHG]

## Connolly's    map 10

| 162 Lower Richmond Road, SW15 1LY | COOKING 2 |
| 01-788 3844 | COST £18–£29 |

Who dares, wins. 'Eamonn Connolly is not afraid of experimenting – smoked chicken with pickled banana; seasonal country salad of mixed leaves, bacon, egg and pickled herring; snails with a kumquat butter. Although some of the combinations sound bizarre, you become convinced that he is not just doing this for the sake of it, but because he has found some excellent taste combinations.' So says one reporter who was brave enough to take a chance along with the chef; but diners who lose their nerve over the odder couplings on the menu can relax in more familiar company: ox-tongue with mustard sauce; pork fillet with apples and prunes; prawn salad. Connolly's sister Kate fronts this new and already popular restaurant, which offers a truncated two-course set menu, or a more extensive *carte*. Some savoury dishes have been overly sweet, but desserts have avoided the trap, among them 'deliciously light' sticky toffee pudding and a 'gorgeous' ice-cream, studded with fragments of kumquat peel that 'should have been served in a *tulipe* only their *tulipe* chef was off sick and it came thinly disguised in the pastry case, and with the kumquat sauce that had been destined for an aborted snail dish earlier in the day.' Thus do the front ends and back ends of modern menus sometimes meet themselves. The wine list is excellent: short, well chosen, competitively priced. Pity more details of makers are not given. House wines from La Vieille Ferme, £6.50. CELLARMAN'S CHOICE : Ch. Lamothe 1985, £8.50; Bourgogne Pinot-Noir 1985, Lahaye, £10.50.

CHEF: Eamonn Connolly   PROPRIETORS: Kate Connolly and Eamonn Connolly
OPEN: Tue to Sun, exc Sun D
CLOSED: bank hols
MEALS: 12 to 2.30 (1 to 4 Sun), 7 to 10.30
PRICES: £15 (£24). Set L and D £10.95 (£18). Cover 75p
CARDS: Access, Visa
SEATS: 40. 6 tables outside. Private parties: 40 main room. Vegetarian meals. Children's helpings (Sun L only). Wheelchair access (1 step). Music

## Cork & Bottle ▼                                                    map 14

| 44–46 Cranbourn Street, WC2H 7AN | COOKING 1 |
| 01-734 7807 | COST £19 |

Don Hewitson's basement wine bar stretches between Cranbourn and Bear Street, but it is easily missed unless you are looking for the narrow door and entrance leading down to the noisy bars. By 7pm on mid-week evenings every table is packed; those in the booths tend to be quieter and give more elbow space for eating. The food, ordered at the bar, is better-than-average wine bar stuff, a mixture of salads, cold pâtés and terrines, hot main dishes of the day and gooey puddings served in generous portions. The raised cheese and ham pie and the Pavlova are renowned, but there have been other good dishes of the day – a duck and lentil terrine or asparagus with pink peppercorn mayonnaise. The wine is good: how exceptional that is in a wine bar! The selection changes, it is investigative and up-to-the-minute, and not expensive. It is pointless to do more than second Don Hewitson's enthusiasm for Champagne, Beaujolais and Australian wines in particular; and note that wine by the glass comes in generous quarter-bottle measure. What bottles we might recommend will be long gone by 1990. Related to Shampers in Kingly Street, W1, and Methuselah's in Victoria Street, SW1.

CHEF: Louie Egham   PROPRIETOR: Don Hewitson
OPEN: all week, exc Sun L
MEALS: 11 to 3, 5.30 to 11 (7 to 10.30 Sun)
PRICES: £9 (£16)
CARDS: Access, Amex, Diners, Visa
SEATS: 60. Private parties: 20 main room, 20 private room. Vegetarian meals. Children restricted. Music. Air-conditioned. Self-service

*Consumers' Association is planning a* **Vegetarian Good Food Guide**, *to cafés and restaurants offering at least one vegetarian main course. Please send reports and recommendations to* **The Vegetarian Good Food Guide**, FREEPOST, *2 Marylebone Road, London NW1 1YN.*

## La Croisette

map 11

168 Ifield Road, SW10 9AF
01-373 3694

COOKING 2
COST £32−£41

This, the original of Pierre Martin's solution for the piscivore of London (see
also Le Suquet), is in a basement with a spiral stairway. It excels at Gallic
atmosphere but 'they are even more civil now and speak to you occasionally.'
The recipe is the same as at the others: a set meal from kir to coffee involving
the plateau de fruits de mer, and a simple *carte* like a fishmonger's price list
with daily specials stuck in. It is all done with style and many do enjoy it. The
wine list may be short but by London standards it is not overpriced. House
wine, £8.50. Who prefers which Pierre Martin branch depends on
temperament.

CHEF: Rob Lanoé  PROPRIETOR: Pierre Martin
OPEN: Tue to Sun, exc Tue L
CLOSED: 25 Dec, Aug
MEALS: 12.30 to 2.30, 7.30 to 11.30
PRICES: £23 (£32), Set L and D £25 (£34). Service 15%
CARDS: Access, Amex, Diners, Visa
SEATS: 55. 3 tables outside. Private parties: 12 main room. Children welcome. Smart dress
preferred. No pipes in dining-room. Music

## Crowthers

map 10

481 Upper Richmond Road West
East Sheen, SW14 7PU
01-876 6372

COOKING 2
COST £20−£34

Even the menu in this converted, none-too-sparkling-from-the-outside shop
might have been Laura-Ashleyed. The food, however, is of the post-nouvelle
modern British variety, owning no precursors save example and illustration
from the 1970s and 1980s. 'This restaurant improves every year,' writes an East
London doctor who makes the journey for semi-suburban solace. 'The
atmosphere is warm and relaxed, the proprietors charming and delightful.' The
set-price menu for three courses may yield sauté scallops and leeks in a
vermouth sauce; a mousse of artichokes; a confit de canard and a pear mille-
feuille straining for flavour as pear dishes always do. It will also show some
direct flavouring: saffron, juniper, marjoram, lime and mixed herbs being the
roll-call on main dishes on a recent menu. Some complain of the slow velocity
of production, some hint at complacency; many find the place charming. The
wine list is organised according to grape type. It is short, quite select, and not
too exorbitant. House French is £8 or £9.25. CELLARMAN'S CHOICE : Petaluma
Chardonnay 1984, £16.80; Gigondas, Dom. de Grand Montmirail 1983, £13.80.

CHEF: Philip Crowther  PROPRIETORS: Philip and Shirley Crowther
OPEN: Mon to Sat, exc Mon and Sat L
MEALS: 12 to 2, 7 to 10
PRICES: Set L £14 (£20), Set D £21 (£28)
CARDS: Access, Amex, Visa
SEATS: 32. Private parties: 32 main room. Children welcome. Wheelchair access.
Air-conditioned

## *Dolphin Brasserie* map 11

Dolphin Square, Rodney House
Chichester Street, SW1V 3LX                 COOKING 1
01-828 3207                 COST £17–£32

The artist Glynn Boyd-Harte worked hard at the neighbourhood brasserie for
Dolphin Square, a giant 1930s village of apartments on the river. The maritime
theme is pressed home by the aquamarine tones and by the architectural
imagery of a liner – the promenade deck looking over the swimming-pool
(unfortunately a view of people's heads, not their legs as in more popular
holiday camps). Many of the customers, at the bar at least, seem on their way
from the squash courts and there's a feeling of rattling in an empty shell on
quiet nights. Quiet they determinedly are not, however, in the Muzak
department. The kitchen seems to communicate by means of some desperate
Morse code, lighting lamp bulbs above the service doors – this makes for
amusing speculation on nights of slow service, which can exist. The cooking,
promised a revamp when Richard Williams took over during 1988, is London
smart-set café food at restaurant prices: pear and watercress soup, mozzarella
salad, a Chinese-style stir-fry of fillet of beef, a skate wing with black butter. It
is not unwholesome and serves a purpose in a residential area with few places
in walking distance. The wine list is intelligent and a Domaine de Trévallon
1984 came out in good condition. House Californian red and French white,
£6.90. CELLARMAN'S CHOICE : Ch. Lyonnat 1983, £14.50; Pouilly-Fumé Les
Loges 1987, £14.90.

CHEF: Richard Williams    PROPRIETORS: Crawley Wilson Restaurants plc
OPEN: all week, exc Sat L
MEALS: 12.30 to 2.15, 7 to 10.45 (11.15 Sat)
PRICES: £16 (£27), Set L £9.80 (£17) to £11.80 (£19). Cover £1.80. Service 12.5%
CARDS: Access, Amex, Diners, Visa
SEATS: 130. Vegetarian meals. Children welcome. Music. Air-conditioned

## *La Dordogne* map 10

5 Devonshire Road, W4 2EU             COOKING 3
01-747 1836                 COST £30

The restaurant pursues the specialities proclaimed by its name: foie gras, confit
de canard, the wines of Cahors and Bergerac. However, it is more serious than
just another memory of last year's holiday: chicken breast with ginger sauce
and panaché de poissons with basil and butter sauce as well as salade
gourmande, Dordogne style. Locals speak softly of its deeply French nature and
of the sometimes diffident approach of staff. Regional menus consitute good
value and are much enjoyed. 'It is the whole experience that attracts us back,
not just the food alone.' The wine list is best for its Jurançon, Bergerac and
Cahors exclusivities. House Bergerac, £6.70. CELLARMAN'S CHOICE : Jurançon
Moelleux, Clos Guirouilh 1985, £7.80; Cahors, Pelvillain 1983, £7.50.

*Report forms are at the back of the book; write a letter if you prefer.*

CHEF: Jean-Claude Paillard   PROPRIETOR: Rachel Bitton
OPEN: all week, exc Sat and Sun L
MEALS: 12 to 2.30, 7 to 11
PRICES: £16 (£25). Cover £1. Service 10%
CARDS: Access, Amex, Diners, Visa
SEATS: 64. 6 tables outside. Private parties: 38 private room. Children restricted. Smart
dress preferred. Wheelchair access. Music

## Dragon Inn                                                       map 11

| 63 Westbourne Grove, W2 4UA | COOKING 2 |
|---|---|
| 01-229 8806 | COST £14–£26 |

Cool and stylish with high ceilings and white walls, the surroundings may
help justify the high prices. The food is good, though, with some authentic fish
cookery and some interesting offerings: translucent shreds of jellyfish dressed
with sesame and chilli; abalone with fish lips (crumpled in sardonic smile), not
tough as is often the case, with a spiky and fresh tasting sauce; fried crispy
intestine, dyed a bright red, of delectable flavour heightened by star anise;
snowy white, firm and sweet prawns sizzled with chilli and garlic; good crisp
broccoli and fried seaweed. Service is amiable; there are a lot of one-plate
dishes to moderate the cost. Another branch is at 12 Gerrard Street in Soho
(01-494 0870). House Loire, £5.50.

CHEF: Sham Yau Wong   PROPRIETORS: Bowell Ltd
OPEN: all week
MEALS: noon to 11.45
PRICES: £14 (£22), Set D £10 (£14) to £16.50 (£21). Service inc
CARDS: Access, Amex, Visa
SEATS: 75. Private parties: 60 main room. Vegetarian meals. Children's helpings. Smart
dress preferred. Music. Air-conditioned

## Dragon's Nest                                                    map 14

| 58–60 Shaftesbury Avenue, W1V 7DE | COOKING 3 |
|---|---|
| 01-437 3119 | COST £9–£29 |

The praise that last year greeted this new arrival to Shaftesbury Avenue has
become less than unanimous, although undoubtedly there is still top-class
Szechuan-influenced food to be had here. The décor, a mixture of traditional
Chinese palace motifs, bevelled mirrors and pale grey brocade panels, is muted
and tasteful. There's a scent of garlic, chilli and ginger in the air and the menu
invites adventurous choices: kidneys with chillis, aubergine Szechuan style,
General Tsang's chicken, yellowfish in a sweet-and-sour sauce. Much else has
been good to excellent, with 'combinations of flavours to knock you off your
feet'. Dazzling successes include 'the best' spring rolls, good-looking prawns in
chilli sauce, 'the best aubergine in bean sauce I have tasted,' outstanding
dumplings and stir-fried tripe, and squid 'mouthwatering with wok-
fragrance'. One reader found it, 'the best Chinese meal I have eaten; at last, all
the components drawn together – food, service, décor.' Others, however, have
been disappointed and found the quality of a few dishes variable. Niggles such
as abrupt or unhelpful service, bill-padding and small portions add to the sour

note. Yet among the surrounding Chinese restaurants of Soho, Dragon's Nest must still stand out for producing convincing regional food with an imaginative modern twist that can be far more than just good. The wine list is adequate.

CHEF: M. Chong   PROPRIETOR: N.L.Yeh
OPEN: all week
MEALS: noon to 11.30
PRICES: £8 (£13), Set L £5 (£9) to £10 (£14), Set D £10 (£14) to £20 (£24). Service inc
CARDS: Access, Amex, Diners, Visa
SEATS: 140. Private parties: 100 main room, 40 private room. Children's helpings. Music.
Air-conditioned

## ▲ Dukes Hotel                                      map 13

St James's Place, SW1A 1NY                              COOKING 3
01-491 4840                                             COST £17−£62

This small hotel tucked away behind St James's Palace, one of the last in private ownership, has fallen to the clutches of Cunard. It has the suavely calming ambience that hotel users – particularly Americans – appear to enjoy. It also has luxurious privacy, in high demand in the district, and at high prices. One set lunch and another of cold roast beef escalated, with wine, to £70. Attention to diners' needs was, on that occasion, virtually non-existent. The *carte* lists delicacies along the lines of turbot slivers with asparagus on a butter sauce; scallops steamed in elderflower wine; fillets of beef in Malmsey sauce. There is always a vegetarian dish. The set menu is simpler: roast of the day (or fish on Fridays), which might be saddle of venison with walnut sauce, plus three or four other possibilities. Bread-and-butter pudding still scores top in the sweets stakes, or there are home-made ices and sorbets. Genteel afternoon teas – smoked salmon sandwiches, madeira cake – are served between 3.30 and 5pm. The wine list does not recognise countries other than France or Germany. Its prices are in line with that of the food, but the Loires, for example, which are at least affordable, are nicely chosen. House French, £10.
CELLARMAN'S CHOICE : Ch. Cissac, Haut Médoc 1981, £29; Chablis 1986, Regnard, £21.

CHEF: Tony Marshall   PROPRIETORS: Dukes Hotels Ltd
OPEN: all week
MEALS: 12.30 to 2.30, 6 (7 Sun) to 10
PRICES: £36 (£52), Set L £17 (£27) to £19 (£29)
CARDS: Access, Amex, Diners, Visa
SEATS: 50. Private parties: 48 main room; 12 private room. Vegetarian meals. Children welcome. Smart dress preferred. Wheelchair access (also WC)
ACCOMMODATION: 62 rooms, all with bath/shower. Lift. B&B £150 to £180. Deposit: £150 to £180. Afternoon teas. TV. Phone. Confirm 2 days ahead

*All details are as accurate as possible at the time of going to press, but chefs and owners often change, and it is wise to check by telephone before making a special journey. Many readers have been disappointed when set-price bargain meals are no longer available. Ask when booking.*

## *Efes Kebab House*

map 13

| | |
|---|---|
| 80 Great Titchfield Street, W1P 7AF | COOKING 2 |
| 01-636 1953 | COST £17–£24 |

The two moustachioed owners beam in ghostly green from the menu cover of the Turkish kebab house long established in 'deceptively cavernous' premises on Great Titchfield Street. An extensive list of mainly vegetarian starters – stuffed aubergine, cream cheese salad – makes way for an even longer list of main courses that are strictly for meat eaters. Every conceivable kind of kebab – lamb, chicken, shish, kofte – is skilfully and succulently grilled on charcoal, and served with rice and salad. To finish there are mountains of fresh fruit or ultra-sweet pastries. Excellent meze. Turkish wines are £7.75, house French is £6.50.

CHEFS/PROPRIETORS: K. Akkus and I. Akbas
OPEN: Mon to Sat
MEALS: noon to 11.30
PRICES: £9 (£17), Set L and D £14 (£19) and £15 (£20)
CARDS: Access, Amex, Visa
SEATS: 150. Private parties: 70 main room. Children welcome. Air-conditioned

## *Faulkner's*

map 11

| | |
|---|---|
| 424–426 Kingsland Road, E8 4AA | COOKING 1 |
| 01-254 6152 | COST £18 |

'There were nine of us and everyone voted it a good cut above the usual', was the enthusiastic comment of a seasoned diner-out, if not a roué of the fish shops of Great Britain. Here, in Hackney streets looking this way towards gentrification and that way to traditional community, John Faulkner, late of the Seashell, Lisson Grove, pursues his ideal fish restaurant. The range is wide, the waitresses efficient, the ketchup is in saucers, the tea in cups. Most white fish, at more than fish shop prices, are well cooked and generously cut. Chips, equally thick cut, come in a separate bowl. Fish soup is imported from France (in cans); no one has reported its taste. Wines number five and are sensationally cheap.

CHEF: Michael Webber    PROPRIETORS: John Faulkner and Mark Farrell
OPEN: Mon to Sat
CLOSED: bank hols, 1 week Christmas to New Year
MEALS: 12 to 2, 5 (4.30 Fri) to 10 (11.30 to 10 Sat)
PRICES: £8 (£15). Licensed, also bring your own: corkage £2
SEATS: 65. Children welcome. Children's helpings. Music. Air-conditioned

---

*This year, in quoting prices for three-course meals at the top of each entry (by the word 'Cost'), we have put a more pessimistic complexion on the upper price by inflating it by 20 per cent. The aim is to prepare the reader for any inflation during the life of the* Guide *and also reflect the price of a meal taken without constant attention to the likely size of the bill. The prices quoted in smaller print below the text remain, as in previous editions, strict computer calculations of an average three-course meal, the price in brackets reflecting an average meal with coffee, service and half a bottle of house wine per person.*

## Fin de la Chasse
map 11

17 Stoke Newington Church
Street, N16 0JL
01-254 5975

COOKING 2
COST £14–£23

'A godsend for the area', was the first news that arrived of this place, coloured as if the fox had spilled its last blood over the walls. It occupies a terraced house and is tight-packed, even to its back yard with tables for summer meal hunts. The cooking seems careful and without excess: good gazpacho; a small slice of poached salmon served cool with a basil and garlic purée that was not as burning as feared; a deep-flavoured sauce Solferino to accompany fillet of beef; saffron sauce for some brill; an intense lemon tart from the Girardet recipe. Vegetables come dear for the quantity served. The welcome is 'charming, the service discreet'. The wine list is short and house wine is £6.10. There is a cheaper lunchtime menu and a table d'hôte to supplement the *carte*.

CHEF: John O'Riordan   PROPRIETORS: Robbie and Carol Richards
OPEN: Tue to Sat
CLOSED: 2 weeks at Christmas, 1 week at Easter, 2 weeks end Aug
MEALS: 12.30 to 2, 7 to 11
PRICES: £12 (£19), Set L £9.50 (£14) to £12.50 (£17), Set D £12.50 (£17). Service 10%
CARDS: Access, Amex, Diners, Visa
SEATS: 40. 5 tables outside. Private parties: 14 main room. Vegetarian meals. Children's helpings. No-smoking area. Wheelchair access (1 step). Music

## Fleet Tandoori
map 11

104 Fleet Road, NW3 2QX
01-485 6402

COOKING 2
COST £10–£17

Up and down it goes, see-sawing along. Currently it is in a good phase. 'No problems this time, the food was delicious, and the service perfectly effective.' Shami kebab, lamb pasanda, mattar paneer, chicken tikka masala and chicken dhansak are among the dishes that have pleased once again. House wine, £4.95. The Sunday buffet at £6.50 is on offer from noon until 5pm.

CHEF/PROPRIETOR: Abdur Rahman Khan
OPEN: all week
MEALS: 12 to 2.30, 6 to 11.30 (noon to 11.30 Sun)
PRICES: £7 (£14); Set Sun L £6.50 (£10). Service 10%
CARDS: Access, Amex, Diners, Visa
SEATS: 52. Private parties: 35 main room, 18 private room. Vegetarian meals. Children's helpings. Wheelchair access

## Fleet Tandoori II
map 10

346 Muswell Hill Broadway, N10 1DJ
01-883 8252

COOKING 2
COST £17

One of a pair (see above). The wedge-shaped, red-carpeted room narrows at the back, and chandeliers attempt to graft a little elegance on to the otherwise simple informality of booths with padded benches. The dishes look standard – chicken, meat and prawn dishes backed up by tandooris and a few specials –

but this is a curry house well above the average: friendly and with fair prices. Crisp, warm poppadums are delivered as you sit down. Mulligatawny soup is a variation on the classic brew, mild with overtones of coconut. Lamb pasanda and chicken tikka masala come with rich and creamy sauces. Prawns in 'home bread' are soft, fresh, succulent and squishy, and pack a spicy punch. Pilau rice is good Basmati with cardamom and coriander; spinach is fresh-flavoured and lightly spiced. Lassi, lager and wine to drink; house wine is £4.95.

CHEF/PROPRIETOR: Abdur Rahman Khan
OPEN: all week
MEALS: 12 to 2.30, 6 to 11.30 (noon to 11.30 Sun)
PRICES: £7 (£14). Service 10%
CARDS: Access, Amex, Diners, Visa
SEATS: 50. Private parties: 50 main room. Vegetarian meals. Children's helpings. Wheelchair access

## Forum Court
map 10

7A−8 High Street
South Norwood, SE25 6EP                                       COOKING 1
01-653 0295                                                   COST £14−£24

Quickly found opposite Norwood Police Station, this useful Chinese restaurant is a cut above the average outer-London standard. Set meals are hung around Szechuan, Cantonese and Peking themes, or there's a gourmet dinner with rainbow bean curd soup, an unfatty version of crispy duck and squirrel fish. On the à la carte menu, many dishes are westernised but in quite an appealing way: for example, frogs' legs with chilli and salt, toffee bananas with chocolate ice-cream. Excellent service. House French, £6.50. Redecoration was scheduled to be finished in the summer of 1989.

CHEF: Chris Harris   PROPRIETOR: Joseph Kwok Ying Loh
OPEN: all week
CLOSED: 25 and 26 Dec
MEALS: 12 to 2.15, 6 to 11.15 (11.45 Fri and Sat)
PRICES: £10 (£17), Set L and D £10.90 (£14) to £16.50 (£20). Minimum £8. Service inc
CARDS: Access, Amex, Diners, Visa
SEATS: 80. Private parties: 80 private room. Music

## ▲ Four Seasons,
## Inn on the Park ♥
map 13

Hamilton Place, Park Lane, W1A 1AZ                            COOKING 4
01-499 0888                                                   COST £25−£58

Bruno Loubet has served his probationary period at this lush affair, coming from Raymond Blanc's Petit Blanc in Oxford (now Gee's; see entry). It is worrying that, although he is one of the better chefs working in Britain today, the *Guide* has received only a few letters about his London performance, while there were sheaves of them during his Oxford stint. Doubtless he is showing his talents to great advantage, but to a very different clientele. Here, customers are asked to deposit their portable phones with the manager before dining.

Walk west on Piccadilly, pass the queue for the Hard Rock Café, and enter a tourist and international business ghetto made up of three or four modern hotels. The landscape is tarmac, bollards, windswept corners, a litter of stretched motorcars that drop off the main stream of the Park Lane north-south cloaca. Once through the door, the restrained tasteless modernism of the exterior is subverted by a blowsy classicism of an even worse sort. Any advantages of a modern structure for interpenetration of light and space is set aside by a management that wants the spurious class given by a deep carpet, chandeliers and wood panelling. The Four Seasons is thus rather depressing to visit, its major advantages being well-spaced tables and comfortable chairs. Reminder of the seasons themselves is restricted to puny little trees outside the large window. In winter, their twigs are a filigree net.

There may have been a linguistic jump (from Quat'Saisons to Four Seasons), but the cooking recalls many successes from the earlier kitchen, not least because M. Loubet has not thrown away his links with regionalism, specifically south-western France. Thus are found a salad of foie gras de canard, small marinated calf's tongues and air-dried duck breast, joined as trois bouchées landaises; breast of duck with a sauce made from liqueur de noix; or ox-tail with red wine and cabbage. Oxford memories come from the sea bass with an aubergine purée with sweet peppers, or the lemon crème brûlée with a jasmin tea sorbet. The menu is longer here, and the flavourings more varied: cumin in a cauliflower soup, ginger with lobster, pickled lime with lamb, juniper with kidneys. Loubet reminds one most strongly of chefs Guérard at Eugénie and Trama at Puymirol, for example in dishes like the home-smoked beef and salmon (quick smoking is popular there, as here) and the apple tart with the apple sorbet. His cooking has always been technically accomplished. A gateau of chicken with wild mushrooms and foie gras has a base of wild mushrooms, an outside carapace of sliced potato and inside a mousseline of chicken wholly suffused with the flavour of foie gras. The sauce, a rich truffled reduction, is given point by well caramelised turnips. By technique, even as humble a joint as shoulder of lamb is elevated to the fancy: boned and trimmed to perfection, turned round a lining of spinach which in turn envelopes a small fillet of lamb. When sliced and served on a good lamb *jus*, it looks like a target. This technique is almost best mobilized on vegetable dishes, for example turnip 'raviolis' filled with wild mushrooms (a big fashion for vegetable 'pasta' at the moment) and a tarte Tatin of celeriac perfumed with truffle, 'the distinctive taste of this apple tart look-alike keeps coming back to me.' Desserts show as much invention, though light on pastry work. An armagnac mousse is three layers – a liquorish mousse below, then a thin sponge, finally a dark chocolate marquise mixture. Bread has not been marvellous. The staff are extremely willing to please and there is no hauteur, save that which comes from the setting, social and architectural. A Clayderman-clone tickles ivories in the adjoining lounge, during lunch *and* dinner.

The wine list is very long; it is also very expensive. Its strength is claret and, to a lesser degree, burgundy and Spain. In the regions of France, it loses interest and, save for some good Italians, its nod towards other countries is cursory. House wine is from £11. CELLARMAN'S CHOICE : Chablis *premier cru* Montmains 1985, Regnard, £35; Santenay, la Maladière 1985, Girardin, £32. It is difficult to understand the argument that in a grand London hotel one should pay double a provincial restaurant's charge for a current wine such as Sancerre.

True, there are a lot of servants and a lot of real estate but so, too, are there a lot of customers, already paying handsome rents. Might that extra charge simply be supporting investors and managers at a higher standard of living than their provincial colleagues? In other words, is it not the operation of greed? There are other aspects of life in this restaurant that are wholly estimable. Care is taken to mark dishes that are low in cholesterol, salt and fats (and three or four such dishes are included in each menu). The lunch menu is spectacular value: good cooking, good service and absolutely no extra charges unless you drink. Not only are you served a small appetiser, but the fine cheeseboard is permitted as well as pudding. One glass of dessert wine is included with the set dinner.

CHEF: Bruno Loubet    PROPRIETORS: Inn on the Park
OPEN: all week
MEALS: 12 to 3, 7 to 11
PRICES: £40 (£48), Set L £19 (£25), Set Sun L £21.50 (£28), Set D £35 (£41). Service inc
CARDS: Access, Amex, Diners, Carte Blanche, Visa
SEATS: 62. Private parties: 10 main room. Car-park, 85 places. No children under 5. Smart dress preferred. No pipes in dining-room. Wheelchair access (also WC). Music. Air-conditioned
ACCOMMODATION: 228 rooms, all with bath/shower. Rooms for disabled. Lift. B&B £195 to £245. Baby facilities. Afternoon teas. Air-conditioning. TV. Phone

## Frith's ♥ 

14 Frith Street, W1V 5TS
01-439 3370

map 14

COOKING 3
COST £37

It's a little unfortunate that Frith's finds itself opposite Alastair Little. There are too many points of similarity for comfort. The decoration of Carla Tomasi's restaurant has modernity but it is softened by warmth of texture, muted wall colour, large paintings and quarry tiles. Her cooking, perhaps, intends the same image of modernity, reinforced by the accession of Robert Ridley of Blakes Hotel to the team. The waiting style, too, is modern: no uniform, much care, and murmurings of 'Enjoy' as forks are lifted. The kitchen produces an ever-changing spread of dishes, in the vein of sweetbreads with pine-nuts, spinach and Parmesan soup to start, monkfish with red pepper and lemon-grass or braised rabbit with dried woodland mushroom sauce as main courses, and apple charlotte with orange cream, chocolate and cinnamon ice-cream with coffee sauce to finish. There is always a vegetarian option. The difficulty for many is that little or no salt is used in the cooking. This leads to insipidity and often to imbalance of tastes. This is a pity because ambitions are very high and Carla Tomasi has a fine intelligence about cuisine. On fine days there is a garden to eat in, and at busy lunchtimes a basement restaurant. Coffee comes in large, sensible cups, with truffles. The wine list may be small but it is perfectly formed. A changing two dozen, often only New World and Italian, it has some delectable bottles: Stag's Leap Hawk Crest Sauvignon Blanc 1986 or Ngatarawa Cabernet Sauvignon 1987 from Hawkes Bay, New Zealand, to name but two. House Italian is £8.50. The mineral water is from New Zealand too.

*The* Guide *relies on feedback from its readers. Especially welcome are reports on new restaurants appearing in the book for the first time.*

CHEF: Carla Tomasi, Nicholas Hawkins and Robert Ridley    PROPRIETOR: Carla Tomasi
OPEN: Mon to Sat, exc Sat L
CLOSED: bank hols, 1 week Christmas to New Year, 5 days at Easter
MEALS: 12.30 to 2.30, 7.30 to 11.15
PRICES: £20 (£31). Licensed, also bring your own: no corkage
CARD: Access, Visa
SEATS: 81. 16 tables outside. Private parties: 40 main room. Vegetarian meals. Children's
helpings. No cigars/pipes in dining-room. Wheelchair access. Air-conditioned

## Fung Shing
map 14

15 Lisle Street, WC2H 7BE                                    COOKING 3
01-437 1539                                                 COST £14–£32

A restaurant for serious eating, frequented by Chinese as well as westerners.
The menu reflects this in dishes that range from straightforward sweet-and-
sours to eel with coriander and crispy fried intestines. That the food is suitably
authentic is demonstrated by advocates' willingness to travel far for it. One
reporter writes: 'Once a year I come from France to eat *du vrai chinois* here. All I
have eaten in this haven of Cantonese cuisine has delighted my palate.' Among
dishes that have left tastebuds in a state of bliss recently have been scallops
with garlic and hot soy sauce; stewed duck in preserved plum sauce; winter
melon soup with dried scallops; stewed belly of pork with yam; barbecued
quail. House French, £7.50.

CHEF: Fu Kwun    PROPRIETORS: Traceflow Ltd
OPEN: all week
MEALS: noon to 11.45
PRICES: £17 (£27), Set L and D £9.50 (£14) to £10.50 (£15). Minimum £8. Service inc
CARDS: Access, Amex, Diners, Visa
SEATS: 85. Private parties: 50 main room, 30 private room. Children welcome. Music.
Air-conditioned

## Galicia
map 11

323 Portobello Road, W10 5SY                                 COOKING 1
01-969 3539                                                 COST £8–£22

North on the Portobello Road, not far from the Spanish school, is home from
home for refugees from Santiago and Coruña. The tapas bar is a long room;
there are tables at the back and in an overflow gallery upstairs. Progress may be
slow when it's busy but make for the Galician dishes when given the chance.
Pulpo (octopus) is still warm on arrival and especially tender, crunchy with
rock salt and slightly hot from the pimentón. Hake is fresh and flaky, cooked a
la Gallega (pimento and potato) or a la Cazuela (sauté onion). Other fish
cooked a la plancha (griddled not grilled) is worthy too. Rough and ready
cooking, but good value and great atmosphere. Tapas are available all day from
noon to closing. House Rioja, £5.50.

*All entries in the* Guide *are rewritten every year, not least because restaurant standards
fluctuate. Don't trust an out-of-date* Guide.

CHEF: Mr Ramon   PROPRIETORS: E. Lage and J. Nieto
OPEN: Tue to Sun
CLOSED: 25 Dec, Aug
MEALS: 12 to 3, 7 to 11.30
PRICES: £13 (£18), Set L £5.50 (£8), Set D £10 (£13) to £15 (£18). Snacks from £2
CARDS: Access, Diners, Visa
SEATS: 48. Private parties: 32 main room. Children welcome. Wheelchair access. Music

## Ganpath

map 11

372 Gray's Inn Road, WC1 8BB
01-278 1938

COOKING 1
COST £6−£13

The scented air is perhaps more fragrant than before and the laminated menus have been usurped by a tattier version, but otherwise little changes at the Ganpath. This is not the place for ambience, although the kindly service is relaxing. Anyway, it's worth concentrating on the food, especially the South Indian first courses. Vada is a firm, fried doughnut, as greaseless as good tempura. Tomato-and-onion utahpum puts pizza dough into the shade with its chewy softness; masala dosa is 'supreme', the thinnest crisp pancake with hearty potato filling and tasty coconut sauce accompaniment. The rest of the menu doesn't come up to these South Indian specialities, although vegetables are superior: crisp, dry and flavourful Bombay aloo; skilfully fried spicy green bananas. Go on Friday (or ask nicely on other days if the staff are not too busy), and try the special payasam dessert, a light, refreshing concoction of tapioca and coconut cooked with milk and sugar. House wine, £4.75.

CHEF: P.G. Ramalingam   PROPRIETORS: P.G. Ramalingam and R. Sivanantham
OPEN: all week, exc Sun L
CLOSED: bank hols, 25 and 26 Dec
MEALS: 12 to 3, 6 to 12
PRICES: £5 (£11), Set L £3.95 (£6). Minimum £4 at D. Service inc set only, alc 10%
CARDS: Access, Visa
SEATS: 50. Private parties: 60 main room. Vegetarian meals. Children's helpings. Separate smoking area. Wheelchair access. Music

## Garbo's

map 11

42 Crawford Street, W1H 1HA
01-262 6582

COOKING 1
COST £24

A restaurant that 'should give ethnic cuisine a good name', with an English chef and Swedish proprietor. The Swedish church and embassy round the corner give the place the feel of a *restaurant du quartier*, cooking is moderate. The menu remains unchanged, full of Swedish stalwarts: herrings; gravlax; Janson's Temptation (potatoes, anchovies, onions and cream, baked); kaldolmar or stuffed cabbage; sole Bernadotte or veal with crab and a béarnaise sauce for the outward looking. Prices are reasonable. The best drinks are the schnapps and the Export lager. House French is £5.45.

*The* Guide *is totally independent, accepts no free hospitality, and survives on the number of copies sold each year.*

CHEF: John Moseley   PROPRIETOR: Ake Lindholm
OPEN: all week, exc Sat and Sun L
MEALS: 12 to 3, 6 to 12
PRICES: £12 (£20). Cover £1
CARDS: Access, Amex, Diners, Visa
SEATS: 50. Private parties: 50 main room, 50 private room. Children's helpings. Wheelchair access. Music. Air-conditioned

---

## Le Gavroche ▼                                            map 13

43 Upper Brook Street, W1Y 1PF                          COOKING 5
01-408 0881                                             COST £29−£79

The legal upset happily behind it, Le Gavroche continues, and Albert Roux is joined by his son Michel. The restaurant is in the basement of a dull mansion block. If the original architect sought to ape the eighteenth century, then the designer of the Gavroche went for a pastiche of the gentleman's club: all greens and russet. The restaurant suffers from the oppression of a low ceiling and skin-deep tastefulness. At night it smothers; the real world breaks in only on a bright summer's day. Suspension of disbelief, promoted by disjunction and envelopment, is anyway useful to cope with the prices − generous only for the *prix fixe* luncheon. The centrepiece is a long *carte*, in French, of laconic titles that demand explication. Oral explanations are graphic, accurate and courteous: you just have to remember them. Prices are denied to women. The style of the cooking is deeply conservative. The best materials, infinite labour, careful design and excellent technique are mobilised to produce dishes that lack nothing. They are presented with such conviction and seriousness that you know you face good cooking. Rare are suggestions of short cuts or economies. This is pleasure and many vouchsafe it. It is comforting to order a consommé de volaille à l'estragon and eat as good a one as you will find − deeply flavoured without stickiness, limpidity itself, with perfect petits légumes, given intensity by small pieces of confit. In like manner, a poulet en vessie once bowled over a correspondent with its archetypical poulet de Bresse, the generosity of the truffles, the clarity of the juices. The deftness of the way it was served and its presentation merely confirmed the diner's satisfaction. Good things are continually reported: fish cooked with langoustines; duck terrine with pistachio; mussels in saffron cream sauce or as a ragoût with potatoes and courgettes; a boudin blanc of chicken; game pie 'like you've never had before'; noisettes of lamb provençale; tarte Tatin of pears with a raspberry sauce; charentais melon filled with red fruits; banana soufflé with rum. These are not, it may be observed, dishes of a modish or 'advanced' kitchen. Starting with the consommé described above, the second course was a feather-light scallop mousse covered with thin-sliced scallops and a plainish eggy sauce. This had perfect technique, though the scallops were barely heated. It attracted by stealth, not by an immediate burst of flavour. The meat course was a tournedos, enriched by bone marrow, sauced by a stock reduction of correct weight, given accent by *pied farci*. Feet (pig's or calf's) figure often as an ingredient in current Roux dishes and make some of them excessively rich, even if 'tasty'. Vegetables were a mixture of peas and broad beans − exquisite, bound with a slight cream that masked their innate quality. Potatoes there were none. The cheese was as grandiloquent and impressive as might be expected. Dessert, a 'cake' of strawberries with red wine, was a thin sponge with a castle mould of red wine jelly set round strawberries. As the fruit was tasteless, it was fortunate that the jelly was of such enticing flavour. Coffee is good, petits fours extravagant and exciting for those who have room. The service is legendary. The waiters' memories are long. There are many staff, always doing something. The only remedy is to lie back and accept it; don't try to break the routine. If length were the measure, the wine list would be faultless. Ignore the rest of the world; just read the classic French regions. There are bottles from about £15. It is wisest to stay in the foothills of the financial mountain. Wine service is good, though not good enough to avoid offering substitute vintages without notice. Both menu and wine list seem to operate on a broad inflation rate of 25 per cent, though sometimes the cellar throws caution to the winds – doubtless in tune with the market. Just as a company revalues its property portfolio to massage its profit figures, so the accountant must run over the stocks here. Thus magnums of Nuits-St Georges Les Pruliers 1978 go from £148.80 to £220 in one year. The percentage mark-up makes good bottles breathtaking in price. A Ch. Grand-Puy-Lacoste 1966 that could be bought on the open market for around £33 comes at £135 (1989 prices); a Ch. Lynch-Bages 1961, though offered retail in Bristol at around £75, takes an outlay of £273. Even humble Ch. Lyonnat 1983 will cost £12.90 a half when the sister restaurant, the Waterside Inn at Bray, charges less than £10. People talk of such quality being good value at any price, but this is stretching too many points. The cynical might recognise themselves. House French is £16.50.

CHEFS: A.H. Roux and Michel Roux Jnr    PROPRIETORS: Le Gavroche Ltd
OPEN: Mon to Fri
CLOSED: 23 Dec to 2 Jan
MEALS: 12 to 2, 7 to 11
PRICES: £54 (£66), Set L £21 (£29), Set D £45 (£57). Minimum £45. Service inc
CARDS: Access, Amex, Carte Blanche, Diners, Visa
SEATS: 60. Private parties: 10 main room, 20 private room. No children under 5. Smart dress preferred. No cigars/pipes in dining-room. Air-conditioned

## Gavvers                                                                    map 12

61–63 Lower Sloane Street, SW1W 8DH                                  COOKING 2
01-730 5983                                                     COST £13–£38

What are we to make of little tadpoles spawned by those masters Albert and Michel Roux? Gavvers opened in 1981 in the former Gavroche premises. By 1983 it had received a 'Best London Value for Dinner' stamp of approval from the *Guide*, and was rated the most popular restaurant in London on the grounds that 'the fixed-price menu formula is what people want.' The formula still attracts. The set dinner price includes everything – and this means everything: a glass of kir, canapés, three courses, half a bottle of wine, water, coffee, petits fours, service and VAT. Gavvers has run up the flag for simple, reliable French food, low prices, and speedy service; and lots of readers have gratefully saluted. The menu markets the Roux name, advertising supplementary dishes under 'Albert' and 'Michel' as if they had a hand in them. Spray-on authentication runs to multiple copies of their books on prominent display along the bar. The welcome can misfire if the chief greeter is otherwise occupied. Some tables are cramped to the point of discomfort; it is not a place for a quiet *tête à tête*. You feel like a package eater just as surely as you would feel like a package tourist had you gone on Safari with Gavvers Tours Inc, where you would end up visiting a mini game-park-cum-zoo with proper toilets and iced drinks, at a comfortable distance from the real jungle. Any excitement the menu may once have shown has been overtaken by events. It is safe and middle of the road. Take cucumber and mint soup, gravlax, a puff pastry case with chicken liver and spinach or, as one of our inspectors did, breast of chicken filled with chicken and mushroom mousse, wrapped in filo pastry and baked. 'We are hardly on the frontiers of cooking are we? Not, so to speak, at the coal-face.' Gavvers now seems like a yellowing snapshot of another era. Surely it is time to cut the apron strings and rethink the style, revitalise the kitchen. In cooking, you cannot afford to stand still. House wine, of course, is Cuvée Roux, from Georges Duboeuf, at £7.

CHEF: Robert Couzens   PROPRIETORS: Roux Restaurants Ltd
OPEN: Mon to Sat, exc Sat L
CLOSED: bank hols
MEALS: 12 to 2.30, 7 to 11
PRICES: Set L £9 (£13) to £15 (£19), Set D £27.50 (£32). Service inc
CARDS: Access, Amex, Diners, Visa
SEATS: 80. Children welcome. Wheelchair access. Air-conditioned

## Gay Hussar
map 14

2 Greek Street, W1V 6NB
01-437 0973

COOKING 2
COST £18–£31

This restaurant, now well launched into a new life, may require a long introduction to describe its qualities and explain reasons for its remarkable fame. Most know it was in the hands of Victor Sassie and sold on his retirement in 1988 to a company of the most canny men among London caterers. Like vultures picking over the entrails of a dying antelope, regular customers peck at weak points to establish if all remains the same. The Gay Hussar is Old Soho. It is all partitions and dark brown downstairs; small and cramped, rather like an old-fashioned railway carriage, upstairs. One newcomer writes, 'It is unpretentious and likeable. The service is agreeable, not at all off-hand. What nicer way to ask someone to leave than to say, "Excuse me, sir, but we will be opening again in half an hour"?' Another, a regular this one, writes that he has had 16 Saturday lunches in the previous six-month period (forming a part of an informal 'Saturday Club'). The range of his eating is indicative of the repertoire: Bulgar salad of peppers, celery, beans, potatoes and Hungarian sausage; fish salad; jellied bortsch; bean soup (white in winter, green in summer); halibut, hake, salmon, jugged hare, saddle of hare, roast grouse, roast pheasant, braised pheasant, roast partridge, Serbian chicken, duck, goose and wiener schnitzel as main courses; cherry strudel, a variety of berries and Christmas pudding as desserts. 'Of all the foods, only the last-named was below a high standard. In some cases, the game birds and hare, the standard was consistently excellent. Now that the phone is answered (an improvement of the new régime), one person can get a table except on the busiest of days.'

There speaks an habitué. This witness is upheld, by and large, by his colleagues. There has been little change in standards, staff or style – though no Mr Sassie himself. Post-Sassie customers will speak of different things. They point out the impossibility of dining upstairs, hugger-mugger, with unhelpful staff unwilling to explain a complex cuisine. They complain of intrusion from neighbouring tables in the crowded downstairs, partitioned or not: 'I sat next to a pair of overweight gentlemen treating a brace of teenage girls who were *not* their grandchildren. On another occasion my neighbour butted into my conversation to challenge my interpretation of schmalz. The last time, there was an echo from the two fellows in the corner, "Did you hear what he said?"' The menu is explained well downstairs, but first impressions are not always as rosy as the memories of old hands: 'dull', 'mediocre', 'no virtue apart from mammoth quantities', 'decent of their sort but not exceptional' are some of the more extreme. There are, too, some more positive eye-openers, even to those more used to the refined cooking of West End altars to Escoffier, 'the best apple strudel I have ever tasted, an excellent version of summer pudding *rote Grütze*, fine Transylvanian stuffed cabbage, and delicious pancakes filled with chicken cream and paprika.' The especial virtues revolve around game cookery, old and famous associations, generous quantities, and reasonable prices. These have less to do with food quality than people sometimes pretend. The quality of the coffee fluctuates; the quality of the house white wine has declined; but there is a range of Hungarian wines that may repay exploration, with care. House wines are £6.50.

CHEF: Laslo Holecz  PROPRIETORS: Magyar Restaurant Ltd
OPEN: Mon to Sat
MEALS: 12.30 to 2.30, 5.30 to 11
PRICES: £17 (£26), Set L £12 (£18) to £14 (£20)
SEATS: 70. Private parties: 20 main room, 10 private room. Children's helpings (L only). Smart dress preferred. Wheelchair access. Air-conditioned

## Gilbert's 🍾

map 12

2 Exhibition Road, SW7 2HF
01-589 8947

COOKING 2
COST £17–£26

The bottom of Exhibition Road is the first outpost of real life after walking through the wasteland of museum and public buildings in South Kensington. The late-Victorian shop buildings strike an incongruous pose and resemble nothing so much as a station parade in the suburbs – which, perhaps, they once were. Gilbert's occupies one of these. Changes and improvements have made it a pleasanter room than it was, though it is still none too comfortable, nor spacious when full. Julia Chalkley cooks food that has been welcomed as 'tasting of itself, and not from the "nage of lobster flesh from the lower lobe, sauce diable, with goats' cheese and baby tomatoes in a pastry basket" school.' A meal of carrot and orange soup; pigeon breasts with marjoram and a light red wine stock sauce, first rate vegetables including Parmentier potatoes (oh! for restaurants that don't serve second-rate gratin dauphinois in tiny discs, or who avoid those ghastly little galettes of grease-laden shredded potato); and a lemon and walnut tart that seems something of a signature dish, came to a fitting end with decent coffee and home-made fudge. Ann Wregg serves, converses and greets in a relaxed and civilised manner. The restaurant has started lighter lunches, there is normally a vegetarian option and they now open on Monday nights. Standards can fluctuate if Julia Chalkley is not cooking. The wine list is a short model. There are so many good merchants around that all such restaurants should be able to do as well, provided they show the intelligence and taste that are evident here. All countries are given a showing, though France preponderates. The organic wines from Terres Blanches in Les Baux are in three colours; there is a 1985 Sauvignon/Semillon from Carmenet in the Sonoma; and the Ch. Hanteillan 1983 is a bourgeois claret that has performed consistently well. Fashionable, yes, but how refreshing and not greedily priced. Five dessert wines by the glass are listed alongside the sweets: not a cliché amongst them. It is interesting to notice that one of the popular wines here, and elsewhere, is François Sack's white Cassis from Provence. Ten years ago it was a minority indeed that found this slightly resinous wine pleasing, but as we have become an outpost of olive oil, sun-dried tomatoes and chillies, so we need something with more coarse attack. House Italian £6.95. CELLARMAN'S CHOICE : Cassis, Clos Ste-Magdeleine 1986, £13.50; Côtes du Rhône, Cru de Coudoulat 1985, Perrin, £12.95.

CHEF: Julia Chalkley   PROPRIETORS: Julia Chalkley and Ann Wregg
OPEN: all week, exc Mon L, Sat L and Sun
MEALS: 12.30 to 2 (2.30 Sun), 6.15 to 10.15
PRICES: Set L £12 (£17), Set D £16.50 (£22)
CARDS: Access, Amex, Visa
SEATS: 32. 2 tables outside. Vegetarian meals. Children's helpings (Sun L only).
Wheelchair access (2 steps). Music. Air-conditioned

---

## *Golden Chopsticks*        map 12

| 1 Harrington Road, SW7 3ES | COOKING 2 |
|---|---|
| 01-584 0855 and 581 8951 | COST £20−£60 |

'The fish is always superb − scallops and soft shell crabs for starters, sea bass, sole and squid.' Mrs Choi, one of the few women Chinese chefs in London, runs a tight kitchen and there have been enough good reports this past year to suggest a return to the *Guide* after an earlier doubtful patch. The menu ranges across the three main regions, but since the cooks are Cantonese, these dishes rather than listed Szechuan specialities are the main attraction. Lobster in black-bean sauce cooked live to order (and how many English restaurants do that?) has been memorably succulent and at perfect pitch; the deep-fried soft shell crabs, a wonderful bonne-bouche, have stood out among a large plateful of appetisers which also includes good jellyfish and shark's fin with bean sprouts; sea bass, steamed or stuffed and re-formed so that it stands up on the plate, is dealt with more than competently. Disappointment has usually come with fried dishes in which toughening or greasiness has spoiled basically good ingredients. Service, run by Mr Choi and waitresses in neat black and white uniforms, is gentle and efficient and the atmosphere airily elegant. Prices have been a grouse in the past and it is true that they do not compare with bargain dinners in Chinatown, but they are not outrageously high considering some of the ingredients. House wine is £7.80.

CHEF: Mrs Choi    PROPRIETOR: C. Choi
OPEN: all week
CLOSED: 25 and 26 Dec
MEALS: 12 to 2.15, 6 to 11.15 (10.45 Sun and bank hols)
PRICES: £34 (£50), Set D £12 (£20) to £30 (£41). Cover 50p. Minimum £10. Service 15%
CARDS: Access, Amex, Diners, Visa
SEATS: 80. Private parties: 50 main room. Children welcome. Air-conditioned

## Good Food                                                          map 14

8 Little Newport Street, WC2H 7JJ                       COOKING 1
01-734 2130                                              COST  £12–£35

The expensive red-and-black decoration brings into focus the old endearing
qualities of south Soho and the new monied Chinese. On the menu are
shredded sea blubber, fried crispy intestine or stewed ox-liver (in all styles).
Reports have been so varied, which is inevitable with such a large menu, that
we perhaps have to conclude that one person's 'abalone and duck's web' may
be another's anathema. House French, £5.50.

CHEFS: Che-Keung Yip and Shun-Yau Wong    PROPRIETORS: Haylin Ltd
OPEN: all week, D only
MEALS: 5pm to 4.30am
PRICES: £19 (£29), Set D £8 (£12) to £10 (£14). Minimum £5. Service inc. Licensed, also
bring your own: corkage £2 each
CARDS: Access, Amex, Visa
SEATS: 75. Private parties: 30 main room, 30 private room. Children welcome. Music.
Air-conditioned

## Gopal's of Soho                                                    map 14

12 Bateman Street, W1V 5TD                              COOKING 3
01-434 1621 and 0840                                    COST  £22

More stylish than many, with bright pink tablecloths and an amiable staff, this
comes from the same mould as Lal Qila and the Red Fort, whose reputation
Gopal Pittal helped to make. To one reader, 'it is the use of coriander and
tamarind' that is memorable. Certainly much is aromatic and much is hot, for
chillies are another strong point. The house thali of chicken tikka, sheek kebab,
king prawn tandoori, keema masala, murgh shahi, saag and pulao rice
impressed more than the vegetarian version. Murgh jalfrezi, chicken cooked
with fresh herbs and green chillies, happily stops conversation. A short wine
list is 'shamefully overpriced', so Kingfisher is a better bet – and more suitable.
House French is £6.75.

CHEF/PROPRIETOR: N.P. Pittal
OPEN: all week, exc Sun D
CLOSED: 25 and 26 Dec
MEALS: 12 to 3.15, 6 to 11.45
PRICES: £13 (£18). Minimum £8.50. Service inc
CARDS: Access, Amex, Diners, Visa
SEATS: 48. Private parties: 50 main room. Vegetarian meals. Children's helpings.
Wheelchair access (1 step). Music. Air-conditioned

## Grafton

map 10

45 Old Town, Clapham, SW4 0JL
01-627 1048 and 8231

COOKING **2**
COST £21−£40

A larger restaurant than meets the eye, it has a pretty room downstairs and two further rooms above. Though in a peculiarly desolate stretch north of the Common that was a bomb-site zone, it occupies an old house. Done out in pine and fabrics, it looks like a bistro but behaves like a fancy joint. The prices reflect the latter. The waiters and waitresses have taken courses in synchronised dome removal − and seem to expect customers to synchronise expressions of awe. This can be tiresome. There is a *carte* and set-price menu at dinner, a big Sunday brunch and an 'executive' menu at lunchtimes that constitutes fair value. The departure of last year's chef and the gathering of the reins in Mr Gabr's hands has led to marked variation in standards, though often acceptable. A foaming soupe aux moules et safran has been pleasant but short on verve; loin of lamb with shallots was well cooked and well arranged but only brought to life by excellent vegetables; puddings still seem a strong point, as do the petits fours. The wide-ranging French wine list, shows house wine at £8.70. Orange juice has come out of a carton.

CHEF/PROPRIETOR: M.W. Gabr
OPEN: Tue to Sun, exc Sat L and Sun D
CLOSED: last 3 weeks Aug, 1 week at Christmas
MEALS: 12.30 to 2.30, 7.30 to 11.30
PRICES: £24 (£33), Set L £12.50 (£21), Set D £18.50 (£27) to £22.50 (£31). Minimum £12.50
CARDS: Access, Amex, Carte Blanche, Diners, Visa
SEATS: 74. Private parties: 20 and 26 private rooms. Children's helpings (Sun only). Children restricted. Smart dress preferred. No-smoking area, no pipes in dining-room. Music

## Great Nepalese

map 11

48 Eversholt Street, NW1 1DA
01-388 6737

COOKING **1**
COST £6−£17

'Still as busy and sharp as ever, the Great Nepalese has not been wrecked by the trendies,' writes a reporter. Certainly the location is far from trendy, just across the road from Euston station, but the food draws many devoted regulars. The menu is more exotic than in most like restaurants. You will find the usual kormas, birianis and tikkas, but alongside these are delicacies like memocha, a light and spicy steamed pastry; kelezo ra chyua, a nicely herbed blend of chicken livers and mushrooms; chicken jalfrezi, a rather dry curry with ginger, peppers and lots of onion. There are unusual pork and duck curries, and a whole list of Nepalese vegetarian specialities. The spicing is lively and the details − breads and pickles − as interesting as the main dishes. Kingfisher beer is available, and house Italian is £4.75 a litre. The experimental no-smoking area has been abandoned.

*All letters to the* Guide *are acknowledged with an update on latest sales, closures, chef changes and so on.*

CHEF: Faruk   PROPRIETOR: Gopal Manandhar
OPEN: all week
CLOSED: 25 and 26 Dec
MEALS: 12 to 2.45, 6 to 11.45
PRICES: £8 (£14), Set L £5 (£8), Set D £7.95 (£12). Minimum £4.50. Service inc L, 10% D
CARDS: Access, Amex, Carte Blanche, Diners, Visa
SEATS: 48. Private parties: 34 main room. Vegetarian meals. Children's helpings. Music

## *Green's*　　　　　　　　　　　　　　　　　　　　map 13

36 Duke Street, St James's, SW1Y 6DF 　　　　　COOKING 2
01-930 4566 　　　　　　　　　　　　　　　　　　COST £46

St James's spawns restaurants of old panelling and marble; centuries have not
affected an English gentleman's taste. Green's, younger than many restaurants
in the district, pursues these ideals. There is a bar with booths for an
assignation or a plot, and a larger restaurant beyond for dining. A test meal of
simple luxuries – the kitchen's benchmark, for it hardly aspires to serious
cooking – took in oysters, carrot soup, a terrine of foie gras de canard and
asparagus hollandaise. Everything was acceptable but with no effort to lift
flavours from ideal ingredients: bland brown bread, monotone soup, insipid
and characterless hollandaise. St James's is a rich purlieu, but more should be
forthcoming for such prices. House French is £9. CELLARMAN'S CHOICE : Ch.
Marquis-de-Terme 1978, Margaux, £20; Sancerre Clos du Roy 1988, £16.

CHEF: Beth Coventry   PROPRIETOR: Simon Parker Bowles
OPEN: all week, exc Sun D
MEALS: 12.30 to 2.45 (12 to 4 Sun), 6 to 11
PRICES: £26 (£38), Snacks from £4.50. Cover £1
CARDS: Access, Amex, Diners, Visa
SEATS: 60. Private parties: 40 private room. Children's helpings (Sun L only). No babies.
Smart dress preferred. Air-conditioned

## *Guernica*　　　　　　　　　　　　　　　　　　　map 13

21A Foley Street, W1P 7LA 　　　　　　　　　　COOKING 3
01-580 0623 　　　　　　　　　　　　　　　　　COST £17–£32

Undoubtedly one of the most interesting Spanish restaurants in London,
Guernica still seems to be developing well. The dining-room remains pink and
airy, with its glass-windowed bay jutting out on to the pavement. Over the last
year and a half the Basque menu has evolved and been slimmed down
considerably to offer a better balance of traditional and new, although for first
and main courses it is still firmly anchored in fish. Excellent brick-brown fish
soup and baby squid in their ink, tender and fragrant in a thick black sauce,
remain. Among chef Benat Arroave's new dishes have been a starter of
asparagus and prawns under puff pastry, a fine hake's tail baked with garlic
and butter and served with oyster mushrooms, and impressive pastelitos de la
casa or miniature sweet pastry tartlets with various fillings. It is always worth
asking about game or fish dishes of the day before making a choice. Service is
made difficult by the restaurant's design. House wine is £7.50.

CHEF: Benat Arroave   PROPRIETORS: Foley 21 Ltd
OPEN: Mon to Sat, exc Sat L
MEALS: 12 to 3, 7 to 11
PRICES: £20 (£27), Set L £12 (£17) to £14 (£19)
CARDS: Access, Amex, Diners, Visa
SEATS: 40. Private parties: 10 private room. Children welcome. Music. Air-conditioned

## Harvey's
map 10

2 Bellevue Road, SW17 7EG                                    COOKING 4
01-672 0114 and 0115                                        COST £25−£44

Like a thin crust on the dough of Tooting Bec, Bellevue Road runs along the
south side of Wandsworth Common. Harvey's, once a wine bar, was
redecorated in 1989, no expense spared. The result is a long room, restful to the
eye, washed yellow and off-white. The plasterwork might be the salon of a
millionaire in a film set. It works well. At the front is a small sitting-out area. A
set-price menu of six or seven choices in each course is offered at both lunch
and dinner and there is a short and cheaper lunch menu. The *carte* does not
change often, Marco Pierre White being a man of a few well-rehearsed dishes
which he does not abandon lightly. First courses show a preoccupation with
shellfish, to the detriment of choice. Foie gras, on the other hand, is not such an
obsession. This lightens the style of the food. Many readers are overcome by
the excellence of the cooking. 'At Harvey's the duxelles of wild mushrooms
inside the eggy exterior of the dariole mould had depth, nuance and flavour of a
type I have never, or hardly ever, encountered.' Another confronted with this
same dish was struck by the most intense truffle flavour encountered outside
Périgord itself. A fellow restaurateur remarked: 'Every flavour in each dish was
evident. Presentation was sublime without being ridiculous. Textures were
perfect. This restaurant is the one to send your chef to.' Success is due to
constant thought and practice; concentration on a few flavours at a time;
inventive presentation; good recipes. Cooking is neither too heavy, rich nor
intense, allowing diners some respite from a culinary bludgeon. A meal in the
summer began with a 'potage of shellfish with chervil'. This was 'almost like a
pyramid' of fish and shellfish with fat scallops seared on the outside, barely
cooked within, layered on top of each other and topped with 'what might have
been spun sugar' but was, in fact, strips of finely sliced carrot. The sauce was a
light reduction that brought out the anise flavour of the chervil. The hallmark of
vertical arrangement runs through every dish: pictures on plates are out; little
towers, tall sandwiches, ziggurats and pyramids are in. Though not invented
here, another trademark is the 'tagliatelle' of vegetables cut into thin strands to
resemble short pasta. More substantial vegetables are scorned in the manner of
expensive French restaurants; a customer who wished for a supplement of
freshly cooked vegetables at mid-summer was denied them. Harvey's is not
primarily about cooking the food that people wish to eat, it is about the power
of the media and the chef to impose taste − however well expressed and well
received − on consenting adults. Marco Pierre White certainly does not enjoy
spoiling his kitchen routine for the sake of pleasing a paying customer. The
next course of this summer meal was Bresse pigeon with a ravioli of ceps, a
confit of garlic and fumet of red wine. This dish can suffer from greasiness and
richness. The mushroom flavour was well handled, the potato disc beneath the

meat less so. Some readers have had truffles on their pigeon, others not. The pigeon itself was very good and balance was introduced by some lentils. (At Harvey's the absence of a specific, listed ingredient can sometimes cause trouble. It is not always announced by the staff; when it is, the telling may be so off-hand as to display arrogance.) Dessert was a slice of lemon tart coated with the finest layer of caramel. The astringent, full lemon flavour of the filling was good, though no better than elsewhere in London. Few dishes served in this restaurant are without recommendation from readers. First courses are consistently more praised than main courses. The trimmings, lack of vegetables apart, are good. Bread is excellent, so is the butter, so are the petits fours. Seasoning, usually the skill most valued in a cook, is surprisingly inaccurate. Too many dishes, in readers' recollection, have suffered from excess of salt. The wine list is improving, while its prices rise, according to reports. Across the stage of this small restaurant walks the figure of its chef, a young man who behaves with a petulance that infects. No other place in this *Guide* excites such volume of complaint about service, though many, it must be said, find the waiters effective and polite and the hospitality, in the widest sense, warm and unaffected. One deep-seated problem is delay. The kitchen takes so long to produce, and especially to arrange, the teetering towers, that rapid or even normal pacing is inconceivable. Three hours for lunch in a half-empty restaurant is too long. More than that for dinner is unacceptable. Too many fingers are poked into too many dishes. A restaurant is a place that serves customers to the best of its ability. Harvey's signally fails to give this image.

CHEF/PROPRIETOR: Marco Pierre White
OPEN: Mon to Sat
MEALS: 12.30 to 2, 7.30 to 11.15
PRICES: Set L £20 (£25), Set D £29 (£39)
CARDS: Access, Visa
SEATS: 45. No children under 16. No pipes in dining-room. Air-conditioned

## Heal's                                            map 13

196 Tottenham Court Road, W1P 9LD                        COOKING 1
01-636 1666                                           COST £21-£37

Buried in the corridors of kitchen fittings and sofas of the first floor of Heal's furniture shop is this low, large restaurant affording quiet, space, comfort and an excess of air-conditioning. It is a pleasant spot for a relaxed lunch. The staff is obliging, the noise level low. Chosen from the short set-price menu, deep-fried calamari with tomato sauce was perfectly decent, as was a tournedos of beef with a proper tomato sauce. Other meals have not achieved this sort of success. Terrible pasta and boring and overcooked vegetables give an air of formula cooking with limited pride in execution. There is usually a vegetarian option. To its credit, the restaurant does a good tea. A buffet laden with sandwiches and cakes will leaven many a visit to the publishers' quarter nearby. For a stiffish set price, you can help yourself to as much as you want. House French is £8.

*County Round-ups listing additional restaurants that may be worth a visit are at the back of the* Guide, *after the Irish section. Reports on Round-up entries are welcome.*

CHEF: Anna Smith   PROPRIETORS: de Blank Restaurants Ltd
OPEN: Mon to Sat, L only
CLOSED: bank hols
MEALS: 12 to 2.30
PRICES: £20 (£31), Set L £15 (£21), Snacks from 95p. Minimum £6
CARDS: Access, Amex, Diners, Visa
SEATS: 80. Private parties: 250 main room. Vegetarian meals. Children welcome.
No cigars/pipes in dining-room. Wheelchair access (also WC). Air-conditioned

## *Hiders*

map 10

755 Fulham Road, SW6 5UU                                              COOKING **2**
01-736 2331                                                         COST £21−£28

A smart neighbourhood restaurant which charges neighbourhood prices and
cooks London food satisfactorily. The set-price menu allows for a 'two- or
three-course' meal (a hefty supplement if you try having two main courses
seems to imply the presence of several sharp customers in the past). A salad of
green and red leaves, green beans and tomatoes with a basil and olive oil
dressing, followed by saddle of rabbit stuffed with herbs and lavender, with
wild rice and a sherry sauce exemplifies the style and pleased one reporter. The
wine list is short and to the point (though lacking vital shippers' names), no
dearer than the menu. House French is £6.50. A 12.5 per cent 'optional' service
charge was still added to the bill long after being discountenanced by
officialdom (see the Introduction) − and the consumer too.

CHEFS: Paul Duvall and Andrew George   PROPRIETORS: Richard and Hilary Griggs
OPEN: Mon to Sat, exc Sat L
CLOSED: bank hols
MEALS: 12.30 to 2.30, 7.30 to 11.30
PRICES: Set L £15 (£21), Set D £17 (£23). Service 12.5%
CARD: Access, Visa
SEATS: 70. Private parties: 40 main room. Children welcome. Wheelchair access

## *Highgate Brasserie*

map 10

1 Hampstead Lane, N6 4RS                                              COOKING **2**
01-341 9736                                                         COST £17−£34

Here is reassuring proof that the brasserie formula, so often a disappointment,
can still work. The mood is relaxed, noise levels in the spacious room are high
but not intolerable and the clientele varies with the long opening hours (from
8am). Appropriately, the food adapts to mood, occasion and taste. A summer
dinner for two started with a warm salad of pink duck on frilly lettuce and firm
Mediterranean prawns grilled in garlic butter, continued with steamed halibut
in a cream and wine dill sauce with shrimps and mussels, and fried calf's liver
with onions and bubble and squeak, then finished adequately with fruit tarts.
Ingredients are good and there are careful details. Service is welcoming and
speeded by electronic whizz-kiddery. Prices can mount quickly, not least
because of the 'optional' 15 per cent service charge. The wine list is well chosen
but works on stiff mark-ups for a brasserie. House Cuvée Georges Blanc, £6.50.

CELLARMAN'S CHOICE : Mâcon-Lugny, Les Genièvres, Latour, £12.50; Fleurie 1988, Georges Blanc, £14.90.

CHEF: Christian Tamm   PROPRIETOR: Sven Hoffelner
OPEN: all week
CLOSED: 25 Dec
MEALS: 12 to 3.30, 6.30 to 12
PRICES: £18 (£28), Set L £10.50 (£17). Service 15%
CARDS: Access, Amex, Diners, Visa
SEATS: 180. 4 tables outside. Private parties: 100 main room. Vegetarian meals. Children's helpings on request. Wheelchair access (2 steps; also WC). Music. Air-conditioned

## Hilaire

map 12

68 Old Brompton Road, SW7 3LQ
01-584 8993

COOKING 3
COST £22−£37

Lunch is the better meal to have, upstairs the better place to sit. Trusthouse Forte has not yet brought down this loner among restaurants: owned by a group, but seeming quite individual. The characters of the executants and the nature of the place − comfort and grandeur on an absurdly small scale − must have something to do with it. Although not a great many people have reported, those who have still approve Bryan Webb's modern cooking. There are many components familiar to habitués of London restaurants but still to percolate beyond − Piedmontese peppers, zampone, lentils − and other features now found everywhere − coriander, gravlax (a national snack, from nowhere to supermarket counter in 10 years), laverbread (not very well dealt with, according to one), wild mushrooms, St-Emilion au chocolat, and so on. The connections with the repertoire of Simon Hopkinson, the former chef, are still pronounced. In many ways, the mode best suits simplicity − thus the attractions of lunch: a little less rich, a lot cheaper. The wine list is nice enough and offers many half-bottles, but is dear. Sancerre can be had on the Welsh borders for under £10, here it will cost £17.50. There is not much attempt to find characterful though lesser wines that would in fact suit better the pronounced flavours of the cooking than do fine burgundies at fancy prices. House Duboeuf, £7.50. CELLARMAN'S CHOICE : Bourgogne Rouge, Hautes Côtes de Nuits, 1985, Guyon, £15.50; Sancerre Rouge 1986, Vacheron, £17.50.

CHEF: Bryan Webb   PROPRIETORS: Distinctive Inns THF
OPEN: Mon to Sat, exc Sat L
MEALS: 12.30 to 2.30, 7.30 to 11
PRICES: Set L £16.50 (£22), Set D £24.50 (£31)
CARDS: Access, Amex, Carte Blanche, Diners, Visa
SEATS: 50. Private parties: 8 main room. Children's helpings. Air-conditioned

## Hung Toa

map 11

54 Queensway, W2 3RY
01-727 6017

COOKING 2
COST £12−£19

'Still the best char sui and roast duck west of Hong Kong' and it's best to hit the place just as they come fresh into the window. 'For a good six months the standards dropped to those of every high street outfit, but now the crisp skins

have returned to the lean ducks and barbecued pork is more thoroughly
marinated. This remains the principal canteen in which a loyal Chinese
clientele eat those dishes, crispy belly of pork and white chicken on a plate of
rice or noodles.' Very cheap if you choose well. Licensed.

CHEFS: Mr Wong and Mr Leong   PROPRIETORS: Jeromglen Ltd
OPEN: all week
MEALS: noon to 11pm
PRICES: £11 (£16), Set L and D £9 (£12), Snacks from £1.20
SEATS: 66. Private parties: 25 main room, 30 private room. Children welcome. Wheelchair
access (3 steps)

## Ikkyu

map 13

Basement, 67 Tottenham
Court Road, W1P 9PA                                        COOKING 1
01-636 9280                                               COST £9–£24

By day, the basement feels as much like a café as a restaurant, with rushed one-
plate lunches being downed at the closely packed tables. At one end of the
dining-room is a long, curving bar and at the other a shelf with bottles of
whisky earmarked for regular customers; between the two the staff dash back
and forth to take orders, deliver food and top up the tea. In the daytime, grilled
fish, sushi and teriyaki set meals come with miso soup and fulfil what they
promise, though the overall effect lacks delicacy. In the evening the menu
lengthens considerably and includes individual pot and yakitori dishes as well
as a wider range of sushi and sashimi, but with a less informal mood the rough
edges of cooking and presentation can make the dishes less acceptable. While
the atmosphere among the clientele is pretty casual, service is impeccably
polite. Sake is most appropriate to drink, but house wine is £6.50.

CHEF: M Suzuki   PROPRIETOR: M. Kawaguchi
OPEN: all week, exc Sat and Sun L, Sat D
MEALS: 12.30 to 2.30, 6 to 10.15
PRICES: £15 (£20), Set L and D £4.80 (£9) to £8.30 (£13)
CARDS: Access, Amex, Diners, Visa
SEATS: 65. Private parties: 30 main room, 12 private room. Vegetarian meals. Children
welcome. Music. Air-conditioned

## L'Incontro ♥

map 12

87 Pimlico Road, SW1W 8PH                                 COOKING 3
01-730 6327                                               COST £25–£47

This one is slick – full of mirrors, black and white pictures of Venice, and an
ice-tank in the window bedecked with dead langoustines. The food is good, no
doubt about that, but it is very expensive. Sure, it's Belgravia, and it's full of
Belgravians pecking at their bresaola, but any dish with white truffles is £28 –
which is nearly twice as much as at the Neal Street Restaurant (see entry), not a
cheap place itself. For the price of lunch here you could eat at Gavroche or Tante
Claire. There is some semblance of regionality, reinforced by the sale of the
owner's book on the till counter, but it's fairly superficial. Fegato Veneziana is
a classic, a far cry from the usual trattoria sludge, and the kitchen would be mad

to desert the mushrooms, game and pork. Plebeian bean soup – perverse in this suave setting – is a good version. Fish is a strong point; sauces can be sharp, vegetables disappoint, and the waiters can be obsessively over-attentive. Espresso puts up the bill as do the wines – house Italian is £10.50, Antinori's super-Tuscan Solaia 1978 is £94. The list, however, is a *tour de force* that includes some of the best Italian drinking you will find anywhere – except at Santini, the sister restaurant, whose list matches closely, though prices are not always the same.

CHEFS: D. Minuzzo and I. Santin   PROPRIETOR: G. Santin
OPEN: all week
MEALS: 12.30 to 2.30 (1 to 3.30 Sun), 7 to 11.30 (10.30 Sun)
PRICES: £26 (£39), Set L £14.50 (£25). Cover £1.50. Service 12%
CARDS: Access, Amex, Diners, Visa
SEATS: 65. Private parties: 30 private room. Vegetarian meals. Children's helpings.
Wheelchair access. Music. Air-conditioned

## Inigo Jones                                              map 14

14 Garrick Street, WC2E 9BJ
01-836 6456 and 3223

*As the Guide went to press, Inigo Jones closed until October 1990,
for major refurbishment.*

# *Jade Garden*
map 14

15 Wardour Street, W1V 3HA
01-437 5065

COOKING **2**
COST £19–£28

Chinese warriors picked out in gold relief take an over-view of the proceedings in this elegantly decorated Cantonese restaurant. A spiral staircase leads to the upstairs balcony section and cunningly placed mirrors add to the spacious feeling. Sunday dim-sum is deservedly popular – queue before midday to be sure of a place. The rewards are impressive: hot, fresh, crispy when crispiness is called for. Although the choice is not hugely different in composition from the usual, there are a few uncommon items, for instance prawn toasts with whole prawns embedded in the surface. For more elaborate meals there's a wide selection of stir-fried, clay-potted, steamed and roasted dishes, a few of which are pretty exotic, while one or two others move towards Szechuan and Peking style. Crab with ginger and spring onion, and mixed seafood noodles generously topped with squid and giant prawns have been good. Steamed cod with ginger was well cooked and lavishly topped with fried pork and black mushrooms. Recently service has been charming, making it worthwhile to ask for recommendations not on the menu. House wine, £6.20.

CHEF: Raymond Bignold   PROPRIETORS: L.S. and P.W. Man
OPEN: all week
CLOSED: 25 and 26 Dec
MEALS: noon (11.30am Sat and Sun ) to 11.30
PRICES: £11 (£19), Set D £19 (£23). Service inc
CARDS: Access, Amex, Visa
SEATS: 160. Private parties: 70 main room, 70 private room. Children welcome. Wheelchair access (1 step). Air-conditioned

# *Jamdani*
map 13

34 Charlotte Street, W1P 1HJ
01-636 1178

COOKING **1**
COST £18–£42

Amin Ali has done great things to revitalise the image of Indian restaurants. Jamdani, so named after the fine-woven muslin of Bangladesh, is a handsome space: rose roughcast limestone with fittings in steel and glass. Handsome yes, comfortable no. The menu is long, with an emphasis on the north, but without

*On 6 May 1990 all London telephone numbers will change, the 01- prefix being replaced by either 071- or 081-. See the front of the* Guide *for a list of which numbers will take which prefix.*

*This year, in quoting prices for three-course meals at the top of each entry (by the word 'Cost'), we have put a more pessimistic complexion on the upper price by inflating it by 20 per cent. The aim is to prepare the reader for any inflation during the life of the* Guide *and also reflect the price of a meal taken without constant attention to the likely size of the bill. The prices quoted in smaller print below the text remain, as in previous editions, strict computer calculations of an average three-course meal, the price in brackets reflecting an average meal with coffee, service and half a bottle of house wine per person.*

the regionality you might expect from the name or the trappings. Reports this year have been very mixed, from cries of rapture for the virtuosity of the non-vegetarian thali to dismay at the crudeness of the navratan korma – reminiscent of many a provincial curry-house. Among the best features have been the rice – kesar pulao fit for a medieval prince – and the dhal and raitas. In other words the trimmings, not the substance. The coconut ice-cream was described as 'the best outside the Singapore Mandarin', so persevere to the end. Service is pleasant and concerned. The immense promise of opening months has not been realised, but hope should not be extinguished. Customer resistance to the restaurant's charms is probably fuelled by the high prices. House Italian, £6.95.

CHEF: Naresh Matta   PROPRIETOR: Amin Ali
OPEN: all week
MEALS: 12 to 3, 6 to 11.30
PRICES: £17 (£27), Set L £15 (£18) to £25 (£30), Set D £20 (£23) to £30 (£35). Minimum £15. Service inc
CARDS: Access, Amex, Diners, Visa
SEATS: 90. Private parties: 30 private room. Vegetarian meals. Children's helpings. Smart dress preferred. Wheelchair access (2 steps). Music. Air-conditioned

## *Jasons Court*                                                    map 13

Jasons Court, Wigmore Street, W1                            COOKING 2
01-224 2992                                                      COST £23–£36

This is the second step in young chef Shaun Thomson's path towards elaborating English nouvelle cuisine. He started at Auntie's in Fitzrovia. Opposite St Christopher's Place, in an alley off Wigmore Street, the restaurant is deceptively spacious for a labyrinthine basement, with artful touches (not to all tastes), good linen and chairs and sea salt in glass pestles and mortars. Reports have been mixed even though everyone seems to eat the same dishes: haggis with neeps and tatties; 'gathering of woodland mushrooms' in puff pastry on a pink peppercorn and coriander sauce; parcels of smoked salmon with a smoked trout mousse on a salmon caviare and chive sauce; crown of Welsh lamb with a toasted oatmeal stuffing and a red berry and mint sauce; Shipdham apple tart; hot fruit soufflé with a honey and ginger sauce. There are many berried and sweet sauces scattered through the menu. Presentation is a strong point, some say too strong, veering to pretension. That taste takes occasional second place may be reflected in the livery wild duck terrine, a bitter tasting oatmeal stuffing to the lamb, and a strawberry soufflé that was more floury than fruity. Cheeses are well described, British and unpasteurised. The team is youthful and very enthusiastic. The long wine list suggests direct links with Ch. Boyd-Cantenac. There is a page devoted to its vintages, back to 1949. There are also some odds and ends, including English-bottled burgundies from the 1950s and 1960s, which may or may not come up to scratch. For the rest, it is ambitious and expensive. House Loire, £7.95. CELLARMAN'S CHOICE : Ch. Boyd-Cantenac, Margaux, 1979, £24.95; Clos Fourtet, St-Emilion 1960, £15.95 (half-bottle).

CHEF: Shaun Thomson    PROPRIETORS: Shaun Thomson and Charles Boyd
OPEN: Mon to Sat, exc Sat L
MEALS: 12 to 2.30, 7 to 10.30
PRICES: £20 (£31), Set L £14.95 (£23)
CARDS: Access, Amex, Diners, Visa
SEATS: 50. Private parties: 50 main room, 6 and 14 private rooms. Children welcome.
No-smoking area. Air-conditioned

## Joe's Café                                                           map 12

126 Draycott Avenue
Brompton Cross, SW3 3AH                                        COOKING 2
01-225 2217                                                      COST £31

A node of fashion, such is Brompton Cross. Joseph Ettedgui, the designer, has
been one of its catalysts. The rubberneck up from the shires may wish to
observe it; the more etiolated, worn down by London life, may wish to share its
whorls. Joe's Café, catering arm of said Joseph, is the place to do both. Black
and white, chrome and glass, very flash or supercool; the bartenders,
suntanned to the last, twirl drinks and flick the knobs of the espresso machine;
waiters in white aprons and maître d's in grey baggy suits dash hither and yon,
ever with a smart Mediterranean aside. The cooking is pretty smart too. Even
the pasta is black and white. The puddings consume themselves with
cleverness: a tall glass has five layers – strawberry coulis, dark chocolate
mousse, milk chocolate mousse, white chocolate mousse, raspberry coulis –
the only difference is sweet (too sweet) and sour (too sour); the result is
horrible. But there among it all is some good cooking, not just smart, in the
style of London brasseries: escalope of salmon with sorrel sauce is correctly
fried, and the sorrel is for once adequate to its role of cutter and acidulator; a
craquelet of duck, shredded duck in a filo parcel, is suffused with smoky
flavour; black and green tagliatelle is dressed with a very good oil, given
texture with toasted pine kernels; fried potatoes are thin and crisp. It's not
cheap but it is the front row of the stalls. Coffee is good. Open much of the day,
and no minimum charge until dinner. House wine, from Chinon and Aix-en-
Provence, £8.

CHEF: James Waters    PROPRIETORS: Joseph Ltd
OPEN: all week, exc Sun D
CLOSED: 25 Dec and 1 Jan
MEALS: 12 to 3.30, 7.30 to 11.30 (Snacks 2.30 to 4.30)
PRICES: £18 (£26). Cover £1. Minimum £7. Service 12%
CARDS: Access, Amex, Carte Blanche, Diners, Visa
SEATS: 95. 2 tables outside. Private parties: 25 main room. Vegetarian meals. Children's
helpings. Wheelchair access. Music

*The* Guide *always appreciates hearing about changes of chef or owner.*

*If you see a certificate in a restaurant bearing the words 'Good Food Guide
(International)', the claim is false (and the restaurant may be in contempt of court in
displaying it) – see the Introduction. Please write and tell us the name and address of the
restaurant.*

## Kalamaras

map 11

76–78 Inverness Mews, W2 3JQ
01-727 9122

COOKING 2
COST £19–£29

A dependable and bustling restaurant that has a more diverting menu than most tavernas, and that is Greek rather than Cypriot. Tacked on to the usual offerings of taramosalata and moussaka is a long list of mysterious specialities – ask for a translation. The outfit is organised by matronly Greek women who will ignore customers who persistently put them under pressure. If the kitchen does not sprinkle dried herbs on the Feta, the salad is first class. The grilled aubergines with a strong garlic dip can be excellent; standard items like hummus and calamaras are above par. All wines are Greek, the house bottle at £6.20. CELLARMAN'S CHOICE : Naossa Boutari, £8; Rosé Santa Laura, £6.80.

CHEF/PROPRIETOR: Stelios Platonos
OPEN: Mon to Sat, D only
CLOSED: bank hols
MEALS: 7 to 12
PRICES: £11 (£19), Set D £14 (£21) to £15.50 (£24). Cover £1. Service 10%
CARDS: Access, Amex, Diners, Visa
SEATS: 96. Private parties: 16 and 28 private rooms. Children's helpings. Wheelchair access. Music. Air-conditioned

## Kanishka

map 11

15 Warren Street, W1P 5RY
01-388 0860 and 0862

COOKING 1
COST £8–£20

The waiter had lately sustained an injury to his thumb while arming the burglar alarm on the manager's car. Thus do the machines fight back on a street once lined with second-hand car dealers. Indian restaurants must now be the dominant trade in Fitzrovia. This is a new-wave Indian restaurant that boasts pink cloths, wicker seats, attentive staff and slices of lime in your cola. The tandoor oven is used with some distinction and whole spices are present in encouraging quantity in many of the dishes. The spinach and coriander korma is an example of how the availability of green coriander in London has transformed the taste of Indian food in the last decade. The menu has an equal bias towards vegetarian dishes but, in all, still promises more than it delivers on the plate. Lunch is a good-value help-yourself from a side buffet.

CHEF: Noor Mohamed     PROPRIETOR: Jagdish Vitish
OPEN: all week, exc Sat L
MEALS: 12 to 3, 6 to 11.30 (Fri, Sat 12)
PRICES: £11 (£17), Set L £6.95 (£8)
CARDS: Access, Amex, Diners, Visa
SEATS: 120. Private parties: 30 main room. Vegetarian meals. Children's helpings on request. No-smoking area. Wheelchair access. Music. Air-conditioned

CELLARMAN'S CHOICE : *A wine recommended by the restaurateur, normally more expensive than the house wine.*

## Kensington Place

map 11

| 201 Kensington Church Street, W8 7LX | COOKING 3 |
|---|---|
| 01-727 3184 | COST £18–£32 |

The Place provokes extreme opinions: of approbation from city dwellers who enjoy a buzz, are happy to shout in the echoing atmosphere of hard edges, bare wood and glass, and like to see and be seen; of dismay from those who expected a restaurant, West End style, and find a brasserie, albeit serving foie gras. One reporter, shocked by the noise level, commented, 'My guests told me that film director X and assorted film stars were at the next table. Had they also told me they were filming *Gone With the Wind*, I wouldn't have been suprised.' Another visited 'only to find the staff arrogant and uninterested and very casually serving rather overpriced food to patrons sitting on highly uncomfortable seats.' More tolerant reports, however, have observed, 'this place deserves all the fuss. Not that it needs it – Messrs Smallwood and Slater must be making a fortune, but a deserved one; perhaps most of all because they offer value for money. Nowhere else seems to be packed, "trendy", jolly good and reasonably priced, all at once.' A recommendation from the heart and pocket.

The same correspondent remarked that Rowley Leigh, a graduate of the 'Roux brothers' school of catering', seems to improve as time passes. That there have been moments when improvement was necessary is undeniable – there are too many barbed comments to ignore – but when he and his team are on form, they produce really good cooking with ambition to delight but without pretension. A meal early in 1989 began with a chicken and goats' cheese mousse topped with olives. The dariole was more custard than mousse, but had an intriguing succession of flavours: 'Ah, chicken … There's the goats' cheese … What a combination!' The olives, a chopped layer on top of the mould, added bite, which was reinforced by a drizzle of gooseberry sauce. Unlikely it may sound, but it worked magnificently. This was succeeded by roast *coquelet* with salsify and a walnut vinaigrette. The fowl, moist within but crisp of skin, was set on a bed of salsify, carrots and green beans that were insufficiently cooked, but the walnut dressing was exactly right in its added flavour, touch of lubrication and zest of acid from the vinegar. Cheese followed, a mixture of French and English well enough kept that only a crottin failed to live up to expectations. Dessert was a grand selection, of which the summits were a lemon tart that draws consistent and deserved praise, and baked tamarillo with passion-fruit sauce. The menu changes frequently and there are daily specials to accelerate the kitchen's response. Essentially, there are a dozen choices in each course. For the first, two or three soups, often an omelette, and dishes that strike one as off the page of a weekend cookery supplement: griddled scallops with rocket; vinaigrette of red peppers with anchovies (a dish of impeccable brasserie breeding in the late 1980s); egg, potato and mâche salad with truffles. Then on to spiced shoulder of lamb with couscous and harissa, calf's liver with beetroot sauce, or grilled rump steak with salsa verde. The worst criticism is that occasionally these dishes are done with too little gusto or conviction and appear dire, wimp-like rip-offs. The trimmings are well thought out; the breads, for instance, are a great selection from the Italian bakery La Fornaia. Some of these are pretty good, some dreadful. The waiting staff has a lot to do – 'They're not rude, just anxious to re-lay your table.' This means you may have to ask for everything twice, but usually it will come with a smile. Coffee is good but sometimes cool. The wine list is short and by no means greedy. It even has a fair proportion of halves. House French is £6.95 for red, £6.75 white. CELLARMAN'S CHOICE : Condrieu 1986, Antoine Cuilleron, £25; Bourgogne Pinot Noir Chante-Flûte 1985, £11.75.

---

CHEF: Rowley Leigh   PROPRIETORS: N. Smallwood and S. Slater
OPEN: all week
MEALS: 12 to 11.45 (10.15 Sun)
PRICES: £19 (£27), Set L £11.50 (£18)
CARDS: Access, Visa
SEATS: 90. Private parties: 90 main room. Children's helpings. Music. Air-conditioned

---

## ▲ Kingfisher Restaurant, Halcyon Hotel

map 11

81–82 Holland Park, W11 2RZ                    COOKING 2
01-221 5411                                    COST £16–£35

To get to this purposely discreet restaurant (perhaps to protect the famous who are reported ever spilling the beans within its purlieu), it is wisest to approach from Holland Park Avenue. Access from the hotel itself is a Thesean labyrinth (and reception is no Ariadne). The goal achieved, the room is deceptively large with restful garden-trellis and washed-colour decoration. The menu is enticingly modern, designed to nourish without excess burden. Rhubarb, sorrel, coriander, onion confit, flageolets and sea urchins are markers enough of affiliation and style. When carefully developed, the combinations may sing. When badly handled, as they can be, they may nauseate: scallops overwhelmed by a black olive and tomato sauce; sashimi of tuna and salmon lost beneath a Chinese consommé as crude as any worked by a new cook playing with his or her first wok; saddle of rabbit swamped by a high, fishy sea urchin and tarragon risotto. Others find more sophisticated skills at work, a greater degree of balance, but it cannot be guaranteed. The wine list is good, few growers are to be discounted. It is also expensive. House French is £8.75. CELLARMAN'S CHOICE : Ch. Millet, Grand Cru Graves 1982, £23.50; Wyndham Oak Cask Chardonnay 1989, £15.75.

---

CHEF: James Robins   PROPRIETORS: Halcyon Hotel Corporation Ltd
OPEN: all week
MEALS: 12.30 to 2.30, 7.30 to 11.30
PRICES: £25 (£28), Set L £15.50 (£15.50) to £19.25 (£19.25), Set D £20.75 (£20.75) to £28.90 (£28.90). Service inc
CARDS: Access, Amex, Carte Blanche, Diners, Visa
SEATS: 66. 6 tables outside. Private parties: 60 main room. Children's helpings. Smart dress preferred. Wheelchair access. Music. Air-conditioned
ACCOMMODATION: 44 rooms, all with bath/shower. Rooms for disabled. Lift. B&B £125 to £175. Deposit: £125. Baby facilities. Afternoon teas. Sauna. Air-conditioning. TV. Phone. Confirm by 6

---

*County Round-ups listing additional restaurants that may be worth a visit are at the back of the* Guide, *after the Irish section. Reports on Round-up entries are welcome.*

---

## Lal Qila
map 13

117 Tottenham Court Road, W1P 9HL
01-387 4570

COOKING 1
COST £16-£32

New-wave Indian is rather old hat these days, and Lal Qila – once excitingly in the vanguard of elegant décor, skilful cooking and suave service – seems to have lost its sizzle. This has been literally true in the case of karahi gosht, where the authentically spitting iron platter of lamb should necessitate dry-cleaning bills at neighbouring tables. However, at least the spicing of that dish was lively. Not so in other reported experiences, such as 'dry and rather tasteless sheek kebab', 'bland, barely spicy murgh chat' and 'feeble' lamb pasanda. Basmati rice and the various breads remain popular, vegetables are fair, and the thalis (one vegetarian) are an acceptable introduction to the genre. Service has slowed noticeably. If good taste forbids such cocktails as Raj Rascal, 'the phantom flasher', there's house wine at £6.75 and various imported lagers.

CHEF: Ayub Ali   PROPRIETORS: Enamul Haque, Abul Kalam and Ayub Ali
OPEN: all week
MEALS: 12 to 3, 6 to 11.15
PRICES: £9 (£18), Set L £10 (£16) to £12 (£18), Set D £15 (£22) to £20 (£27). Service 15%
CARDS: Access, Amex, Diners, Visa
SEATS: 80. Private parties: 40 main room. Vegetarian meals. Children's helpings. Smart dress preferred. Music. Wheelchair access (1 step). Air-conditioned

## Langan's Bistro
map 13

26 Devonshire Street, W1N 1RJ
01-935 4531

COOKING 1
COST £25

In an area still short of acceptable restaurants, the Bistro survives, though looking none too up-to-the-minute. The menu is simple and adequate, the wines include some nice bottles at not extortionate prices. Monkfish with red peppers, grilled lamb cutlets with tarragon and a warm salad of mussels are a few of the dishes that have pleased but not excited reporters. House wine is £7.50.

CHEF: Sean Butcher   PROPRIETORS: Michael Caine and Richard Shepherd
OPEN: Mon to Sat, exc Sat L
CLOSED: 25 and 26 Dec, 1 Jan
MEALS: 12.30 to 2.30, 7 to 11.30
PRICES: £13 (£21). Cover £1. Service 10%
CARDS: Amex, Access, Diners, Visa
SEATS: 38. Children's helpings on request. Wheelchair access. Air-conditioned

*The* Guide *relies on feedback from its readers. Especially welcome are reports on new restaurants appearing in the book for the first time.*

*Several sharp operators have tried to extort money from restaurateurs on the promise of an entry in a guide book that has never appeared.* The Good Food Guide *makes no charge for inclusion and does not offer certificates of any kind.*

## Langan's Brasserie

map 13

Stratton Street, W1X 5SD
01-493 6437

COOKING 2
COST £35

The sad death of Peter Langan has not caused the demise of his brasserie, although he will be sorely missed by many who appreciated the validity of the original conception, and more who fed off stories of his excess. The conception lives on, the framework supplied by the organisational skills of Richard Shepherd. It is still full to bursting, still characterful, still glamorous in the eyes of column readers. It even manages to deliver surprises: 'much better than I ever expected'. The vast menu, changing day by day, offers a mix of English restaurant food of the old school and French or European brasserie dishes. Standards rarely achieve high spots, but are often satisfactory. The quails' eggs tart has a nice enough hollandaise, but the hard-boiled eggs put it firmly in the bistro class. Cooking may be accurate to the second on one day, hit and miss the next. The system, however, does work: food is delivered to the right table by waiters who may be crusty and even crotchety but know their trade. There are few places which achieve this scale with like panache over so long a period. The wine list, entirely French, has as many Champagnes as white wines. House wine is £6.50. CELLARMAN'S CHOICE : Sancerre, Le Grand Chemarin 1987, £13.60; Brouilly 1988, Duboeuf, £11.95.

CHEFS: Richard Shepherd, Dennis Mynott and Roy Smith   PROPRIETORS: Michael Caine and Richard Shepherd
OPEN: Mon to Sat, exc Sat L
MEALS: 12.30 to 3, 7 to 11.45 (8 to 12.45 Sat)
PRICES: £19 (£29). Cover £1. Service 12.5%
CARDS: Access, Amex, Diners, Visa
SEATS: 200. Private parties: 12 main room. Vegetarian meals. Children's helpings. Wheelchair access (1 step). Music. Air-conditioned

## Launceston Place

map 12

1A Launceston Place, W8 5RL
01-937 6912

COOKING 2
COST £34

A restaurant such as this goes in cycles. The result of its spawning so successful a fry as Kensington Place (see entry) has been a concerted effort to iron out the blips in the graph of its own performance by liaison between the two brigades under the guiding hand of Kensington Place's Rowley Leigh. From its inception, Launceston Place has served its immediate community well: not too expensive, a readiness to serve quickly, light and inventive food in civilised though sometimes crowded surroundings. This year has seen some comment about unevenness, but more generally, relief at a return to steadier form. In the full flight of nouvelle cuisine some fairly outrageous combinations were essayed. Today the style is more subdued: lobster salad, quails' eggs and grilled peppers; an omelette terrine with tomato vinaigrette; sea bass with courgettes and rosemary; quail with foie gras and shallots; a vegetarian gratin of turnips, Jersey Royals and morels. The cooking has often been very successful, from well-seasoned soups to ethereal bread-and-butter pudding, 'the best version I have ever eaten'. A short wine list is restrained in price for

Kensington, and sensible in choice. The service can be suave, friendly, considerate and, rarely, haughty and hurried. House wine, £6.95 and £7.85.

CELLARMAN'S CHOICE : Volnay *premier cru* Les Brouillards, 1983, £25; Ch. Doisy-Daëne Sec 1986, £10.75.

CHEF: Charles Mumford   PROPRIETORS: Nick Smallwood and Simon Slater
OPEN: all week, exc Sat L and Sun D
MEALS: 12.30 to 2.30, 7 to 11.30
PRICES: £19 (£28)
CARDS: Access, Visa
SEATS: 55. Private parties: 25 main room, 14 private room. Vegetarian meals. Children's helpings (L only). No pipes in dining-room. Wheelchair access. Air -conditioned

## *Laurent*                                                           map 11

| 428 Finchley Road, NW2 2HY | COOKING 1 |
| 01-794 3603 | COST £19 |

An unpretentious and authentic Algerian-French couscous house much patronised by French customers who are used to finding this type of establishment all over Paris. To start, brik à l'oeuf is a crispy pancake filled with a well-seasoned egg. Main choices are three types of couscous: vegetarian; *complet*, which adds spicy merguez sausage and lamb to the vegetables; and royal, which makes the further addition of a brochette and a lamb chop. The couscous itself is separate and dry, the accompanying sauces well flavoured, the meat tender. A dish of hot chilli sauce is also served. Desserts are ices or crème caramel. Three house French wines from £6 a bottle.

CHEF/PROPRIETOR: Laurent Farrugia
OPEN: Mon to Sat
CLOSED: first 3 weeks Aug
MEALS: 12 to 2, 6 to 10.30
PRICES: £11 (£16). Minimum £5
CARDS: Access, Visa
SEATS: 36. Private parties: 50 main room. Vegetarian meals. Children's helpings

## *Left Bank*                                                         map 11

| 88 Ifield Road, SW10 9AD | COOKING 1 |
| 01-352 0970 | COST £15—£29 |

An astonishing number of people can eat here, once the home of 'Nick's Diner' and now extended with a conservatory. The cooking is modern French bistro, with a praiseworthy cheap menu for the early (7pm to 8pm) and late (10pm to 11.30pm) hours. Go at 9pm, however, and it's à la carte all the way. The wine list is as French as the food purports to be, and house wine from Bergerac is £7.

CHEF: Michael Mannion   PROPRIETORS: Fernando Peire and Keith Wormleighton
OPEN: all week, D only and Sun L
MEALS: 12 to 2.30, 7 to 11.30
PRICES: £16 (£24), Set D early and late eve. £10 (£15) to £12.50 (£18)
CARDS: Access, Amex, Visa
SEATS: 95. 2 tables outside. Private parties: 14 main room, 30 private room. Children's helpings. Wheelchair access. Music. Air-conditioned

## Leith's ♥

map 11

92 Kensington Park Road, W11 2PN
01-229 4481

COOKING **3**
COST £29—£44

From very early in its career, this place was accepted as an institution; a
remarkable achievement. It is a substantial place, occupying a substantial
house, decorated not with frills and furbelows but with cleaner lines, almost
sober – besuited – but with the odd tricksy number like the quasi-office
chairs. 'I have never before visited a restaurant in which there seemed to be a
waiter for every item – even the water.' The New Establishment will feel at
home here. It is a triumph of form over content that the menu occupies an A3
folder yet lists only 15 dishes, in unadorned typography. Such economy is
possible only because the trolleys—hors d'oeuvre, cheese and desserts—assume
so great a role in the choosing of a meal. Round they trundle, affording
involvement, participation and some pleasure when the waiter detailed for this
function is not too blasé. Thomas Alf cooks a modern menu that ranges from
grand luxury – duck-liver and foie gras parfait – to more homely dishes, la
poule au pot, and to a fashionable mixture of the two, as in veal tongue with
wild mushrooms, truffles and port wine sauce. Although the menu is translated
into French, it is a thoroughly British affair, including British cheeses and hot
bread-and-butter pudding. The place is so reliable that it may bore, only
outraging when faults recall to mind the cost of it all: 'the trolley was
interesting although rather bland, the grilled salmon was very salty and the
sweets trolley consisted of a variety of mousses and two forms of fruit salad. An
apple tart did arrive later but was not available to us.' Leith's current claim to
fame is its vegetarian menu, offering dishes such as a salad of spring leaves
with melted goats' cheese croûtons; mille-feuille of asparagus with scrambled
eggs and watercress sauce; or spinach and wild mushroom tartlet glazed with
madeira sabayon, 'well presented and cooked perfectly'. The intermeshing of
carnivore and vegetarian menus is quite interesting: do they use meat stocks in
any of their sauces? do they prepare vegetarian versions every day? Three out of
four sauces on the vegetarian menu are the same as on the meat-eaters'.

The wine list is classic. The few wines from outside France are excellent, for
example, Carmenet Sauvignon Blanc, Edna Valley 1984, and the French bottles
include some greats, not least Chave's Hermitage 1978 which may not yet be
ready but is one of the finest vintages. There are some old clarets, 1966 in
particular, and a strange note on the list that these bins 'have been carefully
stored in our cellars for many years' but customers ordering them do so 'at their
own risk, bearing in mind their maturity'. This is a new area for *caveat emptor* to
operate: do they make no allowance? Four good house wines, £9.75.
CELLARMAN'S CHOICE : Cullens Sauvignon Blanc 1986, Margaret River £19.50;
St-Joseph 1985, St-Desirat-Champagne, £17.50. Tipping 'is positively
discouraged'. Nick Tarayan, the manager, made an observation on no-smoking
zones, which the restaurant has suspended this year. 'We tried very hard to
implement the non-smoking area, despite the fact that our rather warren-like
rooms make it difficult. The result was even more complaints about smokers,
due to the fact that clients would book non-smoking and arrive with smoking
guests.' The lot of a restaurateur is never an easy one.

CHEF: Thomas Alf   PROPRIETORS: Leith's Restaurant Ltd and Prue Leith
OPEN: all week, D only
CLOSED: 3 or 4 days at Christmas, 2 days at Aug bank hol
MEALS: 7.30 to 11.30
PRICES: Set D £24.50 (£29) to £32.50 (£37). Minimum £18.50. Service inc
CARDS: Access, Amex, Diners, Visa
SEATS: 85. Private parties: 24 main room, 10, 24 and 36 private rooms. Vegetarian meals.
Children welcome. Wheelchair access (3 steps). Air-conditioned

## Lemonia

map 11

154 Regent's Park Road, NW1 8XN
01-586 7454

COOKING 1
COST £18

A Greek/Cypriot restaurant serving fresh food of consistent quality 'with confidence and brio'. Meze is popular at £6.90 a head; or there's moussaka served in its own little pot rather than a tranche; stewed and spiced meats; stuffed vegetables and charcoal grills scented with oregano. Greek wine starts at £5.90; house French is £6.90.

CHEF: George Ioannou   PROPRIETOR: Anthony Evangelou
OPEN: Mon to Sat, D only
CLOSED: 2 weeks Aug
MEALS: 6 to 11.30
PRICES: £9 (£15)
SEATS: 85. Private parties: 12 and 14 private rooms. Children welcome. Wheelchair access
(1 step; also WC). Music. Air-conditioned.

## Lilly's

map 11

6 Clarendon Road, W11 3AA
01-727 9359

COOKING 2
COST £34

The wine bar at the rear of this restaurant has been merged into the more important activity of serving food, and Roger Jones continues his determined way of cooking with little fat or cream. This preoccupation with health translates in some reporters' realities to small portions and a surfeit of carrots, but it also reveals an inventive way with combinations and some good cooking. Casserole of pigeon breast with wild mushrooms; poached scallops with fines herbes; baked red mullet provençale; white chocolate mousse with a raspberry sauce are some good items; British cheeses have been less good. The odd voice is raised against three raspberries and a sprig of redcurrants on a green salad: why do we wish to merge all hierarchies of taste? The wine list is short and well explained. House wines from Hill Smith are £6.95.
CELLARMAN'S CHOICE : Pouilly Fumé 1987, Ladoucette, £28; Ch. Musar 1979, £14.95.

*If you see a certificate in a restaurant bearing the words 'Diploma of Merit. The Good Food Guide (United Kingdom)', the claim is false (and the restaurant may be in contempt of court in displaying it) – see the Introduction. Please write and tell us the name and address of the restaurant.*

CHEF: J. Roger Jones  PROPRIETORS: Dr Peter and Mrs C. Lillywhite
OPEN: Mon to Sat, D only
CLOSED: Aug
MEALS: 7 to 11.15
PRICES: £19 (£28)
CARDS: Access, Amex, Diners, Visa
SEATS: 32. 3 tables outside. Private parties: 40 main room. Children welcome. Music

## Los Remos

map 11

38A Southwick Street, W2 1JQ  COOKING 1
01-723 5056 and 706 1870  COST £29

'At last, a reasonable spot near Paddington for the waiting traveller.' It's in a small street in walking distance of the station. Señor Lopez keeps a happy tapas bar in the basement and a restaurant on the ground floor. The octopus in oil and paprika, grilled sardines, ham and chorizo are good as tapas and there is a decent range of Penedès, Riojas and Galicianos to drink with them. The restaurant specialises in grills and does not shirk the garlic. House Rioja, £6.50. CELLARMAN'S CHOICE : Torres Gran Viña Sol 1987, £8.95. There is San Miguel beer.

CHEF/PROPRIETOR: Roberto Lopez
OPEN: all week
MEALS: 12 to 3, 7 to 11 (10.30 Sun)
PRICES: £15 (£24). Cover 50p L, £1 D. Service 10%
CARDS: Access, Amex, Carte Blanche, Diners, Visa
SEATS: 70. Private parties: 70 main room. Children's helpings. Music. Air-conditioned

## Lou Pescadou

map 11

241 Old Brompton Road, SW5 9HP  COOKING 1
01-370 1057  COST £26

The scruffiness may be part of its charm, which continues to attract a certain generation of Londoners. There is no booking, the menu is fish and the restaurant is part of the Pierre Martin stable. Best are the simple dishes, and these are supplied by a very sophisticated marketing operation. Why it should be necessary to import fish from Brittany is a mystery, but this is always cited as the principal attraction of this and its sister restaurants – and it does taste excellent. House wine is £7.50.

CHEF: Laurent David  PROPRIETORS: Oakhelm Ltd
OPEN: Mon to Sat
MEALS: 12 to 3, 7 to 12
PRICES: £15 (£22). Service 10%
CARDS: Access, Amex, Diners, Visa
SEATS: 60. 8 tables outside. Vegetarian meals. Children's helpings. Wheelchair access (1 step)

*The Guide is totally independent, accepts no free hospitality, and survives on the number of copies sold each year.*

## Magno's ♥

map 14

65A Long Acre, WC2E 9JH          COOKING 2
01-836 6077          COST £14−£32

Every year this erstwhile brasserie picks up nearly as many critical notices as favourable. However, it performs a useful function as a pre- and post-theatre location and the praise can be uncommonly warm, for the welcome as well as the cooking, uneven though that may be. There are set meals, one cheaper for pre-theatre suppers, as well as a *carte* and daily specials. Fish dishes have been praised, such as crab galette, 'a superior fish cake', and turbot with Sevruga caviare, of outstanding freshness. Specialities include a feuilleté of Roquefort with a light cheese sauce, a côte de boeuf for two, or a carré of lamb with flageolets. The wine list is very French, for all the half dozen bottles from other parts. It is a small, thoughtful collection from good properties and includes a few surprises from older vintages like de Vogüé's Musigny 1970 or Ch. Léoville-Las-Cases 1964. Outside the classic regions, it offers Chardonnay 1986 from Australia's Basedow and California's Mountain View; the sole Italian is a cracker: Gaja Barbaresco 1974 at £42.50. House French is £6.50.

CHEF: Gilbert Rousset   PROPRIETORS: E. Coliadis and A. Wastell
OPEN: Mon to Sat, exc Sat L
CLOSED: 24 Dec to 2 Jan
MEALS: 12 to 2.30, 6 to 11.30
PRICES: £17 (£27), Set D from £8.95 (£14). Cover 75p. Service inc Set, 12.5% alc
CARDS: Access, Amex, Diners, Visa
SEATS: 50. Private parties: 60 main room. Children welcome. Wheelchair access. Music

## Mandalay

map 10

100 Greenwich South Street, SE10 8UN     COOKING 1
01-691 0443         COST £13−£28

Perhaps the only restaurant in the country serving Burmese food, so for rarity value it may be worth journeying to try 'mohinga' (rice noodles in a fish soup) or 'pet-to' (deep fried pork wun-tun). The menu is explained in detail and Gerald Andrews couldn't be more helpful, steering the uninitiated through the spicy curries or blander noodle dishes. Fresh fish has been praised, with portions so adequate that there's enough for the pets back home. Other satisfactory reports have been of pun-ta-hkawk-swe (egg noodles with chicken slices); duck hsi-byan (a casseroled, marinated duck with ginger, garlic, onion and tomato). House wine, £6.

CHEFS: Gerald Andrews and Alastair Shea   PROPRIETOR: Gerald Andrews
OPEN: all week D, and Sun L
MEALS: 12.30 to 3.30, 7 to 10.30
PRICES: £15 (£23), Set Sun L £7.50 (£13)
CARDS: Access, Amex, Visa
SEATS: 58. Private parties: 26 main room, 26 private room. Vegetarian meals. Children welcome. Music

▲ *This symbol means accommodation is available.*

## Mandarin Kitchen

map 11

14–16 Queensway, W2 3RX
01-727 9012 and 9468

COOKING 2
COST £12–£25

Fish, fresh from Billingsgate, are steamed to retain their delicacy and lobsters are served on noodles to catch their juices. The best of British coastal catches is combined with authentic Cantonese cooking in such dishes as turbot in black-bean sauce; nonetheless, the meat dishes should not be overlooked. Stewed belly of pork with preserved cabbage, a well-known Hakka dish, is both rich and fatty – just as it should be. Malaysian and Singaporean dishes also figure, reflecting the broad-based foundations of this very sound restaurant. House French, £6.50.

CHEFS: Fong Ho and Kwong Wing Man  PROPRIETORS: Stephen and Helen Cheung
OPEN: all week
MEALS: noon to 11.30
PRICES: £13 (£21), Set L and D £8.30 (£12) to £15 (£18). Service inc. Licensed, also bring your own: no corkage
CARDS: Access, Amex, Diners, Visa
SEATS: 110. Private parties: 110 main room. Children welcome. Wheelchair access. Music. Air-conditioned

## Mandeer

map 13

21 Hanway Place, W1P 9DG
01-323 0660

COOKING 1
COST £7–£18

This modest restaurant, tucked away behind a pink facade on a narrow alley a stone's throw from Tottenham Court Road tube station, offers value for Indian vegetarian food. There are set-piece thalis, unspiced or curried vegetables such as fresh spinach or potato, vegan and macrobiotic dishes. More unusual pulse dishes include vadi and onion, a wet curry of ground lentils with onions, and kachori, a starter of spiced mung beans rolled in pastry and then deep fried. Alongside Indian sweets, including shrikhand, a creamy, sweetened yoghurt with spices, there are Loseley Park Farm ice-creams. House French wine (organic), £6.25.

CHEF: Mr Daudbhai  PROPRIETORS: Mr and Mrs Patel
OPEN: Mon to Sat
CLOSED: bank hols and New Year
MEALS: 12 to 2.30, 6 to 10.15 (10.30 Fri and Sat)
PRICES: £7 (£15), Set L £3 (£7) to £5.50 (£10), Set D £5 (£9) to £8.50 (£13). Minimum £5 (D only). Service 10% at D
CARDS: Access, Amex, Diners, Visa
SEATS: 75. Private parties: 100 main room. Vegetarian meals. Children's helpings. No-smoking area. Music. Self-service at L

*If you see a certificate in a restaurant bearing the words 'European Good Food Guide (UK)', the claim is false (and the restaurant may be in contempt of court in displaying it) – see the Introduction. Please write and tell us the name and address of the restaurant.*

## ▲ *Manzi's*                                                                                        map 14

| 1–2 Leicester Street, WC2H 7BL | COOKING 1 |
| 01-734 0224 | COST £32 |

A place for devoted regulars, for the cooking skills are not highly developed
(eat simple things) and the waiters may be parodies or travesties – this
depends on your status. One man asked for pan-fried scallops, to be refused on
the grounds they had no frying-pan. Another, revisiting after all these years,
was refreshed by the marvellous mussels, horrified by the price of the oysters,
pleased by the bargain of the white Corvo. If the fish doesn't have lashings of
butter, then it will have a dollop of tartare. The fresh strawberry tart is reliably
good. The wine list has too few details: the vintage for instance. House wine is
from £5.60.

CHEF: V. Frappola   PROPRIETORS: The Manzi family
OPEN: all week, exc Sun L
MEALS: 12 to 2.30, 5.30 to 11.30
PRICES: £20 (£27). Cover £1.30
CARDS: Access, Amex, Diners, Visa
SEATS: 125. Private parties: 12 main room. No children under 7. Wheelchair access (2 steps)
ACCOMMODATION: 16 rooms, all with bath/shower. Lift. B&B £30 to £50. Deposit: £10.
Confirm by noon

## *Maroush*                                                                                           map 11

| 21 Edgware Road, W2 2JH | COOKING 2 |
| 01-723 0773 | COST £26 |

A strategically placed restaurant for the many local Middle Eastern families
who grace it with their custom. The menu offers the full range of classic meze
such as fried kibbeh, falafel, ful medames, babba ganoush and hummus. Also
on the menu are lambs' tongues and brains, raw liver and a smoked fillet of
beef (basturma). If you don't drink Turkish coffee, Nescafé may be the
alternative. House wine is £9.15.

CHEF: Mr Omar   PROPRIETOR: M.C. Abouzaki
OPEN: all week
CLOSED: 25 Dec
MEALS: noon to 1am
PRICES: £13 (£22). Cover £1
CARDS: Access, Amex, Diners, Visa
SEATS: 80. Private parties: 60 main room, 60 private room. Vegetarian meals. Children's
helpings. Smart dress preferred. Wheelchair access. Music. Air-conditioned

## *Martin's*                                                                                          map 11

| 239 Baker Street, NW1 6XE | COOKING 2 |
| 01-935 3130 and 0997 | COST £26–£44 |

It is a very pretty restaurant this, with pinks and terracottas, a lot of painted
woodwork and a handsome skylight making for a festive air. The carpet is also
pink and absorbs stains and traffic marks poorly. A small bar forms an
attractive prelude to the dining-room at the back. Lunch is *prix fixe*, changing

only for the number of courses consumed, and there is a *carte* at dinner. A seasonal menu is supplemented by daily specials. The catchwords of modish cooking stand out: ravioli, basil, flageolets, two peppers, pear, saffron, morels and oyster mushrooms. The cooking of the lunch menu has reflected the haste of the session and the numbers of the clients: abbreviated, unsubtle and inaccurate. The evening performance is better reported: good salmon quenelles with dill sauce; breast of pheasant with redcurrant game sauce; breast of chicken with basil and wild mushrooms; 'absolutely fantastic' chocolate bombe in caramel; pear poached in red wine with figs and strawberries. It is a good place for a small dinner party; one reader commented warmly on the private room as being one of the few in London that are comfortable and well positioned near the kitchen. The French wine list includes some authoritative bottles from excellent growers but most will pay closer attention to the selection at the beginning, which includes wines from other countries, from £6.75 to £12.75. House Bordeaux (red) and Muscadet and Pinot Blanc (white) are £9.75. CELLARMAN'S CHOICE : Chassagne Montrachet, *premier cru* 1982, Jabot, £32; Ch. Talbot 1979, St-Julien, £28. There is a hefty 15 per cent 'voluntary service charge' added to the bill.

CHEF: Brendan McGee   PROPRIETOR: Martin Coldicott
OPEN: Mon to Sat, exc Sat L
MEALS: 12 to 2.30, 6 to 11
PRICES: £23 (£37), Set L £17.50 (£26). Service 15%
CARDS: Access, Amex, Diners, Visa
SEATS: 60. Private parties: 16 private room. Children welcome. Smart dress preferred. Wheelchair access (1 step). Music. Air-conditioned

## *La Mascotte* map 10

54 Cricklewood Lane, NW2 1HG COOKING 1
01-452 1299 COST £16−£22

Prices are up a bit on last year, but value is still high at this simple restaurant which strives hard to produce an authentic French ambience. Even if you don't feel transported from Cricklewood to Calais, the mood is nicely pitched and, at its best, the cooking is light and warming. The cheaper set menu offers three beginnings and three main courses, while for £14.50 the selection broadens to eight dishes per course. To begin, there might be leek and potato soup or chicken-liver pâté, followed by rack of lamb in celery and apricot sauce or fillet steak in green peppercorn sauce, plus fish and vegetarian dishes according to the market. Puddings are the same for both menus: all the standards, from chocolate mousse to marinated oranges. House French is £6.25.

CHEF: Phillip Kanoun   PROPRIETORS: Rachid and Phillip Kanoun
OPEN: Tue to Sun, D only
MEALS: 7 to 10.30 (11 Fri and Sat, 10 Sun)
PRICES: Set D £10.50 (£16) and £14.50 (£18). Cover 80p. Minimum £12
CARD: Access, Visa
SEATS: 40. Private parties: 40 main room. Vegetarian meals. No children under 5. Music

*Preliminary test of a good restaurant: order fresh orange juice and see what you get.*

## Le Mazarin

map 11

30 Winchester Street, SW1V 4NE
01-828 3366 and 630 7604

COOKING **3**
COST £22–£53

The concept of a bargain here has taken some hard knocks. 'Two Champagne cocktails, an orange juice, a glass of wine and a bottle of Evian at £18 is banditry. The set price for three courses would be bearable if every other choice did not come with a supplement. Add £2.50 for coffee and exorbitant prices for wine...' And where are you? Le Mazarin, indeed, adds supplements to its 'set-price' menu, although not at the newly introduced and cheaper lunchtime meal. Many readers reported the further indignity that women were not handed priced menus (supplements or no). The year has also seen Le Mazarin painting out the note 'service included' from every bill. One hopes the labour was worth it. Service in fact has been generally characterised as 'poor', 'slow', 'inattentive', 'unhelpful' and other such epithets. The food in this often smoke-laden basement is not criticised as much as its incidentals, which include overcrowding. A meal began with a creamy celery soup (consolation for English customers) and an excellent vol-au-vent of langoustine and sweetbreads on a bed of vegetable tagliatelle (everywhere this year) with a morel sauce. More wild mushrooms appeared with a fine pheasant, and the dessert of meringue with honey ice-cream and a bitter chocolate sauce was applauded. There have been favourable accounts of meals here but money has so intruded on the enjoyment that nit-picking is the usual result. However René Bajard is a good cook in the current French style, worthy of his place in this book on this account at least. The wine list has many good (all French) wines, though prices are very high. House wine from £11. CELLARMAN'S CHOICE : Graves, Ch. Millet 1982, £21.30; Chablis, Motte 1987, £14.50.

CHEF/PROPRIETOR: René Bajard
OPEN: Tue to Sat
CLOSED: bank hols, 1 week at Easter, last 2 weeks Aug, 2 weeks at Christmas
MEALS: 12 to 2, 7 to 11
PRICES: Set L £14.50 (£22), Set D £25 (£35) to £32 (£44)
CARDS: Access, Amex, Diners, Visa
SEATS: 55. Private parties: 10 main room. Children's helpings. Music. Air-conditioned

## Melati

map 14

21 Great Windmill Street, W1V 7PH
01-437 2745

COOKING **1**
COST £19–£31

Redecoration and an extended dining area have not altered the essential café character of Melati. The redoubtable Mrs Ong, gimlet-eyed, oversees the swift and casual service. The menu is an instantly recognisable list of Malaysian/Indonesian stalwarts. Here are satays, soups, noodles or rice in top-value one-plate combinations. Bean curd omelette is a speciality and there are other vegetarian dishes. A new menu featuring more fish dishes was in progress as the *Guide* went to press. It was also to include service. Portions are immense; desserts sweet and unusual. House French, £5.95.

CHEFS: S. Alamsjah and H. Hasyem    PROPRIETORS: Mrs M. C. W. Ong and S. Alamsjah
OPEN: all week
CLOSED: 25 Dec
MEALS: noon to 11.30 (12.30 Fri and Sat)
PRICES: £10 (£19), Set L and D £17 (£26)
CARDS: Access, Amex, Diners, Visa
SEATS: 130. Private parties: 50 main room. Vegetarian meals. Children welcome.
Wheelchair access. Music. Air-conditioned

## *Le Mesurier*                                                    map 11

113 Old Street, EC1V 9JR                                        COOKING 3
01-251 8117                                                      COST £31

Enthoven and Enthoven occupy a small terraced house close to the church of
St Luke in Old Street, its fluted obelisk of a tower providing a rare piece of
originality on this dismal stretch. Gillian Enthoven runs a restaurant at ground
level; her husband is an architect on the first floor. The decoration betrays an
architectural affinity. The restaurant is very small, and therefore sometimes
cramped, and sometimes in need of ventilation. It is too serried for
indiscretions. On duty and on form, Gillian Enthoven is a fine cook. She
produces a fast-changing menu of perhaps three or four choices in each course.
They often involve pastry and she seems keen on soufflés. A cheese soufflé as a
first course was matchless; pancakes filled with orange and Grand Marnier
soufflé were exactly cooked and of meltingly piercing flavour. There are two
strains running through her style: one might be termed modern, such as brill
with crab and a mustard crust or lamb with red and green peppers (compare
Alastair Little) or skewered marinated tropical fruit on a bed of rice pudding
(compare Raymond Blanc). The other comes from works on French provincial
cooking: pork with prunes, duck breast with pears, lemon tart. Some
combinations work fantastically: a couple of slices of foie gras cooked as little
as could be, with turnip and potato galettes with a mushroom sauce (again,
compare Blanc); king prawns in filo pastry with a prawn sauce; very good little
pizze for amuse-gueule; nice French cheese. Other dishes are less considered:
poor potato gratin; too many sweet sauces with the meats; incompetent
meringue cake with cherries; bread that should be better; slack wine stocking
and service. But the compensation is that this is a personal restaurant in the
very centre of London serving food that shows care. It is within a short walk of
the Barbican and should be packed out for pre- and post-theatre suppers. There
is usually only one waiter or waitress, which can put a strain on details, just as
one person in the kitchen may strain at the limits of pauses between courses.
The wine list is tiny and deals in very young wines (Chambolle-Musigny 1987
from Amiot), with much from nearby Corney & Barrow. The house wine at
£6.50 tasted pretty moderate but the prices for other and better bottles are not
greedy. CELLARMAN'S CHOICE : Muscadet, Clos de Beauregard 1986, Laroux,
£8; Beaujolais Villages, Domaine des Roches du Vivier 1987, £9.

*All entries in the* Guide *are rewritten every year, not least because restaurant standards
fluctuate. Don't trust an out-of-date* Guide.

CHEFS: Gillian Enthoven and James Hooton   PROPRIETOR: Gillian Enthoven
OPEN: Mon to Fri
CLOSED: 3 weeks Aug, 1 week after Christmas
MEALS: 12 to 3, 6 to 11
PRICES: £19 (£26). Service 12.5%
CARDS: Access, Amex, Visa
SEATS: 24. Private parties: 24 main room. Children's helpings. No smoking. No children
under 5. Wheelchair access

## Mijanou &#124;
map 12

143 Ebury Street, SW1W 9QN                          COOKING 3
01-730 4099                                        COST £20−£49

Characters in *A Dance to the Music of Time* might pace a saraband down Ebury
Street − inexpensive hotels, slightly shabby in parts, old fashioned. Mijanou
takes its place without difficulty: flashy it is not. Ring the front door bell to be
let in − the closed door at least reduces draughts spiralling through the tables
set in the small, low-ceilinged dining-room on the ground floor. The kitchen is
visible across an iron balustrade, opening off a half-landing to the stairs, which
in turn lead to a second dining-room below. There non-smokers may eat
without pollution. Table settings are smart, the kitchen is pleasant indeed, the
decoration is dated. The presence of the Blechs, she in the kitchen, he in the
dining-rooms, is important; this is a very personal restaurant. There is a series
of short, set-price menus, from very reasonable to quite expensive, plus some
daily specials (often at a supplement). Cross-ordering is readily coped with.
There is a vegetarian menu. Sonia Blech's style is inventive. There are echoes of
nouvelle cuisine in the combinations of sweet and sour; there are variations on
peasant cooking ('cassoulets' with lentils, not beans, using pheasant or lamb as
the meat); and there are undertones of the Orient − leaf coriander, lemon-grass,
ginger. One of the nicest aspects is the unexpected: a salmon with a watercress
sauce flavoured with dill and whisky; a marmite des pecheurs with a clear and
light broth with ginger that gave a delicious zing to the excellent fish. Surprise
may also come when the sweet-and-sour theme is indulged to excess. One
vegetarian was sufficiently impressed to attempt incorporation of some of the
dishes into his own repertoire: a wild mushroom timbale on a bed of wild rice
with a saffron sauce succeeded particularly, on grounds of sophisticated texture
contrasts. The meal continues inventive to the end, with good coffee and petits
fours. Service is assiduous and smiling. The wine list is first rate. It shows signs
of intelligence at every turn. Without insult, it is very fashionable, in that
Neville Blech has moved as fast as press and public to snap up examples of the
best of the new. The classic regions are also presented with skill, even
brilliance. Prices are considerate and choices give a more than adequate price
range. Half-bottles are not ignored. A better selection would be hard to find.
House Bordeaux, Sirius 1986, Peter Sichel, £10.50. CELLARMAN'S CHOICE :
Toro Collegiato Tinto 1985, £8.50; Côtes du Rhône, Parallèle 45 1980, Jaboulet,
£8.50; Bienvenue Bâtard Montrachet 1983, Leflaive, £46.

&#124; *denotes an outstanding wine cellar;* &#9851; *denotes a good wine list, worth travelling
for. See the Introduction for a fuller explanation.*

CHEF: Sonia Blech   PROPRIETORS: Neville and Sonia Blech
OPEN: Mon to Fri
MEALS: 12.30 to 2, 7.30 to 11
PRICES: Set L £13 (£20) to £26 (£34), Set D £22 (£30) to £32 (£41)
SEATS: 30. 4 tables outside. Private parties: 24 main room. Children welcome. No smoking
in one dining-room

## *Ming*   map 14

| 35-36 Greek Street, W1V 5LN | COOKING 2 |
| 01-734 2721 | COST £15−£29 |

Owner Christine Yau, not content with simply refurbishing her restaurant in
pale duck-egg blue, has brought in a new chef and introduced an innovative
Peking-style menu. Gone are any Cantonese undertones, and in come a sweep
of dishes inspired by recipes from the great seventeenth-century Ming dynasty.
Initial reports are good. Beef with coriander and onion pancakes, gansu duck,
fried and simmered with herbs, and sizzling prawns with fresh mango feature
alongside standards such as hot-and-sour soup or squid in chilli. Live carp, eel
and lobster are delivered fresh each day. Seasonal specials supplement the long
menu. A lunch began with good wun-tun soup, not stinting on the chilli, and
took in fish steamed with coriander and ginger in a lotus leaf that was best for
its very fresh bream, squid and perfect scallops, then finished with stir-fried
root vegetables and courgettes that had elementary sweet-and-sour seasoning
and lashings of pepper. Ms Yau adds sophistication to the amiable service.
House French is £7.30. Service was still being added to the bill long after the
government's guidelines were issued and contrary to the indication given on
our questionnaire.

CHEF: Chan Kit   PROPRIETORS: Christine Yau and May Yau
OPEN: all week
MEALS: noon to 11.45
PRICES: £14 (£24), Set L and D £10.50 (£15) to £16 (£23). Snacks from £2.55. Minimum £5.
Service 10%
CARDS: Access, Amex, Diners, Visa
SEATS: 80. Private parties: 56 main room, 24 private room. Children welcome. Wheelchair
access. Music. Air-conditioned

## *Miyama*   map 13

| 38 Clarges Street, W1Y 7PJ | COOKING 2 |
| 01-499 2443 | COST £17−£50 |

Eight set lunch menus are still the best bet for value at this calming, white-
painted Japanese restaurant divided by trellises into small groups of tables.
Approached free-style, the cost can be high. There are always comforting
numbers of Japanese among the clientele. Sashimi, teriyaki and miso soup
have all been well reported. Although good value, the lunches do not attain
nearly the quality of the longer, more elaborate meals suggested on the full
*carte*. Service is very helpful and charming. There are two teppan-yaki bars as
you enter, where your food is prepared before your eyes. The wine list is short.
House French is £8, sake £2.40.

CHEF/PROPRIETOR: Mr Miyama
OPEN: Mon to Sat, exc Sat L
MEALS: 12.30 to 2.30, 6.30 to 10.30
PRICES: £20 (£35), Set L £7 (£17) to £9.60 (£20), Set D £26 (£38) to £30 (£42). Cover £1.50.
Service 15%
CARDS: Access, Amex, Diners, Visa
SEATS: 70. Private parties: 18 main room. Children welcome. Smart dress preferred.
Wheelchair access (also WC). Music. Air-conditioned

## Monkeys

map 12

1 Cale Street, Chelsea Green, SW3 3QT
01-352 4711

COOKING 2
COST £15–£46

No one has ever written to say how beautiful this restaurant is. Indeed, one
man suggested, against the grain of course, that a designer be hired – but it
provides the 'sort of French bourgeois cooking which I enjoy as much as
anything Bibendum put my way.' This may be an extreme way of putting it.
The wine list used to be a treasure trove of bin-ends, off-vintages and the like,
as well as lots of good half-bottles. Now it is more day-to-day in its stock and
has little to help a stranger make a choice. House Côtes du Ventoux and
Sauvignon de Touraine are £7.50.

CHEF: Tom Benham    PROPRIETORS: Tom and Brigitte Benham
OPEN: Mon to Fri
CLOSED: 2 weeks at Easter, 3 weeks Aug
MEALS: 12.30 to 2.30, 7.30 to 11.00
PRICES: £29 (£38), Set L from £10 (£15) to £15 (£20), Set D £17.50 (£25) to £25 (£33).
Minimum £16.50 at D
CARDS: Amex, Visa
SEATS: 45. Private parties: 50 main room, 14 private room. Children welcome. No pipes in
dining-room. Air-conditioned

## Mon Petit Plaisir

map 11

33C Holland Street, W8 4LX
01-937 3224

COOKING 2
COST £20–£37

Lunch at a neighbourhood restaurant in Kensington can cost as much as a very
grand meal 400 miles north of London. Is it therefore worth celebrating?
Perhaps not in too many words. So, Mon Petit Plaisir is the smaller relation of
Mon Plaisir (see entry). Done out in the French style it is a pretty restaurant,
delectable on a fine day, when Kensington seems at its best. The food is
perfectly decent, without excessive fuss: first courses have the unnerving habit
of turning up two minutes after the order has been passed. The sauces taste of
their announced ingredients and the staff treat you well. What more should you
expect? Well, the cost is sufficient to ask for more, but money ceases to have
absolute value in parts of Kensington. The wine list is intelligent and short.
House French is £6.95.

*The* Guide *always appreciates hearing about changes of chef or owner.*

CHEF: Philippe Molin  PROPRIETOR: Alain Lhermitte
OPEN: Mon to Sat, exc Sat L
MEALS: 12 to 2.15, 7 to 10.30
PRICES: Set L £11.95 (£20), Set D £18.50 (£28) to £21 (£31). Service 12.5%
CARDS: Access, Amex, Diners, Visa
SEATS: 36. 4 tables outside. Private parties: 20 main room. Children's helpings

## Mon Plaisir

map 14

21 Monmouth Street, WC2H 9DD
01-836 7243

COOKING 2
COST £12–£30

'The last time I was here was some 20 years ago. It hasn't changed much,'
commented one satisfied customer. More than anything, Mon Plaisir seems to
be valued as one of the last refuges of no-nonsense French cooking in central
London. The recorded accordion music, slightly bizarre bistro décor and
spirited service do, indeed, produce a Parisian ambience in the dining-room. It
is nearly always crowded, but with no feeling of hurry to clear the table. The
expected classics – mixed hors d'oeuvre, rough home-made pâté, onion soup
and entrecôte béarnaise – are mixed in with a few less obvious dishes showing
more modern influences as in a pot-au-feu de poussin au gingembre and a
carbonnade made with cider. Although there is some griping about rough
edges and rising prices, many dishes have been recommended: confit of goose
on a bed of warm spinach, sweetbreads in port, pojarsky de légumes – a
vegetarian timbale of spinach, celery, gruyère and wine surrounded by a good
cream sauce – and a delicate cod with *fines herbes*. The cheeseboard is loaded
with ripe, often creamy cheeses, in tip-top condition. Mon Petit Plaisir
(see entry) is of the same stable. House French is £6.95. CELLARMAN'S
CHOICE : Gigondas, Domaine les Pallières 1985, £15.60; Reuilly 1987,
Lafont-Martin, £12.95.

CHEF: Michel Dubarbier  PROPRIETOR: A. Lhermitte
OPEN: Mon to Sat, exc Sat L
MEALS: 12 to 2.30, 6 to 11.15
PRICES: £17 (£25), Set L £11.95 (£18), Set D (pre-theatre) £11.95 (£11.95). Service 12.5%,
inc Set pre-theatre D
CARDS: Access, Amex, Diners, Visa
SEATS: 95. Private parties: 26 main room, 30 private room. Vegetarian meals. Children's
helpings. Wheelchair access. Music

## M'sieur Frog

map 11

31A Essex Road, N1 2SE
01-226 3495

COOKING 2
COST £22–£48

The building was scheduled for demolition and, after 10 years or more, the
Rawlinsons thought the Caribbean would be the place to go. Then, all stop, the
building was reprieved. Nonetheless, the Rawlinsons went and chef Jean-Luc
Guiral took over. Certainly the Frog was becoming a mite tired. Demolition
indeed seemed close at hand. However, reports still speak of good French
provincial cooking, and respite on the building front and a change of
ownership may have the desired effects. Fricassee of giant prawns; mousse of

smoked salmon and smoked mackerel have been approved. Civet of wild boar with few onions (the origin of the word civet) or mushrooms and little wine misses its mark. But contentment returns with prawns with orange and avocado; chicken with crayfish, and chicken liver with pork in a warm salad. The cooking is more restaurant-oriented than the word bistro might imply. Desserts are also quite fancy – none of the crème caramel and apple tart, more of the kiwi mousse in a spun-sugar case. A short but not wholly chauvinist wine list has house wines at £6.25 and CELLARMAN'S CHOICE : Ch. Millet, Graves, 1982, £14.95; St Aubin 1987, £17.15.

CHEF/PROPRIETOR: Jean-Luc Guiral
OPEN: Mon to Sat, D only
CLOSED: 1 week at Christmas, 10 days Aug
MEALS: 7 to 11.30
PRICES: £16 (£24), Set D £16 (£22) to £32 (£40). Cover 75p. Service 10%
CARDS: Access, Visa
SEATS: 63. Private parties: 14 main room. Vegetarian meals. Children's helpings. Wheelchair access

## Nanten Yakitori Bar

map 13

6 Blandford Street, W1H 3HA
01-935 6319

COOKING 1
COST £11–£25

In the centre of the functional, slightly run-down room is a large counter with stools where customers can watch the chef cutting fish and grilling yakitori as they eat. The food is unpretentious and adequately prepared for the prices and level at which the bar aims. At lunchtime, when the clientele is largely English (few Japanese work in the area), the menu offers sashimi, tempura, vegetable salad, noodles or a light five-course set lunch, with yakitori chicken and fine salmon sashimi or grilled fish as main-course choices. In the evening, the dozen or so yakitori choices become the centre of interest. Quantities are large by Japanese standards and service is prompt. There is sake, of course, and house wines are from £7 to £9.

CHEF: Mr Hikichi    PROPRIETORS: Ninjin Ltd
OPEN: Mon to Sat, exc Sat L
MEALS: 12.30 to 2.30, 6.30 to 10.30
PRICES: £9 (£17), Set L £6 (£11) to £11 (£17), Set D £10 (£16) to £15 (£21). Service 15%
CARDS: Access, Amex, Diners, Visa
SEATS: 32. Private parties: 8 main room. Children welcome. Music. Air-conditioned

## Neal Street Restaurant

map 14

26 Neal Street, WC2 9PH
01-836 8368

COOKING 2
COST £43

In its day, the Neal Street Restaurant was as enlivening and eye-opening as Bibendum was last year. This was the first encounter with full-blooded Conranisation. There were a few restaurants using Bauhaus chairs before this one, but not many. It still has style. If properly maintained, the look – enlivened by a Hockney here and there and a touch of marble and brass – will last for years: a classic, as are the menu designs. Although coping well with heat waves, the room's consistent drawbacks are echo and noise. To eat, wild mushrooms and white truffles are the thing: Antonio Carluccio's delight. 'I would compulsively revisit, to try the strong flavours expertly manipulated,' was one comment although others have not agreed. The menu, which is long, sounds interesting and direct in the manner of the best Italian restaurants, though it draws on other nations' specialities for a wider palette. Scrambled eggs with smoked salmon; brandelli of pasta with morel sauce; taglioni with wild mushrooms or pesto; an aïoli garni; parmigiana of courgettes are some of the things listed. Such dishes only succeed if cooked accurately, with deep flavours gained from materials and qualifying sauce or accompaniment. Here are no mousses or stuffings to hide behind. Unfortunately such power, or accuracy, has often been lacking: consistent grumbles of lack of flavour are not encouragement to spend a lot of money on simple food. The expertise of the service is not in question, nor the choice of Italian wines on the wine list. House Sicilian is £7.50.

CHEF: M. Santiago Gonzalez    PROPRIETOR: Antonio Carluccio
OPEN: Mon to Fri
CLOSED: 1 week at Christmas, bank hols
MEALS: 12.30 to 2.30, 7 to 11.30
PRICES: £24 (£36). Service 15%
CARDS: Access, Amex, Diners, Visa
SEATS: 65. Private parties: 24 private room. Vegetarian meals. Children's helpings. Wheelchair access. Air-conditioned

## Neal's Lodge
map 10

Wandsworth Common, SW18
01-870 7484
park in Baskerville Road and
walk across Common

COOKING 2
COST £23–£35

The new chef at this white house and conservatory in the middle of the Common cooks in similar style to his predecessor: nouvelle cuisine à l'anglaise. The customers, too, have stayed the same: products of gentrified terraces. The two are in happy symbiosis. Reports through the year have been mixed, but are improving as we go to press. The Lodge is offering a social service as well as mere catering for those who can afford their evening prices. It is a privatised concession from the local authority, providing teas and all-day refreshments as part of its contractual obligation; the good side of restaurant capitalism perhaps. Most recent visitors have encountered medallions of veal with coriander potatoes and rosettes of lamb in balsamic vinegar sauce as main courses; a soup of scampi, cucumber and dill, and asparagus served with a morel-flavoured butter as first courses; and praline parfait or apple brioche with summer fruits that brought a meal to a 'pleasant and picturesque' conclusion. The cooking has been praised for accuracy and invention. A 'modern' beef à la ficelle revealed a glorious flavour to the meat with the sauce thickened with cream and discreetly spiked with ginger. The trimmings – correct temperatures for wine, wrong vintage for a bottle of wine, a slight sense of short-cut on the decoration – are for once less considered than the cooking. The wine list is short and international. House wines from Hunter Valley,

£9.50. CELLARMAN'S CHOICE : St-Véran 1986, Maufoux, £14.50; Rioja Reserva 1975, Marquès de Riscal, £14.50. Most grouses concern the 'suggested' service added to the bills: 12.5 per cent at lunch, 15 per cent at dinner. Perhaps they pay lower wages at night and need to make up the shortfall. Muzak can be loud.

CHEF: Peter Brennan  PROPRIETORS: Vicki MacCallum and Alex Campbell
OPEN: Tue to Sun, exc Sun D
MEALS: 12 to 3, 7 to 10
PRICES: £14 (£23), Set D £19.50 (£29). Snacks from £2.50. Service 12.5% L, 15% D
CARDS: Amex, Visa
SEATS: 90. 15 tables outside. Private parties: 40 main room, 50 private room. Children's helpings. Separate smoking area. Wheelchair access. Music

## New World
map 14

Gerrard Place, W1V 7LL
01-734 0677 and 0396

COOKING 1
COST £9–£22

In this vast dim-sum emporium it is possible to while away an afternoon listening to the background babble of Chinese chatter and, every now and then, making a choice from the trolleys that wend their way round the three floors until 6pm. Dumplings might be filled with shrimp and pork, or beef, ginger and spring onion. In another steamer could be revealed spare ribs with chilli and black-bean sauce, or boned chicken thighs wrapped in bean curd. Big, steaming bowls of soup teeming with barbecued pork and noodles are ladled freshly from the trolley. Go for a blow-out or a snack and be prepared to queue at peak times. After the dim-sum cease, a more expensive menu comes into operation. House French is £5.40.

CHEFS: Wong Wailam  PROPRIETORS: New World Restaurant Ltd
OPEN: all week
MEALS: 11am to 11.45pm (11pm Sun)
PRICES: £12 (£19), Set L and D from £6 (£9). Service inc
CARDS: Access, Amex, Diners, Visa
SEATS: 600. Private parties: 200 main room, 20, 80 and 100 private rooms. Children welcome. Wheelchair access (also WC). Music. Air-conditioned

## Nichol's
map 11

75 Fairfax Road, NW6 4NN
01-624 3880

COOKING 3
COST £21–£30

Here is a restaurant developing personality through cooking more than décor. Since Susan and David Nichol, both antipodeans, moved into their Swiss Cottage premises in a dull post-war row of shops, they have washed down the tidemarks of previous occupants by swapping busy wallpaper for plain peach and imparting a sense of space. The short, seasonal, three-course menu seems to be evolving rapidly, characterised by unexpected themes. Reports have been consistently good, despite initial scepticism of nouvelle tendencies, emphasising the clean flavours and clever ideas: a warm salad with gleaming flakes of smoked haddock, mixed greenery and sliced golden-fried potatoes dressed in a light chive beurre blanc; refined fish and chips – plaice in a very delicate batter served with beetroot and horseradish relish; ox-tongues served with red cabbage on top of a beurre blanc. A liking for more exotic spicing and flavourings – a peach glaze on guinea-fowl and chilli-hot satay sauce for rare beef with fresh pineapple – have been well judged too. Vegetables, left in serving dishes on the tables, include dark, deep-fried potatoes. Puddings are as varied in inspiration – chocolate marquise, summer pudding, coffee and rum cheesecake – and executed with panache. The wine list allows space for the new countries (old to the Nichols) among an inexpensive French selection. House wine is £8.50, from France, not Australia or New Zealand. CELLARMAN'S CHOICE is more loyal: Te Mata Sauvignon Blanc 1988, £14.50; Wynn's Cabernet Sauvignon 1984, £14.95.

CHEF: David Nichol    PROPRIETORS: Susan and David Nichol
OPEN: all week, exc Sat L and Sun D
MEALS: 12 to 3, 7 to 10
PRICES: Set L £14 (£21), Set D £17.90 (£25). Service 10%
CARDS: Access, Amex, Visa
SEATS: 45. 3 tables outside. Private parties: 18 main room. Children's helpings. Wheelchair access. Music. Air-conditioned

## ▲ Ninety Park Lane, Grosvenor House Hotel

map 13

90 Park Lane, W1A 3AA                                    COOKING 3
01-409 1290                                              COST £32–£71

Ninety Park Lane advertises on the first page of *The New Yorker*. A toll-free transatlantic call will reserve a table. At a summer lunch, a roll-call of the full restaurant yielded one woman and more than 50 men. That woman had preceded her companion to the hotel and business had delayed him. A glass of Champagne was poured, without her being asked first. On the arrival of her partner, he had an orange juice. A while later, they repeated the order. Those four aperitifs cost £20. The dining-room, hung with art, panelled in silk, with great vases of white flowers, is plush – mostly because the seating against the walls is not banquettes but chesterfields, with the plumpest cushions ever seen. The tableware is pretty, a feminine touch in a masculine world. Beyond the *carte*, there is a series of menus, culminating in the Louis Outhier.

M. Outhier, of L'Oasis in La Napoule, is consultant here. Executant is Jean Fouillet who has succeeded Stephen Goodlad. He is French and has held a *Michelin* star in two restaurants of his own, in Beaujolais and Villefranche-sur-Saone. The cooking, as may be imagined, is refined and sometimes daring. There is, apart from the usual procession of luxury ingredients, much marrying of European materials to quasi-oriental flavours. The luxuries can be handled brilliantly; a piece of foie gras wrapped in bacon was lightened and given account at the same time by a sharp reduction sauce. But at the same meal, a lobster was served with Thai herbs: this proved to have a crudely curried cream sauce with orange segments and a sweet taste that overwhelmed the lobster completely. That the touch can be light is seen with langoustines – fresh, plump and firm – served with white asparagus dressed with sesame oil. Unsatisfactory points have surfaced as to quality of materials – fantastic white leaven bread but stale walnut bread with cheese, old broad beans, starchy peas

– and the quality of the co-ordination. One person's pigeon came with a different accompaniment to that described; another's desired soufflé was refused at first because it was too late in the day; wine orders can get muddled. There is skill abounding but at what cost. Until the skill is guaranteed perfection, its value must be questioned. The wine list is just what it should be for France, with less elsewhere. House wines are £11.50. CELLARMAN'S CHOICE : Auxey Duresses 1985, Piguet, £22.50; St-Aubin 1986, Thomas, £23.50.

CHEF: Jean Fouillet  PROPRIETORS: Trusthouse Forte Ltd
OPEN: Mon to Sat, exc Sat L
MEALS: 12 to 2.30, 7 to 10.30
PRICES: £48 (£57), Set L £25 (£32) to £37.50 (£44), Set D £35 (£42) to £52.50 (£59). Service inc. Licensed, also bring your own: corkage £12
CARDS: Access, Amex, Carte Blanche, Diners, Visa
SEATS: 70. Private parties: 80 main room. Vegetarian meals. No children under 6. Smart dress preferred. No-smoking area. Wheelchair access (2 steps; also WC). Music. Air-conditioned
ACCOMMODATION: 468 rooms, all with bath/shower. Rooms for disabled. Lift. B&B £195 to £204. Afternoon teas. Swimming-pool. Sauna. Air-conditioning. TV. Phone

# Ninjin
map 13

244 Great Portland Street, W1N 5MF
01-388 4657

COOKING 1
COST £10–£32

Good-value set lunches are the main attraction at this basement Japanese restaurant, downstairs from its own supermarket. The price includes an appetiser, soup, brightly coloured pickled radish and dessert around a main course: tempura and sashimi have been well reported. There are constant supplies of green tea. In the evening the set-meal price rises, but there are interesting possibilities on the menu, from grilled willow fish to steamed liver of angler.

CHEF: Mr Funakoshi  PROPRIETORS: Ninjin Ltd
OPEN: Mon to Sat, exc Sat D
MEALS: 12 to 2.30, 6 to 10.30
PRICES: £10 (£15), Set L £5.30 (£10) to £15 (£20), Set D £18 (£27)
CARDS: Access, Amex, Diners, Visa
SEATS: 50. Private parties: 10 main room. No children under 5. Music

# ▲ Nontas
map 11

16 Camden High Street, NW1 0JH
01-387 4579

COOKING 1
COST £14

Breakfasts of yoghurt and honey or kateifi and coffee are to be had in the 'Ouzerie', which has a roaring fire in winter, and is open all day and evening for Cypriot snacks, both sweet and savoury. In the restaurant proper the atmosphere is relaxed and easy, 'a rustic informality.' Meze are good, but one reporter was happy to confine the first course to just one dish of talattouri – yoghurt and cucumber – as a preface to her moussaka, well presented and of better materials than many in more prestigious Greek restaurants in London.

There are plenty of daily specials, for example baked fresh cod or chicken with Jerusalem artichokes cooked with red wine. House wine is £5.15, and there are a dozen or more other Hellenic wines.

CHEF: Nontas Vassilakas   PROPRIETORS: Helen and Nontas Vassilakas
OPEN: Mon to Sat
MEALS: 12 to 2.45, 6 to 11.30 (snacks 9am to 11.30pm)
PRICES: £7 (£12). Snacks from 95p. Service 10% for parties of 6 or more
CARDS: Access, Amex, Diners
SEATS: 50. 10 tables outside. Private parties: 25 main room. Children welcome. Wheelchair access. Music
ACCOMMODATION: 12 rooms, 11 with bath/shower. B&B £29 to £43. No children under 12. Afternoon teas. TV. Phone. Doors close at 12.30

## ▲ Oak Room, Le Meridien Piccadilly Hotel ▮

map 13

Piccadilly, W1V 0BH                                     COOKING 4
01-734 8000                                          COST £28−£67

In the midst of Norman Shaw's best baroque manner are flower arrangements so large that Rousseau's tigers might part their fronds. The space they are meant to fill is vast: once enough for 400 diners, now holding just over one tenth of that to allow privacy and quiet. Le Meridien has dropped its gourmet restaurant into a segment of the old dining-room, sending a greater number of customers to the rooftop Terrace Garden (see entry) for less expensive and simpler food. The Oak Room has an English chef and a French consultant: Michel Lorain of Côtes St-Jacques at Joigny in Burgundy − three stars in *Michelin*, no less. David Chambers cooks haute cuisine French food from a French menu of a high standard. The service is impeccable, the tones are hushed (save the piano at night), the atmosphere is cool (thanks to air conditioning set at transatlantic levels). The menu planning is impressive: there is a slowly changing *carte*, a *menu gourmand* of up to seven courses that move with the ebb and flow of supplies, and a supplement of a dozen or more daily dishes. On one day you may be offered two soups, four varieties of fish, three sorts of shellfish, two lambs, two beefs, hare, wild duck and a mixture of game: no offal or chicken. The range of styles is good: beef bourguignonne as well as fillet, salt cod as well as langoustines. This reflects a broad division imposed by Lorain and Chambers between 'cuisine traditionelle' and 'cuisine créative', and the added dimension of David Chambers' specific contribution in the daily dishes. Since never more than a hundred people are served a day, and often many less, the menu is a monument to careful marketing. Skill of cooking apart, it should be all about flavour. One reader, at least, will remember for a long while the intensity of his wild mushroom soup with diced scallops, and another praised scallops lightly cooked with endive and orange. But nerve may fail in certain respects. Truffle, cast with abandon on scallops demi-deuil and over a saddle of hare with wild mushrooms and celeriac purée was as evanescent as most truffle is in this country. A consommé of langoustines with its ravioli, although exquisitely clear, held but a shadow of langoustine taste. The saddle of hare was hardly gamey. Meats come with little copper pans of mixed vegetables. These look pretty but proved to be the now common, next-to-raw vegetables, invariably cold by the time you get to eat them and with as much charm as the bran you scatter over your breakfast cereal. Vegetables really need rethinking. Nonetheless, a kitchen that can produce a plate of daintily sliced lamb fillet, roast with whole cloves of garlic and sauced with a sorrel cream deepened by well-flavoured tomato can be forgiven much. Service until the dessert is all domes and lamps. At that point the trolley appears and the waiter indulges in a deft exercise of slicing, arranging and feathering the sauce. Such display means raspberry or strawberry with *everything* to aid the visuals: this is a dreadful modern cliché. However a fine caramel ice-cream is on offer and a light pastry tart with a frangipane topped with excellent imported raspberries was a high point of a meal early in the year. The wine list is massive, and massively expensive. House Ch. Bellevue La Forêt 1987, Côtes du Frontonnais and Chardonnay Laroche 1986, £12. Half-bottles are at a premium. Lunch, as so often, appears a consummate bargain. See also Terrace Garden, Le Meridien Piccadilly Hotel.

CHEF: David Chambers  PROPRIETORS: Meridien Hotels
OPEN: Mon to Sat, exc Sat L
MEALS: 12 to 2.30, 7 to 10.30
PRICES: £33 (£46), Set L £19.50 (£28), Set D £35 (£45) to £45 (£56)
CARDS: Access, Amex, Carte Blanche, Diners, Visa
SEATS: 50. Private parties: 10 main room. Children welcome. Smart dress preferred. No pipes in dining-room. Wheelchair access (also WC). Music. Air-conditioned
ACCOMMODATION: 284 rooms, all with bath/shower. Rooms for disabled. Lift. B&B £202.50 to £228.50. Baby facilities. Afternoon teas. Swimming-pool. Sauna. Snooker. Air-conditioning. TV. Phone. Confirm 1 day before

---

## Odette's ♥

130 Regent's Park Road, NW1 8XL
01-586 5486

map 11

COOKING 2
COST £34

On a hot summer day, the vivid green awning extended, the front left open, this place is very pleasant. The conservatory at the back, top-lit, is also good – better when the sun beats down less relentlessly. In winter, the gilt-framed mirrored walls (not a picture in sight, they're all in the back room) reflect light and warmth. A good space, then, in all seasons; a cheerful and obliging staff too, making the best of the stylish ambience. The cooking needs to settle down; at the time of writing new chef Wayne Bosworth, ex-Savoy, is playing with novelties that barely hang together. Reports have revealed sauces with no foundation to them, over-sweetened, over-perfumed (with lavender in the case of a boned, stuffed poussin) or over-acidulated. It is very modern cooking, with too much time spent on larding monkfish with strips of pimento and not enough on producing recognisably appetising flavours. Some people do enjoy these adventures, and more would be reconciled to them if the cooking were invariably well-timed and accurate. Aficionados of modern cooking have indeed found the salmon and brill on a warm vinaigrette with chopped fennel and chives perfectly cooked and intriguingly flavoured, and have approved the 'monkfish larded with peppers on a tagliatelle of vegetables scented with Chinese ginger.' Traditionalists might praise the drift towards a lighter cooking shown in these two dishes but query the pusillanimous use of ginger to give substantial flavour, and might also point to the large quantity of butter sauce anointing the plate of mixed vegetables – negating any illusion of health promoted by the principal dish. Breads are minute buns of three or four flavours: herb, cheese, garlic and so on. Mr Bosworth worked in the same kitchen as Gary Hollihead of Sutherlands, another exponent of this style of baking. The wine list is really excellent as a short, and not expensive, essay in good wines, mainly from France. House French from Côtes de Gascogne and Bordeaux, £6.95. CELLARMAN'S CHOICE : Ch. Court-les-Mûts, Bergerac 1985, £8.50 for red and white.

CHEF: Wayne Bosworth   PROPRIETOR: Simone Green
OPEN: Mon to Sat, exc Sat L
MEALS: 12.30 to 2.30, 7.30 to 11
PRICES: £20 (£28). Service 12.5%
CARDS: Access, Amex, Diners, Visa
SEATS: 55. Private parties: 8 and 28 private rooms. Children welcome

## *192* ♥ 

map 11

192 Kensington Park Road, W11 2ES    COOKING 2
01-229 0482    COST £29

This most trendy of wine bars has oscillated in the affections of food lovers, if not inamorati of the scene, over some years. Chefs and cooks come and go: 'win some and lose some' may be the motto of the management. It is, nevertheless, usually full. Just the place to people-watch. Eating goes on downstairs, as well, in a basement hung with oriental carpets. Staff, trendy or no, are pleasant and helpful, even in the chaos of the bustling, long, thin room. Food is ultra modern, dealing in simple things with definite flavours: even scallop mousse has a strong taste. Pigeon comes with lentils and beans; brill is seared, dressed with strong olive oil and served with aubergine purée, tapénade and sweet cherry tomatoes; monkfish is dressed with a pepper vinaigrette. Vegetables are not always brilliant. The menu changes at every meal. The wine list, as one of the owners is a wine merchant, is an exemplary choice of decent bottles at fair prices. A Cruover machine makes a lot available by the glass. The restaurant has sensibly eschewed trying for the great and the old and just offers a fashionable worldwide selection. House Corney & Barrow's French from Lebègue is £6.25. CELLARMAN'S CHOICE : Ch. Thieuley, 1988, £8.75; Ch. du Gaby 1983, Canon Fronsac, £16.

CHEF: Maddalena Bonino   PROPRIETORS: Anthony Mackintosh, Michael Chassay and John Armit
OPEN: all week, exc Sun D
MEALS: 12.30 (1 Sun) to 3, 7.30 to 11.30
PRICES: £16 (£24)
CARDS: Access, Amex, Visa
SEATS: 75. 4 tables outside. Private parties: 10 main room, 30 private room. Children's helpings on request. No cigars/pipes in dining-room. Wheelchair access. Music. Air-conditioned

CELLARMAN'S CHOICE : *A wine recommended by the restaurateur, normally more expensive than the house wine.*

## Orso ♥ map 14

| 27 Wellington Street, WC2E 7DA | COOKING 3 |
| 01-240 5269 | COST £35 |

One of the best and most lively Italian restaurants in the capital. Down the hill from the Royal Opera House, the entrance beckons you (not very alluringly) to a large, stylish basement where the kitchen and wine cellar are on view and the noise bounces off the tiles with more *brio* than a Verdi chorus. The uncharitable would suggest lavatorial as the decorative mode. Life and colour are given to food and table by the intense decoration of the Mediterranean pottery used throughout. Tables are close set. Opinions, as often about places both popular and crowded, are very mixed. The staff, smiling and helpful to some, can, to others, seem brusque. The food gets equally varied comment but should be applauded as a clever and appetising interpretation of Italian cooking. The daily menu has half a dozen choices per course, plus a like number of pizza and pasta dishes. The pizze are extremely thin crusted, therefore ultra crisp to the knife, and suffer from an excess of topping, as in sun-dried tomatoes, roasted peppers and Mozzarella, or Swiss chard, pancetta, olives, Mozzarella and Parmesan. The pasta is well made but a test meal revealed a spinach and ricotta ravioli that was thick, tough and very boring, under-endowed with either spinach or lubrication. Main dishes feature good veal and offal (including, often, calf's brains) and adopt a pleasantly direct approach to seasoning and flavouring. The vegetables, ordered separately, are the best element of all: broccoli with lemon and oil (a favourite) refreshes the palate and offers extra vitamins. Puddings come in for little praise: a chocolate mousse (often as good an indicator as crème caramel used to be) was made with poor chocolate, without necessary bitterness or darkened tones, and served with too much cream. Cheese to finish may be 'Parmesan; a large, delicious lump.' Coffee and bread are good; the wine list an excellent short choice of thoroughbred Italians at not excessive prices (Chardonnay 1987, Bollini, £10.50; Chianti Classico Riserva 1983, Antinori, £12.50). Everything on the menu is in Italian (with an English translation on the facing page), but readers have not yet seen an Italian face on the staff: the ownership is Anglo/American, the staff are well-spoken Englishmen, the chefs seem English too. House wine is £7.50 a litre.

CHEF: Martin Wilson   PROPRIETORS: Orso Restaurants Ltd
OPEN: all week
CLOSED: 25 and 26 Dec
MEALS: noon to midnight
PRICES: £16 (£29)
SEATS: 110. Vegetarian meals. Children welcome

## Otters map 10

| 271 New King's Road, SW6 4RD | COOKING 2 |
| 01-371 0434 | COST £25 |

'Otters was set up with the intention of providing quality food with decent sized portions at a price that is realistic... We quite simply adjust the menu to the demand.' Certainly, the value for money is good compared with that of many restaurants in the King's Road area, but it is hard to believe that the move towards ever more strident flavour contrasts – for example, wild boar on a strawberry and pink peppercorn sauce or peppered Boursin and mango wrapped in filo – is to everybody's tastes. By these standards, clams on pasta with pesto cream, griddled gravlax with mustard mayonnaise or a vegetarian steamed nut and herb mousse wrapped in Savoy cabbage are among the quietest on the menu. Nonetheless, one regular said that she has never been disappointed and there is no doubt that even some of the most bizarre combinations have worked; one sceptic was persuaded by a pink rack of lamb with a rich mustard and golden syrup sauce given body by ground hazelnuts. Ingredients are good and vegetables, thankfully, are left plain. Wines are listed on the back of the menu in a short but seemly group, not overpriced. House wine is £6.95. CELLARMAN'S CHOICE : Ch. Notton 1981, £16.75; Mâcon-Lugny Les Charmes 1987, £11.75.

CHEFS: Neil Stott and Laurence Benson   PROPRIETORS: Julian Sowerbutts and Alexander Shead
OPEN: all week, exc Sun D
MEALS: 12 to 3, 7 to 11
PRICES: £15 (£21)
CARDS: Access, Amex, Carte Blanche, Diners, Visa
SEATS: 52. Vegetarian meals. Children welcome. Wheelchair access (also WC). Music. Air-conditioned

## *Pagu Dinai*                                                      map 10

690 Fulham Road, SW6 5SA                                      COOKING 2
01-736 1195                                                    COST £26

Graziano Lecca opened his restaurant to put the cuisine of Sardinia on the London map. Its name, meaning 'it's good value' in Sardinian, sets the tone – that of a simple trattoria with largely local customers, no pretence and no Italian kitsch on the plain, white-washed walls. Service is also pleasantly low-key: 'For once they do not gyrate around the tables flashing their phallic peppermill in a boring show of machismo.' On both the long *carte* and shorter list of daily additions, it is the Sardinian specialities – for example, semolina gnocchi in a fresh tomato sauce, pasta stuffed with ricotta cheese and saffron, Sardinian fish stew and unleavened, grilled Sardinian bread – that make the most interesting eating. One spring meal of fennel soup, sharpened by just the right amount of grated Pecorino and served with a thick slice of country bread floating in the middle, followed by a large halibut steak sauté in olive oil and thickly covered with a traditional Sardinian garnish of pine kernels, walnuts and breadcrumbs, was first class. To finish, there is sebadas, a delicious Sardinian filled pastry deep-fried in olive oil and doused in honey, and strong espresso. The wine list is short and thoroughly Italian. House Sardinian is £6.05.

*If you see a certificate in a restaurant bearing the words 'Good Food Guide Top Restaurants', the claim is false (and the restaurant may be in contempt of court in displaying it) – see the Introduction. Please write and tell us the name and address of the restaurant.*

CHEF: Giovanni Branco    PROPRIETOR: Graziano Lecca
OPEN: all week
CLOSED: bank hols
MEALS: 12 to 2.45, 7 to 11.45
PRICES: £13 (£22). Cover 95p
CARDS: Access, Amex, Diners, Visa
SEATS: 60. Private parties: 30 main room, 20 private room. Vegetarian meals. Children's
helpings. Smart dress preferred. Wheelchair access (1 step)

## *Phoenicia*                                                          map 11

| 11–13 Abingdon Road, W8 6AH | COOKING 1 |
| 01-937 0120 | COST £12–£24 |

The strain can be taken from ordering if the staff are allowed to produce one of
several selections from the wide range of meze. Otherwise, there are good items
to be had from the charcoal grill. There is a bakery on the premises, so bread
may be better and fresher than that which comes from plastic packets and tastes
like so many flattened sliced-whites. The meze 'are interestingly spicy'
according to one newcomer. There is arak, Lebanese Ch. Musar red, 1980, and
white (n.v.) and a 35-strong list. House French, £6.95.

CHEF: Chaoki Serhal    PROPRIETOR: Hani Khalife
OPEN: all week
MEALS: noon to midnight
PRICES: £11 (£19), Set L £7.95 (£12) to £16.45 (£20), Set D £11.95 (£17) to £16.45 (£20).
Cover £1.25. Minimum £11.95. Service inc
CARDS: Access, Amex, Diners, Visa
SEATS: 80. Private parties: 80 main room, 15, 25 and 40 private rooms. Vegetarian meals.
Children's helpings. Wheelchair access. Music. Air-conditioned

## *Pizzeria Castello*                                                  map 11

| 20 Walworth Road, SE1 6SP | COOKING 1 |
| 01-703 2556 | COST £12 |

There is often difficulty getting a table here: even at 7pm on a Saturday it is
crowded out. Some, who have had to eat in the wine bar downstairs, would
aver that conditions are far from ideal. Nonetheless, the popular vote is
affirmative. 'The pizzas are good, hot and sizzling from the oven, freshly made
and served. There are other pastas, but nothing as good as the pizzas. Staff are
pros, Italian, and often don't speak English, but it doesn't matter. They get the
gist of what it is all about. A pizza, a shared bottle of house wine, a coffee and a
tip, come to about a fiver. Salads are OK, but it is better to eat a lettuce leaf and
a tomato at home. Garlic bread is good as well.' These telescoped notes of an
inspector say it all. In common with a lot of other places, the Castello levies a
10 per cent service charge on parties of seven or more. This rule puts a certain
perspective on how restaurateurs view the 'discretionary' nature of tipping.
House Montepescali, £4.60. CELLARMAN'S CHOICE : Verdicchio 'Il Pallio' 1987,
Monte Schiavo, £6.90; Montepulciano d'Abruzzo 1984, £7.30.

*Report forms are at the back of the book; write a letter if you prefer.*

CHEF: Cicero Calogero  PROPRIETOR: Renzo Meda and Antonio Proietti
OPEN: Mon to Sat, exc Sat L
MEALS: noon (5 Sat) to 11
PRICES: £6 (£10)
CARDS: Access, Visa
SEATS: 180. Private parties: 40 main room. Vegetarian meals. Children's helpings.
Wheelchair access (also WC). Music. Air-conditioned

## Pizzeria Condotti

map 13

| 4 Mill Street, W1R 9TE | COOKING 1 |
| 01-499 1308 | COST £19 |

Out of Apicella and Pizza Express, this may be as good as any pizzeria in
Central London. Certainly it feels the smartest, although the prices are not
upwardly mobile to any great extent. There is a better cooked base than in most
of the others, although Pizza on the Park does well too. The toppings do not
pretend, nor do any others in England, to the Mediterranean fragrance that,
combined with the smell of fresh dough and burning wood, creates the
irresistible charm of a real Provençal/Italian pizzeria. Milk suffers from the
same UHT syndrome as Pizza Express but there is good espresso. House
Italian, £6.20.

CHEF: Mahmoud Eskendry  PROPRIETORS: Enzo Apicella and Peter Boizot
OPEN: Mon to Sat
MEALS: 11.30 to midnight
PRICES: £10 (£16)
CARDS: Access, Amex, Diners, Visa
SEATS: 130. Private parties: 70 main room, 50 private room. Wheelchair access (2 steps).
Music. Air-conditioned

## Poons

map 14

| 4 Leicester Street, WC2H 7BL | COOKING 2 |
| 01-437 1528 | COST £14–£20 |

Indicating its speciality with wind-dried duck, sausages and bacon hanging in
the window, Poons remains one of the most reliable Cantonese restaurants in
Chinatown. As a result, there are often queues outside the door and the tiny
dining-rooms on the ground floor and in the basement can be packed to the
point of claustrophobia (expansion upstairs still hangs upon planning
permission). From the long menu offering over 200 choices, the wind-dried
meats and the hot-pots are the most unusual dishes; the stewed eel with crispy
pork and garlic and the wind-dried duck rice hot pot are both excellent. So, too,
are other plainer dishes or specialities like deep-fried lamb with lettuce leaves.
Prices remain low and service helpful. House French is £5.20.

*If you see a certificate in a restaurant bearing the words 'The Good Food and Restaurant
Guide', the claim is false – see the Introduction. Please write and tell us the name and
address of the restaurant.*

CHEF/PROPRIETOR: W. N. Poon
OPEN: Mon to Sat
CLOSED: 25 Dec
MEALS: noon to 11.30
PRICES: £6 (£14), Set L and D £12 (£17). Minimum £6. Licensed, also bring your own:
corkage £1
SEATS: 100. Private parties: 30 main room. Children welcome. Air-conditioned

## Ports
map 12

11 Beauchamp Place, SW3 1NQ        COOKING 1
01-581 3837        COST £16–£34

Hidden away under the designer fashion shops of Beauchamp Place, this
Portuguese cellar restaurant remains refreshingly unpretentious, offering a
wide range of fish and seafood, a handful of meat dishes and friendly staff who
will guide wary customers around the menu. On the wall there are decorative
tiles to set the Iberian mood. Inevitably, perhaps, some dishes have been
internationalised, but the octopus and salt-cod dishes, such as bacalhau assado
na braza, a thick steak of sun-dried cod grilled over charcoal and served in olive
oil containing pieces of garlic, have an altogether earthier feel. Since portions
are generous, vegetables may not be necessary. To end the meal, there is ewe's
milk cheese, creamy rice pudding and custard tarts. House wine is £7.90.

CHEF: Elio de Andrade    PROPRIETORS: Luis Pimentel and A. Valerio
OPEN: Mon to Sat
CLOSED: Christmas, Easter, bank hols
MEALS: 12 to 2.30, 7 to 11.30
PRICES: £20 (£28), Set L £8.75 (£16). Service 12.5%
CARDS: Access, Amex, Diners, Visa
SEATS: 45. Private parties: 48 main room. Children's helpings on request. No pipes in
dining-room. Music. Air-conditioned

## Le Poulbot
map 11

45 Cheapside, EC2V 6AR        COOKING 3
01-236 4379        COST £40

Once Le Poulbot was taken as seriously as Le Gavroche but there was a change
of direction, a simplification of approach and charging. Now, the red-plush
basement offers the Roux formula of an all-in price from kir to coffee, only
wine being extra. Upstairs is a *casse-croûte* bar of great popularity. There have
been no notes of discord that it serves a purpose – 'it is suitable for business
lunches, which is ideal in the City' to quote their own words. Four meats (beef,
lamb, veal, chicken), two fish, six first courses and recited desserts (sometimes
not remembered) is the routine. The style is French, adequate, sometimes
excellent; the flavours definitely not modern: leaf coriander is for the media-set
further west. The service remains consistently Gallic; unless our language
tuition begins to respond to the prospect of 1992, no one will be able to
understand the menu anyway. The wine list continues to be short and pitched
to the market; there are only four half-bottles on offer. As the management sent
the *Guide* a wine list more than 18 months out of date, our first amazement at the

thought the Roux brothers had *reduced* their prices was sadly disillusioned. The wines stay broadly the same, the prices rise. CELLARMAN'S CHOICE : Chablis, Albert Roux Domaine de la Roche 1987, £15.80.

CHEF: Philippe H. Vandewalle   PROPRIETORS: Roux Restaurants Ltd
OPEN: Mon to Fri, L only
MEALS: 12 to 3
PRICES: Set L £27.50 (£33). Service inc
CARDS: Access, Amex, Carte Blanche, Diners, Visa
SEATS: 50. Private parties: 50 main room. Children welcome. Smart dress preferred. No pipes in dining-room. Air-conditioned

## Le Quai St Pierre

map 11

7 Stratford Road, W8 6RF                    COOKING 1
01-937 6388                                 COST  £37

Reports for Pierre Martin's seafood restaurant vary a great deal when it comes to the cooking, but there are always a few who insist that the unvarying freshness and quality of the seafood make it notable. The menu breaks down into simply grouped dishes: mussels, oysters and scallops various ways, oysters by the half-dozen and shellfish by weight, salads, feuilletés and steaks plus half a dozen simple fish dishes of the day – grilled sole or skate with black butter, for example. The shellfish platter, moules marinière and beurre blanc dishes have been recommended; others have pointed to watery sauces, overcooked vegetables and sketchy desserts. House wine is £8.50.

CHEF: Alain Patrat   PROPRIETOR: Pierre Martin
OPEN: Mon to Sat, exc Mon L
CLOSED: 2 weeks at Christmas
MEALS: 12.30 to 2.30, 7 to 11.30
PRICES: £21 (£31). Cover £1. Service 15%
CARDS: Access, Amex, Diners, Visa
SEATS: 55. 3 tables outside. Private parties: 6 main room. Children welcome. Wheelchair access. Music

## Ragam

map 13

57 Cleveland Street, W1P 5PQ                COOKING 1
01-636 9098                                 COST  £13

Near the Middlesex Hospital; unassuming but clean, with gentle staff. The sweet astringency of South Indian cooking is both refreshing and enticing: coconut, tamarind, lemon and mango. Masala dosai, filled with potato and fried onions; masala vadai, a lentil patty deep fried; avial, a vegetable curry with coconut, yoghurt and curry leaves; and sambar, a tamarind gravy for dosai, are good dishes to try. Licensed.

The Good Food Guide *does not issue certificates of approval and does not allow restaurateurs to refer to* Guide *recommendations in their promotion. If you see such references, please tell us where, when and what you saw.*

CHEFS: J. Dharmaseelan and Mojid Ullah  PROPRIETORS: J. Dharmaseelan, T. Haridas and S. Pillai
OPEN: all week
MEALS: 12 to 3, 6 to 12
PRICES: £6 (£12). Minimum £3. Service 10%. Licensed, also bring your own: corkage £1.50 per bottle
CARDS: Access, Amex, Diners, Visa
SEATS: 34. Private parties: 34 main room, 25 private room. Vegetarian meals. Children's helpings. Wheelchair access (also WC). Music

## Rani
map 10

3 Long Lane, Finchley, N3 2PR
01-349 4386 and 2636

COOKING 2
COST £11−£23

At the time of going to press, the dining-room had just tripled in size by expanding into two neighbouring shops, a non-smoking zone had been introduced, the menu had been extended with new breads, set meal combinations and desserts − dudhi halva made from green marrow and a rich nut pudding − and, predictably, prices had crept up slightly. But the essentials have not changed at this family-owned Indian vegetarian restaurant; the owner's mother and wife are still in the kitchen and the food remains excellent value. Curries are freshly cooked with plenty of coriander and first courses are helped along by home-made date, coconut and mango chutney. The drinks list now runs from Champagne through basic wines to falooda and herbal teas. On the menu is a strict note: 'No service charge and gratuities not accepted. Any change left behind will be donated to charity.'

CHEFS: Kundan and Sheila Pattni  PROPRIETOR: Jyotindra Pattni
OPEN: Tue to Sun, exc Tue L
CLOSED: 25 Dec
MEALS: 12.30 to 2, 6 to 10.30
PRICES: £11 (£16), Set L £5 (£11) to £13.50 (£19), Set D £7 (£13) to £13.50 (£19). Minimum £7 weekdays, £10 weekends
CARDS: Access, Visa
SEATS: 90. Vegetarian meals. Children's helpings. No children under 6. No-smoking area. Music

## Rebato's
map 10

169 South Lambeth Road, SW8 1XW
01-735 6388

COOKING 2
COST £19

There is a certain code of conduct if you wish to enjoy this popular restaurant and tapas bar: go regularly; enjoy yourself; do not suffer inhibitions; don't order the Spanish dishes, for example, paella; don't bother with cheese or pudding; tolerate the coffee. Once observed, the rest is pure fun: characterful and watchful staff; excellent fish and grill cookery (bad vegetables); fantastic ambience of jollification, apparently unforced and unlike most English restaurants; a willingness to provide good food and service for not expensive prices. The wine, too, is cheap. A recent meal took in excellently fried soft roes, grilled fresh sardines, Parma ham (and this a Spanish restaurant) carved there and then, a large Dover sole (for a £1.50 supplement – for once justified), poached salmon hollandaise, halibut meunière and a plate of mixed grilled fish: prawns, salmon, halibut. The fruit salad was fresh. Tapas, eaten in the front bar area, are more akin to Spain. Other places may cook more authentically and sometimes better, but nowhere is so loved. A useful range of Spanish wines, only four costing more than £10; some good Spanish brandies and a few Spanish liqueurs. House Torres, £5.50. Book ahead.

CHEF: Edwardo Carvalho    PROPRIETORS: Tino and Shelia Rebato
OPEN: Mon to Sat, exc Sat L
CLOSED: bank hols
MEALS: 12 to 2.30, 7 to 11.15
PRICES: Set L and D £10.75 (£16)
CARDS: Access, Amex, Diners, Visa
SEATS: 60. Children welcome. No pipes in dining-room. Wheelchair access. Music.
Air-conditioned

## Red Fort                                                    map 14

| | |
|---|---|
| 77 Dean Street, W1V 5HA | COOKING 2 |
| 01-437 2525 and 2410 | COST £18–£41 |

Although it is still possible to have an enjoyable and authentic meal here, a griping note emerges from several reports. Disastrously slow service, poor or nondescript dishes and mean portions – a starter of single king prawn with pickle garnish – have left some reporters disconsolate. Yet when the Red Fort is good, it can be very good, with delicate chicken tikka, well-spiced lamb and prawn curries, a zingy sauce for the muttar paneer and superior kulfi and coffee. A suitably relaxing mood prevails for the Sunday lunch buffet, which is good value, though it offers few of the more interesting dishes found at other new-wave Indian restaurants. House French, £6.95.

CHEFS: Azad Ullah and Hafiz Miah    PROPRIETOR: Amin Ali
OPEN: all week
MEALS: 12 to 3, 6 to 11.30
PRICES: £13 (£22), Set L £15 (£18) to £20 (£24), Set D £20 (£23) to £30 (£34)
CARDS: Access, Amex, Diners, Visa
SEATS: 160. Private parties: 100 private room. Vegetarian meals. Children's helpings.
Wheelchair access (1 step; also WC). Music. Air-conditioned

## River Café ♥                                                map 10

| | |
|---|---|
| Thames Wharf, Rainville Road, W6 9HA | COOKING 3 |
| 01-381 8824 | COST £33 |

Now here's a place that polarises opinion. On the one hand, there are the fans of starched linen who develop mild shock that London prices should be charged in starkly modern premises without soft lighting, soft sounds or hushed professionals. On the hand are those who have craved colour, flavour and vibrancy in a new and simpler cooking served in natural and relaxed conditions. The Café has figured proudly in columns of journalists anxious to claim acquaintance with its famous progenitors and eager to flaunt an intimate knowledge of cookery as practised in Tuscan farmhouses. The cuisine of a certain region will only be as successful as the cachet that is garnered from its recognition. Harrods Repository looms against the orange sky of Barnes and Putney. The wind whips white horses on the dark flow of river below the esplanade formed by the square of warehouse, now office, that is Thames Wharf, workplace of Richard Rogers, architect. Aspects of architectural humour make it an intelligent place to be. In the summer, you can eat outside; in the winter, you may wish to rush for the door. The warehouse lies among the indeterminate terraces of Fulham Palace Road, protected by latterday ravelins and salients created by one-way systems. A taxi ride from central London will cost a bomb. The Café itself has a simple architectural form of shallow rippling barrel vaults supporting the floor above. Not much is decorative: one large window wall, high-tech kitchen and still-room counter, linen with paper slip-cloths, Bauhaus-style chairs. The space echoes to loud conversation. The restaurant is generally busy and booked up – 'packed and cheerful' – and the service is relaxed and often welcoming. People are bound to compare the style and ambience to Alastair Little's. There is a similar direct approach to the art of dining; there is a rapidly changing menu coupled to a short but good wine list; the cooking is high on flavour; it deals in materials at the front of the mind of every food enthusiast: mustard greens, rocket, broccoli sprouts, buffalo Mozzarella, polenta, pancetta, beans of various sorts. Only at pudding stage does Italian inspiration desert the chefs: whisky ice-cream, Elizabeth David's chocolate cake, Richard Olney's apple tart. Opinions on the *success* of the cooking come in several shades: 'Self-confident and expert, but never complacent. The result for me was that I cooked Italian all weekend, inventing as I went. What I mean by exciting cooking, not a sculpted kiwi in sight.' A less happy commentary included reflection of 'a rather pale and gooey version of the classic Pappa Pomodora', an 'altogether dull' slab of warmed Mozzarella on a bed of frisée and a dull (again) brochette of scallops with fried potatoes that desperately needed some sauce to bring out the shellfish. Dullness may come if you choose a relatively simple dish rather than a long-cooked affair such as pheasant braised with cabbage and pancetta or pork braised with milk and lemon served with a spinach and Parmesan torte. The pheasant was well judged in its cooking – brown outside, tender and tasty within –the Savoy cabbage did not lose its crispness entirely and was given some impact by the pancetta, all helped by delectable cloves of garlic. With this was served, by request, some first-rate polenta with a topping of fresh Parmesan – light, tender, 'perfect', said an aficionado. Equally, one seasoned diner admitted that char-grilled squid with fried courgettes was 'sensational'. Some of the more straightforward dishes hardly qualify as cooking. A Mozzarella salad was a few slices of cheese, basil and chilli scattered over, a lot of olive oil, a couple of sun-dried tomatoes and a piece of garlic toast. It was a most unsuccessful assemblage. And it cost £6. The same meal brought an overcooked minute steak served with too much but good horseradish cream, an overdressed rosso, rocket and French bean salad and a gallon of French fries. Fine, but at £11.50? Sanity did not return with a dry crumbly lemon cake with a spoonful of thin cream inadequate to mask the pulverulent texture. A frangipane tart was much better. The chocolate cakes have been well reported and the Italian cheeses are always in good condition – usually offered singly or in pairs. Bread is good London-Italian country bread; the olive oils are always fragrant; many of their own herbs and saladings are home grown. The wine list is very short and may appear on the surface to promise little, but the wines are expertly chosen and the growers very fine. Barbaresco and Barbera from Maria Feyles, Brunello di Montalcino from Talenti and Angelo, Barolo from Conterno and the fruity Soave from Vinicola Suavia are just a few examples. House Abruzzi, £6.25. CELLARMAN'S CHOICE : Chianti Classico 'Il Poggio', 1979, £18.50; Portico dei Leoni Chardonnay 1985, £16. From just lunch, the Café went on early in 1989 to serving dinner. At first the licence imposed an 11pm curfew on customers, but that should have been dealt with by the time the *Guide* is published. Some people have been surprised to find an unannounced service charge added to their bill.

CHEFS: Rose Gray and Ruthie Rogers   PROPRIETORS: Richard and Ruthie Rogers and Rose Gray
OPEN: Mon to Fri
CLOSED: 2 weeks Aug, 1 week Easter, 1 week Christmas
MEALS: 12.30 to 3.30, 7.30 to 9.30
PRICES: £19 (£28)
CARDS: Access, Amex, Diners, Visa
SEATS: 58. 8 tables outside. Private parties: 60 main room. Children's helpings (L only). Wheelchair access (also WC). Air-conditioned

## Rotisserie                                                          map 10

56 Uxbridge Road
Shepherd's Bush Green, W12 8LT                              COOKING 1
01-743 3028                                                  COST £22

The lack of circumflex should indicate the international, not French, nature of the operation. Making a welcome refuge from the dispiriting wasteland of Shepherd's Bush Green, the restaurant hides behind a plate-glass window. Long, narrow, faint green and cream, it succeeds in being pleasantly airy. The menu gets straight to the point: fashionable first courses, a pasta dish, a few salads, then an array of main courses from the rôtisserie or the charcoal grill. Corn-fed chicken, Barbary duck, rack of lamb, Scotch salmon, all get the treatment. Good chips, salads and vegetables are à la carte. Home-made ices, a crumble or crème brûlée to finish; a fair range of teas and coffees. Gripes include overly-thin paper napkins and thoughtless service. A smart and cheap international wine list has house French, £5.75. CELLARMAN'S CHOICE : Rothbury Estate Hunter Valley Chardonnay 1988, £10.50; Firestone Merlot 1985, £11.

CHEFS: Emmanuel Schandorf   PROPRIETOR: Karen Doherty
OPEN: all week, exc Sat L and Sun D
MEALS: 12 to 3, 6.30 to 11 (11.30 Fri and Sat)
PRICES: £11 (£18). Cover 50p. Service 10% for parties of 6 or more
CARD: Visa
SEATS: 76. Vegetarian meals. Children welcome. Wheelchair access. Music

*On 6 May 1990 all London telephone numbers will change, the 01- prefix being replaced by either 071- or 081-. See the front of the* Guide *for a list of which numbers will take which prefix.*

## ▲ *Royal Roof Restaurant,* *Royal Garden Hotel*

map 11

2–24 Kensington High Street, W8 4PT
01-937 8000

COOKING 2
COST £24–£60

Rank Hotels have secured the services of David Nicholls, whose cooking at the Britannia Intercontinental Hotel on Grosvenor Square was good enough to earn him many plaudits. His arrival at this restaurant, whose view is worth the long ride up, may also render it an acceptable place for a meal, so long as the bill (as elevated as the dining-room) does not immediately declare it out of bounds. Hotel cooking is 75 per cent system and 25 per cent inspiration. To date the system suffers from hiccups that in turn obstruct the inspiration. However, there are signs that David Nicholls may win through, in which case, the money question disregarded, a good meal will be secured. Service could be improved for competence and willingness. The wine list is acceptably grand hotel in style. House wine is £14.

CHEF: David Nicholls  PROPRIETORS: Rank Hotels
OPEN: Mon to Sat, exc Sat L
MEALS: 12 to 2.30, 7 to 11
PRICES: £32 (£50), Set L £22 (£24), Set D £32 (£43)
CARDS: Access, Amex, Carte Blanche, Diners, Visa
SEATS: 75. Private parties: 30 main room. Vegetarian meals. Children welcome. Smart dress preferred. No-smoking area. Music. Air-conditioned
ACCOMMODATION: 384 rooms, all with bath/shower. Lift. B&B £125.25 to £163. Baby facilities. Afternoon teas. Air-conditioned. TV. Phone. Confirm by 4

## *Royal Thai Orchids*

map 10

141 Upper Richmond Road, SW15 2TX
01-789 4304

COOKING 1
COST £24

Although the food at this friendly family restaurant has not been without criticism, it provides a useful service in the busy old part of Putney (park at the back of the block). On the main menu there are some 50 dishes running through the usual spicy salads, soups, noodles, meat and seafood. The fried minced pork cakes with garlic and coriander and the mixed seafood soup, with prawns crab claws, scallops and lemon-grass, have been praised and there are good-value, anglicised lunchtime dishes. If flavours are disappointingly unfiery, bowls of fish sauce and fresh chillies are available. Extremely pleasant and helpful service.

CHEFS: B. Suwankumpoo and S. Panrod  PROPRIETORS: The Suwankumpoo family
OPEN: Mon to Sat
CLOSED: 2 weeks Aug
MEALS: 12 to 2.30, 6.30 to 11 (11.30 Fri and Sat)
PRICES: £14 (£20)
SEATS: 110. Private parties: 65 main room, 45 private room. Children's helpings. Music

*See the back of the* Guide *for an index of restaurants listed.*

# RSJ ▼

map 11

13A Coin Street, SE1 8YQ
01-928 4554

COOKING 2
COST £18−£29

As the restaurant developed from what was essentially a brasserie, so it is set to spawn a brasserie of its own in the basement. Nonetheless, readers have observed a few steps back in the restaurant: extra, uncomfortable tables, and paper napkins at lunchtime are two instances reported. It might be replied: at these prices, can you blame them? For both the *carte* and the *prix fixe* menus (set according to whether two or three courses are taken) are still very good value. The cooking takes in the fairly normal and slightly odd mixing of fish and meat and meat and fruit. Lots of main dishes are produced on a bed of vegetables, surrounded by a mousse, stuffed with a scallop and then sauced with something else. People do seem to like it: even dishes like milk-fed French lamb and scallops sliced and layered alternately around French leaves, served with a hazelnut sauce. There are occasional notes of displeasure: 'salmon with avocado slices and an avocado sauce − a rather horrible combination if you think about it − was undercooked, a large slice of salmon with a small amount of sauce, and was also not very hot.' But these are far outweighed by approvals for pleasant service in convivial surroundings, good food and memorable wines. The list has long been a treasure trove for lovers of wines from the Loire. The prices are wonderfully fair, the selections as good as any on this or the other side of the Channel: drink bottle after bottle of Saumur Champigny and feel as trendy as the diners of Paris; choose a Cabernet from Savennières like Clos de Coulaine and discover the subtlety and stature of these wines; learn by practice why Loire sweet wines have as many charms as those of Bordeaux − at a fraction of the price. Other regions are not ignored (three Australians, but nothing else outside France) and each choice seems a good one.

CHEF: Ian Stabler   PROPRIETOR: Nigel Wilkinson
OPEN: Mon to Sat, exc Sat L
CLOSED: 3 days at Christmas
MEALS: 12 to 2, 6 to 11
PRICES: £17 (£24), Set L and D £12.25 (£18) to £13.75 (£20). Service 10%
CARDS: Access, Amex, Visa
SEATS: 60. Private parties: 40 main room, 20 private room. Children's helpings on request. Music. Air-conditioned

# Rue St Jacques ▼

map 13

5 Charlotte Street, W1P 1HD
01-637 0222

COOKING 3
COST £25−£50

As fashionable cooking has moved towards less frenetic combinations, so this restaurant becomes less outlandish even if unrepentantly luxurious. The decoration − the combination of reds and greys, the counterpoint of traditional and modern, the various hues of green in the first-floor rooms, the changing volumes of dining spaces − is immensely skilled. It is a pity that mega-buck deals crowd out normal human relations. There is a long *carte*, but at a fixed price, and a shorter, cheaper *prix fixe* at lunchtimes. Service is extremely personable. When this restaurant first opened, it appeared to be in the grip of a culinary wizard anxious to match the most unlikely products of the world's cornucopia, with the waiting staff a motley crew of the sardonic and the supercilious. Things have improved immeasurably since then. The cooking has remained rich: sweetbreads with langoustine tails and cream sauce; fillet of beef with a slice of foie gras and a rich red wine sauce; quail stuffed with foie gras and truffles on a cabbage salad. The ingredients have continued to be occasionally surprising: coriander in the fish soup with salmon sausages; black-bean and oyster sauce with salmon; Amaretto sauce with breast of duck. The cooking sometimes works sensationally; three oysters are each wrapped in a spinach leaf, served in an oyster velouté. The soup is redolent of oyster, just acidulated enough never to pall. The oysters are not so cooked as to lose their melting substance, their creamy softness; not a hint of shrinkage nor firmness. The spinach, too, was still slightly crisp, with sufficient flavour to point up the taste of the oysters. A masterpiece. This dish was followed in the same meal by a breast of smoked chicken on a bed of endives with a white wine cream sauce. Ideally, the dangerously intrusive smoked taste should be countered by the refreshing bitterness of the endive, itself softened by a cream sauce that only adds breadth and bottom. To start, the breast was too big and too smoky. Second, the bed of endives was merely a few pieces, not really cooked, instead of a luscious mattress of the leaf braised in stock, finished with a little butter and lemon. And third, the cream sauce was rich, too rich, with nothing to balance it. The mousse that followed, mango with a wild strawberry coulis, was also too creamy, the fruit fugitive. The feeling was of a great restaurant that just missed, confirmed by details such as undercooked bread, another bland mousse, ginger this time, and unrelentingly hard meringues. The wine list has had a great deal of thought and money spent on it in the last year or two. It is an impressive cellar, almost wholly French (and other sources affectedly given as 'Nouvelle-Zélande' and 'Hongrie'), but with much more effort than before on lower, middle-priced bottles. It is still dear, but worth close attention. Some say not all the staff know as much as they should; perhaps they will learn. House Ch. Terrefort Quancard 1985, £9.50; Sauvignon de St Bris 1987, Luc Sorin, £9. The lavatories are excellent.

CHEF: Günther Schlender   PROPRIETORS: Jessop and Boyce Restaurants Ltd and Günther Schlender
OPEN: Mon to Sat, exc Sat L
CLOSED: Christmas, Easter, bank hols
MEALS: 12.30 to 2.30, 7.30 to 11.15
PRICES: Set L £17.50 (£25), Set D £29.75 (£42). Minimum £17.50 L, £29.75 D. Service 15%
CARDS: Access, Amex, Diners, Visa
SEATS: 70. Private parties: 25 main room, 12, 25 and 30 private rooms. Children's helpings. No pipes in dining-room. Wheelchair access (1 step). Music. Air-conditioned

## Sabras                                                     map 10

| 263 Willesden High Road, NW10 2RX | COOKING 2 |
| 01-459 0340 | COST £8–£22 |

The tables are so closely packed at this longstanding *Guide* entry that 'you have no choice but to join in the conversation with the neighbours. We had an odd couple next to us, whom I didn't find particularly entertaining.' The lure, small tables or no, is good Indian vegetarian food in scrupulously clean surroundings, which now include a bar. A meal will start encouragingly with a frothy and foaming lassi – even the sweet ones are not so sweet as to fail to refresh – or an actually fresh fruit or vegetable juice. The Gujerati snacks such as onion bhajias and khamans (the first fried, the second steamed) are of good texture and not too aggressively spiced, yet the fenugreek and coriander leaves give real interest. A Hyderabad dhosa (large thin pancake), again very freshly made with accompanying masala of sweet onions, cashews and coconut, is perked up and given fire with a hot sambar. Then shrikhand – curd cheese with honey, saffron, cardamom and pistachios – sticky and sweet but cooling. The teas are good (though perhaps too much ginger for some in the Gujerati masala version) and there is a wide range of bottled beer. Some have found that the opening hours are unpredictable; a few that the food is blander than they had expected. House French wine, £5.50.

CHEFS/PROPRIETORS: Hemant and Nalinee Desai
OPEN: Tue to Sun
MEALS: 1 to 3, 5 to 10 (1 to 10 Sat and Sun)
PRICES: £9 (£18), Set L £4.50 (£8) to £7.50 (£11), Set D £7.50 (£11) to £10 (£14), Snacks from £2.50. Service inc
CARDS: Access, Visa
SEATS: 32. Private parties: 32 main room. Vegetarian meals. Children welcome. Separate smoking area. Wheelchair access (also WC). Music

## St Quentin
map 12

| 243 Brompton Road, SW3 2EP | COOKING 2 |
| 01-581 5131 and 589 8005 | COST £19–£36 |

There is no slicker establishment in Knightsbridge, with a strong local following for the French touch that has more style than the Grill St Quentin, yet is not so long-drawn-out and fanciful as a full-dress restaurant. The table d'hôte menus are conspicuous examples of fair pricing for this district. It is a pity that standards are so up and down, particularly weak on the linkage between dining-room and kitchen. An inspection meal had poor features, such as cod with a tomato sauce that had seen sitting about on the hot plate looking for a waiter for too long to be acceptable. Its requested replacement was excellent, however. The cheeseboard, (thanks, perhaps, to Délices de St Quentin down the road), was also very satisfactory as was an orange tart and the earlier monkfish in fair puff pastry. Watch for escalating bills as extras mount up. House French, £6.90. The Savoy Group have taken a controlling interest in this company, though personnel has not yet changed.

CHEF: Pascal Fioux   PROPRIETORS: St Quentin Ltd
OPEN: all week
MEALS: 12 to 3 (4 Sat), 7 to 12 (11.30 Sun)
PRICES: £20 (£30), Set L £10.90 (£19), Set D £13.90 (£22). Cover £1.30. Service 12.5%
CARDS: Access, Amex, Diners, Visa
SEATS: 85. Private parties: 25 private room. Wheelchair access. Air-conditioned

▲ *This symbol means accommodation is available.*

## San Martino

map 12

103 Walton Street, SW3 2HP
01-589 3833 and 1356

COOKING 2
COST £26

'Simply Tuscan' is the way Costanzo Martinucci describes the cooking at his long-established Chelsea trattoria, which he runs enthusiastically as a family affair. The decoration is a far cry from the designer artiness of many newer Italian restaurants, with heavy silver cutlery that is a matter of some pride. The atmosphere, however, is relaxed; children are made welcome. Much emphasis is placed on the marketing. Fish is bought on Tuesdays and Fridays; other specialities like kid and lamb, langoustines or wild mushrooms arrive according to availability and fresh herbs come from the garden or a specially built greenhouse. Many of the most interesting and beguilingly described dishes − for example 'fantastic fish soup' and 'best mixed hors d'oeuvre in London' − come off the chef's daily recommendations, but spaghetti San Martino, cooked in a paper bag with fish, has been a favourite in the past, grilled meat or fish platters are other specialities and Costanzo himself waxes lyrical about the salads dressed with a balsamic vinaigrette. Espresso coffee is good. The album of a wine list has some excellent new-wave Italian growers among its offerings. Ignore the Champagne prices and be happy with the reasonable mark-ups on the native material including Chianti from Isole e Olena, Rubesco Torgiano from Lungarotti and Dolcetto d'Alba from Gagliardo. House Tuscan is £6.80. Beers from Peroni and Nastro Azzurro.

CHEFS: Costanzo Martinucci, Alfonso Cestaro, Fernando Lima and Tommaso Martinucci  PROPRIETOR: Costanzo Martinucci
OPEN: Mon to Sat
MEALS: 12 to 2.45, 7 to 11.30
PRICES: £14 (£22). Cover £1.15 L, £1.50 D. Service 15%
CARDS: Access, Amex, Diners, Visa
SEATS: 48. Private parties: 65 main room, 24 private room. Vegetarian meals. Children's helpings. Wheelchair access (1 step). Air-conditioned

## Santini ▼

map 11

29 Ebury Street, SW1W 0NX
01-730 4094 and 8275

COOKING 3
COST £23−£67

Although this ultra-smart restaurant on the east end of Ebury Street offers some fine Venetian cooking, there have been cavils at the price/bulk ratio and the service. Nonetheless, the polenta, the pasta, the calamari and the crespedille with the coffee have been energetically praised, as have dishes incorporating wild mushrooms − veal scallopine on one occasion, tagliatelle on another and polenta with two sorts of funghi on a third. The calf's liver too, served with 'raw young spinach', captures the simple refreshment of Italian meat cookery in restaurants. There is a cheaper lunch menu of two courses and coffee, and several daily specials. For some, the service is impeccable, for others it is flippant, arrogant and hectoring. Yet the wine list needs calm, not salesmanship. It is a remarkable collection of Barolos, Chiantis and North Italian whites, to say the least. The prices are pretty steep. One reader was moved to tears by the brilliance of the money-making machine. House

Valpolicella or Soave, £10.50. CELLARMAN'S CHOICE : Venegazzù della Casa 1984, £15.50; Barolo, Rocche dei Manzoni 1979, £47.50. See also L'Incontro, the sister show.

CHEFS: Mr Santin and G. Rosselli   PROPRIETOR: Mr G. Santin
OPEN: all week, exc Sat and Sun L
CLOSED: bank hols
MEALS: 12.30 to 2.30, 7 to 11.30
PRICES: £24 (£37), Set L £12.50 (£23) to £33 (£44), Set D £34 (£45) to £45 (£56). Cover £1.50. Service 12%
CARDS: Access, Amex, Diners, Visa
SEATS: 65. Private parties: 25 main room. Vegetarian meals. Children welcome. Wheelchair access. Air-conditioned

## ▲ *Savoy Grill and River Room*                                    map 14

Strand, WC2R 0EU                                                    COOKING 3
01-836 4343                                                         COST £27–£56

The Grill Room is set to one side, not part of the hotel itself; the River Room is deep in the structure with views over the Thames worth making some fuss to obtain (or you can end up behind a pillar facing the wrong way). The one is modern, the other has red walls, classical columns and mirrors – and a bandstand that looks like a chandelier. The Grill Room makes a greater effort to be a restaurant: there are English specialities on set days of the week (like school) and a modern menu (slightly longer at night) with dishes that do not aimlessly ladle on the luxuries: watercress and lime soup; smoked salmon with asparagus mousse; beef fillet with aubergines and olives, and sea bass on a bed of fennel. Many people (some famous) enjoy it for the tradition of service as well as the much livelier cooking of recent years. The River Room has perhaps a different function and thus less culinary character, though people have also found it greatly improved of late. It is, however, a forbidding place to enter, especially for the tyro; there can also be a whirling rush to the service when the pressure is on. Not one word of the menu seems to be in English. To some people's ears, the music is quite dreadful. The wine list is expensive, without the character of the Connaught's. As this *Guide* went to press, David Sharland was tagged to take over the Grill kitchen in September 1989.

CHEFS: Anton Edelmann and David Sharland (Grill)   PROPRIETORS: Savoy Hotel plc
OPEN: Grill Room Mon to Sat, exc Sat L; River Room all week
CLOSED: Grill Room 3 weeks Aug; River Room L 31 Dec
MEALS: Grill Room 12.30 to 2.30, 6 to 11.15; River Room 12.30 to 2.30, 7.30 to 11.30 (7 to 10.30 Sun)
PRICES: Grill Room £28 (£41), Set D £20 (£27) to £23 (£30); River Room £37 (£47), Set L £20.50 (£27), Set D £25.50 (£31) to £29.50 (£36). Licensed, also bring your own: corkage £8.50
CARDS: Access, Amex, Diners, Visa
SEATS: Grill Room 80; River Room 140. Private parties: 10 main room. Car-park, 30 places. Children welcome. Smart dress preferred. No pipes in dining-room. Wheelchair access. Music. Air-conditioned
ACCOMMODATION: 202 rooms, all with bath/shower. Rooms for disabled. Lift. B&B £142.25 to £172.25. Deposit: £142.25. Baby facilities. Afternoon teas. 60 per cent air-conditioned. TV. Phone. Confirm by 6

## Si Chuen

map 14

56 Old Compton Street, W1V 5PN
01-437 2069

COOKING 1
COST £10—£40

Although in direct descent from the progenitors of Szechuan cooking in
London, it may be difficult to descry this on the menu which includes as many
Cantonese items, and even some from Malaysia, as Szechuan. In many dishes
this restaurant is no better than average, but the shredded pork with fish-
flavoured sauce; twice-cooked pork in hot soya paste; minced meat with
seasonal beans; pelmeni in hot sauce; stewed fish in spiced sauce and other
Szechuan specialities are worth seeking out. House wine £6.

CHEFS: Bing Tzue and K.W. Li  PROPRIETORS: A.Y.C. Cheung and C.M. Liew
OPEN: all week
MEALS: noon to midnight
PRICES: £16 (£27), Set L £4 (£10) to £10 (£16), Set D £7.50 (£13) to £25 (£33). Cover 50p.
Service 12.5%
CARDS: Access, Amex, Diners, Visa
SEATS: 60. Private parties: 30 main room, 30 private room. Vegetarian meals. Children's
helpings. Wheelchair access (3 steps). Music

## Singapore Garden Restaurant

map 11

83—83A Fairfax Road, NW6 4DY
01-328 5314

COOKING 1
COST £15—£38

Massed plants and flowers and the cunningly arranged banks of mirrors
make this restaurant feel like an oriental garden inhabited by mysteriously
disappearing waiters. Service in fact is courteous and attentive, prices
reasonable, helpings huge and the food tasty and authentic. The list of
Singapore and Malaysian dishes repays investigation, as do the fish specialities
like chilli crab or lobster. Fried crisp noodles Mee Hoon have been crisp and
clean, well augmented with prawns, fish cake and much else; satays are also
recommended. House French is £6.50 and there's Tiger beer or sake.

CHEF: Mrs Lim  PROPRIETORS: The Lim family
OPEN: all week
MEALS: 12 to 2.45, 6 to 10.45 (11.15 Fri and Sat)
PRICES: £10 (£20), Set L £10 (£15) to £15 (£21), Set D £15 (£21) to £25 (£32). Minimum
£6.50. Service 12.5%
CARDS: Access, Amex, Diners, Visa
SEATS: 100. Private parties: 60 main room, 60 private room. Children welcome. Music.
Air-conditioned

## Soong Szechuan

map 11

45A South End Road, NW3 2QB
01-794 2461

COOKING 1
COST £15—£25

Superior interior design and classy atmosphere, coupled with friendly service,
are not the only recommendations for this Szechuan restaurant opposite
Hampstead Heath railway station. Although the menu ranges from sweetcorn
soup (Cantonese) to drunken fish in Shaoxing wine from the Shanghai region,

it is possible to eat genuine Szechuan dishes such as prawns flavoured with Szechuan peppercorns or aubergines in fish fragrant sauce. One or two Hunan dishes have also crept into the menu, another cuisine noted for its fieriness. Crab in black-bean sauce, mange-tout with garlic sauce and spiced salt spare ribs have been recommended. House wine, £5.

CHEF: Kok Seng Lee  PROPRIETOR: Soong Yap
OPEN: all week
CLOSED: bank hols, 24 to 26 Dec
MEALS: 12 to 2.30, 6 to 11 (10.30 Sun)
PRICES: £15 (£21), Set D £12.50 (£15) to £18 (£21). Service inc
CARDS: Access, Amex, Diners, Visa
SEATS: 85. Private parties: 100 main room. Children's helpings on request. Music.
Air-conditioned

## ▲ Le Soufflé, Inter-Continental Hotel

map 12

1 Hamilton Place, W1V 0QY                                          COOKING 3
01-409 3131                                                        COST £29–£52

There is not a lot to lift the spirits in the Inter-Continental. The good taste/bad taste either depresses or enervates. The dining-room, called Le Soufflé after the speciality of its highly esteemed chef Peter Kromberg, is lighter in decorative treatment than its forerunner, though it might be a contender for a grand prix of tedium. Its lack of reference to the world outside may cause anomy in the diner unwilling to accept the artificial mores of a vast brigade of service. The cooking has always belied its surroundings and this year sees its crop of reports in favour of the highly skilled international cuisine. Nine of the 12 first courses of the summer menu included smoked salmon or shellfish – leaving the person who wants a surprise in all this 'international' cooking the choice of smoked duck with foie gras and truffles; sweatbread [sic] and goose-liver tartlet; or Wensleydale and walnut soufflé. Menu planners should note that length does not always equal variety. Recommendations have been received for a breast of pheasant wrapped in a strudel parcel with a truffle sauce; a chicken breast wrapped in Parma ham served with subtle spicy vegetables and home-made noodles; rabbit with artichoke, spinach and a sauce spiked with balsamic vinegar; and wild strawberries and a strawberry mousse piled on to a first-class pastry base. Much is wrapped or stuffed. Soufflés are served for dessert: speak early about them to avoid delay. They have been known to be leathery on top, but the kitchen is masterful at them as a rule. The waiters can also be the worst sort of hotel brigade: asked where the Stilton came from, 'Scotland' was the reply; other cheeses are from Philippe Olivier. The wine list is long and expensive. To say the smallest mark-ups lurk among the older clarets is merely to exacerbate a failing apparent through the rest of the list. But then, the Inter-Continental is Club Class and money has less meaning than in Economy. House wines are £13. There is a short list of CELLARMAN'S CHOICE : presented with the daily menu. The Coffee Room at the Inter-Continental is the locale for many guest appearances from cooks and chefs. It is also quite a serious spot for luncheon if that is the place you need to be. It has windows to the street outside.

CHEF: Peter Kromberg   PROPRIETORS: Inter-Continental Hotels Corp.
OPEN: all week, exc Sat L
MEALS: 12.30 to 3, 7 to 11.30
PRICES: £29 (£38), Set L £22.50 (£29), Set D £36.50 (£43). Service inc
CARDS: Access, Amex, Carte Blanche, Diners, Visa
SEATS: 72. Private parties: 10 main room, 700 private room. Car-park, 100 places.
Children's helpings. Smart dress preferred. Wheelchair access (also WC). Air-conditioned
ACCOMMODATION: 490 rooms, all with bath/shower. Rooms for disabled. Lift. B&B £151 to
£176. Baby facilities. Afternoon teas. Sauna. Air-conditioning. TV. Phone

## Soulard                                                          map 11

| 113 Mortimer Road, N1 4JY | COOKING 2 |
| 01-254 1314 | COST £22 |

There is something about uncompromisingly French restaurants, run by
uncompromisingly French people, that strikes a chord in the English psyche.
Provided they do whatever they do with conviction and apologise for nothing,
we take them to our hearts. It is amazing that there are still French restaurants
opening in London in small out-of-the-way premises, with small chauvinist
wine lists and serving snails. Yet they do, and we lap it up. This is Philippe
Soulard's first solo venture, a modestly decorated dining-room in an
unfashionable part of town (best approached from Englefield Road, which runs
between Essex and Kingsland Roads). It is clean and cheerful with plain white
walls, varnished wood, and dark green tablecloths. A large brick chimney
claims centre stage. The welcome is warm, and despite the clichés, the kitchen
delivers the goods: crisp, deep-fried puff pastry oozing with melting
Roquefort; tender, pink, pan-fried calf's liver; poached apple with a caramel
honey sauce, and proper crème anglaise. And it is good to see a trio of sausages:
Toulouse, merguez, andouillette with a Dijon mustard sauce. The wine list is
short, but the whole package is greater than the sum of its parts. It could be just
what this part of Islington needs. House French, £5.75.

CHEF: Christian Veronneau   PROPRIETOR: Philippe Soulard
OPEN: Tue to Sat, exc Sat L
CLOSED: 2 weeks in Aug
MEALS: 12 to 2.30, 7 to 10.30
PRICES: £13 (£18)
CARD: Access
SEATS: 28. 9 tables outside. Private parties: 15 private room. Children's helpings. No cigars
in dining-room. Music.

## Spices                                                          map 11

| 30 Stoke Newington Church | |
| Street, N16 0LU | COOKING 2 |
| 01-254 0528 | COST £14 |

Easy to locate, with a car-park right behind the restaurant, Spices has earned
itself a reputation as a good Indian vegetarian restaurant. Plants, candles and
subdued lighting make for a tranquil, unhurried atmosphere under a false
ceiling of red lattice. Bombay tiffin – a selection of starters – and two thalis

give the opportunity to taste a range of dishes from the short, handwritten menu. Among these, malai baigan, fried aubergines with soured cream and spices, combines well with the spicier pakoras and samosas. The special thali includes cardamom-flavoured rice, fresh spinach and mixed vegetable curries. Among desserts, there are three refreshing kulfis and sweet gulab jamun. Service manages to be attentive but not intrusive. Finish with a fresh pot of Gujerati tea. House French is from £4.25.

CHEF: Khaleda Choudhury    PROPRIETORS: Spices Ltd
OPEN: all week
CLOSED: 25 and 26 Dec
MEALS: 12.30 to 3, 6 to 12 (1am Fri), noon to 1am Sat, noon to midnight Sun
PRICES: £6 (£12). Service 10%
CARDS: Access, Amex, Carte Blanche, Diners, Visa
SEATS: 90. Private parties: 25 main room, 15 private room. Vegetarian meals. Children's helpings. Separate smoking area. Wheelchair access (also WC). Music. Air-conditioned

## Sree Krishna                                                          map 10

194 Tooting High Street, SW17 0SF                                    COOKING 1
01-672 4250                                                            COST £12

The Sree Krishna has changed hands and acquired a new chef, but the menu remains identical, with southern vegetarian specialities of Kerala alongside a short, fairly standard menu. The specialities are listed as dosai (lentil and rice flour pancakes) − there is now a meat as well as a potato version − vadais (fried lentil doughnuts), tangy sambar and vegetable avial; but there are also coconut and lemon rice and green banana bhajis. Vegetable dishes are made with fresh ingredients. There is a basic wine list, Kingfisher beer or lassi to drink.

CHEF: Mullath Vijayan    PROPRIETORS: T. Haridas and family
OPEN: all week
MEALS: 12 to 2.45, 6 to 10.45 (11.45 Fri and Sat)
PRICES: £4 (£10). Minimum £2.50. Service 10%
CARDS: Access, Amex, Diners, Visa
SEATS: 120. Vegetarian meals. Children welcome. Wheelchair access (also WC). Music. Air-conditioned

## Stephen Bull ▼                                                        map 13

5−7 Blandford Street, W1H 3AA                                        COOKING 3
01-486 9696                                                            COST £31

The food and the room in which it is eaten seem to have the same ideas: spare, clean, open, but with unexpected angles and crannies. For central London, and this level of cooking, you eat cheaply. There is no attempt to create a 'brasserie', it is a restaurant, albeit pared down to essentials. There are tablecloths, comfortable chairs and waiting staff, for a price below that of fashionable places offering less. The food is very modern, with a lot of surprising flavours. It is also light in taste and style. There are no rich reduction sauces and rarely any cream or butter emulsions. Quantities are finely judged, not small but never outfacing. The menu changes every week, offering eight or 10 dishes at each course, with occasional extras. There is always a soup: mussel with beef marrow quenelles, sorrel, watercress. Fish is excellent: invariably fresh, nearly always cooked to a moist succulence. Flavourings are edged with some acidity: sorrel, rocket, citrus, vinegar, but the thumping sweet-sour of heavier sauciers is mercifully absent. Spices, another fondness, are also lightly handled. The cooking is influenced by the herb garden and permeates ancillaries as well as centrepiece dishes. The materials deployed are first rate, as they need to be with so fragile a disguise. Desserts are not invariably light: the plate of chocolates contains a St-Emilion so boozy and rich as to stop many in their tracks. Best, for simplicity, is the 'lightest possible cheesecake'. Vegetables are served in small white dishes. They, too, show some invention; chickpeas and couscous are as likely as boiled potatoes. The big question is whether Stephen Bull can persist in charging so little (in West End terms). To succeed in his intention he has to judge finely the balance of staff and material costs. Yet the customers will endlessly press for better service and more elaboration. The service has so far creaked somewhat. Were it to be faultless (within its own set of rules), the pressure could be more strongly resisted. The wine list displays the same approach as the menu: modern, intelligent, fairly priced. It deserves awards for the latter alone. Shippers are good, range is catholic, service is adequate. House wines from £7.

CHEFS: Stephen Bull and Thomas Slowey    PROPRIETOR: Stephen Bull
OPEN: Mon to Sat, exc Sat L
CLOSED: 1 week at Christmas
MEALS: 12 to 3, 6 to 11.30
PRICES: £19 (£26)
CARDS: Access, Visa
SEATS: 60. Private parties: 50 main room. Children's helpings. Wheelchair access (1 step). Air-conditioned

## Suntory

map 13

72 St James's Street, SW1A 1PH                    COOKING 3
01-409 0201                                    COST £26−£65

The surroundings do have class, and the service some inkling of the Japanese ideal: perfectly orchestrated in a formal atmosphere, customers treated as guests. Competence runs through the whole operation, together with a certain opulence. Best here to be advised, for counsel will be fair. The specialities are table-top cooking: shabu-shabu and sukiyaki. More interesting dishes are on the *carte* and there are daily extras advised separately. The wine list has exciting prices although some of the reports about the cost of eating here are exaggerated in the telling. Suntory no longer levies a cover charge. House French is £10 but sake is the proper accompaniment.

CHEF: M. Hayashi    PROPRIETORS: Suntory Ltd
OPEN: Mon to Sat
MEALS: 12 to 1.30, 7 to 9.30
PRICES: £31 (£49), Set L £18 (£26) to £42 (£54), Set D £27 (£39) to £42 (£54). Minimum £18. Service 15%
CARDS: Access, Amex, Diners, Visa
SEATS: 130

## Le Suquet

map 12

104 Draycott Avenue, SW3 3AE
01-581 1785 and 225 0838

COOKING 2
COST £53

The service is best if you are a regular and regulars do like Le Suquet. Whether others can cope with the conditions is a moot point. One reader, upbraided for leaving an inadequate tip, felt not. Le Suquet cooks fish: the beginning salads, simple affairs with ceps, asparagus or warm grilled salmon are recommended, as are grilled langoustines for a first course. Among main courses, the cod with a provençale sauce and the grilled sole or turbot are thought satisfactory. Vegetables usually are not, nor desserts. Tables are cramped. Keep to simple dishes relying on shrewd buying. The wine list includes an excellent Muscadet from Métaireau and an infrequently found Bellet from Provence. House French is £7.80. For a place so lacking in major comforts, a £1 cover charge is just the thing to make the blood boil.

CHEF: Jean Yves Darcel   PROPRIETOR: Pierre Martin
OPEN: all week
MEALS: 12.30 to 2.30, 7 to 11.30
PRICES: £34 (£44). Cover £1
CARDS: Access, Amex, Diners, Visa
SEATS: 50. 4 tables outside. Private parties: 16 private room. Children welcome. Smart dress preferred. Wheelchair access. Music. Air-conditioned

## Suruchi

map 11

18 Theberton Street, N1 0QX
01-359 8033

COOKING 1
COST £5−£12

Though looking too French by half, it is a South Indian vegetarian café, light and airy with hushed classical background music rather than twanging sitar. The menu is a short list of snacks and specialities: alongside crispy bhel pooris and well-flavoured dosa are steamed rice cakes in sambar sauce and excellent value thalis. Spices are well-balanced, textures pleasing. Good ras malai and other sweets to finish. Unlicensed, but no corkage if you take your own wine. A second branch, specialising in seafood, has opened near Newington Green.

CHEFS: Rofique Uddin and Hurun Ahmed   PROPRIETORS: Suruchi Partnership
OPEN: all week
MEALS: 12 to 2.30, 6 to 10.45
PRICES: £7 (£10), Set L £4.10 (£5) to £6 (£7), Set D £4.50 (£5) to £7.50 (£8), Snacks from £1.45. Unlicensed, but bring your own: no corkage
CARDS: Amex, Visa
SEATS: 40. Vegetarian meals. Children welcome. Music

*The* Guide *office can quickly spot when a restaurateur is encouraging customers to write recommending inclusion. Such reports do not further a restaurant's cause. Please tell us if a restaurateur invites you to write to the* Guide.

*All letters to the* Guide *are acknowledged with an update on latest sales, closures, chef changes and so on.*

## Sutherlands ▮

map 13

45 Lexington Street, W1R 3LG
01-434 3401

COOKING 4
COST £33–£48

Small wonder that Siân Sutherland-Dodd, the manager in the young triumvirate that rules, was in advertising. This place reeks of concept and forethought. The point, however, is that it convinces many, despite itself. 'The arrival of the breads made me suspect that, far from being a serious operation, it was a pretentious one,' but, after a lobster soufflé, splendid wild duck with onions and girolles, a charlotte of raspberries that avoided over-sweetness and an excellent Fixin 1984 from Bruno Clair, recommended as a good bottle from a poor year, the correspondent was converted – mimsy rolls and cloudy coffee notwithstanding. The jewel-like interior, the more remarkable for the fashionably drab street-front, sets the tone for the cooking and incidentals – the plates are settings for precise arrangements, the sauces have an intensity of polished diamonds, everything is spare, miniature and considered. This may provoke the urge for gesture, for expansiveness in some – forsooth, things can take a long time from kitchen to table – but it is mediated by a civilised, relaxed formality on the parts of owners and staff. They, at least, know precisely what is going on and why things are done so. A couple placed their order, one choosing monkfish for the principal dish. Out came the ante-prandial 'taster': for one, a bit of monkfish with butter and chive sauce; for the other, a trifle of red mullet so as not to replicate the main choice. The cooking, as if you didn't guess it, is nouvelle, though Garry Hollihead might deny it. It has preserved and developed many of the features of that style: unfamiliar ingredients, surprising combinations, miniature arrangements and working out the balance of sweet and savoury. The repertoire of dishes gives an embarrassment of choice: a terrine of pigeon, duck, partridge and foie gras served cold with a warm sauce of truffles and hazelnuts strewn with raspberries, loganberries and blackcurrants, where the texture of the terrine was flawless and every component played its part, down to 'the acidic nip of blackcurrants cutting into the creaminess of the foie gras'; a John Dory sliced into collops, arranged on a lemon sauce accompanied by slivers of turnip, artichoke, courgettes and asparagus tips, where 'each vegetable retained its flavour, the lemon sauce was sufficiently restrained and the final – almost excessive – touch was a fragile but intensely flavoured lobster mousse just holding its shape on the side of the plate'; or an iced coffee and Tia Maria soufflé on two sauces, one of saffron and vanilla, the other of dark chocolate. A further catalogue is superfluous. Garry Hollihead manages to bring off most that he tries, and he tries so hard that Sutherlands is rather a good place. Not all is praise. Meals occasionally topple into imbalance. The demi-glace sauce may crop up in first and second courses; it is so rich (almost immobile on the plate) that it may overwhelm. The preoccupation with technique is so great that flavour may fly out the window: 'I still can't get used to the microscopically diced vegetables, as they don't taste of anything in the end.' (Other chefs, besotted with their Japanese blades, please note.) More worryingly, there is often cause to complain that components mentioned in the menu specification (accurate word, that) are not perceptible in the finished dish: a lobster soufflé with too evanescent *marc*; a guinea-fowl with sorrel sauce (this features the other sauce foundation of the house, a buttery Jacqueline, chicken based) where the sorrel was indiscernible, as the Noilly Prat had been under a demi-glace in the preceding course; or Parmesan contributing nothing to the rolls so advertised. Balance that against the admission of a seasoned diner-out, while £10 for two people was once an outrage, now we don't think twice about £100 when it's as good as this. Well, we do, but the melancholy fact is that it is probably worth it – by today's standards. The wine continues to be the image of care and value: only 70 items, but each well chosen, with equal weight afforded countries outside France. The Champagnes encompass le Mesnil Blanc de Blancs 1983 and Bruno Paillard 1969; half-bottles are thoughtfully selected; burgundies improve with each new list (just as well); Washington and Idaho provide tongue-twisting food for thought.

CHEF: Garry Hollihead   PROPRIETORS: Siân Sutherland-Dodd, Garry Hollihead and Christian Arden
OPEN: Mon to Sat, exc Sat L
MEALS: 12.15 to 2.15, 6.15 to 11.15
PRICES: Set L and D £23.50 (£33) and £29 (£40). Service 12.5%
CARDS: Access, Amex, Carte Blanche, Visa
SEATS: 50. Private parties: 50 main room, 20 private room. Vegetarian meals. Children's helpings. No pipes in dining-room, no cigars L. Wheelchair access. Air-conditioned

## Tante Claire ♥ map 12

68–69 Royal Hospital Road, SW3 4HP
01-352 6045

COOKING 5
COST £25–£66

Were one to give an annual report, it would have to be, 'Steady as she goes'. Pierre Koffmann does not change things lightly. The menu, for example, although showing variation, has remarkable continuity. Ever-present is the stuffed trotter: with morels one year, with sweetbreads the next. Hare or venison with chocolate and raspberry vinegar are other long stayers. Even fish evinces this same longevity, as in red mullet with cumin. Styles, too, persist. Fish is usually approached in a sturdy, robust manner: salmon with goose fat, turbot with lentils, turbot with cinnamon and lemon. Bold tastes, but never strident, for a craftsman is at work. Pierre Koffmann is a fine baker, whose preference seems to be for a pain de campagne. This affection (in shorthand) for his roots comes out in general cooking with use of cabbage in recipes, that original taming of the sausage for his seafood sausages and other touches of cuisine à l'ancienne, a style that he early espoused. These, allied to a fine judgement and an unwillingness to use luxuries for their own sake, may be pointers to a style. The framework for dining is an exceptionally discreet and relaxing room that has few of the usual hyperbolic mannerisms of decorators. The understatement, of cooking and locale, may indeed contribute to the occasional shock at the size of the final account. Some dishes that have been noted include exceptional appetisers (although other diners have been underwhelmed), for instance, a little pot of brandade or two oysters in an oily aspic. As first courses there have been feuilleté of langoustines on a butter sauce with saffron and pieces of cucumber and tomato; or a salade savoureuse of partridge and 'hauntingly tasty' foie gras. Those do not take in the many references to the signature dish of scallops with a blackened sauce from the ink of squid that still has the visual impact of its original and the many-layered flavours that have continually impressed. Main courses include venison, crusty outside and pink within, with a texture giving bite yet tender, and a sauce of balance between chocolate and fruity vinegar. This sweet-sour theme is repeated in pigeon, arranged round a potato galette and sauced with an elderberry and stock-based reduction. Puddings may be no more complex than a trio of sorbets, but what sorbets! 'More impressive than I have had elsewhere,' was the comment of one faced with kiwi, raspberry and lemon. Ices figure prominently in other people's accounts of dessert: raspberry soufflé with its sorbet; a sandwich of brandy-snaps with a passion-fruit ice-cream and a grapefruit sauce; a real peach Melba. Very great skills are mobilized simply to get things right. The service, too, is often congratulated. It can be so efficient as to make some feel hurried, others feel unloved, but in general it is thought good, the sommelier in particular never recommending too expensive a bottle and pouring and serving with timely accuracy. That coolness observed by a few is extended by them to the cooking. Not that there are faults, merely that it leaves them unimpressed; the symbiosis of the two complaints may be significant. Less favourable are reactions to vegetables, pursued by Pierre Koffmann in a fairly French manner – not a lot of them and often done 'inventively'. This may be an example of a collision of ethnic customs. Perhaps the same might be said of the service charge. Many, for many years, have raised their eyebrows at the consistent refusal to close the bottom line of the credit card voucher, even though 'service included' is written on bills and menus. Mere questioning escalated to outrage when one enquirer was informed that the service charge was used to pay the wages and had 'nothing to do with tips or gratuities'. Restaurants such as this should lead the way in clearing the air of all such nonsense. The wine list is very extensive. Its best characteristic for the private customer with limited funds is the selection of French wines from regions outside the classics. These may still cost dear, but they are well chosen and avoid the danger zone of vintage claret. Seek guidance, for the advice is fair. There is also a body of reporters who feel lunch is a better meal than dinner and that the cheaper set-price lunch, with very few choices, leaves the body fitter for the next segment of the day or evening. It is here, they say, where artifice is more rarely pursued, that Pierre Koffmann's true capabilities can best be seen.

CHEF: Pierre Koffmann   PROPRIETORS: Mr and Mrs Pierre Koffmann
OPEN: Mon to Fri
MEALS: 12.30 to 2, 7 to 11
PRICES: £47 (£55), Set L £19.50 (£25). Minimum £40 alc. Service inc
CARDS: Access, Amex, Diners, Visa
SEATS: 38. Children welcome. Smart dress preferred. Wheelchair access

*Restaurateurs justifiably resent no-shows. If you quote a credit card number when booking, you may be liable for the restaurant's lost profit margin if you don't turn up. Always phone to cancel.*

*If you see a certificate in a restaurant bearing the words 'Good Food and Wine Guide', the claim is false – see the Introduction. Please write and tell us the name and address of the restaurant.*

## ▲ Terrace Garden, Le Meridien Piccadilly Hotel

map 13

21–22 Piccadilly, W1V 0BN
01-734 8000

COOKING 3
COST £21–£31

When Le Meridien was renovated, a brainwave produced this glass-covered terrace across the front half of the building, high above the pavement of Piccadilly. The result is unexpectedly airy and sometimes calming – depending on the time of day and mix of customers. The food is not bad at all, and offers carefully thought out, low-cholesterol, reduced-calorie dishes as well as normal items. The prices are very fair for the district. The style is middle-of-the-road French modern; coffee is thoroughly English, however. House French, £9.75. See also Oak Room, Meridien Piccadilly Hotel.

CHEF: David Chambers   PROPRIETORS: Meridien Hotels
OPEN: all week
MEALS: noon to 11.30
PRICES: £17 (£26), Set L and D £13.50 (£21). Snacks from £4.75
CARDS: Access, Amex, Diners, Visa
SEATS: 130. Vegetarian meals. Children's helpings. Smart dress preferred. No-smoking area. Music. Air-conditioned
ACCOMMODATION: 284 rooms, all with bath/shower. Rooms for disabled. Lift. B&B 203.50 to £225.50. Afternoon teas. Swimming-pool. Sauna. Snooker. Air-conditioning. TV. Phone. Confirm one day before

## Tiny Tim

map 11

7 Plender Street, NW1 0JT
01-388 0402

COOKING 2
COST £12–£23

Marc Peyroche may be a Dickens fan, but the cooking and atmosphere of his restaurant are French in everything from the menu's healthy disregard for London fashions to small details like crisp, fresh baguettes and large pats of unsalted butter. Decoration is rural, with thin blackened beams against white walls. There are mirrors, crisp linen on the tables and the service is pleasant and relaxed. Dishes range from fricassee of snails topped with puff pastry; carré d'agneau finished with mustard; warm calf's liver salad with apples; fillet of lamb with red wine and mint; lemon crème brûlée. The choice is limited – five for each course – but changes frequently and there are daily fish dishes, other specials and a couple of vegetarian options. Artichoke hearts, quail salad, freshly made bisque de langoustines, a piping hot goats' cheese custard and moist guinea-fowl with morels have all been good. An ample plate of crisply cooked vegetables plus a potato gratin is left on the table, and the bread basket is kept full. Puddings, homely rather than elaborate, have included a fromage frais crémet with swirls of cassis, crêpes with various fillings and apricot tart. More places of this standard would make London happier. House wine is £5.50. CELLARMAN'S CHOICE : Sancerre, Domaine des Groux 1987, £8.

*See the inside of the front cover for an explanation of the new 1 to 5 rating system recognising cooking standards.*

CHEF/PROPRIETOR: Marc Peyroche
OPEN: Mon to Sun, exc Sat L, Sun D and Mon D
CLOSED: 2 weeks Aug and 1 week at Christmas
MEALS: 12 to 2 (3 Sun), 7 to 11
PRICES: £12 (£19), Set L £7.50 (£12). Cover 50p. Service 10%
SEATS: 30. Private parties: 30 main room. Vegetarian meals. Children welcome. No cigars/
pipes in dining-room. Music

## Topkapi
map 13

25 Marylebone High Street, W1M 3PE
01-486 1872

COOKING 1
COST £17—£20

It's lively, it's fun, and it can be overcrowded, although the waiters are well
able to cope and actually seem to prefer being rushed. Topkapi sticks to what it
knows it does well: beginnings of kofte (with 'a kiss of garlic'), hummus,
taramasalata and meze all receive honourable mentions. Main courses are
kebabs and more kebabs, with moussaka, roast lamb or stuffed vine leaves by
way of light relief. Sweets, as expected, ooze honey. House French is £6.
Turkish wines are £7.50, Efes Turkish beer £1.50.

CHEF: R. Kalayci   PROPRIETOR: U. Fahri
OPEN: all week
MEALS: noon to midnight
PRICES: £10 (£17), Set L and D £12 (£17). Service 10%
CARDS: Access, Amex, Diners, Visa
SEATS: 50. Private parties: 20 main room. Vegetarian meals. Children's helpings.
Wheelchair access (also WC). Music

## Les Trois Plats
map 12

4 Sydney Street, SW3 6PP
01-352 3433

COOKING 2
COST £22—£28

At the top of Sydney Street, this makes a good daytime stopover, although at a
price that would afford true creativity in the provinces. The Roux brothers have
always had the praiseworthy desire to feed the masses. The Brasserie Benoît in
Old Bailey (now Le Gamin) was an early experiment that introduced a better
class of fairly priced eating to the City luncher. Les Trois Plats makes the same
effort. Upstairs is a café set with small tables, slightly rustic in looks, where
booking is not required and there is something to eat all day. The food does not
offend: a decent mushroom soup; a passable salad of lyonnais sausages, new
potatoes, chives and a good oily dressing; a good steak and chips; a turban of
sole on a leek sauce, the fish cooked correctly, the sauce harmonious and
discreet; then a passion-fruit soufflé with sufficient attack to spur the
slumbering soul. The staff are anxious to please, happy to hurry if requested,
and competent. It's exhausting having everything done in French, often by
Englishmen, but perhaps that's part of the play. Downstairs is a restaurant
open at night with a set price for a short *carte*, which includes an aperitif and
half a bottle of house wine (or an allowance towards a choice from the list). The
restaurant is plush, still very French, dealing in modern clichés of simple
French food. The same criticisms may apply here as apply to Gavvers (see

LONDON

entry). However, the greater social utility of the upstairs café may endear this place to more people's hearts. The wine list is short, but includes M. Roux's Provençal white and rosé, vinified for him by Ch. Minuty. The Cuvée Roux from Duboeuf is £7 a bottle.

CHEF: Nick Reade   PROPRIETORS: Roux Restaurants Ltd
OPEN: Mon to Sat, exc Sat L (D only in restaurant)
CLOSED: bank hols
MEALS: Café noon to 11; Restaurant 7 to 11
PRICES: £19 (£22), Set D £27.50 (£27.50). Service inc set only
CARDS: Access, Amex, Diners, Visa
SEATS: Café 34, Restaurant 50. Children welcome

## Tuk Tuk
map 11

330 Upper Street, N1 2XQ
01-226 0837

COOKING 1
COST £17

The less expensive offshoot of the Lakorn Thai, Tuk Tuk is pleasantly informal and generally avoids 'large sharable hot-pots with everything in them'. A meal of pork-stuffed chicken wings followed by pork curry in a clay pot and a slightly sweet chicken and noodle dish partook of strongly Thai flavours: chilli, lemon-grass, coconut and that sweetness that seems omni-present. Spring rolls are not brilliant. House wines from £5.50.

CHEF: Mr Phongphongsavat   PROPRIETOR: Stephen Binns
OPEN: Mon to Sat
CLOSED: 25 and 26 Dec, 1 Jan, bank hols
MEALS: 12 to 3, 6 to 11
PRICES: £9 (£14). Service 10%
CARDS: Access, Amex, Visa
SEATS: 100. 2 tables outside. Private parties: 60 main room. Vegetarian meals. Children welcome. Wheelchair access. Music

## Turner's ♥
map 12

87–89 Walton Street, SW3 2HP
01-584 6711

COOKING 4
COST £21–£46

There are few restaurants in London more pleasant to be in, more pleasant to eat at. The cooking is deceptively skilled: 'I once tried to emulate a dish of steamed goujons of salmon with salad I had here and mine was leaden by comparison.' Turner's has brought the gentle and low-key to a fine art, with the peak of performance by Brian Turner himself: 'at your shoulder as soon as you looked as if advice would be appropriate.' That it carries through to the whole staff is evinced by the comment that no one pours wine for you unless you ask for it: 'I shall attack the next waiter who, when a person is lingering politely over a tiny sip of wine in the glass, empties the bottle in one slurp – to the brim.' (More trouble is caused by wine service than almost any other aspect of restaurant life. For many people, having to continually say 'no, thank you' is irksome and obnoxious. The balance between discretion and parsimony, attentiveness and excessive zeal is dangerously fine.) The cooking itself at this spacious and comfortable place verges on the discreet: there are few fireworks.

Yet the calm assurance scores many hits: fillets of monkfish served with saffroned John Dory on a light cream sauce with asparagus; a compress of smoked chicken with a salad and a fine olive oil; crab sausages 'as light as a cloud'; roulade of guinea-fowl with girolles and, unusually for central London, a fine Sunday lunch of roast beef and Yorkshire pudding. The menu is set price for the first two courses, then extra for cheese and desserts. Lunch is a bargain. Portions are not large, conforming to the light style. One of the criticisms is that tastes are understated. Another is that an English restaurant might do more for English cheese. The wine list is not interested in much outside France either, though not depressingly full of high-priced wonder-bottles that we may think of but not afford. However the base prices are not exactly low. House wines from £10.50. CELLARMAN'S CHOICE : Bourgogne Pinot Noir, Mongeard Mugneret £15; Ch. Lyonnat, 1981, £15.25.

CHEF: Mark Clayton   PROPRIETORS: Brian J. Turner and Martin Davis
OPEN: all week, exc Sat L
CLOSED: Christmas to New Year's Eve
MEALS: 12.30 to 2.45, 7.30 to 11 (10 Sun)
PRICES: £30 (£38), Set L £15.50 (£21) to £17.50 (£23), Set D £19.50 (£25) to £24.50 (£30). Service inc
CARDS: Access, Amex, Diners, Visa
SEATS: 52. Private parties: 14 main room. Children's helpings on request. Wheelchair access (2 steps). Music. Air-conditioned

## Upper Street Fish Shop

map 11

324 Upper Street, N1 2XQ                                    COOKING 1
01-359 1401                                                    COST £13

It is as much the overall package of value, speed and undiluted Englishness as the fish and chips themselves that pulls in the customers here. Nonetheless, the food is worth coming for: very fresh fish, deep fried to order or, for sole and halibut, shallow fried in an egg batter; the chips thick and dry, but not too crisp. 'Our mushy peas are second to none and are requested especially by all our customers from north of the Watford Gap,' writes Olga Conway. Other dishes, for instance salmon with mange-tout, are kept plain and leave space for the home-made English puddings. Take glasses if taking drink (there are several off-licences nearby). Alternatively, stick to tea.

CHEF: Alan Conway   PROPRIETORS: Alan and Olga Conway
OPEN: Mon to Sat, exc Mon L
CLOSED: bank hols
MEALS: 12 to 2 (3 Sat), 5.30 to 10
PRICES: £9 (£11). Minimum £4. Unlicensed, but bring your own: no corkage
SEATS: 50. Children's helpings. Wheelchair access. Air-conditioned

*The 1991* Guide *will be published before Christmas 1990. Reports on meals are most welcome at any time of the year, but are extremely valuable in the spring. Send them to* The Good Food Guide, FREEPOST, *2 Marylebone Road, London NW1 1YN. No stamp is needed if posted in the UK.*

## *Very Simply Nico*

map 11

48A Rochester Row, SW1P 1JU
01-630 8061

COOKING **3**
COST **£26–£34**

When Nico Ladenis moved to Great Portland Street (see Chez Nico), he did not sell his last premises, but converted them to a place of less elaborate cooking at lower prices. He thus gave the lie to the idea that he would not countenance a well-done steak or serve chips. This parody of his dislikes (his first restaurant in Dulwich used to sport the notice, 'We do not serve prawn cocktails or well-done steaks') is, of course, executed by other people. Very Simply Nico is in the 'designer' style of restaurants – immaterial that the 'name' does not actually cook there, enough that the place is stamped with their mark, in this case the name and a few cartoons. However, the concept is a sound one because Tony Tobin cooks well. The set-price menu features modern brasserie food: smoked mackerel pâté; egg, spinach, chives and haddock en cocotte; garlic mushrooms; boudin blanc; calf's liver; confit of duck; salmon steak; steaks simply grilled; cream caramel; trifle; tarts. The cooking is more serious than that bare list implies, and more elaborate: the confit is proper confit; the mackerel pâté is unctuous and spiked with pepper, at its centre a kernel of spinach, served with an aspic; the steaks come with traditional trimmings, and the meat is fine and well-hung; the chips are superlative; the vegetables include petits pois with lettuce and ham and purée potatoes with little pieces of tomato and chives beaten into them with olive oil; trifle has been pronounced fruity, creamy and alcoholic and the only criticism of sponge cake with strawberries and cream was that the sponge was a mite dry as a vehicle. The dining-room itself has not greatly changed from its last incarnation. There are a few more tables and their covers are oil cloth, but former customers would recognise it. Service is efficient but perhaps cool. The wine list is very short and operates the same mark-ups as the Great Portland Street restaurant. Some effort, however, has been expended to find good bottles that cost under £15.

CHEF: Tony Tobin    PROPRIETORS: Nico and Dinah-Jane Ladenis
OPEN: Mon to Sat, exc Sat L
CLOSED: 3 weeks in summer, 10 days at Christmas
MEALS: 12 to 2, 6 to 11
PRICES: Set L and D £19 (£26) to £21 (£28). Service inc
CARDS: Access, Amex, Visa
SEATS: 48. Private parties: 48 main room. Children welcome. No pipes in dining-room. Wheelchair access (1 step). Air-conditioned

## *Wakaba*

map 11

122A Finchley Road, NW3 5LG
01-722 3854

COOKING **2**
COST **£12–£38**

The pure white panels and the clouded curving window, each stretching unbroken from floor to ceiling, relax the spirit after the mess outside. The spirit cleansed, the cooking may be approached in peace, untrammelled by preconception or prejudice. As the room fills, the hard surfaces of floor, wall, table and roof bounce the sound to and fro. It makes conversation with the monoglot, but willing, waiting staff more than difficult. The best item is the sushi; many other dishes are inadequately cooked on too many nights. Costs can be kept in check but, equally, they may run away with you. House Italian wine, £6.20.

CHEF/PROPRIETOR: Minoru Yoshihara
OPEN: Mon to Sat
CLOSED: 1 week Aug, 5 days at Christmas, 4 days at Easter
MEALS: 12 to 2.30, 6.30 to 11
PRICES: £20 (£27), Set L £7.50 (£12) to £9.80 (£14), Set D £17.80 (£24) to £25 (£32).
Service 12.5%
CARDS: Access, Amex, Diners, Visa
SEATS: 55. Private parties: 60 main room. Children welcome. Wheelchair access (also WC).
Air-conditioned

## Waltons ♥                                                           map 12

121 Walton Street, SW3 2HP                                    COOKING 3
01-584 0204                                                   COST £20–£52

There are still advocates of this long-lived restaurant at the west end of Walton Street. The inside has more fabric than Liberty, sometimes impeding the natural disposition of one's legs. It has never been cheap; nor has its style changed very much over the years. The set-price lunches led the fashion for daytime bargains among West End restaurants; the Sunday lunch and the after-theatre suppers remain fair value. It is nonetheless possible to create a considerable bill even when eating from the table d'hôte. The addition of 15 per cent for service does not help. Ravioli of lobster, scallops and crab on a Champagne sauce; poached loin of veal with creamed parsley and morels; salmon with a confit of leeks and a saffron sauce; the hot soufflé of the day and the baked lemon and almond parcel are some of the dishes that indicate the style – well in the current mode of ingredients, with the execution still harking back to those days of ultra-nouvelle cuisine. Mark that vegetables are 'served with each principal dish' – but they are charged at £2.50 per person. The wine list is not as expensive as many local competitors. There is no automatic inflation on bottles that have been in stock over a long period (mark-ups are historic, not invariably tracking auction prices). The selection is almost entirely French and is not so good for anything other than the Bordeaux and burgundy which dominate the list. The clarets, however, do deserve close study at every level and the burgundies offer famous names as well as some growers who are not so frequently encountered. House Côtes de Provence red and Bordeaux white, £8.

CHEF: Tony Cameron    PROPRIETORS: Waltons Restaurants Ltd
OPEN: all week
CLOSED: Easter and Christmas
MEALS: 12.30 to 2.30 (2 Sun), 7.30 to 11.30 (10.30 Sun)
PRICES: £29 (£43), Set L £13 (£20), Set D £19.50 (£27). Service 15%
CARDS: Access, Amex, Carte Blanche, Diners, Visa
SEATS: 65. Private parties: 33 main room, 12 and 24 private rooms. Children welcome.
Smart dress preferred. No pipes in dining-room. Wheelchair access. Air-conditioned

*The* Guide *always appreciates hearing about changes of chef or owner.*

# Wiltons

map 13

55 Jermyn Street, SW1Y 6LX
01-629 9955

COOKING 2
COST £52

Wiltons is a corner of old England, celebrating the formal glories of plain food. There are lobster, sole, plaice and salmon regimented on the menu. Oysters, langoustines and caviare figure too. Nothing hides under a fussy sauce: grilled sea bass with fennel or roast baby guinea-fowl and herbs are more typical choices. This is also a place to eat game. To follow, what else but strawberries, summer pudding or crème brûlée? Some rate this food highly, 'simply perfect, turbot firm but coming away from the bone, hollandaise exquisite ... I had forgotten how good a piece of fish ... simply prepared could be.' Others think it overpriced. That the Savoy Group should have an interest in this as well as a newly acquired share of St Quentin may be thought an example of commercial bet-hedging: no two culinary and cultural forms could be further apart. The wine list starts high and stays there. House wine is from £10. CELLARMAN'S CHOICE : Ch. D'Angludet 1980, £28; Meursault Poruzots 1985, Jean Germain, £45.

CHEF: Ross Hayden   PROPRIETORS: Wiltons Ltd
OPEN: Mon to Sat, exc Sat L
CLOSED: late July to mid-Aug, Christmas Eve to early Jan
MEALS: 12 to 2.30, 6 to 10.30
PRICES: £29 (£43). Cover £1. Minimum £12.50
CARDS: Access, Amex, Diners, Visa
SEATS: 90. Private parties: 12 main room, 16 private room. Children welcome. Smart dress preferred. No cigars in dining-room. Wheelchair access (1 step). Air-conditioned

# Wong Kei

map 14

41−43 Wardour Street, W1V 3HA
01-437 3071 and 6833

COOKING 1
COST £5−£16

Outside, the Wong Kei looks the sort of place non-Chinese might feel timid about entering. Inside it's like a Hong Kong restaurant: abrupt chaos, lots of chatter and bustle. There are five floors − and you might be hustled up and up to the top when it's busy. The food is fast and filling: great piles of noodles or rice topped with meat or fish; steaming soups; barbecued meats. It's cheap and good: 'you can stuff yourself stupid for £5, with no service charge.' The counterbalance is the service: too uncaring even for old hands. House French, £4.50.

CHEF: T.F. Tang   PROPRIETORS: E. Liu and M.H. Lo
OPEN: all week
MEALS: noon to 11.30pm
PRICES: £8 (£13), Set L £2.20 (£5) to £4.50 (£7), Set D £2.20 (£5) to £5 (£8), Snacks from £1.50. Service inc
SEATS: 550. Private parties: 80 main room, 80 private room. Children welcome. Wheelchair access (also WC)

*Report forms are at the back of the book; write a letter if you prefer.*

# *Zamoyski*

map 11

85 Fleet Road, NW3 2QY                    COOKING 1
01-794 4792                               COST £13–£24

A companionable Polish up-and-downstairs wine-bar-cum-restaurant with a lively atmosphere, where sharing one of the polished wood tables is a necessary part of the experience. Seating is on benches with individual cushions or kitchen-style chairs; the walls are hung with colourful rugs, and all sorts of culinary appurtenances are strung from the ceiling. The food is good value and authentic: apple-filled blini topped with beluga caviare; pickled herring with fresh cream, sultanas and apple rings; bigos, a version of choucroute garni. The Polish staff, one of whom sports an elaborately curled black beard, give fine basic service. There is a shorter, cheaper wine bar menu downstairs. House claret is £6.75, plus Polish and Czech beers and several vodkas.

CHEF: Ala Piechocinska    PROPRIETORS: Kathy and Christopher Witkowska
OPEN: Mon to Sat
MEALS: 12 to 2, 5.30 to 11
PRICES: £9 (£13), Set L and D £10 (£14) to £15 (£20). Snacks £1. Service 10% for parties of 6 or more
CARD: Visa
SEATS: 72. Private parties: 38 main room. Vegetarian meals. Children's helpings. No-smoking area. Smart dress preferred. Music

# *Zen*

map 12

Chelsea Cloisters,
Sloane Avenue, SW3 3DN                    COOKING 2
01-589 1781                               COST £24–£54

The least consistent of this chain of design-conscious hybrid restaurants that seek to re-interpret – perhaps atomise – Chinese cooking: to make it acceptable to a public now weaned on nouvelle cuisine. Atomised certainly were the prawns stuffed with mushrooms and ham; they came as three prawns, three Chinese mushrooms and three tough cubes of ham. The stuffing was conceptual, just as the lesson of nouvelle seemed to have been learned only in portion sizes of the sizzling dishes reported by another reader. However, many are taken by the quality of cooking on occasion: 'Eight Treasures tofu was deep-fried bean curd stuffed with vegetables and served in a tasty sauce, excellent'; the sea-spice braised aubergine with a hot sauce was 'beautifully tender, robustly flavoured and too rich' and plentiful for just one person. Desserts, too, have been praised: sweet dumplings with red bean paste, lighter and better sweetened (with honey) than in most places. Not all experiences have been so happy. An inspection meal was a serious wash-out: food not fresh, cooking slap-dash, service poor (this is an aspect that receives mixed reports anyway). Standards go up and down and the bill may reflect location and clientele too much for comfort. Good wines, the house French at £9.

*All letters to the* Guide *are acknowledged with an update on latest sales, closures, chef changes and so on.*

CHEF: Michael Leung   PROPRIETOR: Lawrence Leung
OPEN: all week
CLOSED: 25 to 27 Dec
MEALS: 12 to 3, 6 to 11.30 (noon to midnight Sat and Sun)
PRICES: £11 (£24), Set D £25 (£35) to £35 (£45). Cover £1. Minimum £8. Service 15%
CARDS: Access, Amex, Diners, Visa
SEATS: 120. 35 tables outside. Private parties: 110 main room, 20 private room. Vegetarian
meals. Children's helpings. Smart dress preferred. No cigars/pipes in dining-room. Music.
Air-conditioned

## Zen Central

map 13

20–22 Queen Street, W1X 7PJ

01-629 8089

COOKING 2

COST £38

There are signs of staining on the water cascade in this oh-so-elegant restaurant
that constituted the most emphatic bid yet for the conjunction of Chinese and
Western tastes in the capital. Prices are higher than in Chinatown and no reader
suggests that the food tastes better, but the place is handsome and the service is
extremely amenable. Dishes that receive favourable comment include sole with
ginger and spiced onions, crispy seaweed with pine kernels, dim-sum of
Peking ravioli with hot sauce, zen zen chicken with yellow-bean sauce and
sizzling veal with black pepper sauce. Portions are not large but this may
enable a greater variety to be chosen without waste, though the bill may mount
rapidly. The wine list is suitably intelligent for the sort of cooking that is
pursued. Here is one of the best places to investigate satisfactory partnerships
of spice and bouquet. House wine is £10.

CHEF: Michael Leung   PROPRIETORS: Blaidwood Co.
OPEN: all week
MEALS: 12 to 2.30, 6.30 to 11.30 (11 Sun)
PRICES: £17 (£32). Cover £1. Service 15%
CARDS: Access, Amex, Carte Blanche, Diners, Visa
SEATS: 110. Private parties: 80 main room, 20 private room. Vegetarian meals. Children
welcome. Smart dress preferred. Wheelchair access. Music. Air-conditioned

## Zen W3

map 11

83 Hampstead High Street, NW3 1RE

01-794 7863 and 7864

COOKING 2

COST £12–£28

Reactions to this, the second of the small Zen chain, have always been extreme,
as is perhaps inevitable in any designer restaurant which claims to break the
mould and charges high prices for it. 'Absolutely fantastic. My guests thought
it the most stunningly designed restaurant they'd seen … smoked-glass floor-
to-ceiling frontage with a huge fig leaf tree dominating the window and a
waterfall running down the bannister! Excellent cooking. Typical eastern
efficiency by androgynous male/female waiters in designer suits.' This year,
however, criticism has been more common than praise. 'One might die of
terminal trendiness in this establishment, which looks more like a cocktail bar
than a restaurant. Portions are tiny, the food sometimes tasty but mostly highly
inauthentic Chinese both in faithfulness and feeling. Dishes described as very

hot have no heat at all. Expensive for the amount of food given.' Another customer has pointed specifically to food that at lunchtime seemed to be reheated leftovers. The menu remains broadly the same, with MSG-free Chinese dishes mainly created for western tastes: deep-fried chicken stuffed with banana, king prawns in a thin orange glaze and charcoal grilled, thinly sliced chicken breast served with a chopped garlic and coriander sauce are examples. As the food is a tantalising hybrid that sometimes works well at marrying Chinese technique and new Western ideas on ingredients and components, the wine lists at Zen are better than many Chinese restaurants bother to assemble. The bottles come from good makers, the world range is catholic, and prices are not avaricious. House wine is £5.50.

CHEF: K. S. Leung   PROPRIETOR: Lawrence Leung
OPEN: all week
CLOSED: 25 and 26 Dec
MEALS: 12 to 11.30
PRICES: £14 (£23), Set L £6.80 (£12). Minimum £5. Service 12.5%
CARDS: Access, Amex, Diners, Visa
SEATS: 135. Private parties: 100 main room, 24 private room. Vegetarian meals. Children welcome. Smart dress preferred. Wheelchair access (2 steps). Music. Air-conditioned

# England

## Raffles

1 The Green, Aldbourne
nr Marlborough, SN8 2BW                                          COOKING  1
MARLBOROUGH (0672) 40700                                    COST  £26

Park close to the duck-pond and the restaurant is a short walk away. Now there
are two overflow rooms upstairs, and the minute bar area has been extended to
take in what was the old kitchen. On the tables there are fresh flowers and
warm, crusty bread. The formula remains simple and brief – half a dozen first
courses and main dishes, plus daily specials, on a set-price, three-course menu.
Cooking shows well in the simplest dishes – for example, lightly sauté
scallops in a cream sauce, asparagus with hollandaise, breast of mallard in a
pink peppercorn sauce, veal with home-made pasta and a marsala sauce. The
kitchen achieves what it sets out to do. Vegetables are plainly and well cooked.
Desserts tend to be fruity, as in a hot apple cake with calvados sauce, or creamy,
and often substantial. House French is £5.95.

CHEF: James Hannan   PROPRIETORS: James and Mary Hannan
OPEN: Tue to Fri L, Mon to Sat D
CLOSED: last 2 weeks Aug, 25 to 30 Dec
MEALS: 12.30 to 2.15, 7 to 10.30
PRICES: £16 (£22)
CARDS: Access, Amex, Diners, Visa
SEATS: 36. 3 tables outside. Private parties: 36 main room. Children's helpings (L only).
Smart dress preferred. Wheelchair access. Music

## Aldeburgh Festival Wine Bar

152 High Street, Aldeburgh IP15 5AQ                         COOKING  1
ALDEBURGH (0728) 453734                                       COST  £13–£20

The wine bar is reached through the arch by the Festival Office. It is housed in
the former Suffolk Hotel, once a small Victorian commercial hotel. It is not easy
to recommend this place, on account of its limited opening hours outside high
season, but visitors to the Festival and town alike should be alerted to Peter
Jansens' honest cooking of sustaining food, well suited to a wine bar. Thick-
cut cold roast beef, nicely pink, with a rémoulade; a dish of fresh pasta with a

generous seafood sauce, and treacle and nut tart are some of the items reported. The wine list is short, but not without interest, and not expensive. House wines, £4.95. Expect queues at Festival time; at least they're cheerful.

CHEF: Peter Jansens   PROPRIETORS: Peter Jansens and Sandy Dahmen
OPEN: all week L and D during Festival; plus all bank hols Mon L. Outside Festival, Tue to Sun L, exc Sat; and Sat D
MEALS: 11am to 7pm (Festival), 12 to 2.30, 7 to 9.30
PRICES: £9 (£13), Set D £9 (£13) to £12.50 (£17)
SEATS: 32. 10 tables outside. Private parties: 32 main room. Vegetarian meals. Children's helpings. Wheelchair access

## ▲ Austins

243 High Street, Aldeburgh IP15 5DN                          COOKING 1
SAXMUNDHAM (0728) 453932                                      COST £23

A blue awning proclaims the name of this pink-washed hotel and restaurant at the lighthouse end of the High Street. Inside is plush and elegant in shades of bluish grey and bitter lemon. Theatrical names are dropped in the bar, which is adorned with assorted memorabilia and photos of the stars. The menu is less glittery and supplements the likes of lamb Wellington, fillet steak and grilled local Dover sole with New Orleans crayfish gumbo and, from time to time, specials such as steamed sea bass on a bed of samphire. Meals are brought to a close with home-made parfaits and ice-creams or concoctions of fresh fruits. The quality of ingredients at an inspection in the summer could have been better and the sauces more intense. The will is there for improvement. A short, modestly priced wine list with house French at £5.05 and CELLARMAN'S CHOICE: Sancerre, Domaine de Villots 1987, Reverdy, £11; Ch. Roquebrune, 1ères Côtes de Bordeaux 1985, £8.

CHEF: Julian Alexander-Worster   PROPRIETORS: Robert Selbie and Julian Alexander-Worster
OPEN: Tue to Sun, exc Sun D
CLOSED: first 2 weeks Feb
MEALS: 12.30 to 2, 7.30 to 10.30
PRICES: £13 (£19). Cover £1
CARDS: Access, Amex, Visa
SEATS: 30. Private parties: 30 main room. Children's helpings on request. No children under 12. No cigars/pipes in dining-room. Music
ACCOMMODATION: 7 rooms, all with bath/shower. B&B £32.50 to £55. Deposit: 10%. No children under 12. TV. Phone. Scenic. Doors close at 1am. Confirm by noon

## Regatta ♥

171–173 High Street, Aldeburgh IP15 5AN                      COOKING 1
ALDEBURGH (0728) 452011                                       COST £23

A cheerful wine bar-cum-restaurant with the good sense to stay open late during the Festival. A whopping nautical mural sets the mood, thronging the wall with mermaids and seagulls, sailing boats and coiled ropes; all of which seems slightly out of keeping with the original cornice above. But no matter; the atmosphere's the thing and it's bustling, friendly and lively. The food is plain and good value, featuring local asparagus, samphire and seafood among more mundane bistro fare. Recommended have been home-made soups, beef in red wine, chicken parmigiano and, above all, fish from the Aldeburgh fleet: grilled, en brochette, in crumbles or pastry seashell. The wine list is almost too good for the setting. Certainly the two main suppliers have done very well and the range is reasonably priced and enticing. Wines by the glass are listed on a blackboard in the wine bar and house Cuvée d'Adrien (described as 'French plonk') is £5.75. CELLARMAN'S CHOICE: Tyrrell's Long Flat Red 1984, £7.50; Allanmere Semillon 1986, £12.75. There is beer from Nethergate Brewery of Clare as well as Beamish's Irish Stout.

CHEF: Sara E. Fox   PROPRIETOR: Peter G.R. Hill and Sara E. Fox
OPEN: all week
MEALS: 12 to 2.30 (12.30 to 2 Sun), 7 to 10.15
PRICES: £14 (£19), Snacks from £1.50
CARDS: Access, Visa
SEATS: 90. 4 tables outside. Private parties: 90 main room. Children's helpings. Wheelchair access (2 steps)

---

**ALFRISTON  East Sussex**                                               map 3

## *Moonrakers* ♥

| High Street, Alfriston BN26 5TD | COOKING 1 |
| ALFRISTON (0323) 870472 | COST £28 |

Slap bang in the middle of a tourist-haunted village, this sixteenth- century cottage comes suitably equipped with its very own smuggling legend. The menu is styled 'small, but exquisite' by one reporter, who clearly remembers Peter Cook's description of Dudley Moore. It changes every four to five weeks, yet somehow remains very much the same. Dishes such as hot Sussex smokie; beef Wellington and roast duck with apples, clementines or kumquats make regular reappearances by popular demand, although the Wilkinsons do add new dishes when the mood takes them. Sole with almonds and pork with Stilton sauce have been applauded, and the home-made frangipane flan comes in copious portions. A very aristocratic wine list, unexpectedly good at reasonable prices. The German selection is better than most. House French from Corney & Barrow is £6.50. CELLARMAN'S CHOICE: Crozes Hermitage, Domaine de Thalabert 1984, £10.80; Tolley Barossa Valley Chardonnay 1986, £11.60.

CHEF: Elaine Wilkinson   PROPRIETORS: Elaine and Barry Wilkinson
OPEN: Tue to Sat, D only
MEALS: 7 to 9.15 (6.45 to 9.45 Sat)
PRICES: Set D £17.40 (£23)
SEATS: 32. 2 tables outside. Private parties: 32 main room. Children's helpings

---

*The 1991 Guide will be published before Christmas 1990. Reports on meals are most welcome at any time of the year, but are extremely valuable in the spring. Send them to* **The Good Food Guide,** FREEPOST, *2 Marylebone Road, London NW1 1YN. No stamp is needed if posted in the UK.*

ALNWICK  Northumberland                                                    map 7

## John Blackmore's

1 Dorothy Foster Court, Narrowgate
Alnwick NE66 1NL
ALNWICK (0665) 604465

COOKING 3
COST £20

Linden Hall might have felt some regret at John Blackmore's striking out on his own in a tiny restaurant in the shadow of the castle, but locals are bound to cheer any reinforcement of good cooking in the region. In the winter, the coal range is lit to warm the stone-flagged floors of an eighteenth-century house – once residence of Dorothy Foster, an ardent Jacobite – which just leaves space for eating. Lunches at Blackmore's are simple, good and cheap. Dinner, on four nights a week only, is more elaborate. A short menu is supplemented by a few daily specials. Reports have come of straight cooking, with a fair number of cream sauces, that but faintly reflects the more advanced styles of further south. This does not detract from the accuracy or taste of the execution. Recommendations have come of a lobster, salmon and prawn soup finished with cream and dill; chicken livers with bacon and grapes; baked eggs with Stilton and celery; fillet with cream and tarragon; salmon with a white wine cream sauce; chicken in a prawn sauce; noisettes of lamb with brandy and cream sauce; chocolate roulade and a compote of strawberries and raspberries. Vegetables are well handled; some have found the presentation mannered; desserts are more elementary, but tasting as pleasant as the first two courses. Service is extremely friendly. The wine list is barely three dozen strong, but the choice is very catholic and the prices are kept low. House wine is £4.75.

CELLARMAN'S CHOICE : Chilean Cousiño Macul, Antiguas Reservas 1981, £9.

CHEF: John Blackmore   PROPRIETORS: John and Penny Blackmore
OPEN: Tue to Sat, exc Tue D
CLOSED: Jan
MEALS: 11.30 to 3, 7 to 9.30
PRICES: £13 (£17), Snacks from 90p. Service inc
CARDS: Access, Amex, Diners, Visa
SEATS: 25. Private parties: 30 main room. Vegetarian meals. Children's helpings. Smart dress preferred at (D). No pipes in dining-room. Wheelchair access (1 step). Music

AMBLESIDE  Cumbria                                                          map 7

## ▲ Kirkstone Foot
## Country House Hotel

Kirkstone Pass Road, Ambleside LA22 9EH
AMBLESIDE (0966) 32232

COOKING 1
COST £23

This hotel in gardens occupied by self-catering units offers peace at the edge of Ambleside – a church tower visible one way, Wansfell the other and streams running through green lawns. The Batemans are a catering dynasty: one daughter and her husband have joined them in running the hotel. Their five-course dinner, hitherto with no choice, has been expanded with the accession of a further chef to the team. The repertoire is unchanging – having pleased generations of local clients and visitors by its value. People who know and love the Batemans tend to return. The cooking is English in style and recipe, with roasts having importance (now regularly matched by a fish dish and a vegetarian option); the trolley of sweets is trundled around the dining-rooms to laudatory murmurs and contains the best offerings of the evening. Breakfasts have received poor notices: no fresh juices or home-baked goods. A short but adequate wine list offers fair value. House French, £5.50.

CHEFS: Jane Bateman and Victor Sharratt  PROPRIETORS: Jane and Simon Bateman
OPEN: all week, D only
CLOSED: Jan to early Feb
MEALS: 8
PRICES: Set D £14.75 (£19)
CARDS: Access, Visa
SEATS: 50. Private parties: 10 main room. Car-park, 30 places. Vegetarian meals. Children's helpings on request. No children under 7. Smart dress preferred. No smoking. Wheelchair access (also WC). Music. One sitting
ACCOMMODATION: 16 rooms, all with bath/shower. DB&B £38 to £76. Deposit: £20. Baby facilities. Pets welcome. Afternoon teas. Garden. Fishing. TV. Phone. Scenic [GHG]

## ▲ Rothay Manor ▼

| Rothay Bridge, Ambleside LA22 0EH | COOKING 2 |
| AMBLESIDE (053 94) 33605 | COST £11–£31 |

Over the years this manor house within the town of Ambleside has preserved a reputation for friendliness and accessible prices. Slight hiccups in standards are barely remembered this year and the chorus of approval has been strong. Self-service at an extensive buffet at weekday lunches and glorious teas promote the pleasure of all participants and there is much effort on the part of the Nixon brothers to create a sense of community among their guests by means of their winter programmes of music, interior design or simple gourmet 'grandes bouffes'. There has long been an emphasis on (old) English cooking, reinforcing the Victorian architecture, furnishing, staff uniforms and image of the hotel. Dishes that illustrate it are indicated on the menu, but recommendations have in fact centred on things of French inspiration: a fine salmon mousse; a well-balanced pork and prune terrine; succulent chicken basquaise, juicy from the tomatoes and peppers, aromatic from the orange; tender and flavourful mallard with red wine sauce. Vegetables and desserts remain more British. A reader had a most successful Burgundy dinner in the winter, wines included, that took in jambon persillé, trout montbardoise and boeuf bourguignonne before offering French cheeses in perfect condition. The cooking may be described as substantial rather than super-sophisticated. The good sense continues in the wine list, even if its lay-out reminds one of tyro days before a word processor. Halves of many whole bottles may be taken at three-fifths the full price and the range is catholic with very fair prices. It is for these more even than the range that it deserves notice. Study the clarets for particular value and the French country wines. Not only are the Nixons welcoming to children but they have made great changes to rooms to improve wheelchair access. Smoking is not allowed in the dining-room and one sitting-room has also been declared smoke free. House Bulgarian Chardonnay and Cabernet Sauvignon £7.50 a litre.

CHEF: Jane Binns  PROPRIETOR: Nigel Nixon and Stephen Nixon
OPEN: all week
CLOSED: last 3 weeks Jan, first week Feb
MEALS: 12.30 to 2 (12.45 to 1.30 Sun), 8 to 9
PRICES: Set L £6 (£11) to £11 (£16), Set D £15 (£21) to £20 (£26)
CARDS: Access, Amex, Diners, Visa
SEATS: 70. Private parties: 12 main room, 30 private room. Car-park, 30 places. Vegetarian meals. Children's helpings. Smart dress preferred. No smoking. Wheelchair access (also WC). Air-conditioned
ACCOMMODATION: 18 rooms, all with bath/shower. Rooms for disabled. B&B £56 to £78. Deposit: £50. Children welcome. Baby facilities. No pets. Afternoon teas. Garden. TV. Phone. Scenic. Doors close at 12. Confirm by noon [GHG]

## Sheila's Cottage

| The Slack, Ambleside LA22 9DQ | COOKING 2 |
|---|---|
| AMBLESIDE (053 94) 33079 | COST £18 |

Janice and Stewart Greaves celebrate 25 years in the old town of Ambleside with a new barn dining-room that will add 12 seats to their crowded cottage café (at the time of writing, scheduled to open in early September 1989). Standards remain as high as ever and there has been little change in the two dozen or so dishes on the lunchtime and afternoon menus. Cumbrian sugar-baked ham served with damson chutney, mustard and home-made bread, warm or potted Solway shrimps and marinated herring fillets are local items; the other clear strand is Swiss, running from cheesy ramekins and gratins through to large cups of drinking chocolate topped with whipped cream. The dozen or so desserts ranging from apricot strudel to lemon ice-cream are a star turn. Some are still served at teatime alongside muffins and teabreads, although there is now also a set afternoon tea which can be pre-booked. House wines, £5.75 a litre. There is a short, refreshingly New World wine list with CELLARMAN'S CHOICE : Delegats Hawkes Bay Sauvignon Blanc 1987 at £10.

CHEFS: Janice Greaves, Jane Sutherland and Keith Anderson
PROPRIETOR: Stewart Greaves
OPEN: Mon to Sat
CLOSED: Jan
MEALS: 12 to 5.30 (L to 2.30)
PRICES: £10 (£15)
SEATS: 38. Private parties: 38 main room. Children's helpings (L only). No smoking. Wheelchair access. Music

## ▲ Wateredge Hotel

| Borrans Road, Ambleside LA22 0EP | COOKING 1 |
|---|---|
| AMBLESIDE (0966) 32332 | COST £11−£28 |

The unruffled waters of Windermere stretch beneath the window of this comfortable hotel restaurant, once fishermen's cottages. The atmosphere, set by the light touch of paint and print, is co-operative and outgoing. A six-course menu, Lakeland style, with two alternatives to begin and a choice of meat or fish, is the evening centrepiece, although shorter lunches are offered every day. For residents, this arrangement is most satisfactory, for the food is competently cooked; chance visitors may suffer from the lack of options. Plain but careful cooking has produced good pastry, soups and roast meats; the occasional elaboration may step too close to needless fancy. Puddings and cheeses are more than adequate: profiteroles with a good butterscotch; high flavour in the raspberry and white wine syllabub. House wine is £7.50.

CHEFS: Michael Cosgrove and Mark Cowap  PROPRIETORS: Mr and Mrs Derek Cowap
OPEN: all week
CLOSED: mid-Dec to Feb
MEALS: 12 to 2, 7 to 8.30
PRICES: Set L £6 (£11) to £12 (£16), Set D £17.50 (£23)
CARDS: Access, Amex, Visa
SEATS: 45. Car-park, 25 places. Children's helpings (D only). No children under 7. Smart dress preferred. Music
ACCOMMODATION: 23 rooms, all with bath/shower. B&B £42.50 to £82. Deposit: £5 No children under 7. Pets welcome. Afternoon teas. Garden. Fishing. TV. Phone. Scenic. Doors close at midnight. Confirm by 5 [GHG]

---

**ASHBOURNE** Derbyshire                                     map 5

# ▲ Callow Hall

| Mappleton Road, Ashbourne DE6 2AA | COOKING 1 |
|---|---|
| ASHBOURNE (0335) 43403 | COST £13–£37 |

A handsome stone Victorian house overlooking the Dove valley, built for a corset manufacturer but now converted to a small hotel. The situation, and the warm hospitality, are attractive. The cooking in the large restaurant, furnished more lightly than the style of architecture or the avocation of the original owner might imply, is announced by a menu (unnecessarily in French) that does not stray far from the expected. Nonetheless, people have approved the asparagus with lime butter sauce; mussels marinière; veal with wild mushrooms; beef en croûte; orange mousse and Callow tart of apples, raisins and marzipan. Sunday lunch is British and traditional. Some people find the Hall too pretentious, the service too callow and the execution stilted. However, there are aspects that present very good value and the intentions are fair. 'Breakfast was fresh fruit, cereals, cooked, croissant and toast. Plenty of it, and good hot coffee too.' The wine list has some nice French bottles, not excessively priced. House French, £5.10. CELLARMAN'S CHOICE : Ch. Fontblanche, 1ères Côtes de Blaye 1982, £11.75; Sancerre, Clos du Roy 1987, Millérioux, £11.30.

CHEF: David Spencer  PROPRIETORS: David and Dorothy Spencer
OPEN: Tue to Sat D, Sun L (other days by arrangement)
MEALS: 12.30 to 2.30, 7.30 to 9.30
PRICES: £20 (£26), Set Sun L £9 (£13) to £11 (£15), Set D £18 (£23) to £26 (£31)
CARDS: Access, Amex, Diners, Visa
SEATS: 80. Private parties: 50 main room, 50 private room. Car-park, 70 places. Children's helpings (Sun L only). Wheelchair access (also WC).
ACCOMMODATION: 11 rooms, 9 with bath/shower. B&B £50 to £75. Deposit: 10%. Baby facilities. Garden. Fishing. TV. Phone. Scenic. Doors close at 11.30. Confirm 1 day before [GHG]

## ASHBY-DE-LA-ZOUCH  Leicestershire map 5

# *Mews Wine Bar*

8 Mill Lane Mews
Ashby-de-la-Zouch LE6 5HP COOKING 2
ASHBY-DE-LA-ZOUCH (0530) 416683 COST £13–£28

This kitchen has regained the esteem of readers. The bar is a pair of rooms in an eighteenth-century house, once a smithy – the lavatories are where stables were. There are daily lunch and supper menus, each quite long, the supper one having a core of fixtures and an evolving periphery. Janet Rishman is a self-taught, fairly traditional cook, yet with a streak of invention. She does not flinch at cream. Recent fashions have left their mark, particularly with sweet-and-sour accompaniments or oriental flavours, as in lamb noisettes on a bed of onion marmalade or stir-fried beef and vegetables. Puddings – spotted Dick is much loved – are definitely British, though even at this stage an exotic fruit terrine has been espied. The wine list is longer and more informative than it used to be, though some details of makers and years may be lacking. Prices are fair and there is a nod towards the New World. It is not as fashionable a list as, say, a good metropolitan brasserie. House claret and Muscadet are £7.85.
CELLARMAN'S CHOICE : Brouilly Pissevieille 1986, £11.85; Penedès, Gran Toc Gran Reserva 1982, £13.50.

CHEF: Janet Rishman    PROPRIETORS: Ian G. Bridge and Janet Rishman
OPEN: Mon to Sat
MEALS: 11.45 to 2, 6.30 to 10 (10.30 Sat)
PRICES: L £8 (£13), D £16 (£23)
CARDS: Access, Visa
SEATS: 56. Private parties: 36 main room, 36 private room. Children's helpings. Wheelchair access. Music

## ASTON CLINTON  Buckinghamshire map 3

# ▲ *Bell* 🍾

Aston Clinton HP22 5HP COOKING 3
AYLESBURY (0296) 630252 COST £20–£50

Here, in a seemly but not grandiose red brick inn with brewery yard across the way, is enshrined a generation's experience of country cooking. The apotheosis across the main road is the Pavilion, a cross between Bexhill and Versailles, where major functions are held. A link with the gourmets of happier times – such as Barry Neame, John Fothergill and Norman Douglas – is found on reading the florid titles of the *carte*. 'La Salade Aphrodite sur son Océan de Perles Noires à la Ville de Reims' sounds much like a pre-war banquet, perhaps organised by André Simon. In the event, it translates as a salad of aphrodisiacs (oysters, etc, etc) on a caviare sauce with a glass of Champagne. Quite a lot of the menu reads like that. Kevin Cape has been chef at the Bell for no more than three years. His arrival galvanised the kitchens from mild lethargy, making those who dismissed it take notice once more. His menus are in tune with modern fashions. Lobster is smoked in the chimney as *chez* Michel Guérard;

pasta dishes and light vegetable mousses crop up here and there; offal is combined with potato and truffle as in the best European establishments. The main *carte* is also one of the most luxurious to be found anywhere. In the summer of 1989, not many of the dishes on offer lacked its special (imported) ingredient: frogs' legs, caviare, wild mushrooms (passim), foie gras and truffles. Nor were many of these allowed to stand alone: foie gras is combined with scallops, salmon and lobster and with sweetbreads. This, however, may be balanced by plainer dishes on the daily, and by no means as expensive, table d'hôte. The power of attraction this inn exerts is expressed in this report: 'I have been making the 210 mile round trip to the Bell on and off for 17 years. We have eaten some very good meals and some moderately good ones. We have had good service and at times sullen, or untrained, or uncomprehending. The fantastic list of fine clarets and the elegance of the dining-room have always been strong attractions. Our latest visit, the first since the new chef took over, delighted us by the transformation of the food and service. We began with délice of wild salmon in pink Champagne sauce, beautifully light and fully flavoured. Hot brown rolls were served with the first course. They never used to be. The excellent sirloin of Scotch beef from the trolley came with large individual Yorkshire puddings and good gravy. Crisp vegetables were on a side plate. From the trolley I had a light chocolate mousse and my companion an apple flan – too much cream and not enough tart apple for her. With coffee, petits fours; when we finished the first plate, another was brought to us.' Sunday lunch is traditional and excellent value. Perhaps because of the prices, there are more reports of the fixed price meals than the elaborate *carte*. Recommendations include kidneys in a bouchée with a red wine sauce; asparagus with hollandaise (though one reader remarked its absence in full asparagus season); monkfish and salmon with langoustines; ballotine of boned quail stuffed with wild mushrooms; a trio of lamb including its liver; a grapefruit soufflé with a blackcurrant sorbet. For what may often be a traditionalist clientele, the reaction to vegetable cookery may be of interest: 'superbly undercooked, a lot of taste to them', said one; 'perfectly cooked' said another; 'a touch too crisp,' for a third; but 'bullet-hard brussels' was the final sting. Generally the verdict is affirmative and the most conflicting messages surround the service. There have been moments when it has not been up to the mark. The slow pacing of the meals may be deliberate, but the longueurs extend too much for a reader who began his simple meal at 8.40 and did not get to the coffee until 11.30. The wine list's length and range confound criticism, nor are its prices extortionate. Provision of a non-alcoholic cocktail, and an extending list of low-alcohol wines, meets extravagant gratitude from the larger and larger numbers who do not hold with liquor of any sort, or who fear the consequences of inebriation when driving. The house wine is £7.95. CELLARMAN'S CHOICE : Chablis *premier cru* Montmains 1987, Rottier-Clotilde, £15.75; Menetou Salon 1987, Pelle, £11.40; Ch. de la Rivière, 1982, £14.50. The staff are good with children.

*All details are as accurate as possible at the time of going to press, but chefs and owners often change, and it is wise to check by telephone before making a special journey. Many readers have been disappointed when set-price bargain meals are no longer available. Ask when booking.*

CHEF: Kevin Cape  PROPRIETORS: The Harris family
OPEN: all week
MEALS: 12.30 to 2, 7.30 to 10
PRICES: £36 (£42), Set L £15.50 (£20) to £19.50 (£24), Set D £16.50 (£21) to £19.50 (£24).
Service inc
CARDS: Access, Visa
SEATS: 100. Private parties: 20 and 200 private rooms. Car-park, 250 places. Children
welcome. Wheelchair access (also WC)
ACCOMMODATION: 21 rooms, all with bath/shower. Rooms for disabled. B&B £76 to £90.
Baby facilities. Pets welcome. Afternoon teas. Garden. TV. Phone [GHG]

---

**AVENING Gloucestershire**                                                    map 2

## Gibbons

Avening GL8 8NF                                                      COOKING 2
NAILSWORTH (045 383) 3070                                           COST £23–£34

The flagstones and walls of this Cotswold house converted to a restaurant
shelter a lover of France and French cooking. Philip Gibbons cooks a short
menu of four or six choices at each stage. It is not as aggressively French as
might appear – even as the strains of *chansonniers* come over the occasional
Muzak. It is, however, good, and does not fall into the English habit of
sweetness or strange combinations. Sea trout with a fromage blanc and sorrel
sauce; duck with caramelised shallots; fine vegetables and good gratin
dauphinoise; hazelnut and coffee ice-cream; St-Emilion au chocolat
(chocoholic's version) and orange cream caramel are dishes that have been
noticed. 'Philip is outward-going with that touch of irascibility that one often
finds in top chefs,' commented one reporter, while others have found the one-
man-band can falter when pressed too hard by a number of customers at once.
The wine list has shrunk a little of late; it remains exclusively French. House
wine is £5.50.

CHEF: Philip Gibbons  PROPRIETORS: Philip and Wendy Gibbons
OPEN: Mon to Sat, D only (L by arrangement)
MEALS: 7.30 to 9.30
PRICES: Set D £18 (£23) to £23 (£28)
CARDS: Access, Amex, Diners, Visa
SEATS: 26. Private parties: 34 main room. Car-park, 11 places. Children welcome

---

**AYLESBURY Buckinghamshire**                                                  map 2

## ▲ Hartwell House

(COUNTY OF THE YEAR RESTAURANT)

Oxford Road, Aylesbury HP17 8NL
AYLESBURY (0296) 747444
on A418, 3m SW of Aylesbury                                         COOKING 3
                                                                    COST £17–£44

Historic House Hotels have drawn another ace from the pack of declining
country houses, or plum from the pudding if you will. Hartwell House is
wondrous. Only three miles from Aylesbury, set in a soft Home Counties
landscape, surrounded by obelisks, temples and ruined Gothick church, it

might be the Elysium it was intended. For two years, work has been unabated. Billeted by troops in the war, occupied by young women at school in the 1960s and 1970s, it has been fully converted to hotel use. The new construction and reproduction that has been necessary – the 'Soane' dining-room is Soane in but name – is remarkable. An architectural historian may be (nearly) muddled, but a guest can only admire the investment and single-mindedness. Whether the charms of the house will be overtaken by bevies of executive meetings and high-rolling travellers is yet to be seen, but the staff (as at Bodysgallen, see Llandudno in Wales) are extremely welcoming and open to all, including visitors for tea from Aylesbury, anxious to catch a glimpse for the first time of what lay behind unscaleable walls. Aidan McCormack was once chef at Middlethorpe Hall (see York), also run by this company. A brief period of independence at 19 Grape Lane (see entry, also York) intervened before he began the kitchen here. The restaurant offers a long *carte* and shortened set-price menus for every meal. The cooking is a satisfactory rendering of the country-house style, technically accomplished and offending no-one. In more humble surroundings it would be acclaimed; in these, it is taken for granted. It is not easy to impress a definite personality on an enterprise that must please so many palates. However, the cooking does not suffer from excesses (fruit, sweetness, spice or ludicrous ornament) nor, at an early meal as we were going to press, is it badly executed. In just one dish, a fillet of sea bass topped with a chicken, salmon and goose liver pâté, did the eater wonder 'Why bother?' Otherwise, a tart filled with accurately creamy scrambled eggs and wild mushrooms; a cream of vegetable soup; a mixture of shellfish on braised Florence fennel with a well-tarragoned sauce, and a Gressingham duck with a none-too-sweetened caramelised wine sauce given edge by turnips were satisfactory, vitiated only by a praline mousse of unctuous sickliness that was not cut by the oversweet currant sorbet. The wine list is nascent and growing. Prices have started high, though at least attention is not confined solely to France. House wine is £9.90, otherwise the base price is £14.95 and rising (fast). This makes a reasonable set-price lunch of £15 become rather punishingly expensive. Drink water.

CHEF: Aidan McCormack    PROPRIETORS: Historic House Hotels Ltd
OPEN: all week
CLOSED: 24 to 26 Dec (exc to residents)
MEALS: 12.30 to 2, 7.30 to 9.45
PRICES: £29 (£37), Set L £12 (£17) to £18 (£23), Set D £25 (£33). Service inc
CARDS: Access, Amex, Carte Blanche, Diners, Visa
SEATS: 75. Private parties: 20 main room, 16 and 30 private rooms. Car-park, 100 places. Vegetarian meals. No children under 8. Smart dress preferred. No cigars/pipes in dining-room. Wheelchair access (also WC)
ACCOMMODATION: 32 rooms, all with bath/shower. Rooms for disabled. Lift. B&B £89.50 to £124.80. No children under 11. Afternoon teas. Garden. Fishing. TV. Phone. Scenic

*If you see a certificate in a restaurant bearing the words 'Good Food Guide Top Restaurants', the claim is false (and the restaurant may be in contempt of court in displaying it) – see the Introduction. Please write and tell us the name and address of the restaurant.*

## Pebbles ▮

Pebble Lane, Aylesbury HP20 2JH
AYLESBURY (0296) 86622

COOKING 3
COST £21–£58

Aylesbury is a county market town torn apart by motor vehicles. The plan may have been to return the centre to the pedestrian, the effect created is of an islet in an ocean of inner ring road and roundabout. Head for the church: owls still live there. A narrow lane connects the churchyard to the shopping street; Pebbles, once a pub, then a restaurant, is a small, seventeenth-century cottage on it. Inside are low ceilings, beams, small rooms and several levels, improved by redecoration. Jeremy Blake O'Connor, chef/proprietor since 1988, has the hopes of England riding on his broad shoulders. Praise has been loud, almost strident, for cooking that is 'worthy of comparison with the best in France.' The jury will remain out for some time, but there is no denying the intentions: proper service, good wine list, complex menu, a preoccupation with supplies (an ex-chef provides the baby vegetables, shoots in Scotland and Yorkshire the game, farmers follow his feeding instructions for rearing chickens), and no false modesty. Within so small a compass, the kitchen offers much. There is a lunch menu (two prices depending on the number of courses); a vegetarian three-course table d'hôte (sounding delicious, although there have been quiet nights when the option disappears); a full single-price *carte* of half a dozen choices at each stage, bolstered by daily market dishes which usually carry a supplement; and an eight-course gourmet surprise menu that must be taken by the whole table. The style is modern European with strong classical overtones – Mr O'Connor retreated to France for mid-career retraining at the beginning of the 1980s and it has left its mark. Dishes of all description seem to capture the rapture: smoked salmon in a basket of radicchio with a cream dressing and three different sorts of caviare; salad of wood-pigeon in a sherry sauce; jambonnette of wild rabbit, boned and stuffed with a herb mousse, wrapped in Bayonne ham and served with the fried saddle of the rabbit with a Sauternes sauce and wild mushrooms; smoked salmon and crab terrine; roundels of Scotch salmon wrapped in leek, or again, with a cumin sauce; a saffron velouté of halibut, turbot, monk and mussels; and sea-bass with morels and asparagus are but a few. There is little doubt that he has gained sufficient technical ability to deliver sophisticated and well-cooked food; accounts of error have not been frequent. However, debate still turns on the digestibility of the food. Is it too elaborate and too rich? Although the gourmet meal is described as light, Mr O'Connor's generosity has left several readers feeling more than post-Lucullan. A dish of roast pigeon consisted of the boned birds laid on a bed of lentils cooked with an equal quantity of bacon. Two birds, the lentils and a good deep red wine and cognac flavoured game sauce were 'garnished' with a too-rich medallion of foie gras. A confit of shallots, some cherry tomatoes and a few morels finished it off. Potatoes there were none, but a green salad was supplied. A dessert of passion-fruit mousse in a mango sauce came on a giant plate under a spun-sugar cage. It was garnished with fans of fruit – 'the greengrocer named it, we had it' – arranged on the perimeter, the garnish outweighing the mousse by two to one. As it was winter, the garnish tasted of nothing. A worrying factor to be observed in the output of English chefs is the similarity of dishes from one place to the next. An idea is born and it is copied very quickly, albeit with variations. Tagliatelle of oysters and scallops served on a Champagne butter sauce, garnished with caviare and chervil; timbale of calf's sweetbreads set in a mousseline of chicken with diced truffles with a cèpe and madeira sauce; fillet of veal topped with a herb purée and a spaghetti of vegetables on rösti potatoes with a green peppercorn sauce: these are three items from Pebbles menus in 1989. A game is to match these to their originals round London. The wine list shows much promise and enthusiasm. It has balance, with fair attention to Italy, Spain, the New World and French country wines; it has some good bottles (Chignin Bergeron 1986, Quenard, Château-Chalon Vin Jaune 1979, Ch. Dauzac, Margaux 1981) and it has halves. Prices are canny. There are two red and two white house wines at £9.50 and £12.50. CELLARMAN'S CHOICE : Ch. Pavie-Decesse, 1983, £23; Montagny *premier cru* Les Coères 1986, Jean Vachet, £17.

CHEF/PROPRIETOR: Jeremy Blake O'Connor
OPEN: all week, exc Sun D and Mon L
MEALS: 12 to 2.15, 7.15 to 10.30
PRICES: Set L £11.50 (£21) and £14 (£25), Set D £25 (£35) and £36 (£48)
CARDS: Access, Amex, Diners, Visa
SEATS: 32. Private parties: 22 main room. Children's helpings. Smart dress preferred. No cigars/pipes in dining-room. Wheelchair access. Music

---

**BABBACOMBE Devon**                                                    map 1

## *Table*

135 Babbacombe Road
Babbacombe, TQ1 3SR                                             COOKING **3**
TORQUAY (0803) 34292                                          COST £24−£37

The young owners are putting heart and soul into their new enterprise, to the delight of locals who have sought them out in this rather dreary street. 'The best meal we have eaten since arriving in this part of the world,' says one reporter. Decoration has been kept simple, with pale yellow walls and flowered curtains, but all the signs of serious cooking are here: sounds of hand-whisking come from the kitchen and shelves are loaded with jars of the chef's own elderflower and balsamic vinegars, orange jelly, lobster-flavoured oil. Trevor Brooks worked at Inverlochy Castle, Michael's Nook and Hambleton Hall. At Table his menu is very modern, with occasional leanings to the classic, using lots of pulses and offal and drawing extensively on his home-made preserves. Aromatic ingredients abound: morels, Gewürztraminer, mango, curry spices, madeira, truffles and marinated strawberries have all appeared in one evening's set menu. A meal sent one reader happy to her home: 'sauté of monkfish with prawns ... outstanding sauce, stock-based but no straightforward fish stock − this was stronger, more fragrant and had a sweetness combined with a slightly acid touch. Roasted quail with haricots and madeira sauce; pinkish, succulent meat, fragrant stuffing of chicken forcemeat with lemon, thyme and garlic, superb sauce, a mound of pale green haricots simmered in white wine, a potato cake scented with Parmesan and freshly grated nutmeg. Caramelised pear tart, containing halved, poached pears beautifully cooked, soft and sweet. On top, a fan of unpoached pears, white, fresh and sharp. And with coffee, a sugary, sticky brandy snap that included chopped marmalade rind.' The haute cuisine background of the cooking has two consequences: first is the complexity of flavours which, when successful, is rewarding; second is an over-elaboration (for instance an unnecessary half-time sorbet) that only serves to muddy tastes, particularly when it is not backed up by a brigade of scurrying assistants. This may also lead to slowness in service (or production) simply through lack of hands. No one, however, can fault the amiability and conviction of Miss Corrigan who runs the front of house. When people attempt to export great hotel cookery to simpler surroundings, they may sometimes do better to take two steps back (in complexity) in order to leap forward: a contradiction that has some truth. The wine list is French, with good choices in all main regions. House Lirac or Muscadet, £8.25 or £9.20. 'Service charges do not exist here and tips are not expected.'

CHEF: T.J. Brooks  PROPRIETORS: T.J. Brooks and J.B. Corrigan
OPEN: Tue to Sun, D only
MEALS: 7.30 to 9.30
PRICES: Set D £17.50 (£24) to £24.50 (£31). Minimum £17.50
SEATS: 20. Private parties: 21 main room. No children under 10. Wheelchair access. Music

---

## BAKEWELL Derbyshire                                         map 5

# Clarity Jayne

| Woodhouse, Bath Street | |
|---|---|
| Bakewell DE4 1BX | COOKING 2 |
| BAKEWELL (062 981) 2687 | COST £35 |

The restaurant is opposite the bowling green and rose garden. The dining-room is spare and slightly country and the cooking so far reported is careful and competent, though prices are not low. Meals are chosen from a very short menu stronger on mousses than pastry. Soups; turbot stuffed with a julienne of vegetables; lamb with a simple but flavoursome tarragon gravy; a warm pigeon salad of carefully chosen meat; plentiful vegetables; a fine cheese soufflé and an iced strawberry soufflé have been recommended. The wine list is succinct, like the menu. House French is £6. Children's helpings are half price. The Fischers, whose restaurant used to be here, are scheduled to open their Baslow Hall restaurant in autumn 1989.

CHEF: Rupert Stenniforth  PROPRIETOR: Peter Robey
OPEN: Tue to Sun
CLOSED: 2 weeks in July
MEALS: 12 to 3, 7 to 10.30
PRICES: £21 (£29)
CARDS: Amex, Visa
SEATS: 60. Private parties: 40 main room, 16 private room. Car-park, 4 places. Vegetarian meals. Children's helpings. Smart dress preferred. No cigars/pipes in dining-room. Wheelchair access (1 step; also WC). Music

---

*The* Guide *relies on feedback from its readers. Especially welcome are reports on new restaurants appearing in the book for the first time.*

## Green Apple

Diamond Court, Water Street
Bakewell DE4 1EW             COOKING 1
BAKEWELL (0629) 814404         COST £10−£25

Roger Green reckons that it was making his small restaurant a no-smoking zone that boosted business, but it may be simply growing local appreciation of his down-to-earth blend of wholefood and traditional British cooking – and the sensible prices – which have done the trick. Snacky self-service lunches – salads, rolls and quiche-type main courses – are replaced in the evening by more substantial three-course set meals with good vegetarian choices. Most of these feature a plainly cooked centrepiece served with a sauce: venison matched with redcurrant and port, nut roast with tomato, steak with bordelaise, and halibut with caviare are examples. Home-made puddings range from the gooey, as in Pavlova and toffee pudding, to the healthy, as in sheep's milk yoghurt. Drinks include real ale, English wines – Rock's elderflower, Breaky Bottom and Lamberhurst Priory – and cider as well as three dozen mixed continental and New World wines. House French is £5.95. CELLARMAN'S CHOICE : Breaky Bottom 1986, £9.95; Fetzer Zinfandel 1984, £10.95. Roger Green plans to stop accepting credit cards in 1990.

CHEFS: Roger Green, Nick Andrews and Pan Wain   PROPRIETOR: Roger Green
OPEN: L Mon to Sat (all week in summer), D Wed to Sat
CLOSED: mid-Jan to mid-Feb
MEALS: 12 to 2, 7 to 10
PRICES: £7 (£10), Set D £10 (£14) and £16 (£21), Snacks from £1.20. Service inc
SEATS: 50. 6 tables outside. Private parties: 50 main room. Vegetarian meals. Children's helpings. No smoking. Wheelchair access. Music

---

**BARHAM** Kent                     map 3

## ▲ Old Coach House

Dover Road, Barham CT4 6SA         COOKING 2
CANTERBURY (0227) 831218        COST £14−£19

The Rozards moved here from the French Cellar – Brighton's highest rated restaurant in last year's *Guide*. Its position in a lay-by behind a Happy Eater on the A2 between Canterbury and Dover determines the style. Lorry drivers eat here, and you can even buy ferry tickets from a mobile office in the grounds. Copper cooking pots adorn the walls; red check cloths and Jean-Claude Rozard's Burgundian background are enough to convince some that France seems nearer than it is. So does the quality of the food, from celery and lovage soup to salad of local crab. Fish outshines meat, and there is game in season. Bar snacks, rather like the tunnel, aim to link up saucisson, jambon de Bayonne and moules farcies with sausage and chips and steak and kidney pie. Vive la différence. Good value and simplicity are the aims – 'gastronauts not welcome' – and 30 well chosen wines follow suit. House wine, £7.50. CELLARMAN'S CHOICE : Mâcon-Lugny, Domaine du Prieuré 1987, £12.50; Brouilly, Ch. de la Chaize 1985, £11.

CHEF/PROPRIETOR: Jean-Claude Rozard
OPEN: all week, exc Sun D
MEALS: 12 to 2, 7.30 to 9
PRICES: Set L and D £8.75 (£14) to £11.50 (£16), Snacks from £2
CARD: Access
SEATS: 28. 4 tables outside. Private parties: 28 main room. Car-park, 60 places. Children's helpings. No cigars/pipes in dining-room
ACCOMMODATION: 14 rooms, 4 with bath/shower. B&B £20 to £30. Baby facilities. Pets welcome. Afternoon teas. Garden. TV. Doors close at 12.30am. Confirm by 6

---

**BARNARD CASTLE   Co Durham**                                          map 7

## *Market Place Teashop*

29 The Market Place
Barnard Castle DL12 8NE                                      COOKING 1
TEESDALE (0833) 690110                                        COST £12

This ground-floor café with upstairs gift shop prides itself on weaning families, as well as consenting adults, off the perils of fast food. Wholesome, sometimes heavy, dishes for meat eaters and vegetarians are produced from quite a large repertoire: good watercress soup, smoked bacon and mushroom pot, a fair carrot and courgette bake, a pot-roast brisket with Yorkshire pudding. The chef goes off to the Orient and Mexico for vegetarian inspiration: samosas and enchiladas. Bertorelli ice-cream; Cotherstone cheese; good bakery bread; haggis sent down from Scotland; and tea served in glorious silver teapots. Licensed.

CHEFS: James Moffat, Bob Hilton and Roy Varndell   PROPRIETOR: Bob Hilton
OPEN: all week, L only
CLOSED: Sun Christmas to Mar
MEALS: 12 to 5.30
PRICES: £6 (£10). Snacks from £1.05
SEATS: 50. Vegetarian meals. Children's helpings. Wheelchair access

---

**BARNET   Hertfordshire**                                              map 3

## *Wings*

6 Potters Road, New Barnet, EN5 5HW                          COOKING 1
01-449 9890                                                  COST £19–31

Fly to the northern suburbs for a smart Szechuan-Peking place with attentive service. Good prawns in a garlicky black-bean sauce, crispy duck and monk's vegetables are possibilities; alternatively a taste of regional dishes can be had with special banquet menus, including excellent bang bang chicken and beef with chilli and carrot from western China and very typical beef and tomato soup from the north. Steamed scallops in a 'wonderfully subtle tangy sauce' and crispy lamb, all fat miraculously dispersed, remain firm favourites. A cover charge seems excessive as it doesn't cover tea but only some lacklustre prawn crackers. House wines, £6.45.

CHEF: Ho Yuen Wan  PROPRIETOR: Pak Wah Tse
OPEN: all week
MEALS: 12 to 2.30, 6 to 10.30
PRICES: £12 (£24), Set D £12.50 (£19) to £18 (£26). Cover 85p. Service 15%
CARDS: Access, Amex, Diners, Visa
SEATS: 80. Private parties: 40 main room. Vegetarian meals. Children welcome. Wheelchair access (also WC)

---

**BARNSTAPLE  Devon**                                              map 1

## ▲ Lynwood House

Bishops Tawton Road
Barnstaple EX32 9DZ
BARNSTAPLE (0271) 43695                                    COOKING 2
on A377, between Barnstaple and Exeter              COST £16−£30

Reports have continued to endorse this restaurant with rooms in a large house overlooking the Taw. The Roberts' two elder sons have joined their parents in the venture – Adam in the kitchen and Matthew in the dining-room. 'The increasing maturity of Adam Roberts in the kitchen alongside his mother has given a new lease of life and adventure to the cooking.' The menu, served in upstairs and downstairs restaurants, includes stalwarts like a fine duck pâté with Cumberland sauce; prawns and wild river-bank garlic in a salad of mixed leaves; the Lynwood seafood pot, of whatever the boats have brought in, with a cheese tarragon cream sauce; flummery; and butterscotch sauce with meringue. It outshines local competition. The wine list is short and sharp, with a modicum of information, but not too highly priced. House French is £6.25.

CHEFS: Ruth Roberts and Adam Roberts  PROPRIETORS: John H. and Ruth Roberts, Adam and Matthew Roberts
OPEN: all week
MEALS: 12 to 2, 7 to 10
PRICES: £19 (£25), Set Sun L £12 (£16). Snacks from £1.50. Service inc
CARDS: Access, Visa
SEATS: 70. Private parties: 70 main room, 24 and 70 private rooms. Car-park, 25 places. Children's helpings. No smoking in dining-room. Wheelchair access (also WC)
ACCOMMODATION: 5 rooms, all with bath/shower. B&B £47.50 to £67.50. No children under 12. Garden. TV. Phone. Scenic. Confirm by 6

---

**BARWICK  Somerset**                                              map 2

## ▲ Little Barwick House

Barwick, Yeovil BA22 9TD                                   COOKING 3
YEOVIL (0935) 23902                                         COST £21−£28

Take the sign to St Mary Magdalene church, opposite the Red House (on the Yeovil to Dorchester road) if you wish to find this newly extended and ship-shape dower house. It is a 'haven of peace' and the Colleys are hospitable. Over the years, many tales of complimentary birthday cakes and timely trays of tea have reached these offices. Veronica Colley is a good cook, reputed for her bread, her meringues and her apple and almond pie. The ethos is that of English cookery, to throw into relief the fine ingredients – the game in winter, venison from Sherborne Castle or very good lamb – but it is not without some sophistication from more modern tendencies. Gravlax which 'melts in the mouth' and smoked trout are produced on site and goodly pies are a fixture. A menu with half a dozen choices is supplemented by a fair number of recited extras. People enjoy the generosity, the robust approach and, most especially, the puddings. One appreciative overnight guest commented on the success of the recent renovation which included creating a breakfast room that faces east. Wines are offered from a fair list that is largely French in origin, but with some nice Spanish, too, of around 40 bins. Prices are reasonable. Little Barwick is deep in cider country and there is local apple juice. Only 10 miles away, England's first 'calvados' is getting into production at Brympton d'Evercy. House Duboeuf, Mosel or Bulgarian Cabernet 7. CELLARMAN'S CHOICE : Dry Muscat 1987 João Pires, £9.

CHEF: Veronica Colley   PROPRIETORS: Mr and Mrs C. Colley
OPEN: Mon to Sat, D only
MEALS: 7 to 9
PRICES: Set D £17.60 (£21) to £19.60 (£23). Service inc
CARDS: Access, Amex, Diners, Visa
SEATS: 40. Private parties: 50 main room. Car-park. Children's helpings
ACCOMMODATION: 6 rooms, all with bath/shower. B&B £66 (for 2). Garden. TV. Scenic. Doors close at 11 [GHG]

---

**BASINGSTOKE  Hampshire**                                        map 2

## Hee's

23 Westminster House, Town Centre,
Basingstoke RG21 1LS                                      COOKING  2
BASINGSTOKE (0256) 464410 and 460297                 COST  £16–£28

A very welcome addition to the Basingstoke scene, once you have managed to find it on the edge of the pedestrian shopping-precinct. Approach it from Upper Church Street and sniff it out, as it lies in unmarked Potters Walk. Praise goes to the ambience – smart and welcoming with not a dragon in sight – and the good-value set meals. Peanut sauce and slivered cucumber accompanying bang bang chicken have been deemed excellent, as was the garnish of a large carved radish, 'presented without being twee'. Praise for careful attention to detail, like removing a tablecloth after the main course, is counter-balanced by gripes about over-zealous wine service and brimming glasses. The wine list is fair by Chinese standards. Portions are generous and, even under pressure, the kitchen seems to cope. Desserts are standard, but the ubiquitous toffee apples and bananas are crunchy and very hot.

---

*Consumers' Association is planning a* Vegetarian Good Food Guide, *to cafés and restaurants offering at least one vegetarian main course. Please send reports and recommendations to* The Vegetarian Good Food Guide, FREEPOST, *2 Marylebone Road, London NW1 1YN.*

CHEF: Mr Leung   PROPRIETOR: Mr Lee
OPEN: all week, exc Sun L
CLOSED: 24 to 27 Dec, Sun of bank hol weekends
MEALS: 12 to 2.30, 6 to 11
PRICES: Set L and D £10.50 (£16) to £16.90 (£23). Service 12.5%
CARDS: Access, Amex, Diners, Visa
SEATS: 90. Private parties: 120 main room. Vegetarian meals. Children restricted after 8pm.
Wheelchair access (1 step). Music. Air-conditioned

---

**BATH  Avon**                                                                     map 2

## ▲ Dower House Restaurant, Royal Crescent Hotel

16 Royal Crescent, Bath BA1 2LS                                          COOKING **2**
BATH (0225) 319090                                                      COST  £29-£54

Draw up in the Royal Crescent, an architectural world first, on a wet winter's
night and you might, save for the cars, be in the eighteenth century. The
lighting is crepuscular; the facade of giant Ionic columns and panelled doors
admits to none of the forced conversion to flats and apartments that has gone on
behind. Make for a glass-paned door flanked by two lamps at dead-centre of
the arc. This is the Royal Crescent Hotel: an English version of the Spanish
*parador*, where you can inhabit an historic monument – at a price. The
threshold breached, the deserted rooms have the air of a museum but with
luxury, of course. Press on, for the restaurant occupies the dower house, a
separate building at the back of the site reached through the hotel and its
garden. Viewed in the glow of floodlights, it is remarkable: it might be a
stylised print from an architectural pattern book, so pure is its form. The trek
through the garden, however, is hazardous in inclement weather. Once inside
the house, first impressions are high, not least because of the oval staircase, an
exercise in architectural fluidity. The main rooms – lounges to the right,
restaurant to the left – are more conventional versions of late twentieth-century
luxury even if the Georgians have left a legacy of draughts not wholly
overcome by modern heating systems. The cooking is conventional-classy as
well and, at that price, should certainly achieve a minimum level of
palatability. Money does not buy consistency, however, nor refined accuracy of
flavouring. While some dishes, such as a ravioli of lobster with a tarragon
sauce, and parcels of pigeon with a pastry case with red wine and mushroom
sauce, have been heartily endorsed, an undercooked and flavourless fillet of
monkfish wrapped in cabbage with an enervated mushroom duxelles and a
plain egg and buttery sauce won prizes only for its lack of character. There is
usually a hot pudding on the set-price, frequently changing menu of half a
dozen dishes in each course. This has also received equal praise and
condemnation: a light ginger sponge with delectable lemon sauce, or boring
chocolate pudding with an over-sweet and thick fudge sauce. (For the national
champion of this latter dish, go to the Old Vicarage at Ridgeway, see entry.)
Overall, Michael Croft may cook a good dinner or a boring one. It will be
professionally served but, for the price, the details need to be improved as well
as the consistency. The wine list, with lots from Eldridge Pope, is as expensive

as the food, though covering a fair range. Go for the bin-ends. House French is
£16. CELLARMAN'S CHOICE : Ch. Haut Pontet 1979, St-Emilion, £27.20;
Sancerre La Guiberte, 1988, £17.90.

CHEF: Michael Croft   PROPRIETORS: Norfolk Capital Hotels
OPEN: all week
MEALS: 12.30 to 2, 7 to 9.30 (10 Sat)
PRICES: Set L £17 (£29) to £21 (£32), Set D £33 (£45)
CARDS: Access, Amex, Diners, Visa
SEATS: 70. Private parties: 70 main room, 20, 36 and 40 private rooms. Car-park, 12 places.
Children's helpings on request. No cigars/pipes in dining-room. Wheelchair access
(1 step). Air-conditioned
ACCOMMODATION: 45 rooms, all with bath/shower. Lift. B&B £99 to £145. Baby facilities.
Afternoon teas. Garden. Air-conditioning. TV. Phone. Scenic. Confirm by 10am [GHG]

# Garlands

7 Edgar Buildings, George Street
Bath BA1 2EE
BATH (0225) 442283

COOKING 1
COST £15–£28

A grey and gold inn sign sways outside the premises, until recently occupied
by the Clos du Roy (see entry, Box). It was taken over shortly before the *Guide*
went to press by Tom Bridgeman, lately at Tarts restaurant, and Will Baber,
who runs front of house. The grey and gold theme continues within to give a
cool, modern feel backed up by botanical prints, jazz in the background and
pleasantly unhurried young service. It is impossible to make hard judgements
at such an early stage, especially since Tom Bridgeman is trying his hand at
more varied and formally presented cooking than that of Tarts. Dishes are
eclectic, individual yet predictably accessorised by filo pastry, walnut and
hazelnut oil, smoked meats, green and red peppercorns, oyster mushrooms and
exotic fruits. Sometimes combinations are well judged, as in first courses of a
puff pastry tartlet with quails' eggs and smoked chicken quenelles balanced
well by its béarnaise, or a terrine of duck with livers and oyster mushrooms set
in its aspic and served with an orange sauce. As yet, though, the execution has
not caught up with the complexity. Vegetables have been well cooked, and
clever puddings, such as crème brûlée with apple topping, work well. House
French is £6.75 on a decent short list.

CHEF: Tom Bridgeman   PROPRIETORS: Will Baber and Tom Bridgeman
OPEN: Tue to Sun, exc Sun L
CLOSED: 25 to 27 Dec
MEALS: 12.15 to 2.15, 7 to 10.30
PRICES: £15 (£23), Set L £9.25 (£15) to £10.95 (£17)
CARDS: Access, Amex, Visa
SEATS: 32. Private parties: 15 main room. Vegetarian meals. Children welcome. Wheelchair
access (1 step; also WC, 3 steps). Music

*If you see a certificate in a restaurant bearing the words 'Diploma of Merit. The Good Food
Guide (United Kingdom)', the claim is false (and the restaurant may be in contempt of
court in displaying it) – see the Introduction. Please write and tell us the name and address
of the restaurant.*

## Moon and Sixpence

| | |
|---|---|
| 6A Broad Street, Bath BA1 5LJ | COOKING 1 |
| BATH (0225) 460962 | COST £13–£30 |

The Moon and Sixpence keeps to a particular modern style which seems either to capture people's imaginations or set their nerves on edge; what some call beautiful presentation, others find too fiddly. Nevertheless, there have been many positive reports. One dinner of vegetable terrine, scallops with dill and ginger, steamed fillet of salmon and turbot wrapped in spinach with a saffron sauce, duck with raspberry sauce, lemon tart and tropical fruit salad earned unstinting praise. During the day, there is a much less elaborate cold table, which has been called tired and overpriced, although turbot and sewin has been well cooked, and the English or continental cheeses make a reliable snack with the good bread and a glass or bottle of wine. The setting, in a lovely stone building with a conservatory extension and covered patio off a courtyard, undoubtedly adds to the effect, although the main rooms can get smoky. Service is friendly but can be slow. House wine, £5.75.

CHEF: Kevin King   PROPRIETOR: Keith Waving
OPEN: all week
MEALS: 12 to 2.30 (2 Sun), 5.30 to 10.30 (11 Fri and Sat)
PRICES: £18 (£25), Set L £7.50 (£13) to £10.75 (£16)
CARDS: Access, Amex, Visa
SEATS: 70. 15 tables outside. Private parties: 30 main room, 25 private room. Vegetarian meals. Children's helpings on request. Wheelchair access. Music

## Popjoy's

| | |
|---|---|
| Beau Nash's House, Sawclose | |
| Bath BA1 1EU | COOKING 2 |
| BATH (0225) 460494 | COST £24–£35 |

When Lord Chesterfield saw the statue of Beau Nash in Bath's Pump Room, flanked by busts of Newton and Pope, he commented, 'Wisdom and Wit are little seen, but Folly at full length.' The fool's mistress, Juliana Popjoy, lived in the house now occupied by the dining-room and kitchen: a glorious high-Georgian building. The discreet taste that marked Stephen and Penny Ross' dramatic revival of this restaurant in the 1970s has been somewhat overlayed by a flamboyance that is not without advocates. Although the place has gone through several changes of ownership, the chef/manager team of Mark Anton Edwards and Mark Heather seems to stick together. In like manner, the style of cooking appears consistent through the last five or six years: very modern, very complicated; what the British have come to expect of restaurants. One meal started with a salmon and turbot terrine wrapped in nori served with a lime pickle and a mixed leaf salad with a mustard dressing, and continued with a pair of boned quail stuffed with a walnut mousse on a sweet/sour Grand Marnier sauce, the plate (large) decorated with sliced kumquats, peeled segments of orange, some diced tomato and lots of sprigs of chervil. Vegetables involved an array of china and cutlery to cope with two sorts of potatoes – gratin and new – a carrot purée, broccoli, green beans and mange-tout peas. Yet space there was for a hazelnut meringue with caramel ice-cream on a coffee sauce. On paper this sounds a mouthful, indeed, but in the event it was much liked. The fish combination seems impossible but each element was delicious, particularly the home-made pickle and especially with the good bread that Popjoy's make to their own recipe. The main course, though over-ornate, had excellent technique in the walnut mousse and a skilled balance in the sweet-and-sour sauce, even if the quail barely supported them. The vegetables (though not potatoes) were cooked fairly well and the dessert showed true and intense flavours. The chef seems to believe in himself. The wine list is arranged according to flavour rather than origin. House Provence wine, bottled for the restaurant, is £7.50. CELLARMAN'S CHOICE: Ch. Musar 1980, £12.20; Sonoma-Cutrer Chardonnay, 1986, £21.50.

CHEFS: Mark Anton Edwards and John Headley   PROPRIETORS: Avon Inns
OPEN: Tue to Sat, exc Sat L
MEALS: 12 to 2, 6 to 10.30
PRICES: L £13 (£17), Set L £18.50 (£24), Set D £22.50 (£29). Service 12.5% for parties of five or more
CARDS: Access, Amex, Visa
SEATS: 36. Private parties: 36 main room. Vegetarian meals. No children under 10 at D. Smart dress preferred. No cigars/pipes in dining-room. Wheelchair access (1 step; also men's WC). Music

## ▲ *Priory Hotel*

Weston Road, Bath BA1 2XT                                      COOKING 3
BATH (0225) 331922                                              COST £18−£50

The Priory has always been classed as a country-house hotel; in fact it is a suburban villa in a late eighteenth-century outgrowth west of the city of Bath. Inside it feels indeed like a country house, although pressure of business has occasioned new bedroom wings and a new-dining room in the last five years. The fine lawn sweeping away from the garden front could never be but suburban. Michael Collom has survived as chef, even if the owners are that canny group, Select County Hotels, who seem quite sensitive in their central control, although themselves undergoing some adjustment of control as we go to press. This kitchen has consistently produced meals of sophistication with essentials properly considered, as well as showing signs of adventurousness. Reports over the past year stress the normal rather than any testing of the bounds of taste. Roast beef, asparagus, gravad lax, watercress soup are praised. As one remarked, 'Not very French, but still very good.' But then, Michael Collom doesn't pretend to Frenchness; and the restaurant does cater for its market as part of the Bath tourist operation (rich division) and shows few signs of dodging its responsibilities. The wine list is priced at all the market can bear, and makes little concession to the impecunious. For example, is it necessary to start red burgundies at £17.75 for a Mâcon? The selection is interesting and the choice of vintages seems acute. House Bordeaux, £8.50. CELLARMAN'S CHOICE: Ch. Bellevue-La-Forêt 1986, Frontonnais, £11.

*All letters to the* Guide *are acknowledged with an update on latest sales, closures, chef changes and so on.*

CHEF: Michael Collom   PROPRIETORS: Select Country Hotels
OPEN: all week
MEALS: 12.30 to 2, 7 to 9.15
PRICES: £26 (£33), Set L £12 (£18) to £17 (£24), Set D £25 (£31) to £35 (£42). Service inc
CARDS: Access, Amex, Carte Blanche, Diners, Visa
SEATS: 64. Private parties: 40 main room, 22 and 40 private rooms. Car-park, 25 places.
Vegetarian meals. Children welcome. Smart dress preferred. No smoking.
Wheelchair access
ACCOMMODATION: 21 rooms, all with bath/shower. Rooms for disabled. B&B £75 to £105.
Deposit: £75. Afternoon teas. Garden. Swimming-pool. TV. Phone. Scenic. Doors close at
12 [GHG]

## Tarts ▼

| | |
|---|---|
| 8 Pierrepont Place, Bath BA1 1JX | COOKING 2 |
| BATH (0225) 330280 and 330201 | COST £26 |

This labyrinth of cellars south of the Abbey is praised for its attitudes. At times,
a party may be smoked out by neighbours in some of the tiny rooms, or
forgotten (as in Château d'If) when the pace hots up but, as one customer
remarked, 'It is a delight when the place is so friendly and the bill not an arm
and a leg.' There is a fixed *carte* and a daily changing short menu of specials –
cheaper and lighter at lunch. The cooking is lifted by its sauces, which
especially pleased an inspector. The style is more than bistro. Earlier this year,
the specials (much more interesting than the *carte*), included chicken livers and
lardons of bacon in a puff pastry with a lustrous shallot sauce; escalope of
salmon with a rosemary butter; and a suitably rich chocolate marquise.
Presentation obviously excites the kitchen: mint leaves on everything and
feathered coulis. Other dishes that have pleased are a ham, avocado and
mushroom pancake, terrine of salmon and sole, guinea-fowl with oyster
mushrooms and a madeira sauce, a Pavlova of mango and passion-fruit and a
chocolate and Grand Marnier mousse. The wine list is ten times better than
anyone might expect: good growers, good prices, very intelligent. House
French is from £5.80 to £8.20. CELLARMAN'S CHOICE : Côtes de Duras Blanc,
Domaine de Laulan 1988, £9.80; Crozes Hermitage, Mule Blanche 1986,
Janboulet Aîné, £12.90.

CHEF: Michel Lemoine   PROPRIETOR: John Edwards
OPEN: Mon to Sat
CLOSED: 3 days over Christmas
MEALS: 12 to 2.30, 6.45 to 10.45
PRICES: £14 (£22). Snacks from £2.20
CARDS: Access, Visa
SEATS: 50. Private parties: 22 main room, 8 and 12 private rooms. Children welcome. Music

*County Round-ups listing additional restaurants that may be worth a visit are at the back
of the* Guide, *after the Irish section. Reports on Round-up entries are welcome.*

*All letters to the* Guide *are acknowledged with an update on latest sales, closures, chef
changes and so on.*

BATTLE   East Sussex                                                          map 3

# ▲ *La Vieille Auberge*

27 High Street, Battle TN33 0EA                              COOKING 2
BATTLE (042 46) 5171                                          COST £14–£28

Battle Abbey has been a useful quarry: La Vieille Auberge is built from its
stones. Though the night-life of Battle may cause the visitor to riot in Hastings,
this hotel/restaurant will give solace to anyone stranded before Senlac. Quite
why it is so studiously French is not revealed: the menu has French
translations for its English titles – perhaps for latter-day invasions – but the
food, and the decoration, is English (modern in the case of the food) through
and through. Paul Webbe is a competent chef. His dishes sound of the
impressive kind, but please visitors by tasting as good as they look. Decent
reports have come of venison sausages (something of a speciality); a too-cold
gazpacho with basil, the perfume sufficient to suffuse the whole, and a little
crescent of filo with a panaché of fish on a hollandaise. Veal, also in pastry –
this time buttery and light – with olives and tomatoes impressed by the well-
judged piquancy of the sauce and careful preparation of the meat. A confit of
duck revealed the English rather than French nature of the kitchen: this seemed
not true confit, rather duck with its skin crisped by a frottage of salt. Generous
and simple vegetables are preludes to a sweet course that may excel the others.
A timbale consisting of honey and lemon ice-creams topped with frozen honey,
sitting on a good vanilla sauce, was full of texture differences as well as
changing intensities of flavour; a trio of chocolates might reconcile everyone to
the charms of white chocolate which comes as a pyramid of mousse, paired
with a heavier dark mousse and a tulip of excellent ice-cream. Coffee has been
stewed. The wine list is almost entirely French and has some decent bottles and
growers at none-too-excessive prices. There are some bottles from the Carr
Taylor vineyard nearby. House French is £6.45. CELLARMAN'S CHOICE :
Mercurey, Chante Flute 1985, Clos l'Evêque, £17; Carr Taylor Schoenburger
1988, £7.95. One French characteristic is to offer more than one set menu as
well as the *carte*. These include a vegetarian meal as well as a gourmet seven-
course affair.

CHEF: Paul Webbe   PROPRIETOR: Stephen P. Dickey
OPEN: all week
MEALS: 12 to 2, 7 to 10
PRICES: £18 (£22), Set L £9.75 (£14) to £18.50 (£23), Set D £14.50 (£19) to £18.50 (£23).
Service inc
CARDS: Access, Amex, Diners, Visa
SEATS: 33. Private parties: 33 main room, 14 private room. Vegetarian meals. Children's
helpings on request. No cigars/pipes in dining-room. Wheelchair access (also WC). Music
ACCOMMODATION: 7 rooms, 5 with bath/shower. B&B £24.50 to £39.50. Deposit: 50%.
Afternoon teas. TV. Phone. Doors close at midnight. Confirm by 6

*'We are constantly offered wine of a different year to that which we ordered from the wine
list. When we complain we are made to seem the unreasonable ones; and there is a look of
blank incredulity, when we suggest we should pay less for a moderate '84, than we should
for a good '85. This seems to be becoming a widespread malaise in good establishments as
well as bad.'* A reader

# China Diner

7 The Highway, Station Road
Beaconsfield HP9 1QD                                    COOKING 1
BEACONSFIELD (0494) 673345 and 678346                  COST £11–£32

Local aficionados have insisted on a full listing for this long-running star in
Beaconsfield's Chinese firmament. Service is invariably attentive, the welcome
warm, the dining-room most memorable for its dark blue venetian blinds,
ceiling fans and dining booths 'owing more to Hollywood than China'.
Seaweed crisp, bang bang chicken, prawns in chilli sauce, succulent and crispy
duck and dry-fried Szechuan beans with savoury topping have come in for
strong recommendations. House wine, £6.50.

CHEF: Robin Yu  PROPRIETOR: Shu Fun Li
OPEN: all week
MEALS: 12 to 2.30, 6 to 11.30
PRICES: £10 (£19), Set L £5.50 (£11) to £12.50 (£18), Set D £12.50 (£18) to £20 (£27). Snacks
from £3. Service 10%
CARDS: Access, Amex, Diners, Visa
SEATS: 90. Private parties: 70 main room. Vegetarian meals. Children welcome. Wheelchair
access (also WC). Music. Air-conditioned

# Leigh House

Wycombe End, Beaconsfield HP9 1XL                      COOKING 2
BEACONSFIELD (0494) 676348                             COST £21–£38

The curiously English, country-house feel of this upmarket Chinese restaurant
carries through into the menu, which takes a westernised gourmet approach to
Peking and Northern Chinese cooking. Working within these limits, the
kitchen is reliably good and consistent. Specialities are fresh lobsters or
scallops done various ways, sizzling frogs' legs and crispy duck falling off the
bone. Some of the most interesting dishes are among the appetisers: paper-
wrapped prawns are said to be superb; steamed dumplings are served with red
wine vinegar and shredded ginger; mixed cold hors d'oeuvre are arranged
around a carved radish flower and spring onion. The careful presentation is not
merely ornamental. Chilli chicken, for example, is served in a fresh pineapple
to temper the heat with sweetness. For vegetarians, there are four vegetables –
baby corn, green pepper, button mushrooms and bamboo shoots – in an
unusual thick, chilli-spiced buttery sauce. The wine list is a cut above most
provincial Chinese restaurants and shows a loyalty to France bar two Mosels
and two Australians from Rosemount. House burgundy or Bordeaux,
£6.50 or £6.90.

'Service in both bar and restaurant was that rare combination of indigenous, friendly and
professional.'  On dining in Gloucestershire

'I returned a glass of English red wine, utterly gone, foul smelling and depraved in taste.
The wine waiter commented, ''Well, the Japanese like it''.'  On dining in London

CHEF/PROPRIETOR: S.W. Tang
OPEN: all week
MEALS: 12 to 2, 6 to 11
PRICES: £13 (£23), Set L and D £15 (£21) to £25 (£32). Minimum £10. Service 10%
CARDS: Access, Amex, Diners, Visa
SEATS: 80. Private parties: 25 main room. Car-park, 8 places. Vegetarian meals. Children welcome. Wheelchair access. Music. Air-conditioned

---

**BECKINGHAM  Lincolnshire**                                                    map 6

## Black Swan

| | |
|---|---|
| Hillside, Beckingham LN5 0RF | COOKING 3 |
| FENTON CLAYPOLE (063 684) 474 | COST £15−£26 |

'An oasis on the edge of a culinary desert,' this pub is off the Sleaford road six miles out of Newark. The River Witham runs at the bottom of the garden. It is a two-generation enterprise, with the younger half doing the cooking, which is unexpectedly ambitious, perhaps more fashion-conscious than mindful of seasons and markets, though the menu does change every three weeks. The set-price dinner is a long affair. It starts with an appetiser, 'la surprise du chef', has a sorbet after the first course and cheese before dessert. Coffee is included in the price; there are three choices in the principal courses. Service is white-gloved, a trifle slow but entirely willing. The staff is also nice to children. Reports are very consistent that this is a reliable kitchen which tries hard, whose imagination shines like a beacon in a fogbound moor. A meal eaten by an inspector started with a brioche with a superbly textured bream mousse surrounding a morsel of salmon sauced with a strong fish stock, lemon and chopped watercress, followed by a piece of monkfish wrapped in spinach before steaming, served on a tomato concasse well flavoured with saffron, finishing with a rum and raisin soufflé that erred on the sweet side. Vegetables are not always chosen with an eye to the taste of the principal dish. Cheese service is elaborate, including fruit, nuts and seven sorts of biscuit, and the condition of the board has been praised. There are often soufflés on the menu, a hangover from Anton Indans's time with Peter Kromberg at the London Inter-Continental. The wine list has improved. House French is £5.75.
CELLARMAN'S CHOICE : Beaujolais Juliénas 1987, £10.85; Rosemount Chardonnay 1987, £9.45.

CHEF: Anton Indans   PROPRIETORS: Anton and Alison Indans
OPEN: Tue to Sat D, Sun L till Easter 1990
MEALS: 12 to 2, 7 to 10
PRICES: Set L £10.50 (£15), Set D £16.80 (£22)
CARDS: Access, Visa
SEATS: 30. Private parties: 24 main room, 12 and 24 private rooms. Car-park, 9 places. Children's helpings (L only). Wheelchair access (also WC). Music

---

'The food is up to **Guide** standard, but not helped by comments such as, at tea, ''God, you must be bored coming here''; at dinner, ''Right troopers, are you ready to order?''; over pre-dinner drinks, ''Do you want orange juice or squash in your vodka?'' ''Juice, please.'' ''Oh good, she's passed the slag test.''' On dining in Gwynedd

---

BEDALE  North Yorkshire                                          map 7

## Plummers ♟

7 North End, Bedale DL8 1AF                              COOKING  2
BEDALE (0677) 23432                                    COST  £18−£28

'There's an artist in the kitchen,' writes one reporter of an immaculately
presented meal, and chef Chris Cope admits to being influenced by colours and
textures. This artist-cook creates a menu from a mix of styles: classic French,
traditional English and Eastern. Results emerge as chicken livers with shiitake
mushrooms in filo pastry; poached beef fillet with tomato and rosemary coulis;
fresh salmon mousse with spring onions and ginger in hollandaise. Reporters
enthuse: 'the duckling was like a superior Sunday lunch ... just the thing to
revive the spirits, cooked with style but without pretension.' 'It was the little
touches that made it so special: tiny crisp chicken wings as appetisers; slightly
sweet home-baked bread; rich vanilla petits fours.' Eat informally in the
downstairs bar from the blackboard menu or go up to the airy high-raftered
restaurant. The wine list is fashionable in the best of senses; for Bedale it is
remarkable. House wines, 30 of them, from £5.75. CELLARMAN'S CHOICE : Ch.
Calon Monségur, Côtes de Castillon 1983, £8.25; Montana Marlborough
Sauvignon Blanc 1988, £8.95.

CHEF: Chris Cope   PROPRIETORS: Guy and Audrey Staniland
OPEN: Tue to Sat
MEALS: 12 to 2, 7 to 10
PRICES: £18 (£23), Set L and D £13.95 (£18) to £17.65 (£23). Snacks from £1.15
CARDS: Access, Visa
SEATS: 40. Private parties: 12 main room, 40 private room. No children under 10.
Wheelchair access. Music

BERKHAMSTED  Hertfordshire                                      map 3

## Cook's Delight

360−362 High Street
Berkhamsted HP4 1HU                                     COOKING  1
BERKHAMSTED (0442) 863584                              COST  £14−£40

A dedicated restaurant that throws itself enthusiastically into all kinds of
vegetarian cooking; there are South-East Asian gourmet evenings, macrobiotic
Sunday dinners, vegetarian quiches, soups, cakes and so on. Claypots of
vegetables − and fish or poultry with prior warning − are also available every
day. 'Lemon meringue looks like Everest.' Organic and chemical-free produce
extends into the wine list with good bottles from France and Italy and less from
the rest of the world, all at fair prices. House Italian, £7.50. The beers are worth
a look, too.

---

*The text of entries is based on unsolicited reports sent in by readers, backed up by
inspections conducted anonymously. The factual details under the text are from
questionnaires the Guide sends to all restaurants that feature in the book.*

---

CHEF: Khai-Eng Tyler   PROPRIETORS: Rex Tyler and Khai-Eng Tyler
OPEN: Thur to Sun, exc Sun D
CLOSED: 2 weeks July or Aug, 1 week after Christmas
MEALS: 9 to 5, 7.30 (8 Sat) to 9 (11 Sat)
PRICES: £11 (£19), Set L £8 (£14) to £15 (£22), Set D £20 (£27) to £25 (£33), Snacks from
£2.50. Licensed, also bring your own: corkage 50p per person
CARDS: Access, Visa
SEATS: 56. 4 tables outside. Private parties: 36 main room, 16, 36 and 40 private rooms.
Vegetarian meals. Children's helpings. No smoking. Wheelchair access. Music

---

**BERWICK-UPON-TWEED  Northumberland**                                    map 7

## *Funnywayt'mekalivin*

53 West Street
Berwick-upon-Tweed TD15 1AS                                        COOKING 2
BERWICK-UPON-TWEED (0289) 308827 and 86437                          COST £14

'From the outside,' wrote an inspector on her first visit, 'this is the most off-
putting, scruffiest-looking place I have seen in the British Isles.' But the cottage
on a cobbled hill leading from Main Street to the river opens into a
'wonderland of small spaces on different levels, under a roof propped up by
rough-looking beams.' It is crammed with miscellaneous objects and fresh
flowers. Elizabeth Middlemiss' restaurant grew unexpectedly from small
beginnings and pleases many people. 'Excellent', 'delightful', 'interestingly
different' are some of the compliments. A set dinner of four courses for one
sitting at 8 is what is on offer. The price is not high and there is no licence (but a
corkage charge). An aperitif is included in the price of the meal in the evenings.
The cook sometimes serves as well; certainly there are few staff, so the cooking
is fairly straightforward. A meal as reported began with a carrot and apple
soup, went on to a smoked salmon Pithiviers, offered a main course of fanned
steak with mustard sauce served with dauphinois, cauliflower and broccoli
before a finish of walnut tart and Brie. Coffee is unlimited. The cooking
manages to strike an imaginative note, vegetarians are never ignored and the
welcome is open and friendly. What defects there are may come from the
balancing of cooking and serving on a basis of too little equipment and staff,
and occasional lack of finesse.

---

CHEF: Elizabeth Middlemiss   PROPRIETORS: Mr and Mrs Middlemiss
OPEN: Mon to Wed L, Fri and Sat D
MEALS: 12 to 2, 8
PRICES: Set D £13.75 (£13.75). Service inc. Unlicensed, but bring your own: corkage £1.50
SEATS: 26. Private parties: 26 main room. Vegetarian meals. No children under 8. No
smoking D, no-smoking area L. Wheelchair access (1 step). Music. One sitting at D

---

*Restaurateurs justifiably resent no-shows. If you quote a credit card number when
booking, you may be liable for the restaurant's lost profit margin if you don't turn up.
Always phone to cancel.*

*The* Guide *office can quickly spot when a restaurateur is encouraging customers to write
recommending inclusion. Such reports do not further a restaurant's cause. Please tell us if a
restaurateur invites you to write to the* Guide.

---

## Lychgates

5A Church Street, Old Town
Bexhill-on-Sea TN40 2HE                              COOKING 2
BEXHILL (0424) 212193                                COST £12–£24

Make for St Peter's church in Bexhill old town; Lychgates is hard by. This small
restaurant in two low rooms of a fifteenth-century Wealden hall – 'lovely and
cool on a hot day' – has received many endorsements in its first year in the
*Guide*. 'Homely', 'friendly', 'not greedy', 'adventurous for the area' are some of
the comments. In truth, the menus do read adventurously at times: a spinach
roulade with cream cheese, prawns, red and green peppers and a tomato
vinaigrette; or a breast of chicken with whisky, coconut, spiced pineapple and
cream sound like clarion calls from the farthest margins of culinary discovery.
Some have thought that John Tyson's cooking is better when kept on a tight
rein of simplicity and lightness. There are two set-price dinner menus of three
or five courses that change every month. These tend towards an individual
interpretation of recent fashion and are of fluctuating success. What can never
be doubted, however, is that the Tysons' hearts are in it. The wine list is short:
Mr Tyson says he is working on its development. House French, £6.75.

CHEF: John Tyson   PROPRIETORS: John and Sue Tyson
OPEN: Tue to Sat (Sat L bookings only)
MEALS: 12.30 to 2, 7.15 to 10.30
PRICES: Set L £7.95 (£12), Set D £12.50 (£18) to £14.95 (£20)
CARDS: Access, Visa
SEATS: 26. Private parties: 18 main room. Children's helpings. No children under 8 (D
only). Wheelchair access

## ▲ Bilbrough Manor

Bilbrough Y02 3PH
TADCASTER (0937) 834002                              COOKING 1
1m off A64, between Tadcaster and York              COST £18–£41

A house that was born as Queen Victoria died, but visitors might think that her
values lived on. The butler, Hyde, figures largely in reports: 'a nice gent, and
very helpful', 'attentive (almost too attentive sometimes) but later he got it just
about right'. Hyde's helpmeets are deferential and properly clad, as must be
customers. It is in keeping with the style of the place that guests are given
unpriced menus. As if status has more to do with it than taste, there is much
elaboration in the cooking. Indeed, it was beginning to appear no longer
acceptable. Slimming down the menu, or possibly streamlining the recipes, has
meant some contented diners are reporting to this *Guide*. Ravioli filled with
duck mousse and a touch of sage with a diced vegetable sauce; a 'sausage' of
chicken breast filled with a tongue mousse and pistachio nuts; lamb and a
mustard sauce; excellent vegetables; perfect new potatoes: all these have been
approved. But invention worked against enjoyment at dessert stage: too many

conflicting flavours or just too much distracting from the point of the dish. There is an adequate wine list, at prices as high as in the other departments. House wines are £8.50. CELLARMAN'S CHOICE : Montagny *premier cru* 1987, Caves de Buxy, £15.50; Ch. Talbot 1986, St-Julien, £18.

CHEF: Idris Caldora   PROPRIETORS: Mr and Mrs Colin C. Bell
OPEN: all week
MEALS: 12 to 2, 7 to 9.30
PRICES: Set L £12 (£18) to £29.50 (£34), Set D £19.50 (£26) to £29.50 (£34).
Minimum £19.80
CARDS: Access, Amex, Diners, Visa
SEATS: 60. Private parties: 30 main room, 20 private room. Car-park, 50 places. No children under 12. Smart dress preferred. No smoking in dining-room. Wheelchair access (also WC). Music
ACCOMMODATION: 12 rooms, all with bath/shower. B&B £75 to £130. No children under 12. Afternoon teas. Garden. TV. Phone. Scenic

---

**BILLESLEY  Warwickshire**                                               map 2

## ▲ *Billesley Manor* ♥

Billesley, B4G 6NF                                              COOKING 2
STRATFORD-UPON-AVON (0789) 400888                      COST £22−£43

For five years (not allowing an interruption caused by devastating fire), Mark Naylor has been cooking at this sixteenth-century (and now reconstructed) hotel just outside Stratford. Although catering for business, conference and swift-passing tourism, the cooking is reliable according to emphatic reports − though the prices may be too reliably high and the insistence that jackets should be kept on all through dinner is idiotically formal. A four-course table d'hôte dinner menu (cheaper at lunchtime) has proved satisfactory restaurant cooking: chicken-liver parfait of fine texture and smooth taste; crab, smoked salmon and fresh salmon bound in a light dill mayonnaise; lamb cutlets cooked exactly right, with interest from a thin herb crust; beef of fair quality with a simple bordelaise sauce neither strong, sweet nor overloaded with alcoholic fumes; desserts plain but good, as was the beetroot consommé that came as second course. If marooned in Stratford, worse fate than lunch here might be one's lot. Formal the staff can be, but amiable too. In the way of such places, the wine list is wildly overpriced. The head office accountant's calculations of profit margins are almost audible. It's a pity the hotel's public is so complaisant. The choice of wines is careful: some interesting growers even if the range is less exciting outside France. House wine is £9.50.

---

*'A strong candidate for the Ghastliest Dish of the Year award. The meat was two half-inch-thick slices of car tyre, on the point of going off, topped with a mixture of finely chopped mushrooms that was utterly tasteless. Topped with very thinly sliced bacon or ham that tasted of a last-minute dash of some liqueur. Encircled with pallid uncooked pastry that strongly resembled a strip of wet blanket. Surrounded by a dark brown, over-caramelised, over-salted puddle of meat extract. Garnished with five baby veg. plus stalks. So hard that one couldn't even prick them with one's fork. On a boiling plate.'* On inspecting in Gloucestershire

---

CHEF: Mark Naylor   PROPRIETORS: Norfolk Capital Hotels Ltd
OPEN: all week
MEALS: 12.30 to 2, 7.30 to 9.30 (10 Fri and Sat)
PRICES: £25 (£36), Set L £15 (£22), Set D £21 (£28)
CARDS: Access, Amex, Diners, Visa
SEATS: 75. 6 tables outside. Private parties: 8 main room, 100 private room. Car-park, 150 places. Children's helpings. No children under 12. Smart dress preferred. No smoking. Wheelchair access (also WC)
ACCOMMODATION: 41 rooms, all with bath/shower. Rooms for disabled. B&B £75 to £105. Baby facilities. Afternoon teas. Garden. Swimming-pool. Tennis. TV. Phone. Scenic. Doors close at 1am. Confirm by 6

---

**BIRDLIP** Gloucestershire                                                    map 2

## ▲ *Kingshead House*

Birdlip GL4 8JH                                                    COOKING 2
GLOUCESTER (0452) 862299                                    COST £14–£26

'I took to it very much for what it was not', wrote a correspondent. By this she meant that the Knocks' conversion of an eighteenth-century coaching-inn high on the Cotswold scarp had none of the pretty-pretty and irritating 'superficial niceties' that pass muster for country-house restaurants in some parts. An honest effort therefore, rarely pretending to more than it is, masking hard work in the kitchen by Judy Knock and much beavering and travelling for supplies and produce by Warren Knock. Lunch is cheaper than dinner, simple but proper snacks are available, and a short set-price menu is there if you need more nourishment. Dinner continues to be an inclusive priced three- or four-course affair with at least a few choices at each stage. There is always a vegetarian main course, such as hot mushroom mousse with wild mushrooms or timbale of courgettes and spinach with red pepper sauce. Judy Knock has admitted interest in old English recipes, as in Lord John Russell's iced pudding, red berry and tea sorbet; spices and strong flavours, as in best end of lamb with ratatouille and garlic fritters, Moroccan lamb with coriander; and French bourgeois cooking – salmon 'cuit d'un côté', canard en civet. She bakes her own bread, makes her own jams and in other ways shows the virtues of self-sufficiency. Criticisms have centred on sauces and a greater timidity of flavour than might be expected from the menu. On the first Friday of the month a lutanist, Rod Willmott, plays guitar and lute. Vegetables are largely organic, supplied by Hill Farm, Birdlip. The one guest room is comfortable, with a decent breakfast. Warren Knock was co-author of a pioneer guide to Britain's beers but his wine list shows respect for the grape too. It is not expensive, with helpful notes, and there are some nice Italians as well as French and others from Thomas Panton of Tetbury, Rose Tree Wines and Windrush. House French is £6.50. CELLARMAN'S CHOICE : Soave, Costeggiola 1987, £8.95; Château La Rivière, Fronsac 1981, £13.95.

---

*'The waitress, when told of our disappointment at the meal, said she was sorry but the owner/chef had gone to Twickenham on Saturday, got drunk and had fallen down some stairs and injured his leg.'*   On dining in Avon

---

CHEF: Judy Knock   PROPRIETORS: Warren and Judy Knock
OPEN: Tue to Sun, exc Sat L and Sun D
MEALS: 12.15 to 2.15 (1.45 Sun), 7.15 to 10
PRICES: Set L from £9.50 (£14), Set D from £16.50 (£22), Snacks from £2.50
CARDS: Access, Amex, Diners, Visa
SEATS: 32. 2 tables outside. Private parties: 36 main room. Car-park, 12 places. Vegetarian meals. Children's helpings. Wheelchair access. Music
ACCOMMODATION: 1 room, with bath/shower. B&B £20 to £28. Garden. Scenic. Doors close at 12. Confirm by 6

---

**BIRKENHEAD  Merseyside**                                                                 map 5

## *Beadles*

| 15 Rosemount, Oxton, Birkenhead L43 5SG | COOKING 1 |
| 051-653 9010 | COST £24 |

The restaurant is not of the kind that cocoons in luxury: it has small simple, tables close to one another and paper napkins. The menu for the month is short, with half a dozen choices for each of three courses. Many customers are satisfied: 'always very sound'; 'this bistro serves the only good food – carefully purchased, thought out and well served – in the Wirral peninsula.' Others have pointed to attentive service, splendid black puddings and Roy Gott's recitation of dishes to each table, which locals apparently 'either admire or cannot stand', not least because it can slow down service and become tedious the sixth time around. Bea Gott gives variety within this short menu. Dishes range from the very simple, like melon and Parma ham, memorable for well-bought ingredients, across a range of national influences – as in first courses of nori roulade, brandade de cabillaud and tabouleh – to traditional and modern British ideas. Individual game pie and calf's liver with star anise glaze are examples among main courses, treacle lick or pear and ginger meringue are typical puddings. Roy Gott is as articulate on his wines as on the food and is happy to offer his customers a glass of new discoveries to sample. House French is £5.50 CELLARMAN'S CHOICE : Morgon, Domaine Les Pilletts 1986, £8.95; Bourgogne Aligoté 1985, Defrance, £8.50. Coffee is unlimited after the first cup is paid for.

CHEF: Bea Gott   PROPRIETORS: Roy and Bea Gott
OPEN: Tue to Sat, D only
CLOSED: Aug
MEALS: 7.30 to 9
PRICES: £13 (£20)
SEATS: 34. Private parties: 30 main room. Children welcome. Wheelchair access. Music

---

'While at the restaurant I heard a lady (whom I know, but she doesn't know me) ask what these white things were in the salad. They were of course pignons – pine kernels. The waiter didn't know either but came back with the answer. The point is that I know that this lady stays a fortnight each at the Connaught, Chewton Glen and Inverlochy Castle and one would think with this and her other travels and culinary experience she would have recognised pine kernels. So what chance do adventurous restaurateurs have up here in the North?'  On dining in Lancashire

---

map 5

# Adil

| 148-150 Stoney Lane, Sparkbrook, B11 8AJ | COOKING 1 |
| 021-449 0335 | COST £10 |

Adil is only one of a number of balti houses in Sparkbrook and some might claim it is not the best but simply the best-known among non-locals because it was the first to open. Be that as it may, its reputation does also rest upon its cooking. 'The manager suggested five baltis to complement one another and we rolled up our sleeves and thoroughly enjoyed ourselves. I cannot believe how far more enjoyable this food is than standard Indian fare. It's quite simple – we'll be back and back again.' The 50-plus baltis, cooked in large cast-iron pans, range from the straightforward meat and chicken with which most sweet-houses began, to more interesting fresh vegetable ones like spinach, pulse and cauliflower. Breads are wonderfully fresh and there is good lassi to drink. A second Adil is nearby at 130 Stoney Lane. Unlicensed.

CHEF: Mr Ashraf   PROPRIETOR: Mr Arif
OPEN: all week
MEALS: noon to midnight
PRICES: £6 (£8). Unlicensed, but bring your own: no corkage
CARDS: Access, Visa
SEATS: 70. Private parties: 50 private room. Vegetarian meals. Children welcome

# Los Andes

| 806 Bristol Road, Selly Oak, B29 6BD | COOKING 1 |
| 021-471 3577 | COST £20 |

Cooking not just from the Andes but the whole South American continent can be had from this *cantina* opposite Sainsbury's. The restaurant is a co-operative that uses food as a means of introducing Latin American culture. The cooking is not refined, but it can be tasty and it is cheap. Live music is played twice a week and loud Muzak at other times – Latin American of course. There are Chilean wines and Mexican beers. House wine is £5.80.

CHEFS: Roque Mella, Freddy Aburto and Alejandro Lira   PROPRIETORS: Freddy Aburto, Greg Grandon and Roque Mella
OPEN: Mon to Sat
MEALS: 12 to 2, 7 to 11.30
PRICES: £10 (£17)
CARDS: Access, Amex, Diners, Visa
SEATS: 66. Private parties: 80 main room. Vegetarian meals. Children's helpings. Wheelchair access. Music

'Resist all recommendations for this restaurant's inclusion in the Guide. The chef is hopeless, the service chummy, verging on slapstick, the cost exorbitant. The menu is pretentious and strewn with adjectives: food on "pools" of sauce is "scented", "subtle", "enhanced" and "romantically married" with flavours that are "enticing", "delicate" or, when all else fails, "traditional".'  On inspecting in Hampshire

# Le Biarritz

| | |
|---|---|
| 148–149 Bromsgrove Street, B5 6RG | COOKING 2 |
| 021-622 1989 | COST £12–£32 |

'An oasis in a rather depressing part of Birmingham.' One of the virtues of this French restaurant, on a corner in the Chinatown quarter close to the Hippodrome, is its reliability. Carl Timms' menus, both *carte* and set-price – bargain business lunches and *dégustation* in the evenings – have developed little over the past couple of years, but recently some of the mannered modern touches seem to have dropped away. Fish remains his first love. Good dishes have included a fruits de mer pancake, crab salad and beautifully presented sea bass, while fixtures such as the hot goats' cheese oozing out of a flaky pastry case and the soupe des pêcheurs earn praise again. Meat dishes, for example a rare roasted rack of lamb, have also been well judged. Service is very attentive. The wine list is as French as the name of the restaurant. It is a surprising collection of clarets, some too young to see their full potential, others at their peak. Prices also vary, with bargains as well as more usual mark-ups. House Duboeuf is £7.50. CELLARMAN'S CHOICE : Ch. Ramage La Batisse, 1981, £16.90; Sauvignon de St-Bris 1988, Brocard, £12.40.

CHEF: Carl Timms   PROPRIETORS: Andrea and Susan Lo Coco
OPEN: Mon to Sat, exc Sat L
CLOSED: 25 Dec to 9 Jan
MEALS: 12 to 2, 7 to 10.30
PRICES: Set L £7.50 (£12), Set D £21 (£27). Service 10%
CARDS: Access, Amex, Diners, Visa
SEATS: 40. Private parties: 50 main room. Car-park, 10 places. Children's helpings. No-smoking area. Smart dress preferred. Wheelchair access. Music. Air-conditioned

# Chung Ying

| | |
|---|---|
| 16–18 Wrottesley Street, B5 6RT | COOKING 2 |
| 021-622 5669 and 1793 | COST £9–£14 |

A giant of a restaurant, still full to the brim on a Sunday with Chinese families and the odd, lone English person. The opinion in the Midlands is that Chung Ying has perked up its standards since the last *Guide*. Reports have come of fine dim-sum; one-plate meals of noodles perfectly crispy on the outside and yielding and savourous within, permeated by the aromas of pork, duck and prawns; fried vegetables in an edible bird's nest of yam strips; beef with ginger and spring onion; and generous portions of food quite palpably fresh. House wine £4.

CHEF/PROPRIETOR: Siu Chung Wong
OPEN: all week
MEALS: noon to midnight
PRICES: £7 (£11), Set L £5 (£9) to £6 (£10), Set D £6 (£10) to £8 (£12)
CARDS: Access, Amex, Diners, Visa
SEATS: 200. Private parties: 200 main room, 100 private room.
Car-park, 10 places. Vegetarian meals. Children welcome. Smart dress preferred. Music. Air-conditioned

## *Chung Ying Garden*

| Thorp Street, B5 4AT | COOKING 2 |
|---|---|
| 021-666 6622 | COST £11–£26 |

'A good beginning is half the battle won' is a Chinese proverb that the proprietors of the Garden took to heart. Nonetheless, the other half remains to be fought and signs are that the vanguard falters. The dim-sum get most praise with stuffed bean curd roll and chicken with glutinous rice among examples. Specialities like fried sliced fillet of beef with ground walnuts or steamed scallops with minced prawn have not always lived up to their descriptions, errors compounded by indifferent service. But fried fish cake and mange-tout; crispy fried stuffed pork intestine with salt and pepper; steamed pork pie with salted egg have been well-noticed. House French, £6.40, lots of tea, rice wine.

CHEF/PROPRIETOR: Siu Chung Wong
OPEN: all week
MEALS: noon to midnight (11 Sun)
PRICES: £13 (£22), Set L £6 (£11) to £10 (£15), Set D £8 (£13) to £15 (£20), Snacks from £1.10. Service 10%
CARDS: Access, Amex, Diners, Visa
SEATS: 300. Private parties: 100 main room, 50 and 100 private rooms. Vegetarian meals. Children welcome. Wheelchair access (side entrance; also WC). Music. Air-conditioned

## *Days of the Raj*

| 51 Dale End, B4 7LN | COOKING 2 |
|---|---|
| 021-236 0445 | COST £10–£23 |

There are dishes of Bombay mix in the pastel-coloured bar area, a collection of Raj photographs hung in the dining-room and a pink transparent curtain veiling the coffee lounge. It may all sound too westernised to expect really good food, but in fact the cooking, largely northern Indian with a Punjabi and Kashmiri bias, is sophisticated and classy. Rogan josh, for example, lamb with a thick intense sauce tasting of cumin and coriander, contrasts well with shikar badami, chunks of lamb served in a creamy, mild almond sauce. As the menu has reduced in size, so some of the more interesting specialities have been lost, but plenty remain: an excellent moghlai kebab, mixed tandooris, chicken jalfrezi and murgh massallum, which has to be ordered two days ahead. Complimentary poppadums come with good fresh pickles. At the end of the meal, a trolley with carefully arranged Indian sweets is wheeled around. Since the restaurant is close to the High Court and owned by a solicitor and barrister, many of the customers are lawyers. House French, £5.95.

CHEFS: Ramesh Chander and Rashpal Sunner    PROPRIETORS: Balbir Singh and P.S. Kulair
OPEN: all week, exc Sat and Sun L
MEALS: 12 to 2.30, 7 (6 Fri and Sat) to 11.30
PRICES: £12 (£19), Set L £5.95 (£10). Minimum £7.50 D only. Service inc
CARDS: Access, Amex, Diners, Visa
SEATS: 120. Private parties: 100 main room, 25 and 30 private rooms. Vegetarian meals. Children's helpings (with prior notice). Smart dress preferred. Wheelchair access (also WC). Music. Air-conditioned

# Henry's

| | |
|---|---|
| 27 St Pauls Square, B3 1RB | COOKING 1 |
| 021-200 1136 | COST £15–£23 |

Henry Wong visits both his restaurants every night, a level of personal involvement which appears to pay off. Henry's is, if anything, slightly smarter than its sibling, Henry Wong, in Harborne High Street, but both pull the crowds most nights. The prices are up a bit on other Chinese restaurants, but the food is first-class. A fashionable menu includes yuk shung (shredded meat in lettuce leaves); king prawns in a bird's nest; sizzling steaks and lamb; and crispy duck in plum sauce. For a party of five or more, the set meal is a useful way to test-drive the menu. House French is £6.

CHEF: C.W. Choi  PROPRIETORS: Henry Wong and C.W. Choi
OPEN: Mon to Sat
CLOSED: one week Aug
MEALS: 12 to 2, 6 to 11 (11.30 Sat)
PRICES: £12 (£19), Set L and D £11 (£15) and £11.50 (£16). Service inc
CARDS: Access, Amex, Diners, Visa
SEATS: 95. Private parties: 80 main room. Children welcome. Music

# Maharaja

| | |
|---|---|
| 23–25 Hurst Street, B5 4AS | COOKING 1 |
| 021-622 2641 | COST £12–£20 |

One reporter says it all: 'Long established in the city centre. Always full, too smoke-filled for comfort at times. It has been under the same management, in the same style, for the 18 years I have known it. Pink these days. Vegetable korma: very nice, different textures, just-cooked ginger, just about crisp peppers and peas stood out nicely above the sauce. Sag paneer – very good, spinach cooked to a pulp and quite hot with lots of coriander leaf with paneer. Nans OK – no more than that. Service OK for a busy, inexpensive restaurant. House white wine was really poor cheap stuff.'

CHEF: Bhupinder Waraich  PROPRIETOR: N.S. Batt
OPEN: Mon to Sat
MEALS: 12 to 2.30, 6 to 11.30
PRICES: £8 (£15), Set L £7.50 (£12) to £9.50 (£14), Set D £8.50 (£13) to £12.50 (£17).
Minimum £6.30. Service 10%
CARDS: Access, Amex, Diners, Visa
SEATS: 65. 18 tables outside. Private parties: 30 main room. Vegetarian meals. Children welcome. Wheelchair access. Music. Air-conditioned

---

*Several sharp operators have tried to extort money from restaurateurs on the promise of an entry in a guide book that has never appeared.* The Good Food Guide *makes no charge for inclusion and does not offer certificates of any kind.*

*The* Guide *office can quickly spot when a restaurateur is encouraging customers to write recommending inclusion. Such reports do not further a restaurant's cause. Please tell us if a restaurateur invites you to write to the* Guide.

---

## Sloans

27–29 Chad Square, Hawthorne Road
Edgbaston, B15 3TQ
021-455 6697

COOKING 2
COST £19–£32

This apparent fixture on the Birmingham scene is in the corner of a small shopping precinct opposite the White Swan on the Harborne road. Cheerful Roger Narbett cooks, the rest of the family oversees the much-redecorated dining-room. There has been a rethink this year to make the place more accessible, less victim of the tag 'exclusive'. Thus the menu has dropped its French and attention is brought to the short lunch offering. People still enjoy the fish: smoked haddock in a cream sauce; sole meunière on a bed of chopped mushrooms; pan-ried salmon trout. Presentation is also praised, although the contents of the trolley of sweets were once disappointing. The wine list offers no bargains, nor much adventure apart from some 1970 clarets, from £38 upwards. The eight house wines offer the best value, all French, starting at £8.

CHEF: Roger Narbett   PROPRIETORS: W.J. Narbett and Roger Narbett
OPEN: all week, exc Sat L and Sun D
CLOSED: bank hols, first week Jan
MEALS: 12 to 2, 7 to 10
PRICES: £19 (£27), Set L £13.50 (£19)
CARDS: Access, Amex, Diners, Visa
SEATS: 60. Private parties: 30 main room. Car-park, 60 places. Children welcome. Smart dress preferred. Wheelchair access (1 step; also WC). Music. Air-conditioned

## Thai Paradise

31 Paradise Circus, B1 2BJ
021-643 5523

COOKING 1
COST £9–£32

Even though it's hard to find, hidden in the concrete jungle opposite the town hall and near the library complex, Thai Paradise is usually full. The atmosphere is noisy and friendly and the food fresh-tasting. The set menus are a helpful introduction to Thai food, and include hot satay sauces, chicken in coconut and crab with oyster sauce. Or dip into the main menu for king prawn soup with kaffir lime or stir-fried squid with basil, chilli and garlic. House French is £6, or drink Thai Singha beer.

CHEF: Surachet Lathe   PROPRIETORS: Preecha and Robert Lathe
OPEN: all week, exc Sat and Sun L
MEALS: 12 to 3, 6 to 12 (1am Fri and Sat)
PRICES: £10 (£19), Set L £4.95 (£9), Set D £12.50 (£18) to £20 (£27). Service 10%
CARDS: Access, Amex, Diners, Visa
SEATS: 60. Private parties: 25 main room. Children's helpings. Smart dress preferred. Wheelchair access. Music. Air-conditioned

*If you see a certificate in a restaurant bearing the words 'Good Food Guide Top Restaurants', the claim is false (and the restaurant may be in contempt of court in displaying it) – see the Introduction. Please write and tell us the name and address of the restaurant.*

| BIRTLE   Greater Manchester | map 5 |

# ▲ *Normandie* ♛

| Elbut Lane, Birtle BL9 6UT | COOKING 3 |
| 061-764 3869 and 1170 | COST £22–£32 |

This hotel overlooking the foothills of the Pennines (when not obscured by low cloud or rain), was a *Guide* favourite in its days of ownership by Yves Champeau. Many owners and many chefs have passed since then, but consistency may be in the grasp of the Moussa family and the chef Pascal Pommier. There have been plaudits for very modern cooking offered as a *carte*, a restricted choice menu, or lighter lunches. A spring visitor praised a meal that began with a red pepper mousse with a tomato concassé, followed by a feuilleté, in the form of an Ali Baba basket, of queen scallops with a julienne of leeks, strips of orange rind and a white wine sauce; a side plate of good plain vegetables with a somewhat unsuitable gratin dauphinoise, and, to finish, a vacherin with a raspberry sorbet and coulis and poached pears. Other successes have been a serving of beef on wild mushrooms; chicken stuffed with vegetables with a light madeira sauce; a good marquise au chocolat; a satisfactory cheeseboard; and a warm gratin of oranges. Many of the dishes are derived from modern masters and their books; sometimes their descriptions and appearance belie their flavour. Service is correct, some say too correct. The wine list has improved this year with greater representation of the New World and other European regions. They have taken in some good Australian and New Zealand reds and whites and three vintages of the embattled Ch. Musar from the Lebanon, as well as making an effort with French country and lesser known wines to keep prices affordable. There is a Quincy as a cheaper alternative to Sancerre, there are some good Beaujolais, and a Toro from Spain, Bodegas Farina 1985, gives fair body and fruit for its low cost. House French Chenin Blanc is £7, Côtes de Thongue Rouge is £7.50. CELLARMAN'S CHOICE: Menetou Salon, Le Petit Clos 1986, Jean Max Roger, £13.50; Ch. d'Issan, Margaux 1984, £22.50. The menu states 'prices are fully inclusive of service charge' and the proprietors say 'we do not believe in tipping.'

CHEF: Pascal Pommier   PROPRIETORS: Gillian and Max Moussa
OPEN: Mon to Sat, exc Mon and Sat L
CLOSED: 26 Dec to first Sun in Jan, exc New Year's Eve
MEALS: 12 to 2, 7 to 9.30
PRICES: £24 (£29), Set D £16.50 (£22). Service inc
CARDS: Access, Amex, Diners, Visa
SEATS: 60. Private parties: 70 main room. Car-park, 60 places. Vegetarian meals. Children's helpings. Smart dress preferred. No cigars/pipes in dining-room. Wheelchair access (also WC). Music
ACCOMMODATION: 24 rooms, all with bath/shower. Rooms for disabled. Lift. B&B £45 to £65. Baby facilities. TV. Phone. Confirm booking by noon

---

*All details are as accurate as possible at the time of going to press, but chefs and owners often change, and it is wise to check by telephone before making a special journey. Many readers have been disappointed when set-price bargain meals are no longer available. Ask when booking.*

BISHOP'S CLEEVE  Gloucestershire                                   map 2

## ▲ *Cleeveway House*

Bishop's Cleeve GL52 4SA
BISHOP'S CLEEVE (024 267) 2585                         COOKING 1
on A435, 3m N of Cheltenham                            COST £28

This is a fine Italianate stone house redolent of the Victorian suburbs of Bath, or
of the Cheltenham just left behind on the Evesham road. That road intrudes if
you stay overnight. The bright, if not garish, decoration of the public rooms is
the setting for a long menu that still is supplemented by daily specials – game
is a fondness. The style is Anglo-French with no specific tilt. Standards seem
less constant than they have been: a fine salmon mousse with salmon eggs and
lobster sauce, and a decent chicken quenelle with very mushroomy sauce were
followed by less impressive main courses and vegetables. Old hands confirm
ambitions appear lower than they were. Bread is bought in, service not always
very informed. The wine list is a pleasant one: traditional, but clear and with
no nasty surprises. House French, £5.80. CELLARMAN'S CHOICE : Brown
Brothers Chardonnay 1986, £13.80; Ch. Meyney 1981, St Estèphe, £21.

CHEF/PROPRIETOR: John Marfell
OPEN: Mon to Sat, exc Mon L
CLOSED: 1 week after Christmas, Good Friday, bank hols
MEALS: 12 to 1.45, 7 to 9.45
PRICES: £16 (£23)
CARD: Access
SEATS: 38. Private parties: 10 main room. Car-park, 50 places. Vegetarian meals. Children's
helpings. No cigars/pipes in dining-room. Wheelchair access (also WC). Air-conditioned
ACCOMMODATION: 3 rooms, all with bath/shower. B&B £28.50 to £45. Baby facilities. Pets
welcome. Afternoon teas. Garden. Air-conditioning. TV. Scenic. Doors close at 1am

---

BISHOP'S TACHBROOK  Warwickshire                                   map 2

## ▲ *Mallory Court*

COUNTY OF THE YEAR RESTAURANT

Harbury Lane
Bishop's Tachbrook CV33 9QB
LEAMINGTON SPA (0926) 330214                          COOKING 3
off A452, 2m S of Leamington Spa                      COST £26–£50

One reader recalls with affection the welcome accorded him on a January
night: of all the country-house hotels, this is the most obviously sybarite.
Mythology has it that certain towns and certain districts are unable to support
good restaurants. The Midlands has suffered from the jibe. Mallory Court is
one of its answers. Signs, however, of playing to its audience do exist. The
menus, with set prices pitched fairly high, have hedonistic leanings: 'Dublin
Bay prawns cooked in garlic oil with herbs and vegetables, diced and bound
with a salmon mousseline, wrapped in tender leaves of Savoy cabbage and
steamed, served with a tomato and olive oil sauce.' The style is
uncompromisingly modern: that olive oil-based sauce (compare with Shaun
Hill's experiments with fragrant oil emulsions at Gidleigh Park, see Chagford);
the use of leaf coriander, ginger, soy sauce and endless white chocolate. The

important thing, observations about the menu notwithstanding, is that people enjoy the cooking (though baulk at the extra £6 for cheese). One reader wrote full of enthusiasm for a meal of classic artichoke hearts farcis à la duxelles, sauce béarnaise; a best-end of lamb with a rosemary sauce and a ratatouille; and a passion-fruit soufflé. Others speak of the punctilious service in the panelled dining-room; others wax eloquent on the bedrooms and formal gardens to this Lutyensesque house. The wine list matches the food for price. Though containing some good 1970 clarets, some fair petits châteaux, and some Côte Chalonnaise wines from André Delorme, it needs work and lower margins to take it into the first rank. Italian and New World selections are boring, there are too many négociants' burgundies, and Spain doesn't get a look in. House French ranges from £7.95 to £11.50. The menu states 'no service charge is made or expected.' This is the right stuff!

CHEF: A.J.G. Holland   PROPRIETORS: A.J.G. Holland and J.R. Mort
OPEN: all week
MEALS: 12.30 to 1.45, 7.30 to 9.30 (10 Sat)
PRICES: Set L £18.50 (£26), Set D £35 (£42). Service inc
CARD: Access, Amex, Diners, Visa
SEATS: 50. Private parties: 50 main room. Car-park, 50 places. No children under 12. Smart dress preferred for D. No cigars/pipes in dining-room
ACCOMMODATION: 10 rooms, all with bath/shower. B&B £87 to £165. No children under 12. Afternoon teas. Garden. Swimming-pool. Tennis. TV. Phone. Scenic. Doors close at 12 [GHG]

---

## BLACKWATER  Cornwall

map 1

### Long's

Blackwater TR8 8HH
TRURO (0872) 561111

*COUNTY OF THE YEAR RESTAURANT*

COOKING 3
COST £14–£28

The Longs are back! There are many in Cornwall who rued the day that Ian and Ann Long left for Somerset. Their emphasis on quality at a reasonable price was deservedly popular. They began in mine buildings (at the Count House, Botallack); they have fetched up this time in the former mine captain's house of Wheal Concord, a granite and slate-roofed Georgian house on the old Redruth road in the centre of Blackwater village. It has been decorated with a feminine touch that no bluff mine captain would ever have contemplated. Sitting amid peach and green, dining off pink linen (which others interpret respectively as sand, turquoise and apricot) – the luxury reflects the hopes of business being brought to a revitalised and expanding Truro. The restaurant is also very much a statement of how the Longs wish things to be. Their daughter Suzanne is now independently established as a maker of conserves and jams, and there are many expressions of the Longs' identity, from the rocking chair and resident teddy bear in the lobby to Ann Long's pictures on the wall and Ian Long's unmissable bonhomie in bar and dining-room. Ann Long has her own style of cooking, born largely out of enthusiasm; so enthusiastic that the soup served as second course in the à la carte dinner is complimentary, to allow her to continue making soups without any restraint from a lack of orders. Many of her dishes involve wrapping: salmon and turbot with cucumber arranged in layers in a filo parcel; spiced lamb in a pastry case; loin of lamb wrapped in puff and served with fennel and laverbread; rabbit in puff; salmon in puff with almonds, sultanas and cumin. Even if there is no wrapping, there may be rolling, as in chicken breast beaten out, layered with smoked salmon and asparagus and rolled up again. When this is sliced it looks magical. When eaten with a lemon butter it has lightness and luxury all at once. Menus are commendably short, changing daily on a rolling basis. First courses may involve cumulation. One enthusiastically reported meal began with a triple mousse of lobster, roe and smoked mussels: khaki, pink and cream stripes (perhaps the colours of Cornwall's tricolor when independence comes); and a selection of terrines and meats – a ballotine of chicken filled with a herb farce, a rough pork terrine, smooth and gamey rabbit pâté, and some rare roast beef that is marinated with chopped black olives. A Sunday lunch began with 'a light mixed beginning', described as 'the best leftovers in the world, three different mousses, marinated mushrooms, tandoori chicken breast and a salad of cherry tomatoes.' Generosity, often interpreted as plenty, continues, both in the vegetables accompanying the main course, and the desserts, which may be very substantial. These live on a table in the centre of the dining-room. The hungry or the curious may try more than one. Chocolate praline mousse, strawberry meringue gateau, apricot crème brûlée, oatmeal meringue topped with raspberries, trifle with black cherries are some that have received mention. Ann Long does not confine herself to the kitchen, coming out frequently to serve or help. Thus one may discuss the merits of these dishes with her. First reactions to the cooking have undoubtedly been as enthusiastic as the Longs themselves, but tempered by thoughts that not every experiment works perfectly. Occasionally the flavours overbalance (when, for example, using lovage – a hazardous herb – in soup), or the tastes do not knit, or there is one layer too many. By contrast, the wine list is a masterpiece of understatement with very few wines but the maximum range of selection at prices never exceeding £20 a bottle. It changes rapidly and always contains novelties, the Gamla wines from Israel as an instance. There are even fewer half-bottles. House French is £5.50. Tipping is 'not encouraged'.

CHEF: Ann Long   PROPRIETORS: Ian and Ann Long
OPEN: Wed to Sat, D only, and Sun L
CLOSED: four weeks during winter
MEALS: 12.30 to 1.45, 7.30 to 10
PRICES: £15 (£23), Set Sun L £9.50 (£14)
CARDS: Access, Amex, Visa
SEATS: 30. Private parties: 10 main room, 10 and 12 private rooms. Car-park, 20 places.
Children's helpings. No children under 12. Smart dress preferred. Wheelchair access
(also WC)

## Pennypots

| Blackwater TR4 8EY | COOKING 2 |
| REDRUTH (0209) 820347 | COST £22 |

On the Redruth to Bodmin expressway, Blackwater has spawned not one but two restaurants in the past twelvemonth. This concatenation is mere coincidence, though it must reflect the changing society of Cornwall in some way useful to future historians. Pennypots is the home of Kevin and Jane

Vyner and has been the locale of restaurants in prior incarnations. The new name and the new style are to rid them of the incubus. Kevin Vyner has taught the army to cook and been part of Britain's team for the Culinary Olympics. Small wonder, then, that his menu reads as it does: 'Fresh smoked Scotch salmon parcel filled with crab, prawns, apple and celery and mixed in a light lemon and horseradish mayonnaise served on a bed of salad garnished with lemon.' The advantage is that he has the technique to bring this off. The main dishes of the *carte* are dominated by beef and there is a fair quotient of stuffing and larding. On a specifically Cornish menu that he cooked during the summer there were indications of this technique and taste: a 'croissant' made of salmon and sole turned round each other in crescent form had fine saffron shellfish sauce, though the fish gained small advantage from being thus twined; a breast of duck was cunningly stuffed with its own liver, wrapped in a layer of spinach leaves, on a good madeira sauce; and the closing column of orange-flavoured cream cheese crémet topped with a layer of chocolate, with a black cherry sauce was impressive to look at and a better marriage of flavours than many strident chocolate/citrus concoctions manage these days. The dangers lie in the fandangos that go with such cooking. Technique becomes an end in itself, taste goes out the window – pushed either by the preoccupations of the chef or the demands of customers for show and display. The homely and gentle charm of Jane Vyner may curb the flights of fancy; then would Blackwater be a privileged place indeed. House wine is £4.95.

CHEF: Kevin Vyner   PROPRIETORS: Kevin and Jane Vyner
OPEN: Tue to Sun, D only (Tue to Sat in winter)
MEALS: 7 to 10.30
PRICES: £15 (£18). Service inc
CARDS: Access, Amex, Diners, Visa
SEATS: 30. Private parties: 12 and 18 private rooms. Car-park, 14 places. Children's helpings on request. Music

---

**BLANDFORD FORUM  Dorset**                                    map 2

## ▲ *La Belle Alliance* ♟

Whitecliff Mill Street
Blandford Forum DT11 7BP                                    COOKING 2
BLANDFORD FORUM (0258) 452842                              COST £22–£28

Take the road from Blandford's fine market square towards Shaftesbury. La Belle Alliance occupies an Italianate Victorian house with columned front porch. The restaurant is as well dressed and formal as the architecture, mediated by the charm and warmth of Lauren Davison. The set-price dinner menu offers four or five choices at each course and changes almost daily. The cooking has a liking for sweet-and-sour – king fish and scallops in a mild curry and pineapple sauce – and for matching fairly assertive flavours to the main vehicle of a dish: halibut with courgettes and cheese; monkfish and scallops on puréed leeks and red pimento sauce; partridge with red cabbage, onions and apples; fillet steak with Stilton and walnuts; pork with sage, red wine and cream. It needs a master to bring these off and all credit to Philip Davison that many readers enjoy his cooking. His ice-creams are excellent too. The wine list has a fair spread and does not overcharge. House wines include the organic Muscadet of Guy Bossard, and are priced from £7.50 to £8.65. CELLARMAN'S CHOICE : Villa Maria Sauvignon Blanc, Hawkes Bay 1987, £10.50; Ch. Bon Dieu des Vignes, Graves 1982, £17.25.

CHEF: Philip Davison   PROPRIETORS: Lauren and Philip Davison
OPEN: Mon to Sat, D only, and bank hol Sun
MEALS: 7 to 9.30 (10 Sat)
PRICES: Set D £18 (£22) to £19 (£23). Service inc
CARDS: Access, Amex, Visa
SEATS: 28. Private parties: 36 main room. Car-park, 9 places. No children under 7. No smoking in dining-room. Wheelchair access. Music
ACCOMMODATION: 5 rooms, all with bath/shower. B&B £38 to £49. No children under 7. Pets welcome. TV. Phone. Scenic. Doors close at midnight. Confirm by 6 [GHG]

---

BOLLINGTON   Cheshire                                                        map 5

## Mauro's

88 Palmerston Street, Bollington SK10 5PW                    COOKING 2
BOLLINGTON (0625) 73898                                          COST £23

Here is a family business providing an honest service with warmth and enthusiasm. It steers a path between design-conscious modernity and the awful Britalian trattoria with some judgement. The Italian staples – melon, Parma ham, saltimbocca alla romana – are not badly done; but the daily specials – the varying fish and the fresh pasta, often with a good garlic aroma and chilli – are the best things. The antipasti from the trolley have pleased with their piquant dressings – aubergine, squid, anchovies and red peppers. Similarly, scallops cooked accurately with a brandied cream sauce and apples to give bite and acidity, were appreciated, save for the bottled artichoke hearts. Cheshire compromise has meant that some few things may come from freezer, bottle or tin. Puddings and sweets are good-looking and fair. Coffee is good. Everyone remarks the quality of service. Sr Mauro emerges from his kitchen, where he can be seen cooking through a glazed archway, and modestly talks to his customers. A short Italian wine list gives too little information about makers and vintages but there are some fine Lungarotti wines as well as super-Tuscans, Sassicaia and Tignanello. House Italian is £6.85. CELLARMAN'S CHOICE : Chianti Vicchiomaggio Riserva 1982, £10.20; Chardonnay del Alto Adige, £9.90.

CHEF/PROPRIETOR: V. Mauro
OPEN: Tue to Sat
MEALS: 12 to 2, 7 to 10
PRICES: £13 (£19)
CARDS: Access, Amex, Visa
SEATS: 50. Vegetarian meals. Children's helpings. Wheelchair access (also WC). Music

---

*Consumers' Association is planning a* **Vegetarian Good Food Guide**, *to cafés and restaurants offering at least one vegetarian main course. Please send reports and recommendations to* The **Vegetarian Good Food Guide**, FREEPOST, *2 Marylebone Road, London NW1 1YN.*

# Randalls

22 High Street, Old Market Place
Bollington SK10 5PH
BOLLINGTON (0625) 75058

COOKING 2
COST £12–£25

Bollington is a stone-built mill village on the line dividing the flat meadows of
Cheshire from the Derbyshire hills. The main square or green, lined with
terraced houses showing signs of Cheshire gentrification, is also the site of this
sound restaurant catering well for its locale. Correspondents spoke at first in
hushed tones of the chef's training at the Dorchester. Rather as Uncle's presence
at Waterloo fitted him for a lifetime's disagreement with von Clausewitz, so a
spell at the Dorchester is qualification to cook for the world. In fact, the chef
who now cooks at Randalls did not train at the Dorchester, though his
predecessor did. No matter, people still approve it. The restaurant is quite
relaxed, not so much as to admit people dressed in jeans, but enough to have
bare board floors, bare tables, cane chairs and a lot of pink and blue paint.
When full, it can be crowded. The seasonal menu is long and is supplemented
by a fortnightly 'market menu'. The style is modern smart bistro: sauté of
artichoke and wild mushrooms with herbs and garlic, thinly sliced smoked
beef on melon; fillet of beef stuffed with hazelnuts and covered with smoked
bacon; veal cutlet stuffed with blue cheese and broccoli with a béarnaise. More
discreet cooking may occur on a reasonably priced gourmet evening where a
longer meal is cooked: terrine of pike and trout; smoked chicken consommé;
sorbet of strawberries and green peppercorns; paupiette of veal with
sweetbreads; and charlotte of rhubarb and plum had moments of real pleasure.
Sunday brunch is popular, black puddings to the fore. There is a short but
inexpensive wine list. House French, £4.95.

CHEF: Lee Allsup   PROPRIETORS: Southdene Ltd
OPEN: Mon to Sun, exc Mon and Sat L, Sun D
MEALS: 12 to 2.30, 7 to 10 (10.30 Fri and Sat)
PRICES: £14 (£21), Set L £7.95 (£12), Set D from £12.50 (£17)
CARDS: Access, Amex, Diners, Visa
SEATS: 50. Private parties: 50 main room. Children's helpings (Sunday L only). Smart dress
preferred. Wheelchair access (1 step). Music

---

**BOROUGHBRIDGE  North Yorkshire**                                    map 7

# La Petite Fleur

4 Fishergate, Boroughbridge YO5 9AL
BOROUGHBRIDGE (0423) 322055

COOKING 2
COST £28

Paul Grindle was London-trained, working at Anna's Place, then moved to
Crabwall Manor at Mollington (see entries). He set up shop in his native
Yorkshire and plies his trade in a way that must have surprised the denizens of
Boroughbridge – so much so that a move is intended, towards the denser
population of Leeds. But his activities were noted, 'a little gem of a place', and
Yorkshire people may be well advised to keep track of his movements. La
Petite Fleur is so called, perhaps, for its size, for the minuscule proportions of
its kitchen, and for the Laura Ashley-style fabrics which, together with carpets

and velvets in deep red, give the place a happy, homely touch – well warmed in winter by live fires. The cooking is by no means petite but serious in intent. The very short weekly menu of three choices in each course proclaims some of its affinities in the flavourings for three main dishes in the springtime: blackcurrant with beef, lemon with duck, tomato and basil with salmon. Thoroughly modern British. Technique and taste seem well allied, improved by an adequate supply of vegetables selected for each meat and disposed around the perimeters of large cartwheel plates. Saucing is light and accurately reduced, for example in a warm salad of fillets of lemon sole on an orange sauce, the citrus giving the correct acidity to an otherwise bland flesh. Puddings continue the metropolitan touch, as in a walnut parfait with a first rate salmon tuile and a mango coulis. Cheeses, both British and French, come from Alan Porter. In this first enterprise, Paul Grindle has sensibly limited his repertoire to ensure high standards (though not yet improving on bought bread). The cost, for Boroughbridge, is high and Leeds may offer a wider audience. House wine is £6.25. From a short list, CELLARMAN'S CHOICE : is Pouilly Fumé, Ch. de Tracy 1987, £13.50; St-Véran, Domaine St-Martin, 1987 Duboeuf, £9.95.

CHEF: Paul Grindle   PROPRIETORS: Paul and Judith Grindle
OPEN: Tue to Sat, D only
CLOSED: 2 weeks at Christmas
MEALS: 7.30 to 9.30
PRICES: £16 (£23)
SEATS: 16. Children's helpings on request

---

**BOTLEY  Hampshire**                                                map 2

## Cobbett's

15 The Square, Botley SO3 2EA                        COOKING 1
BOTLEY (0489) 782068                                 COST £17–£40

From its appearance, the timbered cottage suggests olde worlde tea-shop, but the Skipwiths run their restaurant with enthusiasm for French cooking. Lucie Skipwith, a Burgundian, is no longer in the kitchen, so the cooking is now characterised by the modish inspiration of chef Peter Hayes: fillet of pork has appeared in a 'sauce confuse' of garlicky cooking juices with tomato, orange and lemon segments, while a first-course ramekin of 'saumon mariné' has been flavoured with caviare, diced cucumber and mustard seed. There are still solid provincial dishes on the menus – boudin de volaille aux pommes, rognons de veau à la liégeoise, gigot d'agneau – but they are not always cooked with the verve of past years. A regional gastronomic evening yielded a properly made quiche Lorraine and excellent choucroute and noodles accompanying roast loin of pork stuffed with prunes. The wine list is short and French, but the bottles are nicely chosen with a showing from the Loire and Rhône from Yapp Brothers. House Bordeaux from the family vineyard, £8.50. CELLARMAN'S CHOICE : St-Véran 1987, Duboeuf, £11.33; the first vintage from Wickham, the 1987, John Charnley, £8.50.

CHEF: Peter Hayes  PROPRIETORS: Charles and Lucie Skipwith
OPEN: Mon to Sat, exc Mon and Sat L
CLOSED: 2 weeks summer, 2 weeks winter
MEALS: 12 to 2, 7.30 (7 Sat) to 10
PRICES: £21 (£33), Set L £9 (£17) to £11 (£19), Set D £16 (£24)
CARDS: Access, Amex, Visa
SEATS: 40. Private parties: 40 main room, 15 private room. Car-park, 15 places. No children under 12. No cigars/pipes in dining-room

---

**BOURNEMOUTH  Dorset**                                                    map 2

## Sophisticats

43 Charminster Road
Bournemouth BH8 8UE                                        COOKING 2
BOURNEMOUTH (0202) 291019                                  COST £25

Tucked in a shopping parade, the feline theme much in evidence, this small restaurant is viewed with affection by both residents and visitors: the salvation of no few holidays. Most popular meat dishes are a satay beginning and a Javanese fillet steak but it is fish that perhaps occupies the limelight, that and the desserts where no invention is spared – from praline and armagnac mousse with caramel sauce and candied almonds to a blue pear sorbet. John Knight and Bernard Calligan have assessed their market sensitively and provide fair food at fair prices. The repertoire does not change greatly from year to year, but variety is afforded by weekly specials and the sort of fish available. Bernard Calligan has a good line in soufflés: cheese for the first course, chocolate or chocolate and rum for dessert. On a short wine list beset by split vintages, the best offerings are half a dozen specials at the end. House French is £5.75.

---

CHEF: Bernard Calligan  PROPRIETORS: John Knight and Bernard Calligan
OPEN: Tue to Sat, D only
CLOSED: 2 weeks Jan, 1 week May, last 2 weeks Oct
MEALS: 7 to 10
PRICES: £14 (£21)
SEATS: 32. Private parties: 12 main room. Children welcome. Wheelchair access (also WC). Music

---

**BOWNESS-ON-WINDERMERE  Cumbria**                                          map 7

## Porthole Eating House ▮

3 Ash Street
Bowness-on-Windermere LA23 3EB                             COOKING 3
WINDEREMERE (096 62) 2793                                  COST £29

Surely only an enthusiast would, for 10 years, sponsor a cycling time-trial of 25 miles round Lake Windermere. Gianni Berton is the man. His enthusiasm extends to restaurant, kitchen and wine list: even the bar list is longer than 95 per cent of British restaurants – make for Bowness for an eau-de-vie of figs. The restaurant is old English in decoration and almost bistro in feel. It is close to the lake, across the square from the parish church. The printed *carte* may hint at no more than a British trattoria, but save your appetite for the weekly specialities, a dozen choices of interest and invention combining new creations (breast of chicken filled with pâté and turned in shallots, herbs and mushroom) and Italian cooking that may lean towards the Veneto (Sr Berton's mother was Venetian) or the Tuscan (his Aunt Ancilla is from Lucca). Try, for instance, calf's liver with an agrodolce sauce. The changes are rung fairly regularly, but some constants on this speciality menu are pears Mirabelle, poached in red wine with a Roquefort sauce, a fish cocktail and a very good spaghetti bolognese. Lake District regulars can usually find a sticky toffee pudding here, or various ice-cream specialities created by Judy Berton, who is also the breadmaker. The cooking, marked by a vigorous approach to taste in sauces and flavourings, as well as a trencherman's view of quantity, is noted as improving as the years pass. The wine list is a *tour de force*. Extremely long, it has sections of oldsters (back to the 1920s in clarets) and rarities whose price is given only on enquiry, but it is chiefly remarkable for its Italian, Spanish, Australian and (perhaps the least common) German bins. It is deep enough to do justice to Alsace, the Rhône and other classic regions as well, and it provides a fair choice of halves. Note the run of Châteauneuf-du-Papes, though none earlier than 1981, the Nuits-St-Georges, both red (1983) and white (1981), from Henri Gouges and the Cabernet Sauvignons 1977 and 1978 from Jekel, Montebello, and Joseph Phelps in California. House Merlot and Verduzzo from the Veneto £7 a litre. CELLARMAN'S CHOICE : Gewürztraminer Reserve 1983, Hugel, £18; Riesling Reserve Personelle 1983, Hugel £18; Tinto Pesquera, Ribera del Duero 1985, £18.

CHEF: Michael Metcalfe   PROPRIETORS: Judy and Gianni Berton
OPEN: all week D, exc Tue
CLOSED: mid-Dec to mid-Feb
MEALS: 6.30 to 11
PRICES: £15 (£24)
CARDS: Access, Amex, Diners, Visa
SEATS: 40. Private parties: 36 main room, 22 private room. Children's helpings. Music

---

**BOX** Wiltshire                                                    map 2

## *Clos du Roy at Box House*

Box SN14 9NR                                                    COOKING 3
BATH (0225) 744447                                             COST £18–£43

Philippe Roy's ambition is great. From a tiny restaurant on the high pavement in Bath where one forceful patron could outcrow the rest, he has leapt to a fine eighteenth-century vicarage close to Isambard Kingdom Brunel's Box Tunnel, with seven acres of garden and car-park and future plans that resemble an Albert Speer sanatorium. Not content with just a restaurant, the intentions are big. At present, however, he has his work cut out in the kitchen. There are dining-rooms to feed: all in the grandest of good taste and with much fun from combining all sorts of ingredients. The style that he elaborated at the first Clos du Roy may have once been more in tune with the times than it now strikes some readers. There is a long *carte*, a five-course *menu surprise* and perhaps three or four daily dishes recited at commencement. The menu gives some, but not enough, hint of the profusion on the plate. So far, as well, the staff is not trained to indicate the likelihood of variation from the advertised dish. Illustration of both defects is a main course of wild rabbit with sage butter, and an apple quiche. What actually arrived was a disproportionately small quantity of rabbit, a courgette flower stuffed with diced aubergine and courgette in a blue cheese sauce, a quarter of a skinned tomato, a morel, a penny round of sage butter and some delicious fried sage leaves. This tasted quite at variance with the intention and never achieved homogeneity. A dessert of iced walnut terrine with a caramel sauce was four slices of excellent terrine containing lemon and caramelised nut, an intense sauce feathered with chocolate, a chocolate walnut 'shell' containing a kernel of walnut, a mint leaf, a slice of mango and of star fruit, sprigs of redcurrant, strawberries and raspberries. This is student stuff. Complexity is substituted for good cooking: vegetables, for example, are first rate, even if bread is not and the butter can be old. Less striving, perhaps forced by very high prices, would be to everyone's benefit. The wine list hardly pulls a punch on prices either. Mark-ups are more French than English. The range is almost exclusively French with a few interesting country wines. House wines, from £11.30. CELLARMAN'S CHOICE : Pécharmant, Ch. de Tiregand 1985, £14.50; Cassis, Clos Ste-Magdeleine 1985, £16.50.

CHEF: Philippe Roy   PROPRIETORS: Philippe and Emma Roy
OPEN: all week
MEALS: 12 to 2.30, 7 to 10
PRICES: £27 (£35), Set L £11.95 (£18) to £14.50 (£20), Set D £24.50 (£33) to £27.50 (£36). Service inc
CARDS: Access, Amex, Diners, Visa
SEATS: 55. Private parties: 28 main room, 15, 15 and 30 private rooms. Car-park, 50 places. Children's helpings. No-smoking area. Wheelchair access (1 step; also WC)

---

**BRADFORD   West Yorkshire**                                     map 5

## Bharat

502 Great Horton Road, Bradford BD7 4EG                COOKING 1
BRADFORD (0274) 521200                                 COST £7–£18

Opened late in 1987, the Bharat, found on one of the arterial roads climbing the hill out of town, is now setting standards among the mass of Indian restaurants in the locality. Sequinned pictures glitter on the walls, but otherwise the décor remains plain. The menu is unpretentious, too, running through the standards, with karahis and vegetarian thalis as the chef's specialities. Dishes that are ordinary elsewhere are here lifted by the flavours of good, fresh ingredients and a charcoal tandoor. In lamb tikka, for example, succulent lumps of meat arrive in a rich but not greasy curry sauce. Likewise, home-made kulfi is creamy and studded with pistachios. Peripherals like garlicky poppadums, chapati and pilau rice – not tinted the usually mandatory lurid yellow – are good too. House wine, £5.10. Although there is a no-smoking zone, its tables still have ashtrays on them – the best of both worlds?

---

*See the inside of the front cover for an explanation of the new 1 to 5 rating system recognising cooking standards.*

CHEFS: M Parmar and Mohan Mistry   PROPRIETORS: Mohan and Jantilal Mistry
OPEN: Tue to Sun
MEALS: 12 to 2, 6 to 12
PRICES: £8 (£15), Set L £4.95 (£7), Set D for 2 £19.95 (£22). Service inc
CARDS: Access, Amex, Diners, Visa
SEATS: 48. Private parties: 48 main room. Car-park, 8 places. Vegetarian meals. Children's
helpings. Separate smoking area. Wheelchair access. Music. Air-conditioned

---

## ▲ Restaurant 19,
## Belvedere Hotel ♥

North Park Road, Bradford BD9 4NT                    COOKING 3
BRADFORD (0274) 492559                               COST £33–£42

In a solid Victorian villa in a leafy Victorian suburb, Stephen Smith pursues his
craft. Around him, the hotel upgrades its rooms. The restaurant, occupying the
ground floor, retains original details, done over, picked out and rendered with
a certain Yorkshire flamboyance. A spirit of enquiry hangs round the kitchen,
'What if...?' This year, it has been smoked foods. Having discovered a good
source, the kitchen has developed it. Smoked eel with a gooseberry compote,
smoked salmon, and smoked loin of lamb are some of the results, the lamb
being served with sauté kidney and a gooseberry and sage jelly. A fillet of
smoked pork with a mushroom pudding containing diced Parma ham
reminded one reporter of Austrian frankfurters, 'the kind you get in ski resorts'.
There has been success, it appears, in moderating the smoked taste so as not to
mask the flavour of the raw original. Pickles and jellies are other favourites of
this chef: gooseberry, rhubarb, cucumber and onion, beetroot and radish are
just some of them. The cooking is substantial, the flavours strong but kept in
check: lovage and coriander are two often-used herbs. Some recommended
dishes have been grilled fillet of sea trout with warm potato and sorrel salad;
summer soup of cucumber, lettuce and onion with lovage; saddle of rabbit
with home-made green pasta and a herb cream sauce; sea bass and salmon
baked with basil and tomato; a soup of cherries with cinnamon ice-cream;
peach and almond tart. Vegetables have been integrated into each main course
but diners remain very conservative. The wine list is trimmed down and comes
from new suppliers. The hundred bottles give an even spread (though none
from Italy); the prices are not exorbitant. House wine, £8.50. The bread is good.

---

CHEF: Stephen Smith   PROPRIETORS: Stephen Smith and Robert Barbour
OPEN: Tue to Sat, D only
MEALS: 7 to 9.30 (10 Sat)
PRICES: Set D £23 (£33) to £25 (£35)
CARDS: Amex, Diners, Visa
SEATS: 40. Private parties: 10 main room. Car-park, 16 places. Children welcome. No
smoking in dining-room. Smart dress preferred. Music
ACCOMMODATION: 13 rooms, 3 with bath/shower. B&B £25 to £35. TV. Doors close at
11.30. Confirm by 6

---

*Preliminary test of a good restaurant: order fresh orange juice and see what you get.*

*The* Guide *always appreciates hearing about changes of chef or owner.*

---

## BRAMPTON Cumbria                                           map 7

# ▲ *Farlam Hall*

Brampton CA8 2NG
HALLBANKGATE (06976) 234
on A689, 2m from Brampton (not at                          COOKING 3
Farlam village)                                      COST £24–£30

The atmosphere in this early-Victorian extended farmhouse, with very pretty surrounds, is formal and a touch eccentric, though not unpleasantly so. There are strong overtones of Jane Austen emanating from the Bennet-style family act put on by the owners, but guests would have to be feeling distinctly misanthropic not to enter into the spirit of the mock-Victorian parlour theatre that prevails from the moment of gathering for sherry and a look at the menus to the passing on towards the dining-room. The ambience is comfortable and tables are well spaced, so it's not hard to feel relaxed. And the food is still excellent value on a finely balanced set-price menu. Salmon and sole roulade with a restrained tarragon sauce, Lancashire guinea-fowl with a kumquat sauce, and caramelised raspberry crème brûlée would be a typical meal, well presented and interspersed with winter fruit sorbet, carefully judged vegetables and an English cheeseboard. The wine list is very short, shorter than most country-house hotels. The wines, however, are not ill chosen and prices are fair. House French (red) and English (white) are £5.95.

CHEF: Barry Quinion   PROPRIETORS: Quinion and Stevenson families
OPEN: all week, D only
CLOSED: Feb .
MEALS: 8
PRICES: Set D £19 (£24) and £20 (£25)
CARDS: Access, Amex, Visa
SEATS: 40. Private parties: 30 main room. Car-park, 30 places. No children under 4. Smart dress preferred. Wheelchair access. One sitting
ACCOMMODATION: 13 rooms, all with bath/shower. D, B&B £55 to £90. No children under 5. Afternoon teas. Garden. TV. Phone. Scenic. Doors close at 12. Confirm by 2 [GHG]

## BRAY Berkshire                                             map 2

# *Waterside Inn*

Ferry Road, Bray SL6 2AT                                   COOKING 4
MAIDENHEAD (0628) 20691                               COST £29–£73

The thing that always strikes the newcomer to Waterside is the valet parking. Americans may expect it, but it is a thrill in little old England. Take the signs off the main road to Bray village. Once in the centre, you see that Waterside has been extended the privilege of a council sign. The house is right on the river. The fully glazed extension, framed by willows, affords a smashing view for those on the front row. The back of the restaurant, a semi-circular amphitheatre to that window, is done out as a luxury garden pavilion. True indicators of original Roux taste are found in the centre of the room. Service is by a young army, marshalled by Napoleonic black-coats. It is proficient but humourless; but then, a production such as this needs organisation, not laughs. Although fixtures and fittings are of the highest standard, there are some tables so badly placed as to be impossible. A postage-stamp of space costs, maybe, £1 a minute. Reports of meals do not stint on praise: competence, occasional brilliance, excellence are the least of epithets. Complaint arises when a cog of the machine has slipped. A lunch of sweetbreads and morels with pasta in a cream truffle sauce, salmon and crayfish on a julienne of vegetables and a sharp orange beurre blanc, cheeses (what cheeses!) from Olivier and, finally, a superb light biscuit sandwiching a hazelnut mousse with a custard sauce scattered with praline is a typical meal (at a very fair set price as well) that has pleased many. Nonetheless, there is a mechanical vapidity in the cooking that is put into the shade by the really creative kitchens in the Home Counties, such as Messrs Burton-Race and Blanc. A meal began with langoustines with pasta and scallops in a cream sauce competently executed yet with no spark of ingenuity. A skilled chef's dish, with impeccable ingredients. Young lamb was the meat dish, milk-fed (although not as milky as some) with a simple gravy and a scattering of vegetables. Sauce paloise accompanied it. This was all egg and air, no bite to speed the meat − young meat is rich and needs cutting by a sharp sauce, hence the use of mint. No potatoes with this (many readers hope this tendency of ignoring potatoes will soon die), but a green salad with too sharp a vinaigrette, rather like one in a Routier. Cheese was an array difficult to better, unless British were added to French. Desserts are shown to the table by a waiter: a tray of artificial plastic sorbets and examples of three choices (omitting the half dozen on the real menu). This conversation stopper, as you strain to hear the bad English descriptions, results in an order. A sandwich of fine pastry, a layer of sliced pear, Chantilly cream, strawberry sauce, a tiny portion of flavour in this barren concoction is afforded by some blackcurrants dotted around its perimeter: less satisfying than the cream slices one dreamt of when fielding long-stop at prep school. The item with the greatest flavour in this meal was a tiny diamond of spinach quiche, quite brilliant. Coffee is very good; tea is very strong. The wine list is very long. The bill is very high.

CHEF/PROPRIETOR: Michel Roux
OPEN: Tue to Sun
CLOSED: 26 Dec to 15 Feb, Sun D late Oct to Easter
MEALS: 12 to 2, 7 to 10
PRICES: £49 (£61), Set L £21.50 (£29) to £24.50 (£32). Minimum £25. Service inc
CARDS: Access, Amex, Carte Blanche, Diners, Visa
SEATS: 80. Private parties: 80 main room. Car-park, 30 places. Vegetarian meals. Children restricted. Smart dress preferred. No cigars/pipes in dining-room. Wheelchair access (2 steps; also WC). Air-conditioned

*See the back of the Guide for an index of restaurants listed.*

*This year, in quoting prices for three-course meals at the top of each entry (by the word 'Cost'), we have put a more pessimistic complexion on the upper price by inflating it by 20 per cent. The aim is to prepare the reader for any inflation during the life of the Guide and also reflect the price of a meal taken without constant attention to the likely size of the bill. The prices quoted in smaller print below the text remain, as in previous editions, strict computer calculations of an average three-course meal, the price in brackets reflecting an average meal with coffee, service and half a bottle of house wine per person.*

## Food for Friends

17A – 18 Prince Albert Street
The Lanes, Brighton BN1 1HF                              COOKING 1
BRIGHTON (0273) 202310                                       COST £10

Tourism has not served Brighton well as far as eating places are concerned and it is still curiously difficult to find reasonably priced, ungimmicky food in the centre of town. Here is one exception, an easygoing vegetarian café with a broad mix of customers 'from students and deck-chair attendants to office workers, shoppers and teachers'. The food is not refined, but it says a lot about the quality and value for money that 90 per cent of the customers are not vegetarians. Thick soups, salads ranging from potatoes in cream with garlic to healthy beansprout affairs, substantial hot dishes like stuffed pancakes or vegetable casseroles, and puddings change twice a day. Wholemeal bread and cakes are home made and freshly squeezed juices come from Long's of Pevensey. Inevitably, tables are crowded and older people say that they can feel like interlopers in the community-centre atmosphere. House French is £3.95. There is a no-smoking area and 'shirts must be worn'.

CHEF: Karen Samuel   PROPRIETORS: Simon Hope and Jeremy Gray
OPEN: all week
MEALS: 9am (9.30 Sun) to 10pm
PRICES: £6 (£8). Snacks from £1.15. Service inc
CARD: Visa
SEATS: 50. Vegetarian meals. Children's helpings. Separate smoking area. Wheelchair access. Music

## Langan's Bistro

1 Paston Place, Brighton BN2 1HA                         COOKING 3
BRIGHTON (0273) 606933                                       COST £25

The first aspect of Langan's that continues to impress is its professionalism, even though retaining an aura of amateurism. Place settings of unmatched china add to this. The menu is short, changes weekly with the ebb and flow of supplies and gives equal space to fish and meat. It is not invention one seeks here but freshness, accuracy and reliability. Duck parfait; a salad of grilled tuna; a warm salad of duck; lamb tournedos forestière; halibut meunière; gigot of lamb; orange and Grand Marnier crème brûlée; white chocolate ice-cream and coffee have all been well reported. A short wine list from France offers the necessary. House French is £5.40. This is a cut above most bistros.

CHEF: Mark Emmerson   PROPRIETORS: Coq d'Or Restaurants Co Ltd
OPEN: Tue to Sun, exc Sat L and Sun D
MEALS: 12.30 to 2.30, 7.30 to 10.30
PRICES: £15 (£21). Cover 75p. Service 10%
CARDS: Access, Amex, Diners, Visa
SEATS: 50. Children welcome. Music

# ▲ La Noblesse, Hospitality Inn

| Kings Road, Brighton BN1 2GS | COOKING 3 |
|---|---|
| BRIGHTON (0273) 206700 | COST £23–£46 |

'At last Brighton has a restaurant that compares favourably with London,' was the first news we had in the *Guide* office of a strange phenomenon: the then Ramada Renaissance Hotel, not long opened, had incorporated a gourmet restaurant in its package. Much the same occurred in this chain's hotel in Manchester. Then came commercial upheaval as Ramada was sold and reconstructed, Mount Charlotte Hotels taking on Brighton as the Hospitality Inn, but leaving chef and restaurant manager in place. Richard Lyth has high ambition and the management has high ideas about what to charge. Meals are therefore expensive (although the table d'hôte is markedly cheaper). The menu is also composed with an eye to the likely customer profile: Tory party or Institute of Directors on a jolly. It therefore is boring and stuffed to the gills with luxuries: not enough to have asparagus, but must have both white and green. In May the short *carte*, with only five first courses, had foie gras in two, langoustines, oysters and smoked salmon in the others. 'They do not appear to have heard of anything so cheap as soup or, for that matter, an egg dish.' Nonetheless, in conditions of great luxury (coloured blue, pink and brass), with a willing band of waiters, even if communication in English is stilted, the food is very well cooked. A chicken-liver terrine with a finely balanced Cumberland sauce was a traditional yet satisfactory amuse-gueule; a fillet of sea bass was baked with a mild herb crust on a sauce suffused and infused with crustacea yet not overpowered by them, checked and pointed by a sharpening of anise. A rack of lamb was roasted à point, served with morels and two sorts of asparagus on a sauce that was reduced enough for taste but not so much as to crowd out the savour of lamb stock. Vegetables, a stir-fried mélange, were sweetened with diced tomato and seasoned with chives. The dessert let down this so far impeccable meal. It was a flaccid gratin of strawberries: the fine judgement not exercised, the materials not adequate. Petits fours, in keeping with the style of the place, came on a Christmas tree of a stand and were good. Were the owners to continue to back the chef, Brighton would indeed be fortunate – if a mite poorer for the experience. The wine list is orthodox. House wine is £9.80.

CHEF: Richard Lyth   PROPRIETORS: Mount Charlotte Hotels
OPEN: Mon to Sat, exc Sat L
MEALS: 12 to 2.30, 7 to 12.30
PRICES: £30 (£38), Set L £17.50 (£23), Set D £27 (£32). Service inc
CARDS: Access, Amex, Diners, Visa
SEATS: 50. Private parties: 45 main room. Car-park, 60 places. Vegetarian meals. No children under 14 at D. Smart dress preferred. No pipes in dining-room. Wheelchair access (also WC). Air-conditioned
ACCOMMODATION: 204 rooms, all with bath/shower. Rooms for disabled. Lift. B&B £103.50 to £132. Baby facilities. Pets welcome. Afternoon teas. Swimming-pool. Sauna. Air-conditioning. TV. Phone. Scenic. Doors close at 11. Confirm by 6

*Report forms are at the back of the book; write a letter if you prefer.*

# ▲ Poppies, The Roebuck

Brimfield SY8 4WE                                                         COOKING 2
BRIMFIELD (058 472) 230                                                     COST £36

The last few years have seen rapid evolution at the Roebuck, where the
boundless energy of Carole Evans in the restaurant has a fresh setting in the
conservatory extension. There are guest bedrooms newly converted and John
Evans has revised and expanded the wine list. The pub side continues, with
the pool room and public bar as the domain of the village. Bar food is markedly
superior. The new dining-rooms have occasioned a smart new menu.
Altogether, the existence of the bar side and daily specials must make Carole
Evans one of the most wide ranging of cooks: from cottage pie to quails with
truffles. People are impressed by the enthusiasm and the willingness to push
back the boundaries of what is thought of as pub cooking, as well as the
Evans's encouragement of local growers. As one reader commented,
'strawberries come from the postman and venison from the chap who has just
started up the road'; oatmeal is milled by the local doctor. The garden, in the
hands of John Evans, plays its part: claytonia formed part of a salad in early
January, 'the first I have eaten in a restaurant.' The style of the main *carte* is
decidedly up-to-date (a reflection of Franco Taruschio of the Walnut Tree Inn,
Llandewi Skirrid, a relation by marriage) and meals have included mushroom
soup; scallop mousse with a leek and saffron sauce; John Dory with rhubarb
and coriander; partridge with a wine and tarragon sauce; beef Wellington;
some fine vegetables, better in the buying than in the cooking; hot chocolate
soufflé served with a passion-fruit sorbet; and poppyseed parfait with a ragout
of dates. Execution varies from the sublime to the hamfisted. It is not helped by
knives as blunt as mallets. Some of the intentions do not gel: rhubarb and
coriander hardly apparent; partridge legs too rare; turbot overcooked;
wonderful Guernsey cream occasionally left for too long. Chervil leaves have
figured as decoration on every dish from beginning to end, as far as the petits
fours. The wine list improves, and there are some nice American and
Australian bottles including a 1976 Heitz Cabernet Sauvignon, Fay Vinyard
and four 1978s from Trefethen, Phelps and Mondavi. House Rosemount
Cabernet Sauvignon is £8.50, Anjou Blanc, £7. CELLARMAN'S CHOICE :
Andrew Garrett South Australian Chardonnay 1987, £14.50; Baileys Shiraz
1985, £13.50. Dunkerton's famed cider is available and is used in the cooking.

CHEF: Carole Evans   PROPRIETORS: John and Carole Evans
OPEN: Tue to Sun, exc Sun D
CLOSED: 2 weeks Feb, 25 and 26 Dec
MEALS: 12 to 2 (1.45 Sun), 7 to 10
PRICES: £22 (£30), Snacks from £1.50
CARDS: Access, Visa
SEATS: 40. Private parties: 40 main room. Children welcome. Separate smoking area.
Wheelchair access
ACCOMMODATION: 3 rooms, all with bath/shower. B&B £40 to £60. No children under 10.
TV. Phone. Scenic. Doors close at 12.30. Confirm by 6

## Bistro Twenty One

| | |
|---|---|
| 21 Cotham Road South, Kingsdown | |
| Bristol BS6 5TZ | COOKING **2** |
| BRISTOL (0272) 421744 | COST £25 |

It is possible to eat on the first floor of this determinedly bistro-decorated restaurant where Alain Dubois continues in charge, though having added business interests across the Severn at Cowbridge (Basil's Brasserie). However, the majority stay at street-level, the kitchen in view across the bar, the seating uncomfortable and drifts of smoke sometimes difficult to cope with. The menu is uncommonly long for so small a place, a dozen items at each course being supplemented by daily specials. Pastry and sauces are strong points: feuilleté of seafood with a lobster and cream sauce combines the ingredients to great effect. Cream is a weakness and ordering should take this into account. It may even be coloured blue (with curaçao) to afford a lake on which a choux swan swims. Production from the kitchen has sometimes been leisurely paced. The wine list is better, and more expensive, than in many bistros. House French is £6.50 but 'Vin du Patron' is £8. CELLARMAN'S CHOICE : Macon-Fuissé 1986, £13.50.

CHEF/PROPRIETOR: Alain Dubois
OPEN: Mon to Sat, exc Sat L
CLOSED: 1 week at Christmas
MEALS: 12 to 2.30, 6.30 to 11.30
PRICES: £15 (£21)
CARDS: Access, Visa
SEATS: 40. Private parties: 16 main room. Children's helpings. Wheelchair access. Music

## Edwards

| | |
|---|---|
| 24 Alma Vale Road, Clifton | |
| Bristol BS8 2HY | COOKING **1** |
| BRISTOL (0272) 741533 | COST £11−£20 |

John Selwyn Gilbert, combining the clipped speech of Patrick Moore with the mischievous grin of Keith Floyd, still presides over the dark oak-panelled dining-room with red plush bench seats and decorative Wedgwood plates. It is tucked away in a quiet back street behind Clifton Down shopping centre, next to Alma Vale post office. Gerrard Perry is cooking less French than before − seventeenth-century pea soup (with mace, mint and spinach), lamb chops, and steak and kidney pie, represent something of a British take-over. On Sunday, roast pork with crackling, roast potatoes, a commercial-tasting apple sauce and a rich glossy brown gravy is followed by a spotted Dick and custard straight out of school days, heavy with suet and nostalgia. Fish comes from Cornwall− scampi and monkfish are sauté with pastis, coriander and mushrooms − and vegetarian dishes are always available − 'please ask for details'. If the food is not very sophisticated, then neither is it very expensive. 'If I lived in Bristol I would definitely want to know about Edwards.' The short, inexpensive and largely French collection of wines is helped by a few other European and New

World additions. House French, £5.50. CELLARMAN'S CHOICE : Mâcon-Lugny 1987, Cuvée Eugène Blanc, £9.75; Brouilly, Dom. de St-Charles 1987, £9.75. Coffee is ad lib'.

CHEF: Gerrard Perry  PROPRIETOR: John Selwyn Gilbert
OPEN: all week, exc Sun D
MEALS: 12 to 2.30, 7 to 11
PRICES: £12 (£17), Set Sun and Mon L £7.50 (£11), Snacks from £2.50
CARDS: Access, Visa
SEATS: 44. Private parties: 40 main room, 12 private room. Vegetarian meals. Children's helpings. Smart dress preferred. Wheelchair access (1 step)

## Harvey's ♥

| 12A Denmark Street, Bristol BS1 5DQ | COOKING 1 |
|---|---|
| BRISTOL (0272) 277665 | COST £20–£37 |

This conversion of the cellars beneath a wine merchant's offices was once the talk of the town. It still gives some pleasure for the contrast of painted walls and fine tableware. The restaurant seems to have regressed to a form and content familiar to our grandfathers, down to 'Choix de Fromages sur la Voiture' or 'Sole de Douvre Grillée' and similar. One reader, preferring his langoustines plain grilled, threw the team into disarray for even suggesting a variation to the holy writ of menu. Perhaps the object of a diner's delight will be the wine list which displays a selection of claret and fortified wines that would excite the most blasé among us. Move to new countries and it becomes as old-fashioned and purblind as the menu. House wine is Harvey's claret at £7.75.

CHEF: Thierry Rouvrais  PROPRIETORS: John Harvey and Sons Ltd
OPEN: Mon to Sat, exc Sat L
CLOSED: bank hols
MEALS: 12 to 2.15, 7 (6.30 Sat) to 11.15
PRICES: £21 (£31), Set L £13.75 (£20). Cover £1. Minimum £13.75. Service 10%
CARDS: Access, Amex, Diners, Visa
SEATS: 120. Private parties: 60 main room. Smart dress preferred. No-smoking area. Music. Air-conditioned

## Jameson's

| 30 Upper Maudlin Street, Bristol BS2 8DJ | COOKING 1 |
|---|---|
| BRISTOL (0272) 276565 | COST £26 |

The menu goes on from year to year, but the room gets bigger. Actually, walls were knocked down in this pair of shops opposite the Royal Infirmary to create a more spacious dining-room. The menu is a long one, but the large number of seats no doubt secures adequate through-put for the fish (three sorts), scampi, rabbit, pigeon, venison, veal, duck, chicken, lamb and beef, bought 'on a daily basis'. People have found it cheerful, generous and good for vegetarians. Service sometimes seems unrelated to activities in the kitchen. Avery's Clochemerle is the house wine, at £6.95 a litre. CELLARMAN'S CHOICE :

Tyrrell's Hunter Valley Shiraz 1983, £9.75; Tyrrell's Hunter Valley Chardonnay 1986, £9.75.

CHEFS: Carole Jameson and Ian Leitch   PROPRIETORS: Carole and John Holmes
OPEN: Mon to Sat, D only
MEALS: 7 to 11 (11.30 Fri and Sat)
PRICES: £15 (£22). Service of 10% for parties of 6 or more
CARDS: Access, Visa
SEATS: 70. Private parties: 35 main room. Vegetarian meals. Children's helpings.
Wheelchair access (2 steps). Music

## Lettonie

9 Druid Hill Stoke Bishop
Bristol BS9 1EW                                                  COOKING 3
BRISTOL (0272) 686456                                        COST £18–£30

In the way that like attracts like, René Gaté sold Les Semailles, his small restaurant in a shopping parade of Bristol's inner suburbs, to chefs who practise a comparable mode of cooking – modern, innovatory, sophisticated –though Martin and Siân Blunos may be less assertive in flavours, more fussy in execution. Recommendations this year have been firm and numerous. 'One of the nice things was that even with the canapés before and friandises after, the whole meal was not over-filling and one did not feel bloated.' Trenchermen have found this alarming; others, interested in balance rather than bulk, have regretted the paucity of vegetables, often an integrated, thus minor, component of the main dish; but many will find it refreshing. The befores and afters are certainly essential – in the chefs' view of things. So much work and thought go into them, that they are more than mere extras. Many specific dishes have been applauded: braised lambs' tongues in pastry with a caper sauce; salsify and herbs in a pastry case with a cured ham cream sauce; mushroom ravioli with a shallot sauce; shellfish bisque; fillet of sea bream; salmon with sorrel sauce; lamb with a basil mousse and a basil sauce; venison on a bed of noodles with a liquorice sauce; ox-tail with grapes and snails in a red wine sauce; marquise au chocolat with a rosemary-scented sauce; a parfait of tea and mace; pink grapefruit in a Sauternes jelly. It was once observed that Les Semailles was too good a restaurant for Bristol – another way of saying that there were not enough customers. The original comment was unfair, but it is not easy to make a small place like this, a characterless building in a characterless district, sing. The Blunoses should be given the chance. The wine list is as French as the titles on the menu (Lettonie is French for Latvia, the ancestral home of the chef). It has some age in clarets and burgundies (though 1967 clarets are fairly speculative) and some good makers: Borja's Crozes Hermitage, Filliatreau's Saumur Champigny, Roumier's Morey St-Denis. Some of the prices are very fair. Half-bottles are light. House French from £6.50. CELLARMAN'S CHOICE : Fareham Estate Sparkling, £10.50; Ch. Pillebois, Côtes de Castillon 1985, £8.50. (As we went to press, former owner René Gaté withdrew from Le Renoir at Up Holland in Lancashire.)

▲ *This symbol means accommodation is available.*

CHEFS/PROPRIETORS: Martin and Siân Blunos
OPEN: Tue to Sat
CLOSED: 2 weeks Aug
MEALS: 12.30 to 2, 7 to 10
PRICES: Set L £11.50 (£18), Set D £17.95 (£25)
CARDS: Access, Amex, Visa
SEATS: 24. Private parties: 14 main room. Children's helpings on request. Music

## *Markwick & Hunt* ♥

43 Corn Street, Bristol BS1 1HT
BRISTOL (0272) 262658

COOKING 3
COST £16–£28

In the commercial centre of Bristol, quite a different animal from the elegant terraces of Clifton, are the Corn Street Commercial Chambers, a fine classical building that once was a coffee house for merchants and bankers. The whole street and district has preserved its sense of prosperity, bank after bank, market after market give variety and richness to the townscape. In the undercroft of the coffee-house was established a safety deposit. Then it became a restaurant, now it is again, as Markwick & Hunt. Black and white marble floors, panelling to the vaulted rooms, cast-iron grille doors – all these survive from the original. Add some good modern joinery, some Venetian lamps done as bunches of grapes, good tables, linen and glassware and the result is a fine city-centre restaurant. Stephen and Judy Markwick ran Bistro 21, which offered imaginative cooking at low low prices to a Bristol that needed them. Andy Hunt was chef at Harvey's (see entry, also Bristol) and nearly turned it from a lumbering mammoth to a responsive kitchen offering modern food. They are attempting to provide the same style of Franglais provincial cooking that was served at the Bistro but with a touch more elegance and comfort. Early meals have shown some of the faults of a team out of practice: over salting, more simple sauces than are now customary, a certain roughness of finish; but the value and the good intentions, from the home-made bread to the fudge at the end, are palpable. There is a short weekly *carte* and a very short set-price choice at lunchtime. The range of dishes is not immediately startling: Provençal fish soup, moules marinière, ratatouille niçoise, warm chicken liver salad, spiced lamb with aubergines, boeuf bourguignonne, lamb tournedos with bacon and broad beans, lemon cheesecake, St-Emilion au chocolat. The lineage, from Elizabeth David through Kenneth Bell and George Perry-Smith, is plain. What is refreshing is the chefs' verve and honesty. A pea and ham soup with enough flavour and body to warm anyone on a frosty day; squid stewed with red wine and orange neither too strong nor too tough; turbot and sea bass as fresh and refreshingly cooked as any on the Cornish coast; a diplomat pudding with subtlety of flavour from a discreet use of fruit and yet light and rich. Service is young, though often supervised and humanised by Stephen Markwick himself. The wine list is longer than might be expected, gives fair exposure to countries other than France (which nonetheless has primacy), and is not too expensive. There are two excellent choices from Jean Léon in the Penedès, a good Madiran Ch. Peyros 1985, a pair of expensive Italians from the fashionable Avignonesi and a cheaper experiment with a claret lookalike from Greece, Ch. Carras 1979. House Muscadet or Beaujolais, £8. CELLARMAN'S CHOICE: Gigondas 1985, Amadieu, £9.85; Balgownie Chardonnay 1987, £9.50.

CHEFS: Andrew Hunt and Stephen Markwick   PROPRIETORS: Stephen and Judy
Markwick and Andrew Hunt
OPEN: Mon to Fri
MEALS: 12 to 2, 7 to 10.30
PRICES: £18 (£23), Set L £10.50 (£16) to £12.50 (£18). Service inc
CARD: Access
SEATS: 50. Private parties: 30 main room, 8 and 20 private rooms. Children's helpings

## Muset

| 12 Clifton Rd, Clifton, Bristol BS8 1AF | COOKING 1 |
|---|---|
| BRISTOL (0272) 732920 | COST £14–£19 |

A busy bistro-style operation on three levels, Muset takes an open approach to
good food and wine at sensible prices. The format is a set price for any two or
three courses picked from a choice of half a dozen at each stage. First courses –
for example, pickled salmon fillet sliced and served with a grain mustard
mayonnaise or Somerset soup with cider and Stilton – are more adventurous
than main courses, although these too have been well reported, as in a pork
tenderloin with bacon duxelles in cream sauce. Home-made puddings, such as
crème brûlée, have been memorable, and details are good: well-cooked
vegetables, a lemon sorbet between the first and main courses, and filter coffee.
The short wine list has some good French and Australian bottles with
reasonable mark-ups, but there is no corkage charged for wine brought by
customers. House French is £5.25. CELLARMAN'S CHOICE : Hoffmans Barossa
Valley Cabernet Sauvignon 1985, £8.95; Balgownie Chardonnay 1987, £8.75.
The list is fast changing and vintages are not guaranteed. 'Tips not necessary.
Service included,' say the proprietors.

CHEFS: A. Portlock, D. Wheadon and M. Read   PROPRIETORS: B.Y.O. Holdings
OPEN: Tue to Sat, D only
MEALS: 7 to 10.30
PRICES: Set D £11.75 (£14) to £13.75 (£16). Service inc. Licensed, also bring your own: no
corkage
CARDS: Access, Visa
SEATS: 70. Private parties: 30 main room. Children's helpings. Children restricted. Music

## Orient Rendezvous

| 95 Queens Road, Clifton | |
|---|---|
| Bristol BS8 1LW | COOKING 1 |
| BRISTOL (0272) 745202 and 745231 | COST £20–£25 |

A recent customer described this upmarket Chinese restaurant as one of the
finest he had ever visited in terms of cuisine, ambience and service. Perhaps it
has something to do with the dance floor in the dining-room, or perhaps it is
the more unusual items on the English and Chinese menu, which spans the
three main regional cuisines. Among the appetisers there are half a dozen dim-
sum, cold Szechuan pork in garlic and chilli sauce and fried frogs' legs.
Szechuan dishes of beef, pork, squid and prawns feature heavily among the
half dozen specially recommended main courses. House wine, £5.95.

CHEF: David Wong   PROPRIETOR: Raymond Wong
OPEN: all week
CLOSED: 25 to 28 Dec
MEALS: 12 to 2.30, 6.30 to 11.30
PRICES: £11 (£21), Set D £15 (£20). Service 10%
CARDS: Access, Amex, Diners, Visa
SEATS: 150. Private parties: 150 main room, 10,20 and 45 private rooms. Car-park, 25 places. Children welcome. Smart dress preferred. Music. Air-conditioned

## Plum Duff

6 Chandos Road, Redland, Bristol BS6 6PE                    COOKING 1
BRISTOL (0272) 238450                                       COST £15–£22

The name is hardly appropriate since the food is anything but old-fashioned English, but at a certain level, as reflected by the reasonable prices of the two- or three-course formula, this new restaurant offers some fair cooking. Once occupied by local-boy-turned-media-star Keith Floyd, the corner site has been completely redecorated, with flowery plates and old photographs on the rag-rolled walls, heavy lace half-curtains, a motley collection of chairs and a heather and blue colour scheme now giving the room a quirkily Victorian air. In the kitchen, chef/proprietor James West is still developing the style of the menu, which at present seems divided between dishes of uncluttered simplicity – chicken-liver pâté, monkfish provençale, lamb fillet in a basil cream sauce – and those dressed up by fashionably flavoured sauce, for example, duck with cassis and port, pork with a ginger wine gravy, monkfish with lime and Pernod. Both strands have produced good dishes: an honest gratin of seafood with chunks of fresh salmon, white crab meat, shrimps and undyed smoked haddock under bubbling hot melted cheese; an experimental Peking duck salad with mange-tout and water chestnuts; monkfish in a lime and ginger sauce. But the standard is still erratic, especially where dishes are overloaded with novel flavours, as in a duck breast with an over-rich strawberry sauce. It seems curious, too, that while wholemeal rolls are home made, puddings have been badly let down by commercial flavours and spray-on cream – but perhaps these are anomalies resulting from teething problems which will disappear with time. A decent, very short wine list reveals the house wine at £4.95 and £5.35.

CHEF/PROPRIETOR: James West
OPEN: Tue to Sat, D only
CLOSED: 24 Dec to 10 Jan
MEALS: 7 to 10.30
PRICES: Set D £10.50 (£15) to £13.50 (£18)
CARDS: Access, Visa
SEATS: 34. Private parties: 12 main room. Vegetarian meals. Children welcome. No cigars/ pipes in dining-room. Wheelchair access (1 step). Music

*'The hopes raised by the fact that the telephone booking had to be conducted in French were soon disappointed. Judged by the standards obtaining in the normal run of modest establishments in Normandy or Brittany, this place is pretentious but mediocre.'* On dining in London

# ▲ *Collin House*

Collin Lane, Broadway WR12 7PB
BROADWAY (0386) 858354                  COOKING **2**
on A44, 1m NW of Broadway            COST £13–£25

An old Cotswold building of yellow stone, probably a wool merchant's house originally, Collin House is now a small hotel and relaxed country restaurant. The small dining-room, heavily beamed but not particularly striking, is often packed. The food is well cooked and wholesome, served in generous portions, and traditionally English but not slavishly so. Kedgeree, rabbit braised in cider served with herb dumplings, and jugged hare are typical examples. Other dishes, such as an elderflower sorbet with melon, or poached salmon with leek and vermouth sauce, show a more modern approach. Puddings, a high point, are the most old-fashioned of all: lemon posset, sticky sponges, fruity ice-creams and so on. Light lunches, served in the bar or garden in good weather, overlap with the main menu. The wine list shows signs, in the notes, of John Mills's enjoyment of his cellar. The prices are very fair and the range extends through Spain, Italy and the New World as well as France. Special enthusiasm is reserved for the small lots of wine listed at the back. House French is £6. CELLARMAN'S CHOICE : Mark West Russian River Chardonnay 1981, £14.30; Taltarni Cabernet Sauvignon 1982, £11.80.

CHEFS: Judith Mills and Glyn Musker    PROPRIETORS: John and Judith Mills
OPEN: all week
MEALS: 12 to 1.30, 7 to 9
PRICES: £8 (£13) Bar L, Set D £13 (£18) to £15 (£21)
CARDS: Access, Visa
SEATS: 35. 5 tables outside. Private parties: 30 main room. Car-park, 30 places. Children's helpings. No children under 6. Wheelchair access (also WC)
ACCOMMODATION: 7 rooms, all with bath/shower. B&B £33 to £69. Deposit: £35. No children under 6. Garden. Swimming-pool. Scenic. Doors close at midnight

# *Hunters Lodge*

High Street, Broadway WR12 7DT             COOKING **2**
BROADWAY (0386) 853247                 COST £31

A Jacobean Cotswold house as popular with residents as the tourists who flood Broadway with vehicles and tote bags the year round. It is not compulsory to have a full-blown meal at lunch, and as Kurt Friedli's spirit and portioning is generous, one may not need more. There are encouraging notices: 'no minimum charge–no dress code–no frowns for well-done meat–just a starter and a cup of coffee is no problem.' Careful, substantial cooking of dishes such as a rabbit casserole (roasted at dinner time), veal chop with wild mushrooms, shallots and red wine, fried sole stuffed with scampi, characterises the menu. Dottie Friedli is as efficient as she is affable. The wine list is mainly French, backed up by a small selection of good Germans, with a dozen more expensive clarets and burgundies. But the main collection is more than adequate; note Alsaces from Kuentz-Bas and Reserva 904, 1975 from Rioja Alta. House French is £6.25. The Victorian typography of the wine list and ornament to the menu well complement the feel of the restaurant.

CHEF: Kurt Friedli   PROPRIETORS: Kurt and Dottie Friedli
OPEN: Tue to Sun, exc Sun D
CLOSED: first 2 weeks Feb, first 2 weeks Aug
MEALS: 12.30 to 2, 7.30 to 9.45
PRICES: £17 (£26)
CARDS: Access, Amex, Diners, Visa
SEATS: 55. 6 tables outside. Private parties: 35 main room, 22 private room. Car-park, 20 places. Children's helpings. No children under 8 (D). No cigars/pipes in dining-room. Wheelchair access (also WC)

---

## ▲ Lygon Arms ♟

| Broadway WR12 7DU | COOKING 2 |
| BROADWAY (0386) 852255 | COST £23–£43 |

The process whereby this hotel, for decades a byword of professionalism, should have come to rest in the arms of the Savoy Group, the last bastion of the old-guard hotel companies, is apt. Yet whether metropolitan finesse of management is suitable for a Cotswold village is questionable. The main street is filled with flocks of international sheep and so, too, is the hotel. In the dining-room, men are instructed to guard their jacket and tie, as lambs before shearing perhaps. The tariff card lists numbers in Australia, Japan and Canada on which to make reservations. Clive Howe has his work cut out to make something of this clientele: the menu reflects it, offering complicated cookery, plain grills, simple *prix fixe*, and now even a vegetarian menu. There is some invention: a warm salad of home-smoked duck with marinated vegetables and a honey and sesame dressing, or medallions of beef topped with a soufflé of sweetbreads. Some of the Englishry of the menu, the daily hot puddings for example, is also acceptable. Yet the multiple strands of the menu engenders a committee approach to cooking – no one chef can be excited by all these styles. The scale of business, too, means delegation is necessary and, in truth, those delegated are not up to a great deal. The high cost is not mirrored by high achievement, nor well represented by accessible and delightful service. The wine list is not as dear as may be feared and covers the French side quite well; other countries are given a nod of recognition though not of exploration. House French is £7.25. CELLARMAN'S CHOICE: Ch. Moulin de Launay, 1988 Entre-Deux-Mers, £7.50; Ch. Macquin St-Georges, 1983, £14.

CHEF: Clive Howe   PROPRIETORS: The Savoy Group
OPEN: all week
MEALS: 12.30 to 2, 7.30 to 9.30
PRICES: £27 (£36), Set L £14.75 (£23), Set D £22.50 (£31)
CARDS: Access, Amex, Carte Blanche, Diners, Visa
SEATS: 90. Private parties: 90 main room, 10, 20, 40 and 76 private rooms. Car-park, 150 places. Vegetarian meals. Children's helpings on request. Smart dress preferred. No-smoking area. Wheelchair access (also WC)
ACCOMMODATION: 66 rooms, all with bath/shower. Rooms for disabled. B&B £80 to £122. Baby facilities. Pets welcome. Afternoon teas. Garden. Tennis. Snooker. TV. Phone. Scenic

| BROCKENHURST  Hampshire | map 2 |
| --- | --- |

## ▲ Poussin ♥

| 57–59 Brookley Road | |
| --- | --- |
| Brockenhurst SO42 7RB | COOKING 4 |
| LYMINGTON (0590) 23063 | COST £19–£42 |

The outside is not especially prepossessing but once through the door –
leaving the adjacent former hairdresser's, now the Aitkens' delicatessen, for a
later visit – there is solid luxury and warmth that is sign of serious cooking and
high ambition. The ground floor dining-room (a handsome bar-sitting-room is
upstairs) is pleasantly formal, 'no-one whispers, there is not a hint of
stuffiness'. The room is characterised by big curtains, hunting pictures, comfy
seats and benches, a blazing log fire and a big mirror to add to the sense of
space. Without excesses (menus, for example, are in plain English), the Aitkens
run a surprisingly French establishment: from the cooking to the staff and even
to the pink ribbons used to hold the menu together. The restaurant is by no
means cheap, though the comfortable accommodation is a bargain. This is not a
foie-gras-and-shellfish place, though these ingredients are used. The cooking
steers a good course between the luxurious and the simple, between the light,
as in a salad of calf's liver with orange and a dressing of walnut oil, and the
robust, as with the pig's trotter stuffed with sweetbreads, described to the *Guide*
as 'a blinder; bourgeois almost peasant, big, beefy and brilliant.' One customer
who had not encountered this in more famous surroundings was moved to
observe that anyone who can 'add value to a pig's trotter by boning it, stuffing
it suitably and serving it in a pool of (albeit excellent) sauce, charge more than
£12 and get away with it is deserving of admiration.' Indeed, Alexander Aitken
is. Game seems an especial preoccupation. A tourte of pheasant is a 'solid, juicy
upturned bowl of perfectly cooked succulent meat in crisp, buttery pastry on an
excellent stock.' Four different sorts of venison are served: fallow, roe, red and
sika (the chef's favourite). Another dish is 'Fruits of the New Forest': three
pillows of pastry filled with wild rabbit, venison and hare on a game sauce.
The menu is keen on titles such as rendezvous of … pillows of … festivals of …
More elaborate dishes also appear to work: breast of chicken stuffed with
lobster with two sauces and lobster and chicken, served with wild rice and
shredded courgettes convinced two waverers.

Ancillaries are not below these standards though bread does have its critics;
amuse-gueule receive constant praise; the French cheeses from Olivier seem
always ripe; vegetables are cooked crisp though sometimes unrecognisably.
'There was a greenish substance on my plate, with the consistency of rubber.
When asked what it was, the reply came, 'potato'.' This was comment from one
of the few who thought the cooking sometimes over-ambitious. Desserts have
absorbed the modern love of hot dishes, or chaud-froids, at this stage of the
meal. A passion-fruit soufflé, or a crêpe soufflé filled with crème pâtissière on a
passion-fruit sauce, or gratins of fruits 'in a perfect custard with ice-cream, the
blending of temperatures just right,' are some instances. The service, overseen
by Caroline Aitken, is as impressive as the food. There is an obvious enjoyment
of south-western French wines though the list concentrates on more classic

regions. Although both nicely spread and offering some aristocratic growers and properties, there is less of a price range than could be. House wines are £9.95 and £11. CELLARMAN'S CHOICE : Jurançon Sec, Domaine Cauhapé 1987, £12.50; Madiran, Domaine Pichard 1983, £12.50.

CHEF: Alexander Aitken   PROPRIETORS: Alexander and Caroline Aitken
OPEN: Tue to Sun, exc Sun D (Mon D parties by arrangement)
MEALS: 12.30 to 2, 7 to 10
PRICES: £25 (£35), Set L £9.95 (£19) to £15 (£24), Set D £20 (£30) to £25 (£35)
CARDS: Access, Visa
SEATS: 35. Private parties: 35 main room. Vegetarian meals. Wheelchair access (also WC)
ACCOMMODATION: 2 rooms, with bath/shower. B&B £30 to £50. Deposit: £30. Baby facilities. Doors close at midnight. Confirm by 4

---

**BROUGHTON** Lancashire                                                    map 5

# ▲ Courtyard,
# Broughton Park Hotel

Garstang Road, Broughton PR3 5JB                          COOKING 2
BROUGHTON (0772) 864087                                    COST £17–£62

Although Lancashire is 'an equal opportunities county', women get unpriced menus in this top-of-the-range section of a country club, health club and country-house hotel that sports two restaurants. The refurbished Courtyard in question, approached through a profusion of plants, water and statuary, manages to rise above some of its own sillinesses by dint of good and concerned service and fair cooking. The menu is a florid classic of English, then translated into terse and approximate French. Every commodity is given its place name – breasts of Hornby duckling, Goosnargh chicken, Derbyshire Gritstone lamb. The meals seek to justify high prices by lots of extras: butter carved in roses; a chef's complimentary appetiser of anchovy and tomato concasse; a sorbet between the first and second courses; seven different vegetables served in minute quantity with the main course. None of this is done badly – the saving grace – but one may wonder if the fuss is worth it. A summer dinner included a minestrone of shellfish with saffron-coloured pasta and a good tomato-flavoured fish stock; a warm salad of scallops and smoked salmon; a piece of turbot with a leek, chive, cream and white wine sauce where the kitchen was so impressed by daintiness that the leeks had turned into spring onions; a fillet of sea bass roasted with scallops on a bed of bulb fennel and tomato, with a caviare butter sauce; excellent vegetables; a quenelle of passion-fruit in a spun-sugar cage with raspberry and strawberry sauce; a steamed treacle pudding that tasted more like reheated sponge cake with sauce anglaise. There were many plus points to the meal, especially when initial tastes were clear and piercing. The wine list has been extended. The largest section (15 per cent) is Champagne. There are some classic wines, at a price, which are properly served. House burgundy from Labouré-Roi is £9.50 (red) and £9.95 (white). CELLARMAN'S CHOICE : Mâcon-Lugny les Genièvres 1986, Latour £13.75; House claret, Henri Rodier, £8.50.

CHEF: Paul Heathcote   PROPRIETORS: Country Club Hotels
OPEN: Mon to Sat, D only
MEALS: 7 to 10.30
PRICES: £22 (£32), Set D £10.95 (£17) to £30 (£41) to £40 (£52)
CARDS: Access, Amex, Diners, Visa
SEATS: 30. Private parties: 30 main room. Car-park, 65 places. Vegetarian meals.
Children welcome. Smart dress preferred. No smoking during meal. Wheelchair access
(also WC). Music
ACCOMMODATION: 98 rooms, all with bath/shower. Rooms for disabled. Lift. B&B £75 to
£90. Baby facilities. Afternoon teas. Garden. Swimming-pool. Sauna. Air -conditioning.
TV. Phone. Scenic. Confirm by 6

---

| BRUTON   Somerset | map 2 |
|---|---|

## ▲ *Claire de Lune*

| 2–4 High Street, Bruton BA10 0EQ | COOKING 2 |
|---|---|
| BRUTON (0749) 813395 | COST £15–£25 |

Why Bruton should sprout two restaurants at about the same time may be a
question for social historians of the future: is it all the schools in the district? is
mid-Somerset an economic growth area? will the town, once fat on the profits
of the wool trade, be able to support them both? Claire de Lune is run by a
young couple whose first independent venture this is. The milieu, two shops
knocked into one, with some nautical reference in the pictures and a certain
'antique' feel, is site for modern cooking in the Anglo-French mode. The most
French thing is the menu, with pointless Gallic titles to the dishes lending
credence to combinations that would not necessarily receive French approval: a
chocolate mousse with a sharp lemon tart, for example. The short menu, five
choices per course, is changed monthly but there are daily extras as
supplements. Thomas Stewart has learned his lessons well, his pastry being
especially commended. The rest of the cooking has also received immediate
approval although some note an excess of cream diminishing flavours and
overloading the frames of its consumers. Strips of monkfish cooked with a very
creamy tomato sauce benefited from good raw materials and an excellent use of
tomato to lighten the impact of all that cream. Boned quail on a bed of cabbage
with a green peppercorn sauce was accurately cooked if insipid in taste.
Vegetables are likewise often helped with cream or hollandaise. That chocolate
mousse and lemon tart was praised for each element, if regretted in
combination, particularly with the added ingredient of a Bailey's Cream sauce;
crème brûlée and oeufs à la neige have been praised. Coffee is weak. A wine
list that is not afraid to go outside France and is not highly priced yields as
CELLARMAN'S CHOICE : Champagne Granier NV, £18; Cooks Sauvignon Blanc
1987, £9.95; Raimat Abadia Reserva 1985, £8.95. House French, £7.50.

---

*All letters to the* Guide *are acknowledged with an update on latest sales, closures, chef
changes and so on.*

*On 6 May 1990 all London telephone numbers will change, the 01- prefix being replaced
by either 071- or 081-. See the front of the* Guide *for a list of which numbers will take
which prefix.*

---

CHEF: Thomas Stewart   PROPRIETORS: Thomas and Kate Stewart
OPEN: Tue to Sat, Sun L
MEALS: 12 to 2, 7 to 10 (10.30 Sat)
PRICES: Set L £10 (£15), Set D £15.75 (£21)
CARD: Access
SEATS: 38. Private parties: 40 main room. Children's helpings. No children under 5.
Smart dress preferred. Wheelchair access (2 steps). Music
ACCOMMODATION: 3 rooms, 2 with bath/shower. B&B £20 to £30. TV. Scenic. Doors
close at 10

## Truffles

| 95 High Street, Bruton BA10 0AR | COOKING 2 |
|---|---|
| BRUTON (0749) 812255 | COST £14–£30 |

Bruton consists mostly of one hill. The restaurant – formerly a pair of 300 year-old weavers' cottages – is at the lower end of the High Street. The dining-room is tiny, and the setting is homely with eccentric touches such as the foot-high, pink-shaded, pillar-of-gold candlesticks on each table and colour photos of chef Bottrill's dishes. The three-course set-price dinner, with half a dozen dishes per course, changes monthly. If the menu reads fussily, it is because descriptions are exhaustive: pillows of smoked trout are filled with a light smoked trout mousse, coated with a dill mustard dressing; fillet of pork is wrapped in an aubergine jacket with a herb brioche centre, served on a tomato sauce. The ideas sound a little stiff and old-fashioned – everything comes with a sauce, dishes are a lot of trouble to make, chocolate truffles arrive on gold paper doilies – but the result is much more upbeat. Saucing is light: cream, fish stock and Champagne provide a fragrant background for parcels of salmon filled with spinach and chopped oysters; the sweetness of an orange sauce to partner fanned breast of duck comes from liqueur, not over-reduction, and contrasts with the sharp accompanying redcurrants and citrus fruit. Truffles gateau, typically rich, is a fixture: layers of sponge, meringue and chocolate marquise, with a chocolate sauce. Attention from the husband-and-wife team is charming and enthusiastic. No service charge is made or expected. The largely French wine list is reasonably priced with a good show of half-bottles and dessert wines by the glass. House wine is £6.25. CELLARMAN'S CHOICE : Ch. Plagnac 1983, £13.95; St-Véran, Ch. Fuissé 1985, £13.95.

CHEF: Martin Bottrill   PROPRIETORS: Denise and Martin Bottrill
OPEN: Tue to Sat, D only and Sun L (weekday L by arrangement)
MEALS: 12 to 2, 7 to 9.30
PRICES: Set Sun L £9.50 (£14), Set D £15.95 (£20) to £17.50 (£25)
SEATS: 20. Private parties: 20 main room. Smart dress preferred. Wheelchair access (1 step)

*This year, in quoting prices for three-course meals at the top of each entry (by the word 'Cost'), we have put a more pessimistic complexion on the upper price by inflating it by 20 per cent. The aim is to prepare the reader for any inflation during the life of the Guide and also reflect the price of a meal taken without constant attention to the likely size of the bill. The prices quoted in smaller print below the text remain, as in previous editions, strict computer calculations of an average three-course meal, the price in brackets reflecting an average meal with coffee, service and half a bottle of house wine per person.*

| BUCKLAND Gloucestershire | map 2 |
|---|---|

## ▲ *Buckland Manor*

| | |
|---|---|
| Buckland WR12 7LY | |
| BROADWAY (0386) 852626 | COOKING 2 |
| off A46, 1m from Broadway | COST £35 |

One of the ironies of the English country-house hotel movement is that many of the houses selected are architecturally slightly less than first rate. Exceptions abound, but here at Buckland the good sixteenth-century manor-house that forms the hotel was fatally altered in the last 100 years. The real architectural gem of the village is the rectory, 'the oldest and most complete medieval parsonage in the county still so used.' Hotel guests will not lack for comforts provided by Barry and Adrienne Berman: this is one of the most beautiful hotels in the region, previous comments notwithstanding. The meal is served in a painted, panelled dining-room, on varnished tables with many candles, the windows heavily curtained, the waitresses in frilly aprons. The menu is exhaustingly written in French with descriptions as ornate as the aprons. Spelling is not perfect. A sorbet may be served between the first and main courses. The style of cooking is modern British country-house and has not received invariable adulation. A reported meal began with a cornet of puff pastry (of moderate quality) filled with a delectable mixture of fresh langoustines, mussels and cockles spilling into a pool of madeira cream sauce that set the flavours off just so. This was followed by a cartwheel of boned quails stuffed with a chicken mousse on a caramelly port and raisin sauce accompanied by some excellent vegetables – well timed, fresh, good quality. The desserts are less enterprising: bread-and-butter pudding, chocolate mousse, crème brûlée and the like. The lemon soufflé was distinguished only by its generosity with the zest of lemon. Good coffee. The wine list is quite extensive. House French, £6.75.

CHEF: Martyn Pearn   PROPRIETORS: Adrienne and Barry Berman
OPEN: all week
CLOSED: 3 weeks from mid-Jan
MEALS: 12.30 to 1.45, 7.30 to 8.45
PRICES: £19 (£29)
CARDS: Access, Visa
SEATS: 34. 6 tables outside. Private parties: 10 main room. Car-park. No children under 8. Smart dress preferred. No cigars/pipes in dining-room. Wheelchair access (also WC)
ACCOMMODATION: 11 rooms, all with bath/shower. Rooms for disabled. B&B £125 to £180. No children under 12. Afternoon teas. Garden. Swimming-pool. Tennis. TV. Phone [GHG]

| BURNHAM MARKET Norfolk | map 6 |
|---|---|

## *Fishes'*

| | |
|---|---|
| Market Place, Burnham Market PE31 8HE | COOKING 2 |
| FAKENHAM (0328) 738588 | COST £12–£28 |

A stone's throw from an early work of Sir John Soane behind the church in the 'loveliest village in Norfolk', Fishes' takes its place in a row of fine architecture on the green. It looks not unlike a shop, with counter sales in the mornings from the rear of the dining-room. There is a small stripped pine and linden green dining-room adjoining a turquoise dining-room cum sitting-room with fire, books, watercolours and comfort. People have been seen taking up reading where they left off on the last visit. You come here to eat fish: fresh from Wells, raised from local oyster beds, smoked by the restaurant itself. There is meat, some of it smoked too, but often not more than one dish. The crabs, smoked eel, potted shrimps, fish cakes and oysters are very good. A spring dinner started with smoked eel and a home-made horseradish cream and continued with monkfish cooked in butter and white wine, finished with mussels, mushrooms and parsley. All the flavours stood up – surrounding nose and brain as they enticed the tongue. Quantities are not outfacing; some think them small. Vegetables, bar baked or new potatoes, are not cooked (except some speciality, such as asparagus in season) – you are offered a range of salads. Desserts include home-made ice-cream (try buttered walnut) and fairly simple dishes done honestly: meringues were exactly right in consistency, sandwiched with whipped cream, served with kiwi fruit. Lunch is even better value than dinner. Smoking is discouraged in a civilised way with a note on a card on the tables. The wine list is short, sweet and white (plus three reds and a rosé). House wine, £5.25. CELLARMAN'S CHOICE : Chablis, *premier cru*, Vau de Vey, 1986, Rottiers, £19.50; Mâcon-Clessé 1986, Loron, £10.60.

CHEFS: Carole Bird, Gillian Cape and Paula Rout   PROPRIETOR: Gillian Cape
OPEN: Tue to Sun
CLOSED: Sun D Oct to June, 24 to 26 Dec, 2 weeks Jan
MEALS: 12 to 2, 6.45 to 9
PRICES: £15 (£23), Set L £6.95 (£12) to £9.75 (£15)
CARDS: Access, Amex, Diners, Visa
SEATS: 48. Private parties: 30 main room. Children's helpings. Children under 5 at D by prior arrangement. Wheelchair access (1 step)

---

**BURY ST EDMUNDS  Suffolk**                                          map 3

## *Mortimer's*

30 Churchgate Street
Bury St Edmunds IP33 IRG                                    COOKING 1
BURY ST EDMUNDS (0284) 760623                              COST £24

Seafarers' charts and paintings of life on the ocean jolly up the white walls of this straightforward fish restaurant near the middle of town, under the same management as Mortimer's in Ipswich (see entry). Kenneth Ambler cooks half a week here and half a week there. The menu changes and special dishes are prepared according to what arrives in the daily delivery from Grimsby. Fish might be simply grilled or fried, or might have a sauce incorporating cheese, white wine, mushrooms or herbs. The simpler the dish the better, in the opinion of most readers; consistency is sometimes hard won. There are shellfish and smoked fish, too, and even the coffee comes with fish-shaped chocolates. House French, £6.50. CELLARMAN'S CHOICE : Pinot Blanc 1985, Hugel, £8.95; Torres Viña Sol 1987, £7.75.

CHEF: Kenneth Ambler   PROPRIETORS: Kenneth Ambler and Michael Gooding
OPEN: Mon to Sat, exc Sat L
CLOSED: bank hols, 23 Dec to 5 Jan
MEALS: 12 to 2, 7 to 9 (8.30 Mon)
PRICES: £14 (£20)
CARDS: Access, Amex, Diners, Visa
SEATS: 60. Private parties: 8 main room. Children's helpings. No smoking area/ no pipes in dining-room. Wheelchair access (1 step)

---

**CALSTOCK   Cornwall**                                                                  map 1

## ▲ *Danescombe Valley Hotel* ▼

Lower Kelly, Calstock PL18 9RY                                              COOKING 3
TAVISTOCK (0822) 832414                                                        COST £28

This lovely small hotel on the banks of the Tamar, surveying a bend often populated with pleasure steamers from Plymouth, the railway viaduct bisecting one vista, the woods of Cotehele rising lusciously from the stream, exemplifies some of the contradictions of cooking and eating in Britain today. Martin and Anna Smith were two Londoners who wished to leave the city, to walk taller on a smaller planet, preserve liberty and freedom of expression. Having a gift for hospitality, they elected to run a small hotel. They kept it to a size where they could undertake everything: cooking, buying, greeting, decorating, furnishing, bedmaking – the lot – without outside help. This they have done to a high standard. Bedrooms have every comfort; the house is delectable; the food and wine are good. But the place has very little to do with the world of chefs, head waiters, great hotels and grand restaurants. Its existence in this book by the side of, say, John Burton-Race at L'Ortolan in Shinfield (see entry) is a piece of flawed logic, certainly of classification. Were this the only instance in these isles, it would matter not, but it is a paradigm. There are scores of like establishments dotted across the shires of England, concentrated in the outer zones of Scotland, Wales and the borders. We do not regret their existence, even though they outnumber 'normal' restaurants in some of these regions. What is a pity, however, is that they do not wish to expand their horizons – to make the jump from the super bed, breakfast and evening meal category to something that offers a much wider public service. This is a reflection on the British eating public as much as on the Smiths and their colleagues. The hallmark of Danescombe is studied informality (an inherited London characteristic) within a lovingly decorated small house. The number of bedrooms almost matches the seats in the dining-room, so there is little space for outsiders. Anna Smith cooks a set three-course meal, without choice, on five nights of the week. The extra course of cheese may be uncooked, but such care is taken in its composition that it must take as much time as all the puddings put together. Her style is refined simplicity. On some evenings, the simple gains victory over the refinement. This is a signal cause of her popularity. Not only is the place unlike a restaurant, but so is the cooking. Guests, apprehensive of another dose of fats and proteins, relax at the clean flavours and direct approach. A meal that merited approval started with a warm goats' cheese in pastry, proceeded to a breast of chicken with sorrel sauce, took in the cheeses – all local, all unpasteurised, all ripe – before finishing with a tart of poached pears in a firm custard. Another evening saw a salad of fennel, chicory and peppers, rack of lamb with three mustards and an excellent home-made almond ice-cream and strawberry sauce. Vegetables with the main course are usually simple but good. The wine list is as particular as the rest of the operation. One of the major justifications of places like Danescombe is that they allow the quixotic to shine. Thus Martin Smith's choice is not large, outweighed indeed by the length of his comments, but it is both very good and very cheap. The choices are excellent, the growers invariably first class. There is no doctrinaire concentration on a particular region. There is a fixed mark-up (not percentage) which makes everything very fairly priced. As Martin Smith himself observes, 'We would love to give it all away, but…' House claret is Ch. Méaume 1985 at £6.75 and the white is Sauvignon de Touraine 1987 from the co-opérative at Oisly at £6.

CHEF: Anna Smith   PROPRIETORS: Martin and Anna Smith
OPEN: Mon to Sun, exc Wed and Thur, D only
CLOSED: Nov to Easter
MEALS: 7 to 8
PRICES: Set D £20 (£23). Service inc
SEATS: 12. No children under 12. No smoking in dining-room
ACCOMMODATION: 5 rooms, all with bath/shower. B&B £48 to £56. Deposit: £50. No children under 12. Garden. Golf. Scenic. Doors close at midnight. Confirm by 3 [GHG]

---

**CAMBRIDGE  Cambridgeshire**                                    map 3

## Midsummer House

Midsummer Common,
Cambridge CB4 1HA                                    COOKING 3
CAMBRIDGE (0223) 69299                               COST £18–£43

The house looks as if it had lost its neighbours, a tooth in a gap, bolstered by a conservatory. Space is generous but the best tables are indeed in the conservatory even if it may get warm on a summer's day. The long walk from the nearest car park – the house is reached by a towpath – may be a wet transpontine hike to the accompaniment of low moans of singing wind. The house once reached, comfort is paramount and reports have been glad of this arrival on the Cambridge scene. 'At last, a decent restaurant,' is a cry oft repeated. A monthly menu, with much cheaper lunchtime offerings, and a six-course gastronomic extravaganza (cheap by metropolitan standards), must be exceptional in not offering beef as a main course (in the March menu to hand), save as part of a no-choice set meal. On a Sunday lunch, beef is also absent, the alternatives being lamb or 'rather gristly' sucking pig. This courage is to be applauded. Dishes that have been praised include a stuffed quail en ballotine with a truffle *jus*; wild mushrooms in puff pastry; salmon in cream and Champagne sauce; lamb chops with spinach and bacon. Certain infelicities may creep into the cooking although the standard has done nothing but improve, especially with the sauces and the vegetable accompaniments. A chicken cooked oriental style included cabbage stuffed with rice and bacon, purée of carrot and stuffed Florence fennel. The wine list affords a stroll through most countries, though concentrated on France. Its prices are not outrageous, and the spread is acceptable, though not very enlivening. House wine from Geoffrey Roberts is £8.50. CELLARMAN'S CHOICE : Cousiño Macul Cabernet Sauvignon Antiguas Reservas 1981, £10; Cuvaison Chardonnay 1986, £15.50. The sad death of Michael Smith, one of the founding partners, has not altered the policies or intentions of those who remain.

CHEF: Hans Schweitzer   PROPRIETORS: Chris Kelly and Hans Schweitzer
OPEN: Tue to Sun, exc Sat L and Sun D
MEALS: 12 to 2, 6.30 to 9.30
PRICES: Set L £10.80 (£18) to £13.50 (£21), Set D £18.50 (£27) to £26.50 (£36)
CARDS: Access, Diners, Visa
SEATS: 35. 2 tables outside. Private parties: 35 main room, 12 and 16 private rooms.
Children's helpings on request. Smart dress preferred. Wheelchair access

## Shao Tao

| 72 Regent Street, Cambridge CB2 1DP | COOKING 1 |
| CAMBRIDGE (0223) 353942 and 328739 | COST £17–£35 |

Service, rather than food, has drawn the liveliest comments this year. For example, one reporter found that 'if you dare to complain, the waiter assumes a Bruno-esque expression, as though dying to hit you!' and others have had similarly disquieting experiences. Despite this, reporters do enthuse about the food. The menu straddles the Chinese regions and specialises in hot Hunan and Mandarin saucing, moo shu pork and vegetables and sizzled dishes. There is now a branch in Newmarket, Suffolk. House French is £5.50.

CHEF/PROPRIETOR: Mr Tao
OPEN: all week
MEALS: 12 to 2.30, 6 to 11 (11.30 Fri and Sat)
PRICES: £10 (£18), Set D £12.50 (£17) to £22.50 (£29). Snacks from £2.50. Service 10%
CARDS: Access, Amex, Diners, Visa
SEATS: 100. Private parties: 100 main room, 30 private room. Vegetarian meals. Children's
helpings. Music. Air-conditioned

## Twenty Two ▼

| 22 Chesterton Road, Cambridge CB4 3AX | COOKING 2 |
| CAMBRIDGE (0223) 351880 | COST £25 |

This end-of-terrace house is just past Midsummer Common, close to the river at Jesus Lock. Open the door and the dining-room is there: a high ceiling, delicate greys and pinks, a dresser full of wines and bottles, candles on the tables. In a town of fluctuating restaurant fortunes, this place seems to offer decent cooking (usually) at very fair prices. The menu is short, set-price and changed every month. There are four choices at each course (including a vegetarian dish) with an automatic second course salad. A recent meal included excellent pakoras – spicy vegetable fritters – with a tamarillo sauce; went on to that compulsory salad which had several greengrocer's leaves, marigolds and double daisies as well; some exactly cooked calf's liver with a pesto cream sauce; vegetables that included grated courgettes topped with cheese, steamed cauliflower with flaked almonds and small new potatoes; and finished with a traffic-light trio of sorbets – kiwi, passion fruit and raspberry. All this was good, but the other half of the party fared less well: undercooked pastry in a pear and almond tart; grey and fatty duck; overly firm crab and asparagus mousse. Reports from others have underlined this unevenness. Service is exemplary: intelligent, kindly, well-paced and firm. Coffee is often not good. The wine list is nicely judged for a place of this character. It is not too long, it has some interesting bottles – Jekel's Arroyo Seco Riesling 1986, Wolf Blass Watervale Semillon 1984, Rissardi's Valpolicella Amarone 1982 and Lurgashall Winery's gooseberry wine are examples. It charges fair mark-ups (Krug Grande Cuvée is £19 cheaper than at a restaurant 10 miles down the road). The house Duboeuf white is not as good as the house red, Ch. du Grand Moulas from the Rhône, both at £5.95. CELLARMAN'S CHOICE : Rioja Reserva, Contino 1984, £9.50; Cloudy Bay Sauvignon Blanc 1988, £11.95.

CHEF: Michael Sharpe   PROPRIETORS: Michael and Susan Sharpe
OPEN: Tue to Sat, D only
CLOSED: 24 Dec to 1 Jan
MEALS: 7.30 to 10
PRICES: Set D £15.50 (£21). Licensed, also bring your own: corkage £3
CARDS: Access, Visa
SEATS: 28. Private parties: 28 main room. Vegetarian meals. No children under 12. Music

## Upstairs

| 71 Castle Street, Cambridge CB2 3AH | COOKING 1 |
|---|---|
| CAMBRIDGE (0223) 312569 | COST £12–£18 |

All that's visible from outside is Waffles café, but at the top of the stairs, step on to the set of *The Sheik of Araby*, with black-painted tables, lanterns, Persian rugs, and fretted window screens. The menu, not least the diner-friendly prices, is identical to that of a year ago. Dishes originate from all over the Middle East and Africa: chicken marinated with turmeric and ginger in a lemon sauce from Morocco; stuffed aubergines from Iraq; kala josh, a yoghurt-topped spicy beef dish from Eastern Turkey. To start with there is gagamp, like a cabbage-leaf dolmades, or filfil, a salad of sweet pepper rings. Desserts drip honey. It is an exercise in vicarious travel that enchants some, but leaves others thinking the flavour is stronger in memory than in actuality. A well-judged short and cheap wine list with house wine at £5.74.

CHEFS: Virginia La Charité and Hywel Evans   PROPRIETORS: Virginia and Pat La Charité
OPEN: all week, D only
MEALS: 6.30 to 11.30 (11 Sun)
PRICES: £9 (£15), Set D £7 (£12) to £8 (£13)
CARDS: Access, Visa
SEATS: 36. Vegetarian meals. Children's helpings. Music

---

*The text of entries is based on unsolicited reports sent in by readers, backed up by inspections conducted anonymously. The factual details under the text are from questionnaires the* Guide *sends to all restaurants that feature in the book.*

---

CAMPSEA ASH  Suffolk                                              map 3

## ▲ *Old Rectory* ♟

Campsea Ash IP13 0PU
WICKHAM MARKET (0728) 746524                          COOKING  1
on B1078, 1m E of A12                                COST  £21−£29

It is never easy to recommend without reservation any place as idiosyncratic as
this. Stewart Bassett has converted a long, low, seventeenth-century rectory
into a low-key restaurant with rooms. Its style is laid back and artless,
buttressed by firm ideas about cooking and hospitality and a fine wine list.
When it fails to function, it does so resoundingly, causing apoplexy. When it
works, it will enchant those whom it suits, perhaps to enthusiastic distraction,
but will create some irritation by its refusal to play by universal rules. Much
dining takes place in a large reconstructed conservatory. Menus are not
available, meals are composed either over the phone or by leaving the menu to
Stewart Bassett. The choice of wine may similarly be left to him. The cooking is
not cuisine *à la minute*. Much stuffing, spicing, and longish cooking is indulged.
It can work, as in a first course of salmon topped with a mousseline of pike and
baked in puff pastry, followed by Gressingham duck with a ginger and apricot
sauce. It can also be criticised for bad menu construction, lumpish presentation
and bad vegetables. Cheese is often good; upside-down cakes get an excellent
press. Service does not, although no-one impugns Mr Bassett's civility. The pill
is sweetened by its not being very expensive. The wine list is composed by
Remington Norman, M.W. It, too, is very reasonably priced: enough to
compensate for any shortcomings of service. The range, of vintages as well as of
regions and countries, is enviable. There is something for everyone here.

CHEF/PROPRIETOR: Stewart Bassett
OPEN: Mon to Sat, D only
MEALS: 7.30 to 10
PRICES: Set D £15 (£21) to £17.50 (£24)
CARDS: Access, Amex, Diners, Visa
SEATS: 40. Private parties: 18 main room, 6 and 20 private rooms. Car-park, 20 places.
Children's helpings. No children under 10. Wheelchair access
ACCOMMODATION: 8 rooms, all with bath/shower. B&B £27 to £43. Deposit: 10. No
children under 8. Garden. Doors close at midnight. Confirm by noon [GHG]

CANTERBURY  Kent                                                 map 3

## *Tuo e Mio*

16 The Borough, Canterbury CT1 2DR                   COOKING  1
CANTERBURY (0227) 61471                              COST  £22

This trattoria near the cathedral continues to be well patronised, especially on
Saturday night (which may affect the standards if too pressed). Pasta, fresh and
varied fish and game are offered alongside veal, calf's liver and other Italian
standards. Daily specials are signalled and worth pursuing for the most
interesting variations. Canterbury keeps this place close to its heart. House
wine is £5.50.

CHEFS: Bernardino Lombardo and Tino Guzman
PROPRIETORS: Mr and Mrs R.P.M. Greggio
OPEN: Tue to Sun, exc Tue L
CLOSED: 2 weeks Aug to Sept
MEALS: 12 to 2.30, 7 to 10.45 (10 Sun)
PRICES: £12 (£18). Cover 50p. Service 10%
CARDS: Access, Amex, Diners, Visa
SEATS: 40. Private parties: 20 main room. Vegetarian meals. Children welcome. No pipes in dining-room. Wheelchair access (1 step; also WC). Music

---

**CARTMEL  Cumbria**                                                                 map 7

## ▲ Aynsome Manor

Cartmel LA11 6HH                                                               COOKING 2
CARTMEL (053 95) 36653                                                    COST £11–£25

The house is deceptively large and stately. The view down Cartmel vale from the panelled dining-room is a reminder that it was once the property of the founding family of Cartmel Priory. There have been a few changes in the kitchen with promotions following the departure of Ernest Scott, but the formula and overall policy remain the same. There is a Lakeland-style five-course dinner at a fair set price with three choices before the second-course soup, three main courses, a perambulating sweets trolley and a largely British cheeseboard. The menu changes daily. The usually good vegetables include two sorts of potatoes that, ranging from à la berrichonne to à la forestière to à la boulangère as day follows day, read like a page from the classic *Repertoire de la Cuisine*. A summer meal began with tiny fried sprats, went on to a minestrone, followed by a slightly overcooked salmon with lemon cream sauce. The vegetables were baked fennel and broccoli with hollandaise. The *coup de grâce* was a meringue with crème de cacao. The desserts are still creamy to excess. One diner was struck particularly by the close attention of the staff – well motivated in a hotel that takes training seriously. A place, too, where the staff 'do not expect tips.' The wine list ranges more widely than deeply. There is almost a Louis Latour monopoly of burgundies and Beaujolais. But there are a few good bottles, including Hill Smith's Barossa Valley Semillon 1986, a Ch. Vignelaure 1980 from Provence, and a Quinta de Bacalhoa 1985 from Portugal. House Italian, £6.50 a litre. CELLARMAN'S CHOICE : Beaujolais Régnié 1987, Duboeuf, £8.40; Casteller Schlossberg Silvaner Trocken 1987 Franconia, £11.

---

CHEFS: Tony Varley, Ian Simpson and Ava Hill   PROPRIETORS: Tony and Margaret Varley
OPEN: Mon to Sat D, Sun L
CLOSED: 2 to 27 Jan
MEALS: 1, 7 to 8.15
PRICES: Set Sun L £7.50 (£11), Set D £15.50 (£21)
CARDS: Access, Amex, Visa
SEATS: 35. Private parties: 35 main room. Car-park, 20 places. Children's helpings. No children under 5. Smart dress preferred. No smoking. Wheelchair access
ACCOMMODATION: 13 rooms, 12 with bath/shower. B&B £23.50 to £47. No children under 5. Pets welcome. Garden. Golf. TV. Phone. Scenic. Doors close at 11.30 [GHG]

## ▲ *Uplands*

Haggs Lane, Cartmel LA11 6HD
CARTMEL (05395) 36248 and 36249

COOKING 3
COST £13–£25

Straddling the ridge above Grange-over-Sands, with views of Morecambe Bay, Uplands is a mile out of the village; take the turning opposite the Pig and Whistle. As befits an outpost of Miller Howe, there are echoes of the master, but Tom Peter's cooking and his wife's hospitality have an identity of their own. The house is coolly coloured, almost restrained, and pleases alike its two constituencies of residents and restaurant customers. Most comments begin with a paean to its value, particularly at lunch. Dinner is a set-price four-course meal with coffee. Choice is limited to two or three dishes at each stage until pudding. Soup is the universal second course. The service, although nearly simultaneous for all diners, is not theatrical in the mode of Miller Howe. Lunch is three courses, but just as good. Cooking is as vibrant as John Tovey's – Tom Peter was at Miller Howe for many years–and there are plenty of flavours, many of them sweet and fruit based. Pastry techniques are good, and hot soufflés, particularly of sole, have continued to be well reported. A spring meal started with hot hare soufflé wrapped in chicken breast on a pineapple salad with port and redcurrant sauce; then Jerusalem artichoke soup served in its tureen to each table along with a loaf of malted bread (and knife and board); then sea bass with a sauce of tarragon and shrimps from Morecambe Bay, surrounded by five vegetables, very much in the Tovey style and almost overwhelming; finally a chocolate and Amaretto mousse of exemplary lightness. After that, walking is a necessity; dining again, a pleasure. The wine list is short, fairly priced and best for Australasia. CELLARMAN'S CHOICE : Delegat's Gisborne Chardonnay 1986, £12.20; Ch. la Tour Blanche 1986, St-Emilion, £9.20.

CHEF: Tom Peter   PROPRIETORS: John J. Tovey, Tom and Diana Peter
OPEN: Tue to Sun, and Mon bank hols
CLOSED: 1 Jan to 24 Feb
MEALS: 12.30 to 1, 7.30 to 8
PRICES: Set L £10 (£13), Set D £17.50 (£21). Service 10%
CARDS: Access, Amex
SEATS: 34. Private parties: 34 main room. Car-park, 18 places. No children under 8. No smoking. Wheelchair access. Music
ACCOMMODATION: 5 rooms, all with bath/shower. B&B £24 to £36. No children under 8. Pets welcome. Garden. TV. Phone. Scenic. Doors close at 11. Confirm by 3 [GHG]

---

**CHADDESLEY CORBETT**  Hereford & Worcester                                    map 5

## ▲ *Brockencote Hall*

Chaddesley Corbett DY10 4PY
CHADDESLEY CORBETT (0562) 83876

COOKING 2
COST £18–£47

This extremely swish building in a 70-acre park with a lake, just west of the village, on the Kidderminster road, is brewers' classical, built at the turn of the century for the proprietors of Mitchell & Butler. It was well converted to a hotel in the English country house style (as spurious as brewers' classical) and has Anglo-French owners and a French chef. The style of cooking and presentation belongs about two miles this side of Calais, but is one we seem to have taken to our hearts. The lunch is good value but prices climb in the evening. There is a surprising emphasis on fish; equal numbers of fish and meat dishes are present on menus for both meals. The gravlax of salmon with a spaghetti of vegetables 'oladis de sarazin' has been recommended, as was the fillet of veal with honey and lime sauce. The wine list continues to offer a good range of French wines at French prices. House wine, Bordeaux Supérieur, £11.50; Alsace Pinot Gris, £9.40.

CHEF: Serge Demolliere   PROPRIETORS: Mr and Mrs J. Petitjean
OPEN: all week, exc Sat L and Sun D
MEALS: 12.30 to 2, 7.30 to 9.30
PRICES: £27 (£34), Set L £12.50 (£18), Set D from £31.80 (£39). Service inc
CARDS: Access, Amex, Diners, Visa
SEATS: 38. 5 tables outside. Private parties: 40 main room; 25 private room. Car-park, 45 places. Children welcome. Smart dress preferred. Wheelchair access (also WC). Music
ACCOMMODATION: 9 rooms, all with bath/shower. B&B £58 to £90. Children are restricted. Afternoon teas. Garden. TV. Phone. Scenic. Doors close at 12. Confirm by 6 [GHG]

---

## CHADLINGTON  Oxfordshire
map 2

## ▲ *The Manor* ▮

Chadlington OX7 3LX
CHADLINGTON (060 876) 711

COOKING 3
COST £29

'It's not one of those caricatures of a country house where everyone whispers, looks bored and waits for the next meal.' Indeed, much travail went into its purchase and redecoration and many pantechnicons (not tankers) were required to move the stocks of wine from the Grants' previous venture, Kirkby Fleetham Hall, to this slightly older, more manorial than aristocratic house deep in the heart of England. Chris Grant is again in charge of the cooking (but has been known to carry the bags). Children are welcome, dress rules relaxed, and David Grant observes that charges should always be net of everything: 'You don't tip the man who sells you a car, nor should you have to tip the waiter.' For all that, it is quite grand, certainly handsome, and has been decorated with bold colours and none of that 'spriggery' found in so many country places. The cooking takes the form of a five-course set-price dinner – opening with soup, closing with cheese, three or four choices in between. Chris Grant cooked well in Kirkby Fleetham and there is no reason to suppose it will now be otherwise. At a meal early in this kitchen's career, an inauspicious soup was succeeded by well-made brioche filled with feather-light smoked trout mousse and a vibrant hare terrine with a plum sauce. Plums proved to be a leitmotif, unseasonally decorating many of the dishes. Calf's liver with a blackcurrant sauce was correctly cooked, as was a salmon steak. The vegetables indicated accurate timing and a sensitive eye. Desserts have included a delicious prune and armagnac ice-cream and an airy, cold lime soufflé; hot or English recipes such as sticky toffee pudding and baked bananas evidently find favour. Chris Grant is a conservative yet careful cook, who patently enjoys fruit in saucing and who may have assessed well the palates of her potential customers. The service goes swimmingly with David Grant, who is a real enthusiast on the wine side. The most obvious merits of his cellar are a magnificent range of clarets with depth in Médoc first growths bettered by none – over 40 vintages of Latour back to 1924 – and prices that may make the explorer swoon with anticipation. A few lacunae appear (for example, in the Loire) and red burgundies are more miscellaneous than they might be, but the Jura and German sections are very strong. It is not a new-countries list. Notes are extensive, as is the choice of half-bottles. House Duboeuf is £6.50.

CHEF: Chris Grant   PROPRIETORS: David and Chris Grant
OPEN: all week, D only and Sun L
MEALS: 12.30 to 1.30, 7 to 9
PRICES: Set L and D £19.50 (£24). Minimum £19.50. Service inc
CARDS: Amex, Visa
SEATS: 24. Private parties: 6 and 10 private rooms. Car-park, 16 places. Children welcome.
No smoking in dining-room. Music
ACCOMMODATION: 7 rooms, all with bath/shower. B&B £50 to £100. TV. Phone. Scenic.
Doors close at 11 [GHG]

---

**CHAGFORD  Devon**                                                     map 1

## ▲ *Gidleigh Park* 🍷

Chagford TQ13 8HH
CHAGFORD (06473) 2367 and 2225
from Chagford square, turn R at Lloyd's,                          COOKING 4
then R at first fork; continue 2m                                COST £25–£50

Small wonder that the east side of Dartmoor became an enclave of millionaires at the end of the last century. Grocers, shipping magnates, tea planters and proconsuls built houses – some beautiful, some tedious, most large – in coveys. Summer afternoons witnessed the glide of limousines from tea to tea. Gidleigh Park was an Edwardian shipping magnate's; architecturally it is overstretched. Its reason is the moor at the back and the swoop towards the river plain: wooded, enchanted, be-valleyed. In the garden rushes the Upper Teign, the Hendersons' landscaping allowing the river the force of its true character. This hotel has been made by intelligence and determination. Only vision could create aesthetic pleasure out of such a lacklustre building. Refurbishment is constant, housekeeping never rests, reconstruction is always in view: a new cottage in the grounds, bedrooms redecorated and new croquet lawns – this is the only hotel in Britain with four. Shaun Hill cooks, and the kitchen keeps pace with the quality of the hotel. In two dining-rooms – one smaller and more enclosed than the other, but neither of especial character – he offers three set-price meals, the cheapest at lunch, the most expensive a seven-course gourmet meal served to the whole table only, sandwiching one common to either meal that offers half a dozen alternatives at each stage. Shaun Hill makes some of the best restaurant bread in the country. His feather-light buttermilk white bread is brilliant; so, too, are his Yorkshire puddings. A chef, then, that can deal with the basics (oatmeal biscuits are good as well), yet whose range is wider than most. When he cooked at London's Blakes Hotel, he led the fashion for eclecticism. This taste for the exotic has not left him: Thai soup of chicken and coconut milk with lemon grass, galanga, coriander and chilli, and scallops with lentil, coriander and cumin sauce. While many of his dishes are what we understand as 'modern', his cookery is among the most digestible. His sense of balance is fine and a long meal can be consumed without ill effect. Rather than a catalogue of dishes, here is a gourmet menu as taken by an inspector earlier this year. It began with a *turban* of ribbon-thin fresh pasta dressed in a light cream and covered with shavings of fresh white truffles. For fish there was a firm, fat piece of steamed turbot, flecked with the white spume of freshness and gentle cooking, sitting by a concasse of tomato enriched by oil and sharpened with vinegar. The vegetable course (Mr Hill takes vegetable cookery seriously) was a ragoût of wild mushrooms and baby vegetables – 'a fabulous array of different colours, textures, tastes, each mouthful a burst of new flavour, quite one of my favourite dishes this year.' Four wild mushroom types, tossed in a madeira, stock and red wine sauce with sweetcorn, carrot, green beans, broccoli, cauliflower, mange-tout and asparagus: 'It could have looked higgledy-piggledy; as it was, it was a still-life painting'. Not easy to follow this, but squab with shallots and red wine did well. The bird was carved but reconstructed for presentation. A dark sauce was matched by spinach and scattered pine kernels. Cheeses have long been an event at Gidleigh; it was one of their hallmarks, the second restaurant in Devon (the first was the Horn of Plenty, Gulworthy) to buy their stocks from Major Rance at Streatley. They still deal there, and at other places, like Jeroboams in London. A remarkable array, divided logically on the board, explained clearly by the waitress – with *those* biscuits. Sorbet clears the palate at this stage, no sooner: a lozenge of orange. The last course before coffee is a passion-fruit soufflé. This was cooked the exact time, in personal ramekins, but had separated a little – the one technical error. Non-flour-bound fruit soufflés can be difficult. Coffee is cafetière and strong.

The wine list that goes with this food is of the best. Although never expensive, it is not as cheap now as it used to be. The list may be forbiddingly long but Paul Henderson is free with his asterisks recommending particular bottles to the fledgling or seasoned toper. It is a remarkable collection, particularly of Californians, Jaboulet Rhônes, top-class Italians and old Champagnes, to name but a few. It is silly to recommend anything in particular here. For the curious, there are a few hundred bin-ends that the waitress will look for but may not find. The hotel's brochure hopes that service (which is in actuality just right) is 'always enthusiastic, personal and friendly, sometimes efficient.' This statement illustrates at once the ironic humanity that brightens unexpectedly such a fancy place and a certain take-it-or-leave-it approach that may jar on some customers. Those who don't know him might raise their eyebrows at Mr Henderson's comment at the head of the wine list, 'I have become bored with writing the introduction...' Equally, a few might suggest that the 'optional' levy – which is automatic unless objected to – on all accounts of a charitable gift of 35p to the Arvon Foundation is estimable, but that the hotel might seek to give the money out of its own takings rather than arm-locking its clientele. Playing fast and loose with diners' pocket money is evident again with VAT. Wines are priced exclusive of VAT. Children are welcome in the dining-room but restricted in the hotel, where pets are welcomed. Sense prevails in their attitude to tipping: it is discouraged.

CHEF: Shaun Hill   PROPRIETORS: Kay and Paul Henderson
OPEN: all week
MEALS: 12.30 to 2, 7 to 9
PRICES: Set L £21 (£25) to £29 (£35), Set D £29 (£34) to £37.50 (£42). Service inc
CARDS: Access, Visa
SEATS: 35. Private parties: 18 main room. Car-park, 25 places. Children welcome. Smart
dress preferred. No cigars/pipes in dining-room. Wheelchair access
ACCOMMODATION: 14 rooms, all with bath/shower. B&B £55 to £125. Children are
restricted. Pets welcome. Afternoon teas. Garden. Tennis. Fishing. TV. Phone. Scenic
[GHG]

## ▲ *Teignworthy Hotel*

Frenchbeer, Chagford TQ13 8EX
CHAGFORD (064 73) 3355
3m SW of Chagford: from Chagford Square follow          COOKING 3
signs to Fernworthy, then Kestor and Thornworthy          COST £43

Here is another house on the edge of Dartmoor, reached with difficulty (or close
attention to the signs) from the square at Chagford. Teignworthy, slightly
Lutyensesque, was built for a late-imperial forester. Today, very post-imperial
woodlands (larch and conifer) lap the sight-lines, but the walks among the
rocks and leaping waters of the Upper Teign are delectable. The Newells have
continued redecoration and improvement in the dining-room and reception
area: solidly modern with few weak concessions to nostalgia. Other parts of the
hotel follow other lines: English country domestic, a touch of art deco
furnishings, family Victorian antiques, and so on. The kitchen is devoted to
modern cooking, no nostalgia at all in avocado and mango salad with raspberry
vinaigrette; marinated raw mackerel fillets with lightly pickled squid; fillets of
sea bass topped with a herb and brioche crust; sauté of duck with morels and
ceps in a port and sweet wine sauce; or iced Sambuca parfait with coffee sauce.
David Woolfall is a good cook; there is balance in much he produces and the
basic techniques are sound. Materials are well sought out and their
presentation is neither too elaborate nor too off-hand. The wine list is mostly
from Christopher Piper Wines and affords a decent canter through France with
short walks to Australia (Brown Brothers), Italy and elsewhere. There are some
good Beaujolais. House Duboeuf is £6.80. The drawback with Teignworthy,
averred in too many letters to ignore, is that it is expensive. However, tipping is
'discouraged.'

CHEF: David Woolfall   PROPRIETORS: John and Gillian Newell
OPEN: all week
MEALS: 12 to 2, 7.30 to 9
PRICES: £26 (£36). Snacks from £5
CARDS: Access, Visa
SEATS: 30. 3 tables outside. Private parties: 30 main room. Car-park. Vegetarian meals. No
children under 10 except by arrangement. No smoking in dining-room. Wheelchair access
(also WC)
ACCOMMODATION: 9 rooms, all with bath/shower. B&B £54.50 to £59. No children under
10 except by arrangement. Afternoon teas. Garden. Sauna. Tennis. TV. Phone. Scenic
[GHG]

# Al San Vincenzo

52 Upper Mulgrave Road, Cheam SM2 7AJ                    COOKING 3
01-661 9763                                                                    COST £32

This is not a 'Britalian' trattoria, though you might be forgiven for thinking so
from a cursory glance at the shop-converted-to-restaurant in a manner all too
familiar to generations of English spaghetti-eaters. In a shopping parade giving
on to the railway station of Cheam, this place provides evening comfort for a
population once described in a couplet by a former editor of this *Guide*: 'Daily,
chef's "executive luncheon" feeds the rising men from Cheam.' Their
successors may return to supper at Al San Vincenzo, but in small number.
Provincial restaurateurs would be encouraged by the fact that, close to London
as this is, midweek winter nights can be very quiet indeed. The Borgonzolo
story is impressive. To begin with, a footballer, then a waiter in England from
1967, he taught himself to cook about five years ago. He never wished to fall
into the trattoria mould but to demonstrate the wealth of more complex and
imaginative dishes, principally from southern Italy. To a large extent, he has
succeeded. Perhaps material success, when it comes, will encourage him and
his kind and attentive English wife, who waits at table, to walk a wider stage.
The menu is short and fixed-price; a choice of four dishes in each course. He
takes a pride in being market-led. It may include home-made spicy sausage
served with polenta and sun-dried tomatoes, beef with capers, black olives and
peppers or quail stuffed with pork, parsley and garlic with and *agrodolce* sauce.
Desserts include a range of Italian (only) cheese, home-made ice-cream or
sorbet (not ethnic these – for example a granita of apple and kiwi), or
cantuccini with a glass of Vin Santo. Not every reader has felt that the flavours
are as vibrant as the menu promises, nor the output as swift as it might be. The
wine list is short and Italian, without even any Champagne, only the fragrant
Malvasia Secco Carmiano Frizzante. No house wine, but a Rocca delle Macie
Chianti Classico is £9.50. CELLARMAN'S CHOICE : Tenuta di Pomino
Frescobaldi 1987, £12.95; Valcalepio Rosso 1985, £9.50.

CHEF: Vincenzo Borgonzolo    PROPRIETORS: Vincenzo and Elaine Borgonzolo
OPEN: Mon to Sat, exc Sat L
MEALS: 12 to 2.30, 6.30 to 10.30
PRICES: Set L and D £21 (£27)
CARD: Access, Visa
SEATS: 24. Private parties: 8 main room. Children's helpings. No cigars/pipes in dining-
room. Wheelchair access

*On 6 May 1990 all London telephone numbers will change, the 01- prefix being replaced
by either 071- or 081-. See the front of the* Guide *for a list of which numbers will take
which prefix.*

*If you see a certificate in a restaurant bearing the words 'The Good Food and Restaurant
Guide', the claim is false – see the Introduction. Please write and tell us the name and
address of the restaurant.*

CHEDINGTON  Dorset                                                    map 2

## ▲ *Chedington Court* ▮

Chedington DT8 3HY
CORSCOMBE (093 589) 265                                    COOKING 3
off A356, 4m SE of Crewkerne                                COST £31

The house, built 150 years ago, is made from great blocks of warm yellow
stone. It has curved Dutch gables, mullioned windows, lots of little turrets, and
a balustraded, terraced garden round the back with spectacular views into
Somerset. 'The only thing the Chapmans cannot take credit for – the grassy
hill-top forts overlooking Marshwood Vale – are the gilt on the gingerbread.'
The public rooms have a private and intimate air, and an English formality.
Hilary Chapman keeps to a simple framework: choice of starter, then fish, meat,
a sweets trolley, cheese and coffee. Cheeses and traditional sweets such as
gooseberry crumble are as pervasively English as the fabric. Many dishes
sound quite ordinary: ogen melon with preserved ginger, poached sea-trout
with caper sauce, beef Stroganoff. What sets Chedington apart is a modern
treatment, a straightforwardness, a sense of control and restraint, as if the chef
is standing one step back, involved and yet detached, like a professional of the
best kind. This gives individuality to scallop, salmon, lemon sole and sea bass
in a buttery orange sauce, or to perfectly timed roast rack of lamb, full of flavour
with a very fine breadcrumb and rosemary crust. There are never too many
flavours on the plate nor too many kinds of vegetable. This sort of cooking
makes simple flavours sing. A raspberry mousse, the size of a small cake, is
edged with a palisade of sponge finger biscuits: perfectly wobbly, intensely
fruity, and simply garnished with a blob of cream, one raspberry and a mint
leaf. The wines are impressive in range, countries of origin and price: there
must be hundreds under £10. Allow an extra half hour to look through this
splendid list. There seems to be an upper price limit in operation. With few
exceptions (for example, some old clarets), Mr Chapman seems not to bother
with the fancy names. Oh! but the Spanish and the German choice, the half-
bottles, the little corner of delight. House French is £6. CELLARMAN'S CHOICE :
Ch. des Tour, Brouilly 1987 (red), £11.50 and 1986 (white), £11.50. 'Service is
already paid for so no extra is added or expected.'

CHEFS: Hilary Chapman and Nicolas Alcock    PROPRIETORS: Philip and Hilary Chapman
OPEN: all week, D only
MEALS: 7 to 9
PRICES: Set D £22.50 (£26). Service inc
CARDS: Amex, Visa
SEATS: 30. 2 tables outside. Private parties: 30 main room, 40 private room. Car-park, 20
places. Vegetarian meals. Children's helpings. Smart dress preferred. No cigars/pipes in
dining-room. Wheelchair access (also WC). Music
ACCOMMODATION: 10 rooms, all with bath/shower. B&B £35 to £90. Deposit: £30. Baby
facilities. Garden. Snooker. TV. Phone. Scenic. Doors close at midnight. Confirm by 9
[GHG]

*The Guide is totally independent, accepts no free hospitality, and survives on the number
of copies sold each year.*

## CHELMSFORD Essex                                    map 3

# Melissa

21 Broomfield Road, Chelmsford CM1 1SY               COOKING 1
CHELMSFORD (0245) 353009                             COST £11–£14

At present a daytime café-restaurant, well established for vegetarian and wholefood lunches and snacks, Melissa plans to open in the evenings as well. The lunchtime formula remains the same, with a daily dish such as moussaka or lentil loaf with basil alongside soup and salads, pizza, quiche, mushroom-filled baps and filled baked potatoes – 'design your own jackets.' For gourmet evenings held on the first Friday of each month, the food is of a different order. Goats' cheese in filo pastry with spiced pear, brazil nut loaf with champagne sauce, and vegetables such as parsnip purée with horseradish are some dishes. There is a good choice of coffees and teas. The wine list is short and basic with house bottles at £5. The restaurant is firmly non-smoking.

CHEFS/PROPRIETORS: Rosemary and Melanie Upson
OPEN: Mon to Sat L, first Fri each month D
MEALS: 9 to 4 (L 11.30 to 3)
PRICES: £5 (£11). Set D £10 (£12). Snacks £1.30
SEATS: 24. Private parties: 28 main room. Vegetarian meals. Children's helpings. No smoking. Wheelchair access. Self-service

## CHELTENHAM Gloucestershire                          map 2

# Le Champignon Sauvage 🍸

24–26 Suffolk Road
Cheltenham GL50 2AQ                                  COOKING 2
CHELTENHAM (0242) 573449                             COST £19–£32

Named appropriately after the past year's dominant ingredient. Without doubt, David Everitt-Matthias is aiming at cooking of astonishing complexity. What do you do with a piece of perfectly cooked lamb coated in a too-stiff mousseline of chervil, a strongish lamb reduction, a timbale of cabbage and bacon, a potato lattice propping up the meat and a tartlet of overcooked sweetbreads? The answer may well be, 'start again', especially as this description doesn't include the vegetables. The smart attractive restaurant is close to the Texaco garage and antique shops of Suffolk Road. Service with perfect skill is by Helen Everitt-Matthias in an atmosphere that is friendly and unassuming. This has disarmed many readers who have written again to extol the virtues of hot salmon mousse stuffed with frogs' legs, very fine soups, duck Pithiviers with almonds and Amaretto sauce, chartreuse of pigeons and pheasant with lentils. As with much of this sort of cooking, there are lots of two-sauces, pastry and odd toppings – for instance, deep-fried celeriac – that actually do not amount to much. The French cheeses come from Olivier and are a grand range. The petits fours are in remarkable variety – 18 were counted by one happy diner. To date the ambition runs ahead of the achievement because the form is unsuited to its vehicle, but the prices are not untoward for this level of effort. The wine list of over 100 bins concentrates on well-chosen French bottles, with a nod to the

New World. House French — three reds and three whites — from £6.75.
CELLARMAN'S CHOICE : Draytons Estate Chardonnay, 1986 from Australia,
£13; Châteauneuf-du-Pape, Vieux Télégraphe 1984, £18.30.

CHEFS: David Everitt-Matthias    PROPRIETORS: David and Helen Everitt-Matthias
OPEN: Mon to Sat, exc Sat L
MEALS: 12.30 to 1.30, 7.30 to 9.30
PRICES: Set L £12.45 (£19) to £18.50 (£27), Set D £18.50 (£27)
CARDS: Access, Amex, Visa
SEATS: 34. Private parties: 26 main room. Children welcome. Smart dress preferred.
Wheelchair access (1 step). Music. Air-conditioned

## Finns

| | |
|---|---|
| 143 Bath Road, Cheltenham GL53 7LT | COOKING 1 |
| CHELTENHAM (0242) 32109 | COST £12−£23 |

Iain Gaynor, who ran the *Guide*-featured Rose Tree in Bourton-on-the-Water in
the early 1980s, opened this restaurant to fill what he saw as a gap in the
market for reasonably priced eating out. At lunch there is a short set-price
menu and at dinner a *carte* priced for two or three courses. The atmosphere is
appropriately relaxed, with plants giving both main room and glass-roofed
extension a sub-tropical feel. It is a well-chosen backdrop for the food, which is
Anglo-French but scattered with exotic fruits, fish and flavourings in the
modern style: Seychelles kingfish has been cooked with black butter and lime
or a curry and coriander sauce; papaya stuffed for a first course; chocolate
mousse served on a mango and guava purée. Nonetheless, the menu is clearly
designed to offer something for everybody and there are other more classic
Mediterranean or British ideas such as leek and potato soup or lemon sole with
port jelly sauce. First reports suggest that at the moment it is these plainer
dishes which work best, highlighting the quality of well-bought produce.
Sweetness in savoury dishes may be an unwelcome element. Desserts, more
traditional mouthwatering concoctions such as a towering strawberry
shortcake on crème Anglaise and a stunning iced raspberry and blueberry
soufflé, seem more consistent. The wine list travels in short compass from
house wine at £4.95 to Ch. Pétrus 1979 at £195. This is a deserved indulgence;
for the most part the choice is fair and inexpensive. CELLARMAN'S CHOICE :
Chablis 1986 Beaufumé, £9.50;

CHEF: Mark Lawson Smith    PROPRIETORS: Iain and Diane Gaynor
OPEN: all week, exc Sat L and Sun D
CLOSED: first 2 weeks Aug, 25 and 26 Dec
MEALS: 12.30 to 2, 7 to 10
PRICES: Set L £8.75 (£12), Set Sun L £11.95 (£16), Set D £12.50 (£18) to £13.95 (£19)
CARDS: Access, Amex, Carte Blanche, Diners, Visa
SEATS: 50. 2 tables outside. Private parties: 30 main room. Vegetarian meals. No cigars/
pipes in dining-room. Wheelchair access (2 steps; also WC). Music

*See the inside of the front cover for an explanation of the new 1 to 5 rating system
recognising cooking standards.*

## *Mayflower*

| | |
|---|---|
| 32 Clarence Street, Cheltenham GL50 3NX | COOKING 2 |
| CHELTENHAM (0242) 522426 | COST £9–£28 |

'Possibly the best Cantonese restaurant within a 50-mile radius,' sits centrally in the town's one-way maze behind a red awning. The muted pastel walls and the table settings have none of today's often grandiose pretensions and there are a few rough edges. Sake comes heated in a pint mug of hot water and maraschino cherries make their way into garnishes. But the kitchen works well, the quality of the cooking is consistent and the dining-room is often packed. Flavours are well defined and pull no punches. The hot-and-sour soup, for example, has a peppery chilli, and vinegar cabbage is very spicy and salty, as described on the menu. But flavours can also be subtle, as in the bird's nest of scallops, large fresh prawns and vegetables in a light garlicky sauce on lettuce leaves. Seafood is emphasised in the chef's specialities and the Szechuan crispy aromatic duck is a favourite. Portions are generous and service is of a standard to match the food. There is a broad, reasonably priced wine list including rice wine and high-octane Chinese liqueurs. Dom Pérignon at £48 may constitute a bargain, and there are some nicely chosen bottles on an above-par list. House Mommessin, £5.50. Expansion is scheduled as the *Guide* goes to press.

CHEF: H.S. Truong   PROPRIETORS: The Kong family
OPEN: all week, exc Sun L
CLOSED: 25 to 28 Dec
MEALS: 12 to 1.45, 5.45 to 10.45 (11.15 Fri and Sat)
PRICES: £14 (£23), Set L £4.10 (£9) to £5 (£10), Set D £9.50 (£15) to £13 (£18)
CARDS: Amex, Diners
SEATS: 48. Private parties: 30 main room. Children welcome. Wheelchair access (1 step). Music. Air-conditioned

---

**CHESTER  Cheshire**                                                                 map 5

## *Abbey Green* ♥

*(badge: COUNTY RESTAURANT OF THE YEAR)*

| | |
|---|---|
| 2 Abbey Green, Northgate Street | |
| Chester CH1 2JH | COOKING 2 |
| CHESTER (0244) 313251 | COST £18 |

Abbey Green flourished as the national vegetarian restaurant of 1988/9 and has now been completely refurbished, with new tableware and a landscaped garden for summer eating as well as revamped lilac and pink décor. The menu holds plenty of surprises, since the kitchen takes the global village approach – gougère dijonnais, pasta polenesia, avocado crêpe with lime sauce and spicy courgette kofte were choices on one menu. Such main courses often translate into outrageous combinations: pineapple, avocado and ginger were layered with green pasta and a peanut sauce for the pasta polonesia. Sauces have the same unrestrained feel: whisky, apple and tarragon for a nut roast; coconut and vermouth for stuffed vegetables on rice. Off-putting as this compound of flavours may sound, it seems to work. Even non-vegetarians come away impressed. This may be because beginnings and sweets from the sideboard are far simpler so that, taken as a whole, meals are well balanced. The wine list is none too long (though there are long notes for each bottle) and somehow achieves a good spread at very fair prices. The organic wines are the ones to look out for. Mas de Gourgonnier, Ch. Le Gorre Sauvignon Blanc, A. Verdet's Hautes Côtes de Nuits and St Joseph, Clos de l'Arbalestrier 1984 are very good wines indeed. House Loire, Gamay and Sauvignon are £5.60. CELLARMAN'S CHOICE : Montana Sauvignon 1987, £9.25; Ch. Talbot, St-Julien 1979, £26.90.

CHEFS: Michael Davies, Catherine Kirko and Julia Dunning  PROPRIETORS: Julia Dunning and Duncan Lochhead
OPEN: Mon to Sat, exc Mon D
MEALS: 12 to 2.30, 6.30 to 10.15
PRICES: £11 (£15)
CARD: Access
SEATS: 55. 24 seats outside. Private parties: 8 main room, 24 private room. Car-park, 20 places. Vegetarian meals. Children's helpings. No-smoking area. Wheelchair access (2 steps). Music

---

CHINNOR  Oxfordshire                                                          map 2

## Sir Charles Napier Inn 🍴

Sprigg's Alley, nr Chinnor, OX9 4BX                              COOKING 1
RADNAGE (024 026) 3011                                          COST £16–£36

Sit on the terrace of the Inn on a summer's day facing quintessential Chilterns: Wain Hill, Beacon Hill, Lodge Hill. Around the Inn, about a mile out of Chinnor on the Bledlow Ridge road, is a smallholding with Oxfordshire Sandy and Black Boar, Vietnamese Pot Belly Boars, poultry, American Bronze turkeys, lambs. Eat the consequences. The meats are smoked on the premises, as well as roasted, for quite a long menu that includes a pretty wide range of fur and feather – from wild goose to rabbit. A summer meal of home-made pasta and pesto; salmon with a julienne of vegetables and a white wine sauce; fillet of beef with ginger, madeira and mango; finishing with a chocolate bavarois was pronounced enjoyable, if the coffee was not. There have been votes to the contrary: the somewhat exotic flavours – lime, ginger, coriander, tumeric, relish of kiwi and passion-fruit – have shocked rather than surprised. The staff, even when very busy, 'cope well'. The wine list was called 'short' in last year's *Guide*. That is stretching a point for a cellar of about 200 items fairly spread across the world. Prices are kept reasonable and there are many good bottles to choose from. The first section of about 125 wines is kept under £25, the expensive stuff being in the fine list that includes a run of 1966 clarets. There is an excellent range of sweet wines, including a 1964 Vouvrey Moelleux from Marc Brédif and a Muscat from Cascade Crest in Washington State. House French, £7. Children under seven may not be welcome at dinner, but they are treated royally at lunch.

---

*The* Guide *office can quickly spot when a restaurateur is encouraging customers to write recommending inclusion. Such reports do not further a restaurant's cause. Please tell us if a restaurateur invites you to write to the* Guide.

CHEF: Batiste Tolu   PROPRIETORS: The Griffiths family
OPEN: Tue to Sun, exc Sun D
MEALS: 12 to 2 (3 Sun), 7.30 to 10 (10.30 Fri and Sat)
PRICES: £20 (£30), Set L £9.50 (£16) to £12.50 (£19), Snacks from £4.50. Service 12.5%
CARDS: Amex, Diners
SEATS: 65. 10 tables outside. Private parties: 45 main room, 25 and 45 private rooms. Car-park, 60 places. Vegetarian meals. Children's helpings (L only). No children under 7 at D. No cigars/pipes in dining-room. Wheelchair access. Music. Air-conditioned

---

**CIRENCESTER   Gloucestershire**                                    map 2

## Tatyan's

27 Castle Street, Cirencester GL7 1QD                  COOKING 2
CIRENCESTER (0285) 653529                            COST £13–£25

'In the town that is the world capital of green wellington boots, waxed jackets and Range Rovers, no one might expect a good Chinese restaurant. It doesn't look like one: the decoration is pure Laura Ashley – at least that is in keeping with the town – and the staff and proprietors are slender, springy people who may be living advertisements for the food they cook.' The menu is refreshingly short; Cirencester, after all, is some way distant from the markets Chinese cooks rely on. Szechuan and sizzling dishes take pride of place, though Peking forms the bulk. Spicing has been found subtle and accurate in the Szechuan food and the quality of materials is very high. The Peking duck is properly prepared and comes well recommended. The wine list is equally unexpected: three dozen thoroughbreds, almost all French, from good and fashionable growers. House wines start at £7.50. CELLARMAN'S CHOICE : Sancerre 1988, Henry Natter, £12.50; Ch. Ramage La Batisse 1983, £12.50.

CHEFS: Y. Liang and T.S. Wong   PROPRIETORS: Lookhot Ltd
OPEN: Mon to Sat, exc Sat L
CLOSED: 2 weeks Feb
MEALS: 12 to 2, 6 to 10.30
PRICES: £12 (£20), Set L £8.50 (£13), Set D £11.50 (£16) to £16.50 (£21). Service inc
CARDS: Access, Amex, Diners, Visa
SEATS: 60. Private parties: 60 main room. Children welcome. Wheelchair access (1 step)

---

**CLEEVE HILL   Gloucestershire**                                    map 2

## Redmond's at Malvern View

*COUNTY OF THE YEAR RESTAURANT*

Cleeve Hill, Cheltenham GL52 3PR                      COOKING 3
CHELTENHAM (0242) 6720172                           COST £17–£35

Redmond and Pippa Hayward have flown the nest of Cheltenham to the eyrie of Cleeve Hill. Redmond's, hard by the roadside, is long and low, not as prepossessing as the view, day or night, from which it takes its name. The Haywards have a lot of work in hand to rid the place of the aura of a commercial travellers' stop on the tramp round the West Midlands. They have already succeeded in the dining-room, decorated in simple country style with large old tables, mixed Windsor chairs and some good pictures. Pippa Hayward runs this side of things, assessing the idiosyncrasies of guests, answering the most varied queries with calm aplomb. Redmond sometimes appears, on quieter nights, shyly bearing plates that might otherwise have been delayed. The menu is brief, at two prices depending on whether you take cheese, and shows the preoccupation with materials that was evident when he was in Cheltenham. Skate wing taken off the bone served en feuilleté with a lime and ginger butter; a feuilleté of chicken livers with orange and a port sauce; a light aubergine tart; beef with a garlic purée and a parsley sauce; brill with a parsley sabayon and horseradish; salmon with mussels and a mild curry sauce are some of the dishes recommended. Vegetables have also been mentioned: cooked to time, inventively (carrots with ginger) and attractively. He seems preoccupied with ginger and cinnamon as flavourings, as in hot apple soufflé with cinnamon ice-cream and pears with a ginger sorbet and a caramel sauce. While the quiet skill evokes respect, there have been moments of excess salt (in the bread), too much pepper (in potatoes) and a certain imbalance in flavours: horseradish contributed nothing to fish with a parsley sabayon, a caramel sauce was too bitter to allow the pears any identity themselves. Pastry and soufflés are hallmarks. Lunch is short, good and very reasonable. The wines, from impeccable sources, offer interesting choices (Idaho Chardonnay as well as French, for example), decent half-bottles, and house French from £6.75.

CHEFS: John Redmond Hayward    PROPRIETORS: John Redmond and Pippa Hayward
OPEN: Tue to Sun, exc Sat L and Sun D
CLOSED: first week Jan
MEALS: 12.30 to 2, 7.15 to 10
PRICES: Set L £14 (£17) to £15.50 (£19), Set D £23 (£26) to £26 (£29). Service inc
CARDS: Access, Visa
SEATS: 32. Private parties: 20 main room, 12 private room. Car-park, 16 places. Children's helpings on request. No children under 5. No cigars/pipes in dining-room

---

**CLEVELEYS** Lancashire                                                        map 5

# Cleveleys Wholefood & Vegetarian Restaurant

44 Victoria Road West
Cleveleys FY5 1BU                                              COOKING 1
CLEVELEYS (0253) 865604                                        COST £6–£11

This small restaurant holds its own as much by virtue of its home cooking and good value as by being vegetarian. In the first-floor Edwardian dining-room there is an old-fashioned, rural atmosphere. The menu is English vegetarian but includes birianis, chilli bean casseroles and cashew nut paellas as well as good vegetable soups and various bakes, cobblers and casseroles. On Friday nights there is a set menu offering two first courses and three main courses, but at lunchtimes the choice is wider, supplemented by quiches and open sandwiches. Flavours can be on the bland side, but ingredients are good and fresh. Desserts outnumber all the other dishes and run the gamut of pies, cakes and stickier sweets such as like nougatine meringue or squidgy chocolate roulade. House French wines come by the litre carafe at £5.25. No smoking.

CHEF: Betty Nuttall and Laura Crossley  PROPRIETOR: Sandra Crossley
OPEN: Tue to Sun L and Fri D
MEALS: 12 to 4, 6.30 to 9
PRICES: £5 (£9), Set L £2.75 (£6) to £3.10 (£7), Set D £3.95 (£8). Snacks from 40p
SEATS: 40. Private parties: 40 main room, 40 private room. Vegetarian meals. Children's
helpings. No smoking. Music

---

**CLUN  Shropshire**                                                                            map 4

## ▲ *Old Post Office*

9 The Square, Clun SY7 8JA                                                    COOKING 2
CLUN (058 84) 687                                                            COST £19–£30

Drive south from Shrewsbury and the hills, bare of trees, rear up, archaic slag
heaps set against a westering sun. Come north from Leominster and pass
Stokesay castle, the last vestige of true England before you turn west towards
Wales. At the head of a valley that dives out of the mountains towards the
Shropshire plain lies Clun, a marcher town if ever there was one. A natural
amphitheatre holds town and motte and bailey castle, ramparts dropping sheer
to the river below. The Old Post Office is, as the name implies, a converted
shop, now serving as a restaurant with a couple of bedrooms. The Arbuthnots
have consolidated their position here, are well booked for weekends, and have
redecorated and extended the restaurant into a terrace. It has a very light feel to
it, with grey, white, apricot and some green in the décor, good summer colours.
Continuity with the previous régime is surprisingly strong: parts of the wine
cellar, decorative touches, the importance of the cheeseboard are instances.
However, the music has changed from classical to, on one night at least, an
endless tape of post-Second World War popular songs. A 40-year-old might
sob into the soup as Nat King Cole comes round for the tenth reprise. The menu
is pleasingly short: two fishes of the day tacked on to four other dishes in each
course. Service by Anne Arbuthnot is amiable and informed, especially about
the array of British cheeses. Dining may be a slow procedure on busy nights.
The cooking has been much enjoyed. Appropriately, coming from an erstwhile
*Michelin* inspector, it is modern: warm salad of duck livers with a walnut
dressing; mousseline of sole in a courgette flower served with a red pepper
sauce; breast of chicken with vanilla and orange; lamb with a fresh berry and
wine sauce; cold peach soup with summer berries are examples. Presentation is
good and people like the bread; quantities are generous. There have been times
when the food lacks seasoning, therefore flavour, and when the composition of
tastes is lopsided from injudicious quantities, for instance, of sweetness in a
savoury sauce. The wine list is along the lines of 'small is beautiful.' Reds and
whites, of promiscuous origin, are listed in price order; this makes interesting
reading. The bottles are nicely chosen: Tyrrell's Long Flats from Hunter Valley,
a Rollin Hautes Côtes de Beaune and George Goulet Champagnes are a few.
Half-bottles are sparse and dull. House country French is £6.50 and £6.85.
CELLARMAN'S CHOICE : Juliénas 1986, Monnet, £11.40; Séguret Blanc 1987,
Côtes du Rhônes-Villages, Meffre, £10.50.

---

*The* Guide *always appreciates hearing about changes of chef or owner.*

---

CHEF: Richard Arbuthnot   PROPRIETORS: Anne and Richard Arbuthnot
OPEN: Wed to Sun
CLOSED: 1 week after May and Aug bank hols
MEALS: 12.30 to 1.30, 7.15 to 9.30
PRICES: £13 (£19), Set D £19 (£25)
CARDS: Access, Visa
SEATS: 30. 2 tables outside. Private parties: 25 main room. Vegetarian meals. Children
welcome. No cigars/pipes in dining-room. Music
ACCOMMODATION: 2 rooms. B&B £17.50. Scenic. Doors close at 1am

| COCKERMOUTH   Cumbria | map 7 |
|---|---|

## *Quince and Medlar*

| 13 Castlegate, Cockermouth CA13 9EU | COOKING 2 |
|---|---|
| COCKERMOUTH (0900) 823579 | COST £17 |

This excellent vegetarian restaurant changed hands at the end of 1988, when
the Whitehead-Whitings sold up. Reports, however, stress continuity rather
than change under the new owners, Colin and Louisa Le Voi from Sharrow Bay
Hotel. 'The best vegetarian food we have ever tasted in a restaurant,' wrote one
impressed diner. 'Forget about this being a vegetarian restaurant, the cooking
is more than able to stand on its own feet,' wrote another. The praise is drawn
by a range of dishes which avoid all the old clichés: a parsnip and apple
mousse with pine kernels, an aubergine charlotte with a pasta filling bound by
fresh tomato sauce, a gougère with vegetables in a garlic cream sauce. The
menu changes with the seasons, but old favourites like the twice-cooked
cheese soufflé, seed and nut terrines and sweet-and-sour vegetables have been
kept. Details are good too: pasta is home made, the cheeseboard arrives with
celery and lettuce, coffee comes with fudge brownies. The pleasantly rural
décor has been kept as it was and service is friendly. House French, £4.75.

CHEF: Colin Le Voi   PROPRIETORS: Colin and Louisa Le Voi
OPEN: Tue to Sun, D only
CLOSED: 2 to 3 weeks Jan
MEALS: 7 to 9.30
PRICES: £10 (£14)
CARDS: Access, Visa
SEATS: 26. Private parties: 18 main room. Vegetarian meals. Smart dress preferred. No
smoking. Music

| COGGESHALL   Essex | map 3 |
|---|---|

## *Langan's*

| 4–6 Stoneham Street, Coggeshall CO6 1TT | COOKING 2 |
|---|---|
| COGGESHALL (0376) 561453 | COST £12–£31 |

Mark Baumann has continued cooking here in this gallery of a restaurant by
the market cross in the middle of the village. The brasserie offers a daily menu
of five or six dishes in each course, none overpriced, though neither is it cheap.
Ideas are as modern as in the capital itself: Stilton and shallot mousse; collops

of venison and veal with a tangle of Chinese noodles; hot strawberry soufflé. Tradition reigns at Sunday lunch. Unevennesses may be occasioned by absence or peremptory service. The wine list takes in a wide range of price and origin with none too greedy a mark-up. House French from Gascony, £5.95.

CHEF: Mark Baumann   PROPRIETOR: Susan Langan
OPEN: all week, exc Sun D and Sat L
CLOSED: first 2 weeks Jan
MEALS: 12.30 to 2, 7.30 to 10
PRICES: £20 (£26), Set L £6.50 (£12) to £7.50 (£13)
CARDS: Access, Amex, Diners, Visa
SEATS: 80. Private parties: 30 main room. Children welcome. Wheelchair access (3 steps). Music. Air-conditioned

---

COLCHESTER  Essex                                                      map 3

## Warehouse Brasserie

12 Chapel Street North
Colchester CO2 7AT                                              COOKING 1
COLCHESTER (0206) 765656                                        COST £18

This brasserie continues to satisfy many demands of residents and visitors alike: anyone who has been marooned in Colchester with children in tow on a coolish Friday evening will know the problem. It is not an easy place to find, nor is parking easy. Once achieved, the cheerful impression given by both the decoration and greeting is confirmed by the food: fair eating and fair value. Dishes that have pleased include mussels with garlic butter; mushroom tartlets; a vegetarian couscous dish; char-grilled lamb steak; blackberry and apple crumble and an apricot tarte Tatin. Other hot puddings have been observed, such as a steamed date pudding with vanilla custard and, at the beginning of a meal, soups have been 'rich and nourishing'. House French wines £5.25.

CHEFS: G.C.H. Ford, Larkin Warren, Karen Bussell and Anthony Brooks
PROPRIETORS: G.C.H. and J.N. Ford
OPEN: Mon to Sat
MEALS: 12 to 2, 7 to 10.30
PRICES: £10 (£15)
CARDS: Access, Visa
SEATS: 75. Private parties: 20 main room. Vegetarian meals. Children's helpings. Wheelchair access (1 step). Air-conditioned

---

COLTISHALL  Norfolk                                                    map 6

## ▲ Norfolk Mead Hotel

Church Street, Coltishall NR12 7DN                              COOKING 1
NORWICH (0603) 737531                                           COST £16–£32

Turn right by the church down a long drive leading to this wistaria-and-rose – draped hotel set in a bend of the River Bure. The dining-room is lacy pink and peach, with piped country and western music. Diners can pick and mix from two set menus (plus a third for residents) and a list of specials, all of them modern. The presentation has been enticing in dishes such as grilled breast of duck with calvados sauce and pearls of apple and pear; ravioli of crab with langoustine, tomato and basil; roast saddle of rabbit with shallots and garlic. On the whole, the flavour has lived up to the looks, although there have been instances of disappointing blandness. Hot sweet soufflés are a speciality and reporters have been very taken with the plum clafoutis. Bread and breakfast croissants are home made; pre-dinner nibbles and coffee are good. Wines are not notable for bargains but the house French is £6.75. CELLARMAN'S CHOICE : Montagny *premier cru* 1987, Protheau, £14.75; Ch. Rozier, St-Emilion 1984, £16.75.

CHEF: Chris Hyde   PROPRIETORS: Reginald Davies and Jane Seymour
OPEN: Mon to Sat, D only, and Sun L
MEALS: 12 to 2, 7 to 9
PRICES: Set Sun L £9.95 (£16), Set D £12.95 (£18) to £21 (£27)
CARDS: Access, Amex, Diners, Visa
SEATS: 35. Private parties: 40 main room, 22 private room. Car-park, 45 places. No children under 3. No pipes in dining-room. Wheelchair access (2 steps; also WC). Music
ACCOMMODATION: 10 rooms, all with bath/shower. B&B £43 to £55. Deposit: £10. No children under 3. Garden. Swimming-pool. Fishing. TV. Phone. Scenic. Doors close at midnight. Confirm by 6

---

**CORFE CASTLE  Dorset**                                     map 2

## ▲ *Mortons House Hotel*

East Street, Corfe Castle BH20 5EE                    COOKING 2
CORFE CASTLE (0929) 480988                            COST £17–£30

Corfe Castle is sitting on England's largest onshore oil well. The village has had its part to play in the exploitation of another natural resource: Purbeck marble. The wealth from that created the fine early modern buildings in the village, not least Mortons House itself. Will the oil trade do the same for the more fleeting things of life, cooking for instance? Mortons has taken on a new chef, referred to with some satisfaction as 'coming from Harvey's' – so quickly are reputations made. The kitchen has lost some of its wilder ideas and combinations and seems set on cooking good modern British. Satisfactory verdicts have been received on a warm salad of pheasant and wild mushrooms with walnut dressing; ravioli of seafood with a herb sauce; guinea-fowl with wild mushrooms and port wine sauce; salmon and brill with a herb sauce where the fish alternated in slices round the large plate, the interstices filled with the minutest turned turnips and carrots. The hotel is expanding its rooms; some of the decoration is really fine, parts remain at their restrained best – no carpets or frills. However 'the new rooms have jacuzzi tubs, which I take to be a very bad sign.' This reporter, a cynic as to hotels, was unimpressed by sloppy service. House Fitou, £8.25; Morton Estate Hawkes Bay Sauvignon Blanc, £11.10.

---

'We have all heard of the pub with no beer, but I am now able to report on an Indian restaurant without any rice (in truth without any pilau rice).'   On dining in Leicestershire

---

CHEFS: Tim Hughes and Birgit Heller   PROPRIETORS: Janice E. Hughes and
Gerhard Bockau
OPEN: all week
MEALS: 12.30 to 2, 7.30 to 10
PRICES: £12 (£17), Set D £17.50 (£23) to £19 (£25), Snacks from £1.50. Service inc
CARDS: Access, Visa
SEATS: 40. 6 tables outside. Private parties: 30 private room, 220 hall. Car-park, 30 places.
Vegetarian meals. Children's helpings. Wheelchair access
ACCOMMODATION: 17 rooms, all with bath/shower. B&B £40 to £140. Deposit: 20%. Baby
facilities. Pets welcome. Afternoon teas. Garden. TV. Phone. Scenic. Confirm one week
before [GHG]

---

**CORSE LAWN   Gloucestershire**                                          map 2

# ▲ Corse Lawn
# House Hotel 🍾

Corse Lawn GL19 4LZ
TIRLEY (045 278) 479                                         COOKING 3
on B4211, 5m SW of Tewkesbury                               COST £17–£41

The Lawn is not so much round the house as round the settlement, for it
stretches either side of the road as a long and graceful common fringed with
trees, hedges and scattered houses. The hotel stands alone, a tall double pile in
Queen Anne red brick, a new and conservative extension for bedrooms to one
side, a pond to the front for sitting alongside on fine days, with the ducks. The
Hines have long been in residence and go from strength to strength: more
extensions are envisaged. A bar (where meals may be taken) is on the right of
the front door, the dining-room is a new extension to the left and behind. It is
quite grand; the waiting staff, occasionally lofty, are very proper. Corse Lawn is
a place that excites much correspondence (a good sign), but there are occasions
when enthusiasm is muted although never absent altogether. A large menu is
maintained, both *carte* and *prix fixe*, and the pudding list is almost as long again.
A reader sent her comments after a two-day stay: 'The food is still satisfying in
every way. The house atmosphere easy and human. Perhaps some sauces have
become a little richer, not, to me, an improvement. My first courses were a
bavarois of smoked trout wrapped in smoked salmon – piquant and
refreshing, everything a first course should be; hot crab tart with a hollandaise,
excellent. What a pastry-hand is here!' Main courses at Corse Lawn sound
quite straightforward: poached salmon hollandaise, breast of duckling with
orange sauce, saddle of rabbit with mustard sauce, but the terse descriptions
mask sophistication and finesse of execution even if vegetables 'surprise by
their old-fashioned generosity.' Puddings are also old-fashioned: toffee ice-
cream with butterscotch sauce, a 'custardy' crème brûlée, walnut ice-cream
(there are six or seven ices at any one time) with a 'too sickly' chocolate sauce.
But mango with paw-paw mousse and marinated lime strikes a more modern
note and was adjudged delectable – just as mango and lime for breakfast was
an ideal pick-me-up for a flagging soul. The wine list is much clearer to read
than hitherto and is impressive in its range. The expensive burgundies and
clarets are well balanced by cheaper regional wines and good choices from

Italy, Spain, the United States and Australasia. There are several decent wines by the glass. House Bordeaux is 6. CELLARMAN'S CHOICE : Mâcon-Villages 1983, Leroy, £15.75; Ch. Millet, Graves 1982, £20.30. There is a separate and extensive vegetarian menu (about which we have had no reports) and 'no tips are expected.'

CHEFS: Baba Hine and Tim Earley   PROPRIETORS: Denis and Baba Hine
OPEN: all week
MEALS: 12.30 to 2, 7 to 10
PRICES: £23 (£34), Set L £13.50 (£17) to £15.50 (£19), Set D £19.75 (£23). Service inc
CARDS: Access, Amex, Diners, Visa
SEATS: 45. 8 tables outside. Private parties: 55 main room, 24 private room. Car-park, 50 places. Vegetarian meals. Children's helpings. Wheelchair access (also WC)
ACCOMMODATION: 10 rooms, all with bath/shower. Rooms for disabled. B&B £50 to £65. Baby facilities. Pets welcome. Afternoon teas. Garden. Tennis. TV. Phone. Scenic. Doors close around midnight. Confirm by 6

---

**COSHAM** Hampshire                                                    map 2

## Barnards

109 High Street, Cosham PO6 3BB                          COOKING 2
COSHAM (0705) 370226                                         COST £23

The Cosham gyratory one-way system may leave spinning minds ready for the dark blue calm of this small restaurant run by a young couple of high talent. Look forward to some good food. The menu is short but its execution borrows from good models – even the amuse-gueule is small kebabs of fillet steak and pimento. A meal in spring began with a small tart of good pastry filled with artichoke, quails' eggs and a hollandaise. It was then given a red wine reduction studded with mushrooms and small whole shallots en confit: slightly elaborate, but the individual flavours and textures were preserved before melding into harmony. It was good, though but not surpassing the excellent small fillet of trout with a sole mousse and a beurre blanc. Again flavours were true and execution correct. Interposition of a grapefruit sorbet with little intensity was, as so often, superfluous. The main courses, of salmon with lemon, capers and shrimp, and an entrecôte with a red wine sauce and mint, were very satisfactory, though in a minor key to what came before and after. A fine brioche filled with soft fruit that had been marinated in barely perceptible Amaretto pleased by its balance of two textures and its lingering perfume. Coffee and petits fours kept up the standard. The business is finding its feet as yet; ice-creams are still bought in; the wine list is very short, but Cosham may live in hope. House Bergerac is £6. CELLARMAN'S CHOICE : Ch. Belair 1983, £12; Sancerre 1987, Mallet, £10.60.

CHEF: David Frank Barnard   PROPRIETORS: Mr and Mrs D.F. Barnard
OPEN: Mon to Sat, exc Mon and Sat L
MEALS: 12 to 2, 7.30 to 10
PRICES: £15 (£19). Service inc
CARDS: Access, Visa
SEATS: 20. Private parties: 25 main room. Children's helpings. Wheelchair access. Music. Air-conditioned

## COUNTESTHORPE  Leicestershire
map 5

# Old Bakery

Main Street, Countesthorpe LE8 3QX          COOKING 1
LEICESTER (0533) 778777                     COST £12–£24

At the very end of Main Street, the rebuilt bakery could be mistaken for a private house with parking. Inside, the dining-room is decorated in greys and blues with pictures by local artists on the walls, price tags clearly showing. On both the lunch and dinner set menus the English and Scottish home cooking stands out – vegetable soups, hot meat and game pies with puff pastry crusts, venison in port and old-fashioned puddings with custard. The large dish of mixed vegetables accompanying main courses is in the same style. Thus, too, fruit pies, crumbles, trifles and other down-to-earth puddings score more highly than soufflés, pâtisserie and so forth. Glacier mints come with coffee, which is included in the price. The wine list is not dear. House wine is £5.50.

CHEF: R. Gilbertson  PROPRIETORS: R. Gilbertson, P. Chivers and G. Turner
OPEN: Tue to Sun, exc Sat L and Sun D
MEALS: 12.15 to 1.45, 7 to 9 (9.45 Fri and Sat)
PRICES: Set L £8.50 (£12), Set Sun L £8.95 (£13), Set D £14.95 (£20)
CARDS: Access, Visa
SEATS: 50. Private parties: 50 main room. Car-park, 20 places. Children welcome. Smart dress preferred. Wheelchair access (also WC). Music

## COXLEY  Somerset
map 2

# Ritcher's

Coxley BA5 1RQ                              COOKING 2
WELLS (0749) 79085                          COST £13–£28

Like a Spanish motel, this sits in flat land among vineyards, not in Tarragona but down in Somerset in a converted cowshed – what would Alfred have thought? Nicholas Hart, once assistant to Bill Austin at Blostin's in Shepton Mallet (see entry), cooks a modern bistro menu designed so that many first courses and most desserts can be prepared beforehand, leaving time to concentrate on getting food out to customers. It's 'modern' because some of the classic combinations get jazzed up. So, an excellent game terrine (classic) flavoured with juniper (classic) is set on a pink peppercorn (modern) and port jelly (classic). Lunch and dinner menus are the same, although lunch is somewhat cheaper. The cooking is very competent; a loin of lamb arranged in slices around a filo tart case of rough chopped spinach, sauced with a too highly rosemary-flavoured jus, was pleasingly natural in its impact, as were the accompanying vegetables, including unusually simple red cabbage (often one of the most abused vegetables). Other main courses have been breast of chicken filled with a mango mousse and an individual beef Wellington with oyster mushrooms and bacon to one side. Presentation is much better than 'bistro' might imply, as are petits fours – but not coffee. The wine list may be short, but it is interesting (even if light on growers' details in some instances). It has but one English wine, Coxley of course, but some good Italian and Spanish, including the illustrious Vega Sicilia and a surprisingly large slate of 1972 vintage ports. House wines, including Coxley Seyval Blanc from £5.90. CELLARMAN'S CHOICE : Valdepeñas, Señorio de Los Llanos Les Reserva 1981 £6.95; Boizel Champagne Rosé £16.95. Tipping is 'not encouraged'. There are plans afoot to move to the centre of Wells, so be sure to telephone beforehand.

CHEF: Nicholas Hart   PROPRIETORS: Nicholas Hart and Kate Ritcher
OPEN: Mon to Sat, exc Sat L
MEALS: 12 to 1.30, 7 to 9.30
PRICES: Set L £7.50 (£13) to £11.50 (£17), Set D £11.95 (£18) to £16.50 (£23)
CARDS: Access, Visa
SEATS: 24. 4 tables outside. Private parties: 30 main room. Car-park, 35 places. No children under 8 at D. Wheelchair access (2 steps). Music

---

**CRANLEIGH  Surrey**                                                    map 3

## Restaurant Bonnet

High Street, Cranleigh GU6 8AE                             COOKING 3
CRANLEIGH (0483) 273889                                    COST £12−£31

Jean Pierre Bonnet was chef at La Bonne Auberge, South Godstone (see entry). He has retained links, but is installed, with his wife, as chef-patron of a former wine bar. The dining-room is Surrey 'olde worlde', all beams and Windsor chairs, but the crisp linen, the ultra-modern kitchen and the serious approach of the co-operative young staff indicate greater pretension. The *carte* of eight dishes per course is fixed-price, with not a supplement in sight. Included in the price is an allowance for an aperitif and half a bottle of house wine. Reports of the cooking have been enthusiastic: a tart of soft-boiled quail's eggs, bacon and mushrooms; a crab mousse topped with a slice of smoked salmon; feuilleté of asparagus with a sorrel sauce; salmon on a bed of bean sprouts with a ginger beurre blanc combining good fish cookery, nice contrast of textures and a well seasoned beurre blanc; boned quail pot-roasted, then served with a sauce of vin doux de Banyuls and strawberry vinegar; crisp vegetables and, for once, a correctly creamy gratin dauphinois; moderate meringue; good ice-creams; excellent lime tart that seemed somewhat lemony. Pastry work is top class; cheeses are not exceptional. The restaurant does not suffer from delusions of grandeur, refreshing in Surrey. Lunch reads very like the dinner menu but the price is much reduced. The set-meal alcoholic inducements do not apply at lunch. The wine list is basic but not without enjoyment; it kicks off with Ch. La Tour Bonnet. House French is £6.50. CELLARMAN'S CHOICE : St-Amour, Ch. du Chapitre 1986, Ferraud, £14.80; Pouilly Vinzelles 1986, Ferraud, £18.50.

CHEF: Jean Pierre Bonnet   PROPRIETORS: Jean Pierre and Ann Bonnet
OPEN: Tue to Sun, exc Sat L and Sun D
MEALS: 12 to 2, 7 to 10
PRICES: Set L £11 (£12) to £12.50 (£14), Set D £18 (£20) to £23.50 (£26)
CARDS: Access, Amex, Visa
SEATS: 50. Private parties: 35 main room. Children's helpings on request. Smart dress preferred. No pipes in dining-room. Wheelchair access (1 step). Music

---

*See the back of the Guide for an index of restaurants listed.*

## CRICKLADE Wiltshire

map 2

# Whites ♥

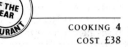

93 High Street, Cricklade SN6 6DF
SWINDON (0793) 751110

COOKING 4
COST £38

There was quite a to-do in Cricklade as Colin White went off to Stapleford Park in Leicestershire and his restaurant was put up for sale. One month later, all change again. Hot dogs weren't on, nor Ritz crackers as amuse-gueule. Whites reopened, north Wiltshire breathed its relief. Well, not north Wiltshire exactly, for local trade does not keep Whites humming and buzzing, but enough readers of the *Guide* do and keep us posted on latest developments. The restaurant occupies a demure stone-built house in a demure town, the dining-rooms either side of a central passage. It makes no great statement, inside or out. Colin White's style is far removed from Girardet's *cuisine spontanée* yet it is abreast of changes in tastes – fairly old-fashioned cooking with an inventive eye. A dish of steamed scallops, mussels and monkfish with lemon-grass, ginger and chilli reflects enjoyment of strong flavours; braised shin of beef with garlic and fresh limes combines that with long cooking. A summer menu had a number of such dishes – which save on staff time at the critical juncture. Both brill and monkfish were baked, the first en papillote with Noilly Prat, vegetables and ginger; loin of pork is marinated, then given a herb crust before pot-roasting. Flavours are from the herb garden: mint with a yoghurt and chickpea soup; thyme with tagliatelle and sweetbreads; rosemary with pork; a mixture with wild mushrooms and blinis. Colin White has avoided courting fruit and sweet flavours in savoury cookery. Tastes are rounded, with no sharp edges, but not smothered in cream. One of the best dishes, a type perhaps, is a roasted guinea-fowl on a bed of lentils with roast red peppers and a sherry sauce; the very description sets the juices flowing. A meal taken after the reopening began with a warm salad of duck livers with sesame and soy sauce, garnished with sprigs of golden marjoram, lemon-balm and parsley. The main course of lamb with a gateau of aubergines topped with breadcrumbs was a perfect piece of lamb, with moisture gained from whole cloves of roast garlic. Vegetables were a pot-pourri, the 11 identified perhaps constituting a record for this type of presentation. Dessert was a featherlight brioche soaked in lemon juice, filled with strawberries and given a further strawberry sauce. Rarely is the flavour of the berries, now so muted by today's plant breeders, so beguilingly heightened. Coffee and petits fours were very good. The setting is one reason for the apparent low key of the venture: a passage to Swindon. This forces concentration on the food, which itself is without theatre. People seem to need theatre, because restaurants have become substitutes for the drama. The wine list is not long. It is notable for having 10 clarets of which five were vintage 1970, one 1971, and four from the 1980s (two out of stock in the spring). The Italian and New World choice, although short, is exceptionally interesting. Good house wine, £8. CELLARMAN'S CHOICE : Watervale Cabernet-Shiraz 1986, £15; Clos du Val Chardonnay 1985, £13.50.

---

*All entries in the* Guide *are rewritten every year, not least because restaurant standards fluctuate. Don't trust an out-of-date* Guide.

CHEF: Colin White    PROPRIETORS: Colin and Gwen White
OPEN: Tue to Sat
MEALS: 12.30 to 2, 7.30 to 9.30
PRICES: £23 (£32). Licensed, also bring your own: corkage £5
CARDS: Access, Visa
SEATS: 32. Private parties: 20 main room, 16 and 20 private rooms. Children's helpings. No cigars/pipes in dining-room. Wheelchair access

CROYDE  Devon                                                    map 1

## ▲ *Whiteleaf* ♥

Croyde EX33 1PN                                          COOKING 2
CROYDE (0271) 890266                                       COST £22

David and Florence Wallington's guest house can produce disappointing first impressions since the house itself is rather characterless and the setting, opposite a working farm and near a bungalow development, is not special. However, misgivings almost invariably drop away in the spacious magnolia dining-room during the excellent, very cheap five-course dinners for residents only. Flo provides the cosseting service and David cooks. 'His stockpot soup was superb and the way he managed five different vegetables with the main course each evening – crunchy courgettes, lemon glazed carrots, herby swede and so on – impressed us immensely.' 'One runs the risk of overdoing the superlatives, but ... this place deserves every accolade for their food.' The choice – at least eight first courses, three soups to follow, eight to a dozen main courses, almost as many desserts and finally cheeses with a full fruit bowl, is also startling for such a small place. Imaginative British ideas such as beef or lamb 'Wallington', served in a brilliantly tender Yorkshire pudding case, simmered duck legs finished with sharp redcurrant or kumquat sauce and pickled pork with spiced oranges are varied with seafood feuilletés and unusual Italian regional dishes. Soups, served with home-made bread, are often a creamy fish chowder, a vegetable or duck consommé and the rich stockpot. Puddings, which are also accomplished, have included a ginger syllabub, poached pear in chocolate with mango sorbet and rich chocolate pudding with clotted cream. The only criticisms boil down to the fact that this is inspired home cooking rather than an attempt at perfect professional performance. Excellent breakfasts open with fresh orange juice and end with toast and home-made marmalade. The wine list is good, cheap and idiosyncratic: almost more Italians than French and only two white burgundies. To cavil is pointless. David Wallington evidently knows and loves his wines and will discuss their characteristics at leisure. The Italians have a good spread and include a 1961 Barolo from Borgogno that alone might make the trip worthwhile. House wines are from £5.90. CELLARMAN'S CHOICE: Alsace Riesling Reserve 1986, Rolly Gassmann, £7.50; Barbera d'Asti 1982, Vincenzo Ronco, £6.80.

*See the inside of the front cover for an explanation of the new 1 to 5 rating system recognising cooking standards.*

ENGLAND

CHEF: David Wallington   PROPRIETORS: David and Florence Wallington
OPEN: all week, D only
MEALS: 7.30 to 8.30
PRICES: Set D £15 (£18). Service inc
CARDS: Access, Visa
SEATS: 16. Car-park, 10 places. Children's helpings. Smart dress preferred
ACCOMMODATION: 5 rooms, all with bath/shower. B&B £27 to £44. Deposit: £25. Baby
facilities. Pets welcome. Garden. TV. Phone. Scenic. Doors close at midnight. Confirm by 7
[GHG]

---

**CROYDON  Surrey**                                                          map 3

## Dijonnais

299 High Street, Croydon CR0 1QL                          COOKING **2**
01-686 5624                                               COST £13–£28

Make for the mussels if they're on, as one of the dishes this slightly untidy little
French restaurant does best. Said shellfish have been known to arrive in a
cream sauce with carrots, celery and leeks, or bathed in delicate curry sauce.
Other dishes to choose from, against a background of taped jazz, have been
wild duck (too rare for some) in a port sauce and a loudly applauded vol-au-
vent of calves' sweetbreads with foie gras and wild mushrooms. There are
short set menus or you can go to the *carte* for frogs' legs and snails. House
wine is £6.95.

CHEF: Lionel Jolivet   PROPRIETORS: Mr and Mrs Lionel Jolivet
OPEN: Mon to Sat, exc Mon D and Sat L
MEALS: 12.15 to 2, 7.30 to 9 (9.30 Sat)
PRICES: £17 (£23), Set L £7.50 (£13), Set D £15 (£21). Cover 60p
CARDS: Access, Amex, Diners, Visa
SEATS: 28. Private parties: 28 main room. Children welcome. Wheelchair access. Music

## Hockneys

98 High Street, Croydon CR0 1ND                           COOKING **1**
01-688 2899                                               COST £14

The name implies artistic loyalties, and they are worn on the sleeve here:
Patrick Procktor etchings on the wall, recommendations from Hockney himself,
Alan Bennett and, for the adjoining and linked Arts Centre, from George D.
Painter and Kathleen Raine. Decoration is a serious thing, as is the karma of an
outgiving institution, but the cooking has long led the field in a practical way:
modern vegetarian cooking that depends on the Orient and India for recipes
and flavours rather than mere leguminous substitution of meaty components.
There are modern recipes too: baked goats' cheese and apple with a
blackcurrant and blue cheese sauce as a starter. Self-service in the day changes
to waited tables at night, by people who pride themselves on involvement.
Reasonable prices – even lower at lunchtime – and unlicensed.

*Preliminary test of a good restaurant: order fresh orange juice and see what you get.*

CHEF: Simon Beckett  PROPRIETORS: Rainbow (Croydon) Ltd
OPEN: Tue to Sat
CLOSED: 2 weeks at Christmas, 1 week at Easter, 2 weeks late Aug
MEALS: 12 to 5.30, 5.30 to 10
PRICES: £9 (£12), Snacks from 95p. Unlicensed, but bring your own: corkage £1 (day), £1.35 (eve)
CARDS: Access, Amex, Diners, Visa
SEATS: 80. Private parties: 25 main room. Vegetarian meals. Children's helpings. No smoking. Music

---

**CUCKFIELD  West Sussex**  map 3

## ▲ *Jeremy's at the King's Head*

South Street, Cuckfield, RH17 5VY                    COOKING 3
HAYWARDS HEATH (0444) 440386                         COST £25

The pub cannot be missed in Cuckfield, on the corner of the lane leading downhill to the church. As the pub continues its merry way, Jeremy Ashpool operates an independent franchise in two dining-rooms and a kitchen. For several years he has been producing very emphatic food, of pronounced flavour, owing no great debt to French or other European tradition. The surroundings are fairly tacky and sometimes give rise to irritation. Equally, the piquant contrast of bare board and fine food, coupled with reasonable charges, appeals to a great section of the Sussex public. An inspection confirmed both the plaudits of readers and some of their comments about a certain roughness that Jeremy Ashpool would not himself always deny. A superlative piece of haddock with finely sliced leeks, tomato pulp, diced red pepper, dill and caraway seeds in a lime dressing was exquisite in its parts but swamped by the flavour of lime. Gressingham duck was described on the menu as being with celery and sage sauce. In fact it came with that, an apple purée and a mango purée. The breast was sliced and interleaved with grapefruit and sliced apple. There was shredded celery under the leg meat and a pile of mushroom and bacon bits in the centre of the plate. This was lubricated by a stock sauce and decorated by more pieces of red pimento. What sounds incredibly messy was, in the eyes of everyone, remarkably successful: it had an 'enjoyable excess' dominated by the flavour of charcoal-grilled duck. The menu is very short, five choices at each course, rapidly changing and not expensive. Ancillaries like bread, butter and vegetables, if not petits fours, are excellent. Almost every main dish has a vegetable accompaniment built in as a foil to the chief ingredient. Even in first courses this sometimes happens: asparagus with an aubergine charlotte, for instance. The wine list is short and sharp.
CELLARMAN'S CHOICE : Ch. Monbousquet, 1983, St-Emilion, £17; Sauvignon de St. Bris 1987, Luc Sorin, £10.

---

*If you see a certificate in a restaurant bearing the words 'European Good Food Guide (UK)', the claim is false (and the restaurant may be in contempt of court in displaying it) – see the Introduction. Please write and tell us the name and address of the restaurant.*

CHEF: Jeremy Ashpool  PROPRIETOR: Peter Tolhurst
OPEN: Mon to Fri, exc Mon D
CLOSED: bank hols
MEALS: 12.30 to 2, 7.30 to 10
PRICES: £15 (£21), Set D £14.95 (£21). Service of 10% for parties of 6 or more
CARDS: Access, Amex, Visa
SEATS: 33. Private parties: 20 main room. Children welcome. Wheelchair access
ACCOMMODATION: 9 rooms, 8 with bath/shower. B&B £34 to £46. Baby facilities. Pets
welcome. Garden. Snooker. TV

---

**DALLINGTON  East Sussex**                                                    map 3

## ▲ *Little Byres*

Christmas Farm, Battle Road,
Dallington TN21 9LE                                              COOKING 3
BRIGHTLING (042 482) 230                                     COST £24–£34

The byres in question once housed cattle. By a near-anagram cows have been
exchanged for chalets, which accommodate guests. The restaurant occupies the
barn and is entered through double, once ecclesiastical, doors. There is a
forceful simplicity to the conversion: rafters, beams and brick are softened by
fabrics. Christopher Davis cooks half a dozen choices at each course from
materials sought from far and near: squab from South Devon, oysters from Loch
Fyne, smoked bacon and meats from Cumbria. He exemplifies that food and
restaurant-based network built up since proper emphasis was laid on the small
producer. Meals have been successful: a tart of buttery shortcrust filled with
browned crisp leeks moistened by reduced stock, covered by slices, as if scales,
of scallops and their corals, then glazed with hollandaise; a saddle of hare with
a rich quatre-épices sauce on a pancake of apple and potato; well flavoured and
simply cooked vegetables; a plate of chocolate desserts – sorbet, white
chocolate ice-cream, marquise and a double mousse sandwich between three
thin almond biscuits. Other good dishes have been cucumber tagliatelle with
salmon and dill; breast of lamb with an onion and courgette roulade; a good
cheeseboard of English and French produce supplied through the Heathfield
Delicatessen. Coffee, petits fours, bread and butter also show invention and
quality. Little Byres continues the promise shown last year and, while there are
criticisms of lack of balance in flavourings and sporadic misses in conception,
the intentions are wholehearted and the results usually appetising. Service is
as individual as the cooking; indeed, Evelyn Stewart seems to do the gardening
and the decorating as well as cooking. Her approach is charming and ingénue;
some suggest too much so when explanations of wine or cheese are needed.
The wine list numbers 50 bins. Almost every one is decent and some are very
good indeed. Many come from Corney & Barrow, whose agencies are
aristocratic to say the least: Penfold from Australia, Heydt from Alsace, Joseph
Roty from Burgundy, Jaboulet and Guigal from the Rhône as well as six decent
halves of sweet wines. The prices are kept to a ceiling so that some mark-ups of
cheaper wines are high while more expensive bottles are quite close to cost
price. House Lebègue and Loron are £6.95. CELLARMAN'S CHOICE : Bourgogne
Blanc les Setilles 1986, O. Leflaive, £14.25; Marsannay 1986, J. Roty, £14.50.

CHEFS: Chris Davis and Evelyn Stewart   PROPRIETOR: Mr and Mrs A.J. Lusted
OPEN: Tue to Sat, D only (Mon for residents)
MEALS: 7 to 9.30
PRICES: Set D £18.50 (£24) to £22.50 (£28)
CARDS: Access, Visa
SEATS: 35. Private parties: 40 main room, 20 private room. Car-park, 18 places. Children's
helpings. Wheelchair access (also WC). Music
ACCOMMODATION: 5 rooms, all with bath/shower. Rooms for disabled. B&B £35. Deposit:
£25. TV. Scenic [GHG]

---

**DARLINGTON   Co Durham**                                                    map 7

# Victor's

| 84 Victoria Road, Darlington DL1 5JW | COOKING 3 |
|---|---|
| DARLINGTON (0325) 480818 | COST £10−£24 |

Peter and Jayne Robinson's restaurant, squeezed inside a small converted shop
near the station, is admirable indeed. Despite the difficulties of buying for an
uneven volume of trade, they cook and serve lunches and dinners drawing
reports of quality and value. Produce is carefully bought, bread and ice-creams
are home made, and variety is packed into the compact daily set-price menus.
At lunchtime dishes have a strong English feel; there are fresh vegetable soups
to start, main courses such as beef in ale with Yorkshire pudding, hot honey
roast ham with spinach purée and marsala sauce or a spiced mushroom tartlet,
and a choice of local cheese or pudding to finish. In the evening, there is a
broader selection of some half a dozen dishes for the three courses, with a
home-made soup or sorbet before the main dish. Both fish and meat may be
sauced with cream or cooking juices appropriately flavoured − white port for
pigeon breasts with olives and almonds, red wine for beef with three vegetable
purées − or finished with more modern touches. Roast duck has been served
with pickled pear, trout in filo pasty with minted cream. Desserts also show a
good range, from French pâtisserie to English puddings, and local cheeses
include Ribblesdale goats' and Mrs Strike's sheep's cheese from Newton Le
Willows. A short wine list of refreshingly low prices. House French, £6.
CELLARMAN'S CHOICE : Wyndham Estate oak cask Chardonnay 1987, £7.95.

CHEFS/PROPRIETORS: Peter and Jayne Robinson
OPEN: Tue to Sat
MEALS: 12 to 2.30, 7 to 10.30
PRICES: Set L £5.50 (£10), Set D £14.50 (£20)
CARDS: Access, Amex, Diners, Visa
SEATS: 26. Private parties: 26 main room. Vegetarian meals. Children's helpings.
Wheelchair access. Music

---

*The* Guide *always appreciates hearing about changes of chef or owner.*

*The 1991* Guide *will be published before Christmas 1990. Reports on meals are most
welcome at any time of the year, but are extremely valuable in the spring. Send them to*
The Good Food Guide, FREEPOST, *2 Marylebone Road, London NW1 1YN. No stamp
is needed if posted in the UK.*

---

## ▲ Billy Budd's

7 Foss Street, Dartmouth TQ6 9DW                                     COOKING 2
DARTMOUTH (080 43) 4842                                              COST £10–£26

The straightforward quality of this small restaurant shines out in both its menu and the favourable reports since it opened early in 1987. 'Our aim is to serve fresh, well-cooked food at reasonable prices,' writes Gilly White. She runs the front of house in the friendliest possible way; Keith Belt does the cooking. During the day, he makes snacky but nonetheless good lunches such as omelettes, salad niçoise and Camembert fritters. In the evening, the tables are transformed with candles and table linen for more formal two- or three-course *prix fixe* dinners. Dishes mix English and continental ideas: brochette of beef with spiced aubergines, lamb soubise, quail braised with apple and thyme, suggest the style and range. Supplies include immaculately fresh fish which is shown at its best in simple dishes like goujons of plaice with a mustard dip or fillet of brill and scallops on a saffron sauce. Puddings, from the blackboard, are largely bistro style and fine. House French is £6.25. CELLARMAN'S CHOICE : Ch. Haut Sociando 1982, Côtes de Castillon, £9.35; Ch. La Garance 1986, Graves, £12.25.

CHEF: Keith Belt   PROPRIETORS: Gilly White and Keith Belt
OPEN: Tue to Sun, exc Sun L
CLOSED: Feb; Tue and Sun in winter
MEALS: 12 to 2, 7.30 to 10
PRICES: L £6 (£10), Set D £14.50 (£20) to £15.95 (£22), Snacks from £1
CARD: Visa
SEATS: 35. Private parties: 35 main room. Children's helpings. No children under 7. Smart dress preferred. Wheelchair access. Music
ACCOMMODATION: 2 rooms. B&B £12.50. TV

## Carved Angel 🍾

2 South Embankment, Dartmouth TQ6 9BH                              COOKING 4
DARTMOUTH (080 43) 2465                                            COST £22–£44

The Angel enjoys a prime site: by the river, overlooking the ferry to Kingswear. Inside it has been smartened up but the carved wooden angel still presides. Like the river, the cooking rolls on, ever changing yet recognisably the same. Like the river, too, it is fed by a wealth of tributaries, its source somewhere in the French provinces. Joyce Molyneux picks up speed to negotiate new ideas – one of Shaun Hill's signature dishes at Gidleigh Park, scallops with lentil and coriander, travels the short distance well – or else meanders leisurely through a repertoire that runs from a plate of duck charcuterie, through matelote of eels and prunes to crêpes Suzette. Provençal fish soup with rouille and garlic croûtons is a staple; the fact that it turns up on every other bistro menu from here to Marseilles does not detract. 'The smell alone takes me back to the south of France; a wonderful colour, shining red, browny and gold almost, full of a rich combination of flavours of fish, stock, vegetables, saffron, oil; it is one of the best versions we have had.' This is just one strand among many, intertwined with old English dishes such as salmon in pastry with ginger and currants, or a Middle Eastern plate of aubergine salad with sour cream and herbs. Ideas come from a fertile imagination that treats boundaries with disdain (even the traditional barrier between kitchen and dining-room is overturned by the open-plan design). Often, dishes plot a well-tried course, sailing home with no more than a tweak of the tiller. Gressingham duck is roasted and served with sweet potato and apple; poached skate comes with virgin olive oil and Chinese pickled vegetables; a pimento bavarois is served with marinated aubergines. This constant reworking produces a freshness that is one of the open secrets of good cooking. If all this fails to reach the greatest creative heights, then no matter; the food impresses for its simplicity, its directness, its assured handling of materials. In spring, for instance, Dart salmon was served with early rhubarb, a pretty dish of two delicate pinks: 'the salmon was lightly cooked, firm-fleshed, creamy, full of flavour; the rhubarb was tender but with enough bite to keep it from being pulpy; the two flavours made a delicious combination, the sharpness of the rhubarb against the almost creamy taste of the salmon. The lightest possible sauce, pale lemon in colour, was dribbled at the side of the plate.' Service has come in for criticism. On the one hand, the staff maintains the open-plan policy, communicating effectively between cook and customer; the waiters really know what is going on in the kitchen because they cook too. On the other, the polish and expertise are not quite what we have come to expect of highly rated and fairly expensive restaurants. Then there is the pricing: £7.50 for a starter, £15 for a main course and £6 for a pudding. Some label them as London prices, but at this rate, 'Dartmouth prices' could become the national yardstick. Or take the fixed-price menus (with a choice of seven or eight items at each stage) which interpose an extra course – sorbet, goats' cheese and hazelnut soufflé, or an English cheeseboard – before the pudding. There is no price reduction for those who wish to skip this and go straight on to dessert; a curious policy. The fixed price does, however, include coffee, petits fours, VAT and service. A few bottles from Italy, Spain, Germany, Australia, California and New Zealand are scattered like herbs over the classic French wines that constitute the main business of a two-hundred strong list. A good selection of half-bottles and an impressive range of ports by the glass add welcome spice. CELLARMAN'S CHOICE : Sauvignon de St-Bris, 1986, Sorin, £11.

---

CHEFS: Joyce Molyneux and Nick Coiley   PROPRIETORS: Joyce Molyneux and Meriel Boydon
OPEN: Tue to Sun, exc Sun D
MEALS: 12.30 to 1.45, 7.30 to 9.30
PRICES: alc L £28 (£34), Set L £17.50 (£22) to £21 (£26), Set D £27.50 (£32) to £32 (£37). Service inc
SEATS: 30. Private parties: 30 main room, 15 private room. Children's helpings. Wheelchair access

---

'Belongs in The Bad Hotel Guide. Also in The Pretentious, Expensive, Run of the Mill Food Guide. Not one of the dishes I ate actually accorded with its menu description, which is irritating. And in the case of the main course and sweet at least, the bits they'd left out were the bits that might have made the dishes interesting.' On inspecting in Wiltshire

## *Mansion House*

Mansion House Street
Dartmouth TQ6 9AG
DARTMOUTH (080 43) 5474

COOKING **3**
COST £23–£35

After a very uneven first six months, Richard and Helen Cranfield now seem to be adapting from the tight confines of Bistro 33 to the vastly increased grandeur and scale of this splendid eighteenth-century house. The early problems seem to have stemmed from trying to take on too much. Ironically, too, the elegance of the house, sparkling with new cream paint, has not helped. 'The food that seemed miraculous served in such unlikely surroundings of the cramped bistro no longer struck us as out of the ordinary once expectations had been raised by such an upmarket setting.' The dining-room itself is upstairs, reached by an imposing sweep of staircase under moulded plaster ceilings, and is tastefully subdued, without a spark of bright colour even in the flowers or menu, against the muted cream, white, grey and black colour scheme. The menu promises well since it is to the point, with only four choices per stage, each one complex and surprising without striving too hard: for example, in one April meal, a cervelas of gurnard on a bed of tomatoes with dill butter sauce was followed by roast Scottish sirloin with garlic scented veal stock, courgette tart and croquette of leeks. As yet, though, the ideas do not translate consistently on to the plate. While the cervelas was fine – a warm mousse-like sausage with a delicate flavour complemented by the sauce – the sirloin lacked flavour and texture, and was unnecessarily cluttered by both the tart and the croquette. Other early meals were underseasoned or let down by technique. Recently, though, reports suggest the threads are being pulled together. Salmon and spinach terrine, turbot in filo pastry, pan-fried calf's liver served on roasted peppers with a sage butter, lamb noisettes with filo parcels of ratatouille and deep-fried parsnip chips have been wholeheartedly recommended. If the final problems of service and pacing (very long pauses between courses) can be ironed out, then there is a chance that the real potential of the restaurant will be showing by the first anniversary of its opening. There is a short wine list with house French at £6.50 and CELLARMAN'S CHOICE : Pouilly Fumé Les Bascoins 1987, £12; Mondavi Cabernet Sauvignon 1982, £15.25.

CHEF: Richard Cranfield   PROPRIETORS: Richard and Helen Cranfield
OPEN: Tue to Sat, exc Sat L
MEALS: 12.30 to 1.30, 7.30 to 10
PRICES: Set L £18.50 (£23), Set D £19.50 (£24) to £24 (£29). Service inc
SEATS: 44. Private parties: 30 main room, 14 private room. Vegetarian meals. Children welcome. No cigars/pipes in dining-room; no-smoking area, exc Sat. Wheelchair access

*This year, in quoting prices for three-course meals at the top of each entry (by the word 'Cost'), we have put a more pessimistic complexion on the upper price by inflating it by 20 per cent. The aim is to prepare the reader for any inflation during the life of the* Guide *and also reflect the price of a meal taken without constant attention to the likely size of the bill. The prices quoted in smaller print below the text remain, as in previous editions, strict computer calculations of an average three-course meal, the price in brackets reflecting an average meal with coffee, service and half a bottle of house wine per person.*

## ▲ Le Talbooth ▮

Gun Hill, Dedham CO7 6HP                                                COOKING 3
COLCHESTER (0206) 323150                                          COST £23–£46

Whether Dedham was the Milsom family's Damascus or the restaurant was always a phoenix that would rise again, something has happened at Le Talbooth. Perhaps it was merely time for a change and this coincided with the arrival, two years ago, of a new chef and brigade. Stephen Blake trained with the French-supervised restaurants of Grosvenor House (Louis Outhier) and Le Meridien Piccadilly (Michel Lorrain). He seconded for David Chambers at the latter place and his brigade is drawn thence in large part. Simultaneously, the Milsom family appreciated that the restaurant itself needed modernising and the result is very much a luxury country affair of carpet, curtains and fine views over the river (the Stour in this case) that can be found for the same expenditure in France or Germany. Gone is the crabbed Tudorbethan style. Gone, too, is the idiosyncratic and surly service, replaced by willingness and suavity. The question remains whether this is the place to go in Essex. Several reports give qualified affirmation. There is skill, imagination, ultra-modern styling – at a price. As one put it, 'This dish gets 80 per cent for execution, but full marks for degree of difficulty.' The kitchen is trying very hard. There are few excesses of the vinegar and fruit school of modern cookery, so offence is rare, but there are occasional lapses in conviction that result in a dish which excites high anticipation being slightly disappointing in the eating. Thus sauté foie gras with deep fried julienne of celeriac and a ginger sauce should have offered contrasting texture from the celeriac and sharpening of taste from the ginger. Yet it failed because the celeriac was soggy and the ginger too faint. So it was just rich (though very good foie gras). There is no cavil about the quality of materials (perfect new potatoes in December) or the pleasantness of the experience. Perhaps, when the menu description 'julienne of vegetables and wine sauce' is matched on the plate, instead of being 'a few shreds of leek in an insipid cream sauce' (for salmon), this kitchen will begin to sing. Have faith. The wine list is not as expensive as it might be (though the food is). There are some very good fine wines and some interesting choices. The Muscadet, Ch. de Coing, which is barrelled in new oak, may seem dear, but it is a novelty rarely seen here or in France and worth investigating. The New World wines also merit a look (especially for value). Some might dismiss Le Talbooth as a tired monster preying on expense accounts and tourism, but that is to do it an injustice. House French wine, £7.50. CELLARMAN'S CHOICE : Montagny *premier cru* £1987, Olivier Leflaive, £15.80; Lake's Folly Cabernet Sauvignon 1986, £18.90.

---

*The* Guide *is totally independent, accepts no free hospitality, and survives on the number of copies sold each year.*

---

*The text of entries is based on unsolicited reports sent in by readers, backed up by inspections conducted anonymously. The factual details under the text are from questionnaires the* Guide *sends to all restaurants that feature in the book.*

---

CHEF: Steven Blake   PROPRIETOR: Gerald M.W. Milsom
OPEN: all week
MEALS: 12 to 2, 7 to 9 (9.30 Sat)
PRICES: £29 (£38), Set L £15 (£23) to £16 (£24). Service 10%
CARDS: Access, Visa
SEATS: 70. Private parties: 70 main room, 24 private room. Car-park, 70 places. Children
welcome. No cigars/pipes in dining-room. Wheelchair access (7 gradual steps)
ACCOMMODATION: 10 rooms, all with bath/shower. Rooms for disabled. B&B £70 to £80.
Garden. TV. Phone. Scenic. Doors close at 10.30 [GHG]

---

**DENT  Cumbria**                                                        map 7

## ▲ *Stone Close*

Main Street, Dent LA10 5QL                                    COOKING 2
DENT (058 75) 231                                             COST £10–£13

Changes have been afoot in Dent, due to the Bonsalls' estimable preoccupation
with British crafts. They have taken on the Dent Craft Centre at Helmside, with
Graham Hudson and Patricia Barber, and redistributed responsibility among
the partnership. They offer all-day eating facilities at the Centre as well as
evening meals at a set price. Stone Close, however, in the downstairs rooms of
a converted seventeenth-century farmhouse, continues to cook good simple
stuff during the day, a blackboard giving details of specials, and a set evening
meal at 7.30 with a choice of three beginnings, one main course and a larger
range of puddings and cheeses (local of course). People are quite overcome by
the price of it all, given how enjoyable it is. 'Chicken pilaff of such freshness
and originality of ingredients; followed by apple pie and Wensleydale, the
pastry superb, with slightly undercooked pieces of apple tasting of apple.'
Another's evening started with ham and pea soup (underseasoned) and a
delicate avocado with lime and lemon sauce; the pork fillet with prunes was
overcooked but well flavoured. It came with carrots with orange, cheesy leeks,
garlic potatoes and mange tout with sesame seeds. The range of puddings,
boozy and creamy, delivered a deceptively light Bakewell tart and a raspberry
Chantilly. Baking is a forte, by contrast wines are not.

CHEFS: Patricia Barber and Hazel Haygarth   PROPRIETORS: Chris and Louise Bonsall,
Graham Hudson and Patricia Barber
OPEN: all week (L Sat, Sun only Nov to Easter)
MEALS: 10.30 to 5.30, 7.30
PRICES: L £6 (£10), Set D £7.50 (£11)
SEATS: 40. Private parties: 25 main room, 20 private room. Vegetarian meals. Children's
helpings. No smoking during meals. Wheelchair access. Music. One sitting at D
ACCOMMODATION: 3 rooms. B&B £11.50 to £20. Deposit: £5. Baby facilities. Pets welcome.
Afternoon teas. Scenic

---

*'On the whole, a most enjoyable evening, tarnished somewhat by a vague bill entry:
"Drinks: £18." We queried this and were offered a more detailed breakdown: "Drinks
before dinner £4.50; after dinner: £13.50." Since only two of us had required after dinner
drinks – one Tia Maria and one armagnac – we requested more details, only given as Tia
Maria £4.00, armagnac: £9.50. "Of course, sir, they were large measures." Indeed they
were – but who ordered large measures?'* On dining in Gloucestershire

DERBY  Derbyshire                                                        map 5

# 524 Brasserie

524 Burton Road, Little Over
Derby DE3 6FN                                                    COOKING 2
DERBY (0332) 294524                                           COST £14−£23

Just beyond the ring road, the old road to Burton (A5250) is edged by a handsome row of shops, now home to this elegant yet informal restaurant which
somehow manages to steer a course between wine bar and modernistic cuisine.
The cooking is by no means throwaway, even if lunch menus start cheaply for a
bowl of pasta and a glass of wine. Dishes the kitchen regards as typical include
glazed woodcock in pastry with a juniper and game sauce; chicken stuffed with
Boursin and served with an asparagus sauce; and a mixture of seafood in a duo
of sauces. Reporters speak warmly of the steak cookery: skilled, good materials
and well judged − not as easy as it may seem. Sweets off the trolley are well
received, as is the hot treacle tart with custard. The wine list is basic, but there
may be extras on the day. House wine from Lichine, £4.95.

CHEF: Stephen Chell    PROPRIETORS: John and Alison Rodgers
OPEN: Tue to Sat, exc Sat L
CLOSED: 2 to 9 Jan and 19 Aug
MEALS: 12 to 2.30, 7 to 10
PRICES: £14 (£19), Set L and D £9.95 (£14)
CARDS: Access, Diners, Visa
SEATS: 36. Private parties: 45 main room. Car-park, 16 places. Children's helpings. Smart
dress preferred. Music

DORCHESTER  Oxfordshire                                                  map 2

# ▲ George Hotel

High Street,
Dorchester OX9 8HH                                               COOKING 1
OXFORD (0865) 340404                                         COST £22−£41

Since our construction of motorways and trunk roads, road-houses have had a
lean time of it. In their capacity of inns and staging-posts, they lived through
one crisis as coach gave way to rail, only to revive in the days of slower motor
travel. Many will recall those long hours of boredom packed with siblings on
the back seat of the car, as the Great North Road, Watling Street or the Fosse
Way passed inexorably by. Stultifying games were the best that were managed
until remission, not invariably blissful, was afforded by an inn. The George at
Dorchester, hard by the bridge and the abbey, was one. For the last few years
there have been signs of greater creativity in the kitchen and latterly the
balance of ambition and restraint has been 'just right'. Add to this a pair of
dining-rooms in (very) traditional English style and a keen though medium-
well-informed young staff and the George becomes a better bargain than once
it was. Neil Cordiner comes from The Swan at Streatley, a few miles
downstream. He cooks good roast beef; blanquette de veau à l'ancienne; ragout
of Cornish fish and asparagus, lime butter sauce; very good vegetables and
good sauces for dishes like noisettes of lamb, sadly overdone when one reader

265

had it. There are some dishes that reflect current fads such as fillet of beef on a prawn sabayon, which underline how taste changes. 'Surf and turf' in one form or another is a preoccupation of restaurants good and bad, just as ultra-sweet sauces were the rage five years ago. People are remarkably tolerant, for this combination will never last, no matter how high the chicken-and-crayfish-classical-cuisine pedigree. Desserts may be to a scale that defies imagination: too large and too sweet. The coffee may not be very strong. Wines are properly served and seem fairly priced for a decent range. Bottles in the inexpensive house selection come between £6.75 and £8.

CHEF: Neil Cordiner   PROPRIETOR: Brian Griffin
OPEN: all week
MEALS: 12.30 to 1.45, 7 to 9.45
PRICES: £22 (£34), Set D £16 (£22)
CARDS: Access, Amex, Diners, Visa
SEATS: 40. Private parties: 30 main room, 20 private room. Car-park, 50 places. Children's helpings. Smart dress preferred
ACCOMMODATION: 17 rooms, all with bath/shower. Rooms for disabled. B&B £49 to 68. Baby facilities. Pets welcome. Afternoon teas. Garden. TV. Doors close at 11. Confirm by 4
[GHG]

---

DORRINGTON  Shropshire                                             map 4

## ▲ Country Friends

Dorrington SY5 7JD                                        COOKING 3
DORRINGTON (074 373) 707
5m S of Shrewsbury on A49                               COST £18–£24

Driving south from Shrewsbury to Ludlow, you see the restaurant standing on a bare grass bank at the road's edge. Neither sign nor house, a Salopian black and white special, can be missed. The interior arrangements show, like a palimpsest, the development from 1600 to the present day. Four bedrooms, divided between main house and coach-house, have been added. The double-room rate must be one of the few that includes a breakfast of scrambled egg, smoked salmon, bucks fizz, toast and coffee for £20 per person. Charles and Pauline Whittaker both cook – she the pastry, he the bread – and serve with a tiny staff who excel at their jobs. The style of their cooking has evolved over the years to what may be termed modern British. Materials are important: many components (bread, pasta, petits fours, even fruit vinegars) are made at home; flavourings and sauces are a long way from the character or constituents we were once used to, and are largely based on personal preference. There is a tendency to sweetness and many of the recipes and compositions are of the type spread by books written in the last 10 years. None of this is meant to be minatory. An inspection meal early this year was consumed with gusto at every stage. A fillet of sole wrapped round a Parmesan soufflé and lubricated with a white wine sauce had crisply fresh sole, perfectly timed with the soufflé, the sauce proclaiming eloquently the good stock, the sufficient wine and the finishing of cream. Lamb with a crab mousse and a curry sabayon, based on a Raymond Blanc recipe, interpreted that combination with skill and success. Vegetables were impressively English, that is, somewhat over-generous and of slight connection to the dish at hand – braised red cabbage with apple, nutmeg and honey, deep-fried cauliflower, a spinach mousse and two sorts of potatoes. Then a gin and lime Queen of puddings. The Whittakers like gin and lime – you can have it with calf's liver (au John Tovey) if you wish. Coffee is occasionally muddy but always well-flavoured. Bread, amuse-gueule and petits fours have all met with approval – especially the unbleached white loaf when eaten with Appleby farm butter. The wine list is perhaps better this year: the odd bottle from the USA, Italy and Germany, a better choice of halves and an improvement in the standard of some of the French wines, mainly from Addisons of Newport. The Mouton Rothschild 1934 has come down from £175 to £150. There is a short table d'hôte at lunchtime, when lighter and cheaper dishes are also available. House French from £6.80. CELLARMAN'S CHOICE : Vacqueyras, Pascal, £10.30.

CHEFS/PROPRIETORS: Charles and Pauline Whittaker
OPEN: Tue to Sat
MEALS: 12 to 2, 7 to 9 (9.30 Sat)
PRICES: £15 (£20), Set L and D £12.50 (£18)
CARDS: Access, Amex, Diners, Visa
SEATS: 40. Private parties: 45 main room. Car-park, 40 places. Children welcome. Wheelchair access
ACCOMMODATION: 4 rooms, 1 with bath/shower. B&B £20 to £32. Garden [GHG]

---

**DREWSTEIGNTON** Devon                                              map 1

## ▲ *Hunts Tor House*

Drewsteignton EX6 6QW                                        COOKING 2
DREWSTEIGNTON (0647) 21228                                     COST £18

This is the sort of homely hotel-cum-bed and breakfast that holidaymakers without children, but with a dog or two to improve fellow guests' asthma and temper, dream about. Run by an engaging couple, it offers excellently cooked no-choice dinners to residents only. The repertoire is more than traditional Devon, but may run to home-made strawberry wine or orange shrub as aperitifs while spinach and cream cheese pancakes, broccoli mousse with fresh tomato sauce, monkfish with a herb sauce, carrot and coriander soup, quail with wild rice and apricots or chicken with sorrel are being cooked. Breakfasts are spot on, from quince through to coffee. A few decent wines are recited before dinner for guests to choose from. The house is a treat, encapsulating a Caroline centre with a verandahed late-classical square-built wrap. House Duboeuf is £6. CELLARMAN'S CHOICE : Muscadet-sur-lie, Domaine la Minière 1987, £7.70; Ch. les Douves de Francs 1985, Côtes de Francs, £10. You can also tipple home-produced raspberry gin and sloe vodka if your appetite leaves room.

CHEF: Sue Harrison   PROPRIETORS: Sue and Chris Harrison
OPEN: all week, D only (residents only)
MEALS: 7.30
PRICES: Set D £11 (£15). Service inc
SEATS: 8. Private parties: 12 main room, 8 private room. Vegetarian meals. No children under 14. One sitting
ACCOMMODATION: 4 rooms, all with bath/shower. B&B £18 to £36. No children under 14. Pets welcome. Doors close at midnight. Confirm by 5 [GHG]

## ▲ Old Inn

The Square, Drewsteignton EX6 6QR                    COOKING 2
DREWSTEIGNTON (0647) 21276                            COST £22

Rose Chapman, who runs this overgrown cottage of a restaurant in its picture-book village, says, 'We stand or fall on our ability to serve fresh local produce honestly, with no flimflam.' Sure enough, there's not a whisper of flimflam on the short, set menus which are recited to guests and focus on English country cooking. Venison always features, with capers and anchovies or blackcurrants. Fish appears less frequently, but when it is on, it's fresher than fresh – Rose Chapman has a hot line to a customer's trawler and knows what's on offer before it hits the quay. There is a separate vegetarian menu, for which vegetables and herbs come from a village allotment. Local cheeses – Devon Garland, Torville – are another speciality, served with home-made rye or milk bread, and puddings are nursery-biased and renowned. There are rooms to let and great breakfasts. The wine list is summary. House wine is £5.50.
CELLARMAN'S CHOICE : Chorey-lès-Beaune Villages 1984, £11.50; Rosemount Estate Chardonnay 1987, £9.95.

CHEF: Rose Chapman    PROPRIETORS: V.L. and Rose Chapman
OPEN: Tue to Sat, D only
CLOSED: weekdays in Feb
MEALS: 7.30 to 8.45
PRICES: Set D £15 (£18). Service inc
SEATS: 20. Private parties: 20 main room. Vegetarian meals. Children restricted. No smoking in dining-room
ACCOMMODATION: 5 rooms. B&B £12 to £24. Baby facilities. Pets welcome. Scenic. Doors close at 11.30. Confirm by 5 [GHG]

---

DULVERTON  Somerset                                          map 1

## ▲ Ashwick House

Dulverton TA22 9QD
DULVERTON (0398) 23868                               COOKING 1
signposted from B3223 N of Dulverton             COST £14–£26

Reports come in confirming that standards have been maintained at this Edwardian house set in glorious surroundings where 'peace comes dropping slow' and the spirit lifts at the sight of the Exmoor landscape. Sadly, Richard Sherwood senior died in 1988. His son, Richard, has taken over the cooking but the recipe remains the same: catering largely for residents but happy to take outsiders at 48 hours' notice. A four-course dinner is offered, and a shorter, but very reasonably priced, Sunday lunch. Alternatives there are for first and last courses, but not in the middle. Broccoli soup; Roquefort mousse with almonds; hazelnut-stuffed mushrooms; salmon with an orange and vermouth sauce; bread-and-butter pudding and Eton mess have been eaten with satisfaction. The wine list is short, cheap, made up of a lot of Averys bottlings and selections and many alternate years. There are two wines and a cider from the Yearlstone vineyard and plenty of half- bottles. House French is £5.80 or £6. CELLARMAN'S CHOICE : Yearlstone Madeleine Angevine, £6; Vacqueyras 1985, Jaboulet, £9.

CHEF: Richard Sherwood   PROPRIETORS: Mrs P.E.Sherwood and Richard Sherwood
OPEN: Tue to Sat, D only, and Sun L
MEALS: 12.15 to 1.15, 7.15 to 8.30
PRICES: Set Sun L £9.75 (£14), Set D £16.75 (£22)
SEATS: 30. 3 tables outside. Private parties: 30 main room. Car-park, 30 places. No children
under 8. Smart dress preferred
ACCOMMODATION: 6 rooms, all with bath/shower. D,B&B £51 to £98. Deposit: £25. No
children under 8. Afternoon teas. Garden. TV. Phone. Scenic. Doors close at 11.30. Confirm
by 6 [GHG]

---

**DUNWICH  Suffolk**                                                          map 6

## *Flora Tea Rooms*

The Beach, Dunwich IP17 3PU                                      COOKING  1
WESTLETON (072 873) 433                                              COST  £6

A beach café, once a hut, now rebuilt to seat vast numbers and offering fresh
fish daily from Lowestoft: excellent fish and chips. Add a long menu of sweets
and home-baked confectionery and here is a refuge from the torrid or the wet
for families cast up on an English shore.

CHEFS: John Elsley and Daphne Gill   PROPRIETORS: Sarah Elsley and Daphne Gill
OPEN: all week
CLOSED: Dec to Mar
MEALS: 11 to 6
PRICES: £4 (£5). Service inc. Unlicensed
SEATS: 103. 16 tables outside. Private parties: 103 main room. Car-park. Children's
helpings. No-smoking area. Wheelchair access (also WC)

---

**EAST BERGHOLT  Essex**                                                      map 3

## *Fountain House* 🍷

The Street, East Bergholt CO7 6TB                              COOKING  2
COLCHESTER (0206) 298232                                        COST  £16−£22

A cottage in Constable-town, as picturesque as it is satisfactory. 'Careful and
imaginative cooking at a very reasonable price' is how one reporter sums it up.
The menu is short: five or six choices in each course for a set price including
coffee. The cooking is not elaborate: a smoked mackerel mousse, 'nicely
presented, in ample quantity'; a breast of chicken with green peppercorn sauce;
fresh vegetables; a selection of sweets, English dinner-party style. The dining-
room is a little small, which can be a drawback if there are too many smokers at
a time. The wine list is ambitious, having grown in a few short years from four
or five dozen bins to pages of very moderately priced yet carefully chosen
bottles, and giving more than fair exposure to the United States, Australasia,
Italy and Spain without ignoring the more traditional districts. There are nice
halves and nice magnums at prices that would be deemed foolish in London's
West End. The list has the merit of not blinding by quantity: there are often no
more than a dozen bottles from a particular region; therefore choice can be

sober, considered and range over the alternatives. House wines at £6 or £6.50. CELLARMAN'S CHOICE : Mâcon Viré 1987, André Bonhomme, £11; Ch. La Lagune, St Julien 1984, £14.

CHEF: Wendy Sarton   PROPRIETOR: James F. Sarton
OPEN: Tue to Sun, exc Sun D
CLOSED: 2 weeks end Feb
MEALS: 12.30 to 2, 7.30 to 10
PRICES: Set L £10.95 (£16), Set D £12.95 (£18)
CARDS: Access, Visa
SEATS: 32. 3 tables outside. Private parties: 16 main room. Car-park, 12 places. Children's helpings. No cigars/pipes in dining-room. Wheelchair access. Music

---

**EAST BUCKLAND   Devon**                                                    map 1

## ▲ *Lower Pitt*

East Buckland EX32 0TD
FILLEIGH (059 86) 243
off A361 at Stags Head, 3m NW of                              COOKING 2
South Molton                                                         COST £23

The long house in sight of the church sits at the edge of Exmoor. You need a map to get there but the North Devon Link Road will make access easier. Although cooking for a strong local audience, its charms for guests further afield are pressing: 'I booked in for one night and stayed three.' There are two dining-rooms, neither especially comfortable but nicely furnished in taste apposite to a rustic situation. Although Suzanne Lyons' cooking might be called 'country', that does not mean unskilled, merely that her vegetable garden contributes its tithe, many of the meats are from the district and the fish is landed not 10 miles distant. The menu is, in fact, longer than might be expected and has been well reported for its generosity, the standard of fish and the vegetable cookery. Cornets of smoked salmon filled with prawns; a brandade of fresh and smoked salmon; loin of pork (from Heal Farm nearby) pan-fried with apples and shallots; home-made ice-creams and the rich chocolate and chestnut gâteau Lyonnais are some favourites from a well-tried repertoire. The wine list, carefully explained and served by Jerome Lyons, comes largely from Christopher Piper Wines. It is very fairly priced and offers all that is needed for the meal. House French is £6.30 a litre. CELLARMAN'S CHOICE : Brown Brothers Chardonnay 1987, £9.20; Brown Bros Cabernet Sauvignon 1986, £8.30. 'No service charge is made or expected.'

CHEF: Suzanne Lyons   PROPRIETORS: Jerome and Suzanne Lyons
OPEN: Tue to Sat, D only
MEALS: 7 to 9
PRICES: £14 (£19)
CARDS: Access, Amex, Visa
SEATS: 28. Private parties: 14 main room. Car-park, 25 places. Children's helpings. Music
ACCOMMODATION: 3 rooms, all with bath/shower. B&B £25 to £40. Deposit: 10%. No children under 11. Garden. Scenic. Doors close at 10.30. Confirm by 6 [GHG]

---

*Report forms are at the back of the book; write a letter if you prefer.*

---

**EAST GRINSTEAD   West Sussex**                                        map 3

## ▲ *Gravetye Manor* 🍾

Vowels Lane, East Grinstead RH19 4LJ                          COOKING **4**
SHARPTHORNE (0342) 810567                                   COST £28−£52

The Elizabethan house and Victorian garden, epitomising England, are in the Wealden forest south of East Grinstead. We may have turned our forests into woods, but Gravetye is still splendid in its isolation, the park now restored by Herculean labours and a successful fund appeal after the great storm of 1987. Combining country-club, hotel and restaurant, and long in the same ownership, it has an atmosphere of belonging that eludes many similar establishments. Leigh Stone-Herbert made an impressive solo debut as chef when he joined his father at Gravetye but, as we write, he is in Australia. In his absence, Mark Raffan heads the kitchen, having worked at the Manor these eight years past. People love the close-panelled dining-room and comfortable English sitting-rooms that form the locale of eating: some movement between the two is inevitable when dining at Gravetye. The perspective of the kitchen, which depends on its own gardens, its own smoke house, and many local suppliers, is modern with the 'gimmicks of nouvelle under strict control'.

The menu is long, featuring first courses such as home-smoked salmon and venison as well as modern classics like a plump fish sausage, described as 'a sausage-shaped mousse in a cream sauce with ginger − now a taste of shellfish, now of halibut, all amounting to near-perfection, with a sauce of very good fish stock, cream and finely shredded spring onions.' Another fine beginning is a tartlet of poached quails' eggs with button mushrooms, crisp bacon and buttery port sauce. English cooking is not ignored, as in lamb with dumplings, braised in a light lamb sauce, or the range of savouries − grilled goats' cheese, soft roes, Brie fritters − offered at the same time as dessert. The handling of separate flavours, noted above, has also been praised in a wild mushroom salad served with an artichoke mousse and a crab mousse with scallops. This skill would also have been apparent in the case of a civet of game, with grand venison and wild duck and a satisfyingly vinous sauce, had the pheasant been more savage than the currently insipid hand-reared birds so often supplied. Among puddings, the prune, armagnac and mascarpone tart has impressed, but the Bramley apple confections, be they crumbles or pies, have not. Invention continues, even at this late stage of the meal: a terrine of citrus and honey, a ravioli of apricots and a poached William pear with lemon-grass sabayon, for example. Service is high in number, low in age. Some diners find the evident willingness and enthusiasm heart-warming. Others, perhaps happier with less voluble treatment, long for encounter that does not end with exhortation as one pursues one's daily round. The hotel needs a large staff to marshal the very large numbers of visitors and guests: Saturday night has the precision of an army drill, but there can be long waits on other nights while the kitchen builds up its head of steam. The wine list and service of wine are exemplary. The list is long − starting with 58 Champagnes of varying size and age − and best suits people with capacious wallets, because at the top lie the true rarities. However, even among less exalted bottles rests a Ch. Roquetaillade Lagrange, Graves 1985, a Crozes Hermitage 1983 from Jaboulet, or a Lake's Folly Cabernet Sauvignon 1985 from the Hunter Valley, good wines by any account. Among burgundies, there is not quite the range of growers one might expect: Jadot and Latour, Latour-Giraud and Tollot-Beaut are fine, but it is good to see more resolute exploration. Half-bottles are generously supplied and the German selection is worth long contemplation. Gravetye is one of a few country establishments that persists in quoting all prices before the addition of VAT. This abominable practice is now very rare. It makes choice of wine more complicated (given that cost comes into the decision at some point) and must create much bad blood at bill time. A false modesty about money, if not coyness, has already been evinced by the dishing out of unpriced menus to women. House Latour Burgundy is £16.10. CELLARMAN'S CHOICE : Crozes Hermitage, Domaine de Thalabert, Jaboulet 1978 £40.25; Ch. Coutet, Barsac 1980, £32.20.

CHEF: Mark Raffan  PROPRIETORS: Peter Herbert and Leigh Stone-Herbert
OPEN: all week
CLOSED: 25 Dec D to non-residents
MEALS: 12.30 to 2, 7 to 9.30 (10 Sat)
PRICES: £28 (£43), Set L £15 (£28), Set D £19 (£32). Service inc
SEATS: 50. Private parties: 10 main room, 20 private room. Car-park, 30 places. No children under 7. Smart dress preferred. No smoking in dining-room
ACCOMMODATION: 14 rooms, all with bath/shower. B&B £70 to £130. No children under 7. Garden. Fishing. TV. Phone. Scenic. Doors close at 12 [GHG]

---

**EASTBOURNE  East Sussex**                                              map 3

## Byrons

6 Crown Street, Old Town
Eastbourne BN21 1NX                                           COOKING 2
EASTBOURNE (0323) 20171                                        COST £24

Reading about this small, personal restaurant set well back from the seaside zone leads to speculation about the relaxed determination it takes to run such a place for 18 or 19 years. Marian Scrutton has always impressed with her warmth and skill as a hostess; determination shows in her remark last year that 'we still run it as though we have guests for dinner each night – and consider it frightfully rude, not to mention disruptive, if the guests turn up late without ringing.' On time or late, the cooking will satisfy for its materials – organic meats, fresh deliveries from New Covent Garden, Eastbourne-caught fish and British cheeses – and its exploration of a happily moderated modern style. Reports have come of duck with blackberries, duck with a port sauce (the leg braised slowly in rich stock, the breast grilled pink); home-made ravioli of salmon trout with a herb sauce; terrine of tip-top crab with avocado; and, favourite hardy perennials, an orange variation of Bakewell tart and lemon syllabub. Herbs are used generously, here and there to excess; flavours are pronounced. A short and satisfactory wine list that demands small ransoms. House Mommessin, £6.20. CELLARMAN'S CHOICE : St Véran 1987, Pierre Ferraud, £14.65; Roussillon La Tour de France 1985, £7.60. Discount for cash of 5 per cent. 'We have been known to open for lunch by special arrangement.' Service is included and tipping is unnecessary.

CHEF: Simon Scrutton   PROPRIETORS: Simon and Marian Scrutton
OPEN: Mon to Sat, D only
CLOSED: 1 week at Christmas
MEALS: 7.30 to 10.30
PRICES: £14 (£20). Service inc
CARDS: Amex, Diners, Visa
SEATS: 22. Private parties: 10 main room; 10 private room. Children welcome. No smoking during meals. Music

---

**EDENBRIDGE  Kent**                                                   map 3

# Honours Mill

87 High Street, Edenbridge TN8 5AU                          COOKING  3
EDENBRIDGE (0732) 866757                                     COST  £20−£40

The Goodhew brothers' restaurant has continued to attract favourable reports, as well as relieved notice that the back of the property is being tidied up, giving space for occasional aperitifs in the sun. Giles is the front man and discusses the menu in the bar before guests go upstairs to the spacious, low-beamed dining-room at the top of the converted corn mill. Cooking, by Neville Goodhew and Martin Radmall, has included some good things on occasion: garlicky fish soup, sea bass and beurre blanc with tomatoes and basil, an 'impeccable' pot-au-feu of duck, ox-tail, beef and salt pork and a 'triumph' of a Sussex pond pudding. Fish changes daily, but for the rest there is a seasonal set-price *carte*. Sunday lunch is simpler and a palpable bargain. While successes have been frequent, there are the odd failings, mainly of conception rather than execution. Service is friendly without intrusion, and incidentals of bread, butter and petits fours are to the mark, with very good coffee. House French is £7.85.
CELLARMAN'S CHOICE : Ch. Lyonnat 1981, £17.60.

CHEFS: Neville Goodhew and Martin Radmall   PROPRIETOR: Neville, Giles and Duncan Goodhew
OPEN: Tue to Sun, exc Sat L and Sun D
CLOSED: 2 weeks after Christmas, 2 weeks in June
MEALS: 12.15 to 2, 7.15 to 10
PRICES: Set L £15.75 (£20) to £28.95 (£33), Set D £25.95 (£30). Service inc
CARDS: Access, Diners, Visa
SEATS: 38. Private parties: 20 main room. Children under 12 Sun L only

---

**EDGWARE  Greater London**                                            map 3

# Wing Ki

29 Burnt Oak Broadway, HA8 5LD                               COOKING  1
01-205 0904                                                  COST  £12−£30

The menu is shorter and the cooking less authentic than at many comparable restaurants, but Wing Ki scores highly on service and cleverly adapted flavours which make it popular with the local community. Wing Ki is from Hong Kong but was trained in England by northern chefs. His Irish wife, Hannah, 'a star turn' as one customer put it, runs front of house. Dishes are largely from

Peking and Szechuan, with most of the pork dropped to satisfy local kosher tastes, and a high proportion of seafood and vegetables. These and the appetisers are the most unusual dishes. Mushrooms with chilli are lethally hot, green beans, broccoli or okra heavily garlicked. The set menus have been praised. 'Every course of the Szechuan feast was beautifully presented and left a memorable taste. They were even kind enough to wrap the remaining crispy beef and chicken in sea-spice sauce for us to take home.' There is a proper vegetarian menu. House French, £5.90.

CHEF: Wing Ki Yeung  PROPRIETORS: Wing Ki and Hannah Yeung
OPEN: all week
MEALS: 12 to 2.30, 6 to 11.30
PRICES: £14 (£25), Set L £6.50 (£12) to £7.50 (£13), Set D £14 (£20) to £17 (£23). Minimum £5. Service 12.5%
CARD: Access, Visa
SEATS: 56. Private parties: 60 main room. Vegetarian meals. Children's helpings. Smart dress preferred. Wheelchair access (also WC). Music

---

**EGHAM  Surrey**                                                    map 3

## La Bonne Franquette

5 High Street, Egham TW20 9EA                           COOKING 2
EGHAM (0784) 439494                                      COST £19–£43

A small cottage at the western end of the High Street, wholly devoted to a very French, English-run, restaurant. Dining occupies three rooms, the bar a fourth. Refurbishment has lifted what was beginning to fray. The cooking excites debate. Some people tend to see 'Surrey-man's' liking for fancy French restaurants being for the trimmings and conspicuous expenditure – hang the flavours. These people then proceed to squash La Bonne Franquette into this mould. It fits sporadically. A meal of asparagus mousse with oysters and chive sauce; duck breast with honey and sesame seeds in an astringent sauce; warm lemon tart on a raspberry coulis with a lemon sorbet, pleased one writer enormously, let down only by the vegetables. Others have been equally pleased by some parts of their meal, for example, ravioli of lobster with a tagliatelle of vegetables on a shellfish sauce (not too distantly related to a host of lookalikes/progenitors in a score of smart restaurants at the time of writing) and a very finely judged mignon of beef with a mushroom fumet and confit of shallots. However, not all is as dandy: the stale, the overcooked and the leaden have also been mentioned. Referred to also has been the incompetence of the waiting staff. In a restaurant that thinks so much of its skills, this goes down badly. Perhaps the recruitment of a new brigade will improve matters. There is a multiplicity of menus: inclusive, dégustation and so on: some cannot be taken at weekends, most cannot be mixed and matched at one table. Lunch is much cheaper, indeed constitutes a possible bargain. The wine list is French bar seven wines. It contains some quite nice choices but not at bargain prices. Some of the clarets are simply prohibitive, others – less well known – relatively fair. Little attempt is made to seek out interesting, less expensive burgundies, though they do exist, or to balance the classics by the far better value new regions – in France, as well as the rest of the world. French house

wine is £7. CELLARMAN'S CHOICE : Petit Chablis 1985, Moreau, £18; Ch.
Montus 1983, Madiran,£17.

CHEF: David Smart   PROPRIETORS: David Turvey and David Smart
OPEN: all week, exc Sat L
CLOSED: bank hols
MEALS: 12 to 2, 7 to 9.30
PRICES: £24 (£32), Set L £15 (£19), Set D £18 (£22) to £32.50 (£36). Service inc
CARDS: Access, Amex, Diners, Visa
SEATS: 46. 3 tables outside. Private parties: 20 main room, 8 private room. Car-park,
14 places. Children welcome. Smart dress preferred. Wheelchair access. Music

---

**ELLAND   West Yorkshire**                                          map 5

## *Berties Bistro*

7–10 Town Hall Buildings
Elland HD1 2TA                                              COOKING  1
ELLAND (0422) 71724                                         COST  £18

A cheerful, cosy bistro of the old mould: Victoriana, blackboards, moussaka. In
all, cheap and substantial. Quality does seem to go up and down in waves but
the restaurant remains popular. The menu runs to about 10 ten items per
course, changing weekly or more often. Onion soup, mussels marinières,
grilled wing of skate with garlic, prawns and cognac and a filo parcel of
Chinese vegetables with sweet-and-sour sauce are some of the dishes reported.
No credit cards and no bookings. The wine list is a peach: only a couple of
dozen bottles but at low prices and from good négociants or growers; if your
merchants are Loeb & Company and Yorkshire Fine Wines, that's what you
should get. House French is £5.75 a litre. CELLARMAN'S CHOICE : Crozes-
Hermitage, Jaboulet 1985, £8.50; Chablis *premier cru* Montmain 1986, £16.

CHEF: Michael Swallow   PROPRIETOR: Brett Woodward
OPEN: Tue to Sun, D only
MEALS: 7 (6 Sat) to 11 (5 to 10 Sun)
PRICES: £12 (£15). Service inc
SEATS: 110. Private parties: 40 private room. Car-park, 60 places. Vegetarian meals.
Children's helpings. Smart dress preferred. Wheelchair access. Music. Air-conditioned

---

**ELY   Cambridgeshire**                                            map 6

## *Old Fire Engine House* ▼

25 St Mary's Street, Ely, CB7 4ER                          COOKING  2
ELY (0353) 662582                                          COST  £22

*COUNTY OF THE YEAR RESTAURANT*

Over 20 years for Ann Ford and Michael Jarman is a fine achievement, pleasing
almost generations of visitors to Ely cathedral with their flower-surrounded
house on the western extension of the close. It is indicative of the place that
Terri Kindred, recently appointed manager, has worked for them almost as
long as they have been running, since she was 13. There is a sense of family, of
the domestic, with open arms and smiles. What it does is serve sound food,
often good, generously, to as many people as can afford their sensible prices.

A reader commented that 'you walk into the hall and you are met by a smiling waitress with a warm welcome. Pink walls, lots of brass and some lovely paintings being exhibited for sale. Hung on the stairs to a family bathroom for toilet facilities are more paintings worth lingering over.' If the dining-room is full, lunch can be taken in the bar, with good Adnams beer or Aspall cider. There is a sound emphasis on quantity, even second helpings, as well as an exploration of local materials in dishes such as pike mayonnaise, Brancaster mussels in white wine, eels baked in white wine, marsh samphire, zander with piquant sauce, roast stuffed leg of pork with apple sauce or pigeon pie. It is the epitome of English restaurants, even to the syllabub, stem ginger and cream, apple Betty and treacle pudding. What it aims to do, it does. The wine list is masterly, with few duds, excellent prices and breathtaking bin-ends. Read the uncondescending notes with attention and buy with confidence Ch. du Tertre, 1978, £19; Erdener Treppchen Riesling Kabinett 1987, Max Ford Richter, £7.65, or Châteauneuf-du-Pape, Ch. de Beaucastel 1984, £16.50. They are great to children and like warning for vegetarian meals. House red Vaucluse and Gaillac white, £5.40, Mosel £6. CELLARMAN'S CHOICE : Concha y Toro: Chardonnay 1987, Cabernet Sauvignon 1985 £5.60; Barossa Valley Shiraz-Cabernet 1985, £5.50.

CHEFS/PROPRIETOR: Ann Ford and Michael Jarman
OPEN: all week, exc Sun D
CLOSED: 24 Dec for 2 weeks, and bank hols
MEALS: 12.30 to 2, 7.30 to 9
PRICES: £13 (£18)
SEATS: 36. Private parties: 36 main room, 22 private room. Car-park, 8 places. Vegetarian meals, by arrangement. Children's helpings. No smoking in main dining-room

---

**EMSWORTH  Hampshire**                                          map 2

## 36 on the Quay

47 South Street, Emsworth PO10 7EG                    COOKING 3
EMSWORTH (0243) 375592                                 COST £42

This stylish restaurant continues to draw good reports for a complex style of cooking that is served intelligently and attractively in a suite of three rooms once occupied by a steak house. This year, a steak would be lightly smoked over oak, flash grilled, topped with flambé foie gras and sauté pleurottes, ceps and morels and served on a beef *jus* flavoured with truffles. This might surprise customers of the earlier incarnation of the house. Likewise, fillets of salmon, sea bass, turbot, scallops and lobster encased in a fine wall of salmon mousseline topped with a compressed pastry lid, enhanced with a white wine and tarragon sauce may give a mild jolt to someone seeking a simple fish dinner. Things tend to be hunted in packs by Vivian Abady. Even soups come as 'duets', cleverly splitting the bowl between tomato and leek, for instance. Birds, too, are shot in groups; a dish well reported over the years has been breasts of pigeon and duck fanned round a boned quail served with three sauces. This cooking is the result of much work, learning and enthusiasm and is received with pleasure. People speak of the tastes somehow remaining discreet within these compositions and being approached in a less ponderous manner than might be feared. There is a unique system of bells on each tables so that one may play the dowager and ring when one has finished. House wine, £7.45 (white), £8.45 (red).

CHEF: Vivian Abady    PROPRIETORS: Tim amd Vivian Abady
OPEN: Mon to Sat, D only
MEALS: 7 to 11
PRICES: £26 (£35)
CARDS: Access, Amex, Diners, Visa
SEATS: 42. Private parties: 22 main room, 10 private room. Car-park, 8 places. Vegetarian meals. Children's helpings. No children under 5. Smart dress preferred. No cigars/pipes in dining-room. Music

---

**EPWORTH** Humberside                                                    map 5

## Epworth Tap 🍾

9–11 Market Place, Epworth DN9 1EU                              COOKING 1
EPWORTH (0427) 873333                                          COST £15–£19

Would that all wine bars were like this one in the heart of the Isle of Axholme. John Wynne has had a bout of bad health, but his wife's hand has kept the Tap flowing smoothly. A satisfied correspondent reflected on his bottle of Ch. Gruaud-Larose 1962 followed by a Meyney of the same year (for comparative purposes, don't you know). The wine list would afford many such essays in grading: Ch. La Lagune in four vintages; nine different Gevrey Chambertins of Rousseau, Bachelet-Ramonet, Dujac or Burguet from 1982, 1983 and 1985; six vintages of Châteauneuf-du-Pape from Ch. de Beaucastel; or perhaps a cross tasting of Chardonnays from the New World taking in Lindeman's, Bannockburn and Rosemount from Australia and Ch. St Jean, Joseph Phelps, Mondavi, Jordan and Firestone from California. Prices are very reasonable and the service intelligent. There is not much old wine, but that is not the same as it all being too young. Mr Wynne intends to beef up his Spanish selection and apologises for offering a generic Hock, 'but I always tell them it constitutes the poorest value.' Helen Wynne cooks a short menu displayed on a blackboard. The hypercritical point out that it changes slowly but are the first to admit that it is always freshly made and that the 'gravies/sauces are well prepared and of good quality.' There are good French cheeses. Lasagne, beef with red wine and lamb with courgettes are among the staples. Sticky toffee pudding, cheesecake and chocolate pot give a little more body to the end of the meal. House Italian, Australian, French and Hock £5.95 (whites) and £6.95 (reds). CELLARMAN'S CHOICE : Crozes Hermitage 1983, Jaboulet, £11.50; St-Véran 1986, Corsin, £12.50.

CHEF: Helen Wynne    PROPRIETORS: Helen and John Wynne
OPEN: Tue to Sat, D only
MEALS: 7.30 to 10 (10.30 Sat)
PRICES: £10 (£15), Set D £11.50 (£16)
CARD: Access
SEATS: 74. Private parties: 50 main room, 24 private room. Vegetarian meals. Children welcome. No-smoking area. Wheelchair access (3 steps). Music

## ERPINGHAM  Norfolk

map 6

# Ark

| | |
|---|---|
| The Street, Erpingham NR11 7QB | COOKING 2 |
| CROMER (0263) 761535 | COST £20 |

'Tucked away in the middle of rural Norfolk, but within five minutes of such
delights as Blickling Hall, the little pantiled, red-brick cottage looks for all the
world as though it should be called "L'Auberge Fleurie" and should be in the
depths of the Cantal. It is excellent on its own terms, which are that of a simple
cottage operation serving good food in generous portions.' The restaurant's
real-life name, taken from that of the house, apparently seemed appropriate
when the skies opened for several days on end. A simple gravelled yard gives
way to a cottage door and red-tiled hallway: this is a family home, with a
kitchen garden providing the herbs and many of the vegetables. Mike and
Sheila Kidd have been here for six years and her short three-course *carte* in the
Elizabeth David style, with dishes of various cuisines built around a backbone
of French provincial cooking, has many local devotees. A summer lunch for
two explains why. First courses of a moist, fresh mushroom terrine, made with
two varieties, and a goats' cheese and fresh herb pâté with orange salad were
followed by rack of lamb flavoured with lemon thyme and a tiny Yorkshire
pudding and perfectly cooked, asparagus with a fluffy, sharp lemon cream.
Vegetables were plainly cooked but tasted of the garden. To finish, lemon tart
in the French manner was satisfyingly sharp and an apple and cinnamon
crunch was a simple but delicious layered pudding. Service, by father and
son, is well timed and careful. A short wine list is fairly priced; house French,
£5.50 and £6.

CHEF: Sheila Kidd    PROPRIETORS: Mike and Sheila Kidd
OPEN: Tue to Sat D, and Sun L
MEALS: 12.30 to 2, 7 to 9.30 (10.30 Sat)
PRICES: £12 (£17)
SEATS: 38. Private parties: 38 main room. Car-park, 15 places. Vegetarian meals. Children's
helpings on request. No smoking. Wheelchair access (1 step; also WC)

## ESHER  Surrey

map 3

# Les Alouettes

| | |
|---|---|
| 7 High Street, Claygate, Esher KT10 0JW | COOKING 3 |
| ESHER (0372) 64882 | COST £31–£44 |

Manifesting in decoration and trim the pinks and blues of a classy restaurant,
this serves local businesses and private residents with a careful and genuine
version of French modern cooking. When the bill can rise as fast as it may, even
though base prices appear quite reasonable, the heretic customer may wonder
if a few miles more to central London may not be worth the small extra outlay.
This is a dilemma faced by all cooks and all customers: the price difference
between the good, better and best is often too small. But Michel Perraud is a
craftsman and does cook reliably. Les Alouettes also delivers the food with
grace and comfort. A light lobster bisque allows the shellfish flavour to come

through its slight masking of cream, just as the butter sauce for the cassolette of scallops is handled with finesse and a light mousseline of lobster has been well noticed on another occasion. First courses comprise four shellfish, a foie gras, smoked salmon, an asparagus and mushroom vol-au-vent and jambon de Bayonne. If crustacea are forbidden for reasons of dislike or reaction, the choice becomes severely limited. Main courses have been praised for their sauces; cheeses are from Olivier (though uniformly under-ripe at one meal); desserts need not drown the already sinking soul. The wine list is long, classic and expensive. Lupé-Cholet house wine, £8.50.

CHEF: Michel Perraud   PROPRIETOR: Steve Christou
OPEN: Mon to Sat, exc Sat L
CLOSED: 1 to 12 Jan, 12 to 28 Aug, bank hols
MEALS: 12.15 to 2, 7 to 9.30 (10 Fri and Sat)
PRICES: Set L £24 (£31), Set D £29 (£37). Service 12.5%
CARDS: Access, Amex, Diners, Visa
SEATS: 75. Private parties: 85 main room. Children's helpings. Smart dress preferred. Wheelchair access (3 steps). Music. Air-conditioned

## Read's

| 4 The Parade, Claygate, Esher KT10 0NU | COOKING 2 |
|---|---|
| ESHER (0372) 65105 | COST £22-£36 |

Book well in advance, as locals are still flocking in to fill this small, welcoming restaurant. The menu has changed to a set price, with a choice of four dishes per course over three courses, plus the option of salad or cheese. Combinations of ingredients are enterprising and can be elaborate, as in rosette of English lamb with a brioche crust, a basil and mustard sauce and a filo bag of ratatouille; or supreme of guinea-fowl with limes and cranberries garnished with a sesame seed and guinea-fowl sausage. Simpler dishes have been well reported: 'extremely light parfait of duck'; 'delightfully fragrant beef in red wine and shallot sauce'. Sweets are 'individual dishes in their own right, not rearrangements of standard components', and one reporter is still dreaming about the plum duff on a sabayon with armagnac and stem-ginger ice-cream. The cheeseboard, from James's of Beckenham, consists entirely of new-style British cheeses. A wide ranging wine list at ungrasping prices. House burgundy, £6.50. CELLARMAN'S CHOICE : Washington State Staton Hills Merlot 1986, £16.75; Alfred Gratien Champagne, £23.50.

CHEF: Stephen Read   PROPRIETORS: The Read family
OPEN: Tue to Sat, exc Sat L
MEALS: 12.15 to 1.30, 7.30 to 9.30
PRICES: Set L £14.95 (£22), Set D £21.95 (£30). Minimum £14.95
CARDS: Access, Amex, Visa
SEATS: 28. Children's helpings (L only). Smart dress preferred. Wheelchair access. Music. Air-conditioned

*Restaurateurs justifiably resent no-shows. If you quote a credit card number when booking, you may be liable for the restaurant's lost profit margin if you don't turn up. Always phone to cancel.*

ETON  Berkshire                                                    map 2

## *Eton Wine Bar*

82–83 High Street, Eton SL4 6AF                          COOKING 1
WINDSOR (0753) 854921 and 855182                        COST £22

The food makes fair wine-bar eating, around a menu of half a dozen daily items at each course. Some of them are predictable, for instance pâté, others more adventurous – baked smoked salmon, smoked fish and scallop risotto with a red pepper sauce. The French wine list (containing items which can be bought by the case from a sister enterprise) is not overpriced and makes good wine-bar reading. Complaints of a cold environment have been countered by the installation of a 'real gas fire'. Service, however, is anything but cold. House wine, £6. CELLARMAN'S CHOICE : Sauvignon de St-Bris 1988, £8.25; St-Nicolas de Bourgeuil 1986, Max Cognard, £8.95.

CHEFS: Caroline Gilbey, Linda Gilbey, the Hon. William Gilbey, Deborah Wicks, and Natalie Gould
PROPRIETORS: The Hon William Gilbey, Caroline Gilbey, the Hon. Michael Gilbey and Linda Gilbey
OPEN: all week
CLOSED: 24 to 27 Dec
MEALS: 12 to 2.30, 6 (7 Sun) to 10.30 (11 Fri and Sat)
PRICES: £11 (£18)
CARDS: Access, Visa
SEATS: 110. Private parties: 35 main room. Vegetarian meals. Children welcome. Wheelchair access (also WC). Music

ETTINGTON  Warwickshire                                            map 2

## ▲ *Chase Hotel*

Banbury Road, Ettington CV37 7NZ                        COOKING 1
STRATFORD-UPON-AVON (0789) 740000                      COST £16–£31

This is an unspectacular Victorian Gothic pile just outside the village of Ettington on the Banbury Road. Once inside, an inappropriate extension slips out of view and there are magnificent views over the grassy terrace to rolling countryside. Gary Thompson, the chef, who arrived with the change of management early in 1988, cooks a concise choice. By contrast with the setting, the menu is unequivocally modern, leaning heavily towards fruity sauces or garnishes and old-fashioned British dishes that are given a contemporary twist. There have been successes and there have been failures, the latter largely confined to the complicated dishes. People are unanimous in praising the fresh enthusiasm of the service, despite the silver-plated domes. The wine list is without prejudice, informative and contains some nice bottles and growers. Prices fluctuate from good to very high. House French is £6.50. CELLARMAN'S CHOICE : Mâcon-Lugny, Les Charmes 1987, £10.15; Ch. Cissac 1984, £14.30.

*'The young boy who took us to our room told us we must have dinner early as the chef was in a hurry to go off for a meal at Hintlesham Hall.'*  On dining in Suffolk

CHEF: Gary Thompson   PROPRIETORS: B.H.I. Hotels
OPEN: all week, exc Sat L and Sun D
CLOSED: 26 Dec to 2 Jan
MEALS: 12.30 to 2, 7.30 to 9
PRICES: Set L £11.50 (£16) to £12.50 (£17), Set D £15.50 (£22) to £18.95 (£26). Snacks from £4.25
CARDS: Access, Amex, Visa
SEATS: 65. Private parties: 65 main room. Car-park, 50 places. Children welcome. No cigars/pipes in dining-room. Wheelchair access (also WC). Music
ACCOMMODATION: 12 rooms, all with bath/shower. B&B £50 to £66. Garden. TV. Phone. Scenic. Doors close at 3am. Confirm by 6pm

---

**EVERSHOT Dorset**                                                    map 2

## ▲ *Summer Lodge* ?

Evershot DT2 0JR                                              COOKING 3
EVERSHOT (093 583) 424                                      COST £15−£25

'So many things have changed for the better in this peaceful oasis,' says one report. After 10 years in this white-painted rural Georgian house, the Corbetts have decided to move with the times. The repertoire has opened up, and a new pair of hands in the kitchen has begun to serve lighter dishes. The choice is between a starter and soup, then fish or meat, with cheese or pudding. Soups are made from good-flavoured stocks and left in a tureen on the table; fish varies from John Dory to gurnard (poached or grilled); and local cheeses are served with Dorset knobs. Now and again a little more flair shows through. Smoked salmon comes on a bed of warm, shredded cabbage with a gentle oily dressing; fillet of pork with sorrel crust is served with a herb soufflé. Puddings are traditional. A large selection of claret is the highlight of a reasonably priced, mainly French list, which also sports a handful of English wines and 40 half-bottles. House French from £5.75. CELLARMAN'S CHOICE : Ch. Franc-Grâce-Dieu 1981, St-Emilion, £12.25; Montagny, Les Bonnevaux 1986, £12.25.

---

CHEFS: Margaret Corbett and Jeffry Condliffe   PROPRIETORS: Nigel and Margaret Corbett
OPEN: all week
CLOSED: 2 to 23 Jan
MEALS: 12.30 to 1.30, 7.30 to 8.30
PRICES: Set L £12.50 (£15), Set D £18.50 (£21). Service inc
CARDS: Access, Visa
SEATS: 48. 28 tables outside. Private parties: 28 main room. Car-park, 30 places. No children under 8. Wheelchair access (also WC)
ACCOMMODATION: 17 rooms, all with bath/shower. Rooms for disabled. B&B £50 to £80. No children under 8. Pets welcome. Afternoon teas. Garden. Swimming-pool. Tennis. Phone. Scenic. Doors close at midnight. Confirm by 6 [GHG]

---

*All entries in the* Guide *are rewritten every year, not least because restaurant standards fluctuate. Don't trust an out-of-date* Guide.

*Several sharp operators have tried to extort money from restaurateurs on the promise of an entry in a guide book that has never appeared. The* Good Food Guide *makes no charge for inclusion and does not offer certificates of any kind.*

---

EVESHAM   Hereford & Worcester                                    map 2

## ▲ Cedar Restaurant, The Evesham Hotel ▼

Cooper's Lane, Evesham WR11 6DA                          COOKING 1
EVESHAM (0386) 765566                                    COST £20

The determinedly facetious tone of menus and wine list masks a sensible
approach to hospitality. The hotel lies on the east side of the Avon as it runs
through Evesham. John Wesley used to call here; his humour was not the
same. The Jenkinsons have a new chef but, although the extremes of
eclecticism have given way to a slightly more traditional approach, and slightly
less cream, the spirit of the kitchen has not changed. Turkey breast with apricot
sauce and a salmon and caviare terrine have been well reported; scallops of
monkfish cooked with butter and finished with lime and cream may have
suffered from too much lime, but contained excellent raw materials. The
cooking is cheerful and not very refined. Service and ambience are also
cheerful. There are good-value buffet lunches. The wine and bar lists give full
rein to humour and a desire to instruct. The bar stocks more strong liquor than
known to most people, starting with five dozen single malts and a like number
of brandies. It includes Rose, a 'nasty sweet Bulgarian drink smelling like, and
made from, roses. Rather like drinking Chanel No. 5 blended with Brut'. This
gives the tone of the humour. The wines – from an eclectic clutch of suppliers
– include four Champagnes and an Eiswein; otherwise it ranges the world.
From Zimbabwe, Holland, the United States, Australia and elsewhere;
selections are impressive and don't cost a lot. Try a bottle of Ruby NV from the
Crimea if you are brave. Half-bottles increase in number; hitherto the problem
has been solved by serving half a bottle at half-price. House wines are Concha y
Toro Cabernet/Merlot from Chile, Soave dry and Bulgarian Riesling medium
whites, £7.60 a litre. CELLARMAN'S CHOICE : Rosemount Show Reserve Merlot
1985, £13; Te Mata Castle Hill Sauvignon Blanc 1987, £14; Texas Vineyards
Gewürztraminer 1986, £8.20. The Jenkinsons' approach to children is
thoroughly sane, as is their dislike of tipping. The hotel is expanding.

CHEF: Ian Mann   PROPRIETORS: The Jenkinson family
OPEN: all week
CLOSED: 25 and 26 Dec
MEALS: 12.30 to 2, 7 to 9.30
PRICES: £14 (£17). Service inc
CARDS: Access, Amex, Diners, Visa
SEATS: 55. Private parties: 12 main room, 15 private room. Car-park, 50 places. Vegetarian
meals. Children's helpings. Wheelchair access (also WC)
ACCOMMODATION: 40 rooms, all with bath/shower. B&B £46 to £62. Baby facilities. Pets
welcome. Afternoon teas. Garden. TV. Phone. Scenic. Doors close at 12. Confirm by 6
[GHG]

---

*If you see a certificate in a restaurant bearing the words 'Good Food and Wine Guide', the
claim is false – see the Introduction. Please write and tell us the name and address of the
restaurant.*

EXETER Devon                                                      map 1

# Tudor House

Tudor Street, Exeter EX4 3BR                              COOKING 1
EXETER (0392) 73764                                       COST £14–£24

Jean Cooke has made a smooth transition from Henderson's in Tiverton
(previously a *Guide* entry) to this wonderful Tudor town-house, a survivor of
air-raids and 'improvements'. Warm brickwork runs up the front façade, on
either side of armorial crests and half-timbered upper stories, to a quaintly lopsided roof; inside, beams and carved ceilings are well preserved and the busy,
ornate feel has been reinforced by reproduction Gobelin tapestries, floral
upholstery and old furniture. The menu hedges its bets with a mixture of
styles; there is modern tressed fish, pink rack of lamb, duck in yellow-bean
sauce and plainly cooked vegetables, but steaks, fish and even cheese soufflé
come with rich cream and butter sauces. Carrot and coriander soup, chicken
marinated in wine and ginger with a white wine and cheese sauce, thick
alcoholic syllabub and fruit Pavlova – called The Folly on the menu – have
been enjoyed. Jean Cooke prefers to work in tandem with another chef, so the
choice of a recruit, when it happens, will be important to the success of the
venture. Changes may be seen. Wines are a good selection, listed by dryness or
flavour, in a catholic mix. There are some mature clarets, a lot of alternate
vintages, and some useful comments all through the listing. Prices are very fair.
House Duboeuf is £5.75.

CHEF/PROPRIETOR: Jean Cooke
OPEN: Tue to Sun, exc Sat L
MEALS: 12.15 to 1.45, 7.15 to 9.45
PRICES: £14 (£20), Set L £8.95 (£14)
CARDS: Access, Amex, Diners, Visa
SEATS: 44. Private parties: 65 main room. Vegetarian meals. Children's helpings.
Wheelchair access (2 steps; also WC). Air-conditioned

FARNHAM Surrey                                                   map 3

# Krug's

84 West Street, Farnham GU9 7EN                          COOKING 1
FARNHAM (0252) 723277                                     COST £29

Once through the door, Surrey drops away and Austria appears: the waitresses
are dressed in dirndls, the walls are hung with decorative plates and Tyrolean
scenes, baskets of home-made rye bread sit on the tables, and jolly, thigh-
slapping music lilts along in the background. Gerhard Krug, chef when this
was the Tirolerhof but now also proprietor, has made the menu
uncompromisingly Austrian, but it offers some good eating and especially
distinctive first courses: sweet marinated herring fillet with a salad of onions
and cream; smoked pork and horseradish sauce; a mushroom soup made with
good stock, sliced Frankfurter sausages and a spoonful of garlic soured cream.
Main course fondues and fried pork, veal and steaks with various rich sauces
are more than ample, but carefully cooked so that they are not defeatingly

heavy. Wiener schnitzel is well fried in a light coating of home-made breadcrumbs and served with a buttery potato gratin and red cabbage cooked with apple and cloves. Another typical dish is sauerkraut with bratwurst and dumpling. Those with a sweet tooth should leave space for the large, calorie-laden desserts – Sachertorte and Apfelstrudel and cinnamon and poppy seed ice-cream, the house speciality – or, for the uncomfortably full, there are *alcools blancs*. House wine is Austrian at £7.50.

CHEF: Gerhard Krug  PROPRIETORS: Gerhard and Karin Krug
OPEN: Tue to Sat, D only
MEALS: 7 to 10.30 (11.30 Sat)
PRICES: £19 (£24). Service inc
CARDS: Access, Visa
SEATS: 90. Private parties: 50 main room, 50 private room. Children welcome. Wheelchair access. Music

---

FAVERSHAM Kent                                                    map 3

## Read's ♟

Painters Forstal, Faversham ME13 0EE                     COOKING 2
FAVERSHAM (0795) 535344                               COST £20–£38

Here is the place to eat the best lunch in Britain. Sanity prevails, too: 'Please tell us if you have limited time available'; and there is a children's menu that includes neither fish fingers nor hamburgers. In fact, the full menu belies both the unprepossessing exterior and any hint of simplicity that may be given by the foregoing remarks; it is a luxurious mix, from caviare down to fish soup, lobster with asparagus to veal normande. Some of the cooking is mere juxtaposition of luxury: a fillet of farmed salmon is placed next to a fillet of the wild, on a red caviare sauce with beluga trimmings. Comparisons obviously attract David Pitchford: he cooks English and Argenteuil asparagus and asks for comments. The cooking leans to a more international slant than anything French provincial, though ox-tail with tomato and madeira sauce as a first course sounds substantial enough for any peasant. Service is outgoing and generous. The wine list is in two halves, the second being 'odd and unusual'. Throughout there are marks of an enthusiast, sometimes chancing his arm a little with dubious origins of old bottles that simply may never last the course; however, with advice there are some real gems at none too high a price in clarets and burgundies. House French, £9. CELLARMAN'S CHOICE: Gigondas, Domaine de St-Gayan 1981, £11.50; Chablis *1er cru* Fourchaume 1985, Jean Durup, £17.50.

CHEF: David Pitchford  PROPRIETORS: David and Rona Pitchford
OPEN: Tue to Sun
MEALS: 12 to 2, 7 to 10
PRICES: £21 (£32), Set L £12 (£20)
CARDS: Access, Amex, Diners, Visa
SEATS: 60. 3 tables outside. Private parties: 60 main room. Car-park, 30 places. Children's helpings. Wheelchair access (1 step; also WC). Music

---

*Report forms are at the back of the book; write a letter if you prefer.*

---

**FELSTED Essex** map 3

## *Rumbles Cottage*

Braintree Road, Felsted CM6 3DJ COOKING **2**
GREAT DUNMOW (0371) 820996 COST £14–£24

Guests who are happy to take gastronomic risks should visit Rumbles on Tuesday, Wednesday or Thursday nights and ask for the 'guinea pig' menu. Chef/proprietor Joy Hadley uses this device to canvass opinion before adding dishes permanently to her repertoire. For £9.50, diners sample three experimental courses, with coffee and petits fours included, and must give their verdicts in return. The main menu reflects this desire to cook creatively, often successfully. The desire to cater for vegetarians is seen in the main course vegetarian dish on the à la carte menu. A beginning of marinated trout and grapefruit has worked well; likewise duck Wellington, stuffed with juniper, served on an apple and calvados sauce; and chicken slivers with water-chestnuts in a ginger, garlic and cardamom sauce, 'very tasty and unusual.' Vegetable selections are just as innovative: Jerusalem artichokes cooked with egg and soft cheese; red and white cabbage strips with leek and bacon. Puddings lean to the creamy and satisfying but have less zing. Good coffee. House French wine is £6.25. Non-smokers can book a separate dining-room.

CHEF: Joy Hadley PROPRIETORS: Joy Hadley and M. Donovan
OPEN: Tue to Sat D, Sun L
CLOSED: 3 weeks Feb, 1 week Aug
MEALS: 12 to 2, 7 to 9
PRICES: £14 (£20), Set Sun L £10.50 (£15), Set D Tue to Thur £9.50 (£14)
CARDS: Access, Visa
SEATS: 46. Private parties: 24 main room, 8 and 10 private rooms. Vegetarian meals. Children's helpings. No-smoking area. Wheelchair access

**FLITWICK Bedfordshire** map 3

## ▲ *Flitwick Manor* 🍷

Church Road, Flitwick MK45 1AE
FLITWICK (0525) 712242 COOKING **3**
off A5120, S of Flitwick COST £24–£53

Flitwick is a good manor house, the feel is right, the books in the library are interesting, the displays of china instructive, the grounds handsome and the architecture not too overwhelming. The cooking, and it is fish that is the attraction, can also be good: 'spot-on fresh seafood, cleverly piled together – sea bass, turbot, excellent salmon, a wonderful huge scallop and a lobster claw – well timed and full of flavour on a light cream sauce with bite from grain mustard. Around the plate were two boiled potatoes, a fanned courgette, two pieces of broccoli and two tiny carrots with tufts.' Very nice, thank you. Such food can come with the most affectionate service. A summer meal cost as much as our 'adjusted for inflation' estimate so this place should be good. That, indeed, it was, showing proper attention to detail in dishes such as smoked trout mousse wrapped with smoked salmon; chilled pear and watercress soup; a hot lobster with a duo of sauces (truffle and a light lobster sauce); and fillet of salmon with a light meat based madeira and shallot sauce. However, this is dear for neither particularly inventive, nor technically surprising food. What is more, there have been too many criticisms for comfort: of tired fish, undercooked vegetables, meagre portions and incompetence or indifference. Perhaps the accession of new blood to the kitchen will return this place to the position it deserves. The wine list is an impressive one, though with more reds than whites while the menu needs tilt the other way. There is evidence of care in picking both suppliers and growers. Prices, however, remain firmly Home Counties. Although France supplies the bulk, an Australian awakening is noticed. House wine, £11.50 (red), £10.80 (white). CELLARMAN'S CHOICE : Ch. de la Rivière, Fronsac 1979, £19.50; Pernand-Vergelesses Blanc 1986, Laleure-Piot £21.

CHEF: Shaun Cook   PROPRIETORS: Somerset and Hélène Moore
OPEN: all week
MEALS: 12.45 to 2, 7 to 9.30
PRICES: £33 (£44), Set L and D £16.50 (£24) to £27.50 (£36)
CARDS: Access, Amex, Visa
SEATS: 60. 6 tables outside. Private parties: 65 main room, 10 and 20 private rooms. Car-park, 70 places. Vegetarian meals. Children's helpings. No pipes in dining-room. Wheelchair access (also WC)
ACCOMMODATION: 15 rooms, all with bath/shower. Rooms for disabled. B&B £67.50 to £90. Deposit: 50%. Baby facilities. Garden. Tennis. Fishing. Golf. Snooker. Air-conditioning. TV. Phone. Scenic. Confirm 7 days ahead [GHG]

---

FOWEY  Cornwall                                                      map 1

## Food for Thought

Town Quay, Fowey PL23 1AT                                    COOKING 3
FOWEY (072 683) 2221                                       COST  £20–£30

It would be a surprise if this quayside restaurant, formerly the Customs House and now done out in Laura Ashley pinks with Portuguese lamps, did not have a good line in fish. What *is* surprising, given the disappointing record of our coastal restaurants, is how far it goes beyond run-of-the-mill seafood. Shelled mussels come with fresh spinach pasta and a saffron cream sauce; scallops are served with a Sauternes and leek sauce; and there is a grilled fish of the evening'. The Billingsleys cure their own salmon for gravlax. The simplicity of grilled lobster or roast rack of lamb shows off the produce – and the kitchen's sense of timing – to best advantage, and saucing, although sometimes rich, doesn't complicate: chive butter with salmon; langoustine with fillet of sole wrapped around salmon mousse. Puddings continue the feeling of reassurance with warm sticky toffee pudding, treacle tart with clotted cream and marquise of dark and light chocolate. Fine ingredients, good execution, attractive presentation, attention to detail, and good value mark this place. There are some supplements on all the set-price menus. The wine list is good, not too long, outward-looking, fairly priced. House Roussillon and Muscadet, £6.50.

---

CELLARMAN'S CHOICE : *A wine recommended by the restaurateur, normally more expensive than the house wine.*

---

CHEF: Martin Billingsley    PROPRIETORS: Martin and Caroline Billingsley
OPEN: Mon to Sat, D only
CLOSED: Jan and Feb
MEALS: 7 to 9.30
PRICES: Set D £14.50 (£20) to £19.50 (£25)
CARDS: Access, Visa
SEATS: 38. Private parties: 20 main room. No children under 5. Wheelchair access

---

**FRAMPTON-ON-SEVERN  Gloucestershire**                              map 2

## *Saverys*

The Green, Frampton-on-Severn GL2 7EA                    COOKING 2
GLOUCESTER (0452) 740077                                   COST £25

Idylls are created at such places as Frampton-on-Severn, with its serene houses
and mansions, its village pool, its family of swans. Saverys is an old brick
house on the green – not just any old green, but the longest in England. The
owners, John Savery and Patricia Carpenter, quit the rat-race to set up shop
here in a tiny pink-painted room with prints, plants and ruched curtains. The
blackboard menu, which changes frequently, is in the main straightforward
and British – pork and madeira terrine in Cumberland sauce; lamb with
redcurrant sauce – with some more modern dishes, such as warm salad of
chicken livers and citrus fruit, and white chocolate terrine with strawberry
coulis. Well-hung, quality meat comes from the butcher two doors away;
salmon started life in the nearby Wye or Severn and arrives at the table with
chive and butter sauce. Abundant vegetables are full of flavour and carefully
timed. And at the end of it all can come a honey and almond parfait of
'unusually intense flavour'; a trio of sorbets in fresh lime syrup; or the
ubiquitous sticky toffee pudding. The wine list is deliciously short, the bottles
are not a bad selection. House Beaujolais, £7.75; Vouvray Demi-Sec, £7.45.
CELLARMAN'S CHOICE : Lirac, Ch. St-Roch 1987, £9.20; Ch. des Annereaux
1985, £13.85. Coffee, served with complimentary chocolates, is extra
but unlimited.

CHEF/PROPRIETORS: John Savery and Patricia Carpenter
OPEN: Tue to Sat, D only
MEALS: 7 to 9.15
PRICES: Set D £15.95 (£21). Service inc
CARDS: Access, Diners, Visa
SEATS: 26. Private parties: 26 main room. No children under 12. No pipes in dining-room.
Wheelchair access. Music

---

*'We asked for the "English cheeseboard". Young waiter arrived with plate dotted about
with six bits of cheese, each one square inch in size, and a sculpted arrangement of sliced
apple and grapes. He looked dismayed when asked to bring whole cheeses on a board, and
10 minutes later head waiter appeared with basket, some fruit sculpture and freezing cold
hunks of dead Cheddar, pallid smoked Austrian, unripe French Brie, a black waxed
Culworthy and some dry Stilton. Asked for, and got, two minute slivers of Cheddar and
Culworthy, Culworthy good for nothing, Cheddar maybe could be used in a sauce. Price,
£3 each.'* On inspecting in Hampshire

---

FRESSINGFIELD  Suffolk                                    map 6

## Fox and Goose ♥

| Fressingfield IP21 5PB | COOKING 2 |
|---|---|
| FRESSINGFIELD (037 986) 247 | COST £21–£37 |

The inn was originally a 'Church house' and the freehold is still owned by the neighbouring church. A fine sixteenth-century timbered building, its historic atmosphere is perhaps less of an attraction than Adrian Clarke's cooking. He has largely stuck to his father's idea of advance orders from a menu sent out when tables are booked, which allows for a wide range of dishes – for example, haunch of venison, grouse and partridge in season – but there is now also a shorter seasonal menu for those who go on the spur of the moment. Meals are pleasantly old-fashioned with many French classics on the menu – salmon in sorrel sauce, boeuf en croûte, sweetbreads in a wine and cream mushroom sauce, quenelles, garlicky fish casserole. Dishes of buttered vegetables are left on the table and bread is home made. There may be nothing very novel in this, but it is all well cooked and well presented, with an eye for detail. Cheeses, for example, are carefully kept and come as a selection of three – perhaps Cheddar, Stilton and Camembert, or Chaumes, Old Gouda and Dolcelatte – with a small salad, grapes and apple. Rachael Clarke and a new manager, Philip Dickson, run the front of house efficiently but with many friendly touches, and the club with quarterly dinners for members and newsletters about other special evenings flourishes. The wine list is strongest on clarets. Adrian Clarke finds New World wines difficult to sell but has increased his stocks of Italian bottles – by some very good makers. The list is well annotated and some of the wines are given very helpful tasting notes. House wine is £9. CELLARMAN'S CHOICE : Ch. Les Ormes-de-Pez 1982, £21; Ch. de Rolland, Barsac 1980, £14.

CHEF: Adrian Clarke   PROPRIETORS: Adrian and Rachael Clarke
OPEN: all week, exc Tue L and D and Sun D; Sun D on bank hol weekends only
CLOSED: 2 weeks Jan to Feb, 2 weeks mid-Sept, 4 days at Christmas
MEALS: 12 to 1.30, 7 to 9
PRICES: £25 (£31), Set L and D £16 and £16.50 (£21). Snacks from £2.50. Service inc.
Licensed, also bring your own: corkage £4
CARDS: Access, Amex, Diners, Visa
SEATS: 26. Private parties: 32 main room. Car-park, 30 places. No children under 10.
No smoking

FROGHALL  Staffordshire                                   map 5

## Wharf

| Foxt Road, Froghall ST10 2HJ | |
|---|---|
| IPSTONES (0538) 266486 | COOKING 1 |
| just off A52 | COST £13–£24 |

The Caldon canal, built by James Brindley, celebrated in 1989 the tenth anniversary of its restoration by volunteer labour. The Wharf restaurant was one of the by-products of that venture; horse-drawn barges carried the curious for afternoon trips, who then needed feeding and watering. The more elaborate dinners cooked at the Wharf were just the gilt on the catering gingerbread. Julia Sargent left to look after her new baby and Mrs Young has returned to the stove in the long low warehouse that was restored at the same time as the canal. There is no disguising her vegetarian preferences and the menu includes some inventive cooking for those of a like mind as well as plenty for carnivores. One reader was struck by her skill with wholemeal pastry – never the easiest thing to handle. Experiment comes easily, with dishes like deep-fried scallops coated in cashew nuts, and crab Battenburg, a chequerboard of light and dark crab mousses wrapped in a Parmesan roulade. Sauces, perhaps with the vegetarian background exerting influence, are not merely cream and wine but also purées of fruit or vegetable. The restaurant is self-supporting in bread, sorbets and after-dinner chocolates. The wine list is short but adequate. House French is £6.70. If you get lost, look for the Wharf in the canal-side picnic area.

CHEF: J.M. Young    PROPRIETORS: R. and J. Young and M.L. St Claire
OPEN: Tue to Sat D, Sun L
MEALS: 12 to 1.30, 7.30 to 9.15
PRICES: £16 (£20), Set Sun L £9.50 (£13). Service inc
CARDS: Access, Visa
SEATS: 32. Private parties: 32 main room. Car-park, 50 places. Vegetarian meals. Children's helpings. Wheelchair access (1 step; also WC)

---

GILLINGHAM  Dorset                                                    map 2

## ▲ Stock Hill House

Wyke, Gillingham SP8 5NR                                    COOKING 3
GILLINGHAM (0747) 823626                                    COST £21–£29

There are few more enticing scenes in spring than Stock Hill and its grounds, a mile west of Gillingham. Black-faced sheep on either side of the beech avenue, a serried vegetable garden, walls, stream, fountain and broad lawns form a complex equation redolent of Charlotte M. Yonge. It is inhabited by a zither-playing Austrian chef and his wife who have furnished it with much sensitivity, a taste for colour and panache, and a great deal of labour; 'several recent improvements to décor have made the house even more attractive.' His cooking in the years since he moved from Sark seems also to have moved from Austrian baroque to a closer relationship with hedgerow, field and barn. Touches of central Europe survive: a brioche in the shape of a lamb sliced to eat with cheese, fancy rolls, swans at sweet time, mice in meringue are a few of the jeux d'esprit. Cooking duck with plums and an estimable wiener schnitzel are other indications of origin. However, produce of the garden, the fishing boat and the Dorset butchers sound nearer to home and indicate a true love of cooking 'sur place'. One reader was pleased to report 'rich sauces, strong flavours'. Venison hung for two weeks, then soaked in oil for another seven days, cream of young nettle soup – proclaimed 'excellent' – diced salmon and bream steamed in rice paper, sweetbreads wrapped in spinach and baked in strudel pastry, salmon in a sauce of Martini and fennel are well recommended from the set-price small carte (cheaper and simpler at lunchtime) with half a dozen alternatives for each course. Desserts have to be a strong point and the ample portions should be paced to take into account such enticements as dates stuffed with a chocolate mousse in a coffee sauce, an Austrian chocolate torte, prunes marinated in alcohol and served with a cinnamon ice-cream. There are also good cheeses, which arrive with good walnut bread, then good coffee and petits fours, including animals in meringue. The wine list is a judicious short selection of French bottles. With Yapp Brothers so near, it is strongest on Rhône and Loire (though note the two Austrian choices); it only touches the surface of the complexities of these regions however. House Gamay de L'Ardèche and Muscadet are £6.95. CELLARMAN'S CHOICE : Gigondas, Domaine St-Gayan 1983, £12.80; Cassis, Clos Ste-Magdeleine 1986, £9.75.

CHEF: Peter Hauser    PROPRIETORS: Peter and Nita Hauser
OPEN: Tues to Sun, exc Sat L and Sun D
MEALS: 12.30 to 1.45, 7.30 to 8.45
PRICES: Set L £16 (£21), Set D £22 (£24)
CARDS: Access, Visa
SEATS: 26. Private parties: 12 main room, 12 private room. Car-park, 25 places. Children's helpings (L only). No children under 7. Smart dress preferred. No smoking in dining-room
ACCOMMODATION: 7 rooms, all with bath/shower. B&B £65. No children under 7. Afternoon teas. Garden. TV. Phone. Scenic. Doors close at 12. Confirm by 8 [GHG]

---

GLASTONBURY  Somerset                                             map 2

## ▲ Number 3

Magdalene Street, Glastonbury BA6 9EW                    COOKING 1
GLASTONBURY (0458) 32129                                   COST £36

Not far from the abbey stands this Georgian house, shielded from fierce light by trees and ivy. Behind is a romantically wild town garden, interplanted with culinary herbs. The dining-rooms and sitting-room are strongly coloured and vibrantly decorated: raspberry red and floral prints. It is spotlessly clean. The waiting and the wine is John Tynan's province. He rules it with enthusiasm and pride. Ann Tynan learned her cooking in Scotland. It, and the service, is formal. It also makes use of excellent materials. The elaborate descriptions on the menu, 'A taste of the sea: usually produces crab, prawns and scallops meeting together in a little pastry pot and served with lobster sauce,' may accurately reflect some of the cooking style. There is quite a lot of cream, fruit comes up in too many first courses, the desserts are heavy. Dishes do, however, taste very pleasant. A salmon in filo pastry was cooked too long but its creamy shellfish sauce proved a good sweetish foil. Lamb rolled in a herb and mustard crust was timed correctly and the meat proved superlative. Vegetables have been spankingly fresh and exactly cooked. Addicts of rich chocolate are well served by the chocolate truffle terrine. The kitchen improves year by year and the intentions are the right ones. 'This is the first time in months that as soon as I got in I did not have something to settle my stomach,' wrote a travelling hotelier. There is an album of a wine list. House French is £8.50.

---

*'What a change of attitude up here to good food! Even the prawn cocktail, (well-done) steak Diane, and Black Forest gateau set are beginning to want something more, and more places are stretching to meet the demand at every level.'*  A Scottish inspector

CHEF: Ann Tynan   PROPRIETORS: John and Ann Tynan
OPEN: Tue to Sat, D only
CLOSED: Jan
MEALS: 7 to 9.15
PRICES: Set D £22 (£30)
CARDS: Amex, Visa
SEATS: 28. 2 tables outside. Private parties: 12 main room. Car-park, 8 places. Children's
helpings on request. No children under 5. Smart dress preferred. No smoking
ACCOMMODATION: 3 rooms, all with bath/shower. B&B £38 to £50. No children under 2.
Garden. TV. Phone. Scenic. Doors close at 11.30. Confirm by 6

---

**GLEMSFORD  Suffolk**                                                        map 3

## Barretts  ♥

31 Egremont Street, Glemsford CO10 7SA                         COOKING  3
GLEMSFORD (0787) 281573                                        COST  £15–£31

Once a shop, now a double-fronted small restaurant with a sitting-room and
dining-room on either side of the entrance. Proceedings are directed by Diane
Barrett who, French patronne-like, has a generalissima's vantage point at a
desk unless greeting, serving or genially talking. The predominant tone is
apricot, the ambience is restrained; neither is enlivened by the pictures nor the
usually subdued level of human converse. Small restaurants may have that
effect. Nicholas Barrett's menu is eclectic: a pastry case of crab with spring
onion and ginger; a tomato and basil consommé; and prawns with a curry
sauce. Main courses, like beef fillet with caramelised mushrooms and a port
and stock reduction, are plainer, though fantasy has its extravagant reign with
grilled sea-bass and a caviare butter sauce. Vegetables are substituted by salad
if you so wish. Soufflés at the end of the meal continue to be well reported: a
hot almond soufflé was well supported by a vanilla ice-cream and a fragrant
raspberry coulis. A white chocolate parfait was not so enjoyed: but who can
make white chocolate taste of more than the most vulgar confectionery? It
should be banned. For a possible £30 a head, details should be better. Bought
bread, packet orange juice, crisps with aperitifs are not marks of quality. The
wine list, out of Lay & Wheeler, is nicely chosen and fairly priced, with a good
selection of half-bottles. Ch. Pétrus 1970 at £295 is a bargain, improbable as it
may seem. There is plenty under £10, including a Lungarotti 1986 Chardonnay
and a Mâcon Viré Les Donzelles 1986. House wines from the Plaimont
cooperative, £6.50. CELLARMAN'S CHOICE : Australian Robson Chardonnay
1986, £13.95; Cabernet Sauvignon Reserve 1982, Simi, £16.95.

---

CHEF: Nicholas Barrett   PROPRIETORS: Nicholas and Diane Barrett
OPEN: Tue to Sat, D only, and Sun L
MEALS: 12 to 2, 7 to 9.30
PRICES: £22 (£26), Set L £11.95 (£15) and £12.95 (£16). Service inc
CARDS: Access, Visa
SEATS: 18. Private parties: 12 main room. Car-park, 10 places. Children's helpings (Sun L
only). Wheelchair access

GLOUCESTER  Gloucestershire                                      map 2

## College Green

| 9 College Street, Gloucester GL1 2NE | COOKING 1 |
|---|---|
| GLOUCESTER (0452) 20739 | COST £13–£23 |

On the first floor of a half-timbered building with fine views of the cathedral,
its floors so steeply sloping that a child might slide down them, this bistro
continues its way unchanging from year to year. David Spencer's menu and
repertoire do not change greatly either, but please lunch customers for skate or
a casserole of beef, or evening diners who enjoy his essays in modern British
cooking: lambs' kidneys with raspberry and port; duck with apricot sauce;
pork with blue cheese; monkfish with garlic sauce. The wine list may seem
unpretentious but it contains some decent choices. Mr Spencer has selected
mostly good produce from good merchants, and prices are sensibly in keeping
with the style of the place. House wine is £6.25. CELLARMAN'S CHOICE : Côtes
du Rhône Blanc, Domaine St-Gayan 1986, £7.95; Bandol, Mas de la Rouvière
1982, £11.95.

CHEF: David Spencer  PROPRIETORS: David and Frances Spencer
OPEN: Mon to Sat, exc Mon and Tue D
CLOSED: bank hols
MEALS: 12 to 2, 6.30 to 9.30
PRICES: £15 (£19), Set L £8.50 (£13) to £12 (£16). Service inc. Licensed, also bring your
own: corkage £3
CARDS: Access, Amex, Visa
SEATS: 30. Private parties: 44 main room, 30 private room. Children's helpings

GOLCAR  West Yorkshire                                           map 5

## Weavers Shed

| Knowl Road, Golcar HD7 4AN | COOKING 1 |
|---|---|
| HUDDERSFIELD (0484) 654284 | COST £17–£28 |

Peter McGunnigle's brother, Ian, has joined him in the kitchen to allow a
greater choice and to beef up the standard of first and last courses in this
converted eighteenth-century stone cloth-mill that is 'still cold in temperature
but warm in welcome'. Catherine McGunnigle and her helpers attend the
customers at the front of the house in true Yorkshire style. The Gallery has been
given a new roof, which affords extra room for dining: another reason for
increasing the brigade. Ambitions are certainly higher: there is a move to more
luxurious ingredients, such as wild mushrooms, truffles and foie gras, as may
be observed in hundreds of similar places. It is not necessarily to be applauded
– the Weavers Shed had rather a good British repertoire in the first instance –
but it may give chefs stimulus to experiment and improve. The regularly
changing menu offers four courses (the second is soup or sorbet) at fair prices,
and praise has been given to the venison with wild mushrooms in a port wine
sauce and the sticky-toffee pudding – showing the Sharrow Bay influence to
the last. Sharrow Bay would not approve however the clumsiness of some of
the puddings, nor the poor vegetable cookery that has been reported. Good
British cheeses are listed carefully on the desserts card, as are three sweet wines

by the glass. Breads are enterprising and home baked. The wine list is short, sensible and astute, with a fair range taking in a Chilean Chardonnay from Cousiño Macul as well as more expected French, Australian and US wines. House wine is French, £5.95. CELLARMAN'S CHOICE : Pulham Magdalen Rivaner 1985, £7.95; Montana Marlborough Chardonnay 1987, £10.85.

CHEFS: Peter McGunnigle and Ian McGunnigle   PROPRIETORS: Peter and Catherine McGunnigle
OPEN: Tue to Sat, exc Sat L
CLOSED: first 2 weeks Jan, last 2 weeks July
MEALS: 12 to 2, 7 to 9 (9.15 Sat)
PRICES: L £10 (£17), D £16 (£23)
CARDS: Access, Amex, Visa
SEATS: 70. Private parties: 40 main room, 30 private room. Car-park, 40 places. Children welcome. Smart dress preferred

---

**GOOSNARGH** Lancashire                                                        map 5

## Solo

Goosnargh Lane, Goosnargh PR3 2BD                              COOKING 1
BROUGHTON (0772) 865206                                         COST £14–£26

Now brightly redecorated and the potholes covered in the car-park, this family-run restaurant a hundred yards from the village green continues in its way of steaks, veal and salmon with daily or weekly extras such as baby squid with garlic and tomato, good fish soup, crab and lobster minimally garnished with salads or oysters. Other substantial main dishes, for instance the speciality of ox-tongue with salsa verde, come with vegetables the reverse of simple: agrodolce onions, cabbage with garlic or paprika, battered cauliflower. House wine is £7.20 a litre.

CHEFS: Rafaele Arrellaro and Simon Eastham   PROPRIETORS: Vincent and Susan Villa
OPEN: all week D, plus Thur, Fri and Sun L
CLOSED: 26 Dec
MEALS: 12 to 2, 7 to 10
PRICES: £15 (£22), Set Sun L £8.25 (£14)
CARDS: Access, Carte Blanche, Visa
SEATS: 48. Private parties: 50 main room. Car-park, 50 places. Children welcome. No cigars in dining-room. Wheelchair access (also WC). Music

---

**GORING-ON-THAMES** Oxfordshire                                        map 2

## Leatherne Bottel

Goring-on-Thames RG8 0HS                                       COOKING 1
HENLEY (0491) 872667                                            COST £26

The spelling may worry, as will the steep approach (when common cars have to be manoeuvred dangerously close to tens of thousands of pounds worth of executive coachwork), but the view, and the food, may dispel dark clouds. Keith Read was last heard of at Read's in Old Brompton Road. His and Annie

Bonnet's purchase of this pub bodes well for riverside eating. So far the food is light, herby and fresh. Reports are not sure how far it has settled down, but it is not expensive by Home Counties standards and the wine list, though short, is unusual. The charcoal grill is made to work hard; a vegetarian salad of avocado, fresh basil and olives, and a lettuce and borage soup whose flavour was extended by lemon have been reported favourably. House wine, £6.50.

CHEF: Keith Read   PROPRIETORS: Keith Read, Annie Bonnet and Roger Kingsmill
OPEN: all week
CLOSED: 25 Dec
MEALS: 12 to 2.30, 6.30 to 10 (7.30 to 9.30 Sun)
PRICES: £16 (£22)
CARD: Amex
SEATS: 45. 15 tables outside. Private parties: 20 main room. Car-park, 60 places. No pipes in dining-room. Wheelchair access

---

**GRAMPOUND  Cornwall**                                                    map 1

## Eastern Promise

1 Moor View, Grampound TR2 4RT                                   COOKING 2
ST AUSTELL (0726) 883033                                         COST £19–£34

Grampound is a handsome village strung along the high road to Truro. Once coaching was its *raison d'être*; now it seems to be antique shops. Unlikely spot, then, for a Chinese restaurant – perhaps catching trade in equal proportion from Truro and St Austell. Sizzling dishes remain the high spot of the repertoire but crab and lobster with black-bean sauce can be had if ordered in advance, or there's crispy aromatic duck. A short wine list –better than many such restaurants, and others – includes five Chinese wines, two sakes, Chinese liqueurs and Tsing Tao beer. French house wine, £5.20.

CHEF: Liza Tse   PROPRIETOR: Philip Tse
OPEN: Mon to Sun, exc Wed, D only
MEALS: 6 to 11
PRICES: £19 (£28), Set D £13.50 (£19)
CARDS: Access, Amex, Diners, Visa
SEATS: 40. Private parties: 24 private room. Car-park, 8 places. No children under 3. Music

---

**GRASMERE  Cumbria**                                                      map 7

## ▲ Michael's Nook

Grasmere LA22 9RP                                                 COOKING 2
GRASMERE (096 65) 496                                            COST £27–£43

The poetic connotations of the name, and the name itself, may lead you to expect something quaint: not a bit of it. This is a substantial house, not a Lakeland cottage. You reach it from the A591, just north of Grasmere; it is set on the side of a hill, behind the Swan Hotel. Though stuffed with smart gentility, it has a slightly faded air, but there is every reason to think this is by design. To its advantage is a lack of ornate pretension. A good place to relax; but messages about whether a good place to eat are very mixed. The daily menu begins with a recommended selection and then lists alternatives. It is worth noting that one reader, after trying things from each half, reckoned the chef's choice was decidedly inferior. Meals have elicited this sort of comment: the menu promised more than the palate detected, flavours were muted, the enterprise vitiated by compromise. Good things have been eaten, however: a quail and pigeon salad to start, a well-hung Gressingham duck served with a light stock sauce and exotic fruits, a pungent fillet of pork with Stilton sauce. The cheeses are British and a good range, impressive but on one occasion found too mild. An inspector felt the restaurant had possibilities but was resting on laurels of long service and easy pickings from tourists. The staff receive similarly contradictory notices, described on the one hand as excessively courteous, even over-solicitous if the night is quiet and there are too few customers to occupy them; on the other, slow and inadequate. The wine list fits the bill as a classic gentleman's cellar, French in origin. Burgundies depend unhealthily on the skills of Louis Latour and there are too many alternate vintages. CELLARMAN'S CHOICE : Caillou Blanc du Château Talbot 1985, £10.50; Vosne-Romanée 1978, Latour, £26.50.

CHEF: Heinz Nagler   PROPRIETOR: Reg Gifford
OPEN: all week
MEALS: 12.30 to 1, 7.30 to 8 (7 to 9.15 Sat D)
PRICES: Set L £21 (£27), Set D £29.50 (£36)
CARDS: Amex, Diners
SEATS: 45. Private parties: 35 main room. Car-park, 20 places. Children's helpings by arrangement. No children under 12. Smart dress preferred. No smoking
ACCOMMODATION: 11 rooms, all with bath/shower. B&B £88 to £128. Garden. Fishing. Golf. TV. Phone. Scenic. Doors close at 11.30

## ▲ White Moss House 🍾

Rydal Water, Grasmere LA22 9SE                    COOKING 4
GRASMERE (096 65) 295                                   COST £36

One couple take a few days every year at White Moss House, once owned by Wordsworth and a remarkably handsome 'cottage'. They have been doing this for years, staying in Brockstone, a dependent cottage (200 feet above the main house), having all the advantages of peace and isolation spiced with pleasing anticipation of a fine dinner served at 8 sharp. It is refreshing that Susan and Peter Dixon no longer insist on the exclusion of children nor on smart dress. The House 'is as formal or as informal as the guests wish to make it'; the sense of hospitality here is very strong indeed. Peter Dixon's cooking has always been characterised as 'British' and he makes an effortless virtue of first-rate supplies and an avoidance of whimsy. It is not exactly traditional British, 'escalope of salmon poached in white burgundy with eight-leaf salad and rose petal dressing, asparagus and sorrel sauce' is never old fashioned; nor is stir-frying green and yellow courgette balls in walnut oil. But nor is it French, nor wild and outrageous. The repertoire may change a little over the years (though the form of the set meal does not), but there is a very strong continuity. There are also points of similarity and a sense of community with other Lakeland hotels. Regular visitors will be assured of their favourite dishes reappearing often enough. This is not a criticism: the cooking is thoughtful and considered.

Careful treatment and purchase of meats is one hallmark: 'our chicken had been hung as if it were game, this caused disagreement' – but not disgust. Another is strong, pronounced sauces or accompaniments: port, plum and Pinot Noir with crispy duck, or fine apple and mint jelly that almost overpowered the venison. Puddings allow the diner a choice, as does the immaculate English cheeseboard. Always there is a traditional pudding: Kentish well (Sussex pond), bread-and-butter, guardsman's; and usually a sorbet – pink Champagne is very popular. Soups start the meal: celeriac and fennel, 'quite, quite exquisite, two haunting tastes that made a perfect blend'; wild mushroom, marjoram and marsala, 'the delicate taste of the fungus went well with the herb and the wine gave a pleasing caramel finish.' A cook of real quality; and Susan Dixon is always there to gently distribute or to explain. Would that more people could enjoy the fruits of their labours. For some, the reason for a visit is the wine list. Again, this is always improving. Its annotations are sane, its range is satisfactory, the choices are delectable and the prices very fair indeed. The clarets have to be the high point, going back to 1961, but there are wines to ponder from every country, even if only two Italian reds. It is wisest to take Peter Dixon's advice: his eye for quality and his lack of rapaciousness make it reliable. House wines start at £7 for a litre but there are many, and changing, offers by the glass to accompany the meal. The Dixons will not be drawn to a CELLARMAN'S CHOICE, merely observing that there are many half-bottles and that a number of their wines are offered below replacement cost – 1961 clarets, for example.

CHEF: Peter Dixon   PROPRIETORS: Susan and Peter Dixon
OPEN: Mon to Sat, D only
CLOSED: mid-Nov to mid-Mar
MEALS: 8
PRICES: Set D £19.95 (£30)
SEATS: 18. 18 tables outside. Private parties: 18 main room. Car-park, 10 places. Children welcome. No smoking. Wheelchair access. One sitting
ACCOMMODATION: 7 rooms, all with bath/shower. B&B £58. Garden. Fishing. TV. Phone. Scenic. Doors close at 11. Confirm by 4 [GHG]

---

**GRAYSHOTT  Hampshire**                                              map 2

## Woods

Headley Road, Grayshott GU26 6LB                          COOKING 2
HINDHEAD (042 873) 5555                                      COST £36

Almost the first shop in Hampshire, once a butcher's, but now a restaurant – all tiles, pine, white tablecloths, shining silver. Eric Norrgren's skills as a chef, and as a pâtissier, too, have never been doubted. He continues to produce food that has a steady local following. Although there are a couple of things that pay homage to a Scandinavian background – gravlax and matjes herrings – the menu is standard modern fare: tomato and basil soup; timbale of asparagus spears and leeks; fillet of beef with a sauce of wild mushrooms and vin jaune; a tulip of apple sorbet and poached apples; a fine chocolate truffle cake. The language of the menu has refreshingly moved from French to English this year. Service can occasionally leave much to be desired. One couple was shocked at the youth of Mr and Mrs Norrgren's offspring, clearing tables in their nightclothes. The wine list is short and sharp; there is a nice white Lirac, La Fermade 1985 from Maby, and a Givry 1983 from Baron Thénard. House French is £6.20.

CHEF: Eric Norrgren   PROPRIETORS: Eric and Dana Norrgren
OPEN: Tue to Sat, D only
MEALS: 7 to 10.30
PRICES: £21 (£30)
CARDS: Access, Amex, Diners, Visa
SEATS: 35. Private parties: 12 main room. Children's helpings. Wheelchair access (also WC)

---

**GREAT DUNMOW  Essex**                                      map 3

## Starr 🍷

| | |
|---|---|
| Market Place, Great Dunmow CM6 1AX | COOKING 1 |
| GREAT DUNMOW (0371) 874321 | COST £22−£47 |

Inside reveals more of the half-timbered original than does the exterior, although both have character. The theme is emphatically that of English country restaurant. Visitors may be surprised at the display and talking-through of the large blackboards that serve as menus. This cannot be avoided, though some may prefer to be left alone. Prices are set and inclusive (though not of service) and are cheaper for lunch as well as on Wednesday nights, when the kitchen offers a Billingsgate menu after shopping for fish. Nearly half the principal menu consists of fish dishes: crab with pink grapefruit and mint mayonnaise; avocado with a walnut dressing and fresh anchovies; shrimps and strips of smoked salmon and trout; paupiettes of lemon sole with crab and saffron; turbot with Dublin Bay prawns and fennel, or just plain Dover sole. Meat dishes have not been badly reported: duck breast with orange and raisin sauce was properly cooked and the sauce was sufficiently restrained not to crowd out the flavour of the meat. Puddings have been less successful. All this comes for a lot of money; too much in some people's eyes. The raw materials are good but assembled with little conviction for the preeminence of flavour. The wine list is a romp through Lay & Wheeler's stock: who better? It is informative, the prices are not greedy, there are a few Australian bottles to bolster the mainly French selection and 20 useful half-bottles. A 1987 Chinon, Les Gravières from Couly-Dutheil is an interesting choice from the Loire, good value at £9 odd, and was very well treated in the serving and delivered that 'earthy flavour of mulberries and bilberries'. If you need to bed down, there will be eight new rooms in the stables behind. House Beaujolais and claret, £9.50. CELLARMAN'S CHOICE : Chardonnay, Brokenbach Vineyard 1987, Rothbury Estate, £10.25.

---

*All letters to the* Guide *are acknowledged with an update on latest sales, closures, chef changes and so on.*

*On 6 May 1990 all London telephone numbers will change, the 01- prefix being replaced by either 071- or 081-. See the front of the* Guide *for a list of which numbers will take which prefix.*

---

CHEF: Mark Fisher  PROPRIETORS: Mr and Mrs B. Jones
OPEN: all week, exc Sat L and Sun D
CLOSED: 3 weeks mid-Aug, 2 weeks at Christmas
MEALS: 12 to 1.30, 7 to 10
PRICES: Set L £15 (£22) to £16.50 (£25), Set D £15 (£22) to £30 (£39), Snacks from £2.50.
Service 10%
CARDS: Access, Diners, Visa
SEATS: 60. Private parties: 8 main room, 12 and 30 private room. Car-park, 15 places.
Children's helpings. Wheelchair access (also WC). Music

---

## GREAT GONERBY  Lincolnshire                                          map 6

# Harry's Place

17 High Street, Great Gonerby NG31 8JS                          COOKING 3
GRANTHAM (0476) 61780                                               COST £40

The Hallams started in the centre of Grantham, but have found a more suitably
formal setting in a Georgian house in a village outside the town, just off the A1.
Their approach is particular and strict: no more than 10 people at one time,
reservations only, strict injunctions to arrive on time and minimal stripped
pine décor to throw all attention on to Harry's cooking. This, together with an
air of correct formality, can produce a strained atmosphere in the two small
dining-rooms. 'Their model is Nico Ladenis and they seem to have the same
attitude towards their customers as he is reported to have.' Even those who find
this off-putting have been sufficiently impressed to return. It is not the menu
which makes meals memorable – the half dozen choices for each course could
be found in many French restaurants, merely nod towards seasonality and
change very slowly – but the judgement and quality coming from the
seriousness of intent, which shows in dishes of all kinds. In a breast of chicken
baked with tarragon, basil, olive oil, tomatoes and Bayonne ham, each of the
simple, strong tastes stood out clearly against a lightly cooked tomato concasse
and *jus* accented by Pernod. A fillet of sea trout had a finely balanced wine,
butter and cream sauce. Among first courses, chicken livers sauté with cognac
and herbs till dark and slightly crisp on the outside but pink and moist on the
inside, and a crab mousse without a hint of blandness have pleased mightily.
Vegetables may perhaps include a small green mound of asparagus tips mixed
with fine beans and mange-tout, a pastry boat of turnip and celeriac purée, a
miniature gratin dauphinoise and carrot batons with fresh coriander. Cheeses
are unusual, including Manchego and Epoisses, and the largely French desserts
– mille-feuille, crème brûlée, chocolate mousse and so on – call forth
superlatives. 'Vanilla ice-cream, which was the best I have tasted, was served
with a spoonful of strawberry sauce.' 'Harry's bread-and-butter pudding is out
of this world.' With all this in mind, it can only be the prices, merited perhaps
but very steep for this area, which leave tables empty. The wine list is very
short indeed and mixes French, German, Spanish and Italian in a collection of
19 bottles. It cannot help but be unbalanced, but it is a courageous attempt at
not being forced into dreadful mediocrity while resisting too large a capital
investment. CELLARMAN'S CHOICE : Blanc-Fumé de Pouilly 1987, Figeat,
£12.75; Protos Gran Reserva 1976, Ribera del Duero, £35.

CHEF: Harry Hallam    PROPRIETORS: Harry and Caroline Hallam
OPEN: Tue to Sat
CLOSED: 25 Dec, bank hols
MEALS: 12.30 to 2, 7 to 9.30
PRICES: £25 (£33)
CARD: Access
SEATS: 10. Private parties: 10 main room, 4 private room. Car-park, 4 places. Children's
helpings on request. No smoking

---

**GREAT MILTON   Oxfordshire**                                              map 2

# ▲ Le Manoir aux Quat'Saisons ?

Church Road, Great Milton OX9 7PD                              COOKING 5
GREAT MILTON (0844) 278881/2/3                                 COST £35−£85

The more indigent may begrudge the price of a meal here but it would be
churlish to deny that M. Blanc seems to apply his effort and thought to better
end than almost any chef now working in England. You pay, therefore, for the
best and often you get something close to it. It is unfortunate that the best has to
wrap itself in such expensive surroundings, when the food would be as
eloquent in a village hall, but that is the way of the world. The Manoir lies in a
barely perceptible hollow on Milton Common, part of a wide (almost
continental) plain that extends south and east of Oxford. Approaching the calm
dignity of the Manoir gates, one reader was struck with flashback to a scene at a
nearby roadhouse 30 years ago. He had repaired to his first solo dinner dance:
properly dressed and anxious to impress. That first gay night, he drank Mateus
Rosé. Times change. The buildings at Great Milton are preternaturally English:
a nest of church, house and barns in honeyed stone, the tone dappled by green
of lawn and tree, deepened by brown of earth. High stone walls protect from
the Ural-blast that sweeps across the Common. Inside is less impressive. Done
over in French restaurant designerese, comfortable but full of bad art, the
dining-room is oppressive, low, heavily beamed, with little aspect and
unsuited to the food it serves. A second room is better but too small. Pink is the
dominant colour and the table settings are refined and pleasing. Best of all is
lunch outside on a summer's day. The bedrooms, say all, are crackers for luxury
and forethought, if not view. It seems to strike few people as strange that this
vessel should be brimfull with French. If an English traveller were to drive out
of Florence to a Renaissance palace and find there a French restaurant from
food, to staff, even to the signs on the lavatories she or he would pronounce it
surreal. Why not here? Approval, even gratitude, is the sense of the chorus of
letters received at the *Guide*'s offices. Cross the threshold, sit in the lounge with
drinks and tip-top appetisers showing an example of each branch of the
pâtissier's work − a croissant, a choux bun, a sablé, a straw, a croûton − and
read the menu. Its design is witty and an improvement on most British
offerings: three pages of printed fare, changing with the seasons, one page of
type-written specialities, a *menu gourmand* and a daily menu of two or three
choices at a set price. The English translations are notable for their poor
spelling and grammar and florid prose. The repertoire will be familiar to

anyone who saw Raymond Blanc on TV's *Take Six Cooks*, or has read *Recipes from Le Manoir aux Quat'Saisons*. This last may prove the vade-mecum to English catering of a certain level for the next five years. On a base of *grande cuisine* and the modern French love of tinkering with bourgeois cooking, coupled to a determination to extract the best materials from his environment, M. Blanc has erected a tower of immense invention and delight. The consistency of his production seems radically improved this year and it remains studded with brilliant diamonds. One of these was a mille-feuille de confit de canard where he sandwiched the duck between brittle layers of shredded potato, 'the smokey and gamey' duck put into relief by a salad dressed with walnut oil, the whole a complex of differing flavours and textures. At the main course stage, he seems to have loosened his approach to saucing. One reader detects fuller and more robust flavours, in greater quantity. Thus a grilled fillet of brill has a 'medium-weight sauce based on chicken stock and accented by miniature onions, rosemary and lardons', powerful tastes which the fish just managed to keep in check. A dessert of exemplary wit is the café crème. A demi-tasse and saucer are fashioned (separately) out of finest chocolate and refrigerated. The cup is filled with some of the best bitter coffee ice-cream and given a cappuccino top of a spume of sabayon sprinkled with chocolate. The recipient of this is constrained to smile and savour to the end of the meal – what a delight! The *menu gourmand* takes a whole table through a range of favourites. In previous years, this has not been adjudged the best way of testing the field but it has received more praise this year. An assiette apéritive that may be a dulcet mousse of red peppers sharpened by a concasse of fresh tomato starts proceedings that run through a ballotine of foie gras with a salad of French beans dressed with truffle oil; tagliatelle sprinkled with fresh truffles sauced with a rosemary cream of infinitely subtle flavour; a pavé of warm smoked salmon; pink grapefruit and champagne sorbet; a breast of Barbary duck with port and a quince relish; to end with trois petits bonheurs du Manoir, a portmanteau description of a composite dessert changing according whim and supplies. Petits fours are as carefully thought out as the appetisers, the fruit ones the best. The bread is among the best in England for eating with restaurant food, the crust perfect, the dough a balance between the insipid and the too demonstrative. The coffee is very strong. Service is very young for such a fine restaurant. It has not, however, come in for as much criticism as in previous years. The d'Artagnan-style sommelier is impressive and helpful. You need guidance if your wallet is not bulging. However, the selection of growers is very good even if the prices are high. The country wines are the ones to pursue: Arbois from the Jura, a Côtes de Buzet or a Côtes du Frontonnais. House Sancerre from Delaporte, red and white, £18.50. CELLARMAN'S CHOICE : Chignin Bergeron 1987, Savoie, Quenard, £16.80; Bourgogne Pinot Noir 1985, Regis Rossignol-Changarnier, £22.

---

*See the back of the* Guide *for an index of restaurants listed.*

*All details are as accurate as possible at the time of going to press, but chefs and owners often change, and it is wise to check by telephone before making a special journey. Many readers have been disappointed when set-price bargain meals are no longer available. Ask when booking.*

---

CHEF: Raymond Blanc  PROPRIETORS: Blanc Restaurants Ltd
OPEN: Tue to Sun, exc Tue L
CLOSED: 4 weeks from 22 Dec
MEALS: 12.15 to 2.30, 7.15 to 10.30
PRICES: £53 (£71), Set L £23 (£35) to £48 (£60), Set D £48 (£60). Service inc
CARDS: Access, Amex, Diners, Visa
SEATS: 70. 4 tables outside. Private parties: 10 main room, 45 private room. Car-park, 45
places. Vegetarian meals. Children's helpings. Smart dress preferred. No smoking.
Wheelchair access (also WC)
ACCOMMODATION: 10 rooms, all with bath/shower. B&B £150 to £300. Deposit: £100. No
children under 7. Baby facilities. Pets welcome. Garden. Swimming-pool. Tennis. TV.
Phone. Scenic [GHG]

---

**GREAT YARMOUTH  Norfolk**                                           map 6

## *Seafood Restaurant*

| | |
|---|---|
| 85 North Quay, Great Yarmouth NR30 1JF | COOKING 2 |
| GREAT YARMOUTH (0493) 856009 | COST £36 |

Pick the fish that takes your fancy from slab or tank in this Greek-run
restaurant, near the station. While your chosen specimen is cooking, there are
over 30 fishy beginnings to toy with. The dozen or more 'fish of the day', fresh
from Lowestoft, are offered grilled, poached, batter-fried or cooked in a variety
of 'saucey dishes'. Shellfish get classic treatments, as in lobster thermidor or
scallops Newburg. Steaks and Stroganoff are the only possibilities for meat
lovers. Although the style is predominantly French, the owners' national
influence gets a toehold with Feta salad, taramosalata, 'boulabais' (Greek
bouillabaisse, which bears very little resemblance to its Massilian original) and
'good Greek coffee in large cups'. The wine list is unexpectedly long and
mostly French. However there are three Cypriot wines to choose from,
adequate half-bottles and sufficient Germans to give variety to the selection.
House French is £7.50 a litre. CELLARMAN'S CHOICE : Bourgogne Aligoté 1987,
£9.50; Traben-Trarbacher Krauterhaus Riesling Kabinett Halbtrocken 1986,
Haussmann, £9.80.

---

CHEF: Mark Chrisostomou  PROPRIETORS: Christopher and Miriam Kikis
OPEN: Mon to Sat, exc Sat L
MEALS: 12 to 2, 7 to 10.45
PRICES: £20 (£30)
CARDS: Access, Amex, Diners, Visa
SEATS: 40. Private parties: 40 main room. Children's helpings. Smart dress preferred. Music

---

*This year, in quoting prices for three-course meals at the top of each entry (by the word
'Cost'), we have put a more pessimistic complexion on the upper price by inflating it by 20
per cent. The aim is to prepare the reader for any inflation during the life of the* Guide *and
also reflect the price of a meal taken without constant attention to the likely size of the bill.
The prices quoted in smaller print below the text remain, as in previous editions, strict
computer calculations of an average three-course meal, the price in brackets reflecting an
average meal with coffee, service and half a bottle of house wine per person.*

GRIMSTON   Norfolk                                                    map 6

# ▲ Congham Hall

Lynn Road, Grimston PE32 1AH                              COOKING 3
HILLINGTON (0485) 600250                                  COST £14–£47

The Hall is a low Italianate villa, in the style of John Nash, with intersecting
cubes and deep eaves against the autumn rains. Clive Jackson has taken over
the cooking for the now larger dining-room – an 'orangery' extension has
made it half as large again. There is a continued emphasis on local produce and
modernistic cooking exemplified by the local goats' cheese on the cheeseboard,
the new herb garden now cropping strongly, and dishes such as medallions of
beef with a sweet chilli relish and a lime cream on a châteaubriand sauce. In
truth, not everything is as daring, even outlandish, as that sounds. Some
readers have even suggested the sauces generally need deepening and
rendering more distinct one from the other. However, most are agreed that
mistakes are rare and much is truly excellent, 'I'd kill for that brioche with wild
mushrooms and truffle.' Good reports, for instance during an early summer
weekend stay, have come in for: beef with a herb crust, white wine and tomato;
well-cooked Gressingham duck, tasting better than if cooked too pink; quail
stuffed with pistachios in a madeira sauce with grapes; first-rate cheese; for
instance a Chaource, Stilton, Brie; blackcurrant parfait with vanilla sauce. A
pianist plays on Saturday nights. Herbs from the garden figure in many things
and guests are told this fairly regularly; the honey is also home made. There is a
set-price *carte* and a six-course *menu gourmand* changing twice a week and called
'Hobson's Choice'. Sunday lunch is very much cheaper for a more traditional
menu. The wines have a great dependency on Jaboulet-Vercherre for
burgundies but there are some good Italians to compensate. House Côtes du
Rhône and Muscadet are £7.75. CELLARMAN'S CHOICE : Ch. Fourcas Hosten
1983, £21.50; dessert wine, Anjou Moulin Touchais 1979, £20. Children are
welcome in the restaurant though they cannot stay under age 12.

CHEF: Clive Jackson   PROPRIETORS: T.C. and C.K. Forecast
OPEN: all week, exc Sat L
MEALS: 12.30 to 2, 7.30 to 9.30
PRICES: Set L £8.50 (£14) to £12.50 (£18), Set D £25 (£32) to £32 (£39), Snacks £2
CARDS: Access, Amex, Diners, Visa
SEATS: 50. Private parties: 8 main room; 12 private room. Car-park, 50 places. Children
welcome. Smart dress preferred. No smoking. Wheelchair access (also WC)
ACCOMMODATION: 11 rooms, all with bath/shower. B&B £65 to £85. No children under 12.
Garden. Swimming-pool. Tennis. TV. Phone. Scenic. Doors close at 11.30. Confirm by 6
[GHG]

*The Guide relies on feedback from its readers. Especially welcome are reports on new
restaurants appearing in the book for the first time.*

*If you see a certificate in a restaurant bearing the words 'Diploma of Merit. The Good Food
Guide (United Kingdom)', the claim is false (and the restaurant may be in contempt of
court in displaying it) – see the Introduction. Please write and tell us the name and address
of the restaurant.*

**GUILDFORD  Surrey**                                   map 3

## *Rumwong*

16–18 London Road, Guildford GU1 2AF                COOKING **2**
GUILDFORD (0483) 36092                                COST £15–£20

Supple diners can eat their Thai dinner from low tables while reclining on cushions in the Khan Tok Room. If that doesn't appeal, withdraw to the à la carte room to study the 100-dish menu. Satay is ever popular, also golden-thread fish topped with pickled plum, ginger and spring onion, squid in fish sauce and garlic and beef with mushroom. There are soups and salads as well as curries and all manner of fried dishes flavoured with fresh herbs. Desserts and other sweets do not light fires of enthusiasm. For a quick lunch or supper, there's a list of noodle- or rice-based dishes, each of which is a complete meal in itself. The wine list seems to include much that is unavailable, but the prices are far from greedy. There are 17 cocktails and the house French wine is £6.60 a litre. Otherwise, there's Singapore beer.

CHEF: Keow Sae Lao   PROPRIETORS: Wanjai and Lumyai Poonum
OPEN: Tue to Sun
CLOSED: 2 to 15 Aug
MEALS: 12 to 2.30, 6 to 10.45 (10.30 Sun)
PRICES: £8 (£16), Set L £10 (£15), Set D £12.50 (£17). Service 10%
CARDS: Access, Visa
SEATS: 100. Private parties: 70 main room, 30 private room. Children's helpings. Smart dress preferred. Wheelchair access. Music. Air-conditioned

---

**GUISELEY  West Yorkshire**                           map 5

## *Harry Ramsden's*

White Cross, Guiseley LS20 8LZ                       COOKING **1**
GUISELEY (0943) 74641                                 COST £10

The change in ownership, a take-over by corporate interests, and the prospect of an American branch have not affected the queues, but they have shocked long-time visitors who relish not the folksy 'Harry's wholesome Yorkshire broth' or 'Harry's steamed ginger pudding and custard'. Some maintain that fish and chips are still consistent, still fresh, still fried and served at all speed; but for others, 'those large fillets of haddock with large milky white flakes, so fresh they tasted of the sea, encased in the thinnest, crispest layer of batter' are but occasional. The hunt, for a successor perhaps, is on. Licensed.

PROPRIETORS: Merryweather Ltd
OPEN: all week
CLOSED: 25 and 26 Dec
MEALS: 11.30am to 11.30pm
PRICES: £7 (£8)
CARDS: Access, Visa
SEATS: 186. Car-park, 200 places. Children's helpings. Wheelchair access (also WC). Music

**GULWORTHY Devon** map 1

## ▲ *Horn of Plenty* 🍷

Gulworthy, PL19 8JD
TAVISTOCK (0822) 832528 COOKING 3
3m W of Tavistock, off A390 COST £18–£37

The Horn is in its fifth lustrum; plenty has flowed continuously for more than 22 years and Sonia Stevenson remains at the stoves, as well as giving her 'courses for sauces'. Rooms, with balconies giving on to the valley below, have added economic bottom to the enterprise. Patrick Stevenson often presides, his approach mellowed by many seasons, no longer carrying the burden of combativeness that would have Devon talking for months on end. There is virtue in consistency and this restaurant still possesses it for many who revisit. For newcomers, the style of the dining-room may give some clues to age; the style of the cooking may do the same. It is a bastion of 1960s eclecticism, drawing from a host of countries – Romania, Austria, Turkey, even China – in a quite insouciant way. In parallel with this is the strong vein of French classical cooking typified by the quenelles of salmon with a white wine and cream sauce and sweetbreads in a brioche served with two sauces, white and brown, that Sonia Stevenson first cooked at Maxim's in 1976. There is also the strand of French bourgeois or provincial cooking, demonstrated by the regional menus that have been a feature since opening, and the Stevensons' determination to expose the materials and wealth of their own district to customers. In this, and so many other ways (roasting young lamb on a spit over the dining-room fire, for one), the Stevensons have anticipated specific shifts in taste, though they have not gone along with the underlying drift towards lightness and transparency. Reports this year have included disappointments, occasionally stemming from dishes of too great simplicity for the surroundings or mere misfires of taste and technique. However, the impression left is that of profligacy: hollandaise comes on the dish and in a jug besides; clotted cream arrives by the pound, not the ounce. Staying the night may well be advised, to take best advantage of the style. The wine list has always been prepared in consultation with David Wolfe. Again, it anticipated by many years our quests for value and good drinking beyond France and Germany. There is invariably some novelty that is worth pursuing and, because of David Wolfe's London connection, it is often fashionable as well. House wine costs as little as £6 for white; £8.70 for red. The set lunch includes a choice of wine, though its cost may be allowed against something from the list if that is preferred. Real beer is kept for Mr Stevenson. Coffee is unlimited.

CHEFS/PROPRIETORS: S. and P.R.N. Stevenson
OPEN: all week, exc Thur and Fri L
MEALS: 12 to 2, 7 to 9.30
PRICES: £24 (£31), Set L £16.75 (£18), Set D £25 (£31), Snacks £5
CARDS: Access, Amex, Visa
SEATS: 60. 6 tables outside. Private parties: 25 main room, 10 private room. Car-park, 30 places. Vegetarian meals. Children's helpings (L only). No children under 10 at D
ACCOMMODATION: 6 rooms. Rooms for disabled. B&B £68 to £73. Garden. TV. Phone. Scenic [GHG]

**HADLOW** Kent                                                                          map 3

## *La Crémaillère*

The Square, Hadlow TN11 ODA                                    COOKING 2
HADLOW (0732) 851489                                               COST £26

Back in the *Guide* following a change of hands, La Crémaillère is now owned by
Austrian Walter Monz. He describes the food as French provincial, but a whiff
of wiener rostbraten and beef goulash wafts through the menu. There are two
dining-rooms, one with inglenook fireplace, the other a vine-covered
conservatory. The menu changes monthly and is kept very simple, three
courses with five or six choices for each. Everything is well and carefully
cooked. Beginnings might be stuffed aubergine, piled with a rich, brick-
coloured crab filling; or fried whitebait, lightly floured and tossed in black
pepper. Main course salmon steaks come with a spiced, slightly sweet butter
melted over; lamb noisettes stuffed with mint and cucumber are dressed with a
well judged pan reduction. Vegetables, served super-hot in copper pans, are
absolutely non-nouvelle: crunchy potatoes sauté with chunks of smoky bacon,
garlic-laden spinach. Puddings such as chestnut parfait or crêpes stuffed with
frangipane are memorable. The wine list is short, the bin ends are worth
looking at. House French, £5.30. 'No extra expected' when it comes to tipping
time.

CHEF: Walter Monz   PROPRIETORS: Walter Monz and Tilda O'Neil
OPEN: Mon to Sat, D only (L by arrangement, exc Sat)
MEALS: 12 to 2, 7.30 to 10
PRICES: Set D £16.50 (£22). Licensed, also bring your own: corkage £5
CARDS: Access, Visa
SEATS: 25. Private parties: 16 main room, 14 and 16 private rooms. Children welcome.
Smart dress preferred. Wheelchair access (2 steps)

---

**HAMBLETON** Leicestershire                                              map 6

## ▲ *Hambleton Hall* 🍾

COUNTY OF THE YEAR RESTAURANT

Hambleton LE15 8TH
OAKHAM (0572) 756991                                              COOKING 4
off A606, 3m SE of Oakham                                    COST £25–£49

Hambleton should be visited to see the hotel as an art form in itself. Some may
find the Englishness and the class overbearing in its discretion and good taste.
An essay could be written comparing the styles of Mallory Court (see entry,
Bishop's Tachbrook) and Hambleton. It would be difficult to better the
standards of the bedrooms, the treatment of the public rooms, the personal
commitment of the staff, or the condition of ancillary niceties – flower
arrangements and the like. Nor can there be better relationships between land
and water than this strange peninsula created by the artificial Rutland Water, a
giant dew-pond that commemorates a drowned county. The dining-room has
always been the nub of Hambleton's existence. It has been redecorated in
lighter colours and benefits from them. Well-spaced tables, heavy napery and
decent cutlery and china give a solid bottom to what may be a long stint of

dining. There is a *carte* that seems to overwork the adjective 'little', as in 'a little stew of lobster and tarragon'. There are six choices of first course, fish or middle course, meat dish, then dessert. This runs on a rolling change. Every meal also has a set-price four-course table d'hôte, coffee included. Lunch is cheap by contrast. Not much pastry turns up on either menu and the kitchen appears keen on sabayons – but then, which isn't? What may be a rumble of battles past surfaces in a note printed on the menu: 'Many of our dishes are served warm rather than hot.' A meal that began happily with some excellent biscuits, canapés and house Champagne that earned credit points for quality went on to a relative standard at Hambleton: pan-fried foie gras served with a pile of mango *mirepoix* on a bed of lamb's lettuce. This was sauced with a strong, sweet pan-juice reduction, the liver cooked with exactness and the combination of mango and liver, the balance of sweet and savoury, memorable. The next course was a pot-roasted squab with roast garlic, roast potatoes and an intense sauce that did not mask flavour. After some first-rate cheese, with tip-top bread (they do several varieties), the meal finished with three sorbets – passion-fruit, lemon with Perrier, and a bland coconut – with a raspberry coulis and a scattering of pomegranate seeds. This was adjudged a success: greater than a slightly muted companion meal that kicked off with a fine *nage* of lobster and mussels but seemed to lose its way with a cabbage roulade stuffed with herbs and red peppers accompanying a loin of lamb that exemplified the perils of over-elaboration. The past year's enthusiasm seems to have been scattering flowering herbs over everything: occasionally they intrude. Coffee and petits fours are as good as you would expect. The wine list runs long and French, with a nod elsewhere. Stocks are quite fluid. Clarets are a particular joy, but there is not a duff grower in the whole list. Prices follow the market but are not extortionate. The short list is a useful canter through a few lower-priced entries, if your stamina is not up to the long handicap. House wine: Ch. Montalivet, Graves 1983; Mâcon- Lugny les Charmes 1987, both £12.
CELLARMAN'S CHOICE : Venegazzù 1981, Conte Loredan, £12; Pinot Blanc d'Alsace, Zind-Humbrecht 1987, £11. 'No additional payment expected' is written on the bottom of each bill.

CHEF: Brian Baker    PROPRIETORS: Timothy and Stefa Hart
OPEN: all week
MEALS: 12 to 1.45, 7 to 9.30
PRICES: £27 (£35), Set L £19 (£25) to £25 (£34), Set D £25 (£31) to £33 (£41). Service inc
CARDS: Access, Amex, Diners, Visa
SEATS: 60. Private parties: 45 main room, 20 private room. Car-park, 40 places. Children's helpings. Smart dress preferred. No cigars/pipes in dining-room. Wheelchair access (also WC)
ACCOMMODATION: 15 rooms, all with bath/shower. Rooms for disabled. Lift. B&B £75 to £98.50. No children under 9. Baby facilities. Pets welcome. Garden. Tennis. Fishing. Golf. TV. Phone. Scenic. Doors close at 12 [GHG]

CELLARMAN'S CHOICE : *A wine recommended by the restaurateur, normally more expensive than the house wine.*

*County Round-ups listing additional restaurants that may be worth a visit are at the back of the* Guide, *after the Irish section. Reports on Round-up entries are welcome.*

## Drum and Monkey

| | |
|---|---|
| 5 Montpellier Gardens, Harrogate HG1 2TF | COOKING 2 |
| HARROGATE (0423) 502650 | COST £23 |

'The Drum and Monkey is deservedly popular. The atmosphere appeals to a wide variety of people; it is civilised, professionally run and engagingly formal... The collection of stuffed fish in both the downstairs bar and upstairs dining-room is a star feature.' William Fuller's seafood restaurant is given character by his old-fashioned courtesy. The cooking of both fish and shellfish is undoubtedly best in plain dishes, such as grilled lobster or Dover sole, a hot shellfish platter in garlic butter or poached salmon trout, although there are plenty of other more adventurous ideas among three dozen or so dishes on the menu. Among these, seafood medallions — scallop, monkfish, sole and sea trout baked with sauce béarnaise — and a spinach mousse filled with prawns and tomato in mayonnaise are excellent, though clumsy sauces and overcooked fish have been noticed. The high atmosphere of hectic lunches is very different from the quiet mood of the evenings, when tables are kept free for regular customers. A short wine list is chosen to complement the fish and includes Bruno Paillard Champagne and a fair range of bottles at reasonable price. House Duboeuf is £5.25.

CHEF: Patrick Laverack    PROPRIETOR: William Fuller
OPEN: Mon to Sat
CLOSED: Christmas to New Year
MEALS: 12 to 2.30, 7 to 10.15
PRICES: £13 (£19)
CARDS: Access, Visa
SEATS: 48. Private parties: 8 main room. Children's helpings

## Millers

| | |
|---|---|
| 1 Montpelier Mews, Harrogate HG1 2TG | COOKING 3 |
| HARROGATE (0423) 530708 | COST £29 |

In its previous incarnation, Millers was a 'fish brasserie'. Simon Gueller still cooks fish, and offers daily market selections, but the partners have changed the overall direction towards a more orthodox restaurant. His background is impeccable and therefore much of the cooking is skilled. The dining-room, as befits an area replete with antique shops, is a comfortable eclectic mix. The menu of six items in each course is nicely judged, the food does not appear heavy, and the sequence of flavours — thyme, herbs, fresh ginger and chillies, coriander, tarragon, shallots, mushrooms, basil — are definite and enticing. The style is direct. A fillet of lamb is in a good feuilleté whose function is to take up the intense thyme sauce. Scallops have a delicate flavouring of green ginger and chilli that is not allowed to overpower the bivalves themselves. Lamb with a tarragon gravy is offset by spinach cooked without the habitual mask of butter or cream. Only in a sea bass with a scallop mousse did the restraint give way to over-elaboration. The fish and the light cream sauce of its juices needed no mousse to enhance its impact. Even the appetiser, a halibut tartlet with a beurre blanc, was exceptional for flavour and technique. A hazelnut praline on a raspberry sauce did not disappoint at the close of a meal though coffee is served with few accompaniments. The professionalism both in the dining-room and kitchen of this new restaurant promises well. The wine list is short, from a good merchant. House wine, £6.95.

CHEF: Simon Gueller  PROPRIETORS: Simon Gueller and Rena Polushka
OPEN: Mon to Sat, exc Mon D
CLOSED: 10 days at Christmas, 1 to 15 Aug
MEALS: 12 to 2, 7 to 10
PRICES: £17 (£24)
CARDS: Access, Visa
SEATS: 24. 4 tables outside. Private parties: 24 main room. Children's helpings. No cigars/pipes in dining-room. Wheelchair access (also WC). Music

---

**HARROW  Greater London**                                                    map 3

## Country Club

160 College Road
Harrow-on-the-Hill HA1 1BH                                     COOKING 2
01-427 0729                                                    COST £15–£34

T.A. Chu comes from Shanghai via Taiwan and can cook up a storm of Shanghai food if you ask him to. His work poses the dilemma of so many Chinese restaurants in this country: their cooks are talented, but they waste their skills on an ersatz and monotonous cuisine that can be recommended only because it outstrips steak bars and restaurants of double the price. But how are English diners to know of this latent ability? Here is one to try: telephone and book a dinner of Shanghai food. French house wine, £6.10.

CHEF/PROPRIETOR: T.A. Chu
OPEN: all week, D only
MEALS: 6 to 11
PRICES: £14 (£21), Set D £11 (£15) to £24 (£28). Minimum £7. Service inc
CARDS: Access, Visa
SEATS: 55. Private parties: 14 private room. Car-park, 50 places. Children welcome. Music

---

**HARWICH  Essex**                                                            map 3

## ▲ The Pier at Harwich ▼

The Quay, Harwich CO12 3HH                                    COOKING 2
HARWICH (0255) 241212                                         COST £14–£35

The two restaurants here look largely to local, fresh fish, which they serve even on a Sunday. Downstairs is cheap and cheerful, serving half pints of prawns, whitebait and fish pie as well as fish and chips. Upstairs there's an altogether smarter dining-room with dishes to match. Some, such as lobster mayonnaise or plaice on the bone, rely largely on the quality of the seafood; others, such as home-made ravioli of lobster, prawns and crab or steamed fillet of sea bass, are more ambitious. Among these, the crab salad with two types of mayonnaise and the seafood pancakes full of scallops, prawns and turbot have been well reported. The non-stop piano may please some, or ruin conversation and pleasure for others. The wine list has more whites than reds and does not charge overly for very decent bottles from France and elsewhere. Would it be otherwise on a list chosen by Lay & Wheeler? House Colombard, Côtes de Gascogne 1988, £6.20; Tyrrell's Long Flat Red 1985, £9.60. CELLARMAN'S CHOICE : Tyrrell's Long Flat White 1988, £9.60; Chardonnay du Haut-Poitou, £8.50.

CHEF: C.E. Oakley   PROPRIETOR: G.M.W. Milsom
OPEN: all week
MEALS: 12 to 2, 6 to 9.30
PRICES: £19 (£29), Set L £7.75 (£14) to £9.50 (£16). Service 10%
CARDS: Access, Amex, Diners, Visa
SEATS: 80. Private parties: 85 main room, 50 private room. Car-park, 10 places. Children's helpings. Wheelchair access (2 steps). Music
ACCOMMODATION: 6 rooms, all with bath/shower. B&B £35 to £55. Afternoon teas. TV. Phone. Scenic

---

**HASLEMERE  Surrey**                                                    map 3

## Morels ▼

25–27 Lower Street, Haslemere GU27 2NY                    COOKING 4
HASLEMERE (0428) 51462                                    COST £23–£42

Marooned, like a ship in full sail on a sandbank, on a high pavement above the narrow road, this place needs be approached on foot from the parking-place reached via the broader main street. As business grew, so did the restaurant, taking in neighbouring cottages to make up a complex series of volumes. The design is outstanding: calm blue and white with fine lighting and a cool sense of space that belies the low ceilings. There are few better eating rooms in England, complemented by good table settings (and cracking lavatories!). Before we get enthusiastic about French coolth, note that Mary Anne Morel is English: she is the designer and has absorbed her lesson well. Service is by Mme Morel herself, efficient and intelligent, and young French staff who stand out by their pleasantness and ability to cope with customers ranging from young business parties to crusty Carthusians down on a visit. This aspect is all of a piece with the design of the restaurant: first class. Jean-Yves Morel may emerge affably from the kitchen during the evening, but his energies are properly expended at the stove – to our benefit. There is a *carte* of eight choices and, on various weekday nights, a cheaper, shorter table d'hôte and a six-course *menu gastronomique*. The cooking is as modern as might be expected; some gutsy flavours from soy sauce, green coriander, black olives; some mixing of shellfish and meat; some fresh pasta. The dishes are interesting, making it difficult to choose: a terrine of ox-tail; ravioli of lobster and monkfish with ginger and soy; roast veal with ravioli of morels and balsamic vinegar sauce. Yet there is sufficient orthodoxy to reassure newcomers: blinis with smoked salmon; feuilleté of asparagus, sauce maltaise; peppered fillet steak with mushrooms and a wine sauce; duck with an apple and Seville orange tart. Execution is skilled and presentation fine. Tartlets filled with well-drained diced cucumber in sour cream and topped with a thin slice of raw salmon had pastry so light and thin that it defied the weight of the contents. John Dory with a chive butter sauce (the most popular sauce with fish this year) was cooked (and bought) to perfection. Boiled potatoes with this were outstanding (a rarer and rarer event in British restaurants besotted with dauphinois and other badly executed potato 'dishes'), even if the vegetables were boring. M. Morel is able to bring off some surprising combinations, for example pigeon breasts with langoustines, although the careful discretion essential to flavouring a sauce for wild rabbit with leaf coriander was lacking. The favourite herb (after basil) of the late 1980s, leaf coriander is in fact the most difficult to use − its odour of stale cat's urine is rank and many western chefs are incompetent at adding it to otherwise attractive food. When used sensitively, it can add an imperceptible tang and exoticism in a wonderful way. Puddings can be good, the grand plate of desserts always causing oohs and aahs. However, the coffee and petits fours are the stars of the meal's end. Although praise of the cooking has, in general, been very warm, a few dissenting voices have expressed concern that press and popularity have caused a brash attitude. The wine list is French with some good, though never inexpensive, bottles. Clarets, especially, contain some good vintages, old as well as new: Ch. Nenin, Pomerol 1964; Ch. Gloria, St Julien 1970; Ch. Fieuzal, Graves, 1978. Burgundy growers just miss the top rank, particularly in the most expensive bottles. Although the lesser regions are not closely explored − nothing from the south-west or Provence − watch for the Jura Ch. d'Arlay from le Comte de Laguiche and the Alsaces from Rolly Gassmann. House Torres Coronas and Sichel Côtes du Rhône and Bordeaux Sauvignon, £9. CELLARMAN'S CHOICE : Mâcon-Clessé 1986, René Michel, £15; Côtes de Nuits Villages 1985, Gérard Julien, £19. There are too many supplements on the *prix fixe*.

---

CHEF: Jean-Yves Morel   PROPRIETORS: Jean-Yves and Mary Anne Morel
OPEN: Tue to Sat, exc Sat L
CLOSED: 25 Dec, bank hols (exc Good Fri), 2 weeks end Feb, 2 weeks Sept/Oct
MEALS: 12.30 to 1.45, 7 to 10
PRICES: £25 (£35), Set L £14 (£23), Set D £17 (£26)
CARDS: Access, Amex, Diners, Visa
SEATS: 45. Private parties: 12 main room. Children's helpings. No pipes in dining-room. Wheelchair access (1 step)

---

**HASTINGLEIGH** Kent                                                      map 3

## ▲ *Woodmans Arms Auberge*

Hassell Street, Hastingleigh TN25 5JE                          COOKING 3
ELMSTED (023 375) 250                                         COST £18−£32

Hospitality is ingrained in some people − it courses in their bloodstream. The Woodmans Arms stands for the Campions' perseverance and apparently open-ended commitment to welcome. What rules there are − no smoking anywhere, a single time for eating, no choice on the menu − are the few limits on untidy reality. Life's apprenticeship has been long served. The Auberge was once an inn; it has three double bedrooms and a commensurate dining-room. Non-residents, therefore, may eat here but rarely, when space permits. For sybarites, cosseted by the luxuries, yet stressed by the din of city life, the Woodmans Arms is a haven of light, air and silence. The cooking will bring them back to a more substantial earth. Susan Campion prepares, and Gerald Campion serves, a meal sometimes of four courses, sometimes of three, with the addition of cheese. The food is fresh – chicken from the farm, leaves from local gardens – and the style is fine domestic. A spring meal began with a smoked salmon mousse 'a cut above the usual served in larger establishments, smooth, well flavoured and not too salty', then went on to a partridge with a good wine, onion and mushroom sauce given body by proper reduction of the stock. Vegetables were new potatoes and spinach 'well cooked, not pappy.' Cheese was adequate, not a feature. Dessert was a trio of very fine ice-creams, chocolate, prune and vanilla, 'not a crystal in sight'. The same reporter commented that the Campions 'make the whole business look very easy, which it isn't. They are both such pleasing and enjoying characters, the professionalism gets overlooked.' The wine list runs through 70 bottles (including a few halves) with a few from Australia and New Zealand. The selection of *cru* Beaujolais is interesting. As haphazard visiting is fruitless, check first and ask for directions if booked in.

CHEF: Susan Campion   PROPRIETORS: Susan and Gerald Campion
OPEN: all week, D only
CLOSED: 1 week Apr and 3 weeks from 1 Sep
MEALS: 7.30
PRICES: Set D £12.50 (£18) for residents, £21.50 (£27) for non-residents. Service inc
SEATS: 8. Private parties: 8 main room. Car-park, 6 places. No children under 16. No smoking. One sitting
ACCOMMODATION: 3 rooms, all with bath/shower. B&B £40 to £65. Deposit: 25%. No children under 16. Garden. TV. Phone. Scenic. Doors close at 11.30 [GHG]

---

HAWKSHEAD  Cumbria                                              map 7

## ▲ *Field Head House* ♥

Outgate, Hawkshead LA22 0PY                          COOKING 2
HAWKSHEAD (096 66) 240                                 COST £25

One mile north of Hawkshead village, this verandahed house sits amid fine scenery: quintessential Lakeland. People report the pleasure of staying here and the hospitality of the Dutch couple who own it. Bob van Gulik, in a letter to the *Guide*, remarked that 'we eat the same food we prepare for our guests', unlike many professionals in more exalted kitchens. 'Le patron mange ici' may be a tired joke, but it is never reassuring to find that the star chefs actually prefer boiled eggs to pan-fried foie gras on a bed of lentils. On offer here is a five-course set dinner with a choice only between two English cheeses and a hot or cold pudding. The style is English Lakes: soup comes as the second course; the puddings include sticky toffee. As their butcher is Richard Woodall, producer of Cumbrian air-dried ham, the meat is often good. Mr van Gulik improves in his technique and the house is self-sufficient in bread and incidentals. The wine list shows care and affection: it is happy to go to different countries, it serves whole bottles by the half (at two-thirds the whole price), its prices are fair, the classic regions are represented by careful choice. The contents and the comments on the list seem to indicate true enthusiasm. A few fine wines (probably not often sold) include a Ch. Lynch-Bages 1961 at £78. Smoking is not allowed in the dining-room, one of the sitting-rooms and the bedrooms. Tips are not expected. Children are welcome as long as parents can convince others that they are in full control (hear, hear!). House Bulgarian Cabernet Sauvignon is £5; Bulgarian Chardonnay is £5.50. CELLARMAN'S CHOICE : Palmela Dry Muscat 1987, João Pires, £8.30; Ch. Tour Grand Mayne 1985, Côtes de Castillon £8.80.

CHEF: Bob Van Gulik    PROPRIETORS: Bob and Eeke Van Gulik
OPEN: all week D only, exc Tue
CLOSED: last 2 weeks Jan, week before Christmas
MEALS: 7.30 for 8
PRICES: Set D £18 (£21). Service inc
SEATS: 12. Private parties: 18 main room. Car-park, 15 places. No smoking. Wheelchair access (3 steps; also WC). One sitting
ACCOMMODATION: 7 rooms, all with bath/shower. B&B £33 to £50. Deposit: £20. Baby facilities. Pets welcome. Garden. Fishing. Golf. TV. Scenic. Doors close at 12. Confirm by noon [GHG]

---

## HAWORTH  West Yorkshire                                          map 5

# Weavers

| 15 West Lane, Haworth BD22 8DU | COOKING 2 |
| HAWORTH (0535) 43822 | COST £15–£25 |

This cosy rabbit-warren of a restaurant in a group of converted weavers' cottages opens off the cobbled street beside the Brontë museum car park. A four-bedroom extension is expected to be on stream during the currency of this *Guide*. Colin and Jane Rushworth 'bake our own bread, make our own puddings, search out local ingredients and use old-fashioned vegetables.' Their style is 'honest northern' but lighter, and with decided 'echoes of France' made visible in some of the fixtures and fittings. Reports praise specific dishes – salmon in pastry with spinach; roast duck breast with rhubarb sauce – and are particularly keen on the value and standard of the set Sunday lunches. On the evening menu most dishes have a homely feel: ox-tail stew, shepherd's pie and 'Yorkshire pud wi' onion gravy'. These latter are 'as big as a flying saucer, crisp and as light as air'. Puddings such as sticky toffee, or Manchester tart are not easily resisted. The place seeks to convert people to rabid enthusiasm for the honesty of it all and the genuine palatability. Turn up at 7 any night but Saturday for the 'early doors' menu of three courses, three choices for £9.50. House French is £7 but better to go for something from the reasonably priced short wine list. CELLARMAN'S CHOICE : Bandol, Moulin des Costes 1986, £8.95; Montagny *premier cru* 1987, Vignerons de Buxy, £10.95.

---

*If you see a certificate in a restaurant bearing the words 'Good Food Guide Top Restaurants', the claim is false (and the restaurant may be in contempt of court in displaying it) – see the Introduction. Please write and tell us the name and address of the restaurant.*

---

CHEFS/PROPRIETORS: Colin and Jane Rushworth
OPEN: Tue to Sat, D only, and Sun L (Oct to Easter)
CLOSED: 3 weeks June/July, 1 week at Christmas
MEALS: 12.30 to 1.30, 7 to 9
PRICES: £14 (£21), Set L £9.50 (£15), Set D £10.50 (£17) Snacks from £1.50
CARDS: Access, Amex, Diners, Visa
SEATS: 60. Private parties: 14 main room, 14 private room. Vegetarian meals. Children's helpings. Music. Air-conditioned

---

**HAYDON BRIDGE** Northumberland                                                    map 7

## General Havelock Inn

Radcliffe Road, Haydon Bridge NE47 6ER                             COOKING 1
HAYDON BRIDGE (043 484) 376                                       COST £12–£26

Angela Clyde's cooking is appropriate to the stone inn beside the South Tyne with blazing log fire and olde worlde furniture. The dining-room overlooking the river is often full at lunchtime, when there are roasts and plainly cooked fish; in the evening, steaks, made dishes and simple produce like asparagus hollandaise are added to the four-course set dinners, but nothing is dressed up. Fish and shellfish are excellent, as in a large pile of moules marinière or a Shield's smokie of smoked cod in a wine, mustard and cheese sauce. For pudding there are rich pies, chocolate concoctions and home-made ice-creams. Service, by Angela Clyde and young helpers, is efficient yet relaxed. More informal meals in the bar can be spoiled by television. House wine is £5.50. CELLARMAN'S CHOICE: red Ch. Thieuley, 1986, £9.50; Mâcon-Prissé 1987, Duboeuf, £10.50.

CHEF: Angela Clyde    PROPRIETORS: Ian and Angela Clyde
OPEN: Wed to Sun, exc Sun D
CLOSED: first two weeks Jan, second week Mar, last week Aug, first week Sept
MEALS: 12 to 1.30, 7.30 to 9
PRICES: £8 (£13), Set Sun L £7.50 (£12), Set D £14 (£19) to £17 (£22). Snacks from £1
SEATS: 28. 4 tables outside. Private parties: 30 main room. Car-park, 12 places. Vegetarian meals. Children's helpings. Wheelchair access (1 step; also WC)

---

**HENLEY-ON-THAMES** Oxfordshire                                                  map 2

## As You Like It

60 Bell Street, Henley-on-Thames RG9 2BN
HENLEY-ON-THAMES (0491) 410071                                   COOKING 1
and 410068                                                       COST £13–£26

Re-opened since the last *Guide*, this Chinese restaurant is a cut above the competition in decoration with a striking façade, tinted windows, gold and blue interior and a 'gold' spoon and bowl per setting. Above-average food has been reported, though tempered with a certain ennui. Unusual dishes, such as crispy aromatic lamb wrapped in lettuce, and a choice of hot-pots, balance the lemon chicken and beef with chilli. Try the sizzling Tappan dishes for a touch of drama, or the lobster if you want to break the bank; the set menus offer little inspiration. The service is friendly and capable. Extra touches, for instance scented towels and fortune cookies make it one of the better places to eat after a day on the river. House French, £5.50.

CHEF: Edmond Tze   PROPRIETORS: PTK Enterprises Ltd
OPEN: all week
CLOSED: 25 and 26 Dec
MEALS: 12.30 to 2.15, 6.30 to 11 (12 Fri and Sat)
PRICES: £9 (£18), Set L £8 (£13) to £10 (£15), Set D £10 (£15) to £15 (£22). Minimum £7.50. Service 10%
CARDS: Access, Amex, Visa
SEATS: 80. Private parties: 100 main room. Vegetarian meals. Children's helpings (Sun and L only). Smart dress preferred. Wheelchair access (1 step; also WC). Music. Air-conditioned

---

**HEREFORD   Hereford & Worcester**                                    map 2

## Fat Tulip

The Old Wye Bridge
2 St Martin's Street Hereford HR2 7RE                          COOKING 1
HEREFORD (0432) 275808                                         COST £26

A useful addition in a badly served area, the Fat Tulip is a brasserie next to the old bridge over the River Wye. At present squeezed into a high, old building, decorated in 1980s brasserie mode, there are plans to open up views over the river. The short menu is more restaurant than brasserie, with half a dozen choices at each course and some extra daily dishes: home-made soups and pies at one end of the spectrum, more elaborate dishes like roast stuffed quail in madeira sauce at the other. Fish is well reported and ranges from smoked marlin – bought in from Vin Sullivan of Abergavenny and served with a horseradish mayonnaise – to freshly cooked seafood salad, grilled sardines or kebabs of river prawns. Vegetables are well timed and tasty. To finish there is locally made ice-cream, such as rich prune and armagnac, or a predominantly French cheeseboard. A choice of four coffees. Service can disappoint. The bill can mount fast for relatively simple cooking, making this a safer bet for a snack and drink than a meal. The wine list is better (and pricier) than many provincial eating places of this sort. France is the source of all bar half a dozen, but the bottles come from some good négociants and growers – Jean Thévenet, Durup, Pascal, Viénot – as well as one very good Italian Montepulciano d'Abruzzo 1985 at £7.50. Eight house wines from France start at £6.95.

CHEF: Kevin Powles   PROPRIETORS: Kevin and Susan Powles
OPEN: Mon to Sat
MEALS: 12 to 2, 7 to 9.30
PRICES: £18 (£22), Snacks from £2.25. Service inc
CARDS: Access, Amex, Visa
SEATS: 35. Private parties: 20 main room. Children welcome. Wheelchair access (1 step). Music

---

*See the inside of the front cover for an explanation of the new 1 to 5 rating system recognising cooking standards.*

HERSHAM  Surrey                                                           map 3

# La Malmaison

17 Queens Road, Hersham KT12 5ND                          COOKING 3
WALTON-ON-THAMES (0932) 227412                          COST £17–£36

The area south-west of London is not just a limbo shaped by Drives, Avenues
and Crescents. There are talented chefs working. One may think that proximity
to the capital means prosperity. Not necessarily. The house occupied by
Malmaison and Jacques and Lisa Troquet is handsome. Its dining-room affords
generous space and quiet grey and red decoration; the windows overlook a
small courtyard rather than Sunset Strip, Walton-on-Thames style. M. Troquet
was once chef to the French Ambassador; his cooking makes few concessions
to his host country. It is skilled, shows appreciation of texture and flavour and
is professionally served by his wife and a helper. Meals have included an
excellent salad of bass, sole, salmon and scallops marinated with lime, green
peppercorns and dill with a chive and sour cream sauce; a warm salad of lightly
braised sweetbreads atop an artichoke heart with a lemon dressing; steamed
sea bass with a thick carrot butter sauce, the fish as good as any on the coast; a
generous fillet of lamb, accurately cooked, on a sauce of red peppers with a not
so successful sweetcorn pancake; turbot cooked on a bed of shallots with a very
mushroomy thin sauce; a lot of tomato roses littered on most dishes and labour-
intensive puddings such as an apple and apricot mixture inside the lightest of
pancakes with a dark caramel sauce. Cheeses are extensive, in good condition
and French, of course. Chocolate, too, is good: fine sweetmeats with the coffee,
'an arterio-sclerotic' plate of chocolate treats for dessert. This is as good as any
of the Surrey competition. The wine list is briefly French, though more English
in its mark-ups. House French from Paul Reitz, £6.50. CELLARMAN'S CHOICE :
Chablis 1986, Couperot, £12.80; Châteauneuf-du-Pape, Domaine du Grand
Tinel, 1981, £17.50.

CHEF: Jacques Troquet    PROPRIETORS: Jacques and Lisa Troquet
OPEN: Mon to Sat, exc Sat L
MEALS: 12 to 2.30, 7 to 10
PRICES: £22 (£30), Set L £12.50 (£17). Service 10%
CARDS: Access, Diners, Visa
SEATS: 40. Private parties: 60 main room. Wheelchair access. Music

HERSTMONCEUX  East Sussex                                             map 3

# Sundial

Gardner Street, Herstmonceux BN27 4LA                     COOKING 2
HERSTMONCEUX (0323) 832217                               COST £20–£38

Eat on the terrace looking down the valley in summer, or retreat to the black-
beamed, cottagey dining-room if the weather is unkind. The menus, both set
and à la carte, are long and complicated. Giuseppe Bertoli has not varied his
formula to any great extent for some years. The black peppercorns with the
entrecôte have become green, the milk-fed lamb (winter and summer through)
has progressed from being roasted with rosemary to being wrapped in pastry.

It is a grand French-style menu (though langouste is not lobster in any language). Wise diners will look for the less elaborate offerings, since, as one reporter extolling the virtues of simplicity observes, 'complexity leads to gastronomic confusion'. There is a regularly changing series of shorter *prix fixe* menus and fish is always a strong feature, varying with the seasons. By contrast the *carte* is very old-fashioned: how can they, for instance, always have the odd half dozen snails or Mediterranean prawns to hand for the occasional dinner à la carte, or offer foie gras pâté only to a minimum of two people? One might think, having made the foie gras pâté, that they would want to sell it as quickly as possible. A host of creamy gateaux wait patiently for their turn on a packed side table. The wine cellar is well stocked with claret, including some Pauillacs of fine breeding from the 1950s and 1960s. Burgundy growers include Jayer, Gros, Rousseau, Clair Dau and de Vogüé but at a price. There are some nice Rhônes including a Lirac at a fair price. House French is £8.95.
CELLARMAN'S CHOICE: Mâcon-Villages 1983, Leroy, £18.25; Gigondas 1982, G. Meffre, £15.75.

CHEF: Guiseppe Bertoli   PROPRIETORS: Laurette and Giuseppe Bertoli
OPEN: Tue to Sun, exc Sun D
CLOSED: mid-Aug to Sept, 25 Dec to 20 Jan
MEALS: 12.30 to 2 (2.30 Sun), 7.30 to 9.30 (10 Sat)
PRICES: £21 (£32), Set L £12.50 (£20), Set D £17.50 (£29). Service 10%
CARDS: Access, Amex, Diners, Visa
SEATS: 70. 8 tables outside. Private parties: 50 main room, 22 private room. Car-park, 25 places. Children's helpings. No smoking in dining-room. Wheelchair access (also WC). Music

---

## HETTON   North Yorkshire                                          map 5

# Angel Inn

Hetton BD23 6LT                                            COOKING 3
CRACOE (075 673) 263                                    COST £16–£25

Denis Watkins continues his campaign for Real Food. Bar food and restaurant dishes alike are cooked 'to order, with great care. We go weekly to Manchester market at 4am. The produce available to us improves all the time – most exciting!' Business is booming, and enthusiastic reports continue to arrive: 'Friday night's menu is augmented by a large blackboard full of superlative fish dishes. There's nothing comparable for miles around.' 'The various combinations, particularly meat and seafood as in breast of guinea-fowl with mousseline of crab may at first shock; however, they all work when tasted.' 'The Provençal fish soup is full of flavour, thick and very satisfying.' The menu carries something for everyone, from a platter of prize-winning pork sausages on a bed of red cabbage, to 'little money-bags' of seafood baked in filo and served on lobster sauce. There are obvious signs of going up-market: the food becomes more ambitious and the wine list improves. This is a steady process of a region at a time, for example red burgundies have taken in some aristocrats from the 1970s and 1960s. But the coverage remains fair – a good Italian selection – and the prices (operating a fixed, not percentage, mark-up) are very good indeed. The food prices still remain ultra-competitive. This is a pub as pubs should be. House French, £5.95. CELLARMAN'S CHOICE : Vernaccia di San Gimignano 1986, Cusona, £8.35; Meursault Rouge 1985, Latour-Giraud, £15.50.

CHEFS: Denis Watkins and John Topham    PROPRIETORS: Denis and Juliet Watkins
OPEN: Mon to Sat D, Sun L
CLOSED: 1 Jan
MEALS: 12.15 to 2, 7 to 9.30
PRICES: £12 (£16), Set L £10.75 (£16), Set D £15.50 (£21), Snacks from £1.35. Minimum £15.50 (restaurant only)
CARD: Access
SEATS: 36. 15 tables outside. Private parties: 40 main room. Car-park, 17 places. Children's helpings (L only). Smart dress preferred. No pipes in dining-room. Wheelchair access (also WC). Music

---

**HINTLESHAM  Suffolk**                                                          map 3

## ▲ *Hintlesham Hall* 🍾

| | |
|---|---|
| Hintlesham IP8 3NS | COOKING 3 |
| HINTLESHAM (047 387) 268 | COST £22–£46 |

The house sails over a sea of corn a few chains west of Ipswich. Elizabethan outline, Georgian front and Caroline interiors have been converted to one of England's most luxurious country-house hotels, which grows apace with an almost annual programme of added rooms and facilities. Ruth and David Watson temper the hedonism with down-to-earth straight-talking that almost reconciles the £900 charge for a Newmarket weekend. At the same time they reinforce the luxury with a thoughtful decorative schema where nothing comes from a catalogue: pieces, pictures and fabrics have been chosen, not ordered over the telephone. Consequently, the hotel is a fine place to stay: the trimmings are all there, even if fake gas logs in the main public rooms caused a little raising of the eyebrows. Breakfasts are well reported. The restaurant has to run hard to keep up with these standards. In the autumn of 1988 there was a change of chefs: Robert Mabey left to work on his own (see entry, Sudbury) and Alan Ford joined them from a training at the Dorchester. Ruth Watson confesses to a preference for 'positive flavours and textures ... with a positively anti main course, meat-and-two-veg ethos.' The difficulty is that, as you aim for luxury, genius is needed to get the flavours to push through the trappings of display. Alan Ford's links with suppliers are as strong as Mabey's: well-hung meats, excellent fish and an impressive cheeseboard of French and English examples all feature. There has been marked a countervailing tendency to detract from this quality by giving too much at a sitting, to provoke imbalance by too rich and creamy a sauce, or to lose vividness by careless seasoning or a failure of nerve. There is a short and cheaper menu at lunchtime (which one ingrate described as falling short of certain expected trappings), and a long *carte* at both meals, bolstered by a *menu gastronomique* at dinner. These change with the seasons and do not always have extra daily specials to tie them closer to the markets. There has not been an obvious shift of emphasis with the change of chefs but there have been signs that Alan Ford has gained assurance in the first year of working here. Given a certain level of skill, confidence is the most important element in anyone's cooking. Good dishes have included a salad of

317

marinated tuna and scallop ranged round a centrepiece of mussels, scattered with shredded mange-tout and dressed with a fruity olive oil vinaigrette, and cannelloni of seafood in a ginger sauce and noisettes of lamb accompanied by intensely flavoured tomato and basil. A very fine caramelised apple tart with custard restored one disconsolate luncher and a white and dark chocolate marbled mousse with a supremely viscous chocolate sauce was the high point for another. The tops and tails of a meal – vegetable tempura with the drinks, bread and butter in the middle, petits fours with the coffee – have pleased many. If the Watsons and Ford continue to pursue positive flavours, there is much going for Hintlesham. The staff is young (but isn't it everywhere?) and often as keen as mustard. Pockets of ignorance and excessive relaxation have been exposed but the Watsons are generally good on motivation. The wine list is a good one, informatively annotated, eclectic and with lots of half-bottles. There is a broad *tranche* of clarets from mostly good vintages, impressive names in burgundy and the Rhône, exciting New World wines, and a helpful selection of reasonably priced 'country wines'. House wine: Edmond Coste Claret 1986, £12.50; Quincy 1988, Mardon, £12.55. CELLARMAN'S CHOICE : Torres Gran Coronas Reserva 1983, £13.65; Nobilo Sauvignon Blanc 1986, £20.10.

CHEF: Alan Ford   PROPRIETORS: Ruth and David Watson
OPEN: all week, exc Sat L
MEALS: 12 to 1.45, 7 to 9.30
PRICES: £30 (£38), Set L £15.50 (£22), Set D £30 (£37), Snacks from £3.50. Service inc
CARDS: Access, Amex, Diners, Visa
SEATS: 65. 6 tables outside. Private parties: 34 main room, 80 private room. Car-park, 100 places. Vegetarian meals. No children under 10. Smart dress preferred. No smoking. Wheelchair access
ACCOMMODATION: 33 rooms, all with bath/shower. Rooms for disabled. B&B £65 to 90. No children under 10. Pets welcome. Garden. Tennis. Fishing. Snooker. TV. Phone. Scenic. Doors close at 12. Confirm 3 days before [GHG]

---

**HINTON CHARTERHOUSE  Avon**                                        map 2

## ▲ *Homewood Park* ▼

Hinton Charterhouse, Bath BA3 6BB
LIMPLEY STOKE (022 122) 3731                         COOKING 3
off A36, 5m S of Bath                                COST £21–£34

There are claims that this was the abbot's house attached to the Carthusian monastery opposite, across the Bath–Warminster road. In truth, monastic associations are now out of place: an eighteenth-century core is overlaid by a Victorian country house with new additions to increase accommodation. The inside lifts the soul more than does the exterior. Stephen and Penny Ross have pitched the level of luxury and price just right, and the hotel manages to avoid the pitfalls of over-ornament or depressing luxury while offering all that anyone could reasonably want (except, in winter, more protection on the way from the car-park to the front door). From the outset, Homewood was conceived as a hotel, not a restaurant with rooms. This is an important distinction. Nonetheless, the praise from diners, as from residents, is constant: indeed the *Guide* is often accused of not rating the food highly enough. There are three dining-rooms in which good fabrics, proper pictures, antique furniture and acres of carpeting set the mood. The menu, priced for two or three courses, offers seven or eight choices at each stage. It is well thought out. The main ingredients range widely and each dish attracts by a distinctive flavour: a sauté of scallops with cumin on a bed of chicory with orange sauce, or veal fillet, kidney and sweetbread with a piquant caper sauce. As in the decorative scheme, a course is set between interest and over-elaboration. Some of the cooking is highly competent: those scallops have cumin mixed with the crumbs before frying, and a vivid orange sauce that manages to combine richness with sufficient acidity. Skill is also manifested in the hot banana soufflé and fine gratin dauphinois, though this comes occasionally with lacklustre vegetables. Not all is rosy: there are reports of oversalted bread, dryish lamb and a lamb stuffing of apricots and wild mushrooms that tasted more of pine kernels than either of these things – but then, how many people can handle wild mushrooms, that most overrated of components? The service at Homewood has remained determinedly young, intelligent and natural. There is none of the pomp of the country house. This is the beneficent effect of the owners, who remain consummate hosts and thoughtful hoteliers. If Homewood is full, or guests are without a car, the Rosses have the Queensberry Hotel in Russel Street, Bath. In three houses by the architect John Wood, the dozen rooms are as comfortable as Homewood but there is no restaurant. A shuttle service takes guests between the two places for dinner. The wine list is well judged. Yapp Brothers, Eldridge Pope, Domaine Direct and Reid Wines figure prominently; the balance is tilted towards France, but by no means exclusively. There are plenty of half-bottles and the prices are fair. There are 11 house wines from £8.50 for the Geoffrey Roberts Reserve (California), red and white, to £19.50 for the Pommery Brut Royal champagne. CELLARMAN'S CHOICE : Sauvignon de St Bris 1987, Sorin, £11; Givry 1986, Ragot, £15; Gigondas, Domaine St Gayan 1984, £15.

CHEFS: Stephen Ross and Darren McGrath    PROPRIETORS: Stephen and Penny Ross
OPEN: all week
CLOSED: 2 weeks from 23 Dec
MEALS: 12 to 1.30 (2 Sun), 7 to 9.30
PRICES: Set L from £16.50 (£21), Set D from £23 (£28). Service inc
CARDS: Access, Amex, Diners, Visa
SEATS: 50. 3 tables outside. Private parties: 36 main room, 12 and 25 private rooms. Car-park, 30 places. Children's helpings by arrangement. No smoking. Wheelchair access (also WC)
ACCOMMODATION: 15 rooms, all with bath/shower. Rooms for disabled. B&B £85 to £115. Baby facilities. Afternoon teas. Garden. Tennis. TV. Phone. Scenic. Doors close at 12 [GHG]

HOCKLEY HEATH  West Midlands                                            map 5

## ▲ Nuthurst Grange

Nuthurst Grange Lane
Hockley Heath B94 5NL                                        COOKING 2
LAPWORTH (056 43) 3972                                       COST £21–£42

Although the house, surrounded by large gardens, may soon be on the frontier of motorways, it attracts a large weekend crowd. Determinedly chintz in decoration, the linked rooms that make the restaurant are quieter in pattern than others. There are three set-price menus on offer, a cheaper one at lunch and two at night, each with a different degree of choice and complexity. The style smacks of larding an already fat capon: there are few direct approaches to a single ingredient. Veal has sweetbreads with it, lobster has crab, turbot has salmon, and salmon gets both brill and salt cod. Many of the sauces or accompaniments are themselves highly flavoured: Brie, horseradish, Roquefort. This manner does occasionally tip over into caricature, and the dishes that result are sometimes conflicting and over-fussy, or they descend into a sort of monotony. However, there is an equal number of accounts that praise the kitchen, 'simple, enjoyable, clean, clear tastes'. Perhaps some of the disparity arises from differing seasons or differing staff conditions. There is, all are agreed, no lack of desire to please. The wine list is quite long and affords a reasonable spread from round the world. However, it is a merchants' list: all Californians are Mondavi, most Australians are Brown Brothers. Value is fair. House wines, from £6.90. CELLARMAN'S CHOICE : Bourgogne Blanc, Les Clous 1986, de Villaine, £14.95. Tips are 'neither expected nor encouraged'.

CHEFS: D.L. Randolph and S. Wilkes    PROPRIETORS: D.L. and D.A. Randolph
OPEN: all week, exc Sat L and Sun D
MEALS: 12.30 to 2, 7 to 9.30
PRICES: Set L £15.50 (£21), Set D £24.50 (£30) and £29.50 (£35)
CARDS: Access, Amex, Diners, Visa
SEATS: 50. 5 tables outside. Private parties: 30 main room, 20 private room. Car-park, 40 places. Vegetarian meals. Children's helpings. Wheelchair access (1 step)
ACCOMMODATION: 8 rooms, all with bath/shower. B&B £75 to £125. Baby facilities. Garden. TV. Phone. Scenic. Doors close at midnight [GHG]

---

**HOLDENBY  Northamptonshire**                                    map 3

## ▲ *Lynton House*

Holdenby NN6 8DJ                                         COOKING 2
HOLDENBY (0604) 770777                                   COST £18–£28

This former rectory is on the Church Brampton to East Haddon road, just east of Holdenby with its ruins and gardens of the wonder house built for Sir Christopher Hatton, Elizabeth I's favourite and Lord Chancellor. The rectory's predominant colour is red, from the brick used in its building to carpets and walls, lightening to pink in the dining-room and conservatory. The house, expected to expand its hotel side in the next year or two, continues in the Italian vein, reinforced by the voluble welcome of Carlo Bertozzi and the cooking style of his wife Carol. The menu, fixed-price with a few surcharges, is long for a country restaurant. Readers have approved the spinach and ricotta tortellini, the medallions of venison with port and berries sauce and the coffee and walnut meringue cake. Some dishes have had little flavour: courgette and almond soup, and scallops poached with white wine, for example. Coffee is neither brilliant nor plentiful. The Bertozzis are good at keeping the dining-room free of smoke; have an excellent attitude to tipping – that is, discourage it; are not so brilliant at maintaining a good gentlemen's lavatory. The short wine list is stronger and cheaper on Italian than French, with nothing else allowed entry. It is light on such details as vintages and shippers. House

Corvo from Sicily, £9.75 a bottle. CELLARMAN'S CHOICE : Nebbiolo d'Alba, Bersano, £12.75.

CHEF: Carol Bertozzi   PROPRIETORS: Carlo and Carol Bertozzi
OPEN: all week, exc Mon and Sat L, Sun D
CLOSED: 2 weeks in summer, Christmas
MEALS: 12.15 to 1.45, 7.15 to 9.45
PRICES: Set L £11.50 (£18) and £12.75 (£19), Set D £16.95 (£23). Service inc
CARDS: Access, Visa
SEATS: 45. Private parties: 55 main room, 20 private room. Car-park, 30 places. Children's helpings (Sun L only). No children under 6. Smart dress preferred. No cigars/pipes in dining-room. Wheelchair access
ACCOMMODATION: 5 rooms, all with bath/shower. B&B £52 to £65. No children under 6. Garden. Golf. TV. Phone. Scenic. Doors close at 12.30. Confirm by 9am

---

**HOLT  Norfolk**                                                        map 6

# Yetman's

37 Norwich Road, Holt NR25 6SA                             COOKING 2
HOLT (0263) 713320                                              COST £22

Holt is one of the more attractive small towns in Norfolk, with small shops and rows of flint cottages. The restaurant is on the outskirts, just up the road from the church, in a row of old houses with hanging baskets and window boxes. The Yetmans almost sound as if they were provoked into the venture. 'We have been coming to this area for the last 20 years and we are running the sort of restaurant that we would like to have found here.' They opened in November 1988 with two pale primrose dining-rooms and a new set of tables and chairs. They lean heavily on organic produce and local fish and shellfish: paupiette of lemon sole is stuffed with smoked salmon butter; crab salad comes with an avocado mayonnaise strongly flavoured with basil. The small *carte* − choice of three, three, cheese and three − is changed each meal-time, and a vegetarian option is standard: courgettes stuffed with finely chopped peppers and onion on a bed of mushroom, topped with a well-flavoured Parmesan sauce, for example. Cheeses are as British as spotted Dick. A first-rate peach Melba combines firm, fleshy, skinned peaches, home-made vanilla ice-cream, cherry meringue, and a nicely sharp raspberry purée. Unlimited coffee and complimentary truffles. Wines are from Lay & Wheeler and reflect their varied choice and good value. Eight house wines, from £5.50. There is also a home-made lemon cordial.

CHEF: Alison Yetman   PROPRIETORS: Alison and Peter Yetman
OPEN: Wed to Sun
MEALS: 12.30 to 2, 7.30 to 9
PRICES: £13 (£18)
SEATS: 32. Private parties: 20 main room. Vegetarian meals. Children's helpings. No smoking in dining-room. Wheelchair access (1 step)

---

*The* Guide *is totally independent, accepts no free hospitality, and survives on the number of copies sold each year.*

## HOPTON CASTLE  Shropshire

map 4

## ▲ *Park Cottage*

Hopton Castle SY7 0QF
BUCKNELL (05474) 351
off B4367, 11m W of Ludlow

COOKING **3**
COST £10–£20

Not content to have a Norman keep in the adjoining field, nor to live in ultimate English picturesque surroundings (still unpolluted water, fresh and bracing air), the Gardners have a house of seventeenth-century origin, all black and white with a more modern timber-clad extension and conservatory. They are familiar to readers of the *Guide* from their stint at Veryan in Cornwall whence they moved in 1988. They have persisted in their approach: a homely scale – there are only two bedrooms and the oak-panelled dining-room can seat no more than a dozen – combined with assured professionalism. This does not extend to adventure (in big city parlance), for 'it seems a shame to serve such excellent local produce with out-of-character sauces which seems the modern trend.' Wye salmon is 'poached in the lovely chemical-free water, a touch of white wine, origanum, seasoning and a little olive oil to maintain the fish's oiliness' then served hollandaise. Leg of lamb is parsleyed and served with garden mint sauce; double-smoked gammon simply boiled. Vegetables, from the garden on good days, are simple yet generous. French cooking (which may shock a Salopian) still appears: duck offset by a slightly bitter prune and red wine sauce; fillets of plaice (Salopians are none too keen on sea fish either) niçoise. Puddings have survived the move from Cornwall: toffee-edged soft meringue filled with cream and raspberries sent a man into swoons. All this on an Aga, 'my third in 25 years of cooking'. Service by Josephine Gardner is nicely judged. Prices are eminently reasonable for a menu of, maybe, three choices until dessert; cheese a good Cheddar and a good Stilton. Sunday lunch is good value too. A very short wine list from Tanners. House wine, £5 or £5.50.
CELLARMAN'S CHOICE : Fleurie 1988, Loron, £10; Stoneleigh Marlborough Sauvignon-Blanc 1988, £10.

CHEF: John Gardner   PROPRIETORS: John and Josephine Gardner
OPEN: all week (advance booking out of season)
MEALS: 12 to 1.30, 7.30 to 8.30
PRICES: £12 (£17), Set Sun L £7 (£10) to £7.50 (£11)
SEATS: 12. 2 tables outside. Private parties: 10 main room, 8 private room. Car-park, 8 places. Children's helpings. No children under 7
ACCOMMODATION: 2 rooms, both with bath/shower. B&B £17 to £32. Deposit: £10. No children under 7. Afternoon teas. Garden. TV. Scenic. Doors close at 10. Confirm by noon

## HORTON  Northamptonshire

map 3

## *French Partridge* 🍾

Horton NN7 2AP
NORTHAMPTON (0604) 870033

COOKING **3**
COST £28

Perhaps the bird escaped in the first instance from the menagerie of the now-vanished great house in the village? More likely, it is a reference to David Partridge's sojourn in the Tarn long years ago, when France was a way of life treasured and, in a sense, displayed upon homecoming. One reader recalls the Partridge in its earliest days, the repository of genuine French cooking (no chi-chi pretence) for the district, visited but once yearly on an income of £750 per annum but worth all the pennies scraped. For some, the very continuity indicates tedium, but there are countless others who would deny that: enjoying the slight yet firm ritual, the slow tempo, the very Englishness of style and interior, and proclaiming the cooking as good as ever. Over the years, perhaps it has been naturalised – in 1987/8 the menu language changed from French to English – there are certainly some quintessentially English dishes on the four-course set-price menu (introduced in 1972) as well as those which display French origin or technique: melon with ginger wine; smoked mackerel pâté and smoked salmon roll; crispy roast duckling with citrus fruits might be examples of the first, while chicken livers on a salad dressed with walnut oil; mussel chowder; lambs' tongues with charcutière sauce; or wild rabbit with a leek cream sauce are instances of the second. Not every meal is perfect, one but moderately impressed visitor felt theirs was saved by the especially ordered vanilla ice-cream and the wine list. This latter is indeed impressive. The prices put others to shame; the selection, although young, is exemplary for France and Germany. The enthusiasm still shines through. The most enjoyable sections are the *vins de pays*, but who could resist burgundies from Gagnard-Delagrange, Clerget and Bachelet and Ch. Cissac 1981 at £16.50? To say nothing of the many thoughtfully chosen half-bottles. The German section should be renovated. House wines there are in profusion (up to Domaine de Trévallon 1985 at £12.50), starting at £5.50. CELLARMAN'S CHOICE : Gewürztraminer Cuvée Réservée 1986, Jean-Michel Deiss £8.50; Madiran, Domaine Bouscausse 1979, £8.90.

CHEFS: D.C. Partridge and Justin Partridge    PROPRIETORS: D.C. and M. Partridge
OPEN: Tue to Sat, D only
CLOSED: 2 weeks at Christmas and Easter, 3 weeks July to Aug
MEALS: 7.30 to 9
PRICES: Set D £18 (£23). Service inc
SEATS: 50. Private parties: 10 main room. Car-park, 50 places. Children welcome. Wheelchair access

---

**HUDDERSFIELD  West Yorkshire**                                    map 5

## Pisces

84 Fitzwilliam Street
Huddersfield HD1 5BD                                           COOKING 2
HUDDERSFIELD (0484) 516773                                  COST £17–£29

A converted mill, using two floors for dining, the name indicates that it is principally a fish restaurant, though it has introduced more meat dishes. This is particularly evident at lunchtime, now an à la carte affair, where three out of 10 main courses feature meat. The choice narrows in the evenings when a set menu offers three fish choices and one meat, perhaps medallions of pork with mushroom and green peppercorn sauce. But it is, after all, for the fish, cooked to order, that most customers come. 'We've been back four or five times, and never been disappointed,' says one regular, and other reports wax enthusiastic over paupiette of lemon sole in a cream and orange sauce, monkfish stew, and smoked salmon salad. Presentation and service are also praised. The wine list offers a short range from France with a few German bottles to top up and a very few half-bottles. House white, from the Loire, is £5.45. CELLARMAN'S CHOICE : Côte du Lubéron Blanc 1988, £6.95; Ch. Thieuley 1987, £8.25.

CHEF: Serge Nollent   PROPRIETORS: T.Y. and S.J. Wormald
OPEN: Mon to Sat
MEALS: 12 to 2, 7 to 9.30
PRICES: £17 (£24), Set D £12.95 (£17)
CARDS: Access, Visa
SEATS: 50. Private parties: 50 main room. Car-park, 22 places. Children welcome. Smart dress preferred. Wheelchair access. Music. Air-conditioned

---

**HURSTBOURNE TARRANT  Hampshire**                                          map 2

## ▲ *Esseborne Manor*

Hurstbourne Tarrant SP11 0ER
HURSTBOURNE TARRANT (026 476) 444
on the A343, 1m N of                                          COOKING 3
Hurstbourne Tarrant                                          COST £12–£36

The hotel changed hands mid-1988, since when reports have been drifting in of the companionable atmosphere and 'serious cooking'. The Yeo family moved down from Scotland and run their new establishment as 'a country-house hotel in its purest form'. It's small for a manor, but suavely done up with luxuriously draped curtains and plump sofas that just fit the rooms. The menu works to an unusual formula. Alongside a set, five-course menu which changes daily is a constant list of five other main courses – including scallop-stuffed chicken; beef fillet with two sauces; and duckling breast with citrus fruits – any of which may be chosen for a £2.50 supplement. In style the food is ultra-modern and seems sophisticated, using lots of spices, herbs and exotic fruits. Chef Mark Greenfield applies a vivid palette of colour: lilac chive flower petals on a smoked monkfish salad; blood red tomato sauce with fresh tuna fish: shocking yellow saffron sauce with chicken; ethereal green frozen mint mousse. There have been disappointments when sub-standard basic ingredients have slipped through, and sauces can be too complex to taste of their stated flavourings. Local game is made much of in season, for jugged hare or teal breasts in blackcurrant liqueur sauce. A single woman was treated less well than she felt she merited. Men 'will feel more comfortable in a jacket' at Esseborne, say the proprietors, although they have begun to be less stringent in their insistence on ties. Tipping is 'no longer expected'. House wines, Tyrrell's Long Flat Red and White, £8.90. CELLARMAN'S CHOICE : Woodstock McLaren Vale Chardonnay 1986, £14; Ch. Lynch-Bages 1978, £32.50.

---

*The text of entries is based on unsolicited reports sent in by readers, backed up by inspections conducted anonymously. The factual details under the text are from questionnaires the Guide sends to all restaurants that feature in the book.*

CHEF: Mark Greenfield   PROPRIETORS: Michael and Frieda Yeo and family
OPEN: all week
MEALS: 12.30 to 2, 7.30 to 9.30
PRICES: Set L £7.50 (£12) to £10.50 (£15), Set D £23 (£28) to £25.50 (£30)
CARDS: Access, Amex, Diners, Visa
SEATS: 36. 10 tables outside. Private parties: 28 main room, 10 private room. Car-park, 20
places. No children under 12 (exc Sun L). Smart dress preferred. No cigars/pipes in dining-
room. Wheelchair access
ACCOMMODATION: 12 rooms, all with bath/shower. B&B £65 to £78. No children under 12.
Afternoon teas. Garden. Tennis. TV. Phone. Scenic

---

**ILKLEY**  West Yorkshire                                                    map 5

## Box Tree

29 Church Street, Ilkley LS29 9DR                              COOKING 4
ILKLEY (0943) 608484                                          COST  £23−£54

No place that survives so long can fail to accrete resentment, even outrage, from
visitors who wonder what it's all about. The costs don't help, nor the elderly
plumbing, nor the ineluctable fading of the decoration. But regulars insist that
the quality continues. The staff may be younger, less outgoing and more
obsequious, and the owner may often be absent, but the cooking is good and
the service more than proficient. The tone can grate on some ears: excessively
ornate, moneyed, the pianist playing Dylan tunes as if they were Noël Coward.
But why change what Yorkshire seems to want? Edward Denny still cooks a
fine French dish, like the dariole of mushrooms that has entered the repertoire
of younger, more modish chefs. The menu is cast all in French, with ornate
English translations that do little to convince the new customer of the
undoubted quality of ingredients and fine judgement in many of the sauces,
still lightening in response to changed fashion. The texture of the langoustines,
the chewy girolles, the blush on the milk-fed lamb and the handling of the
vegetables, reconciling one even to cauliflower, indicates the priority accorded
to marketing. Combinations such as salad of grilled crottin with cashew nuts
and pine kernels, iced parfait of tea with mango sauce, and the perennial
timbale of strawberries with a rose sorbet show the sophisticated appreciation
of flavours. A meal in high summer offered queen scallops of impeccable
freshness served in a soup bowl on a mound of fresh pasta sauced with a fruit-
laden olive oil, grain mustard, fresh tomato and tarragon. Clear tastes, good
textures, an edge to the richness, a sweetness and a powerful aroma all in one
dish. This was succeeded by fillet of lamb arranged round a centre of spinach,
with a tomato and wine sauce given point by fennel. The finish was a feuilleté
(good pastry here) of blackberries and blueberries with a vanilla custard:
simplicity marked by perfect technique. A high point, perhaps, but a sign of
how Edward Denny can rise to the occasion. The wine list is often discounted:
a single merchant, little discrimination on the part of the establishment, and
punishing charges. There are too many alternate vintages, and the big
burgundies are often too young, but there are some nice clarets, a page of
Germans and a trio of Texan wines for the curious. No house wine, but there
are at least 10 bottles under £10. CELLARMAN'S CHOICE : Mâcon Clessé 1986,
Jean Thévenet, £17.85; Penfolds Grange 1981, £49.40.

CHEF: Edward Denny  PROPRIETOR: Eric Kyte
OPEN: Tue to Sat, D only, and Sun L
CLOSED: 25 and 26 Dec, 1 Jan
MEALS: 12.30 to 2, 7.30 to 9.45
PRICES: £30 (£45), Set L £14.25 (£23), Set D £17.50 (£27)
CARDS: Access, Amex, Diners, Visa
SEATS: 50. Private parties: 30 main room, 16 private room. Children welcome. Smart dress preferred. No cigars/pipes in dining-room. Wheelchair access

---

**INKPEN  Berkshire**                                               map 2

## Swan Inn

Lower Inkpen, Newbury RG15 0DX                         COOKING 1
INKPEN (048 84) 326                                        COST £24

It's unexpected to find a Singaporean meal in a Berkshire pub but that is the evening offering at the Swan – Esther Scothorne is the reason, for she is of Singaporean origin. At lunch the kitchen keeps to more orthodox recipes, good nonetheless, they say. The dinner menu is short, but supplemented by daily specials including quite spicy dishes: 'watch the thom yam soup does not blow your head off.' Sometimes the portions appear small, so it is wiser to order, say, six dishes for four people to compose a more balanced meal. Then, quantities are right. Rendang and dill-flavoured rice delighted one traveller who had been trying for some time to make sense of the maze of lanes around Inkpen. Approach from the Hungerford end and it is very clear from the main road. House French is £6.50 and £7.50 but there are Hook Norton, Brakspear and Flowers beers – and Singapore Slings to stay in keeping.

CHEF: Esther Scothorne  PROPRIETORS: Mr and Mrs J. Scothorne
OPEN: Tue to Sun, exc Sun D
MEALS: 12 to 2, 7 to 9.30
PRICES: £10 (£20), Snacks from £2.50
CARDS: Access, Visa
SEATS: 38. 7 tables outside. Private parties: 38 main room. Car-park, 50 places. Smart dress preferred. Music

---

**IPSWICH  Suffolk**                                              map 3

## Kwok's Rendezvous

23 St Nicholas Street, Ipswich IP1 1TW                  COOKING 1
IPSWICH (0473) 256833                                   COST £11–£20

Serious wine is the last thing one expects from a Chinese restaurant, but with such notable suppliers as Lay & Wheeler and Champagne de Villages, the list makes interesting reading. The menu is short, but covers all the regions from fiery bang bang chicken, not a contender for a bottle of Réserve de la Comtesse (Pichon's second wine), to a more suitable partner, the excellent aromatic and crispy duck. Hot-and-sour soup and gan-shaw prawns have been praised and a new menu from early August promised more local fish. House French, £5.95.

CHEF: Thomas Kwok    PROPRIETORS: Lucia and Thomas Kwok
OPEN: Mon to Sat
MEALS: 12 to 2, 7 to 10.30
PRICES: £9 (£17), Set L from £6.50 (£11), Set D from £8.50 (£14). Minimum £8.50
CARDS: Amex, Diners
SEATS: 50. Private parties: 30 main room. Car-park, 50 places. Vegetarian meals. Children
welcome. Smart dress preferred. Wheelchair access (also WC). Music

## Mortimer's on the Quay

Wherry Quay, Ipswich IP4 1AS                         COOKING 2
IPSWICH (0473) 230225                                 COST £24

The sister establishment to Mortimer's at Bury St Edmunds (see entry). On the
waterfront, in a converted warehouse near the old custom-house, this airy,
glass-roofed restaurant serves Grimsby fish, delivered daily, and Scottish
smoked fish. It seems inappropriate that seaside towns go so far for a resource
on their very doorstep, but it has long been so. Victorian residents of Hope
Cove, a fishing village in Devon, used once to wait for the Grimsby delivery to
come through on the train and, even today, the Grimsby lorry does a night-time
round of South Devon fish and chip shops. The menu here changes daily,
offering perhaps plaice, trout, hake, lemon sole, halibut, monkfish, tuna, turbot
and salmon at fair prices and in lavish quantity. Cooking is both plain and
classic, with an eye to the recipes of greats, like Mme Prunier. Beginnings
include a couple of soups, Loch Fyne oysters and smoked fish and about 10
other choices. Sweets are good, if rudimentary. The wine list is short and fairly
priced. House French £6.50. CELLARMAN'S CHOICE : Viña Sol, Torres 1987,
£7.75; Pinot d'Alsace, Hugel 1985, £8.95.

CHEF: Kenneth Ambler    PROPRIETORS: Kenneth Ambler and Michael Gooding
OPEN: Mon to Sat, exc Sat L
CLOSED: bank hols and day after, 24 Dec to 5 Jan
MEALS: 12 to 2, 7 to 9 (8.30 Mon)
PRICES: £14 (£20)
CARDS: Access, Amex, Diners, Visa
SEATS: 88. Private parties: 8 main room. Children's helpings. Smart dress preferred.
No-smoking area. Wheelchair access (1 step)

## Orwell House Restaurants

4 Orwell Place, Ipswich IP4 1BB                       COOKING 2
IPSWICH (0473) 230254                                 COST £11–£34

When the restaurant and bistro opened in 1986, they were welcomed as
additions to the limited choice for good eating in the centre of town. Built
within a Georgian town-house, they are designed as open-plan and split-level,
but decoration and furnishings reflect a provincial respectability appropriate to
the setting. Downstairs, there is a short monthly *carte* with simple bistro food:
in June, for example, it offered a smooth watercress and lemon soup, skate
wing meunière with a small pool of lemon butter, lamb cutlets Reform and a
hot side-plate of vegetables that included a julienne of courgette and carrots, a

biscuity tartlet of broccoli au gratin and new potatoes. Puddings, such as a orange bavarois, vanilla ice-cream and summer pudding, have been a notch above the average because they draw on the restaurant desserts. Upstairs, the three-course *carte* is built around more elaborate ideas and luxurious ingredients, with first courses including a crayfish timbale and boned roast quail filled by a pistachio and basil duxelles, followed by carefully sauced main dishes – some traditional or modern French, others oriental. Lobster, oysters and smoked salmon from the Orford oysterage are usually a feature. Salmon served with a black-bean and oyster sauce and loin of pork accompanied by a gooseberry, mint and sherry sauce have shown skill. Service is attentive and skillfully directed by a head waiter in wing collar and tails. A short wine list offers house Bergerac at £6.95.

CHEF: John Gear  PROPRIETOR: Michael Mosesson
OPEN: Mon to Sat, exc Mon D and Tue D
MEALS: 12 to 2, 7 to 9.30 (10 Sat)
PRICES: £19 (£28), Set L £5 (£11) to £11 (£17), Set D £9.25 (£15) to £15 (£22)
CARDS: Access, Amex, Visa
SEATS: 80. 4 tables outside. Private parties: 20 bistro, 20 lounge, 40 restaurant. Car-park, 12 places. Children's helpings. No smoking. Wheelchair access (also WC) in bistro. Music

## Singing Chef

200 St Helen's Street, Ipswich, IP4 2RH
IPSWICH (0473) 255236

COOKING 2
COST £18–£37

Those with long memories will recall the restaurant of this name in Connaught Street in London (now Le Chef, see entry) where Kenneth Toyé cooked substantial French food, then sang substantial French songs across gingham and candlelight. His love for both has never diminished, even in East Anglian rustication. His Ipswich restaurant pursues the bistro form to the death: café chairs, paper tablecloths, tricolors (for the bicentenary celebration), white-painted brick walls. It also pursues music: Kenneth Toyé may be persuaded to sing a chanson and there are regular jazz evenings. The menu explores a different French province each month. This gives occasion for wheeling out old favourites, from flamiche to fish soup, and the offering of dishes not often seen in English restaurants in the current climate of cooking *à la minute* and light or seemingly light sauces. Estouffade de boeuf arlésienne, lapin à la gitane, coq au vin blanc, côtes de porc avesnoise are a few examples. Success may depend on the tastes of the consumer, who needs to be fond of a casserole. An inspection meal yielded a large fillet of halibut with a carrot, tomato and green pepper sauce (flétan aux tomates normand) and a civet de mouton. The difficulty was the weight of food on a hot summer's day rather than its execution. The desserts need more imaginative finish, but desserts are hardly part of the tradition Mr Toyé is exploring. Green salad, by contrast, is excellent. Ipswich obviously prefers weak to strong coffee. The place may be mournful on a quiet night if the Toyés' presence does not galvanise the troops. The wine list has more Champagnes than anything else – not the ideal accompaniment for the style of cooking – and is light on some details in the largely French list. House French, £6.75; CELLARMAN'S CHOICE : Bergerac Blanc Sec £9; Champagne Brut, Jean-Paul Arvois, £17.50.

CHEFS: Kenneth and Jeannine Toyé   PROPRIETORS: Cynthia and Kenneth Toyé
OPEN: Tues to Sat D, L by arrangement
MEALS: 7 to 11
PRICES: £17 (£31), Set D £11.50 (£18)
CARDS: Access, Visa
SEATS: 35. 4 tables outside. Private parties: 20 main room, 15 and 20 private rooms.
Children's helpings. No-smoking area. Wheelchair access (also WC). Music

---

**IXWORTH  Suffolk**                                                map 6

## Theobalds

68 High Street, Ixworth IP31 2HJ                         COOKING 2
PAKENHAM (0359) 31707                                  COST £22–£32

A small restaurant that has been thriving in the same ownership for a number
of years, in what was once a shop. The cooking of Simon Theobald has
continued to draw favourable notices. It is quite a long menu, priced by the
main course chosen, and has certain hardy perennials: twice-baked cheese
soufflé; mushroom cups with some sort of stuffing; fillet steak with brandy and
green peppercorns; lemon tart. Quite a lot of the sauces are cream-based, and
sweet/sour combinations are sometimes favoured. In short, a steady country
restaurant providing service 'of the highest order', good presentation and fair
cooking such as we could do with across the land. The wine list also give
reasonable coverage and plenty of half-bottles. The Chinon and Saumur from
Couly Duthiel are a couple of good Loire reds; Les Plantiers du Haut Brion 1974
is a wonderful dry Graves, the second white from Haut Brion, most unexpected
in the circumstances. House wines, £7.25. CELLARMAN'S CHOICE : Brouilly,
Domaine de Pierre Bleue 1987, £13.25; Pinot Blanc 1985, Hugel, £11.40.

---

CHEF: Simon Theobald   PROPRIETORS: Simon and Geraldine Theobald
OPEN: all week, exc Mon L, and Sat L and Sun D
MEALS: 12.15 to 2, 7.30 to 10
PRICES: Set L and D £16.50 (£22) to £21.50 (£27)
CARDS: Access, Visa
SEATS: 36. Private parties: 36 main room. Children's helpings (Sun L only). No children
under 8. Separate no-smoking area. Music

---

**JEVINGTON  East Sussex**                                          map 3

## Hungry Monk

Jevington BM26 5QF
POLEGATE (032 12) 2178                                   COOKING 2
on B2105, between Polegate and Friston                   COST £23–£30

Perhaps East Sussex's longest running production, the Hungry Monk has
achieved its majority, always under the watchful eyes of the Mackenzies. The
two cottages afford a succession of little rooms through which diners progress
at each stage of their meal. First, a drink and ordering in a minute sitting-room;
thence to the dining-room, itself close packed; then, the meal finished, back to
another sitting-room for coffee and that complimentary glass of tawny port. On

winter nights it is all fires and candlelight; in summer the clematis blooms, the twilight falls on garden and the trees beyond. An idyll with a heart of steel, for the consequences of leading with the wrong foot will be the collapse of the stately pavane, delays at the commencement of the ritual, muttering in the ranks. It must be stressed again: most diners are willing; they enjoy the routine, the intimacy of the small rooms and the kindly attentions of staff and owners. The food has not changed gear since coming under the well-trained hand of Claire Burgess, nor has it declined, though the modernisation has continued apace. The Hungry Monk is famed for continuity. Portions remain generous, cooking stays robustly familiar to those who have haunted English country restaurants these last two decades. An inspector found all sauces too highly seasoned: calf's liver with raspberry vinegar sauce too acid; quail with port and raisin sauce too sweet. But few are the complaints; the honest food is rarely ruined. Puddings remain a strong point: a crème brûlée, with wafer-thin and brittle crust, as creamy and unctuous as it should be. One cavil is the vegetables. Each diner gets the same – red cabbage with fish is never a pretty sight – which results in some being overcooked while waiting for those which need longer heating. The wine list has a sprinkling of everything and perhaps is most remarkable for its English section, including the excellent Breaky Bottom. There are also some nice French country wines. House wine from £6.90. CELLARMAN'S CHOICE : Coonawarra Rouge Homme Chardonnay 1987, £15.66; Ch. Fabas, Minervois 1985, £7.35. Smoking is now forbidden in the dining-room. There are some pleasant function rooms for larger parties.

CHEF: Claire Burgess  PROPRIETORS: Nigel and Susan Mackenzie
OPEN: all week D and Sun L (other days by arrangement for large parties)
MEALS: 12.15 to 2.30, 7.15 to 10.30
PRICES: Set Sun L £15.95 (£23) to £16.95 (£24), Set D £15.95 (£23) to £17.45 (£25). Service of 10% for parties of 8 or more
SEATS: 36. 2 tables outside. Private parties: 38 main room, 10 and 16 private rooms. Car-park, 17 places. Vegetarian meals. Children's helpings. No children under 3. Smart dress preferred. No smoking

---

KENDAL Cumbria                                                        map 7

## Moon

| | |
|---|---|
| 129 Highgate, Kendal LA9 4EN | COOKING 1 |
| KENDAL (0539) 29254 | COST £19 |

Behind its shop-like façade, the restaurant has expanded yet again. This time, a beamed bar, strikingly decorated in lemon and black, has been added upstairs as an overspill waiting area. The arrival of a full-time manager has also allowed more experiment in the kitchen, so that the small menu – half a dozen first and main courses – draws on an broader repertoire. Brioches with fillings of leek, garlic, cream and mushroom and the like are among the vegetarian additions. Steak and chicken are often given strong, spicy treatments, as in Moroccan prune- and honey-baked chicken breast. Customers point to large portions and say, regretfully, that they don't always make it to the rich home-made puddings, trifles and ice-creams. There is cafetière coffee and a very short but careful wine and beer list, with largely New World bottles, Rock's elderflower wine and Samuel Smith's real ale. House French, £6.25 a litre. CELLARMAN'S CHOICE : Orlando Cabernet Sauvignon 1986, Rowland Flat, £6.79; Orvieto Classico 1987, Torricella, £6.95.

CHEFS: Dianne Kinsey, Sharon Moreton and Val Macconnell
PROPRIETOR: Val Macconnell
OPEN: all week, D only
MEALS: 6 to 10 (10.30 Fri and Sat)
PRICES: £10 (£16)
CARDS: Access, Visa
SEATS: 40. Vegetarian meals. Children's helpings. Wheelchair access. Music

---

**KENILWORTH** Warwickshire                                                   map 5

## Restaurant Bosquet ♟

| 97A Warwick Road, Kenilworth CV8 1HP | COOKING 3 |
|---|---|
| KENILWORTH (0926) 52463 | COST £23–£36 |

The main high road of Kenilworth is hardly fuel for the imagination: that is supplied by the castle or, in lower key, by the old town beyond. One might be forgiven, therefore, for not expecting great things from the undistinguished building that houses this grove of French cooking. The style is not bourgeois: lots of foie gras, wild mushrooms, mousses and wrappings; oysters wrapped with thin slices of salmon, steamed on a bed of seaweed served with a cream white wine and oyster liquor sauce; terrine of red mullet with peppers, wrapped with aubergine and served with pepper sauce; breast of guinea-fowl wrapped with cabbage stuffed with foie gras served with a carrot and Sauternes sauce. The execution continues to be of a high order: 'outstandingly the best meal this year', wrote one couple travelling out of North Wales, 'oozes with professional expertise, he *loves* food and cooking. It was refreshing to see the commis chef on his knees cleaning the kitchen floor.' Equally, it was heartbreaking to watch a drunken party calling for more beer, burnt steaks and 'none of that fancy sauce'. A more local reader accepts that it is the best in the district but regrets that it is not more of an event, too much 'like eating in someone's front room'. Still, if the food warrants it... The wine list is really good. Wholly French, that goes without saying, but finely balanced between regions, interest and affordability. Some unknown hand endorsed a previous list as 'my ideal of the perfect restaurant wine list', and the comment would stand discussion. Look for the south-western wines and seek guidance on some of the lesser clarets. There is a short and reasonably priced set menu served every night bar Saturday; lunch is by prior arrangement. CELLARMAN'S CHOICE : Jurançon, Domaine de Cauhapé 1987, £11; Madiran, Ch. Montus, Cuvée Prestige 1985, £19.

CHEF: Bernard Lignier   PROPRIETORS: Bernard and Jane Lignier
OPEN: Tue to Sat D; Tue to Fri L by prior arrangement
CLOSED: last 3 weeks in July
MEALS: 12 to 1.45, 7 to 10
PRICES: £22 (£30), Set L and D £16 (£23)
CARDS: Amex, Visa
SEATS: 28. Private parties: 30 main room. Children welcome

# ▲ Brundholme Country House Hotel

Brundholme Road, Keswick CA12 4NL
KESWICK (07687) 74495
take Keswick Road from A66 roundabout,
then first L after garage

COOKING 2
COST £14–£29

The stranger will not find this easy to reach, just on the outskirts of Keswick above the River Greta. One reporter was lucky to find a postman: luckier still that he knew the locality. The house, a Regency villa, is by the good architect George Basevi. The Charltons, who have moved here from the Yew Tree at Seatoller, could have called it 'The Delicious Situation' Hotel, since those were the words used by Coleridge to describe the position of the house looking out over the fells. Other literary connections of its builders, the Calverts, included Wordsworth, spared by their beneficence from the awful necessity of working for a living. In the present day, the connections are all supply lines: from farmers and dealers bringing in Borrowdale trout, Windermere char, Herdwick lamb, Cumberland ham and local game. Chefs Ian Charlton and Bruce Jackson work this produce into a satisfactory modern menu, shorter and simpler at lunch, that remains competitively priced. Cumberland ham is wrapped around cream cheese and served with a leaf and fruit salad, or around a lamb steak which is then served with a celeriac croquette; Borrowdale trout is marinated in rose petal vinegar and pink peppercorns and served with an apple and Jerusalem artichoke salad; the game is turned into a coarse and tasty terrine; Cumberland cheese is the base of a hot soufflé garnished with caramelised shallots. They can handle flavours well, a paupiette of sole turned round a dark purée of mushrooms is served in decent flaky pastry, the cooking juices of the fish thickened with cream, the whole accompanied by crisp mange-tout and splendid wild mushrooms; vegetables, although dressed with sauces, in fact achieve coherence, even as accompaniments. There is a strong Englishness to parts of the repertoire: very hearty soups, cobbler of lamb, jugged hare and lots of English puddings, though a sticky date and nut pudding was 'not as sticky or as sweet as it should be'. Decent coffee and vegetarian fare. A short wine list with bottles from Chanson, Deinhard, Babich and Hugel. House Duboeuf, £6.50. CELLARMAN'S CHOICE : Ch. La Gurgue, Margaux 1983, £13.10; Babich Henderson Valley Pinot Noir 1985, £10.90.

CHEFS: Ian Charlton and Bruce Jackson   PROPRIETORS: Ian and Lynn Charlton
OPEN: all week
MEALS: 12.15 to 1.30, 7.30 to 8.45
PRICES: Set L £8.50 (£14) to £12.50 (£18), Set D £14 (£20) to £18 (£24). Snacks from £1.25
CARDS: Access, Visa
SEATS: 50. Private parties: 55 main room, 55 private room. Car-park, 25 places. Vegetarian meals. Children's helpings on request. No children under 12. Smart dress preferred. No smoking in dining-room. Wheelchair access (also WC)
ACCOMMODATION: 11 rooms, all with bath/shower. B&B £30 to £60. Deposit: £10. No children under 10. Garden. TV. Phone. Scenic. Doors close at 11.30. Confirm by 6

## La Primavera

Greta Bridge, High Hill
Keswick CA12 5NX
KESWICK (076 87) 74621

COOKING 2
COST £25

Giuseppe and Pamela Guarracino owned a pub in Bassenthwaite before moving just outside the congested Lakeland town of Keswick. Their restaurant is to be found opposite the pencil mill, beloved object of geography quizzes. It is housed in a former industrial school of art and is a good example of sound Britalian cooking. There is a long menu for the restaurant and an additional list of daily dishes, mainly pasta, available for meals in the bar. Recommendations for both have been received. Authentic Italian items get the cream of the comments: antipasto of salami, aubergine and roasted red peppers in garlic; a bubbling hot dish of melanzana parmigiano with finely sliced aubergine, fresh tomato and mozzarella; a smoothly sauced penne alla mascarpone. Nonetheless, the quality of the grilled steaks has been described as outstanding. There are careful touches, like Cumbrian farmhouse cheeses. Be prepared for a leisurely pace. The service is exemplary. House wines from the Veneto are £6.80 per litre.

CHEF: Giuseppe Guarracino   PROPRIETORS: Giuseppe and Pamela Guarracino
OPEN: Tue to Sun
CLOSED: mid-Jan to mid-Feb
MEALS: 12 to 2, 7 to 10
PRICES: £15 (£21). Snacks from £2.50
CARDS: Access, Visa
SEATS: 90. 20 tables outside. Private parties: 80 main room. Car-park, 20 places. Vegetarian meals. Children's helpings. Wheelchair access (also WC). Music. Air-conditioned

---

**KING'S LYNN  Norfolk**　　　　　　　　　　　　　　　　　　map 6

## Riverside Rooms

King's Lynn Arts Centre, 27 King Street
King's Lynn PE30 1HA
KING'S LYNN (0553) 773134

COOKING 1
COST £23

From the windows of the restaurant, which is built inside a fourteenth-century National Trust building, there are interesting views out over the River Ouse. Inside there is a theatre and coffee-shop as well as the restaurant, in a warehouse, with rough brick walls and beams; a bar has just been added. Both lunch and dinner menus are long, catering for different pockets and tastes, and have a largely British feel. They have changed little although there are some new dishes: rack of lamb with a chive and cream sauce, beef Wellington, Narborough trout baked with butter and green ginger. Shellfish from Cromer varies with availability. Among the desserts, there are many roulades and always a hot steamed pudding. House wine is £7.50 a litre. CELLARMAN'S CHOICE: Côtes de Beaune Villages 1983, £11.75; Clos des Jacobins 1978, St-Emilion, £25.50. There are often bin-end bargains.

CHEF: Dennis Taylor    PROPRIETORS: Michael and Sylvia Savage
OPEN: Mon to Sat
MEALS: 12 to 2, 7 to 10
PRICES: £12 (£19)
CARDS: Access, Visa
SEATS: 65. 24 tables outside. Private parties: 75 main room. Car-park, 10 places. Vegetarian meals. Children's helpings. No-smoking area. Music

---

**KINGHAM   Oxfordshire**                                              map 2

# ▲ Mill House Hotel and Restaurant

Kingham OX7 6UH
KINGHAM (060 871) 8188                                          COOKING 1
off B4450, 5m from Stow-on-the-Wold                          COST £19–£38

A brief hiatus as the chefs changed, is over, bringing the reemergence of this hotel set on the edge of the village in a windswept landscape. A mill stream runs through the grounds, flagged floors remind the visitor of earlier activities but the predominant tone, in dining-room at least, is pink – from ruched curtains to chairs and carnations on the table. The restaurant continues the tradition of modern cooking established in previous years: red pepper and tomato soup finished with a saffron cream, fricassée of monkfish and asparagus flavoured with shallots and tarragon with a mussel sauce, braised salmon with quenelles of brill in a sorrel sauce, breast of duck with mango and a lime sauce, hot prune and Armagnac soufflé with a kirsch cream, a chocolate mousse with a chocolate and Grand Marnier sauce. There is a limited-choice, set-price menu that changes daily and a longer *carte* of half a dozen dishes at each stage that reads slightly more ambitiously. A meal in the spring revealed an unevenness in execution that might be improved if the kitchen limited its sights to a smaller menu and less needless elaboration. A feuilleté of chicken livers and bacon in a port and rosemary sauce had good buttery pastry and well-judged sauce but overcooked livers; a breast of chicken filled with a spinach and hazelnut mousse revealed tip-top chicken, a technically correct but bland mousse and a madeira sauce of exceptional mediocrity. Vegetables went from good carrots to hard beans. A hot soufflé was risen but leathery and with no more flavour than the ginger cream that came with it. The Mill House is popular, the postbag has been full, it is convenient for Stratford, letters convey many yeas but too many nays. Service has been appreciated: all of it seems informed. The wine list has grown over the years and charges fair prices for a reasonable range. House French is £7.50. CELLARMAN'S CHOICE : Mâcon-Viré, Domaine de Roally 1987, £14.75; New Zealand Chardonnay, Marlborough 1987, £14.25.

---

*The 1991 Guide will be published before Christmas 1990. Reports on meals arc most welcome at any time of the year, but are extremely valuable in the spring. Send them to* **The Good Food Guide**, FREEPOST, *2 Marylebone Road, London NW1 1YN. No stamp is needed if posted in the UK.*

CHEF: Stanley Mathews    PROPRIETORS: Mr and Mrs John Barnett
OPEN: all week
MEALS: 12.30 to 2, 7.30 to 9.30
PRICES: £24 (£32), Set L £11.50 (£19), Set D £16.50 (£24), Snacks from £2. Licensed, also
bring your own: corkage £7.50
CARDS: Access, Amex, Diners, Visa
SEATS: 60. Private parties: 30 main room. Car-park, 60 places. Children's helpings. No
children under 5. No cigars/pipes in dining-room. Wheelchair access (3 steps)
ACCOMMODATION: 21 rooms, all with bath/shower. Rooms for disabled. B&B £42.50 to
£65. Deposit: £10. No children under 5. Afternoon teas. Garden. Fishing. TV. Phone.
Scenic. Doors close at midnight. Confirm by 6

---

**KINGSBRIDGE** Devon                                                    map 1

## ▲ Queen Anne Restaurant, Buckland-Tout-Saints Hotel ▼

Kingsbridge TQ7 2DS
KINGSBRIDGE (0548) 3055                                          COOKING 3
2m NE of Kingsbridge                                           COST £24–£42

Buckland-Tout-Saints, its own church tucked at the back of the shrubbery, is a
fine Queen Anne house a few miles off the Totnes to Kingsbridge road: follow
the signs. Inside looks and feels like an Edwardian stockbroker's signal that he
has joined the ranks of the landed, though the bedrooms have a lighter touch.
The success of the hotel was unexpected and shows the effect of youthful
determination and a good chef. In its way, it is a college text-book example of
how to present a country hotel where many lessons from colleagues and
competitors have been well absorbed. The dinner menu is offered at two prices,
dependent on the choice of cheese and/or dessert. There are half a dozen
alternatives at each course. Alastair Carter, the chef, pursues his study of British
cooking to produce dishes in the modern style that never slide into the
ludicrous, and that keep materials and their quality to the fore. A meal that
pleased all readers began with a feuilleté of scallops and mussels with spinach
in a saffron and tomato sauce followed by rack of lamb with an onion purée
and a madeira sauce. The lamb was hung sufficient time to develop its flavour.
Dessert was an iced lemon soufflé, full of zest to cut the cream, with almond
sablés. Cheese, supplied usually by Ticklemore Cheese Shop in Totnes – run
by the makers of Beenleigh Blue – is English and mostly Devon. Coffee, served
in one of the halls or sitting-rooms, comes with good sweets. Ancillaries, at
breakfast as much as lunch or dinner, are home produced and please many:
breads, croissants, jams, pickles, even smoked meats and fish. Service is
invariably keen and concerned. Getting the food up from the basement to the
dining-room without deterioration is achievement enough. Teas on the terrace
are not stinted: and the view of valleys, woods and green hilltops is at its best
then. The wine list is a range of French with adequate buttressing from newer
countries and Germany. There are enough halves; the pricing is not giveaway.
It's a wine merchant's list, carefully composed, not the product of some wild
enthusiast. The notes and introductions tend to overshadow the wines
themselves. The hotel operates the strange practice of adding a small sum as a

charitable gift (this time to conservation) to customers' bills. Vicarious giving is fun, but the management could stump up out of their own takings. A reader tried to book a Mother's Day lunch only to find children under eight were not welcomed. To the Shephards, at least, mothers only have rights in their own homes. House wines from three countries, from £11.40. CELLARMAN'S CHOICE : Clos du Marquis 1983, £24.05; Brown Brothers Cabernet Sauvignon 1978, £21.90.

CHEF: Alastair Carter    PROPRIETORS: Mr and Mrs Victor Edward Shephard
OPEN: all week
CLOSED: 2 or 3 weeks from 2 Jan
MEALS: 12.15 to 1.45, 7.30 to 9
PRICES: Set L £14 (£24) to £18.50 (£27), Set D £21.50 (£32) to £26 (£35). Service inc
CARDS: Access, Amex, Diners, Visa
SEATS: 30. Private parties: 8 and 10 main room, 12 and 20 private room. Car-park, 14 places.
No children under 8. No smoking
ACCOMMODATION: 12 rooms, all with bath/shower. B&B £65 to £125. Deposit: one night's stay. No children under 8. Afternoon teas. Garden. TV. Phone. Scenic. Doors close at midnight. Confirm by 4 [GHG]

## KINGSTON UPON THAMES  Surrey

map 3

## *Ayudhya* ♥

14 Kingston Hill
Kingston upon Thames KT2 7NH
01-549 5984

COOKING  2
COST  £24

In the last two years, Somjai Feehan has invested heavily in furnishings with an appropriate Thai feel – teak panelling plus murals – as well as a water-cooled Chinese cooking range. This reflects the continuing success of the restaurant, one of the first of its kind outside central London, and it is now wise to book at weekends. The menu has new additions which suggest a refreshing lack of compromise: salads of papaya, aubergine or green mango are chilli-hot with a spiced dressing or there are stir-fried morning glory greens. There is also a new vegetarian menu and daily specials which reveal the range of flavourings: breast of duck with tamarind sauce, fried rice with minced coconut, fresh fish balls in a green curry, frogs' legs in a red curry paste flavoured with basil. Coffee is a 'bottomless cup'. The wine list is much improved. It is arranged by grape or taste/vinification type: thus there is a group of oaked Chardonnays, spicy reds and spicy whites. The range is not doctrinaire at all and includes some good bottles, none costing more than £20 and most under £10. House French is £5.90 (white) and £6.25 (red). CELLARMAN'S CHOICE : Cabernet Schlumberger, £8.60.

CHEF/PROPRIETOR: Somjai Feehan
OPEN: all week, exc Mon L
CLOSED: Suns before bank hols, and 25 Dec, 1 Jan, Easter Sun
MEALS: 12 to 2.30 (3 Sun), 6.30 to 11 (11.30 Fri and Sat)
PRICES: £12 (£20). Service inc
CARDS: Access, Amex, Diners, Visa
SEATS: 84. Private parties: 30 main room, 20 and 24 private rooms. Vegetarian meals.
Children welcome. Wheelchair access. Music

## Restaurant Gravier

9 Station Road
Kingston upon Thames KT2 7AA
01-549 5557 and 547 1121

COOKING 1
COST £38

It has been observed by its denizens who also write to the *Guide*, that francophone Surrey is a pretty dull affair but that English people, rushing home from a day's enterprise in the City, seem happy to listen to its siren charms. This small restaurant, made up of three small cottages in the shadow of Kingston's medical quarter, seems anxious to practise its English, for the menu of the day is recited at breakneck and often incomprehensible speed. There is a *carte* as well, between them offering a total of maybe a dozen dishes in each course – no prices given to women. The speciality is fish: fish soup, crab gratin, turbot with a robust stock sauce, salmon with scallops, monkfish in lobster sauce, barracuda, sea-bass, lobster et al. What meat there is may only be fillet steak and that new hoary standby confit de canard (with a salade de gésiers in the first courses). So far, the standard of the cooking has been reported as very mixed, good enough to stand out like a beacon in Kingston, not good enough to justify its pleasure in being French. The cheeseboard from Olivier is excellent. The wine list is interesting, disregarding the first growths. Obviously it only has French wines, but there are some interesting Loires from Guy Saget and generic burgundies from Luc Sorin; neither group will break the bank. Half-bottles are conspicuous by their absence. House French is £6.45.

CHEF: Joanne Gravier  PROPRIETORS: Jean-Philippe and Joanne Gravier
OPEN: Mon to Sat, exc Sat L
MEALS: 12.15 to 2, 7.15 to 10
PRICES: £23 (£32)
CARDS: Access, Amex, Diners, Visa
SEATS: 40. 4 tables outside. Private parties: 50 main room. Children's helpings. Wheelchair access (1 step). Music

**KINGTON**  Hereford & Worcester

map 4

## Penrhos Court ♥

Kington HR5 3LH
KINGTON (0544) 230720

COOKING 2
COST £13–£30

The half-timbered gables of the large farmhouse surrounded by a host of ancillary buildings, making a hamlet without external support, mask a long and complicated history. The Court was first built in the reign of Edward I and has been added to and adapted at one- or two-hundred-year intervals ever since. In 1972 Martin Griffiths, subsequently joined by Daphne Lambert, assumed the burden of restoration, which continues to this day. Anxious that the work ethic that moulded it should not be tarnished by a simplistic heritage culture, its restoration is financed by self-generated surplus. The restaurant that operates in one of the barns is essential for the scheme. Daphne Lambert cooks a thoroughly interesting menu that preserves some home invention, interprets modern literature, and has an eye on centuries of culinary development in England and beyond. Her work on medieval cookery bears fruit in regular banquets (more considered than many) as well as literary work. The menu that she offers runs to six dishes per course. A meal earlier in the year began with a ragout of fish with saffron and aïoli that demonstrated fine timing, well balanced sauces and a pleasing enrichment from the lightly garlicked mayonnaise. Main course was an invention: chicken stuffed with prawns, topped with a claw of lobster in a rich butter, cream and white wine sauce. This combination of flesh and shellfish, though having its attractions, is one of the most depressing aspects of cookery at the turn of the decade. It has to be a blind alley of taste, as is the over-fruiting of savoury dishes that once ruled the roost (and still crows on many middens). However, as such dishes go, this was a good one and displayed good sources of supply, as did the rest of the meal. Desserts divide between a couple of pastries and home-made ice-creams. Breads are excellent and there is a welcome lack of twiddly bits and pieces before and after the meal. Vegetables also have shown the merit of good suppliers (or gardeners). Over the years of Daphne Lambert's practice, there has been some lightening and much effort at improvement and taking notice of other people's work: this does not translate as derivative but rather as honest craftsmanship in a fine location. The meal is enthusiastically supervised by Martin Griffiths. His short wine list, drawing much from Bibendum (wine merchants, not restaurant), is totally non-doctrinaire, fairly priced and good. House wines are £6. CELLARMAN'S CHOICE : Ch. Rouet, Fronsac 1983, £12; Basedow Barossa Valley Semillon 1987, £11.50.

CHEF/PROPRIETOR: Daphne Lambert
OPEN: Wed to Sat, D only, and Sun L
CLOSED: 25 and 26 Dec
MEALS: 12.30 to 2, 7.30 to 10
PRICES: £17 (£25), Set Sun L £9 (£13)
SEATS: 20. 10 tables outside. Private parties: 50 main room. Car-park, 100 places. Children's helpings (under 5s eat free). Wheelchair access (also WC)

---

KINTBURY  Berkshire                                    map 2

## ▲ *Dundas Arms* ▮

Station Road, Kintbury RG15 0UT                    COOKING 1
KINTBURY (0488) 58263                              COST £20−£37

The only snag about the setting of this early Victorian pub is the proximity of the main London to Bristol railway line, a touch too close for comfort. In between trains the setting is idyllic: beside the Kennet and Avon canal, water on three sides. The pub is popular and can be crowded, and the dining-room, decorated in calming greens and pinks, becomes a refuge from scores of cars dotted crazily round the car-parks and rooms close-packed with happy Berkshire drinkers. The three-course set menu is strong on sauces and can be very good: mussels with saffron, fresh and tasty, the cream sauce well judged; smoked pigeon breast, 'a great treat for those who like strong meat'; excellent fish terrine with crayfish sauce. Another meal included fresh spinach of prime quality; nice amuse-gueule; 'authentic' bread in large chunks; but dreadful coffee and, sometimes, puddings that needed more thought. Puddings that have been well reported include lemon mousse and brown-bread ice-cream.

There is a certain take-it-or-leave-it approach to service, slow at the best of times, and standards have slipped badly on an off-day. The kitchen looks in danger of more inconsistency than is acceptable. The wine list retains its French interest and considerable appeal. The wealthy can indulge in a lot of vintage comparisons among clarets: Chasse Spleen, La Lagune, Haut Bages Monpelou, Grand Puy Lacoste, Latour, Haut Bailly all come in more than one year. The burgundies are an aristocratic selection and the prices are fair. House Côtes de Duras, £7. CELLARMAN'S CHOICE : St-Véran, Domaine les Deux Roches 1987, £14.50; Ch. de Marbuzet, 1983 (the second wine of Cos d'Estournel), £18. If replete, guard against the hump-back bridges on driving away, they may cause much discomfort.

CHEF/PROPRIETOR: David A. Dalzell-Piper
OPEN: Tue to Sat
CLOSED: Christmas to New Year
MEALS: 12.30 to 1.30, 7.30 to 9.30
PRICES: Set L £12.50 (£20) to £18.50 (£26), Set D £20 (£28) to £25 (£31), Snacks from £1.20
CARDS: Access, Amex, Diners, Visa
SEATS: 36. 10 tables outside. Private parties: 22 main room. Car-park, 40 places. Children's helpings. Smart dress preferred. No cigars/pipes in dining-room. Wheelchair access (2 steps; also WC)
ACCOMMODATION: 5 rooms, all with bath/shower. Rooms for disabled. B&B £46 to £52. TV. Phone. Scenic. Doors close at 11.30. Confirm by 6

---

**KIRKHAM  Lancashire**                                                        map 5

## *Cromwellian*

16 Poulton Street, Kirkham PR4 2AB                          COOKING 2
KIRKHAM (0772) 685680                                    COST £13–£27

The street frontage is so narrow that you may miss it in the main street of this Lancashire village of long heritage. The Fawcetts' experience since the last *Guide* (their standards seem to be steadily rising) is instructive. They have thrown out the old French menu descriptions, with anglo-subtitles, in favour of an all-English card. The food has not changed, just the packaging of the monthly changing menus. The report is that business has climbed in consequence. This speaks volumes for sound Lancastrian sense. A family business – father out front, mother in the kitchen – the Cromwellian impresses by its warmth. The cooking can be very satisfying: a trifle of filo pastry wrapped round cream cheese and broccoli with aperitifs; a broccoli and fennel soup, or a parsnip and ginger soup with green ginger wine; a salmon with lime, white port and ginger butter sauce; trout with spinach, prunes and almond stuffing (salmon and trout are more often found than white fish from the ocean); chicken breast with hazelnuts, grapes, bacon and a sherry cream sauce are the things that have pleased reporters. Vegetables are not so brilliant, but puddings are obviously a weakness (ie strength): butterscotch meringue pie, spiced apple cheesecake, hot almond sponge, rhubarb brown betty, all these seem substantial and are wildly praised. Is this the secret of going English? The wine list is as fairly priced as the food, short (but growing) and wholly French. House French, £6.50. CELLARMAN'S CHOICE : Mercurey, Dom. de la Renarde 1984, £12.50; Pouilly Fumé 1987, Dagueneau, £13.50.

CHEF: Josie Fawcett   PROPRIETORS: Peter and Josie Fawcett
OPEN: Tue to Sat D, Sun L
MEALS: 12.30 to 3, 7 to 10.30
PRICES: Set Sun L £8.50 (£13), Set D £13.95 (£21) to £16.45 (£23)
CARDS: Access, Visa
SEATS: 30. Private parties: 17 main room, 12 private room. Vegetarian meals. Wheelchair access. Music

---

## KNUTSFORD   Cheshire
map 5

## ▲ *Belle Epoque*

60 King Street, Knutsford WA16 6DT
KNUTSFORD (0565) 3060

COOKING 2
COST £37

Keith and Nerys Mooney are keen, in their wine list for example, to stake their claim to be considered a 'French' restaurant. This justifies their small number of German, Italian and Spanish bottles. Their menu, too, is written in French, with English sub-titles. Yet their kitchen team is, and always has been, English; they serve only cheeses from the British Isles; they are proud to serve fish straight from the coast; lamb is from Cheshire, duck from Lancashire and the blue cheese (used in two particular dishes) from Cashel. Why do they persist in thinking they are French? Their recipes certainly are not: calf's liver served with fresh cranberries and orange; quail stuffed with nuts and nectarines, glazed with honey and served with nectarine and honey sauce; breast of duck on an apple purée with a sausage of the leg meat in a port sauce perfumed with cinnamon. This is sweet-and-sour British cooking with a vengeance, and has received many plaudits over the years. The materials are indubitably chosen carefully and their treatment is inventive. Fashioned as a monument to art nouveau, the Belle Epoque is one of Cheshire's most popular restaurants. Accommodation available to diners only, Monday to Friday.

CHEF: David Williams   PROPRIETORS: Keith and Nerys Mooney
OPEN: Mon to Sat, D only
CLOSED: first week Jan
MEALS: 7.30 to 10
PRICES: £21 (£31). Service 10%
CARDS: Access, Amex, Diners, Visa
SEATS: 70. Private parties: 60 main room, 20, 60 and 80 private rooms. No children under 10. No pipes in dining-room. Music
ACCOMMODATION: 5 rooms, all with bath/shower. B&B £30 to £45. No children under 10. Garden. TV. Scenic. Doors close at 12. Confirm by 2

---

'On arriving at the restaurant I noticed that the "Closed" sign was still up, but pushed on the door, since the restaurant had just confirmed on the telephone that it was open. The door was open – despite the sign – but the restaurant was not. A gentleman with a moustache was sitting near the door. When I asked if we could sit down, he said that I should have read the sign outside. When I said that we had just called to make sure that the restaurant was open before we drove over, he said that he couldn't be responsible for what other people said, and that I shouldn't "have a go at him".'   On dining in Buckinghamshire

# ▲ At the Sign of the Angel

Church Street, Lacock SN15 2LA                         COOKING 1
LACOCK (024 973) 230                               COST £21−£30

Changes there are afoot in this old inn; yet they are not too great: 'Time seemed
to have stood still,' wrote one reporter after a seven-year intermission in visits.
However, telephones and televisions are in all the rooms (no longer a TV in the
upstairs lounge where you take aperitifs); the menu, which used to be recited,
is now written out (but is apparently innocent of any indication of price); the
single main course (with half a dozen items either side) has been replaced by
an invariable roast − often beef, but also boned, rolled and stuffed lamb or
duck, for example − a fish dish and a vegetarian main course; the hours of
dinner have been slightly extended. The inn, it goes without saying, is
quintessentially English, beautiful and embedded in a National Trust village of
paramount charm. The restaurant reflects the consequent pressure, from
American visitors for one, but the rare-cooked beef shows the kitchen has not
entirely succumbed to it. Walking the flagged passages, climbing the stairs of
polished treads and carved balusters, sitting before logs in flames, dining off
glossy tables (with worm-holes, if lucky) with good silver and glassware is a
sure ticket to gentility. The cooking, too, is English: 1960s first courses like
salmon mousse, three pâtés, avocado vinaigrette, kidneys in madeira are
followed by that roast, then a hot pudding or home-made ice-creams,
meringues, 'treacle lick' or fresh-fruit salad. 'Honest' is the first description to
occur, 'expensive' the second. The cooking is often good: vegetables get the
modern, not Mrs Beeton's, treatment; Yorkshire pudding can be light − but
reheated for late-comers. It is not always thus: on such a small base, errors tend
to be magnified. The service is amiable and very willing. The wine list is not
expensive and affords a fair selection from France and elsewhere. House
Labastide de Levis (no relation), £6.40. CELLARMAN'S CHOICE : Ch. Les Forts
de Latour, Pauillac 1979, £28.50; Vouvray Demi-Sec 1985, Pichot, £9.50.

CHEF: L.M. Levis   PROPRIETOR: J.S. Levis
OPEN: all week, exc Sat L and Sun D
CLOSED: 22 Dec to 4 Jan
MEALS: 1 to 1.30, 7.30 to 8
PRICES: Set L £16 (£21) to £20 (£25), Set D £20 (£25)
CARDS: Access, Amex, Visa
SEATS: 40. Private parties: 20 main room, 20 private room. No children under 8. Smart dress
preferred. One sitting
ACCOMMODATION: 8 rooms, all with bath/shower. B&B £55 to £70. No children under 8.
Pets welcome. Garden. TV. Phone. Scenic. Doors close at midnight. Confirm by 5.30 [GHG]

---

▲ *This symbol means accommodation is available.*

*The* Guide *office can quickly spot when a restaurateur is encouraging customers to
write recommending inclusion. Such reports do not further a restaurant's cause.
Please tell us if a restaurateur invites you to write to the* Guide.

# ▲ *Northcote Manor*

Northcote Road, Langho BB6 9BB
BLACKBURN (0254) 40555
on A59, 7m E of M6 exit 31

COOKING 3
COST £11−£38

The house is a red brick, stone and half-timbered Edwardian jumble rather grander in name than presence but 'young entrepreneurs' Messrs Haworth and Bancroft have put in much effort to make the inside spick, span and welcoming. The dining-rooms (the larger one sometimes with a live pianist) have that well-upholstered, pink-tableclothed feel of comfortable restaurants; the tables are not cramped, there are lots of fresh flowers and Craig Bancroft's cheerful greeting is reinforced by the competence of the waiting staff. Although catering to a well-heeled public, they do not ignore value for money: luncheons are decidedly cheap, Sunday lunch only a little dearer (half-price for young children). Nigel Haworth's cooking is pitched towards luxury: the terrine of foie gras was decorated with a langoustine, but readers have felt he does not lard the joint to excess; there is much good cooking, including a layered terrine of salmon, smoked salmon and monkfish set in a fennel butter, with a warm lemon butter sauce; oysters on a granary croûton with a julienne of smoked salmon and a little beluga caviare; fillet of beef on a pancake of roasted barley with a sauce spiked with ox-tail; loin of veal wrapped in a cabbage leaf, surrounded by a veal and basil mousse, covered with a lattice of short-crust; double chocolate and kirsch torte; 'Double Delight' a sandwich of hazelnut sablé filled with pear and cinnamon cream, accompanied by a chocolate and Grand Marnier bavarois. Signs of gilding the lily abound but often to good effect: a lemon-flavoured tuile filled with a lime sorbet was great, even if a basket filled with melon balls, strawberries and grapes might overload the already substantial chocolate torte. Others have suggested that on some nights the flavours, fighting hard to get out, are muddied. Coffee is good. The sensible practice prevails of charging very little for a small portion of cheese as a nibble to finish the wine. The wine list is too expensive for its length. House French is £6.85. CELLARMAN'S CHOICE : Bourgogne Passetoutgrains 1983, Ponnelle, £11.60; Mâcon-Vinzelles, Loché 1986, £14.80. Although the credit card voucher of our inspector was left open, tipping 'should not be expected', according to Mr Bancroft.

CHEF: Nigel Haworth   PROPRIETOR: Craig J. Bancroft and Nigel Haworth
OPEN: all week, exc Sat L
MEALS: 12 to 1.30, 7 to 9 (10 Sat)
PRICES: £23 (£32), Set L £7.85 (£11) to £8.95 (£12)
CARDS: Access, Amex, Diners, Visa
SEATS: 70. Private parties: 60 main room, 20 private room. Car-park, 50 places. Children's helpings. Smart dress preferred. Music
ACCOMMODATION: 6 rooms, all with bath/shower. B&B £49 to £59. Pets welcome.
Afternoon teas. Garden. TV. Phone. Scenic. Confirm by 3 [GHG]

*'Too many of the items on the short menu were "not available" including tea, coffee (!), and ice-cream.'*  On dining in London

## ▲ *Langley House Hotel*

Langley Marsh, TA4 2UF                                          COOKING 2
WIVELISCOMBE (0984) 23318                                  COST £18−£30

A picture book of a small country house in west Somerset, whose dining-room
is in mint green and peach. The decoration has reduced the sense of
claustrophobia, although the colour does run riot. Peter Wilson cooks to a set
five-course menu with no choice until the sweet stage is reached, when there
are half a dozen productions in the National Trust style of cookery. The
repertoire is fairly limited: a regular visitor from year to year was served exactly
the same first three courses as the year before last. The order runs: a cold made
dish, soup, fish, meat, sweet or cheese. The good things about the cooking are
the use of locally or home-grown vegetables and great care when there is no
pressure of clients or service. A cucumber and mint terrine was finely judged
and light as a feather; a carrot and orange soup showed exquisite balance; but
salmon trout stuffed with vegetables was inadequately cooked and mignons of
beef were overwhelmed by a strong mustard topping that drowned any other
flavour. There are serious problems with the salt and pepper pots in the
kitchen: an excess of application. A charming apple and cinnamon shortcake
proved a satisfying conclusion. Service can be vexed by numbers, even while
imposing its own timing on coming to table. The wine list is made up of nicely
chosen bottles. House French is £6.75. CELLARMAN'S CHOICE : Côtes du
Rhône, Cru du Coudoulet, Perrin, 1985, £12.75; Pouilly-Vinzelles 1987,
Mathias, £14.85.

CHEF: Peter Wilson   PROPRIETORS: Peter and Anne Wilson
OPEN: all week, D only
MEALS: 7.30 to 9
PRICES: Set L £12.75 (£18) to £15.75 (£21), Set D £17.50 (£23) to £19.75 (£25)
SEATS: 18. Private parties: 35 main room, 18 private room. Car-park, 10 places. Vegetarian
meals. Children's helpings. No children under 7. No smoking. Wheelchair access (also WC)
ACCOMMODATION: 9 rooms, all with bath/shower. B&B £50 to £75. Deposit: £10. No
children under 7. Baby facilities. Pets welcome. Afternoon teas. Garden. Fishing. TV.
Phone. Scenic. Doors close at midnight. Confirm by 6

## ▲ *Great House*

Market Place, Lavenham CO10 9QZ                            COOKING 1
LAVENHAM (0787) 247431                                       COST £8−£34

Stephen Spender, the poet, once lived in this merchant's house, classically
fronted yet medieval at the core, and one envies him. He is memorialised in the
new Spender Suite. The story goes, apocryphal no doubt, that an American
stayed a night, bought the house the next morning, and installed a French team
to run a Gallic enclave in an arch-typical English country town. It certainly is
French, though the wine list commendably includes English and Australian
bottles. Venison with port, pork fillet with calvados (they have Roger Groult's
here, a good man), deep-fried mushrooms with aïoli have pleased, if not sent

into ecstasy. Mean portions and unimaginative vegetables and vegetarian alternatives have been causes for complaint, also some inflexible service. House Gaillac is £7.85.

CHEF: Regis Crepy  PROPRIETOR: John Spice
OPEN: all week
CLOSED: last 3 weeks Jan
MEALS: 12 to 2.30, 7 to 10.30
PRICES: £19 (£28), Set L £6.90 (£8) to £9.90 (£11), Set D £12.75 (£23), Snacks from £2
CARD: Access, Carte Blanche, Visa
SEATS: 65. 7 tables outside. Private parties: 50 main room; 30 and 50 private rooms.
Vegetarian meals. Children's helpings. No cigars/pipes in dining-room. Music
ACCOMMODATION: 4 rooms, all with bath/shower. B&B £40 to £70. Deposit: £20. Baby
facilities. Pets welcome. Afternoon teas. Garden. TV. Phone. Doors close at 1am. Confirm by
midnight [GHG]

---

**LEDBURY  Hereford & Worcester**                                              map 2

## ▲ *Hope End* ▮

Hope End, Ledbury HR8 1JQ
LEDBURY (0531) 3613
2/3m N of Ledbury, just beyond                                    COOKING 3
Wellington Heath                                                      COST £31

It is not easy to stay a fortnight at a hotel that is only open from Wednesday to Sunday but there are people who do. On their nights in the wilderness, digestions and sleep are left to the mercy of other hoteliers. Perseverance, however, yields dividends. One reader reflects that while she may eat five dinners at the Hegartys' without suffering the consequences, she could not do the same in London. It is a very particular place, set in a hollow. The sound of sheep is the loudest to be heard; even the wind avoids the minaret surviving from the old mansion. Country house it may be, but the pine-clad bedrooms, the furniture, the multitude of paintings by Crispin Thornton-Jones and the use of natural Welsh fabrics are of the twentieth century, not the never-never times when the gentry ruled. The cooking, too, is a response to our times: organic produce, wholemeal flour, few fats, little salt. No wonder it is digestible. Flavour comes from freshness and a bold approach to spicing. Chocolate truffles are made with chocolate, perforce, but also four varieties of ground nut to provide the vehicle. There are criticisms levelled at the style. To some the chocolate truffles are not truffles at all and would be better dispensed with altogether. This is the argument about nut rissoles masquerading as 'meat' that was used against vegan cooks: attempt not simulacra. Similarly, using yoghurt in ice-cream leaves out an essential from the concept. More worrying to some, bread without salt is often not very good bread. The recipe developed by the Hegartys of a meal with no choice of main course is also difficult for a few, particularly the casual visitor. These are not root and branch criticisms: Patricia Hegarty's cooking and John Hegarty's quiet humour carry all before them. The conviction and the execution are persuasive. A summer meal caught some ingredients at their prime. Soups are ever a strong point, asparagus soup was 'luscious, very green, impeccable flavour, containing slim, young asparagus tips, cooked but crisp.' A casserole of lamb which had been marinated in lemon and herbs with fresh-ground spices was then cooked in stock to produce 'subtle yet strong flavours that were clearly distinguishable.' Steamed new potatoes were the epitome of a material and its cookery. The vegetable dish was stir-fried cabbage, field mushrooms and almonds. This, as the basil, radish and lettuce salad that followed, with a scattering of pine nuts, had perhaps one flavour (nuts) too many. Three British cheeses, whole, with Bath Olivers and apples, were, as always, of the highest quality. Puddings, a choice of three, included that ice-cream. Coffee is taken in a sitting-room, from a communal and frequently replaced pot. There smoking is allowed. Service is by Mr Hegarty. If Thoreau or, latterly, John Seymour had been gourmets, they would have lived like the Hegartys. The wines to accompany this are exemplary (though served too cold for one traditionalist). Half-bottles are numerous. Prices are by no means excessive. The range takes in the world, even if claret remains the most desirable. House French is £6. CELLARMAN'S CHOICE: Mâcon-Viré 1986, Bonhomme, £11; Ch. Arnaud de Jacquemaud, St-Emilion 1983, £11. As the decade turns, Hope End celebrates its 10th anniversary. May it continue to the turn of the century.

CHEF: Patricia Hegarty   PROPRIETORS: John and Patricia Hegarty
OPEN: Wed to Sun, D only
CLOSED: Dec to Feb
MEALS: 7.30 to 8.30
PRICES: Set D £23 (£26). Service inc
CARDS: Access, Visa
SEATS: 24. Private parties: 6 main room. Car-park, 10 places. No children under 14. Smart dress preferred. No smoking in dining-room. Wheelchair access (2 steps)
ACCOMMODATION: 9 rooms, all with bath/shower. B&B £58 to £64. Deposit: £30. No children under 14. Garden. Phone. Scenic. Doors close at 11. Confirm by 6 [GHG]

---

LEEDS  West Yorkshire                                                          map 5

# Bryan's

9 Weetwood Lane, Headingley
Leeds LS16 5LT                                                       COOKING 1
LEEDS (0532) 785679                                                     COST £8

'Bryan's fish is beautiful.' That's what they say about the place many rate as one of the best chippies in Leeds. Haddock, plaice and sole, plus halibut and hake, when available, are lightly battered, crisply fried in lard, and eaten with chips, mushy peas and pickled onions. Surroundings are utilitarian, with Formica tabletops and plastic seats, but service is cheerful and attentive, portions gargantuan, prices very reasonable. In the rivalry with Harry Ramsden's, Bryan's might get the upper hand for the quality of its fish and batter as well as its décor.

CHEFS: Alan Germain   PROPRIETOR: Jan Fletcher
OPEN: Mon to Sat
MEALS: 11.30 to 11.30
PRICES: £5 (£7). Minimum £2.89. Unlicensed
SEATS: 140. Private parties: 100 main room. Car-park, 50 places. Children's helpings. Wheelchair access. Music. Air-conditioned

## *Grillade*

| | |
|---|---|
| Wellington Street, Leeds LS1 4HJ | COOKING 1 |
| LEEDS (0532) 459707 and 459952 | COST £14–£26 |

A lively, simple French basement café with whitewashed brick walls and a vibrant atmosphere. Food is mainly grills – steak and frites and so on – but there are interesting daily dishes on the blackboard. House French is £6.20.

CHEF: Orenzo Padolino   PROPRIETORS: Meritlight Ltd
OPEN: Mon to Sat, exc Sat L
CLOSED: bank hols and Christmas week
MEALS: 12 to 2.30, 7.30 to 11
PRICES: £16 (£22), Set L and D £10.80 (£14). Service inc
CARDS: Access, Visa
SEATS: 62. Children welcome. No cigars/pipes in dining room. Air-conditioned

## *Jumbo Chinese*

| | |
|---|---|
| 120 Vicar Lane, Leeds LS2 7NL | COOKING 1 |
| LEEDS (0532) 458324 | COST £16 |

This bustling basement restaurant, devoid of frills and fripperies, serves up good food with speed and efficiency. A fairly predictable menu offers Peking crunch duck and king prawn with OK sauce, and hot-and-sour soup and lemon chicken receive good reports. Unfortunately, dim-sum is no longer served without main course dishes, but even so, prices mean that two can eat well for under £20. House wine, £4.80.

CHEFS: Yat Sun Lo and Lin Dai Lai   PROPRIETORS: Lin Dai Lai, Tony Kwan and Yat Sun Lo
OPEN: all week
CLOSED: 25 to 27 Dec
MEALS: noon to midnight
PRICES: £7 (£13). Service inc
CARDS: Access, Amex
SEATS: 150. Private parties: 150 main room. Children welcome. Music. Air-conditioned

## *Mandalay*

| | |
|---|---|
| 8 Harrison Street, Leeds LS1 6PA | COOKING 2 |
| LEEDS (0532) 446453 and 446340 | COST £10–£24 |

'The price of greed' (to be eaten by a tiger) is the title of a cautionary tale printed in the Mandalay's menu – a timely warning against the triumph of ravenous eyes over inextensible stomach when ordering. The selection is of penetratingly flavoured, freshly spiced dishes which have been universally well reported. For the first course, dhal soup has been 'very wholesome, garnished with fresh coriander'; aloo tikki 'firm in texture, with an appealing flavour'. Favoured main courses have included 'wonderful, fragrantly spiced vegetable biriani'; 'simple, barbecuey Irani shashliks'; 'tandoori mix – highest quality, deeply marinated'; and not-too-rich chicken makhari with the cream content 'just about right'. There are passion-fruit and mango sorbets to finish.

Set menus include one for vegetarians. Service, unless the restaurant is very full, is generally swift and attentive. House French is £5.95.

CHEFS: Khalid Mohammed, Mohammed Ramzan and Bashir Ahmed
PROPRIETORS: P. Chappelow, P. Breaks and W. Prior
OPEN: Mon to Sat, exc Sat L
MEALS: 12 to 2.30, 6 to 11.30
PRICES: £10 (£19), Set L £4.95 (£10), Set D £11.50 (£16) to £13 (£20). Service 10% (D only)
CARDS: Access, Amex, Diners, Visa
SEATS: 95. Private parties: 30 main room. Vegetarian meals. Children's helpings.
Wheelchair access (1 step; also WC). Music. Air-conditioned

## Olive Tree

| | |
|---|---|
| Oaklands, Rodley Lane, Leeds LS13 1NG | COOKING 1 |
| LEEDS (0532) 569283 | COST £7−£23 |

Run with enthusiasm by George and Vasoulla Psarias, this Greek restaurant breaks away from the stereotype with its green bistro décor, courteous bow-tied service and more unusual dishes. It is a winning formula and the various rooms on the ground floor are usually packed. Often, the best is off the daily blackboard where souvla − fillet of leg of lamb marinated in lemon sauce and charcoal grilled − appears alongside the fish dishes. First courses include louganiko, a smoked wine sausage, and pan-fried sardines with tomatoes; the house dessert is stafidhopitta, filo pastry with sultanas and orange liqueur. House wine from Boutaris is £5.95. Early birds for dinner get a three-course meal and a half-bottle of wine for £8.95, from 6.30 to 7.30pm.

CHEFS: George Psarias and Andreas Iacovou   PROPRIETORS: George and Vasoulla Psarias
OPEN: all week, exc Sat L
CLOSED: 25 and 26 Dec, 1 Jan
MEALS: 12 to 2, 6.30 to 11
PRICES: £12 (£19), Set L £5.95 (£7), Set D (6.30 to 7.30pm) £8.95 (£10)
CARDS: Access, Visa
SEATS: 100. Private parties: 45 main room, 30 private rooms. Car-park, 30 places.
Vegetarian meals. Children's helpings. Wheelchair access (1 step; also WC). Music

| LEICESTER Leicestershire | map 5 |
|---|---|

## Lai's

| | |
|---|---|
| 14−16 King Street, Leicester LE1 6RJ | COOKING 1 |
| LEICESTER (0533) 557700 | COST £16−£35 |

Descriptions of Lai's curiously luxurious dining-room range from 'cosmetically plush' to 'a small, intimate cocooned world', a setting apparently intended as much for business lunches as romantic evenings. However, when it comes to food, the fripperies end with the brief recitation as each dish is delivered to the table. The cooking itself is straightforward and good. Dishes are a mixture of Cantonese, Pekinese and Szechuan: shredded pork in lettuce, diced chicken with green pepper, a speeded-up version of crispy aromatic duck are recommended. Bang bang chicken comes as a vast pile of cucumber strips topped with tender chicken strips in a sesame and chilli laced peanut sauce;

fried aubergine is coated in a powerful garlicky black-bean sauce. An eight-course Szechuan feast or ten-course lobster seafood dinner, based on the produce of a local fish farm, provide grander alternatives. House French £6.50 on a short yet adequate wine list.

CHEF: John Lau    PROPRIETORS: Brian Lai and John Lau
OPEN: all week
MEALS: 12 to 2, 6 to 11
PRICES: £12 (£19), Set L and D £12 (£16) to £25 (£29). Service inc
CARDS: Access, Amex, Diners, Visa
SEATS: 100. Private parties: 60 main room, 40 and 60 private rooms. Vegetarian meals.
Children welcome. Wheelchair access (3 steps; also WC). Music

## Rise of the Raj

6 Evington Road, Leicester LE2 1HF                           COOKING 1
LEICESTER (0533) 553885                                       COST £9–£17

The Raj shows no sign of falling at this upmarket Indian restaurant which, unlike many others in Leicester, has cottoned on to the mood of the moment in ethnic eating and offers cocktails, smooth service and a serious attitude to cooking. Prices are reasonable and the food first class. Much of it comes from northern India and house specialities include murgh jalfrezi, chicken with green chillies; a non-vegetarian thali of many components; bingan masala, which is a spicy dish of aubergines, tomatoes and green peppers. There are also tandooris, fresh breads and pretty rice. Hot towels and a dish of tiny sweets are proffered at the end of the meal. House wine £5.25.

CHEFS: Abdul Bashir and Rouf Ullha    PROPRIETOR: Abdul Bashir
OPEN: all week
CLOSED: 25 Dec
MEALS: 12 to 2.30, 6 to 11.45
PRICES: £7 (£14), Set L £5 (£9) to £9 (£13). Minimum £6.95. Service 10%
CARDS: Access, Amex, Diners, Visa
SEATS: 70. Private parties: 40 main room, 45 private room. Vegetarian meals. Children's
helpings. No children under 5. Smart dress preferred. Wheelchair access (2 steps). Music

## Water Margin

76–78 High Street, Leicester LE1 5YP                         COOKING 1
LEICESTER (0533) 516422 and 24937                            COST £7–£29

The strengths of this plainly decorated restaurant are its old-style Cantonese specialities, such as deep-fried chicken and a wide range of seafood dishes, its one-plate noodle meals and excellent dim-sum, served from lunchtime till six in the evening. Among them have been steamed bean curd roll, steamed prawn dumplings and pancakes stuffed with prawns, pork and coriander. The one weakness is the service, which is friendly enough but, especially at busy times, can be chaotic. There are basic and fine wines or, more sensibly, tea or sake.

*See the back of the* Guide *for an index of restaurants listed.*

CHEF: K.F. Lam    PROPRIETOR: Y.W. Lam
OPEN: all week
MEALS: noon to 11.30
PRICES: £15 (£24), Set L £3.20 (£7) to £6.50 (£10), Set D £4.50 (£9) to £8.50 (£13).
Service 10%
CARDS: Access, Amex, Diners, Visa
SEATS: 170. Private parties: 100 main room, 100 private room. Children welcome.
Wheelchair access. Music

---

**LEIGHTON BUZZARD  Bedfordshire**                                    map 3

## ▲ *Swan Hotel*

High Street, Leighton Buzzard LU7 7EA                COOKING 1
LEIGHTON BUZZARD (0525) 372148                       COST £8–£36

Market stalls jostle the white-pillared portico, while from the dining-room
there are glimpses of a pretty conservatory and courtyard. Cooking style is
traditional English with broad hints of the novel, and sauces are stock based
and flavoured with alcohol and vegetable purées. The *carte* changes with the
seasons, the set menu weekly. Alongside a straightforward selection of steaks
and roasts are wider ranging ideas: fillets of plaice on a bed of fresh roes; duck
livers deep-fried in sesame batter with spiced sauce; vegetable brochette with
peanut butter dressing. The sight – and taste – of a hot salad of field
mushrooms was a pleasing preface to guinea-fowl marinated in coriander and
spices, then braised in a dark veal gravy with a rich, deep flavour. Desserts
range through nursery bread-and-butter pudding to coconut-milk ice-cream
with lemon shortbreads. The cheaper table d'hôte and Sunday lunch menus
may suffer from the extra press of business, but not the service – characterised
as 'attentive, friendly yet anonymous' which may represent to many how
waiting staff should be. The wine list addresses all tastes, from Mateus Rosé to
Ch. Pichon-Longueville-Baron, with such unexpected bargains as Laurent
Perrier 1982 Brut at £25, and Ch. Coutet Sec 1985 at £11.65. House Gascogne,
£5.95. CELLARMAN'S CHOICE : Wynn's Coonawarra Chardonnay 1987, £12.95;
Côtes du Rhône 1983, Pascal £8.15.

CHEF: Stephen McNally    PROPRIETORS: Eric and Felicity Stephens
OPEN: all week
MEALS: 12 to 2, 7 (7.30 Fri) to 9.30 (10 Fri, 9 Sun)
PRICES: £22 (£30), Set L £5.25 (£8) to £11.50 (£15), Set D £15 (£18) to £17.50 (£21), Snacks
from £1.50
CARDS: Access, Amex, Diners, Visa
SEATS: 80. 3 tables outside. Private parties: 80 main room, 40 private room. Car-park,
10 places. Vegetarian meals. Children's helpings. Wheelchair access. Air-conditioned
ACCOMMODATION: 38 rooms, all with bath/shower. B&B £65 to £85. Baby facilities.
Afternoon teas. Air-conditioning. TV. Phone. Doors close at midnight. Confirm by 1

---

*Restaurateurs justifiably resent no-shows. If you quote a credit card number when
booking, you may be liable for the restaurant's lost profit margin if you don't turn up.
Always phone to cancel.*

LEWDOWN Devon map 1

# ▲ *Lewtrenchard Manor*

Lewdown EX20 4PN
OKEHAMPTON (056 683) 256 and 222

COOKING 3
COST £20–£40

This large country house is set below the ridge carrying holiday traffic west to Launceston from Okehampton. The house and church, a close group, resemble nothing more than a Victorian dream of Shakespeare's England. The Victorian who realised it was Sabine Baring-Gould, squarson and author of 'Onward Christian Soldiers'. The gardens, which are pleasant, were designed with advice from Gertrude Jekyll. Conversion of this pastiche (even bad nineteenth-century copies of English art on the walls) to a hotel has been halting in its appreciation of decorative detail but is gathering pace under the new owners, James and Sue Murray. The kitchen has been in the charge of David Shepherd under this and the previous regime. His cooking might be described as Anglo-French country-house self-sufficiency. When shops, let alone delicatessens, are distant, you fend for yourself, down to sugar paste baskets for the petits fours. The style is as rich as often encountered but not impossibly so. Flavours come out, and difficult ones, for instance rosemary in a duck sauce, are deftly handled. The dining-room, full of candles, is a very good panelled parlour with Victorian decoration. The waitresses serve quickly and nicely and Mr Murray deals with the wine. Menus are a five-course set price or a short *carte* of half a dozen choices. A good meal ran through mussels in a brioche with orange sauce; a salad of quails' eggs with Roquefort; breast of Gressingham duck with rosemary sauce and an array of six vegetables (a worrying green mousse among them); cheese, mainly English in medium condition, with home-made oatmeal biscuits on the sweet side; and finally, a meringue swan with a blackberry yoghurt ice-cream. Swans are enjoyed: they have been seen in choux paste with a savoury cream as an amuse-gueule. The tastes were clean and the meal not overloaded. Wines occupy a list of 50 bins including burgundies from Latour-Giraud and a few New World and Spanish bottles to bolster the French selection. This is a good isolated spot; there is a chance it may become a stage of distinction. House French from £7.50. CELLARMAN'S CHOICE : Côtes de Beaune Villages 1985, Latour-Giraud, £14; Chablis *premier cru* Vaillous 1986, £19.

CHEF: David Shepherd   PROPRIETORS: James and Sue Murray
OPEN: all week D, Sun L
MEALS: 12 to 2.30, 7.15 to 9.30
PRICES: £27 (£33), Set L £14.50 (£20), Set D £23 (£29)
CARDS: Access, Amex, Diners, Visa
SEATS: 40. Private parties: 8 main room, 16 and 50 private rooms. Car-park. No children under 8. Smart dress preferred. No cigars/pipes in dining-room. Wheelchair access
ACCOMMODATION: 8 rooms, all with bath/shower. B&B £50 to £90. No children under 8. Pets welcome. Afternoon teas. Garden. Fishing. TV. Phone. Scenic. Doors close at midnight
[GHG]

---

*'The service was appalling; there were inordinate delays between every course. When coffee was ordered we were told we would have to wait until people at other tables had finished so that their cups could be washed.'* On dining in Lothian

---

## Kenwards ▮

Pipe Passage, 151A High Street
Lewes BN7 1XV                                                   COOKING 3
LEWES (0273) 472343                                             COST  £31

Not only has this restaurant begun opening for lunch, but it is possible to buy
cheese and other produce from the boutique next door in the narrowest of
passages leading on to the main street. John Kenward is helped in this
expansion by Janet Pattisson, whose co-run restaurant, Pattisson's, was in last
year's *Guide*. John Kenward was an architect in the 1960s and 1970s and
Kenwards has an architect's interior. It uses changes of level for effect, it leaves
relics of previous occupation in situ, it has a spareness that never transgresses
taste. It has been typified as austere, but that is mitigated by softer lighting,
curtains and tablecloths. The cooking, too, is often described as austere;
unfussy may be more accurate. There is a weekly changing menu, clearly
describing what to expect: turbot and oysters with sorrel and vermouth;
artichokes and leeks with ginger and parsley; Bonchester cheese with
courgettes, the cheese baked until runny and served with a few strips of
courgette. Turbot with mussels comes with a light butter sauce garnished with
fronds of fennel. The success depends on the quality of ingredients and the
sense of relief in the diner's mind (and stomach) that layers of meaning, hints
of significance, do not have to be interpreted to be appreciated. The pitfalls of
such cookery is that if the basic material is less than good, or the cooking less
than accurate, the point may be missed before it has even been perceived. In
general, Kenwards avoids such pitfalls. There is some complexity to back up
the apparent simplicity; a clear vegetable soup with a small julienne of
vegetables and a spike of oloroso sherry will not be done in seconds.
Vegetables and herbs bulk large in this repertoire, for themselves or as
flavourings – more important than cream or mousses, for example. Puddings
continue to emphasise England. At lunch there is a cold buffet on the fill-your-
plate-for-a-single-price principle and a shortened version of the dinner menu.
The wine list has been described as 'the best I have ever seen' for this type of
restaurant and the food it serves. At its front is a short selection, all priced at
£8.50 or £4.50 for halves. A new departure, this, which John Kenward says
attracts more than half his customers. At those prices, who can blame them?
The rest of the list, rationalised from previous years and now about 100-strong,
is exemplary too. It eschews the *premiers crus* that are only for bankers. But the
quality of the next rung down is well represented, at very generous prices, and
decently serviced. 'There is hardly a dud on those pages,' wrote one who had
given up the effort of choice; why choose when John Kenward has already
chosen? CELLARMAN'S CHOICE : Mercurey Blanc 1987, Juillot, £13.90;
Gigondas, Les Pallières 1984, £10.90. Kenwards does not operate a percentage
mark-up on wines. There is also a note on the menu, 'We do not expect tips'.
Service is fine and it may even involve John Kenward himself popping out of
the kitchen; it is not formal.

▲ *This symbol means accommodation is available.*

CHEFS: John Kenward and Janet Pattisson    PROPRIETORS: John and Caroline Kenward
OPEN: Mon to Sat, exc Sat L and Mon D
MEALS: 12 to 2.15, 7.30 to 9.30
PRICES: £20 (£26). Service inc
CARD: Access, Visa
SEATS: 25. Private parties: 10 main room. Children welcome. No smoking

---

**LIFTON  Devon**                                                                 map 1

# ▲ *Arundell Arms*

Lifton PL16 0AA
LIFTON (0566) 84666                                                    COOKING 2
on A30, 3m E of Launceston                                         COST £15–£34

Anne Voss-Bark's creeper-clad coaching-inn on the A30 has been pleasing the
*Guide's* fisherfolk for decades (it has 20 miles of its own water, on the Tamar
and its tributaries), as well as those happier with gun, binoculars or map in
hand. Provisioning encompasses packed lunches, a buffet in the cocktail bar,
special feasts for St Valentine's Day and so on, as well as daily set meals and a
seasonally changed *carte*. Philip Burgess, the chef since 1981, has been made a
director in recognition of his services, described in the hotel brochure as
'traditional English and French with just that little extra imaginative touch'. If
your imagination flinches at caramelised orange and dill sauce with the pan-
fried scallops and monkfish, or braised ox-tail with prunes and orange zest, or a
brochette of vegetables with Roquefort sauce and pilaff rice, there are also
plainly grilled meat and fish, all with fresh vegetables or salad. House wines
from £6.75. CELLARMAN'S CHOICE : Sancerre 1987, Chavignol, £11.50; Ch.
Coufran 1979, £16. Children, but not smoking, welcome in the dining-room;
'no service charge added nor tips expected.'

---

CHEF: Philip Burgess    PROPRIETOR: Anne Voss-Bark
OPEN: all week
CLOSED: 4 days at Christmas
MEALS: 12.30 to 2, 7.30 to 9
PRICES: £23 (£28), Set L £11 (£15) to £12 (£16), Set D £18 (£22)
CARDS: Access, Amex, Diners, Visa
SEATS: 70. Private parties: 80 main room, 30 private room. Car-park, 80 places. Vegetarian
meals. Children's helpings. No smoking in dining-room. Smart dress preferred. Wheelchair
access (2 steps)
ACCOMMODATION: 29 rooms, all with bath/shower. B&B £41 to £67. Baby facilities. Pets
welcome. Afternoon teas. Garden. Fishing. TV. Phone. Scenic. Doors close at 11.30 [GHG]

---

*'I asked for Badoit and was given a blank look and then a warm bottle of Malvern water,
which was then changed for a flash-cooled bottle. The food varied: the gravlax was
pronounced good; the meat in the warm duck salad was overcooked. The sauces were
creamy or tasteless. Veg. consisted of the usual mange-tout, dauphinois potatoes, broccoli
and baby carrots. I did love my pud, though, which was the assiette of ice-creams, tarts etc.
There was no decaffeinated coffee, the cream jug was cheap cut glass very badly chipped on
the lip. The petits fours served with the coffee were the sort of thing my son makes at school
with evaporated milk and coconut. Final moan, the bill was just broken down into food
and drinks.'* On dining in Gwent

**LINCOLN** Lincolnshire                                          map 6

# Harvey's Cathedral Restaurant/Troffs

1 Exchequergate, Castle Square
Lincoln LN2 1PZ                                          COOKING 2
LINCOLN (0522) 510333                                    COST £10–£26

Bob Harvey is a restless man anxious to try out new ideas. His name is often
mentioned for one or other 'scheme' to entice more customers through the door,
whether it be 'pay as you drink' or resoundingly good-value lunches. 'The soup
set the standard of a £4.95 set lunch: it was made from fresh field mushrooms,
not a hint of a tin. The steak and kidney pudding relied on good-quality
ingredients. As near to good home cooking as I have encountered in an English
restaurant.' If you can do the cheap things well, the more expensive may come
naturally and there have been satisfactory reports of a menu that leans quite
heavily on pies, casseroles and warm enveloping sauces: old-fashioned in that
sense. It is eclectic, too, with a number of curried items appearing. The wine
list is good, fair and informative. There are plenty of halves, as well as the 'pay
as you drink' scheme, and Bob Harvey's growers are interesting and sought out
with much care. Some prices are especially good and nothing is more than it
should be. House wines are numerous, two of which are Muscadet-sur-lie from
Bossard and Vin du Pays du Comté Tolosan at £6.50. CELLARMAN'S CHOICE :
Mâcon-Viré, Domaine de Roally 1987, £12.50; Crozes-Hermitage 1985,
Desmeures, £12.95. Aqua Libra is stocked. Troffs is a bistro above the main
restaurant and is Bob Harvey's vehicle for appealing to as broad a spectrum as
possible. As he himself remarked, 'Simple food is more difficult than ritzy food.
You soon discover that as long as you have the décor, the grovel and the garnish
you can get away with murder. Not that we want to do so or ever knowingly
adopt such an approach.' Troffs may one day crack the formula.

CHEFS: Bob Harvey, Andy Gibson and Marion Chambers   PROPRIETORS: Adrianne and
Bob Harvey
OPEN: Harvey's all week, exc Sat L and Sun D; Troffs all week D, and Sat and Sun L
CLOSED: 26 Dec
MEALS: Harvey's 12 to 2, 7 to 9.30; Troffs 5 to 10.15 (11am to 11pm Sat and Sun)
PRICES: Set L £4.95 (£10) to £7.95 (£13), Set D £11.95 (£18) to £15.95 (£22); Troffs £9 (£14),
Snacks from £3.45
CARDS: Access, Visa
SEATS: Harvey's 50. Troffs 70. Private parties: 60 main room, 32 private room. Vegetarian
meals. Children's helpings. Music

# Wig & Mitre

COUNTY
OF THE
YEAR
RESTAURANT

29 Steep Hill, Lincoln LN2 1LU                            COOKING 3
LINCOLN (0522) 535190                                     COST £30

'Don't be surprised if you find a judge sitting to one side of you and a bishop to
the other.' The pub is latitudinarian (and libertarian) towards its customers,
serving 'everyone from vegans to gluttons'; 'the waitresses are extremely quick,
alert and pleasant and cope with large numbers.' Recipients of an award from

the Polite Society, Michael and Valerie Hope are welcoming hosts. They converted the property hard by the cathedral into a pub in 1977, a standard-bearer (they would say) of a revival both commercial and aesthetic in the old centre of the city. After starting well, there was a period in the doldrums, overcome by the appointment of chefs Paul Vidic and Lino Poli. This is the New Pub: all things to all people – good bar food, restaurant food, last orders at 11pm every night, open every day for both meals. There is an Italian tilt to some of the cooking that one person felt was being held in check by 'French imperialism'. If that tilt were pushed further, the food might be lightened still further to make even more immediate appeal. As it is, warm recommendations have come for home-smoked monkfish with green beans and a hazelnut dressing, the nut and smoke making a fine combination; terrine of salmon with samphire which had no mimsy finesse but, rather, moist chunks of delectable salmon and strands of samphire held together by a white fish mousse; a really well-butchered rack of lamb with a stock and tomato reduction spiked with pungent basil for sauce; a chicken breast with Parma ham, wrapped in pastry, with perhaps too sweet a sauce; a super-rich chocolate and pear trifle; and an Italian finale of langues de chat soaked in bitter, dark coffee, topped with mascarpone and sprinkled with chocolate, 'just what one wants to indulge in.' The return of better eating to this place, observed another reader, 'seems to stem from a policy change away from buying cheaper, sub-standard ingredients and turning them into cheap, off-beat pub food to selecting quality ingredients and cooking them accordingly.' Of course, we cannot know the truth of that statement, but we can assert that the transition is perceived by outsiders. The wine list is perfectly decent and so is the beer. House wine is £7.10. CELLARMAN'S CHOICE: Côtes du Rhône Blanc 1987, Guigal, £14.30; Ch. de Grand Moulas 1987, £10.45. Tipping is 'not encouraged'.

CHEFS: Paul Vidic, Lino Poli, Peter Dodd and Simon Shaw   PROPRIETORS: Valerie and Michael Hope
OPEN: all week
CLOSED: 25 Dec
MEALS: 8am to 11pm
PRICES: £18 (£25)
CARDS: Access, Amex, Diners, Visa
SEATS: 50. 6 tables outside. Private parties: 30 main room. Children's helpings. Children restricted. Wheelchair access (1 step; also WC)

---

**LITTLE WALSINGHAM  Norfolk**                                             map 6

## ▲ *Old Bakehouse*

33 High Street
Little Walsingham NR22 6BZ                                    COOKING 2
WALSINGHAM (0328) 820 454                              COST £14–£24

'A friendly local restaurant, not standing on ceremony, serving attractively presented and well-cooked fresh food', is a description many restaurateurs would relish and customers would travel far to experience. Add to it resoundingly good-value and comfortable bedrooms in a remarkable Georgian house opposite the ancient Priory gate and you have a grand combination. The ovens to this former bakery are at the rear of the building, passed on the way to the 'granny-killing' steps down to the bar. Upstairs again at street level, the dining-room, with ladder-back chairs and pink napery, is dominated by a giant fireplace and large baker's scales. It may sound dismissive to describe Christopher Padley's cooking as moving along predictable lines, but that is not the intention. Names of dishes will strike a familiar chord to veterans of restaurants of the early 1970s: grilled grapefruit, smoked trout with a mustard mayonnaise, venison, walnut and apple paté with orange and port sauce as first courses, or Barbary duck with brandy and orange sauce and pork with prunes for main courses. Vegetables are good. Cointreau and marmalade ice-cream is an old favourite and whisky chocolate cake might sink souls not inured to richness. Residents have the chance to eat a fixed-price short dinner menu – again, extremely reasonable. Mr Padley still cares about bread: he has it made at the village bakery. Helen Padley serves with charm and intelligence. Her acolytes may be as charming, but not always as informed. Progress may slow on busy or understaffed nights. The wine list is short but fair; watch for bin-ends. House French £5.75. CELLARMAN'S CHOICE : Côtes du Ventoux, Jaboulet 1985, £8.40; Mâcon-Lugny, Cuvée Eugène 1986, £11.95.

CHEFS/PROPRIETORS: Christopher and Helen Padley
OPEN: Tue to Sat D (plus Sun L July and Aug)
CLOSED: 3 weeks Feb; 2 weeks Oct to Nov; Tue to Thur Jan, Feb; Tue and Wed Mar
MEALS: 7 to 9.30
PRICES: £14 (£20), Set D £10 (£14)
CARDS: Access, Visa
SEATS: 36. Private parties: 40 main room. Vegetarian meals. Children's helpings (Sun L only). Smart dress preferred. Music
ACCOMMODATION: 3 rooms, 1 with bath/shower. B&B £13.50 to £32. Deposit: £7. Confirm by 6

---

**LIVERPOOL** Merseyside                                      map 5

## *Armadillo*

20–22 Matthew Street, L2 6RE                                 COOKING 1
051-236 4123                                                 COST £12–£19

Each year this becomes more of a restaurant, though never shedding its café origins altogether, either in price range or rickety stairs to the loos. Liverpool continues to score over Manchester (except in respect of Chinese food) as a place to eat out as a day-to-day experience, helped by Armadillo. It makes no excessive fuss, indeed too little, some say, about the staff, but manages to deliver good-hearted food: smoked fish terrine, fish and mussel soup, confit of duck with cranberries, red mullet with pesto and pheasant with cream, cider and mushrooms are some of the dishes mentioned with pleasure. Desserts, too, continue the enjoyment with a pear and ginger crumble, light and spicy in taste with a spongy toffee'd topping. Food that is 'generous in spirit and in portion' may sometimes approximate, not conform to one's anticipation but nonetheless provides a proper context for a relaxed atmosphere in which to while away a few hours from the 'ravaged and half-renovated city around.' House wine is £6.40 a litre. The early dinner menu from 5 to 7 Tuesday to

355

Friday is the same price as lunch. Lunch is served non-stop from 11.45am to 5pm on Saturday.

CHEFS: John Scotland and Martin Cooper    PROPRIETORS: Martin and Angela Cooper
OPEN: Tue to Sat
CLOSED: bank hols, 24 to 26 Dec
MEALS: 11.45am to 3 (5 Sat), 7.30 to 10.30
PRICES: L and early D £8 (£12), D £12 (£16), Snacks from £1.95
CARD: Access, Visa
SEATS: 65. Private parties: 75 main room. Vegetarian meals. Children's helpings on request. Music. Air-conditioned

## La Grande Bouffe

48A Castle Street L2 7lQ                                          COOKING 1
051-236 3375                                                   COST £13–£24

A regular visitor to this city-centre cellar bistro – found directly opposite the Town Hall and easily picked out by a neon sign in the window – cites a long list of dishes tried over a period of time. They reflect a clever internationalism around a core of French dishes: watercress and walnut soup, crab spring roll, smoked halibut fillet with Chinese cabbage, rack of lamb with apple and mint jelly, fillet steak with Roquefort and walnut butter, fillet of brill with onion compote and a fresh tomato and butter sauce, lemon galette with raspberry sauce, apple pie with treacle and cinnamon. These come from the evening *carte*, when the long narrow main room becomes a restaurant with full table service and there is often live jazz or a classical guitarist. Occasionally, there are regional or other special dinners. At lunchtime, it is a self-service brasserie. House wines, £5.50.

CHEFS: Jean Kassim, Terence Lewis and Philip Bradley    PROPRIETOR: Frank Nyland
OPEN: Mon to Sat, exc Sat L
MEALS: 12 to 2.30, 6 to 10.30
PRICES: £14 (£20), Set L £7.50 (£13). Snacks from 95p. Service 10%. Licensed, also bring your own: corkage £2
CARDS: Access, Amex, Visa
SEATS: 80. Private parties: 60 main room. 24 private room. Vegetarian meals D. Children's helpings. Music. Air-conditioned. Self-Service L

---

**LIVERSEDGE   West Yorkshire**                                    map 5

## ▲ Lillibet's

Ashfield, 64 Leeds Road,
Liversedge WF15 6HX                                            COOKING 2
HECKMONDWIKE (0924) 404911                                    COST £13–£25

The weatherbeaten grey stone house is severe in its squareness, but once inside the dining-room, feminine pink doth rule. There is variety on the concise menu, though it may run on familiar lines of baked avocado, cheese beignets and seafood roulade; lean meat, fried or grilled and served with cream sauce – escalope of veal with sherry and mustard for example – roast duckling with fruit sauces; simply poached or baked fish. Nothing wild or outrageous perhaps, but proof is in the eating. Here Elizabeth Roberts scores highly. A June meal of duck-liver pâté, roast duck then a hazelnut, orange and kiwi Pavlova could have been ordinary but was impressive: the pâté smooth and intense; the duck succulently moist under a crisp skin, with a satisfyingly piquant sauce and well-cooked plain vegetables; the Pavlova light and airy, the meringue carefully balanced by the cream and fruit. The 50-odd bottles on the list are supplemented by a dozen extras noted on a blackboard. The prices are fair and offer decent drinking across the board. House French, £6.50.

CELLARMAN'S CHOICE : Gigondas, Domaine des Bosquets 1984, £10.70.

CHEF: E.J. Roberts   PROPRIETORS: J.M. Roberts and E.J. Roberts
OPEN: Mon to Sat, D only, and L by arrangement only (parties of 10 or more)
CLOSED: 1 week between Christmas and New Year, 2 weeks end Aug
MEALS: 12 to 1.45, 7 to 9.30
PRICES: Set L £9 (£13) to £13 (£17), Set D £12.25 (£17) to £15.95 (£21)
CARDS: Access, Amex, Visa
SEATS: 42. Private parties: 50 main room. Car-park, 23 places. Vegetarian meals. Children's helpings. Music
ACCOMMODATION: 7 rooms, all with bath/shower. B&B £36 to £55. Garden. TV. Phone.
Doors close at midnight

---

**LONG MELFORD  Suffolk**                                                          map 3

## Chimneys

Hall Street, Long Melford CO10 9JR                          COOKING 3
SUDBURY (0787) 79806                                        COST £17–£37

Diamond, twisted, octagonal and spiralling chimneys are indeed staple diet to this part of East Anglia. Add to them half-timbering, a lattice-work of studs and beams, and lead- and small-pane windows and the estate agent's cocktail is well mixed. Sam and Zena Chalmers' restaurant takes full profit from the setting and acts as an attractive frame for a meal far-distant from Tudor predilections, in tune with modern tastes. Ravioli of wild mushrooms and asparagus, and calf's liver with lemon and blackcurrant sauce are two dishes to set the style of six choices at each course. Much satisfaction is reported of a Sunday lunch that began with a 'breathtaking' passion-fruit sorbet – tart and peppery – then some of those ravioli, the filling for once being 'assertive', and a medley of fish in a court bouillon with saffron. Traditional dishes such as sweetbreads in the 'lightest possible' brioche with a port, cream and demi-glace sauce are equally well received. Ice-creams and sorbets appear to be very well done: white chocolate; soft cheese with a really sharp lemon sauce; and a strawberry sorbet with two coulis. Cheese is also fine: whole British truckles make a still-life of grandeur. At the end, the mignardises were 'better than any I have tasted', reflected one who had lived in Brussels, chocolate capital of the world. Rural may be the situation, but the Chalmers' operation appears reassuringly professional. House French, £7.50. The list numbers about 120 bins with a fair spread of origin.

---

*County Round-ups listing additional restaurants that may be worth a visit are at the back of the Guide, after the Irish section. Reports on Round-up entries are welcome.*

---

CHEF: Colin Liddy   PROPRIETORS: Samuel and Zena Chalmers
OPEN: Tue to Sun, exc Sun D
MEALS: 12 to 2, 7 to 9.30
PRICES: £24 (£31), Set L £11.50 (£17), Set D £18 (£24) to £23 (£29)
CARDS: Access, Visa
SEATS: 50. Private parties: 50 main room. Vegetarian meals. Children's helpings. No cigars/
pipes in dining-room. Wheelchair access (1 step)

---

**LOUGHBOROUGH  Leicestershire**                                    map 5

## Angelo's

| 65 Woodgate, Loughborough LE11 2TZ | COOKING 1 |
|---|---|
| LOUGHBOROUGH (0509) 266704 | COST £16 |

A brick house on a wide one-way street in the centre of Loughborough: tiled
floor, whitewashed walls and wooden tables give a Mediterranean ambience
often fugitive in Midland fogs. Apart from the set menu, which has remained
constant for the last couple of years, there are daily specials: pheasant, guinea-
fowl, quails or chicken cacciatore, depending on availability. Game is
something of a speciality. Portions are generous, the meat cookery on the whole
better than that of the vegetable. Service is friendly and fairly efficient. The
menu states that for the 'choice of extra Italian specialities available, see
Angelo'. You will need to see him, too, for an explanation of the short Italian
wine list beyond 'Barbera, £9'. One reader noted 'apparently a good under-
counter wine list but not offered'. House Italian, £5.60.

CHEF: Pramrod Patel   PROPRIETORS: Ann and Angelo Marcelli
OPEN: Mon to Sat
MEALS: 12 to 2, 7 to 10 (10.45 Fri and Sat)
PRICES: £10 (£14). Service 10%
SEATS: 50. Private parties: 30 main room. Car-park, 12 places. Vegetarian meals. Children's
helpings. Wheelchair access (1 step; also WC). Music

---

## Restaurant Roger Burdell

| 11–12 Sparrow Hill, LE11 1BT | COOKING 1 |
|---|---|
| LOUGHBOROUGH (0509) 231813 | COST £26–£35 |

For Loughborough, this is a serious restaurant indeed, occupying an old manor
house, modishly decorated, equipped with all the accoutrements of expensive
meals: the silver cloches are out in full force. The welcome, though, is warm
and the two dining-rooms comfortable. Roger Burdell is a professional chef;
his cooking has thus been accused of an excess of complexity and a
preoccupation with appearance. Some there are this year who consider his style
simplified, less prone to surprising combinations, and (save for desserts) less
excited by the look of the thing. Performance, however, is uneven, materials
not invariably of the best quality. Loughborough is not an easy place to cook up
a storm and the prices make few concessions to the Midlander's sense of
economy. The wine list is not so highly priced and house selections start at £8.
CELLARMAN'S CHOICE: Ch. Haut-Sarpe 1981, £20.50; Antinori, Tignanello
1982, £18.50. As for tipping, 'All prices are inclusive.'

CHEF/PROPRIETOR: Roger Burdell
OPEN: Mon to Sat, exc Mon L
MEALS: 12.30 to 2, 7.30 to 9.15
PRICES: £20 (£26), Set D £21 (£27) to £23.50 (£29). Service inc
CARDS: Access, Amex, Visa
SEATS: 80. Private parties: 56 main room, 24 private room. Children welcome. No cigars/pipes in dining-room. Wheelchair access

---

**LOWER BEEDING  West Sussex**                                    map 3

## ▲ *South Lodge*

Brighton Road, Lower Beeding RH13 6PS                  COOKING 2
LOWER BEEDING (0403) 891711                            COST £23−£41

A rambling 'Tudorbethan' house built by an explorer and botanist who has left his mark on the gardens: a high-Victorian collection of azaleas, rhododendrons and a massive rock garden. As Ian Nairn once remarked, 'Some lodge!' In its refurbished state, it offers neo-Victorian public rooms, modern-comfort bedrooms and country-house hotel cooking, this year from a new chef, at country-house prices. There is a limited choice *prix fixe* at lunch and a *carte* at dinner. The new regime has received guarded approval for dishes such as wild mushroom soup with green coriander; salmon with a chive butter sauce; chicken with wild mushrooms in a port sauce; and a 'South Lodge chocolate Torte'. Sunday lunch, the busiest meal, is not necessarily the best. The wine list is from good sources, and house French is £8.

CHEF: Tim Franklin   PROPRIETORS: Laura Hotels Ltd
OPEN: all week
MEALS: 12.30 to 2.30, 7.30 to 10 (10.30 Fri and Sat)
PRICES: £25 (£34), Set L £15 (£23). Snacks from £2
CARDS: Amex, Carte Blanche, Diners, Visa
SEATS: 34. Private parties: 8 main room, 14, 45 and 50 private rooms. Car-park, 80 places. Children's helpings. Smart dress preferred. No cigars/pipes in dining-room. Wheelchair access
ACCOMMODATION: 39 rooms, all with bath/shower. Rooms for disabled. B&B £73 to £121. Afternoon teas. Garden. Tennis. Golf. TV. Phone. Scenic

---

**LOWER BRAILES  Warwickshire**                                  map 5

## ▲ *Feldon House* ♥

Lower Brailes OX15 5HW                                COOKING 2
BRAILES (060 885) 580                                 COST £17−£24

'About 70 per cent of our business is repeat, so we must be doing something right,' was Maggie Witherick's comment when returning our questionnaire. Indeed the proprietors are, in this Victorian house that is firmly within the ambit of Banbury and its growing business. There is a dining-room in the conservatory and a new terrace for drinks in fine weather. 'Rather like dining in a private house; no good turning up without a booking.' Allan Witherick cooks a no-choice meal at lunch and dinner. The short menu card reads summarily but it may  hide complexities only realised on the plate or explained by Mrs Witherick in person. 'Superb examples of English cooking at its best', observes one reader as he details parsnip and ginger soup with a swirl of cream and a scattering of poppy seeds; grilled salmon with fresh nectarine and accompanied by sauté cucumber and a hollandaise; noisettes of lamb with mushrooms and a home-made plum jelly; and good English puddings like a Queen of puddings or more gooey affairs like a chocolate and hazelnut meringue. Although there is no choice, some adjustments may be feasible to allow for refusal to eat cooked cheese or not liking avocado – such are the perils of short menus. The wine list is also short, but it is not greedily priced and holds some nice choices, adequate for most people. House Mâcon rouge, £7.75 and Sauvignon de Touraine, £7.25. CELLARMAN'S CHOICE : Gisborne Semillon-Chardonnay 1988, Babich, £11; Moulin-à-Vent 1987, Loron, £11.75.

CHEF: Allan Witherick   PROPRIETORS: Allan and Maggie Witherick
OPEN: all week, exc Sun D
MEALS: 12.30 to 2, 7.30 to 8.30
PRICES: Set L £13.50 (£17), Set D £16.50 (£20). Service inc
CARDS: Access, Visa
SEATS: 14. Private parties: 8 main room, 6 conservatory. Car-park, 9 places. Children's helpings (L only)
ACCOMMODATION: 4 rooms, all with bath/shower. B&B £25 to £35. No children under 11. Phone. Garden. Scenic. Doors close at 11 [GHG]

---

LUDLOW  Shropshire                                                          map 4

## ▲ Dinham Hall

Ludlow SY8 1EJ                                               COOKING 2
LUDLOW (0584) 6464 and 3669                          COST £11–£37

Ludlow has not figured in the *Guide* for a few years. Marian and Paul Johnson set out to rectify the omission in this conversion of a late-Georgian merchant's house (lately a boys' school) close to the River Teme, overlooking Whitcliffe Common. No false modesty clouds their pride in a scheme of comfort and warmth that has drawn criticism only for the pictures (there's no pleasing everyone). A propitious start was glory in national competitions won by chef Chris Galvin (once at the Ritz, Inigo Jones and the Swan at Streatley) and his assistant Richard Brown. Galvin was also once executive chef at Ménage à Trois in New York. The cooking, predictably, is very modern. There is a menu of six or seven choices at dinner, a set-price *menu gourmand* of five courses and a reasonably priced short menu at lunch. The further you get from London, the cheaper the lunches, it seems. The *carte* includes a vegetarian dish in each of the first two courses: for example a salpicon of assorted beans flavoured with cheese and chives wrapped in pastry, followed by a tian of provençale vegetables accompanied by a tomato butter sauce. Although the kitchen has sorted out what the food should look like, there appears to be less certainty about flavours. A timbale of lemon chicken filled with a ragoût of brill marinated in Thai dressing was bland in the extreme; mango and lemon bavarois served on a sablé biscuit accompanied by a rhubarb compote looked wonderful but lacked identity or dexterity in textures. More skill is evident in soups, such as Cornish crab bisque with Grand Marnier and mussel velouté with a julienne of root vegetables, and in sorbets. For one reader, her clementine and lime ice was the meal's high-point. The meal as a whole is an exercise in the dying art of nouvelle cuisine: small portions, two sauces for many things, strong reductions, little platforms of potatoes for the meats and touches of the unfamiliar. If the kitchen can settle its style and achieve consistency, the place will be a credit to the town. The service is willing, young, and often French. The wine list began with a distinct lack of half-bottles and a short range, so has also to find its feet. The house red does no credit. The enthusiasm of the place, however, is palpable: the Johnsons wish to please. House French is £9. CELLARMAN'S CHOICE : Volnay, Clos des Chênes 1983, £25.70; Puligny-Montrachet 1982, £22.

CHEF: Chris Galvin  PROPRIETORS: Paul and Marian Johnson
OPEN: all week, exc Sun D
MEALS: 12.30 to 2.15, 7.30 to 9.15
PRICES: £22 (£31), Set L £4.60 (£11) to £10.95 (£17), Set D £16.95 (£21) to £22.50 (£27)
CARDS: Access, Diners, Visa
SEATS: 40. 10 tables outside. Private parties: 40 main room, 24 private room. Car-park, 17 places. Vegetarian meals. Children's helpings. Smart dress preferred. Wheelchair access (2 steps). Music
ACCOMMODATION: 10 rooms, all with bath/shower. B&B £43 to £87. Deposit 33%. No children under 4. Garden. Sauna. Fishing. Golf. TV. Phone. Scenic. Doors close at 1am. Confirm by 8 [GHG]

---

**LUTTERWORTH  Leicestershire**                                          map 5

## ▲ *Denbigh Arms*

| High Street, Lutterworth LE17 4AD | COOKING 1 |
|---|---|
| LUTTERWORTH (045 555) 3537 | COST £14−£29 |

A refurbished market-town inn that offers a better standard than many in the area. People have applauded its value, especially as it operates seven days a week. Bar food is also a cut above the norm – a fish pie included salmon, vegetables were cooked properly and salads were crisp and colourful. The kitchen has not always been well supported by the front of house staff. House French, £6.50.

CHEF: Albert Clinch  PROPRIETORS: Mr and Mrs E.J. Stephens
OPEN: all week
MEALS: 12 to 2, 7 to 9.30 (10 Fri and Sat)
PRICES: £17 (£22), Set L £11 (£14) to £14 (£17), Set D £15 (£18) to £21 (£24), Snacks from £1. Service inc
CARDS: Access, Amex, Diners, Visa
SEATS: 70. Private parties: 30 main room, 50 private room. Car-park, 45 places. Children's helpings. Smart dress preferred. No pipes in dining-room. Wheelchair access (1 step; also WC). Music
ACCOMMODATION: 34 rooms, all with bath/shower. Rooms for disabled. B&B £57.50 to £70. Baby facilities. Afternoon teas. TV. Phone. Confirm by 6

---

*Report forms are at the back of the book; write a letter if you prefer.*

---

map 2

## ▲ *Provence*

The Gordleton Mill, Silver Street
Hordle, Lymington SO41 6DJ                                    COOKING **3**
LYMINGTON (0590) 682219                                       COST £19–£31

Provence has had a good year. The handsome converted mill set in large
gardens (including the *potager*) by the side of the road from Lymington to Sway
contains pretty guest bedrooms and a couple of dining-rooms with exposed
pink brick walls and good table settings. On the walls hang the great, wide
wooden shovels used when it was a mill and the stream, now so picturesque,
powered the wheel. It is a pure French restaurant in the middle of the English
countryside: Italian and French staff and French cooking. Initial impressions
are that it is pleasantly free of the overblown though for some the conversion is
ruched and 'finished' to extinction. The menu deals in short descriptions: eel
cooked in red wine, shoulder of lamb cooked with sage, duck cooked with
fresh figs in Provence red wine, almond cake, hot pancake filled with orange.
These, however, conceal some artifice and invention. There is a short set-price
lunch menu of perhaps four choices at each course (not expensive) with a half-
dozen more elaborate dishes that carry a supplement. At dinner there is a one-
price menu of seven or eight choices and a simple table d'hôte. The main menu
has supplements – lobster and foie gras among them. A meal started with a
lobster salad with a saffron vinaigrette and a supremely intense ravioli of
Dublin Bay prawns and red mullet cooked in a foil envelope with rosemary.
Meat dishes included a fillet of beef with mushrooms and a truffle sauce and
noisettes of lamb scented with thyme and served with a light garlic mousse and
lamb jus. Dishes involving star anise seem to occur quite frequently. An Olivier
cheeseboard, with walnut bread, was savoured for four of the strongest
examples: suitably ripe and pungent. The dessert that caught the eye was a
feuilleté of almond pastry and a mango ice-cream. Good coffee and petits fours.
Other dishes that have been recommended have been foie gras de canard on a
potato galette; mussels with a leek sauce; morels and skate on a celery julienne;
iced hazelnut soufflé and a truly French apple tart. Praise, although vociferous,
has not been in unison. There have been niggles at the service, slow and
occasionally begrudging, as well as at unnecessary insistence on proper
clothing in order to enjoy the food and poor heating (perhaps that's why the
clothing is required). The wine list is French in its entirety, with a fair selection
of around 60 wines at not too high a price. It is not as surprising as the food. It
is good to see the Côtes du Rhône, Domaine de Bel Air 1987 from Ryckwaert
and the interesting dozen bottles from Jean-Pierre Novi's native Provence,
including Terres Blanches red and the house Mas du Gourgonnier white and
red from les Baux at £9. See under Hordle in *The Good Hotel Guide*.

---

*The 1991 Guide will be published before Christmas 1990. Reports on meals are most
welcome at any time of the year, but are extremely valuable in the spring. Send them to
The Good Food Guide, FREEPOST, 2 Marylebone Road, London NW1 1YN. No stamp
is needed if posted in the UK.*

---

CHEF: Jean-Pierre Novi  PROPRIETOR: William F. Stone
OPEN: Tue to Sun, exc Sun D
MEALS: 12.30 to 2, 7.30 to 10
PRICES: Set L £11.90 (£19), Set D £19.50 (£26). Service inc
CARDS: Access, Amex, Diners, Visa
SEATS: 30. Private parties: 30 main room, 12 and 14 private rooms. No children under 8.
Wheelchair access. Music
ACCOMMODATION: 6 rooms, all with bath/shower. B&B £30 to £48.50. Deposit: £30 No
children under 8. Garden. TV. Phone. Scenic. Doors close at 1am [GHG]

---

LYMPSTONE Devon                                                    map 1

## ▲ River House

The Strand, Lympstone EX8 5EY                              COOKING 2
EXMOUTH (0395) 265147                                      COST £25–£40

There is a strong affinity between restaurants and water, demonstrated to
perfection here, where high tide might lap the foundations of this extension to
a riverside house, once a village shop, by the Exe estuary. Bring binoculars for
wader-spotting at low water. The Wilkes are energetic. He bustles around the
dining-room, an amiable host who knows his customers, has drunk his wines
to some purpose and knows what his wife, equally active at the stove top, has
cooked for the day. The cooking takes a modern view – sorrel and onion tart
with a courgette and watercress sauce; guinea-fowl braised with an orange,
grape and walnut sauce – but it is rarely outlandish. Fish is good, as it should
be; vegetables come in several dishes; desserts and home-made ices are
substantial. It is a fine place for Sunday lunch, which has the advantage of
being cheaper. Were any criticism to be levelled, it would have to be that the
prices are high. The wine list, much from Corney & Barrow and Christopher
Piper, has some decent choices from Chile as well as France. House wines from
£5.70. CELLARMAN'S CHOICE : Rully Rabourcé, *premier cru*, 1987, Olivier
Leflaive, £15.40; Robert Mondavi Cabernet-Sauvignon Reserve 1980, £27.50.

CHEF: Shirley Wilkes  PROPRIETORS: Mr and Mrs J.F.M. Wilkes
OPEN: Tue to Sun, exc Sun D
MEALS: 12 to 1.45, 7 to 9.30 (10.30 Sat)
PRICES: £17 (£25), Set L and D £23.50 (£31) to £27.50 (£33). Minimum £8.25
CARDS: Access, Amex, Visa
SEATS: 35. Private parties: 25 main room, 14 private room. Children's helpings. No children
under 5. Smart dress preferred.No cigars/pipes in dining-room
ACCOMMODATION: 2 rooms, all with bath/shower. B&B £48 to £62. Deposit: £10. No
children under 6. TV. Scenic

---

*This year, in quoting prices for three-course meals at the top of each entry (by the word
'Cost'), we have put a more pessimistic complexion on the upper price by inflating it by 20
per cent. The aim is to prepare the reader for any inflation during the life of the Guide and
also reflect the price of a meal taken without constant attention to the likely size of the bill.
The prices quoted in smaller print below the text remain, as in previous editions, strict
computer calculations of an average three-course meal, the price in brackets reflecting an
average meal with coffee, service and half a bottle of house wine per person.*

---

**LYNTON** Devon                                                            map 1

## ▲ *Hewitt's*

North Walk, Lynton EX35 6HJ                                          COOKING 2
LYNTON (0598) 52293                                                   COST £12–£34

David Lamprell is the chef and has been ever since the restaurant's incarnation
four years ago. He cooks well, and it is unfortunate that his talents are not
allowed full rein by virtue of location and clientele. Hewitt's is a dramatically
sited late-Victorian house, its gardens (once terraces) dropping sheer to the sea
below. The architect had his idiosyncrasies and, while the outside is busy with
turrets, balconies and beams, inside has a good line in the sepulchral, not
helped by the current decoration. The central hall might be a setting for an E.C.
Bentley murder tale with candidates for accusation or extinction expected to
pop out of a multitude of doors on any number of levels. The dining-room is
not much more cheerful. The set-price dinner suffers from elaboration, midway
sorbet (even though a good one), and needless decking out, but Mr Lamprell is
able to handle techniques and flavours: a fine duck-liver terrine went well with
its Guérard-style onion and grenadine sauce; a cassis and stock sauce with
breast of duck was praised for its intensity and balance. Soufflés are his
especial delight and, whether fruit or the central European salzburger
Nockerln, have lightness and flavour. Coffee is good, as are some of the petits
fours. The summary wine list reveals little about the makers but is not too dear.
House Ch. Fonscolombe from Provence, £7.25.

---

CHEF: David Lamprell   PROPRIETORS: Robert and Susan Mahon
OPEN: all week, D only and Sun L (weekday L by arrangement)
MEALS: 12.30 to 2, 7 to 9
PRICES: Set L £8.25 (£12) to £15 (£19), Set D £15.50 (£20) to £24 (£28). Snacks from £1.50.
Service inc
CARDS: Access, Amex, Diners, Visa
SEATS: 26. 4 tables outside. Private parties: 50 main room. Car-park, 12 places. Vegetarian
meals. Children's helpings (6 to 7pm). Smart dress preferred. No smoking. Wheelchair
access. Music
ACCOMMODATION: 12 rooms, 9 with bath/shower. B&B £28 to £52. Baby facilities.
Afternoon teas. Garden. TV. Phone. Scenic. Doors close at 11. Confirm by 6

---

**MAIDSTONE** Kent                                                          map 3

## *Suefflé*

The Green, Bearsted, Maidstone ME14 4DN                              COOKING 1
MAIDSTONE (0622) 37065                                               COST £15–£36

The spelling is merely because the proprietor's given name is Sue. On the
'oldest green in England' (though who can tell that?) stands a Kent cottage
older on the inside than its façade might reveal. A little front garden, good for
summer eating, hides behind bushes, the main door hides behind the house.
An attic has been converted to a sitting-room, but dining takes place among
exposed stud-work downstairs. Some people hemmed in by these timbers,
representing privacy long demolished, must feel like gorillas in a peculiarly
sturdy cage. Graham Clarke, whose prints of village life adorn ten thousand

walls, lives nearby: a positive gallery of his work hangs here. There are three prices of menu available, although only the dearest is offered at weekends. The range of cooking is not large, is professional in character and is satisfactory. Watercress soup made on a proper base has true flavour though dark, not emerald, green. A ragout of beef is stir fried with onion so that there is perceptible seizing of the outside without toughening or overcooking the interior. Mixed with a medley of vegetables and tomato, finished with a stock sauce and tarragon, it makes a sustaining lunch dish. Stuffed breast of chicken, fillet of beef, saddle of lamb, Scotch salmon and monkfish fill the roll call at dinner. Summer pudding is called 'Pouding d'été à l'Anglaise.' The wine list is quite ambitious and includes some good bottles, not least a Peter Lehmann Semillon and a couple of wines from Lungarotti. House French is £7.50.

CHEF: Andy Blyth   PROPRIETOR: Sue Dunderdale
OPEN: Tue to Sat, exc Sat L
CLOSED: 25 Dec to 7 Jan
MEALS: 12 to 2, 7 to 10
PRICES: Set L and D £9.95 (£15) to £25 (£30). Minimum £9.95. Service inc
CARDS: Access, Amex, Carte Blanche, Diners, Visa
SEATS: 44. 6 tables outside. Private parties: 46 main room. Car-park, 14 places. Vegetarian meals. Children's helpings. Wheelchair access (3 steps). Music

---

**MALDON  Essex**                                                          map 3

## *Wheelers*

13 High Street, Maldon CM9 8TB                                      COOKING 1
MALDON (0621) 853647                                                   COST £12

At the bottom of the menu there is a small note, 'As all fish is cooked to order, please allow 15 minutes.' Here is a real fish and chip shop, run by the Wheeler family, with tasty home-made soups and puddings as well as wonderful fried fish in thin crisp batter. Chowder and minestrone have appeared alongside thick, well-textured fish soup. The sweets trolley is hard to resist and includes knock-out trifle and apple pie. House wine is £7.70.

CHEF: R.H. Wheeler   PROPRIETORS: W.H.G. Wheeler, R.H. Wheeler and V.A. Wheeler
OPEN: Tue to Sat
CLOSED: 2 weeks Sept
MEALS: 11.30 to 1.45, 6 to 9.30
PRICES: £5 (£10)
SEATS: 52. Private parties: 52 main room, 52 private room. Children's helpings. Wheelchair access (also WC)

---

*'Meal quite pleasant but very salty. Upon enquiry told that chef/owner should have been on duty but was taking an extra night off – hence the extra salt. Two months later, starters consisted of two soup bowls of large lettuce leaves and radicchio swimming in raspberry vinegar, one topped by a mush of duck and the other bacon. Main-course beef was of reasonable quality and, as requested, rare. Rack of lamb sent back as running in blood and undercooked. Returned, now cooked, but too fatty to be edible. Vegetables a mushy mixture: mashed mounds of potatoes were again over-salted.'*  On dining in Avon

MALVERN WELLS  Hereford & Worcester                                                map 2

## *Croque-en-Bouche*

221 Wells Road, Malvern Wells WR14 4HF                                    COOKING 4
MALVERN (0684) 565612                                                            COST £36

By reason of the schools and the location, Malvern has retained its gentility. Perhaps this is why one report called the appearance of the Jones's restaurant 'petit bourgeois'. In fact it is a good deal smarter than it used to be, although the formula of a two-person operation, short menu of impeccable judgement and incomparable wine list has not altered. Its scale determines its type, one the British hold in esteem: 'where there are few pretensions, everything is plain and simple, with a lack of flourishes and expense accounts.' It is ranked equal to the more fancy places because good cooks are so rare in Britain. In Europe, perhaps, more flash and nonsense would be necessary to stand out from the crowd. Thus, like La Potinière, Gullane, Altnaharrie Inn, Ullapool, or the Carved Angel, Dartmouth, luxury ingredients or grand international styles are not required. This assists the relaxation of cook and customer both, and affords a natural approach that brings out inherent flavours without artifice. Marion Jones's cooking often seems to stem from the herb garden. A May menu started with summer savory in the lettuce, pea, spring onion and ham soup; leg of lamb was stuffed with lemon thyme, marjoram and wild rice and came with a mint béarnaise; wild rabbit was marinated with basil and lemon; chicken was prepared with red shallots and tarragon, then sent out with a cep sauce. Butter or oil emulsions are important too, making this a cookery of traditional feel: maltaise with fillet of salmon; paloise with lamb; aïoli with rabbit on that same menu. The herbs contribute to substantial flavours: fillet of sea bass wrapped in cabbage with a chive butter sauce was the best dish of one party's meal; and another had 'pheasant roasted then served with a jammy madeira sauce flavoured with a generous heap of 'porcini secchi' – this heap of onions, lardons and wild mushrooms was so herby, aromatic and gutsy that it takes over completely the pheasant meat, which can be rather dull.' This earthy Italian robustness may be contrasted to a simple piece of poached skate, 'the timing is split second and the abundance of herbs in a beurre blanc manages to envelop each piece of fish with the exact amount of sharpness and sweetness.'

The descriptions so far might indicate a French bourgeoise cooking her heart out, but there are more modern touches, for instance marinated salmon and accompanying vegetables, or cannelloni stuffed with crab, ginger and coriander leaves served on avocado and tomato. Cheese has now become an entirely British affair; it would be superogatory to suggest they were never in the best of condition. Puddings (in English style, there is greater choice at the end than the beginning), have reverberations from down the years: 'ginger meringue on coffee sauce is still good', sorbets and ice-creams, a trio on a single fruit sauce, still delight. This cooking is very good. Its service, by design, is simple – as well it might be with a score of diners and a single pair of hands. When people compare notes on the rebarbative (and there seems to be competition among restaurateurs to see who can be the *most* outrageous), Robin Jones often figures. 'Seriously obnoxious service – even when you try to be friendly,' is one comment. In the end, it is self-defeating – and worse, self-perpetuating. There are indubitably a thousand happy customers to one unhappy one, but the niggles recur from year to year, and the point of this *Guide* is to reflect consumers' experiences, not defend the restaurateur. The excellent value of the food, which should not be ignored, is complemented by that of the wine list. Superlatives have often been expended on it, none more than by Robin Jones himself. It is, in truth, an eye-opener for range and scale and is unwilling to offer second best. Sections come and go. This year, one person reflected, was not so good for red burgundy. Last year was less exciting for Rhônes, but by now this very region is the one that pleases Mr Jones the most. Preliminary indications are indeed impressive. Many things on the list are available retail from the restaurant's cellars. Advance ordering is often an advantage; and do not ignore the aperitifs or digestifs. CELLARMAN'S CHOICE : Stoneleigh Sauvignon Blanc 1988, £9,80; Rouge Homme Shiraz-Cabernet 1984, £9.90. There are two pages of house wines, starting at £5.70 for a white wine from Valencia and rising to £8.70 for Viña Ardanza 1981. 'Tips are not expected.' Children are welcome.

CHEF: Marion Jones   PROPRIETORS: Robin and Marion Jones
OPEN: Wed to Sat, D only
CLOSED: before Christmas to first week of Jan
MEALS: 7.30 to 9.15
PRICES: Set D £25 (£30). Service inc
CARDS: Access, Visa
SEATS: 24. Private parties: 8 private room. Children welcome. No smoking. Wheelchair access

---

**MANCHESTER   Greater Manchester**                                   map 5

## Blinkers French

| | |
|---|---|
| 16 Princess Street, M1 4NB | COOKING 2 |
| 061-228 2503 | COST £15−£35 |

This comfortable basement − with overtones of stables persisting among the decent table settings − is a bastion of European cooking on the verges of Chinatown. A new chef has not changed the modern style of cooking but the format has been extended to a daily fish menu and a *prix fixe* dinner. Catering largely for the businesses in central Manchester, prices reflect expense-account, not privy-purse, economics. Recommendations include parcels of smoked salmon filled with an avocado mousse; veal medallions with a copious madeira sauce; lamb in pastry with a herb and sherry sauce; turbot in a mushroom sauce; dark and luscious chocolate truffle or mousse on a coffee sauce; nougat parfait with a passion-fruit sauce; and good coffee. Muzak is Richard Clayderman-style faves and raves. The wine list has a short page of fine wines and otherwise a sound selection. House French, £7.50. CELLARMAN'S CHOICE : Alsace Pinot Gris 1985, Dopff & Irion, £9.95; Ch. Paybonhomme les Tours, 1ères Côtes de Blaye 1985, £10.50.

---

*Restaurateurs justifiably resent no-shows. If you quote a credit card number when booking, you may be liable for the restaurant's lost profit margin if you don't turn up. Always phone to cancel.*

---

CHEF: Anthony Murphy    PROPRIETORS: Lewes and Christine Gerezdi
OPEN: Mon to Sat, exc Sat L
MEALS: 12 to 2.30, 7.15 to 10.30
PRICES: £19 (£29), Set L £8.95 (£15), Set D £15.95 (£23). Service 10%
CARDS: Access, Amex, Diners, Visa
SEATS: 45. Private parties: 70 main room. Children's helpings. Children restricted. Smart
dress preferred. Music

## Brasserie St Pierre

57−63 Princess Street, M2 4EQ                                        COOKING 2
061-228 0231                                                        COST £8−£20

There are those who find the surroundings less than enticing, though improved
somewhat by the pictures on the walls. The food and service, however, rise
above that, providing good value for lunches as well as a *carte* day and night.
John Nelson and James Sines of the High Moor at Wrightington (see entry) are
making their Manchester mark. A smoked haddock soufflé, baked golden
brown, on a bed of spinach with a generous buttery sauce was a propitious
start to a meal that might go on to a rack of lamb or strips of beef quickly fried
with mushrooms and green peppercorns or a well-flavoured duck roasted to
time with a lemony mango sauce. Vegetables can be very good indeed and
'would put more pretentious kitchens to shame'. Puddings are adequate, but
coffee is good. 'An important local resource,' says one Mancunian. The wine
list is French, short and carefully chosen. People speak well of the vin de pays,
Collines de La Maure, from near Beziers. House wine starts at £5.75. A glass of
wine is included in the £7.50 set lunch.

CHEF: David P. Bolan    PROPRIETORS: John Nelson and James Sines
OPEN: Mon to Sat, exc Sat L
MEALS: 12 to 2, 6.30 to 11
PRICES: £11 (£17), Set L £7.50 (£8), Set D £9.50 (£15). Snacks £1.50
CARDS: Access, Amex, Diners, Visa
SEATS: 65. Private parties: 80 main room. Children's helpings on request. Wheelchair
access (1 step; also WC). Music

## Café Istanbul

79 Bridge Street, M3 2RH                                            COOKING 1
061-833 9942                                                        COST £7−£17

A modest, glass-fronted café with Turkish artefacts and cooking in full view
from the tables, the Istanbul offers both obvious and more unusual dishes at
very reasonable prices. The longish menu, around 35 dishes in all, starts with a
range of meze, including a clutch of vegetable dishes, börek and a
recommended shredded chicken with walnut sauce, then moves on to meatier
main courses, most of them based on lamb and many grilled over charcoal.
Properly prepared doner kebab and mixed grill are specialities. At lunchtime,
there is also a bargain set meal which changes every day. Finish with Turkish
coffee and home-made pastries. There is a short wine list, largely French,
and house French is £5. CELLARMAN'S CHOICE : Buzbag, a dry red Turkish
wine, £6.75.

CHEF: Hasan Bicer   PROPRIETOR: Sacit Onur
OPEN: Mon to Sat
CLOSED: 25 and 26 Dec
MEALS: 12 to 3, 6 to 11.30
PRICES: £10 (£14), Set L £4.20 (£7)
CARDS: Access, Visa
SEATS: 40. Private parties: 45 main room. Children's helpings. Smart dress preferred.
Wheelchair access (also WC). Music

## Hong Kong

| | |
|---|---|
| 47 Faulkner Street, M1 4EE | COOKING 1 |
| 061-236 0565 | COST £8–£24 |

Recently refurbished and with a new chef and management, the Hong Kong
has reorganised the menu and expanded it slightly to include sizzling dishes.
Prices still seem very reasonable, and first reports indicate that the standard is
as reliable as ever. House wine, £5.30.

CHEF: Mo Hon Kit   PROPRIETOR: Kevin Wong
OPEN: all week
CLOSED: 25 and 26 Dec
MEALS: noon to midnight
PRICES: £11 (£20), Set L £3.50 (£8), Set D £10.50 (£15). Service 10% (D and weekends)
CARDS: Access, Amex, Diners, Visa
SEATS: 350. Private parties: 160 main room, 260 private room. Children welcome. Music.
Air-conditioned

## Hopewell City

| | |
|---|---|
| 45–47 Faulkner Street, M1 4EE | COOKING 1 |
| MANCHESTER 061-236 0091 and 0581 | COST £8–£26 |

Flashing neon lights signal this Chinatown basement restaurant. The
Cantonese menu is unusually extensive and includes dim-sum. Reports have
pointed up salt and pepper ribs as being 'very meaty and well flavoured';
'gingery braised noodles with plenty of small, fat slices of pork'; and good
Szechuan prawns and seafood soup with bean curd. Adventurous eaters be
warned, however. Although there are many enticingly unfamiliar dishes on the
menu, it has sometimes been found 'almost impossible to get any rapport with
the waiters', who have been known to warn customers off the more authentic
Chinese dishes. House wine £6.50 per carafe, or drink beer or tea.

CHEF: Kam Hung Yung   PROPRIETORS: Henry C.Y. Yu and Michael K.C. Chow
OPEN: all week
MEALS: 12 to 2, 2 to 11.45
PRICES: £13 (£22), Set L £3 (£8) to £5 (£9), Set D £6 (£11) to £10 (£15). Service 10%
CARDS: Access, Amex, Diners, Visa
SEATS: 100. 20 tables outside. Private parties: 140 main room. Children welcome. Music.
Air-conditioned

*The* Guide *is totally independent, accepts no free hospitality, and survives on the number
of copies sold each year.*

## Kathmandu Tandoori

42–44 Sackville Street, M1 3WE          COOKING 1
061-236 4684          COST £9–£17

The menu at this basement restaurant, situated on the fringe of Chinatown, is more or less standard tandoori, although there are a few more unusual dishes of lambs' kidneys and fresh fish. Business thrives, which has allowed complete refurbishment of the dining-room, bar and kitchen. There are quibbles about value for money, and reports suggest that food can be hit and miss through overcooking, lukewarm temperatures and heavy-handed spicing. This may be balanced by praise for the vegetarian menu, chicken dishes and tasty wet curries. Tikkas, makhan chara – diced chicken in butter with tomato and fresh cream – and lamb pasanda remain popular standards. House French, £5.50.

CHEFS: Ram Das, Abdul Hamid and Ashfaq Ahmad    PROPRIETOR: Gopal Mohan Dangol
OPEN: all week
CLOSED: bank hols
MEALS: 12 to 2.30, 6 to 12
PRICES: £6 (£13), Set L £4.50 (£9), Set D £8.25 (£14), Snacks from 95p. Service 10%.
Licensed, also bring your own: corkage £1
CARDS: Access, Amex, Diners, Visa
SEATS: 250. Private parties: 120 main room, 120 private room. Vegetarian meals. Children welcome. Wheelchair access. Music. Air-conditioned

## Koreana

Kings House, 40 King Street West, M3 2WY        COOKING 1
061-832 4330          COST £8–£24

'Finally seems to be achieving some of the success it deserves.' Now five years old, this excellent family-owned restaurant in the centre of town has fierce Chinese competition and an uninviting basement frontage. The menu concentrates on staple Korean dishes, such as kim-chee, pickled cabbage and crispy meat dumpling. The bulgogi banquet, which has been well reported many times, epitomises the style: a choice of cold vegetables – including wonderful spinach, dressed with a vast quantity of garlic and some sesame oil after steaming, then left to cool – then soup, fried fish or a light bean- flour pancake topped with vegetables and a main course of marinated sliced beef, chicken or pork cooked on a metal shield, before a delicious rice cake cooked in soy sauce. There is a set menu for vegetarians of three of five courses. Service, by waitresses in national costume, is knowledgeable and very helpful. Drink Korean saké, tea or French house wine, £6.80.

CHEF: Hyun K. Kim    PROPRIETORS: Koreana Restaurant Ltd
OPEN: Mon to Sat, exc Sat L
MEALS: 12 to 2.30, 6.30 to 10.30 (11 Fri and Sat)
PRICES: £12 (£19), Set L £4.20 (£8) to £4.70 (£9), Set D £8.65 (£13) to £15.50 (£20).
Service inc
CARDS: Access, Amex, Diners, Visa
SEATS: 56. Private parties: 60 main room. Vegetarian meals. Children welcome. Smart dress preferred. Music

## Kosmos Taverna

| | |
|---|---|
| 248 Wilmslow Road, M14 6LD | COOKING 1 |
| 061-225 9106 | COST £13–£18 |

A very cheerful Greek restaurant offering the full range of taverna dishes, made on the premises. People do enjoy the visit, often volubly, and staff react well to happiness. One reader observed that 'the whole is greater than the sum of its parts' – perhaps a mark of the truly successful restaurant. Eat taramosalata, hummus, tahini, falafel and sometimes the grilled fish with absolute confidence; fish plaki has lots of flavour and the moussaka has been recommended. House wine £5.90 a litre.

CHEF: Loulla Astin   PROPRIETORS: Stewart and Loulla Astin
OPEN: all week, D only and Sun L
CLOSED: 25 and 26 Dec, 1 Jan
MEALS: 12 to 2.30, 6.30 to 11.30
PRICES: £10 (£15), Set D £8.50 (£13) to £9.50 (£14)
CARDS: Access, Visa
SEATS: 80. Private parties: 40 main room. Children's helpings. Wheelchair access (also WC). Music. Air-conditioned

## Lime Tree

| | |
|---|---|
| 8 Lapwing Lane, West Didsbury, M20 8WS | |
| 061-445 1217 | COOKING 2 |
| 2m from M56 exit 10 | COST £15–£23 |

A recent extension into the garden has nearly doubled the number of tables, but the popularity of the restaurant is such that it has not entirely relieved the pressure on space. Nearly every aspect has come in for praise – the unpretentiously bare décor in green and white, happy and helpful staff, easygoing atmosphere – stopping short of approval of strident music and long waits before the kitchen gets into its stride on busy evenings. The most enthusiastic plaudits are still for the food. The menu, à la carte with a choice of eight first courses and main dishes, is built round a core of straightforward French dishes such as beef fillet with shallot and tarragon jus, chicken-liver parfait and asparagus with orange beurre fondue. However, this is balanced by a strand of more modern flavours. Thus, on a spring menu, there were turbans of lemon sole filled with ginger and orange mousse served with a vermouth sauce, or roast duckling with orange and mango sauce. Judging by the many recommended dishes, ranging from a crab and trout salad to a brandy-snap basket of vanilla ice-cream with raspberry coulis, the execution has become more careful and consistent since the kitchen brigade was expanded. The wine list is short, better for bourgeois clarets than run-of-the-mill burgundies, with but a nod to Rioja and Chianti. Prices are fair. House Gros Plant from Bossard and Vin de Pays d'Oc, Domaine Anthea, both good and both organic, £7.50. CELLARMAN'S CHOICE : Rasteau, Cuvée Prestige, 1985, Vignerons de Rasteau, £9.75; Valdepeñas Gran Reserva 1978, los Llanos, £7.95. The Lime Tree branch at 9–11 Wilmslow Road, Rusholme (telephone 061-227 7108) is cheaper and has its own keen supporters.

CHEFS: Patrick Hannity, John Holmes and Simon Haywood   PROPRIETORS: Patrick
Hannity and Robert Williams
OPEN: Tue to Sat D, Sun L
MEALS: 12 to 2, 6.30 to 10.30
PRICES: £12 (£19), Set L £8.50 (£15)
CARDS: Access, Visa
SEATS: 80. 4 tables outside. Private parties: 50 main room. Vegetarian meals. Children's
helpings (Sun L only). Wheelchair access. Music

## Little Yang Sing

| 17 George Street, M1 4HG | COOKING 2 |
|---|---|
| 061-228 7722 | COST £21–£32 |

'Perfect' sea bass in black-bean sauce reflects daily buying while prawns with
chilli and salt, duck in honey and lemon sauce, and crab and sweetcorn soup
point to the emphasis on Cantonese cuisine. Dim-sum, including 'superb'
spring rolls, and one-plate dishes such as deep-fried rice sticks and beef, cater
to a lower budget. Even the free jasmine tea has come in for praise, but the
wine list is not over priced either (house French, £5.95). The staff may try to
persuade the novice diner to select the top-priced banquets. Such
blandishments are exhausting, and the food is not sufficiently interesting to
justify the higher prices.

CHEF: Warren Yeung   PROPRIETORS: Warren Yeung
OPEN: all week, D only
MEALS: 5.30 to 11.30 (11.45 Fri, 12 Sat)
PRICES: £11 (£21), Set D £21 (£27). Service 10%
CARDS: Access, Amex, Visa
SEATS: 80. Private parties: 80 main room. Children welcome. Music. Air-conditioned

## Market Restaurant

| 104 High Street, M4 1HQ | COOKING 2 |
|---|---|
| 061-834 3743 | COST £20 |

Fifties-style green and cream sets the tone in this cosy restaurant facing the old
Smithfield markets. The menu changes monthly. Recently, apple and chive
soup, Javanese chicken in satay sauce with avocado, and vegetable koulibiaka
have met with approval. A new-found supplier has enabled fish to return to the
fore, in dishes such as monkfish with ginger and poached trout fillets with
pears. One or more vegetarian dishes are always available. Stalwarts with a
sweet tooth can test their endurance to the limits at the 'Pudding Club' which
meets monthly (book well ahead). At a typical event, participants tackled
spotted Dick, moved on to coffee cheesecake, Chester pudding and poached
pears and finally arrived, pale, but still conscious, at dark chocolate and praline
terrine. The wine list is sufficient to accompany the food. There are some fun
sparklers, but otherwise not a lot to wash down the puddings. There is an
exceptional range of bottle-conditioned beers from Belgium (including fruit-
flavoured ones), Germany and Britain. House French is £3.50 per 50cl carafe;
house Rock's elderflower is £4.35 a bottle. CELLARMAN'S CHOICE : Peter
Lehmann's Shiraz 1985, £7.95; Bourgogne Blanc 1988, Aujoux, £8.95.

CHEF: Lin Scrannage   PROPRIETORS: Peter O'Grady, Anne O'Grady and Lin Scrannage
OPEN: Tue to Sat, D only
CLOSED: 1 week in spring, 1 week at Christmas, Aug
MEALS: 5.30 (7 Sat) to 9.30
PRICES: £13 (£17)
CARDS: Access, Amex, Visa
SEATS: 40. Private parties: 40 main room, 25 private room. Vegetarian meals. Children
welcome. Music

## Mina-Japan

63 George Street, M1 4NS                                           COOKING 1
061-228 2598                                                  COST £23–£30

Established for a few years now but still little known, this basement restaurant
in a quiet part of George Street, just behind the Odeon Cinema, advertises its
presence only by a small, hand-made, unilluminated sign. As time goes by,
odd artefacts and ornaments – dolls and bonsai trees – have accumulated to
add a Japanese feel to the rather worn trattoria décor surviving from earlier
days. The menu, illustrated like a scrapbook, runs through the limited range of
classics possible with the available ingredients, makimono and nigiri – rolled
and made-to-order sushi – as specialities and a number of multi-course set
meals built around main dishes. The quality of cooking is essentially good,
although the prices give pause for thought. Crispy deep-fried bean curd in a
superb soy sauce, seaweed-wrapped salmon sushi, clear vegetable soup with a
juicy piece of monkfish, and chicken yakitori grilled with sweet onion are the
introductory courses to a teriyaki of seared beef still rare on the inside. Flavours
can be blander than elsewhere. 'Timing is generally sensitive to the quality of
raw materials, but some of the table cooking perhaps overcooks slightly,
probably in response to local demand.' Service is informative and
knowledgeable. House wine, £6.90 (white), £6.95 (red).

CHEF: Yasuto Kawano   PROPRIETOR: Nori Shibahara
OPEN: Mon to Sat, D only
MEALS: 7 to 11.30
PRICES: £16 (£23), Set D £18 (£25). Service 10%
CARDS: Access, Amex, Visa
SEATS: 65. Private parties: 28 main room. Children welcome. Music. Air-conditioned

## Moss Nook

Ringway Road, M22 5NA
061-437 4778
on B5166, 1m from Manchester airport,                             COOKING 3
M56 exit 5                                                    COST £28–£38

An example of old English Anglo-French, north-western style. It is run by
English people in an unprepossessing brick house with quasi-Victorian
interior: all plush and scarlet. The menu is unnecessarily in French: 'boudin
noir notre façon', translated as 'Lancashire black pudding sliced and sautéd,

with petit French black puddings served on a mustard sauce with apple and salad garnish.' For all that, reporters confirm that the cooking is accurate and enjoyable. There are signs of excess: peppered fillet of beef topped with foie gras and truffle served with a mild garlic and honey sauce is an example. However, the seven-course tasting menu, not as highly priced as it might be, is slightly more restrained: a chicken and mushroom tartlet with a curry cream; terrine of lobster, disclosing layers of lobster and other fish; halibut with a lemony beurre noisette; courgette flower stuffed with minced duck; well-composed carrot and lemon soup; loin of lamb on a sauce of tomato and sultanas; passion-fruit mousse with crème de menthe ice-cream. The vegetables are good, though again complicated. Fruit and sweet ingredients outnumber herbs as a source of flavour. There is quite a long wine list, strongest on Champagne, claret and burgundy, although the house Champagne is nothing to write home about. There are three Swiss wines – not often encountered – including a Dézaley from Testuz. House white from £7.75, red at £8.50. CELLARMAN'S CHOICE : Côtes du Rhône Blanc de Blancs, Seguret, 1986, £10.50; Ch. Vieux Landat 1982, Haut Médoc £16.50. Service is kind, pleasant and proficient and prices are 'totally inclusive' – no supplementary tips expected.

CHEFS: Robert Thornton and Kevin Lofthouse   PROPRIETORS: Pauline and Derek Harrison
OPEN: Tue to Sat, exc Sat L
CLOSED: 24 Dec for 2 weeks
MEALS: 12 to 2, 7 to 9.30 (10 Sat)
PRICES: £26 (£32), Set L and D £24 (£28). Service inc
CARDS: Access, Amex, Diners, Visa
SEATS: 50. 8 tables outside. Private parties: 10 main room. Car-park, 50 places. No children under 12. Smart dress preferred. No cigars/pipes in dining-room. Air-conditioned

## Mr Kuk's

| 55A Mosley Street, M2 3HY | COOKING 1 |
|---|---|
| 061-236 0659 | COST £13–£31 |

Chef Lau continues to run a good Peking kitchen, turning out recommended dishes which range right across the board from hot-and-sour soup, well marinated cold meats, smoked fish and superb seaweed to lightly cooked cod in wine sauce and moist braised duck with assorted vegetables. Flavours are strong but subtle, ingredients are good. Soup noodles and dim-sum are as strongly represented as more complex banquet dishes, to be ordered in advance. Among the most unusual offerings are braised sea cucumber and oil-dripped chicken. The basement dining-room is fairly plain and neat, much used for entertaining visiting Chinese dignitaries and business people, and service is friendly and usually efficient. Fragrant tea is served in western cups. House French wine, £5.50.

CHEF: Mr Lau   PROPRIETORS: Stephen Kuks and Geoffrey Cohen
OPEN: all week, exc Sun L
MEALS: noon to midnight
PRICES: £17 (£26), Set L and D £8.50 (£13) to £18 (£23). Service 10%
CARDS: Access, Amex, Diners, Visa
SEATS: 95. Private parties: 95 main room. Children's helpings. Music. Air-conditioned

# Sanam

145–151 Wilmslow Road,
Rusholme, M14 5AW                                COOKING 1
061-224 1008                                      COST £8

The Sanam is a sweet house and restaurant, and authentic Asian sweetmeats are dispensed along with containers of curry over the take-away counter behind the red and gold shop front. To the right is the dining area, brightly lit and closely packed with marble-topped tables. 'Cheap, cheerful and clean – better than most in the area,' is the general feeling among reporters, though a warning note of less than thoroughly cooked chicken on one occasion has been heard. Quails have disappeared since last year but lamb's brain is still on the specialities list along with spicy mackerel, lamb on the bone and a huge Sanam mix comprising quantities of tandoori, tikka and assorted bits of kebab. Unlicensed.

CHEFS: Abdul Jabbar, Ala Uddin and Guzar Ahmed    PROPRIETORS: Abdul Ghafoor Akhtar and sons
OPEN: all week
MEALS: 12 to 5, 5 to 12
PRICES: £6 (£7)
CARDS: Access, Visa
SEATS: 150. Private parties: 100 main room, 60 private room. Vegetarian meals. Children's helpings. Wheelchair access (also WC). Music. Air-conditioned

# Siam Orchid

54 Portland Street, M1 4QU                            COOKING 1
061-236 1388                               COST £7–£29

No longer the sole Thai restaurant in Manchester since the owners opened a second branch, the Royal Orchid, just round the corner in Charlotte Street. Service is courteous and help is offered in achieving a balanced meal from the 100-plus dishes on the menu. Lavish use of coriander and cumin, tamarind and lime, lemon-grass, basil and coconut, makes a refreshing change from the preponderance of Cantonese food in nearby Chinatown. Spicy salads and seafoods are a speciality, while the satays and noodle dishes can rival the best on offer elsewhere in the city. House French, £5.20.

CHEFS: C. Sirisompan and Doy Parry    PROPRIETORS: C. Sirisompan and K. Sisrisambhand
OPEN: all week, exc Sat and Sun L
MEALS: 11.30 to 2.30, 6.30 to 11.30 (6 to 11.30 Fri and Sat, 5 to 11 Sun)
PRICES: £12 (£22), Set L £3.90 (£7) to £18 (£24), Set D £7.40 (£12) to £18 (£24). Service 10%
CARDS: Access, Visa
SEATS: 55. Private parties: 55 main room. Children welcome. Music. Air-conditioned

*All details are as accurate as possible at the time of going to press, but chefs and owners often change, and it is wise to check by telephone before making a special journey. Many readers have been disappointed when set-price bargain meals are no longer available. Ask when booking.*

# That Café

1031 Stockport Road
South Levenshulme, M19 2TB                    COOKING 2
061-432 4672                                  COST £16–£22

Half a mile out of Manchester in an area of small terraced houses, That Café is
undisturbed by traffic noise despite being on the main Stockport road. Outside
are green awnings and there is a jungle of greenery in the window. Inside, the
restaurant shows its origins as an antique shop in the eccentric, decidedly
1930s posters, teapots and memorabilia. Joe Quinn and his staff are calm and
friendly, serving a menu that has vegetarian undertones but doesn't leave
meat-eaters feeling deprived. The selection ranges from six-bean casserole, and
broccoli and Brie crêpes, to beef olives and pigeon in honey sauce. Fresh fish is
always available – delicate salmon kedgeree, trout en papillote – and desserts
are along the lines of hot fudge sundae and treacle tart. House French, £8.
CELLARMAN'S CHOICE : Sparkling Gooseberry English Country wine, £6.95;
Raimat Abadia Reserva, £7.95.

CHEF/PROPRIETOR: Joe Quinn
OPEN: Tue to Sat D, Sun L
MEALS: 12 to 2.30, 7.30 to 10.30
PRICES: £12 (£18), Set D £9.95 (£16)
CARDS: Access, Amex, Visa
SEATS: 50. Private parties: 50 main room, 25 private room. Vegetarian meals. Children's
helpings. Music

# Woodlands

33 Shepley Road, Audenshaw, M34 5DJ          COOKING 1
061-336 4241                                  COST £17–£31

This well-dressed restaurant in a Victorian house in the suburbs of eastern
Manchester continues to offer fairly cooked, elaborate French-style restaurant
food to a number of satisfied customers. Set-price menus at lunch and dinner
offer cheaper alternatives to the *carte* of eight dishes at each course. A short
wine list; house French is £6.

CHEF: William Mark Jackson    PROPRIETORS: Mr and Mrs D. Crank
OPEN: Tue to Sat, exc Sat L
CLOSED: first week Jan, 1 week after Easter, two weeks Aug
MEALS: 12 to 2, 7 to 9.30 (10 Sat)
PRICES: £19 (£26), Set L £10.50 (£17), Set D £12.50 (£19)
CARDS: Access, Visa
SEATS: 36. Private parties: 22 main room, 14 private room. Car-park, 12 places. Children's
helpings. Smart dress preferred. No cigars/pipes in dining-room. Wheelchair access`
(3 steps). Music. Air-conditioned

---

*'Mostly the problem is Monday. You know it is no use trying to eat out on Mondays because
every restaurant within 50 miles of wherever you are is closed. In Lancashire, though, it is
different. The problem is Saturday lunch. Everywhere in the* Guide *in Lancashire closes
for Saturday lunch. Can anybody explain this?'* A senior inspector

---

# Yang Sing

34 Princess Street, M1 4JY                                    COOKING **3**
061-236 2200                                              COST **£16−£38**

'How can we eat in Carlisle after this?' was one reader's plaint after a meal that began with light spring rolls and was followed by sesame toasts, crispy seaweed, fish dumplings, prawns in their shells with a chilli dip, chicken and nuts with lettuce and hoisin sauce, spare ribs, mange-tout with straw mushrooms and sizzling veal chops in black-bean sauce. A damp December day might dawn as spring after that. Yang Sing is in a basement. Its kitchen is visible (and audible) and may afford amusement for the wordless visitor but is deafening if you sit too close. It is busy for much of the time, deservedly so by all accounts, though some opine that missed reservations and similar slips are due to an administration under pressure; service can also be quite brusque on bad days, though helpful and chatty on better ones. The Cantonese menu is vast yet the kitchen is still more experimental than much of the opposition. Try to ignore the banquet suggestions and choose your own meal. Popularity eventually takes its toll and banquet selections are one area of compromise in tastes and techniques. There was an advertisement in the trade press for a chef before Christmas 1988 and a reader did comment that Harry Yeung's chief activity now seemed to be adding up bills at a desk in the restaurant. Balance against that steamed sea bass that 'cannot be improved' and usually excellent dim-sum on offer until 6pm every day. The wine list does its best. House wine from £5.95.

CHEF: Harry Yeung    PROPRIETORS: Yang Sing Restaurant Ltd
OPEN: all week
CLOSED: 25 Dec
MEALS: noon to 11
PRICES: £9 (£16), Set L and D £10.25 (£16) to £25.50 (£32). Service 10%
CARDS: Access, Amex, Visa
SEATS: 140. Private parties: 220 main room, 30 and 70 private rooms. Children welcome.
Wheelchair access. Music. Air-conditioned

---

**MASHAM** North Yorkshire                                            map 7

# Floodlite Restaurant ♥

*COUNTY OF THE YEAR RESTAURANT*

7 Silver Street, Masham HG4 4DX                               COOKING **2**
RIPON (0765) 89000                                        COST **£10−£22**

A little more effort − or money − put into the surroundings would ensure a more positive response to the Floodlite. As it is, that name is inappropriate: the downstairs bar is dark and fusty, the upstairs restaurant dull. The menu is poorly presented and, at first glance, over-ambitious, but the food is princely. To quote one astonished reporter: 'The rosemary and garlic sauce with the roast loin of lamb was excellent beyond belief, richly flavoured, well reduced, a hint of rosemary, natural juices, red wine, light textured but heavily flavoured. Given the surroundings, *we just couldn't believe this*. Roast saddle of hare served with wild mushrooms was equally excellent, with a very rich and wholly natural sauce, the meat tender and of superb quality… There was a fabulous

puréed fruit sauce with the blackcurrant and apple bread-and-butter pudding.'
Also on the menu have been king prawns and squid with ginger and soy sauce;
fillet steak topped with mushroom purée and glazed with hollandaise sauce;
banana-stuffed chicken with fruity curry sauce. Sunday lunches are 'delicious
and imaginative'. The table settings and the service are far better than the
decorative framework. This is a young couple who have talent. At least their
priorities are right. The wine list is an excellent short selection with a proper
range and fair prices. House French is £5.25. CELLARMAN'S CHOICE : Ch. Haut
Sociondo 1983, £8.95; Villa Maria Hawkes Bay Private Bin Sauvignon Blanc
1987, £11.50.

CHEF: Charles Flood    PROPRIETORS: Charles and Christine Flood
OPEN: Tue to Sun D, Fri to Sun L (other days by arrangement)
MEALS: 12 to 2, 7 to 9.30
PRICES: £13 (£18), Set L £6.25 (£10)
CARD: Visa
SEATS: 36. Private parties: 28 main room. Vegetarian meals. Children's helpings on request.
No-smoking area. Music

---

MELMERBY  Cumbria                                                      map 7

## Village Bakery

Melmerby CA10 1HE                                          COOKING 2
LANGWATHBY (076 881) 515                                     COST £14

The Bakery is a house and barn (actually pigsty and chicken-loft) conversion
looking over a village green bisected by the road to Penrith. It is run by Lis and
Andrew Whitley on organic principles (now we would say 'green') using
wholefoods and organically reared meats and poultry, firing their bread oven
with wood, using flour from organic wheat ground at Little Salkeld water-mill.
It sounds twee, certainly evoking sandals and homespun tweed, but it isn't.
The Whitleys are sharp, intelligent folk who know what they're doing and do it
well. The bread is commercial as well as good – and how many whole-earth
bakers in England can say that? The cooking in their daytime restaurant (no
smoking please) is robust and flavoursome. It avoids the deadweight of many
vegetarian places because it is organically carnivore: joints baked in the oven
are good. Breakfasts, served from 8.30 to 11am and 9.30 to 11 on Sundays, are
the sort to set up anyone for a day's walking. It is a civilised place, and it is
licensed. House organic Gros Plant from Bossard and a Côteaux de Ceze £4.95;
also Jennings Bitter from Cockermouth, Aspall Cyder, or Hugh Rock's
gooseberry or elderflower wines.

CHEF: Diane Richter    PROPRIETORS: Lis and Andrew Whitley
OPEN: Tue to Sun, breakfasts and L only
CLOSED: Christmas to Easter
MEALS: 12 to 2
PRICES: £8 (£12), Snacks from 70p
CARDS: Access, Visa
SEATS: 40. Private parties: 25 main room. Car-park, 8 places. Vegetarian meals. Children's
helpings. No smoking. Wheelchair access (1 step)

**MELTON MOWBRAY** Leicestershire map 6

## *Elizabethan*

44-46 Sherrard Street
Melton Mowbray LE13 1XJ COOKING 2
MELTON MOWBRAY (0664) 67871 COST £12–£35

Although Melton Mowbray may not be on the map for its restaurant tradition, there are intriguing precedents for the high gastronomic ambitions Brian Keeley-Whiting has brought to the town. Here in this old market town Francatelli was *chef de cuisine* to an aristocratic gentlemen's club before he achieved fame and glory as Queen Victoria's chef. Brian Keeley-Whiting and his mother – the Elizabeth after whom the restaurant is named – restored a semi-derelict building with much effort before opening in the summer of 1988. Now, it has a comfortingly old-fashioned English air behind its tea-room frontage. The waitresses wear a neat black dresses and white gloves to serve. The cooking, by contrast, is undiluted modern British, described by the chef himself as 'nouvelle but bigger', reflecting his training under Anton Edelmann of the Savoy and then Jeremy Blake O'Connor, now in Aylesbury (see entry). This translates into warm salmon terrine on a saffron sauce, wild mushroom soup, whole poached lobster with a Sauternes sauce, which have been well executed. Take a main dish of best end of lamb in a pastry case with madeira sauce; the lamb, delicately pink in the middle, was encased in melting pastry, garnished with a few fresh wild mushrooms and finished with a rich madeira reduction. Vegetables, served separately on a crescent plate, included baby corn, tiny roast potatoes, mange-tout and cauliflower garnished with grated red peppers. The only slip that has been noted is over-reduced sauces. Everything else thoroughly impressed: a lobster bouillon as the complimentary chef's surprise, good seed-topped rolls, a plateful of desserts, cheeses from Long Clawson and polished petits fours. For all this, prices are very reasonable, especially for the set menus. The next year will see if this ambitious yet unlikely mixture can prosper in the Midlands. Chef Keeley-Whiting does a table tour at the end of a meal and one reporter commented, 'he is in his twenties, depressingly slim...I think he deserves encouragement.' The wine list is short but pointing in the right direction, particularly for its prices. House French is £5.50. CELLARMAN'S CHOICE : Canard Duchêne Champagne NV, £17.50; Ch. Cos d'Estournel 1976, £21.50.

CHEF: Brian Keeley-Whiting PROPRIETOR: Elizabeth Wooldridge
OPEN: Tue to Sun, exc Sat L and Sun D
MEALS: 12 to 2, 7 to 10
PRICES: £22 (£29), Set L £6 (£12) to £7 (£13), Set D £12.50 (£19). Minimum £5
CARDS: Access, Visa
SEATS: 50. Private parties: 30 main room, 20 private room. Children's helpings on request. Wheelchair access. Music

*'The reason for the falling off of their reputation is quite simple – the hand that stirred the pot now rocks the cradle and it is not quite confident enough a hand to train the kitchen which is badly in need of direction.'* On inspecting in Sussex

MIDHURST  West Sussex                                              map 3

## Hindle Wakes ▼

| 1 Church Hill, Midhurst GU29 9NY | COOKING 2 |
|---|---|
| MIDHURST (073 081) 3371 | COST £22–£33 |

Named after a medieval Lancashire chicken dish, this pantiled red brick
restaurant is owned by Christopher Ross, a constant presence in the dining-
room, and Lisa Francis-Lang, doctor turned chef and now half in, half out of the
kitchen. The décor is designer-peach, summery, pastel and ultra-pretty, and the
menu is short and promising, with four to six modern British choices per
course and not a boring-sounding dish among them. Appealing flavour
combinations, as in hot chicken-liver mousse with cranberry and madeira
sauce, are mostly on the classical side without being old-fashioned. There is a
heavy leaning towards old recipes, but cooked in up-to-date variations. There
is also a 1980s preoccupation with sweet sauce for meats. Mead from the
nearby Lurgashall winery is used in marinades and sauces, and the
cheeseboard is British and includes the very local Gospel Green. Lisa Francis-
Lang clearly has all the right ideas and can pull them off, but her results are
uneven. One meal is encapsulated thus: 'a nice, fresh sole terrine; solid and
dull Gressingham duck; the worst vegetables I've had for years; excellent, very
flavourful brown-bread ice-cream'. It is to be hoped the doctor has the knack of
curing herself. The wine list is a fine miniature and not overpriced. House
Côtes de Duras, £6.25. CELLARMAN'S CHOICE : Ch. La Tour St Bonnet, 1979,
£13.50; Saumur-Champigny 1986, Filliatreau, £9.25.

CHEFS: Lisa Francis-Lang and James O'Meara   PROPRIETORS: Christopher Ross and Lisa
Francis-Lang
OPEN: Tue to Sat D, Wed to Fri L (Sat by arrangement)
MEALS: 12.30 to 1.45, 7 to 9.30
PRICES: Set L £12.50 (£22), Set D £16.50 (£27). Licensed, also bring your own:
corkage £6.25
CARD: Access
SEATS: 20. Private parties: 16 main room. No children under 12. No cigars/pipes in dining-
room. Music

## Maxine's

| Red Lion Street, Midhurst GU29 9PB | COOKING 2 |
|---|---|
| MIDHURST (073 081) 6271 | COST £13–£25 |

It is possible to drive through Midhurst, catch a glimpse of Cowdray Castle,
and pass on. Don't. Turn off the main road and see the market square, the
church and a fine country town. On an island site in the centre, flanking the
Swan Inn, is this small restaurant, half-timbered with a vengeance. Robert de
Jager has been cooking, and his wife Marti serving, meals of consistent quality
for the past eight or nine years. They have attracted loyal regulars as well as
steady approval from travellers. 'Excellent value for money.' The slowly
changing repertoire began with bistro favourites like garlic bread, mushrooms
fried in garlic butter and duck with orange and Grand Marnier sauce, but has
moved with the times to encompass calf's brain croquettes served with a

chicory salad or fillet of hare with juniper served with admirable celeriac purée, grated carrots, green beans and dauphinois potatoes. Fashion takes its toll with a lightly grilled wedge of Brie coated with almonds and served with a raspberry sauce but let's hope the vogue is evanescent – the more sensible diner can at least relax with a slice of warm Dutch apple pie (one of the few concessions to the de Jagers' origins). The cooking is skilled, in particular the rich, fairly creamy, sauces – for example sorrel with a small piece of salmon and a tarragon and madeira sauce with fillet of lamb in one test meal. These bore no resemblance to the slovenly, over-worked reductions so commonly served nowadays. Intelligence showed yet again in the fine flavour of a trio of sorbets and that Dutch apple pie. The restaurant is not *bravura* and the service, when busy, may not be of the fastest, but Marti de Jager knows her trade and her produce. The wine list is short, seemly and largely French, including Mâcon-Lugny les Genièvres 1986 from Latour. There are proportionately many half-bottles. House French is £5.50.

CHEF: Robert de Jager  PROPRIETORS: Robert and Marti de Jager
OPEN: Mon to Sun D, exc Tue, Wed to Sun L
MEALS: 12 to 2, 7 to 10
PRICES: £17 (£21), Set L and D £8.50 (£13). Service inc
CARDS: Access, Amex, Diners, Visa
SEATS: 27. Private parties: 30 main room. Children's helpings

---

**MILFORD-ON-SEA  Hampshire**                                     map 2

# Rocher's

69–71 High Street
Milford-on-Sea SO41 0QG                                   COOKING 3
LYMINGTON (0590) 42340                                   COST £12–£24

The minimum has been spent on surroundings at this pleasant small restaurant run by an Anglo-French couple. Originally some sort of shop, its sole decoration is French travel posters proclaiming the glories of the châteaux of the Loire, the region from which Alain Rocher comes (via Chewton Glen, see New Milton). Eschewing any big hotel tricks, his cooking is straightforward, with an attractive mixture of fairly classical and fairly modern French. The sauces are unusually good, very French and almost always cream or alcohol based. Vegetables, too, are excellent; desserts tasteful and quite simple. A meal of monkfish with paprika and pimento sauce; marinated fillet of beef 'en chevreuil' and bombe glacée of chocolate was more than sufficient solace for a seaside evening for one reporter. Trimmings, bread especially, do not do the place justice, although the service does. The wine list is cheap, short but nicely chosen – though lacking many essential vintages. It is expanding into better representation of the Loire as M. Rocher brings in his own shipments. House Cuvée Boisset is £4.95. CELLARMAN'S CHOICE : Mâcon Viré, Domaine de Roally, £12; Chinon Rouge, Ch. de Ligre, £9.50. Travellers who may recall all those *gésiers de canard* consumed driving down the western side of France, can eat them here in a salade tourangelle. They are translated as 'giblets'; 'gizzard' would be more accurate. Sunday lunches are simpler and much cheaper. At the bottom of the dinner menu is the legend, 'No pipes, cigars or children in the main restaurant.' One wonders whether they gave any thought to priorities in that instruction.

CHEF: Alain Rocher  PROPRIETORS: Alain and Rebecca Rocher
OPEN: all week D, and Sun L
CLOSED: 14 Jan to 14 Feb
MEALS: 12.30 to 2, 7 to 10
PRICES: £16 (£20), Set L £8.50 (£12)
CARDS: Access, Visa
SEATS: 30. Private parties: 30 main room. Smart dress preferred. No cigars/pipes in dining-room. Wheelchair access. Music

---

## MOLLINGTON Cheshire                                                    map 5

### ▲ *Crabwall Manor* ♟

Mollington CH1 6NE                                          COOKING 3
GREAT MOLLINGTON (0244) 851666                          COST £18–£41

The clock tower and stables nearly dwarf this red-brick neo-gothic house just outside Chester. Inside, a great deal of fabric and much plasterwork has been expended on a Hollywood vision of life in the English country house. Cooking by Michael Truelove is in the modern international vein: a French-language menu, refreshingly few major luxuries, with flavours familiar to eaters across the land – ginger, lemon-grass, wild mushrooms, coriander. He has had eloquent support for fine, delicate sauces and well-balanced flavours. 'I would look forward to a meal there with excitement.' Loin of lamb Clamart, on a tarragon gravy, with a pastry coffin of peas; duck with cabbage, carrots and courgettes on a honey sauce; a very fine duck and chicken-liver parfait with an onion relish, have all been well reported. There may have been a tilt towards larger portions and perhaps less refined flavours in more recent meals; reporters have found themselves outfaced by quantities, overwhelmed by sweetness. Service is very willing and capable, though the link between dining-room and kitchen sometimes breaks, and other niggles have surfaced. The wine list is a good one with excellent coverage, good choice of growers, a fair number of halves and only one drawback: the price. Commendably, there is a page of bottles costing under £10 but this does not dissolve the surprise at seeing two vintages of Ch. Trotanoy, 1970 and 1979, at mark-ups sufficient to pay for a night's accommodation upstairs. House burgundy is £7.95.
CELLARMAN'S CHOICE : Mercurey, Ch. de Chamirey 1987, £21; Seppelts Cabernet Sauvignon 1985, £16.75.

CHEF: Michael Truelove  PROPRIETORS: Carl A. Lewis and Julian Hook
OPEN: all week
MEALS: 12.30 to 2, 7 to 9.30
PRICES: £22 (£34), Set L £12 (£18) to £15 (£21), Set D £21 (£28), Snacks £1.50
CARDS: Access, Amex, Diners, Visa
SEATS: 120. Private parties: 16 main room, 50 and 100 private rooms. Car-park, 120 places. Children's helpings. No children under 5. Smart dress preferred. No-smoking area. Wheelchair access (3 steps; also WC). Air-conditioned
ACCOMMODATION: 48 rooms, all with bath/shower. Rooms for disabled. B&B £77.50 to £105. No children under 5. Afternoon teas. Garden. Tennis. TV. Phone. Scenic. Doors close at midnight [GHG]

MONTACUTE Somerset                                                          map 2

## ▲ *Milk House*

17 The Borough, Montacute TA15 6XB                                    COOKING 1
MARTOCK (0935) 823823                                                 COST £12−£22

Lee and Bill Dufton's restaurant has been a labour of love. Over the past couple
of years, they have restored this wonderful fifteenth-century ham-stone
building opposite Montacute House and furnished it. They have also brought
the garden back to order and grow vegetables for the restaurant. Orders are
taken in a splendid beamed sitting-room and there are two dining-rooms, the
main one at the back, with an inner rough-stoned wall and old well, and an
inner one with a huge log fire used in winter. Both are furnished with antique
polished tables and matching sets of old chairs. The atmosphere is gentle, the
pace relaxed and reports comment on the evident sincerity of spirit. 'We limit
our intake to 22 people per evening, because we make everything ourselves
and we prefer it that way.' A self-taught cook, Lee Dufton puts as much
emphasis on the raw ingredients, which are organic wherever possible, as on
the dishes themselves, which are sensibly unambitious. Rough terrine de
gibier; salade de maison with smoked quail's eggs and an apple vinaigrette;
smoked salmon roulé with celery and walnut stuffing have all been good first
courses for the quality of the produce. Among the main dishes, gourmet
vegetarian ideas like filled crêpes and nut fricadelles pop up among classic
French dishes − salmon with sorrel sauce, venison braised in red wine, roast
duck with reduced cooking juices and orange zest. Home-made puddings range
from rich to healthy and, to round off, there are petits fours filled with organic
fruit pastes, nuts and liqueurs. Bread is from the Ceres bakery in Yeovil −
wholegrain of course. The wine list includes a few organics, though this area
could profitably be explored further, to complement the cooking. Its range is
catholic, its pricing charitable. House Duboeuf is £5.30, as are two organics
from Lubéron and the Var. CELLARMAN'S CHOICE : Châteauneuf-du-Pape 1984
Pierre André (organic), £14.20; Mâcon-Lugny 1986, Duboeuf, £9.10.

CHEF: Lee Dufton   PROPRIETORS: Lee and Bill Dufton
OPEN: Wed to Sat D, Sun L
MEALS: 12.30 to 2, 7.30 to 9.15
PRICES: Set Sun L £9 (£12) to £11 (£14), Set D £12 (£15) to £15 (£18). Service inc
CARDS: Access, Visa
SEATS: 22. 3 tables outside. Private parties: 40 main room, 20 private room. Vegetarian
meals. Children's helpings. Smart dress preferred. No smoking in dining-room.
Wheelchair access
ACCOMMODATION: 2 rooms, all with bath/shower. B&B to £58. Deposit: £10. No children
under 12. Garden. Confirm by 6

'This year it struck us that standards in Scotland have improved vastly since we first
inspected there for the Guide in 1973 when some of the nominations still had sauce bottles
on the tables! Now we saw sliced bread at only one place and found Scottish bread very
good – fresh and crusty and accompanied by good butter. Menus are more adventurous, in
fact there is a danger that wood-pigeon is becoming the scampi of the future!' A senior
inspector

map 2

## Sheridans

High Street, Moreton-in-Marsh GL56 0AX COOKING 2
MORETON-IN-MARSH (0608) 50251 COST £16–£31

This occupies a stable block to the manor house; the stone floors and walls remind the visitor of its original function, softened by plants and curtains. Marc Sheridan has opened a delicatessen next door – rather than letting bedrooms – in symbiotic relationship with his kitchen: buy his bread rolls in the morning, or meat or terrines, or some of the good preserves. The restaurant remains ambitious, opening seven days a week, lunch and dinner, yet there are fewer signs of ultra-luxury ingredients than formerly. Perhaps Cotswold residents, though well housed, are careful with their money. Trademarks, such as twin sauces dividing a plate, persist. A test meal revealed an acceptable kitchen though flavours were occasionally spoiled by inattention. It opened with a hot scallop mousse with Champagne sauce, following with fillet of beef with a burned bourguignonne sauce. Vegetables are ample but also need care. A hallmark dish ended the meal, marquise au chocolat. This seems to have been on every menu since opening. The wine list, from Bablake Wines, is one hundred per cent French, mostly burgundy and claret. It is adequate, but not cheap. The Mouton Rothschild 1970 comes at £185. Try it at the Old Fire Engine House (see entry, Ely), last seen in the bin-ends – it will only cost you £55. The one is steep, the other a bargain. House wine, £6.95.

CHEF/PROPRIETOR: Marc Sheridan
OPEN: all week, exc Sun D
MEALS: 12 to 2.30, 7 to 10
PRICES: £17 (£26), Set D £10.95 (£16). Cover 75p (L only)
CARDS: Access, Visa
SEATS: 40. Private parties: 30 main room, 12 and 12 private rooms. Children welcome. No-smoking area. Wheelchair access (also WC). Music

 map 7

## La Brasserie

59 Bridge Street, Morpeth NE61 1PQ COOKING 1
MORPETH (0670) 516200 COST £10–£29

Upstairs in a very pretty room of pinks and greens, 'a setting that makes you feel spoilt', is an ambitious all-day venture with *carte*, and fixed-price menus at every level to suit all pockets. The range, giving a fair crack to the vegetarian whip as well, goes from prawns baked in filo to chicken cacciatore. There may be rough edges of service or cooking, but chiefly the spirits are very willing. The wine list is enterprising, on the Italian side, though it does not state much about growers or shippers when it comes to France. It is fairly priced. Wines of the month replace house wine and come at £7.50. CELLARMAN'S CHOICE : Gewürztraminer, Réserve Particulière 1985, Kuehn, £9; Barbera d'Asti 1985, Guasti, £8.95.

CHEF/PROPRIETOR: R.H. Wilkinson
OPEN: Tue to Sun, exc Sun D
MEALS: 11.30 to 2, 6.30 to 11
PRICES: £17 (£24), Set L £4.50 (£10) to £6.95 (£13), Set D £9.50 (£16) to £11.50 (£18)
CARDS: Access, Amex, Diners, Visa
SEATS: 50. Private parties: 30 main room, 50 private room. Car-park, 6 places. Vegetarian
meals. Children's helpings

---

**MOULSFORD**  Oxfordshire                                                          map 2

## ▲ Beetle & Wedge

Moulsford OX10 9JF                                                          COOKING 1
CHOLSEY (0491) 651 381                                                      COST £23–£36

Richard and Kate Smith, who have made such a splash at the Royal Oak,
Yattendon (see entry), have positively dived into the water with their
expansion to this riverside Victorian pub-hotel with a terrace and a converted
boat-house. 'A good position opposite water-meadows with cows, there are
(on a Sunday) a lot of gin palaces mooring alongside and cracking of bottles of
Champagne to go with the langoustines and crab brought on board from the
restaurant by the extremely well turned out staff.' As at Yattendon, this is a
brave attempt to be all things to all people: bar food and restaurant food of a
palpably higher quality than was once associated with such places – though no
ice-cream for a child having Sunday lunch. There are set-price and à la carte
menus changing every day. The former is a variation on the theme of 'things
one likes to eat out': one spring day the first courses read seafood, duck livers,
avocado and prawns, smoked salmon, mushroom, melon, asparagus, kidneys.
Each was dealt with in a direct manner, with little artifice but much resulting
pleasure to reporters. Dishes mentioned include seafood, mushrooms and
pasta; halibut or salmon and turbot with saffron sauce; duck with apples and
calvados; apple and raspberry crumble; hot Cointreau soufflé with a raspberry
coulis. Puddings, especially hot ones like beignets and soufflés, are a strong
point. Vegetables, as at Yattendon, are also plentiful and good. The cooking
appears substantial and very creamy; 'one or two more astringent dishes'
would have eased the return home of one family. Delays have been noticed at
busy times but the welcome is genuine and the staff intelligent. A big wine list
gives help with notes, though saying a wine is 'lovely' does not advance
knowledge very far. House wine is £7.50.

---

CHEF: Richard Smith    PROPRIETORS: Kate and Richard Smith
OPEN: all week, exc Sun D
MEALS: 12.30 to 2, 7.30 to 10
PRICES: £17 (£24), Set L and D £17.50 (£23) to £23.50 (£30)
CARDS: Access, Amex, Visa
SEATS: 60. 21 tables outside. Private parties: 60 main room, 50 private room. Car-park, 35
places. Children's helpings. Smart dress preferred in dining-room. No cigars/pipes in
dining-room. Wheelchair access (also WC)
ACCOMMODATION: 13 rooms, all with bath/shower. B&B £55.50 to £65.60. Baby facilities.
Pets by prior arrangement. Afternoon teas. Garden. Fishing. TV. Phone. Scenic. Doors close
at midnight. Confirm by 6 [GHG]

MOULTON  North Yorkshire                                              map 7

## Black Bull

Moulton DL10 6QJ
BARTON (0325) 377289                                          COOKING 3
1m SE of Scotch Corner, 1m from A1                       COST £14–£34

Unruffled by passing fashions, the menu at the Bull alters little from year to
year. Nor does the decorative scheme, mock-Victorian for the seafood bar and
private rooms, traditional plush for the splendid converted Pullman carriage
from the Brighton Belle, and stylish elegance for the plant-draped
conservatory. The menu is built on two main strands: excellent fish and
shellfish, such as Dublin Bay prawns, lobsters and scallops, and steaks and
roasts. It is the seafood that is the main glory, particularly in its plainest guises:
poached salmon, grilled Dover sole, cold lobster or prawns, sauté scallops. A
meal of seafood pancake with a mustard-flavoured Mornay sauce restored that
dish's reputation and other choices showed a fair hand with a beurre blanc.
Very fresh scallops with bacon and broccoli come with a teriyaki sauce; a
halibut steak is wrapped in the crispest filo and given a seasoning layer of
smoked salmon. Some sauces can be heavy handed, but vegetables back up
main dishes well. Good restaurant desserts, though crème brûlée has been
known to fail. Service is by adults. It may be observed that incompetence
among waiting staff (except in places like this) is very, and regrettably,
widespread. Why should we, who pay for the privilege, support unaided the
YTS programme? House Duboeuf, £5.75. As the proprietors are also wine
merchants, the wine list should be good.

CHEF: Stuart Birkett   PROPRIETORS: Mr G.H. and Mrs A. Pagendam
OPEN: Mon to Sat
CLOSED: 23 to 31 Dec
MEALS: 12 to 2, 6.45 to 10.15
PRICES: £21 (£28), Set L £8.95 (£14), Snacks £1
CARDS: Access, Amex, Visa
SEATS: 100. 4 tables outside. Private parties: 30 main room, 10 and 30 private rooms. Car-
park, 80 places. No children under 7. Wheelchair access (also WC)

---

NAILSWORTH  Gloucestershire                                          map 2

## Flynn's

3 Fountain Street, Nailsworth GL6 0BL                        COOKING 2
NAILSWORTH (045 383) 5567                                 COST £14–£28

The Australian background of Garry Flynn, who cooks, and Deborah Reid,
who manages the front of house, ensures a multi-cultural approach to food and
cooking and a relaxed and open friendliness of service. They also have some
style, having redecorated the stark modern building in soft grey/lilac and hung
a series of paintings of Flynn's food by local artist Terry Cripps. The result is
'classy and elegant'. Much experiment is going into the cooking, arranged as a
couple of short set-price menus, which customers can mix as though à la carte,
with daily specials as well. The presence of William Beeston's wet-fish shop
and delicatessen in the next building gives good supplies; fish features largely

on the choice available. Marinated salmon with horseradish cream; roast monkfish on spinach with a herb and vegetable vinaigrette and poached oysters; a sauté of redfish in black-bean sauce are some of the things reported, borrowing from French, English and Asian cuisines for inspiration. Meat is not forgotten, pigeon, sometimes tough, being a regular ingredient as in a rather crude breast of pigeon on Parma ham with a potato and braised onion galette. Quail with an apricot and pecan stuffing has also featured. Desserts continue the stylishness as in the white chocolate cone filled with a chocolate mousse on a coffee sauce, or the passion-fruit mousse with excellent coconut langue de chat biscuits. The wine list is short but has very good French bottles from Windrush Wines in Cirencester and is expanding its Australian stocks which, to date, have been surprisingly low. House French is £6. CELLARMAN'S CHOICE: Seaview Chardonnay 1987, £8.50; Ch La Mongie, Bordeaux Supérieur 1986, £7.50. 'Tipping is not encouraged or expected.'

CHEFS: Garry Flynn, Nicola West and Robert Dew    PROPRIETOR: Garry Flynn
OPEN: Mon to Sat, exc Mon L
MEALS: 12.30 to 2.30, 7 to 9.30
PRICES: £17 (£23), Set L £11 (£14), Set D £15.50 (£19) to £19.95 (£23). Service inc set only
CARDS: Access, Visa
SEATS: 40. Private parties: 50 main room. Vegetarian meals. Children's helpings

## Markey's Stone Cottage

| Old Market, Nailsworth GL6 0BX | COOKING 1 |
|---|---|
| NAILSWORTH (045 383) 2808 | COST £17–£29 |

Ian and Ann Markey moved west from Lingfield to open this small cottage with two dining-rooms. It feels indeed cottagy, the stone walls reminding you of the Cotswolds outside. Ian Markey's cooking is robust, stopping short of over-seasoning but with sit-you-up tastes. A meal of salmon with a tarragon sauce, lamb with an apricot sauce, and marquise au chocolat with a coffee sauce had plenty of character. It's bistro cooking with a bit more finesse: made good, too, by the quality of the raw materials. Weak coffee. There is a short wine list with house Duboeuf at £7.

CHEF: Ian Markey    PROPRIETORS: Ian and Ann Markey
OPEN: Wed to Sat, D only and Sun L (L and D parties by arrangement other times)
MEALS: 12 to 2.30, 7.30 to 10
PRICES: Set L £10.95 (£17), Set D £17.95 (£24)
CARDS: Access, Diners, Visa
SEATS: 32. Private parties: 22 main room, 10 and 22 private rooms. Vegetarian meals. No children under 12. No pipes in dining-room. Wheelchair access (also WC). Music

---

*From a menu in Kent: 'King Prawn Tails marinated in Dijon Mustard and White Wine, lightly grilled, served on a pulse of Horseradish emulsified with Cream; A Parfait of Skate studded with Dublin Bay Prawn, enveloped with young Spinach leaves, served with it's fume spiked with Chives; Chicken Pate enhanced with Tarragon, forced into a boned leg of Spring Chicken and lightly poached in it's own liquor served cold on a Redcurrant Coulis; Whole Quail gently roast in Goose dripping, the juices acidulated with Red Wine and served over with a garnish of Wild Cepes.'*

# ▲ *Rookery Hall* ▼

Worleston, nr Nantwich, CW5 6DQ
NANTWICH (0270) 626866                                          COOKING **3**
on B5074, off A51                                                    COST £24–£54

Moving away from private ownership, Rookery Hall is now a partner of
Ettington Park, the Priory in Bath and other swish establishments that have, by
increasing the ratio of rooms to seats in the restaurants, reversed the original
concept of the country-house hotel that gained currency 15 years ago. At
Rookery Hall the new rooms are yet to be built, but there is the intent. The
question is whether the restaurant and kitchen have the same priorities under
the new regime. The Hall is set in pleasant parkland on the extreme edge of
Nantwich. A pastiche of France, gothic-renaissance, rococo and institutional
Victorian, the house has an unfinished look on the outside. Within, there are
more carpets and curtains than formerly and some of the redecorated public
rooms impress the eye. Service is on a par with surroundings, punctilious and
concerned. Manager David Tearle goes far to provide the care of the individual
proprietor. The restaurant offers the usual country-house arrangement of set
prices, with a reasonable charge for lunch. The *carte* certainly offers enough
choice and has been seen to succeed where not too much is attempted. Thus a
lunch of Cheshire sausages (a form of cheese croquette) and salmon on a bed of
spinach with a saffron sauce was quite excellent, whereas a more complex
terrine, or hure, of seafood lacked any identifiable flavour. Meat cookery: beef
with onion and mushroom or veal with pasta and a light curry sauce is sound.
Fluctuations in execution or in conception have been infrequently observed,
from bad vegetables to a 'summer' pudding produced in March. The
cheeseboard continues to be good, as do the amuse-gueule and petits fours. It is
hoped that serious attention will make performance consistent with price. The
wine list is long, good – and very expensive. House burgundy is £13.
CELLARMAN'S CHOICE : Savennières 1987, Baumard, £15; Savigny-lès-Beaune
*premier cru* 1984, £22.

CHEF: Christopher Phillips    PROPRIETORS: Select Country Hotels plc
OPEN: all week
MEALS: 12.15 to 2.15, 7 to 9.30
PRICES: Set L £13.50 (£24) and £15 (£27), Set D £27.50 (£40) and £32.50 (£45).
Minimum £13.50
CARDS: Access, Amex, Diners, Visa
SEATS: 60. Private parties: 40 main room, 20 private room. Car-park, 30 places. No children
under 10. Smart dress preferred. No smoking. Wheelchair access (also WC)
ACCOMMODATION: 11 rooms, all with bath/shower. Rooms for disabled. B&B £70 to £110.
Deposit: one night's stay. No children under 10. Afternoon teas. Garden. Tennis. Fishing.
TV. Phone. Scenic. Doors close at 1am

---

*If you see a certificate in a restaurant bearing the words 'Diploma of Merit. The Good Food
Guide (United Kingdom)', the claim is false (and the restaurant may be in contempt of
court in displaying it) – see the Introduction. Please write and tell us the name and address
of the restaurant.*

---

NETHERFIELD  East Sussex                                              map 3

# ▲ *Netherfield Place*

| Netherfield TN33 9PP | COOKING **2** |
|---|---|
| BATTLE (042 46) 4455 | COST £14−£32 |

Although Michael and Helen Collier run Netherfield Place as a country-house hotel, it is as much an upmarket restaurant − he is the chef and she is front of house − and this year, for the first time, there has been a steady trickle of positive reports. It is certainly encouraging that in the spacious grounds surrounding the red-brick house, built in rambling 1920s style, there is a mature walled kitchen garden which provides an array of herbs, fruit, flowers and vegetables for the restaurant. Inside, a pleasant bar leads into the lounge and thence to the wood-panelled dining-room. The menus − there are separate set lunches and dinners but the same *carte* for both meals − are all in the modern style: soups of scallop and saffron or wild mushroom and hazelnut, oak-smoked loin of venison with a cranberry tartlet, fried goats' cheese in sesame and breadcrumbs. Lunchtime set-menu dishes are more straightforward: grilled lamb cutlets, beef forestière and scampi in a curried cream sauce. One mid-summer lunch, for example, started with garden-grown crudités served with a mayonnaise dip and warm home-made rolls, then moved on to a rich cold avocado soup with wild strawberries, spoiled only by over-chilling, then to an excellent main-course dish of fresh, moist salmon with scampi in a delicate Champagne sauce. Curiously, however, vegetables included inedibly oversalted carrots. Puddings returned to standard with strawberries from the garden, accompanied by a home-made ice-cream full of little wild strawberries and a brandy-snap, vanilla bavarois in a chocolate case with lemon and lime sauce and good cafetière coffee. The staff are young and friendly but tend to be unobservant. The wine list reportedly contains fine old wines bought at auction. House wine is £6.95. CELLARMAN'S CHOICE : Ch. Les Ormes de Pez, 1981, £27; Moulin-à-Vent, Domaine de la Tour du Bief, 1987, £17.50. See under Battle in *The Good Hotel Guide*.

CHEF: Michael Collier   PROPRIETORS: Michael and Helen Collier
OPEN: all week
MEALS: 12.30 to 2, 7 to 9.30
PRICES: £20 (£27), Set L £12.50 (£14) to £13.50 (£15), Set D £16.95 (£23). Snacks from £1.75
CARDS: Access, Amex, Diners, Visa
SEATS: 75. 4 tables outside. Private parties: 85 main room, 18 and 40 private rooms. Car-park, 50 places. Vegetarian meals. Children's helpings. Smart dress preferred. Wheelchair access (1 step)
ACCOMMODATION: 14 rooms, all with bath/shower. B&B £45 to £95. Baby facilities. Afternoon teas. Garden. Tennis. TV. Phone. Scenic. Confirm 2 to 3 days before [GHG]

*'There are two dining-rooms: red for smokers "but no pipes please or cigars", and blue for non-smokers. Only the blue was open, however, much to the chagrin of my companion, who muttered darkly. She also muttered darkly about other rules written in the inevitable folder, e.g. "Casual wear such as jeans, corduroy, tee shirts and sweatshirts are not acceptable evening wear", but "trouser suits for ladies may be worn", and "on hot nights men need not wear a jacket".'*  On dining in Scotland

# ▲ *Marryat Room,*
# *Chewton Glen Hotel* 🍷

Christchurch Road, New Milton BH25 6QS                      COOKING **3**
HIGHCLIFFE (0425) 275341                                     COST  £22−£47

Places that have gone full tilt for recognition in the world of international
tourism always excite strong feelings in an English breast. Such places are
single-minded, ruthlessly new and so spankingly clean. They appear to hijack
all that was treasured in the English country firmament and return it in terms
acceptable to foreign visitors. Yet such energy must be applauded, and the
efforts of Martin Skan are foremost among his colleagues. That some of the
measures necessary make it expensive or take it outside the usual English
experience should not be invariable reason to criticise. Chewton Glen,
therefore, is slightly unreal, in the way of glossy magazines. The decoration is
overstated, the luxury is palpable. For many, it works a treat. The restaurant
has always looked to Europe for staff and inspiration. Here is *grand luxe* of the
French variety: no trouble spared to introduce truffles, shellfish and foie gras.
But there are signs of movement with the times: a first course of home-cured
duck with a warm lentil salad, for instance. Equally, there are indications of a
welcome directness in the cooking, as in a breast of duck served with a wild
rice and duck-liver risotto with a plain but true stock reduction, 'a wonderful
dish: straightforward, strong and simple'. An inspection meal confirmed these
attributes. There was a wide choice, there were plentiful trimmings of high
standard (though not the bread), there was good coffee. Perhaps with a nod to
the sort of customer most often present, some flavours were muted, even if
techniques were never deficient. Whether the experience is worth the money
may depend on the individual's reaction to the sybarite approach to life. Some
have praised to infinity the standard of service: tolerant, winning, concerned,
evenly paced. Others have been less impressed. Indeed it is service that has
caused most furrowed brows, according to our post-bag. Supercilious,
inattentive and badly trained are some reflections, spiced with regret on the
part of regulars at the disappearance of the daily table d'hôte, except at
luncheon. The wine list, had it been submitted, might have gained a bottle
award. It is very long, very fancy and includes some interesting French country
wines as well as overseas selections that keep prices within the possible.
House French is £7. CELLARMAN'S CHOICE : Ch. Lamothe Cissac 1985, £12;
Rothbury Semillon Brokenback Vineyard, 1987, £12. Vegetarians are
generously provided with their own menu.

---

*The* Guide *office can quickly spot when a restaurateur is encouraging customers to write
recommending inclusion. Such reports do not further a restaurant's cause. Please tell us if a
restaurateur invites you to write to the* Guide.

*The text of entries is based on unsolicited reports sent in by readers, backed up by
inspections conducted anonymously. The factual details under the text are from
questionnaires the* Guide *sends to all restaurants that feature in the book.*

---

CHEF: Pierre Chevillard   PROPRIETOR: Martin Skan
OPEN: all week
MEALS: 12.30 to 2, 7.30 to 9.30
PRICES: Set L £18 (£22), Set D £35 (£39). Minimum £25. Service inc
CARDS: Access, Amex, Diners, Visa
SEATS: 120. 6 tables outside. Private parties: 20 main room, 6 and 80 private rooms.
Car-park, 100 places. Children's helpings. No children under 7. Smart dress preferred.
No cigars/pipes in dining-room
ACCOMMODATION: 46 rooms, all with bath/shower. Rooms for disabled. B&B £138.
Deposit: £138. No children under 7. Afternoon teas. Garden. Swimming-pool. Tennis. Golf.
Snooker. TV. Phone. Scenic. Doors close at midnight [GHG]

---

**NEWBRIDGE   Cornwall**                                          map 1

## Enzo's

Newbridge TR20 8QH                                    COOKING 2
PENZANCE (0736) 63777                                    COST £22

When Anne and Bill Blows, who came from Scotland, bought this Italian restaurant from Enzo, the temptation to call it McEnzo's must have been strong. But they have continued the Italian drift of the menu although the fish and cream impart a Cornish stamp, just as Scotland sneaks in at the pudding stage. The conservatory, which is a no-smoking area, is hung with plants and has ringside seats on the kitchen. Thence comes all manner of good things, of which fish is best: turbot with scallops in cream and wine sauce; salmon with herb sauce; Mediterranean fish soup, roundly flavoured with saffron and garlic. Italian dishes – an antipasto trolley, veal and pasta – are decently done and desserts travel by trolley as well. The ubiquitous tira mi su – Italy's new-wave answer to trifle – sits there alongside a Scottish crowdie. An Italian wine list and Italian house wine at £6. Son Hamish cooks with Anne Blows. On Wednesday out of season there is a set-menu dinner at £11.50.

CHEFS: Anne and Hamish Blows   PROPRIETORS: Anne and Bill Blows
OPEN: all week, D only
CLOSED: 2 weeks Feb and 2 weeks Nov
MEALS: 7 to 9.30 (9 Sun)
PRICES: £11 (£18)
CARDS: Access, Amex, Diners, Visa
SEATS: 70. Private parties: 50 main room, 40 private room. Car-park, 25 places. Vegetarian meals. Children's helpings. No-smoking area. Wheelchair access (1 step). Music

---

**NEWCASTLE UPON TYNE   Tyne & Wear**                        map 7

## Café Procope

35 The Side, Quayside, NE1 3JE                        COOKING 1
091-232 3848                                            COST £14

All is not roses here, but the dedication of the team of young women who run this all-day café under the Tyne bridge deserves notice. The menu pillages the world's cuisines for jambalaya, hummus, falafel, and bourride. The international beers are bottled but excellent, the wine list is really inventive at the price, and vegetarians get a look in. 'Mushroom Stroganoff is good and cheap and enough to feed one for a day.' Comments are made that it is shabbier and less well organised than it need be. House wines £5.20 (red) and £4.95 (white). CELLARMAN'S CHOICE : Texas Vineyards Riesling 1986, £6.50; Brown Brothers Cabernet Sauvignon 1986, £6.70.

CHEFS: Karen Kennedy and Angela Deutschman  PROPRIETOR: Karen Kennedy
OPEN: Tue to Sun
MEALS: 9.30am to 10.30pm (5 Sun)
PRICES: £8 (£12), Snacks from 60p
SEATS: 50. Private parties: 50 main room. Vegetarian meals. Children's helpings. Separate smoking area. Wheelchair access (1 step; also WC). Music

## Dragon House

30–32 Stowell Street, NE1 4XQ                         COOKING 2
091-232 0868                                          COST £7–£25

Opened in 1987 by Barry Yu, a young Sino-Geordie, and his wife Beverley, the restaurant has quickly gained popularity. The winning formula has been a clever combination of authentic and 'creative' Chinese cuisine, with every taste catered for somewhere on the 200-dish main menu, a separate vegetarian and health menu, and four set meals or list of chef's recommendations – all without the usual accompanying hike in prices found in third-generation restaurants. Recommendations have focused on the more adventurous dishes – monkfish in sweet-and-sour sauce, fresh asparagus rolls stuffed with seafood in a creamy crabmeat sauce, very tender da da chicken marinated in oyster sauce and stir-fried in a hot pot – but more traditional Hong Kong roast duck and peppery Singapore vermicelli have been reliable too. The Yus are always in evidence running front of house, staff members are friendly and intelligent, and the success of the business is already showing in the air-conditioning. There is a decent wine list, containing lots of premier brandies, Korean ginseng and Chinese liqueurs. House wine is £5.75. The Sung Dynasty Menu of five courses is served from noon to 3pm on Sunday at £5.50 and must be booked.

CHEF: Ling Yee  PROPRIETOR: Barry Yu
OPEN: all week
CLOSED: 25 Dec
MEALS: 12 to 2, 6 to 12 (noon to midnight Sun)
PRICES: £15 (£21), Set L £3.75 (£7), Set Sun L £5.50 (£9), Set D £10.50 (£15) to £15 (£20)
CARDS: Access, Amex, Diners, Visa
SEATS: 150. Private parties: 70 main room. Vegetarian meals. Children welcome. Wheelchair access. Music. Air-conditioned

## Fisherman's Lodge

Jesmond Dene, NE7 7BQ                                 COOKING 3
091-281 3281                                          COST £19–£44

The Cetolonis' restaurant, in a Victorian conversion beside a stream, has been going for some years. Their diversion to Fisherman's Wharf is now over. The Lodge shows the benefits of concentration: a new chef, added space, a constant level of smartness and cleanliness. Local observers remark both on the difficulty of getting a table, 'on a wet Tuesday the earliest booking I could get was ten in the evening and as we left at midnight, people were being served their first course,' and on the encouraging continuity of the staff: 'the young head waiter when I first went must now be approaching middle age.' The cooking has not got any simpler, nor cheaper. Many things are popped in bags, wrapped in pastry, prime materials mixed on a single plate. But the kitchen preserves its commitment to fish, only a trio of meats being offered. The elaboration may be seen from this meal: in the bar one may start with two unlikely bowls of peanuts and pickled onions, then at table some appetisers of prawn pastry parcels and gravlax; a first course of three seafood parcels, one king prawn, ginger and peppers, one salmon and spinach, one cod and spring onions; at the same table, another beginning of langoustines arranged, with the help of mint leaves and courgettes, as a butterfly on a wash of butter sauce. The first main course was monkfish, fanned out like a white breast of duck, with a vermouth sauce; to balance was another parcel (the chef must have been a postal worker) this time of lobster and asparagus. The second was scampi with a lobster sauce, the richness cut by smoked salmon shavings. No parcel on this, but an envelope of pasta filled with fish mousse. This may sound disconcerting, but many find it very successful: not outfacing, not muddy-flavoured, save on those occasions when textures or techniques do not combine or tastes appear bland. 'Halfway I got tired and stopped eating,' said one visitor after his monkfish and seafood parcel, who also felt rushed enough to liken the place to a sausage factory. Puddings keep up the good work, coffee and petits fours may be passable or too heavy for an overstrained stomach. The wine list takes in a respectable number of bottles, none too highly priced. For a fish restaurant, there is less of an emphasis on whites than might be expected. House French is £8 a litre. CELLARMAN'S CHOICE : Clos du Château de Meursault 1985, £20.70; Chianti Classico, Riserva di Fizzanno 1982 Rocca delle Macie, £14.70.

CHEF: Steven Jobson   PROPRIETORS: Franco and Pamela Cetoloni
OPEN: Mon to Sat, exc Sat L
CLOSED: 25 Dec to 2 Jan
MEALS: 12 to 2, 7 to 11
PRICES: £27 (£37), Set L £13 (£19)
CARDS: Access, Amex, Diners, Visa
SEATS: 70. 3 tables outside. Private parties: 14 main room, 14 and 40 private rooms. Car-park, 45 places. Children's helpings. No children under 6. Smart dress preferred. Wheelchair access

## Rupali

6 Bigg Market, NE1 1UW                                    COOKING 1
091-232 8629                                              COST £8−£23

Owner Abdul Latif is now also the chef, and maintains the consistent quality of the food in his restaurant above a shop in Bigg Market. The styles of dish, each from a different Indian region, are carefully explained on the menu and there's a plethora of intriguing choice, from mild, fruity Malayan dishes to fiery Madras curries. There are three types each of nan, chapati and paratha, nearly a page of vegetables and, unusually, an enticing section of vegetarian main courses including aubergines with lemony lentils and okra with tomato and onion. Locals go for the cheerful ambience and exceptional value. Turn up at lunchtime or early evening for rock-bottom prices, or on Thursday nights for a three-course set menu, glass of wine and liqueur coffee all for £6.95 a head. The wine list won't break the bank either. House French, £5.50.

CHEF/PROPRIETOR: Abdul Latif
OPEN: all week, exc Sun L
MEALS: 12 to 2.30, 6 (7 Sun) to 11.30
PRICES: £11 (£19), Set Thur D £6.95 (£8)
CARDS: Access, Amex, Diners, Visa
SEATS: 54. Private parties: 50 main room. Vegetarian meals. Children's helpings. Music

## Sachins

Forth Banks, NE1 3SG
091-2619035

COOKING 1
COST £13–£28

Once a pub, now a Punjabi restaurant that has excited differing views but latterly more praise than censure. Chicken jalfrezi is 'not a dish for the faint-hearted' but it has been joined by a chilli masala version for those with a penchant for the truly hot. Chicken makhani, lamb cooked in a karahi and the first courses from the tandoor, shared between two people, have received praise. Some find the waiters press too hard, others that they are 'attentive and efficient'. Camerons beers available. House wine £6.95.

CHEF/PROPRIETOR: Dinesh Rawlley
OPEN: Mon to Sat
CLOSED: Easter and Christmas
MEALS: 12 to 2.15, 6 to 11.15
PRICES: £14 (£23), Set D for 2 £23 (£25) to £26 (£29)
CARDS: Access, Amex, Diners, Visa
SEATS: 98. 3 tables outside. Private parties: 60 main room, 40 private room. Car-park, 6 places. Vegetarian meals. Children welcome. Wheelchair access. Music

## 21 Queen Street

COUNTY
OF THE
YEAR
RESTAURANT

21 Queen Street, Princes Wharf
Newcastle-upon-Tyne NE1 3UG
091-222 0755

COOKING 3
COST £17–£35

As the Newcastle quayside has been transformed by redevelopment into the most fashionable quarter of the city in which to live, work and play, so the restaurants have been moving in. Terence Laybourne arrived after seven years developing his skills as the head chef at Fisherman's Lodge (see entry), and his stylish but serious restaurant has moved smoothly into gear to become one of the most respected eating places in the city. Decorated in muted tones of violet, aquamarine and grey, with abstract flower paintings on the walls, the dining-room is airy and relaxed, with service run professionally by Susan Laybourne. A clutch of daily fresh fish dishes and scattered ideas from further afield and at home – stir-fried king prawns, gravlax, honey-roast duck, smoked haddock risotto and mixed grill with black pudding – give a down-to-earth breadth to the largely Anglo-French *carte* and set-lunch menu, but it is the care with which both familiar and new ideas are executed and finished that makes dishes work. A double crab mousse, made like a slice of gateau with a thin layer of aspic separating the top and bottom halves, was garnished with dill leaves and served with a cucumber salad and toasted brioche; nouvelle vegetables, for example broccoli in a tartlet, braised celery and a square of gratin dauphinoise, are varied to suit main courses; noodles to accompany a sauté of rabbit in a creamy mustard sauce are home-made. Puddings are more predictable: home-made ice-creams and sorbet, the ubiquitous sticky toffee pudding and banoffi pie. Occasional rough edges include disappointing bread, but coffee and petits fours are good. A short, wholly French, wine list has some fashionable labels (Bruno Paillard, Alain Roy, Guigal) and very fair prices. House wine is £7.20.

CHEF: Terence Laybourne   PROPRIETORS: Susan and Terence Laybourne
OPEN: Tue to Sat, exc Sat L
CLOSED: 25 and 26 Dec, 1 Jan
MEALS: 12 to 2, 7 to 10.45
PRICES: £21 (£29), Set L £11.40 (£17)
CARDS: Access, Amex, Diners, Visa
SEATS: 50. Private parties: 50 main room. Children's helpings on request. No pipes in dining-room. Wheelchair access

---

**NORTH HUISH  Devon**                                               map 1

## ▲ *Brookdale House*  ▮

North Huish TQ10 9NR                                        COOKING 3
GARA BRIDGE (0548 82) 402 and 415                            COST £34

The house is not as grand as some and the trees on the slopes around – looking as if part of a W.H. Hudson rain-forest or an M.R. James ghost story, depending on weather or time of day – press hard on the new arrival approaching the Gothic hallway. Inside, however, all is light and comfort. Conversion has made a silk purse out of a locally considered pig's ear. Carol Trevor-Roper has ceded the stove to Terry Rich but Charles Trevor-Roper continues his relaxed yet correct supervision of the front of house. (His playing of 1960s pop music entrances some, enrages others – it is inaudible in the dining-room and, indeed, in much of the rest of the house.) There has been evolution in the style of the cooking. Not least, prices have over the years become more competitive; but more important, there has been conscious effort to lighten some of the cooking: 'the ability to continually eat rich food is the sole preserve of *Guide* inspectors,' writes Mr Trevor-Roper. 'It seems to me bad business to kill off our customers too quickly.' Sound sentiments. Translated, in the eating, into dishes such as hot chicken mousse with roast shallots and a port sauce; warm salad of scallops and mange-tout with an orange dressing; always a soup – watercress, celeriac and saffron, carrot and tarragon; brill with mussels and leeks or John Dory with herbs and fresh noodles – fish, as it should be, is good; an automatic cheese course, usually British from Ticklemore Cheese Shop in Totnes; and a variety of puddings – where sometimes the desire to give variety outruns the ability to deliver balanced tastes. Bread, butter and ancillaries all the way to coffee are *comme il faut*. The wine list has long been the Trevor-Roper pride and joy, since their days as restaurateurs in Berkshire. When they moved to Devonshire, they began again and the result is not a cellar of aged wonders, the fruits of years of collecting, but a remarkably adept selection of modern bottles at decent prices. The list is broadly arranged by weight (red) and sweetness (white). It is not doctrinaire: next to a Côte de Beaune Blanc 1981 from Lescure is a Sauvignon 1985 from Togni, California; following St Joseph 1982 from Jaboulet is Stags Leap Cabernet Sauvignon 1984. It is a fashionable list, in the best sense: here will be found subjects of many articles, much comment: Ch. Le Tertre Rôteboeuf 1982, ZD Chardonnay 1985, Cloudy Bay Sauvignon 1988, and Juillot's Mercurey 1985. There are sufficient halves. Ten house wines from £7.80. CELLARMAN'S CHOICE : Hawk Crest Chardonnay 1987, California, £11.95; Medalla Real Cabernet Sauvignon, Chile, 1985, £13.45. There is draught beer, mainly for the proprietor, and almacenista sherries for those who know and love them.

CHEF: Terry Rich   PROPRIETORS: Charles and Carol Trevor-Roper
OPEN: all week, D only
CLOSED: 2 to 23 Jan
MEALS: 7.30 to 9
PRICES: Set D £21 (£28)
CARDS: Access, Visa
SEATS: 24. Private parties: 16 main room. Car-park, 15 places. No children under 10. No smoking in dining-room. Wheelchair access
ACCOMMODATION: 8 rooms, all with bath/shower. B&B £60 to £90. No children under 10. Garden. TV. Phone. Scenic. Doors close at midnight. Confirm by 6 [GHG]

---

NORTHLEACH  Gloucestershire                                                    map 2

## ▲ *Fossebridge Inn*

Fossebridge GL54 3JS
FOSSEBRIDGE (0285) 72071                                          COOKING 3
on A429, 3m from Northleach                                       COST £22—£40

Hugh and Suzanne Roberts have a mission in life: to convert the English pub into a useful social institution. They did it first at the White Bear, Shipston on Stour, and they have succeeded at this handsome place by the River Coln, complete with lake, island, lawns and the patina of long usage. The Roberts call their place a 'country inn hotel'—the best of all worlds. The first floor dining-room offers set-price short menus in semi-formal surroundings, but the same kitchen beavers away at really good food for the Bridge Bar downstairs, priced somewhat lower to reflect the simpler level of service. Bruce Buchan has left to start his own business and Chris Fisher has taken over at the stove. Reports continue to be in favour of the cooking, which is not so much refined as honest, direct and colourful. A meal began with a salad of cured scallops with lime and ginger, went on to an excellent loin of lamb with spinach and wild mushrooms and finished with an apple crumble and hot apricot sauce. More peasant fare, as in a cassoulet de Toulouse or a warm salad of bacon and grated Parmesan have also been recommended. Hot puddings are obviously enjoyed: Amaretto soufflé and baked apples are two. Fish and shellfish, from Brixham, figure often—Dart salmon, crab, scallops, red mullet, Dover sole. One reader remarked that the sauces were satisfactory but not memorable and there have been occasional mutterings about the size of portions. The bread is often praised and the staff's willingness to please is remarked upon, even when the pace hots up on a Saturday night. The wine list has continued to grow; it has taken in more Australian and New Zealand bottles. It is surprisingly expensive for the philosophy of the rest of the house. The cheaper bottles are not very exciting – except, perhaps, for the Alsace bins – and a reader remarked that many of them were out of stock at the beginning of the season. House claret, burgundy and Muscadet from £7.50 to £7.95. CELLARMAN'S CHOICE : Ch. Talbot, St Julien 1978, £37.25; Ngatarawa Hawkes Bay Chardonnay 1987, £22.30. Vegetarian dishes are always on the menu. See under Fossebridge in *The Good Hotel Guide*.

CHEF: Chris Fisher  PROPRIETORS: Hugh and Suzanne Roberts, Janis and Andy Rork
OPEN: Tue to Sun, exc Sun D
MEALS: 12.30 to 2, 7.30 to 9.30 (10 Fri and Sat)
PRICES: £24 (£33), Set D £16.50 (£22) to £22.50 (£28), Snacks from £3.50
CARDS: Access, Amex, Diners, Visa
SEATS: 60. 4 tables outside. Private parties: 36 main room, 24 private room. Car-park, 50 places. Vegetarian meals. Smart dress preferred
ACCOMMODATION: 13 rooms, all with bath/shower. Rooms for disabled. B&B £45 to 65. Deposit: £45. Baby facilities. Pets welcome. Garden. Fishing. TV. Phone. Scenic. Doors close at 11. Confirm by 4 [GHG]

## Old Woolhouse

| The Square, Northleach GL54 3EE | COOKING 3 |
|---|---|
| COTSWOLD (0451) 60366 | COST £36 |

'Where else does the chef's head appear in the open hatch of his front door as one parks one's car? Where else is the front door opened as one approaches by the owner in his chef's whites?' The chef continues to monitor customers' progress once they are inside the well-dressed, though still rustic, dining-room of this small house. If a stranger, you may find it unsettling – but the distinction at the Old Woolhouse is that most customers are friends. It can be as difficult to obtain a booking, especially if you are on your own, as to gain the keys to Heaven, but some have managed it. The Astics have pursued their rather individual and exclusive course with a persistence that elicits much respect, doubtless because it rather suits them. It certainly agrees with many aficionados. As one of them wrote, 'I remain an enthusiast of the Astic formula. Not a place for too-frequent visits, nor for those seeking a budget meal, but always a great night out.' The repertoire has gradually evolved over the years, but it is not large. For a set price, there is a choice of two first courses, one fish and one foie gras, then three main dishes – two meat and one chicken – accompanied invariably by a gratin dauphinoise, followed by a salad – never vegetables – before moving on to St Marcellin cheese (from the Isère) and dessert. New things noted this year have been a hot foie gras mousse of clear flavour with an ornament of chanterelles, that made one person's view of other chanterelles 'so many button mushrooms', and a fine stock reduction with cream for sauce; and a red mullet with fennel and Pernod sauce, given an alternative dimension by the use of fresh thyme for tang and fresh tomato dice for sweetness and depth. The cooking has perceptibly lightened in some people's view – less cream and more stock in the sauces. It may be thought that so concentrated an effort would mean invariable perfection, but a test meal did reveal miscalculations in the usually excellent gratin dauphinoise and in the use of the salt and pepper pots. The wine list is as individual as everything else: top-hole clarets and burgundies with a few Champagnes, most costing over £25. Less than a handful of halves. No house wine, but they serve something by the glass – its price depends on their choice that day. The cost can be fairly steep, and you have to ask hard if you don't want a shock. As you will be best of friends, that doesn't really matter.

CHEF: Jacques Astic   PROPRIETORS: Jacques and Jenny Astic
OPEN: Tue to Sat D (Sun D by arrangement), L by arrangement
CLOSED: Christmas
MEALS: from 8.15
PRICES: Set L and D £25 (£30). Service inc
SEATS: 18. Children welcome

## Wickens ♥

| Market Place, Northleach GL54 3EJ | COOKING 3 |
|---|---|
| COTSWOLD (0451) 60421 | COST £28 |

To call this a simple restaurant might appear condescending. It is not. The Wickens' approach, now developed over several years of cooking in the Cotswold region, is direct and simple in the best sense of the words. You know what you will get and it will come with intelligence and style and no dreadful fuss. The restaurant itself has grown: the outside lavatories have been brought inside by the expedient of bridging the gap with a conservatory. The series of small rooms, each on its own level, is locale for a short menu that has moved on to a single set price for three courses, cheese and coffee. It makes no bones about what it offers: whole prawn platter with garlic dip; smoked loin of beef with Ogen melon; roast duckling with a plum and armagnac sauce; scallops baked in lemon, lime and parsley. And the cooking is similarly direct, usually with clear flavours, though no great subtlety or technical ambition – none the worse for that as the materials are the best the region can provide. Successes this year have included beef casserole; a seafood tartlet with a perfectly dressed salad; breast of chicken with a honey and mustard glaze; most excellent vegetables; good English cheeses – not too many at a time; substantial English desserts – sticky toffee or bread-and-butter pudding, chocolate meringue cake. The wine list was praised last year for its estimable value and obvious effort in seeking value for money. It is divided into three price levels (£6.50, £7.75, £11.75) for the bulk, then a few individually priced bottles and a special feature, for instance the wines of the north-western states of America. Nothing is overpriced. The selection at the time of writing is more tilted towards France than it has been, but the virtue of keeping a small cellar is that accents can change rapidly. There is a desire to promote English wines, mainly the fine Three Choirs from Hereford. House wines at £6.50 include Three Choirs Dry 1984; Domaine de Rieux, Côtes de Gascogne 1988, Grassa; Fitou 1986, Caves du Mont-Tauch. CELLARMAN'S CHOICE : Tollana Shiraz/Cabernet-Sauvignon 1982, £11.75; Apremont Vin de Savoie, Apremont 1987, £7.75.

CHEFS/PROPRIETORS: Christopher and Joanna Wickens
OPEN: Tue to Sat, D only
MEALS: 7.15 to 9.15
PRICES: Set D £17.50 (£23)
CARDS: Access, Visa
SEATS: 36. Private parties: 22 main room. Children welcome. No smoking. Wheelchair access (4 steps; also WC). Music

---

**NORTON ST PHILIP**   Somerset                                                    map 2

# ▲ *Bath Lodge Hotel & Restaurant*

---

Norton St Philip BA3 6NH                                              COOKING 2
BATH (0225) 723737                                                     COST £30

Take the Bath road for a mile or so east of Norton St Philip to this pint-sized castle, complete with battlements, towers and portcullis. All is not as it seems, however, for this was not the stronghold of some erstwhile stunted despot, but merely a gatehouse, built during the early nineteenth century to serve Farleigh House. The inside has been painstakingly restored and comfortably furnished with antiques. A conservatory bar overlooks the gardens and deer forest and the small stone-walled dining-room has a beamed ceiling and an open fire. John Morris welcomes visitors at the door and explains the menu, Pam Morris sometimes oversees goings-on in the kitchen, and chef Jeremy Shutter cooks. He used to be at Beechfield House, Beanacre. What comes out of the kitchen is a traditional set menu with modern touches. To begin there could be a home-made soup, wild pigeon and mushroom terrine or a warm salad of monkfish and bacon. Of main courses sampled by reporters, sirloin steak in a seed mustard sauce has been 'a beautiful piece of meat in a perfect sauce', and a mild piece of venison with port wine and orange has had 'tangy sauce with good flavour.' For pudding, two chocolate mousses, moated by juxtaposition of sauce and cream, was much more intense than anything with white chocolate deserves to be, and a puff filled with fruit and served with a 'fine' mango coulis came with the fruit unexpectedly raw, not poached. Coffee is unlimited but costs extra. The use of the building is really ingenious and the kitchen nearly matches it, though some northern reporters felt that Bathonians ate less than they should for the money. House French from the Beaujolais négociant, Gobet, £7.95 a litre. A good wine list with old (and dear) as well as young, but an even spread outside France and giving a fair crack at half-bottles. It is not a cheap selection but it will do justice to the food.

---

CHEF: Jeremy Shutter   PROPRIETORS: John and Pam Morris
OPEN: Tue to Sat, D only
MEALS: 7 to 9
PRICES: Set D £18.75 (£25). Minimum £18.50
CARDS: Access, Amex, Visa
SEATS: 27. Private parties: 30 main room. Car-park, 16 places. No children under 10. Smart dress preferred. No smoking in dining-room. Music
ACCOMMODATION: 4 rooms, all with bath/shower. B&B £50 to £85. Deposit: 50%. No children under 10. Garden. TV. Phone. Scenic. Doors close at midnight [GHG]

## NORWICH  Norfolk

map 6

### Adlard's

79 Upper St Giles, Norwich NR2 1AB
NORWICH (0603) 633522

COOKING 4
COST £26–£34

David and Mary Adlard have taken shelter in Norwich, leaving their
Wymondham restaurant to the Jennings (see entry) for the former premises of
the Brasserie de l'Abri. Amid shades of green, tables are arranged on two levels
and Wymondham customers will be pleased to see the chairs have cushions.
The great quality of this restaurant is its natural, matter-of-fact approach to the
business of eating, coupled with very fine kitchen techniques. The menu is
short, four first, four main and three or four sweet dishes. The price is not high.
The meal includes an alternative of a green salad or cheese between the second
and third course. Luxuries – foie gras, truffles, langoustines – do not often
figure, hence the naturalness. Dishes combine three elements at the most; there
is no hectic search for harmony that so often dissolves into dissonance. David
Adlard appreciates the limitations of his situation and perfects what he can
rather than striving for the unreachable. This may explain the calm
contentment of many of his customers. They, too, do not have to strive.
Chicken-liver parfait with toasted brioche is no more than that, with a small
salad properly dressed: the parfait smooth, the brioche light and melting.
Others nowadays would have put in a bit of foie gras. A puff pastry pillow
envelops oyster and French breakfast mushrooms and is surrounded by a
darkly intense wild mushroom sauce. Meats arrive with one accompaniment
and a sauce: lamb, properly trimmed, with a gateau of tomato and aubergine
and a *jus*; pheasant with a game mousse and a madeira sauce. Desserts continue
the approach: orange sauce with a mango sorbet; rhubarb sorbet with rhubarb
fool. Cheeses are British and French, from the Mousetrap in Norwich. Coffee is
either filter or espresso. Assurance combined with the demure friendliness of
Mary Adlard is a fine recipe for a good restaurant. The wine list kicks off with
'bin beginnings', a short page of extras from the New World. Succeeding pages
reveal a medium-length list with not one unconsidered bottle: France, Italy,
America, Australasia, Spain, Germany and England – excellent growers, good
vintages, very fair prices. It is not a collector's list, with only a few old clarets,
but it shows how intelligence (well away from London) can assemble an
exquisite dilemma for any wine drinker. House wine is from Gascony at £6.40
a bottle. CELLARMAN'S CHOICE : Mâcon-Clessé, Domaine de Bon Gran 1987,
£13; Ch. du Grand Moulas, Côtes du Rhône, 1987, £7.30. 'The price of the meal
includes service.' In the features section towards the end of this *Guide*, Mary
Adlard writes about the trials of running a small restaurant.

---

CHEF: David Adlard   PROPRIETORS: David and Mary Adlard
OPEN: Tue to Sat, D only
MEALS: 7.30 to 9
PRICES: Set D £21.50 (£26) to £22.75 (£28). Service inc
CARDS: Access, Visa
SEATS: 30. Private parties: 35 main room. Children's helpings on request. Wheelchair
access (also WC)

## Brasted's

| | |
|---|---|
| 8–10 St Andrews Hill, Norwich NR2 1AD | COOKING 1 |
| NORWICH (0603) 625949 | COST £34 |

This small place is in the boudoir style of interior design – drapes, mirrors and intimacy. One of the two rooms has been converted into a bar and reception area, and John Brasted has a new chef from France who cooks a surprisingly long menu. Reports have indicated that things go along much the same: quite high prices; some fair fish; some ultra-modish combinations such as lamb and scallops with a Dubonnet sauce (why, when people have such close calls with good cooking of the simplest things, do they persist in trying these combinations?); some traditional fare – potted crab, steak, kidney and oyster pie. Service is fine, or was until the waiter 'appeared with two cafetières and asked if we could tell from the colour which was the decaffeinated coffee.' The wine list is short, the longest section of whole bottles being Champagne. House French, £7.25. CELLARMAN'S CHOICE : Mercurey 1986, Jean Raquillet, £14.30; Pouilly Fumé 1987, Guy Saget, £13.90.

CHEF: J.C. Deledicq  PROPRIETOR: J.D. Brasted
OPEN: Mon to Sat, exc Sat L
MEALS: 12 to 2, 7 to 10
PRICES: £18 (£28)
CARDS: Access, Amex, Diners, Visa
SEATS: 22. Private parties: 14 main room. Children welcome

## Marco's

| | |
|---|---|
| 17 Pottergate, Norwich NR2 1DS | COOKING 1 |
| NORWICH (0603) 624044 | COST £18–£31 |

Still going strong after 19 years. Restaurant and kitchen were scheduled for refurbishment during 1989, but the menu that keeps the customers satisfied continues much the same, with Italian fare of the crespoline/saltimbocca/gelato variety. Special mentions from dispatches: 'well-presented and generous melon and Parma ham'; 'mussels superb, cheeseboard very impressive, service off-beat but pleasant'; 'The chef (Marco himself) will always prepare a vegetarian dish, without a moment's notice, quite the best performance in a non-vegetarian restaurant I can remember'. House Italian is £6. CELLARMAN'S CHOICE : Barolo 1978, £20; Chianti Bacco 1985, £9.50.

CHEF/PROPRIETOR: Marco Vessalio
OPEN: Tue to Sat
CLOSED: 20 Aug to 20 Sept
MEALS: 12.30 to 2, 7.30 to 10
PRICES: £16 (£26), Set L £11 (£18)
CARDS: Access, Amex, Carte Blanche, Diners, Visa
SEATS: 40. Private parties: 12 main room, 16 private room. Vegetarian meals. Children's helpings. Wheelchair access. Music

*All entries in the* Guide *are rewritten every year, not least because restaurant standards fluctuate. Don't trust an out-of-date* Guide.

NOTTINGHAM Nottinghamshire                                   map 5

# Les Artistes Gourmands/
# Café des Artistes ♀

61 Wollaton Road, Beeston
Nottingham NG9 2NG                                      COOKING 2
NOTTINGHAM (0602) 228288                               COST £15–£32

With one eye on the economic mood, one of the restaurant's dining-rooms has
been turned into an informal bistro – Café des Artistes. Meanwhile, the
restaurant proper continues to show well. It is conventional, clean and tidy
rather than smart, with somewhat cramped tables. The set-price, four-course
meals are, however, ambitious. There is a choice of half a dozen dishes at the
first and second stage. Some, like the game, are gutsily full-flavoured – a
ragout of wild boar, for example, or roast mallard served pink with a mild
cream of garlic, or fillet of beef served with a port and liver sauce on a bed of
shallots – while others are deliberately light and modern, with cleaner
flavours. In this vein, escalope of salmon rolled around a sole mousse, then
steamed and served with a sorrel sauce, and poached seafood baked with
avocado and finished with a crayfish sauce have both been recommended. A
French chef-pâtissier turns out fine sorbets and other home-made desserts.
There have been criticisms – of flavours that could be stronger, rough edges to
the service, cheeses nowhere near their prime and a general air of
pretentiousness – but these seem harsh for a restaurant with a continuously
developing kitchen. Café des Artistes runs a long bistro *carte* that draws on the
skills of the pâtissier (pasta and pastries) as well as upmarket (that is, food of
the 1980s) dishes involving wild boar, walnut oil and salmon. There is a no-
smoking room, described as 'very successful', and a new, healthy lunch menu
of 800 calories to keep Nottingham trim. The wine list is a model of short sense
in French. The growers are reliable, the choices of area and vintage sound, the
prices very fair. House wines from £7.90. CELLARMAN'S CHOICE : Pouilly
Fumé, Ch. de Tracy 1987, £14.50; St Aubin 1984, Lamy, £15.80. 'No obligation
to tip. Prices all inclusive.'

CHEF: J.L. David   PROPRIETOR: Eddy Keon
OPEN: Tue to Sat, exc Sat L
CLOSED: 1 week Jan, 1 week Aug
MEALS: 12 to 1.30, 7 to 10.30
PRICES: Restaurant: £21 (£27), Set L £10.50 (£15) to £15.50 (£20), Set D £15 (£20) to £22
(£27). Café: £12 (£16). Service inc
CARDS: Access, Amex, Diners, Visa
SEATS: 35. Private parties: 35 main room. Vegetarian meals. Children's helpings. No
smoking in dining-room. Wheelchair access. Music

'A few notes on our holiday in Scotland. 1) It was expensive! We could have gone to a
decent hotel in the sun for what we spent. 2) Not one restaurant or hotel catered for
vegetarians. There was not any mention of a vegetarian dish. I made a point of asking all
the restaurants and hotels; they all said they would find a dish for them. Otherwise
nothing. 3) They are not yet into designer water. Ask for water and you still get iced tap
water. They will soon, I am sure, cotton on to some extra money.'   An inspector

# Ocean City

100–104 Derby Road
Nottingham NG1 5FB                                   COOKING 2
NOTTINGHAM (0602) 475095                         COST £23–£34

An excellent restaurant, slightly out of town near the University, with a
Cantonese kitchen said by some to be as good as any in Manchester or
Liverpool. The English menu includes well-executed standards such as fried
squid in garlic and casseroled duck in plum sauce, plus a long list of Cantonese
house specialities such as whelks, duck webs, beef with bitter gourd and crabmeat braised in milk. Just as good, according to reports, are the cheaper one-
plate dishes – moist barbecued pork or roast duck and crunchy vegetables on
rice, for example – which are only on the Chinese menu. Service is up and
down, but always seems to be friendly. House wine is £5.50. Wan Fu Chinese
medium dry white is £7.

CHEF: Mr Wong   PROPRIETORS: Dragon Wonder Ltd
OPEN: all week
CLOSED: 25 Dec
MEALS: 12 to 3, 6 to 11.30 (noon to midnight Sat, noon to 10.30 Sun)
PRICES: £19 (£28), Set L £17 (£23), Set D £17 (£23). Minimum £7.50. Service 10%
CARDS: Access, Amex, Diners, Visa
SEATS: 250. Private parties: 200 main room, 80 and 120 private rooms. Vegetarian meals.
Children welcome. Wheelchair access (also WC). Music

# Sagar

473 Mansfield Road, Sherwood
Nottingham NG5 2DR                                  COOKING 1
NOTTINGHAM (0602) 622014                         COST £20

Opposite Sherwood library, out in the suburbs of Nottingham, this Regency-
style Indian restaurant is well liked for the reliability of its traditional menu.
The list has been expanded slightly to add cream-and-almond-enriched
moghlai dishes and kaallan curries, cooked with mango, yoghurt and coconut,
to the range of tandooris, birianis, kormas and vindaloos. Prices remain
extremely reasonable. Service is courteous and attentive and the food is fresh
and competently prepared. House French, £6 a litre.

CHEF: Amjaid Habib   PROPRIETOR: Mohammed Khizer
OPEN: all week
CLOSED: 25 Dec
MEALS: 12 to 2.30, 5.30 to 12.30
PRICES: £10 (£17)
CARDS: Access, Amex, Visa
SEATS: 45. Private parties: 45 main room. Car-park, 6 places. Vegetarian meals. Children's
helpings. No pipes in dining-room. Music. Air-conditioned

---

'One of the waitresses was seen spooning soufflé from the sweets trolley into her mouth and
then left the spoon in situ. The worst meal I have ever had.'  On dining in Derbyshire

---

OAKHAM  Leicestershire                                              map 5

# ▲ *Whipper-in*

Market Place, Oakham LE15 7DT                         COOKING 2
OAKHAM (0572) 756971                                     COST £17–£36

This hotel is out of the same stable as the Feathers at Woodstock: quite creative
cooking within a traditional setting. Oakham is a market town (once proud
possessor of the only set of traffic lights in Rutland). The much-refurbished inn
copes with commercial as well as private diners. This may keep the prices high,
as well as occasioning plain offerings from the grill in addition to a fairly long
*carte*. The cooking can be ambitious and work better than expected. A breast of
wood pigeon is baked in pastry with a subtle mushroom and apple filling on a
well-judged calvados sauce; a fillet of lamb is stuffed with a sweetbread and
chicken mixture and served sliced on a madeira sauce. The lamb is well cooked
but the flavours are retained and, bar the burned rösti, work well. Vegetables
may not always be so successful. The kitchen tries different combinations
(although not outlandish), which do not always work: a brown-bread ice-
cream went uninterestingly with a competent savarin with cashew nuts for a
sickly effect. Other reports point to unevenness, though never lack of
derring-do. Service is not so informed, especially when rushed or dealing with
wine. There is a competent wine list. House Bergerac, £6.95. CELLARMAN'S
CHOICE : Champagne de Horsey NV, £17.25; Cuvaison Cabernet- Sauvignon
1981, £17.95.

CHEFS: Paul Cherrington and David Toffiluck   PROPRIETORS: FSI plc
OPEN: all week
MEALS: 12.30 to 2, 7.30 to 9 (9.30 Sat)
PRICES: £22 (£30), Set L £11.95 (£17), Set D £16.95 (£23)
CARDS: Access, Amex, Diners, Visa
SEATS: 50. 3 tables outside. Private parties: 46 main room, 14 and 40 private rooms.
Vegetarian meals. Children's helpings. Wheelchair access. Music
ACCOMMODATION: 24 rooms, all with bath/shower. Rooms for disabled. B&B £42.50 to
£84. Baby facilities. Afternoon teas. TV. Phone

OKEHAMPTON  Devon                                                  map 1

# *Partners*

38 Red Lion Yard, Fore Street
Okehampton EX20 1AW                                      COOKING 1
OKEHAMPTON (0837) 4662                                   COST £11–£19

Jane Beazley runs the dining-room with flair while David Beazley cooks.
Regulars reckon that Partners is 'well worth a detour', and it's open all day,
serving visitors to the newly built shopping-precinct with morning coffee and
cakes and cream teas, as well as lunches and dinners. The brief set menu makes
sensible use of West Country foods: chicken livers with woodland fungi;
roasted local pigeon; ribs of Devon beef; Curworthy cheese. Monthly 'theme
dinners' are a new departure and have so far included 'East meets West' and
'Abused Foods' – no, not beaten eggs and whipped cream, but dishes like
peach Melba and tomato soup made *properly*. The short wine list is well

balanced for the style of place and demands no ransom. House Duboeuf is £5.40. CELLARMAN'S CHOICE : Brown Bros Shiraz 1986, £8.80; Bourgogne blanc, Chardonnay 1986, Labouré-Roi, £9.20.

CHEF: David Beazley   PROPRIETORS: David and Jane Beazley
OPEN: all week, exc Mon and Sun D (Mon L only summer)
MEALS: 12 to 2.30, 7 to 9.30
PRICES: Set L £8.25 (£11), Set D £13.50 (£16). Snacks from £1.15. Service inc
SEATS: 40. 3 tables outside. Private parties: 45 main room, 45 private room. Vegetarian meals. Children's helpings. No cigars/pipes in dining-room. Wheelchair access (also WC)

---

ORFORD  Suffolk                                                        map 3

## Butley-Orford Oysterage

Market Hill, Orford IP12 2PQ                              COOKING 2
ORFORD (0394) 450 277                                       COST £17

It was a brilliant idea of Richard Pinney, who died in early 1989, to start growing oysters in the freshwater creeks of the Orford River over 20 years ago. Now, 50,000 oysters a year disappear down the eager gullets of diners in this plain, no-nonsense café near the church. Visitors can also opt for freshly cured smoked wild salmon or skate, crabs, sole and lobsters caught from the Pinneys' three fishing boats. The establishment may leave something to be desired in accoutrements – though regulars remark on the constant expansion – but the fish can't be faulted; forget other dishes – fish is what the Pinneys do best. 'The chap in front spends his life "doing" crabs and opening oysters. Very, very slick.' The shop next door is good for supplies to take home. There's a short, reasonable wine list including a dozen or so half-bottles.

CHEF: Mrs M. Pinney   PROPRIETORS: Mrs M. Pinney and William Pinney
OPEN: all week, exc Sun D Oct to Mar
MEALS: noon to 2.15, 6 to 8.30
PRICES: £10 (£14)
SEATS: 75. Private parties: 25 main room. Car-park, 20 places. Children welcome. Wheelchair access (also WC)

---

OXFORD  Oxfordshire                                                    map 2

## Al-Shami

25 Walton Crescent, Oxford OX1 2JG                       COOKING 1
OXFORD (0865) 310066                                        COST £20

There are enough travellers and anthropologists in Oxford to provide a willing audience for this small and understated Lebanese restaurant, not to speak of those who merely enjoy the flavours for what they are and appreciate the freshness of the food. The menu does not stray far beyond basic perceptions of Arab identity – lots of baba ganoush, ful medames and tabouleh. For once, the cover charge brings dividends in the form of a dish of tomato, cucumber, lettuce, radishes, beetroot and olives to nibble with bread while waiting, for example, for lambs' brains cooked with onions and sharp spices – and a hint of cloves – or kibbeh, the stuffed, ground meat dish beloved of all Eastern

Mediterranean countries. Main courses are generous – the shawarma was almost more lamb than one reporter, fond though she was of the cumin spicing, could eat at a sitting. Dessert pastries have been said to be better than the normal run. Lebanese coffee, with cardamom and rosewater, is a better bet than European coffee. House wine, £6.50.

CHEF/PROPRIETOR: Mimo Mahfouz
OPEN: all week
MEALS: noon to midnight
PRICES: £10 (£17). Cover £1. Service of 10% for parties of more than 6
SEATS: 40. Private parties: 60 main room. Vegetarian meals. Children welcome. Wheelchair access (also WC). Music

## ▲ Bath Place Hotel

4–5 Bath Place, Holywell Street
Oxford OX1 3SU                                          COOKING 2
OXFORD (0865) 791812                                    COST £23–£47

Down the already narrow street of Holywell is the narrower entry to Bath Place, a small court for a pub and a collection of seventeenth-century cottages now converted to a handsome restaurant with rooms above. Blue seems the dominant colour, against a background of pink. The Fawsitt family, who engineered the conversion, have brought in two chefs, Didier DeVille from Carcassonne and Peter Cherrill. M. DeVille resembles a character from Astérix. All kitchens take time to settle down and this one, having opened in the summer of 1989, is no different. Early reports have been mixed. They identify a modern French approach that embraces robust flavourings and attractive presentation. They applaud some excellent combinations such as foie gras served with a fan of roast peach with a Muscat sauce, or lamb with a caper butter sauce. But there has been irritation with a less than warm service, a muddle over availability of dishes on a Sunday night, and a thought that not all the dishes have much inherent flavour: a veal chop with kidney and a morel *jus*, and roast lamb with garlic cloves both depended only on one element (kidney or garlic) for taste. Fish from Cornwall has been commended and may take in lobster, red mullet and sea bass. Execution of desserts has been enjoyed though invention does not run riot. The menu, which persists in poor French, lists summer pudding as 'pudding d'été'. The wine list is mainly French and contains some odds and ends that make for fun if not enjoyment, like Clos Fourtet 1952. Prices are not impossible and some of the growers are unusual and worth investigating. There is a chance that this place will develop into consistency, power and invention, though Oxford has a way of smothering restaurants as well as nurturing them. House French wine is £7.50.
CELLARMAN'S CHOICE : Ch. De Selle Rosé 1987, Domaines Ott, £18; Hautes Côtes de Nuits Blanc 1986, Gilles, £15.

---

*'Service varied from curt to downright uncooperative. Head waiter, as vegetables ran out before our party was half served, said, "Sure, sir, you pay more, you get more, OK?"'*
On dining in a Suffolk hotel

CHEFS: Didier DeVille and Peter Cherrill   PROPRIETORS: The Fawsitt family
OPEN: Tue to Sun
MEALS: 12 to 2.15, 7 to 9.45 (10.15 Fri and Sat)
PRICES: £29 (£39), Set L £15 (£23). Service 10%
CARDS: Access, Amex, Carte Blanche, Diners, Visa
SEATS: 34. 4 tables outside. Private parties: 10 main room, 10 private room. Car-park,
4 places. No children under 10. Wheelchair access. Music. Air-conditioned
ACCOMMODATION: 8 rooms, all with bath/shower. B&B £65 to £95. No children under 10.
TV. Phone. Doors close at midnight. Confirm by 10.30am

## Cherwell Boathouse ♥

| | |
|---|---|
| Bardwell Road, Oxford OX2 6SR | COOKING 1 |
| OXFORD (0865) 52746 | COST £13−£20 |

The Boathouse sometimes runs through choppy waters, although ever-popular
with undergraduates. The simple arrangement is a weekly menu, at an
affordable price, that gives a choice of two or three dishes in each course. In a
summer week these may be borshch or asparagus to begin; chicken with
sesame or fish quenelles in a truffled cream sauce for main courses; gooseberry
crumble or praline ice for dessert. Choice, for instance if you like neither
aubergine nor tahini, may be more circumscribed than appears in the list
above. Execution is not so assured as to make this a bargain. The comfort level
is not high, nor the standard of decoration, but the location by the river is worth
any privation. So, too, is the wine list. Cheap and brilliant is the simple
description: certainly not encyclopaedic, but everything is worth trying. House
French is £5. CELLARMAN'S CHOICE : Alsace Riesling Muenchberg 1983,
Ostertag, £11.50; Côtes de Nuits-Villages 1983, Rion, £13. 'Smoking is
discouraged' and a complete ban was under consideration at the time of
writing.

CHEF: Gerard Crowley   PROPRIETOR: Anthony Verdin
OPEN: Tue to Sun, exc Sun D
MEALS: 12 to 2, 7 to 10
PRICES: £11 (£16), Set L £9 (£13) to £12 (£16), Set D £12.50 (£17)
CARDS: Access, Amex, Diners, Visa
SEATS: 50. 5 tables outside. Private parties: 50 main room. Car-park, 12 places. Vegetarian
meals. Children's helpings. Wheelchair access (1 step; also WC)

## 15 North Parade

| | |
|---|---|
| 15 North Parade, Oxford OX2 6LX | COOKING 1 |
| OXFORD (0865) 513773 | COST £17−£32 |

Only in Oxford perhaps would North Parade be south of South Parade − the
name signifies the northernmost extent of the Royalist fortifications in the Civil
War. The restaurant at number 15 is fresh; not as elegant as Gee's in the
greenhouse round the corner (see entry), but sharing the same degree of coolth-
with-comfort. There has been a change of chef. A winter meal began with
tomato and fennel soup; goats' cheese wrapped in filo and marinated salmon.
Main courses were medallions of lamb in a garlic sauce ('And I thought
nouvelle cuisine had been sent packing by now,' was one person's comment

about this dish); a vegetarian dish of cheese choux pastry with grilled vegetables (the sous chef is a vegetarian and there is a daily vegetarian choice); tender venison with madeira and celeriac sauce, and fillet of beef with a cep sauce. The food avoids 'the present trap of pretentiousness' while being light and sufficiently inventive. There is a streak of unevenness which leads to things being improperly executed and flavours inadequately expressed. Details, such as bread, have been below par. Disenchantment has also been noted with the wine list because too many bottles were not in stock. Though this possibility is presaged in the notes, it is small comfort at the time. This apart, it is a good, short, fast-changing selection of modern wines not outrageously priced. Wines are listed by grape variety, and whites are numbered on a sweetness scale. There is a sensible approach to corkage, evinced by a note to the effect that 'We would take it as a compliment if you would like to bring your own Fine Wine to our restaurant; we will charge our House Wine price.' Many problems in licensed premises arise from customers wishing to save money by supplying their own wines. Reasonably enough, many owners protest – especially if the customer brings wine already listed for sale. But it is nice to accommodate true enthusiasts who wish to drink some favourite. Georgina Wood's compromise seems nearly fair – had she charged the *profit* on a bottle of house wine, it would perhaps have been fairer. House wines from Berry Bros are £6.75. CELLARMAN'S CHOICE : Cahors, Clos de la Pinerie 1983, £10; Chablis *ler cru*, Montée de la Tonnerre 1985, £21.75.

CHEF: Thomas Thomsen   PROPRIETOR: Georgina Wood
OPEN: all week, exc Sun D
MEALS: 12 to 2, 7 to 10
PRICES: £20 (£27), Set L £10.75 (£17) to £13.75 (£21). Minimum £9.50. Licensed, also bring your own: corkage £6.75
CARD: Access, Visa
SEATS: 55. Private parties: 50 main room. Vegetarian meals. Children's helpings. Wheelchair access (also WC). Air-conditioned

## Gee's

| 61 Banbury Road, Oxford OX2 6PE | COOKING 1 |
|---|---|
| OXFORD (0865) 53540 | COST £25 |

After serving as the second restaurant of Raymond Blanc, this Victorian conservatory has reverted to the name of the mid-1980s. It is a stunning locale for a dinner; always full; pleasantly served by a refreshingly intelligent staff. Reports have not been invariably supportive – perhaps people have been expecting the fireworks of Bruno Loubet when it was Le Petit Blanc – but curious Londoners, weary of designer food, were much taken by the directness of the flavours and competence shown all round. There is a short menu, quite 'designer' enough, of carpaccio, pastrami, stuffed tomatoes, a ratatouille lasagne, seafood risotto and the like, but a meal of good stock-based carrot soup; a vegetable soufflé of courgettes and mushrooms; pork fillet in paprika cream sauce; chicken grilled with rosemary and lemon; a fruit vacherin and a crème brûlée reconciled one couple to the possibilities of less expensive eating (if not absolutely cheap). Coffee is weak. The wine list is short but will do very well. It is not expensive, though why there is a need to stock Dom Pérignon

Rosé is beyond the wit of some. House Paul Bocuse selection is £6.25.
CELLARMAN'S CHOICE : Sancerre Rosé 1987, Dezat, £12.75; Torgiano 1986, Lungarotti, £10.75.

CHEF: David Allison   PROPRIETORS: Gee's Ltd
OPEN: all week, exc Sun D
MEALS: 12 to 2 (11am to 4 Sun), 6 to 11
PRICES: £15 (£21). Service 10% for parties of 5 or more
CARDS: Access, Visa
SEATS: 70. 4 tables outside. Private parties: 30 main room. Vegetarian meals. Children's helpings. Wheelchair access. Music. Air-conditioned

## Munchy Munchy

6 Park End Street, Oxford OX1 1HH                            COOKING 2
OXFORD (0865) 245710                                         COST £10−£17

With longstanding plans for expansion expected to have become a reality by the time the *Guide* is published, queuing may be a thing of the past. Nonetheless, speed is of the essence: to keep the prices down, they serve you fast and, equally, you're not expected to hang around. Ethel Ow's style is entirely her own, with Malaysian and Indonesian spices played off against one another and against more western flavourings to produce unpredictable combinations, sometimes ferociously hot and at other times subtly fruity. Long-term visitors say that the intensity of spicing has lessened, but that may depend on the choice. The formula is simple: half a dozen or so constantly changing daily dishes written up on the blackboard and kept hot behind the counter where you order. (Table service will come with renovation.) Main ingredients usually include fresh king prawns − once, for example, with lemon-grass and coconut milk, another time with mustard, fenugreek, paprika and lemon-grass − duck, beef, lamb and chicken. Typically hybrid ideas are chicken with cardamom and nutmeg in a papaya sauce with chopped pine kernels, or sliced beef with cinnamon, cloves, fresh lime leaves and juice in star-fruit sauce. Stir-fried fresh eastern chives with flowerbuds, flown in from the East, are unexpectedly sweet and complement spicier dishes beautifully. Peripherals − rice to sop up the spiced oils and juices, salads, exotic ice-creams and sorbets − are left plain. Take your own wine for a small corkage charge. Vegetarians are well served unless dishes are running out at the end of the day.

CHEF: Ethel Ow   PROPRIETORS: Tony and Ethel Ow
OPEN: Tue to Sat
CLOSED: 3 weeks Aug, 3 weeks Dec
MEALS: 12 to 2.10, 5.30 to 9.40
PRICES: Set L and D £8 (£10) to £12 (£14). Service of 10% for parties of 5 or more. Unlicensed, but bring your own: corkage 50p
SEATS: 42. Private parties: 7 main room. Children restricted. No cigars/pipes in dining-room

*The* Guide *is totally independent, accepts no free hospitality, and survives on the number of copies sold each year.*

**PADSTOW** Cornwall                                                          map 1

## ▲ *Seafood Restaurant* ▼

Riverside, Padstow PL28 8BY                                         COOKING 4
PADSTOW (0841) 532485                                          COST £25–£48

This has been a good year for the Steins. Rick's book on fish was given the
Glenfiddich Award for the best cookbook of the year; their restaurant was
variously be-laureated. Hardly surprising, for by any standards it is
exceptional. Padstow is a small north Cornish fishing town now much
prettified and improved. The approach takes in a Victorian grand hotel as it
drops to a river front of car-parks and fishermen's hangars. If one's
presuppositions are informed by Betjeman's elegies of Cornish holidays – of
Jennifer's games with Mr Pedder, of 'experience at Budleigh Salterton' keeping
'Bonzo steady at the net' – they may be in for a shock at the Seafood. It has a
lightness, a zing and a fizz unlike most English country restaurants. This comes
from bright lighting, stark white walls, a great sense of space (except the little
bar area), lots of colour from the posters and pictures, a holiday feel from
basket-work chairs and a great deal of noise bouncing off hard floors and
surfaces. Pitch into this a pianist on some nights, a normally full restaurant,
some fine food and drink and the recipe is unique. The cooking is as up-to-date
as Alastair Little's, Simon Hopkinson's or anyone else's in London. It has many
ideas that amuse by their intelligence; it joins simple and direct flavours
together to great effect; it does not seek to impress by complexity. Yet the
techniques – pastry, emulsions, cooking times– are satisfactory. The repertoire
may be wide, but there are some constant elements, or at least long-lasting
ones. There has been the usual praise for the fish soup, the seafood platter, the
oysters and the combination of three fish and three sauces in one dish. Some of
the characteristics of the kitchen can be seen from this spring menu: a tempura
of fish and shellfish (Rick Stein enjoys playing with oriental flavours and
skills, as any fish cook would); char-grilled monkfish with tomato, courgettes
and fennel; scallops sauté with mange-tout and parsley; Dover sole grilled
with lime and sea salt; grilled lobster 'with herbs from our garden and a little
butter'; grilled crawfish with a chervil and tomato fumet; ravioli of lobster with
spinach and a tarragon sauce. There seems to be an excess of grilling here, but
other techniques (en papillote, steaming, baking and frying) are all used, and
competently. Puddings continue the same direct use of contrasting flavours
(often doubling up with contrast of temperature or texture): rhubarb poached
with red wine, served with a cinnamon ice-cream; chocolate mousse cake with
kumquats. Haute cuisine this is not. The staff are young, local and cheerful.
When the place is full, they run. At moments of extreme stress, for instance
halfway through a holiday Saturday, the system may not be able to cope as it
should. The wine list shows the same intelligent approach as the rest of the
enterprise, but though only a couple of meat dishes are on offer at any time,
there is not the preponderance of whites that might be expected. There are
some surprising gaps: very little white Rhône and only one dry white
Bordeaux. Yet there is a Vin Jaune d'Arbois from the Jura, and sound white
burgundies from Olivier Leflaive, Jean Durup and Robert Ampeau, for
example, as well as some first-rate Australians from Robson, Penfolds and
Rosemount. Although the kitchen plays with some good strong flavours –

chillies, coriander, ginger and the like – they seem to feel that American wines are too fat, too strong for their cooking. Thus there is very little from California and nothing from the north-western United States. Prices are very fair. House Bourgogne Pinot Noir, Guy Chaumont 1985, £9.50; Sauvignon du Haut-Poitou 1987, £7.50. CELLARMAN'S CHOICE : St Amour, Ch. de St Amour 1985, Chanut, £10.20; Delegats Hawkes Bay Sauvignon Blanc 1987, £15.50.

CHEF: Richard Stein    PROPRIETORS: Richard and Jill Stein
OPEN: Mon to Sat, D only
MEALS: 7.30 to 9.30 (10 Sat)
PRICES: £31 (£40), Set D £19 (£25)
CARD: Access, Visa
SEATS: 75. Private parties: 24 main room. Children's helpings. Air -conditioned
ACCOMMODATION: 10 rooms, 8 with bath/shower. B&B £20 to £60. Deposit: £20. Baby facilities. Pets welcome. Fishing. TV. Phone. Scenic. Confirm by noon [GHG]

---

PAULERSPURY  Northamptonshire                                    map 2

## ▲ Vine House

100 High Street, Paulerspury NN12 7NA
PAULERSPURY (032 733) 267                          COOKING 3
off the A5, 2m S of Towcester                      COST £21–£41

The long house of pale stone – more Cotswold than the deep honey ironstone of central Northamptonshire – converted well to a restaurant with rooms and is now run with much style by the Snowdons. The sitting-rooms may feel cottagy but the dining-room – all pink – has more light and space than that implies. The cooking is in the hands of Karen Snowdon and Jonathan Stanbury. She has experience of catering and management; he was trained at the Connaught. The result is most impressive. Flavours are not mashed together, nor avoided through pusillanimity. The style is not over-complex. Materials seem fresh and fashionable. Techniques are more than competent. A terrine of chicken livers and baby leeks, with fashionable garnish of sprue, had clean flavours and sound execution. A salad of marinated spring vegetables and a goats' cheese mousse was exact, the dressing precisely the required strength, the mousse light and interesting. A main course of grilled fillets of red mullet with a warm potato salad may sound fashionable but the mullet was fresh and crisp, the oil used on the potatoes fragrant and the whole might be more likely on the shores of Provence than the periphery of Milton Keynes. A dish of duck accompanied by filo parcels of coriander and onion with a ginger and soy sauce had the same judgement as to the effect of flavours. Fair cheese and fair desserts: a winner of apple soufflé, apple sorbet and balls of apple, unadorned, has been reported. The aplomb with which some meals have been achieved is hope for a steady future. The wine list is adequate and makes no great financial demands. If the cooking were to continue in this vein, the quality of the stock would need improving. House French, £7. Children are welcome too.

---

CELLARMAN'S CHOICE : *A wine recommended by the restaurateur, normally more expensive than the house wine.*

---

CHEFS: Karen Snowdon and Jonathan Stanbury    PROPRIETORS: Karen and
Christine Snowdon
OPEN: Mon to Sat, exc Mon and Sat L
CLOSED: 25 Dec, 1 Jan, 2 weeks end of Aug
MEALS: 12 to 2, 7 to 9.30
PRICES: £21 (£28), Set L and D £13.95 (£21) to £26 (£34)
CARDS: Access, Visa
SEATS: 43. Private parties: 30 main room, 12 private room. Car-park, 15 places. Vegetarian
meals. Children's helpings. No cigars/pipes in dining-room. Wheelchair access. Music
ACCOMMODATION: 6 rooms, all with bath/shower. B&B £49 to £59. Afternoon teas. Garden.
TV. Phone

---

**PETWORTH   West Sussex**                                                    map 3

## *Soanes*

Grove Lane, Petworth GU28 OHY
PETWORTH (0798) 43659                                          COOKING 2
1m S of Petworth                                               COST £19–£32

The manor-cum-farmhouse is wrapped round with a modern conservatory
where drinks are taken, affording views out – to the garden and field – and in
– to see Carol Godsmark at work in her kitchen. The dining- room, divided by
the skeletons of earlier partitions, is cool in colour, made warm by domestic
touches of books and antiques. The cooking style is by no means antique. Rich
sauces come with ravioli of lobster, poached turbot and rack of lamb in a
brioche crust. Their flavours – Sauternes, ginger and chive, saffron – at times
fight the taste of the main ingredient but there's no denying their competence,
nor the good techniques that Carol Godsmark has taught herself. A visiting
chef opines that the learning process is continuing and that the food improves
each time he goes there. The menu runs to six dishes at each stage, couched in
unnecessary French. On Sundays there is an abbreviated choice of two roasts
and a fish pie flanked by dishes that will appeal to a staider market. Soanes
takes itself seriously, but reports are too mixed to endorse its own valuation.
However, the intention is there. The wine list is short but decent, French but
not grasping. Ten wines can be taken by discretionary quantity, the customer
being charged only for what is consumed. Two special purchases of Ch. Danon
and Ch. Giscours 1970 are sold at very fair prices. Corkage is high. House
Muscadet or Côtes du Rhône is £8.

---

CHEF: Carol Godsmark   PROPRIETORS: Carol and Derek Godsmark
OPEN: Wed to Sat D and Sun L (other days by arrangement)
MEALS: 12.30 to 3, 7.30 to 11
PRICES: £21 (£27), Set L £13.50 (£19), Set D £14 (£20). Service inc. Licensed, also bring
your own: corkage £8
CARDS: Access, Amex, Carte Blanche, Visa
SEATS: 24. Private parties: 30 main room. Car-park, 16 places. Children's helpings (Sun L
only). No pipes in dining-room. Wheelchair access (2 steps). Music

---

*See the inside of the front cover for an explanation of the new 1 to 5 rating system
recognising cooking standards.*

---

map 3

# La Giralda

66 Pinner Green, Pinner HA5 2AB                             COOKING 1
01-868 3429                                                 COST £13−£20

At £11.50, the fixed-price menu represents good value for three courses with a
choice of eight or nine dishes in each, although it will cost a couple of quid on
top for Mediterranean prawns or châteaubriand. There's a perceptible nod
towards Spain in dishes like chicken Sevillana and entrecôte Santa Cruz.
However, it is easy to forget that this is a Spanish restaurant and eat a meal
composed entirely of Euro-food. Not that the punters are complaining, viz one
reporter's satisfaction with: 'fresh smoked salmon, succulent halibut bonne
femme and proper crème brûlée, the like of which I have not tasted in a year or
more.' Witness another reporter who chose the Spanish accent: 'I had (OK, call
me boring) paella. It looked fantastic and had every kind of seafood you could
imagine.' There are daily fish specials and the service, generally good, warms
up as the evening wears on. Wines are firmly Spanish, ungreedily priced
and minimally described (sometimes even lacking vintage). House
Cariñena is £5.75.

CHEFS: David Brown and Derek Knight   PROPRIETOR: David Brown
OPEN: Tue to Sat
MEALS: 12 to 2.30, 6.30 to 10.30
PRICES: Set L £8 (£13), Set D £11.50 (£17)
CARDS: Access, Amex, Diners, Visa
SEATS: 120. Private parties: 50 main room, 16 and 35 private rooms. Vegetarian meals.
Children's helpings. Wheelchair access (also WC). Air-conditioned

---

**PLUMTREE  Nottinghamshire**                              map 5

# Perkins Bar Bistro

Old Railway Station, Plumtree NG12 5NA                     COOKING 2
PLUMTREE (060 77) 3695                                     COST £19

Trains may no longer run, but the station is signposted and the tracks are down
for testing purposes. Lucky ones actually see an engine. The bistro started as a
love affair with France and classical cooking. Over the years, Tony Perkins'
menu has been somewhat anglicised but he continues happily to serve salmon
Dugléré, pork Holstein, blanquette à l'Amienne, lamb cutlets réforme. The
place is more spacious and attractive than a bistro, and benefits from friendly
and effective service. Menus change regularly, with lunchtime snacks at the bar
for those with a light appetite. Readers have reported favourably on kidneys,
bacon and grapes on a bed of rice, and avocado with a seafood filling, pork
stuffed with prunes and apricot that was tasty but a little dry, and fine
casseroles of lamb − blanquette indeed − and ox-tail. Vegetables are charged
separately, which results in a substantial surcharge. The wine list is short, but
with a wide range and a generous price structure. House French is £4.90.
CELLARMAN'S CHOICE : Rosemount Show Reserve Chardonnay 1987, £11.50;
Ch. Beychevelle 1981, £23.

CHEF: Tony Perkins   PROPRIETORS: Tony and Wendy Perkins
OPEN: Tue to Sat
CLOSED: 1 week at Christmas
MEALS: 12 to 10, 7 to 9.45
PRICES: £11 (£16), Snacks from £1.95
CARDS: Access, Amex
SEATS: 90. 6 tables outside. Private parties: 24 main room. Car-park, 60 places. Children welcome. Wheelchair access (1 step). Music

---

PLYMOUTH  Devon                                                     map 1

## Barretts of Princess Street

| Princess Street, Plymouth PL1 2EX | COOKING 1 |
| PLYMOUTH (0752) 221177 | COST £20 |

Stephen Barrett has moved his restaurant to the basement of a monolithic, pre-war office block behind the theatre, renamed it (from Mister Barretts), and given it a revamped, café/restaurant image. The style is sharp, art deco black-and-white with good prints, good jazz. The man himself adds a lot to the atmosphere, bouncing out of the kitchen clad in chef's apron and designer stubble to chat to customers. Snacks and light meals – pasta, vegetarian bakes, salads and rolls – are served all day from the café menu. More serious eaters may take fish landed at the Barbican, which might be offered as a sauté of scallops, squid and prawns; John Dory and orange; or skewered monkfish. Local game is a speciality: hare comes with chocolate and there is wild boar in a pudding, served with 'real' mash. Produce is Devonian, from the organic ham and sausages and farm-reared chickens to the 'very local' lamb (summer only) and the cheeses. For desserts, ice-cream from Salcombe Dairy or Lovely Lovely cake, which is. Everything is better when Steve Barrett is cooking, not talking. Wines are few in number but intelligently chosen. House French and Australian from £5.95. CELLARMAN'S CHOICE : Morton Estate Sauvignon Blanc 1988, £11.95; Ch. Haut Brisson 1983, £14.95.

CHEFS: Stephen Barrett and Elaine Parker   PROPRIETORS: Stephen Barrett and Geoffrey Rogers
OPEN: Mon to Sat
MEALS: 10.30am to 10.30pm
PRICES: £10 (£17). Snacks from £4.95
CARDS: Access, Visa
SEATS: 50. 6 tables outside. Private parties: 50 main room. Car-park, 35 places. Vegetarian meals. Children's helpings. Music. Air-conditioned

---

## Chez Nous

| 13 Frankfort Gate, Plymouth PL1 1QA | COOKING 4 |
| PLYMOUTH (0752) 266793 | COST £27–£48 |

Frankfort Gate has its own multi-storey car park with a footbridge for crossing back over the dual carriageway – so parking is not a problem as the new centre of Plymouth is radically pedestrianised. Jacques Marchal manages to produce a meal closer in character to those of a small-town, one-star *Michelin* restaurant in France than almost anyone else in England. The bistro lookalike of a dining-room, its windows shuttered from the excess of pigeons and Lowry figures scurrying across the square outside, might be somewhere in the Limousin – until you go out the door. The food exceeds its surroundings. The menu is on a blackboard, neatly written, but take glasses and a French dictionary. Jacques Marchal works in the small kitchen but will sometimes emerge – shy, Gallic and humorous. Suzanne Marchal takes charge of the customers, and spreads a certain calm. Staff there are, some long serving, but they are few. The cooking, clearly taking a leaf from Girardet, is rapid (often steamed) and light. There are moments, due to the lightness of touch, when flavours are not thrown into sufficient relief. It can then be boring, but always pleasant. At best it is masterly. Fish, meat, and especially vegetables are of the highest quality. There is a large choice at every meal, changing seasonably as produce rolls in or passes out, and a shorter set-price menu. Exemplar dishes might be John Dory with tomatoes and basil, escalopes of foie gras with a julienne of cabbage, breast of chicken with mustard, scallops with ginger: they sound not unfamiliar but they are achieved with a freshness of approach that is arresting. Desserts are classic French, lots of pavés, mousses, fruits and coulis, with not much pastry in evidence. The wine list is long and French, with some good older bottles. The prices, as for the food, are not low. House French is £7 a litre. CELLARMAN'S CHOICE : Ch. Léoville-Poyferré 1975, £33.50; Mercurey Blanc, Les Bacs 1985, Charles Genot, £18.50.

CHEF: Jacques Marchal   PROPRIETORS: Suzanne and Jacques Marchal
OPEN: Tue to Sat
CLOSED: first 3 weeks Feb and Sept, bank hols
MEALS: 12.30 to 2, 7 to 10.30
PRICES: £29 (£40), Set L and D £19.50 (£27)
CARDS: Access, Amex, Diners, Visa
SEATS: 30. Private parties: 30 main room. Children welcome. Wheelchair access (also WC). Music. Air-conditioned

---

**POLPERRO  Cornwall**                                                    map 1

## *The Kitchen*

The Coombes, Polperro PL13 2RQ                              COOKING 2
POLPERRO (0503) 72780                                       COST £19–£28

The façade is in keeping with all the houses in this much-visited fishing-harbour town: very small and very charming. In fact, it is tiny to the point of being bijou: pink inside and out, and simply furnished. 'We are fortunate,' write the Batesons, 'that there is a daily supply of fresh fish and shellfish from the busy and growing fish market, and we try to reflect this on our menu. For example, crab and lobster arrive freshly boiled, still warm, and we spend a couple of hours a day picking the crab out - a tedious job, but rewarded by the taste.' The freshness shows in a crisply browned filo pastry parcel filled with lobster – lots of it, and nothing else – which sits in an intensely flavoured, bright pink lobster sauce. Vegetarian dishes are taken seriously too. Cashew-nut and cheese pâté is garlicky and light; marinated mushrooms swim in a strongly coriander-flavoured juice. Five fixed menus (including one for children) provide a wide choice. The Batesons both cook and serve, and bake their own bread. The 30-bottle wine list is reasonably priced (though it sports too many alternative vintages). House Bergerac and Muscadet are £6.25. CELLARMAN'S CHOICE : Ch. Lemoine Lafon Rochet, Haut Médoc 1986, £10.25; Sancerre, Côtes des Roches 1987, £10.15.

CHEFS/PROPRIETORS: Ian and Vanessa Bateson
OPEN: all week, D only (L in summer by arrangement)
MEALS: 6.30 to 10
PRICES: Set D £13.50 (£19) to £17 (£23)
CARDS: Access, Visa
SEATS: 24. Private parties: 12 main room. Vegetarian meals. Children's helpings (6.30pm and L). No children under 5. Wheelchair access. Music

---

**POOL IN WHARFEDALE  West Yorkshire**                                map 5

## ▲ *Pool Court* ♟

Pool Bank, Pool in Wharfedale LS21 1EH                      COOKING **3**
LEEDS (0532) 842288                                            COST £21−£49

This is professional, pitched accurately at West Riding commercial business. Yet there is no restriction on children, even offering them smaller portions. Nor are vegetarians scorned, being given a whole menu to themselves, nor is the customer who chooses the succinct £10 set meal, downed with a bottle of Piesporter, made to feel out of place. Chauffeur-driven limousines may fill the forecourt, the number of staff may appear YTS-inspired, but many people enjoy coming here. From the three-tier fountain outside to the choice of literature in the lavatories, the place is considered. Appointments and decoration are formal and of impeccable propriety. The service is polite, well informed and well drilled. The small menu aside, the offering is of a four-course meal with a price set by the choice of the main course. The range is good, the style is modern-conventional. There are reverberations of regionalism (black puddings and Yorkshire puddings) but few 'modern' flavours of the leaf coriander sort, even if soy, cardamom and basil do make an appearance. The level of technical expertise has remained high as the new kitchen team works its passage: good pastry, accurate cooking of vegetables, a light touch with some sauces and with mousses. What is sometimes questioned, however, is whether the palpable effort and thought translate into palatable dynamite, lifting a meal of luxury to a meal of delight. The pretty seafood sausage with a dill butter sauce had a uniform taste, unlike a salmon, sole and spinach mousse where each component was distinctly perceptible. A salad of avocado with pine kernels and croûtons had not enough character to lift it to stand-alone status, though pleasant enough for an accompaniment. A selection of turbot, monkfish and scallops was bland, perhaps because presentation demanded small pieces, and it was then overpowered by a red wine sauce sufficient for light meat but too salty and rich for this. Black pudding was less than impressive. Further signs of luxury rather than delicate balance are seen in the gratin of summer fruits, awash with too much sauce, rescued by its further complication of honey ice-cream. The wine list is catholic in its inclusion of New World selections, north-western America and California, but gives away few bargains. But just as the house is mindful of its social responsibility in pricing some of the food, so there are some good cheap wines (organics too) under £10. House selections are a Bordeaux and a St Véran at £13.95. CELLARMAN'S CHOICE : Bandol, Domaine de Pibarnon 1985, £19.50; Pouilly-Vinzelles 1985, Mathias, £21.50.

CHEFS: David Watson and Guy Alabaster    PROPRIETOR: Michael W.K. Gill
OPEN: Tue to Sat, D only, and L by arrangement for parties of 10 or more
CLOSED: 2 weeks Jul to Aug, 2 weeks at Christmas
MEALS: 7 to 10
PRICES: Set D £10 (£21) to £28.50 (£41). Service of 10% for large private parties
CARDS: Access, Amex, Diners, Visa
SEATS: 65. Private parties: 30 main room. Car-park, 65 places. Vegetarian meals. Children's helpings. Smart dress preferred. No cigars/pipes in dining-room. Wheelchair access. Air-conditioned
ACCOMMODATION: 6 rooms, all with bath/shower. B&B £60 to £75. Garden. TV. Phone [GHG]

---

**POOLE  Dorset**                                                                                      map 2

## Le Select

129 Parkstone Road, Park Gates
Poole BH15 2PB                                                                     COOKING 1
PARKSTONE (0202) 740223                                                     COST £29

The setting is unlikely for a French restaurant: find the Poole Municipal Buildings and it is opposite. At first the décor is surprising, too, with photos, drawings and paintings of various French sights vying for attention with sculptures of female nudes. Nigel Popperwell arrived in 1988 and the menu has developed a firmer character. Thus, meals have started with mussels in a curried sauce and a salad of melon and pink grapefruit flavoured with Beaumes de Venise, and main courses have been tournedos bordelaise, lamb served with a rosemary sauce, and chicken in a wild mushroom cream sauce. Desserts have included a chunky home-made nougat glacé, served with various sharp fruit coulis, and peach mousse in a tuile basket. Cooking is more approximate than precise. Service by the proprietors is attentive. A vegetarian dish is now a standard item on the menu. House wine is £5.85.

CHEF: Nigel Popperwell    PROPRIETOR: Omer K. Inanir
OPEN: Tue to Sat, D only
CLOSED: 2 weeks Feb and Oct
MEALS: 7 to 10.15
PRICES: £16 (£24). Service 10%
CARDS: Access, Amex, Diners, Visa
SEATS: 28. Private parties: 12 main room, 24 private room. Vegetarian meals. No children under 7. Smart dress preferred. No-smoking area. Wheelchair access (also WC). Music

---

*If you see a certificate in a restaurant bearing the words 'Good Food Guide (International)', the claim is false (and the restaurant may be in contempt of court in displaying it) – see the Introduction. Please write and tell us the name and address of the restaurant.*

## *Warehouse*

| | |
|---|---|
| Poole Quay, Poole BH15 1HJ | COOKING 2 |
| POOLE (0202) 677238 | COST £14–£32 |

A natural advantage is the quayside site. Fishing boats unload; yachts, battered tugs and flash launches chug hither and yon; the parade goes on through the evening and tables in the first-floor restaurant have grandstand seats. Make especially for the fish. The cooking is natural and the materials are good. Meat has not been spurned – magret of duck with pears and a cinnamon and port sauce is one recommendation. Vegetarians are catered for. Puddings finish strongly, though cheese may not. A pleasant place for an evening, or for a cool lunch away from trouble, with time to rehearse maritime ambitions. The wine list seems extensive. House wine, £5.95. CELLARMAN'S CHOICE : Savennières, Clos du Papillon 1987, £11.25; Rully Varot 1983, Delorme, £17.35.

CHEF: Mark Goodey   PROPRIETORS: Mark Goodey and Jane Tyler
OPEN: Mon to Sat, exc Sat L
MEALS: 12 to 2, 7 to 10 (11 Fri and Sat)
PRICES: £21 (£27), Set L and D £10.50 (£14) to £15 (£18). Service inc set only
CARDS: Access, Amex, Diners, Visa
SEATS: 85. Private parties: 85 main room, 20 and 50 private rooms. Vegetarian meals.
Children's helpings. Music

---

**POUGHILL  Cornwall**                                                      map 1

## ▲ *Reeds*

| | |
|---|---|
| Poughill EX23 9EL | COOKING 3 |
| BUDE (0288) 2841 | COST £25 |

In brief, this is a licensed private house in several acres within sight of the sea, where you can spend a long weekend in the care of its owner, an energetic woman of considerable charm. In the middle of the week she turns to gardening. Although only cooking for her staying guests, Margaret Jackson is happy if they, in turn, invite friends to share their table: it is itself like staying with friends. The no-choice dinners are composed with specific people in mind – by consultation and adjustment – and they are accomplished and satisfying. Dishes such as smoked trout mousse, roast rack of lamb coated with a herb crust, pie of stuffed quail in a red wine sauce, and apple pie are made memorable by garden or local produce and a careful eye to detail. This extends to the excellent cheeses, supplied by a delicatessen in Bude, and the vegetables – from gratin dauphinois to a purée of leeks or a ratatouille. As befits the location, fish is often a feature: mousseline of salmon and sole with a sorrel sauce as a beginning, paupiettes of plaice in a white wine sauce with prawns and mushrooms, or lemon sole poached in vermouth as a main course. Breakfast is exemplary; bread is home made. The wine list has a good two dozen modern French bottles from the Devon merchant Christopher Piper, and there are some vintage clarets and burgundies remaining from the cellar of Mrs Jackson's late husband. A reporter had a Ch. Langoa-Barton 1966, (Berry Bros bottling) to go with his lamb and was well pleased. Prices are very reasonable. House French from Duboeuf, £6.

CHEF/PROPRIETOR: Margaret Jackson
OPEN: Fri to Mon, D only (L by arrangement)
CLOSED: 25 Dec
MEALS: 8
PRICES: Set D £17.50 (£21). Service inc
SEATS: 10. Private parties: 10 main room. Car-park, 10 places. No children under 16. Smart dress preferred. One sitting
ACCOMMODATION: 3 rooms, all with bath/shower. B&B £35 to £60. Deposit: £10. No children under 16. Garden. Scenic. Doors close at 12. Confirm by 1 [GHG]

---

**POWBURN  Northumberland**                                        map 7

## ▲ *Breamish House*

Powburn NE66 4LL                                            COOKING 2
POWBURN (066 578) 266                                    COST £17–£26

This worthy-looking, substantial, classical house affords happy respite from care. Above all, it is comfortable – 'log fires and double-glazing.' It has changed hands since the last *Guide*, Graham Taylor giving way to Doreen and Alan Johnson, but Pat Portus remains in charge in the kitchen. Opinion is divided as to the impact of the sale: 'the standard of rooms and food is still the same, and I mean excellent.' However, price rises in food and wine have been detected - but then, inflation has also had its effect. The style continues, with a set-price meal of very small choice (until puddings) with a soup course as number two. 'Good food like mother's professionally done,' with intermittent failings rather like mother's too, seems to sum it up. A main course of pork fillet with a light curry sauce and beautifully cooked rice comes with excellent English-style vegetables. Puddings are always good: a light walnut meringue proved memorable, just as did a lemon cream meringue. Soups and baking seem other strong suits of the kitchen. The wine list has seen changes in the bottles and some quite large percentage rises, but none in overall structure. It remains a fair choice at none too high a cost. Details are not as full as they could be. House Fitou or Plaimont Colombard, £4.95. CELLARMAN'S CHOICE : Seaview Chardonnay 1987, £9.70; Mâcon Burgy, Domaine de Chervin 1983, Goyard, £9.95.

CHEFS: Patricia Portus and Doreen Johnson   PROPRIETORS: Doreen and Alan Johnson
OPEN: all week, D only, and Sun L
CLOSED: Jan
MEALS: 12.30, 7.30
PRICES: Set L £12.95 (£17), Set D £17.95 (£22)
SEATS: 30. Private parties: 22 main room. Car-park, 30 places. No children under 12. Smart dress preferred. No smoking in dining-room. Wheelchair access (also WC). One sitting
ACCOMMODATION: 10 rooms, all with bath/shower. B&B £38 to £62. Deposit: £25. No children under 12. Afternoon teas. Garden. TV. Phone. Scenic. Doors close at midnight

---

*The 1991* Guide *will be published before Christmas 1990. Reports on meals are most welcome at any time of the year, but are extremely valuable in the spring. Send them to* **The Good Food Guide,** FREEPOST, *2 Marylebone Road, London NW1 1YN. No stamp is needed if posted in the UK.*

## ▲ *Three Horseshoes*

Powerstock DT6 3TF
POWERSTOCK (030 885) 328                                    COOKING 1
4m NE of Bridport                                          COST £13–£35

A Victorian/Edwardian pub with a new restaurant extension and a
matchboarded interior in a village that, like the rest of Dorset apart from
caravan and camp sites, demands the epithet 'Hardyesque'. It's a pity the area
can't produce another writer, though Fowles may have laid claim to Lyme
Regis. The cooking is reputed for good materials, especially fish, and a fairly
straightforward approach. Reports have endorsed these two virtues but have
reflected an unevenness of execution during busy periods and questioned the
prices. More recently, the ambition of the cooking seems to have moderated,
which may lead to dullness. Vegetables have been excellent, also spinach
pancake with fresh spinach. One view is that there was a long hiccup while the
extension was absorbed into the operation. 'All is now calm, apart from the
occasional missile thrown across the kitchen in full view of those entering the
restaurant.' House French is £5.20. The list continues to be short and sweet but
has added the CELLARMAN'S CHOICE : Bulgarian Cabernet Sauvignon 1984 and
Chardonnay 1986 at £5.95. There are good beers from Palmers.

CHEF: Pat Ferguson   PROPRIETORS: Pat and Diana Ferguson
OPEN: all week
MEALS: 12 to 2 (3 Sun), 7 to 11
PRICES: £22 (£29), Set L £8.50 (£13) to £10.50 (£15), Set D £12.50 (£18) to £16.50 (£24),
Snacks from £1.50
CARDS: Access, Visa
SEATS: 60. 12 tables outside. Private parties: 28 main room, 16 private room. Car-park, 30
places. Children's helpings. Smart dress preferred. Wheelchair access (also WC). Music.
ACCOMMODATION: 3 rooms, 2 with bath/shower. B&B £20 to £37.50. Deposit: £20. Pets
welcome. Garden. Scenic. Doors close at midnight. Confirm by 6.30

## *Auctioneer*

ADT, Walton Summit, Bamber Bridge
Preston PR5 8AA                                             COOKING 1
PRESTON (0772) 324870                                      COST £11–£22

Junction 29 on the M6, an industrial estate and acres of car parking are the
neighbours of this first-floor restaurant overlooking the car auction ring below.
Customers in the day may be here for business, but at night the free parking
encourages an exodus from towns nearby. 'Inspired bistro' is the tone of the
menu, given solid bottom by English café dishes, especially at lunchtime.
Apart from the standards – gammon, roast beef, roast duck and the like – a lot
of meats are stuffed: chicken with peppercorns, lamb with pâté. Vegetarians
are catered for, children welcomed and smiles frequent. The prices are sensible
and offer real value. House French is £6.50 a litre.

CHEF/PROPRIETOR: Nigel Brookes
OPEN: Mon to Sun L, exc Tue and Sat; Wed to Sat D
MEALS: 12 to 2.30, 7 to 9.30 (10 Fri and Sat)
PRICES: £12 (£18), Set L £5.95 (£11), Set D £6.95 (£11), Snacks from £1.50
CARDS: Access, Visa
SEATS: 100. Private parties: 100 main room. Car-park, 500 places. Vegetarian meals.
Children's helpings. Music. Air-conditioned

---

## PULBOROUGH  West Sussex                                    map 3

### Stane Street Hollow

| Codmore Hill, Pulborough RH20 1BG | COOKING 3 |
| PULBOROUGH (079 82) 2819 | COST £13–£29 |

Fresh eggs from the ducks and chickens that scuttle about outside, home-grown vegetables and home-smoked fish and meat are used to good effect in René Kaiser's Swiss restaurant. On a chilly day guests can choose a table close to the open log fire and work their way through a comforting menu of robust dishes well suited to lunch in a cold climate. Home-cooked ham in caper sauce, on lambs' kidneys and sweetbreads in red wine arrive surrounded by sauté potatoes, carrots with onions and parsley and leeks in a cheese sauce. Before that come minestra Ticinese, a vegetable and tripe soup, or vol-au-vent filled with local pheasant in port and juniper sauce. And desserts demand equal stamina, with banana fritters, Black Forest torte or Swiss rhubarb tart, although there are home-made ices and sorbets for the faint-hearted. The menu changes monthly, and offers fish specialities each day. One reader remarked that Anne Kaiser's welcome 'is unvaryingly cheerful and not just for those of us who have been coming here for over 10 years.' The wine list is not unfairly priced. It kicks off with two Swiss wines but concentrates on Bordeaux and burgundy. House French from the Pyrenées and the Loire are £8 a litre. CELLARMAN'S CHOICE : Côte Rôtie, Chapoutier 1980, £15.25; Blanc-Fumé de Pouilly 1986, £11.35.

CHEF: René Kaiser  PROPRIETORS: René and Ann Kaiser
OPEN: Wed to Sat, exc Sat L
CLOSED: 3 weeks May and Oct, 24 Dec to 5 Jan
MEALS: 12.30 to 1.15, 7.30 to 9.15
PRICES: £16 (£24), Set L £6 (£13)
SEATS: 35. Private parties: 24 main room, 16 private room. Car-park, 14 places. Children's helpings

---

## RAMSBOTTOM  Greater Manchester                             map 5

### Village Restaurant ▮

COUNTY OF THE YEAR RESTAURANT

| 16 Market Place, Ramsbottom BL0 9HT | COOKING 3 |
| RAMSBOTTOM (070 682) 5070 | COST £31 |

A terraced cottage (with wine bar next door) in a Lancashire town as forgettable as the decoration within. To have created a place of celebration is an achievement in itself. While little money is lavished on externals, the table settings live up to the food. This is the modern English formula taken to extremes: six courses without choice (save the sweets) served at 8.30pm on four nights a week. Begin with a cold hors d'oeuvre, pass through soup to a cooked fish dish, rest with a roast meat and six vegetables, gain breath with cheese, then subside with puddings (not desserts). This will take up to five hours, punctuated by description and explanation by Chris Johnson and many long pauses between courses. It will taste, on a good night, fantastic. In all, an eccentric folly that people anticipate with pleasure and revisit with glee. Forewarned is forearmed. The formula guarantees no staff costs, no waste and a fair living. It could only be England, which seems to hate the idea of bustling, changing, noisy and vibrant restaurants, that supports such a thing. Mr Johnson and Ros Hunter are quixotically obsessive about the sources of their ingredients. This shows in the flavour of their hormone-free meats, the freshness of their organically grown vegetables, the quality of their Little Salkeld mill organic flour and the odour of their unpasteurised cheeses (British one and all). The obsession is further revealed by the fact that Ms Hunter seems to cook without salt. Dishes that have been praised this year include, again, air-dried spiced fillet of beef; a mushroom soup pointed with lemon and sherry; good smoked salmon from Loch Fyne (vitiated by a garnish of chopped onion and hard-boiled egg); chicken cooked two ways (done with guinea-fowl too), the legs casseroled with tarragon and cider, the breasts roasted with a mustard mousseline sauce; the vegetables that might be plain carrots, beetroot with lemon, kale with raisins and sour cream, parsnips with nutmeg, swede with pine kernels and parsleyed potatoes, all served in appetising array; and hot apple pie that will not be cooked until the main course has been sent out. Exemplary home cooking on a professional basis: when it works, it's very fine; when it does not, it may be lacklustre.

The wine list is another folly, often an act of charity. Mr Johnson operates a fixed, not a percentage mark-up, so the cost of good wines is reasonable indeed. The list is set out by style or grape variety, where appropriate, clear even with several hundred wines to scan. The roster of great names is too long to mention individuals, but Alsace is especially well covered and Australia and America are given their due (including fine botrytised dessert wines). The sight of old clarets, Rhônes, white burgundies, even Australian Grange Hermitage and Californian Cabernet Sauvignons at prices little higher than in the auction room or at a specialist wine merchant is too much for many to resist. Mr Johnson serves these expertly; he also offers to diners who wish to abdicate choice his own selection of wines by the glass to match the dinner of the evening. Many others may be had by the glass for concocting an individual running order. In fairness to this remarkable restaurant, Ms Hunter and Mr Johnson know it may not be everyone's medicine. Their approach is firmly indicated in any preliminary telephone conversation.

CHEF: Ros Hunter   PROPRIETORS: Ros Hunter, Chris Johnson, Peter Johnson and Lynda Johnson
OPEN: Wed to Sat, D only
MEALS: 8 for 8.30
PRICES: Set D £19.50 (£26)
CARDS: Access, Visa
SEATS: 16. Private parties: 8 main rooms. Children welcome. No smoking. Music. One sitting

---

**REDLYNCH** Wiltshire            map 2

## ▲ *Langley Wood*

Hamptworth Road, Redlynch SP5 2PB      COOKING 1
ROMSEY (0794) 390348          COST £15−£25

'Almost like staying in a fairly simple private house, though the cooking is
*much* better than that,' was one reporter's verdict, after an overnight stop at this
part-Victorian/part-sixteenth-century country house off the A36 south-east of
Salisbury. David Rosen is a welcoming and helpful host. Sylvia Rosen takes
care of the cooking, and her menu centres on roasts, grills and steaks, well
flavoured and interestingly accompanied: beef with Stilton and walnut
stuffing; garlic roast pork with spiced apricots. Among old faithfuls are some
less expected departures: courgette and Gruyère pie; Caribbean pepperpot, a
casserole of pork and chicken; eel from the River Test, cold-smoked in oak.
House French is £5 a bottle, or there's a list of nicely chosen French wines, with
half a dozen Germans, at very fair prices. CELLARMAN'S CHOICE : Ch. Tours des
Combes 1983, St-Emilion, £11.75; Chablis Côte de Léchet 1986 *premier cru*,
Defaix, £16.

CHEF: Sylvia Rosen   PROPRIETORS: David and Sylvia Rosen
OPEN: Wed to Sat D and Sun L
MEALS: 12.45 to 2, 7.30 to 11
PRICES: £15 (£21), Set Sun L £10.75 (£15)
CARDS: Access, Amex, Diners, Visa
SEATS: 30. Private parties: 65 main room. Car-park, 25 places. Vegetarian meals. Children's
helpings. No cigars/pipes in dining-room. Wheelchair access (also WC). Music
ACCOMMODATION: 3 rooms. B&B £14 to £28. Baby facilities. Pets welcome. Afternoon teas.
Garden. Scenic

---

**RICHMOND** Surrey            map 3

## *Chez Max* ▼

*COUNTY OF THE YEAR RESTAURANT*

291 Sandycombe Road
Richmond TW9 3LU          COOKING 3
01-940 3590          COST £22−£34

This is the metropolitan particular of the year. Max and Marc Renzland are
twin brothers. One cooks, the other waits. One waits, the other cooks. Which
one? Probably Max waiting and Marc cooking. Each seems consumed by a
dream of wanting to run a French restaurant − more precisely a *bistrot à vins*.
The restaurant was lovingly slotted into a space left by a failed wine bar. The
art nouveau front was shipped from Lyon; the bar was found in Normandy,
restored and reconstructed; the light fittings were bought in Paris; the bench
came from a French church; even the lace curtains are from Nouvelles Galéries.
The menu is written out for each meal, in French of course: not particularly
grammatical and quite illegible. It is then explained to you by Max (or Marc) in
French and English. He will persist in speaking French to the customer
throughout the meal. The dream extends to the rhythm of the meal itself.
Nothing is allowed to break it: the menu must be explained, then you may
have a bottle of wine; the nibbles don't come until the order is made, then they

are delicious rosette de Lyon, a few herby olives and nice rillettes, with fair bread and decent butter. After the main course, you take cheese (but what good cheeses, and how lovingly cared for), then you take dessert. No choice: three little slices of pastry – a tarte Tatin, a chocolate morsel, and a lemon or custard item – and two sorbets, maybe poire, strawberry or prune and armagnac. The ritual, the meaningless linguistics, the thoroughness of it all may grate on an unsympathetic ear (not all the waiters are as enthusiastic). The longueurs in the kitchen and the form of production may just irritate. Because the brothers so enjoy eating, quantities are worryingly large. The style is more ambitious than bistro, though the broad approach is French bourgeois – it is coloured by no English considerations. It is also old-fashioned: lapin à la moutarde had an egg and cream liaison of a richness and copiousness to sink a post-war stomach. Materials are made much of, though all imported. Even the raspberries are Provençal – and mighty good too. Quail have been especially flavoursome – for once kept properly. It is the sort of place to go when feeling in need of food: the soup of white beans and ham was the sort that would keep a traffic warden on duty throughout the coldest snap. There is also a hazy appreciation of cost. Where else in the London orbit can you get a lobster for a mere £3.75 supplement on a £14.95 menu? Or a giant bowl of simple morels and girolles with a cream sauce (no stinting on the morels) for £4 extra? So excited are customers by the cheapness of it all that they splash out on the wine list. With that, coffee, addition of service charge and the like, the bill becomes substantial, but the opportunity for fair eating is there. The cooking is not all perfection. There are frequent delays, sometimes at the cost of quality. There are miscalculations of salting, for instance and, more rarely, of flavouring. And there have been errors of judgement: a greyish artichoke, elderly vegetables. Enthusiasm has almost got the better of them with the wine list. This gets longer by the month and more extravagant. As the restaurant is neither spacious nor comfortable, it may not be the best place to spend £420 on a 1955 Yquem. Overall, wines are not cheap. Some clarets are bargains, other wines quite pricey. All have been chosen with conviction and are explained to anyone who asks. Only French (save a few sweeties) of course. House wines from £7.

CELLARMAN'S CHOICE : Madiran 1985, Plaimont, £9.50.

CHEFS: Marc and Max Renzland and Marc Spindler    PROPRIETORS: Marc and Max Renzland
OPEN: Tue to Sun
CLOSED: 25 and 26 Dec D
MEALS: 12 to 2.30, 7 to 10.30 (9.30 Sun)
PRICES: Set L £14.95 (£22) to £19.95 (£28), Set D £19.95 (£28). Service 12.5%
CARDS: Access, Amex, Diners, Visa
SEATS: 50. 3 tables outside. Private parties: 34 main room, 14 and 16 private rooms. Children's helpings (L only). No children under 8. No pipes in dining-room. Wheelchair access. Air-conditioned

*If you see a certificate in a restaurant bearing the words 'Good Food Guide Top Restaurants', the claim is false (and the restaurant may be in contempt of court in displaying it) – see the Introduction. Please write and tell us the name and address of the restaurant.*

## *Lichfield's*

13 Lichfield Terrace, Sheen Road
Richmond TW9 1AS
01-940 5236

COOKING 3
COST £22–£37

There has been no criticism of Gerald Haslegrave's cooking. It continues to be careful, modern, composed, and with good flavours. Some ideas in the first courses – honey-roast quail served on·oyster mushrooms and lamb's tongue salad and crispy bacon; artichoke heart filled with goats' cheese and spinach wrapped in puff pastry served with red wine sauce – seem excessive but cause no cavil. Main courses are more straightforward, in externals at least. There is a fair-priced lunch with a trio of choices per course; in the evenings a *carte* of six choices per course comes into play. Although ineffably polite, the staff seem slightly distant, according to all reporters, and the place is a mite subdued. The joy of eating is as important as the joy of living. The wine list is short and fairly aristocratic, though decent exposure is given to half-bottles. What cheap wines there are, are good ones: House French is £10. CELLARMAN'S CHOICE : Ch. La Tour de By, Médoc 1980, £15.

CHEF: Gerald Haslegrave   PROPRIETORS: Gerald and Stephanie Haslegrave
OPEN: Tue to Sat, exc Sat L
MEALS: 12.15 to 2.30, 7.15 to 10.30
PRICES: £22 (£31), Set L £16.50 (£22). Service inc
CARDS: Access, Amex, Visa
SEATS: 40. Private parties: 40 main room. Children's helpings. Wheelchair access(1 step).
Air-conditioned

---

**RICHMOND** North Yorkshire                                    map 7

## ▲ *Howe Villa*

Whitcliffe Mill, Richmond DL10 4T
RICHMOND (0748) 850055

COOKING 1
COST £13–£19

Leave Richmond and go towards Leyburn and Reeth, turn left at the Tyre Service Station and follow the signs to Howe Villa, a square, porticoed Georgian house with views over the River Swale. The dining-room has been extended 'not really to get in lots more people, but to make it more spacious.' The set dinners are amazing value. There are decisions to ponder over at either end of the menu, which centres on a traditional English roast: beef with airy Yorkshire; pork loin with orange. Preceding this might be watercress soup or sole au gratin; succeeding it, raspberries in red wine jelly or miniature apple strudels. The whole affair is rounded off with local cheese, coffee and mints. The place is unlicensed but not totally dry, since a crafty aperitif is included in the price and there is no corkage for bringing a bottle.

---

*The text of entries is based on unsolicited reports sent in by readers, backed up by inspections conducted anonymously. The factual details under the text are from questionnaires the* Guide *sends to all restaurants that feature in the book.*

CHEF: Anita Berry  PROPRIETORS: Tom and Anita Berry
OPEN: all week, D only
CLOSED: Dec to end Feb
MEALS: 7 to 7.30
PRICES: Set D £12 (£13) to £14 (£16). Unlicensed, but bring your own: no corkage
SEATS: 12. Private parties: 12 main room. Car-park. Children's helpings by arrangement.
No children under 8. No smoking in dining-room
ACCOMMODATION: 4 rooms, all with bath/shower. D,B&B £65 for 2. Deposit: £20. No
children under 8. Garden. TV. Scenic. Doors close at 11.30 [GHG]

---

**RIDGEWAY** Derbyshire                                           map 5

## Old Vicarage 🍷

Ridgeway Moor, Ridgeway S12 3XW
SHEFFIELD (0742) 475814
off A616, on B6054 nearly opposite                      COOKING 4
village church                                           COST £22−£44

This is a Victorian house and garden set in a small village not far from the
abrupt margin of Sheffield. High plantings shelter it from the moorland rains.
Passage through the front door, complete with guttering lantern, might
convince you of the possibility of time-travel, but the two dining-rooms, one in
a beflowered conservatory, are in warm creams with good rugs and curtains,
affording comfort and avoiding pretension. Tessa Bramley cooks, her husband
and son run the remainder. Her training was a good English domestic science
college, and the rest was self-taught. The resulting amalgam of absolutely
sound technique, the best of English habits from a life of cooking for family
and friends, and a certain amount of book learning is first rate. The inspiration
is mostly horticultural. The Bramleys have always grown their own herbs and
vegetables, once in a Sheffield garden, now in greater space with two full-time
gardeners. Every dish is informed by what is going on out there. The leaf and
floral decoration that occurs seems to be a message from the gardener, not
designer nonsense plopped on to every plate. The second course of any dinner
is a composed salad from the garden or some vegetable in season cooked in an
appropriate way. Menus will include a herb-garden salad with exotic fruits
and hazelnut dressing; a thyme flower jelly with a game liver parfait; geranium
jelly with a wild rabbit and walnut terrine; or apricot, mint and chive flower
stuffing to a leg of lamb. The only cooks here that would produce the sort of
range Tessa Bramley now practises would probably have been French chefs to
earls who had been on the Grand Tour, for she is not happy restricted to simple
roasts. Luxury ingredients are bought in, from foie gras to wild mushrooms.
They are also handled in an assured 'restaurant' manner; this is not the cooking
of an ingénue. Dishes that have been applauded include escabèche of pigeon;
great soups, from leek and cauliflower to fennel and almond; a sole mousse
with salmon served on a leek sauce; pancakes filled with mussels in a herb
sauce; calf's liver and foie gras served with a simple gravy; a hotch-potch of
game birds with a lemon compote and a sauce of wood blewits; a stunning hot
chocolate sponge with a fudge sauce and an English custard; simple fools,
possets, pies and trifles as puddings (Sunday lunch is a good time for the more

substantial of these). Vegetables, as befits a gardening kitchen, are excellent, often stir-fried with an interesting oil to add a light variation. One reader remembers white cabbage stir-fried with caraway as reconciling him to that herb after years of self-denial. Service is informed, gentle and proper (white gloves for hot plates). A few find it verges on the stiff. The wine list is the province of Andrew Bramley. It bespeaks as much care as in the rest of the house. It kicks off with a collection of Champagnes, including a Salon and a Dom Ruinart 1976 as well as six Krugs back to 1961, that might show Sheffield to be the last resort of the Champagne Charlies of England. So far, it avoids going out of Europe, nor does it touch Italy, though Spain and Germany are given some space. There are not a lot of bargains, but the prices are fair. As so often, the real gifts occur among the very expensive: the Ch. Haut Brion 1955, the Roederer Cristal 1981, the Krug Blanc de Blancs 'Clos du Mesnil' 1979. Clarets are more interesting than burgundies, but the best of the cheaper drinking is among the Loires and Beaujolais. It is in any case unreasonable to criticise any restaurant that manages to field more than 30 wines, all decent, some more than that, at under £10. House Bourgogne Rouge, Jayer, £13.50; Sancerre, André Dézat, £13.50.

CHEF: Tessa Bramley   PROPRIETORS: Tessa, Andrew and Peter Bramley
OPEN: Tue to Sat D, Sun L (Tue to Sat by arrangement)
MEALS: 12.15 to 2.30, 7 to 9.30
PRICES: Set L £11 (£22) to £15 (£26), Set D £17 (£28) to £26 (£37)
SEATS: 50. Private parties: 30 main room 30 private room. Car-park, 25 places. No children under 12. Smart dress preferred. No smoking in dining-room

---

**RIPLEY Surrey**                                                            map 3

## Michels' ♥

13 High Street, Ripley GU23 6AQ                              COOKING 2
GUILDFORD (0483) 224777                                      COST £23–£43

The restaurant has undoubtedly benefited from its redecoration in the last two years, a lighter feel in bar and dining-room being more in tune with the modern style of the cooking. Much bodes well, from the table settings, the crudités and the breads to the welcome at the door. The menu is large and changes often enough, though items in the repertoire resurface regularly. Variety is the name of the game: cooking techniques, materials and ingredients in a single dish bulking larger than flavour. 'I had rabbit, so complex that it was hard to recognise. I have never before had rabbit that looked less like rabbit and took so long to eat.' Chefs of the seventeenth century would have been proud to have such comment passed. On a summer menu, five main dishes out of eight were stuffed with something or very closely paired: bourgeois with scallop mousse; lamb with a tarragon mousse; chicken with langoustine; oxtail with sweetbreads. The pasta for vegetarians just has to be ravioli. Some of the variety is wholly praiseworthy: main courses each have their own potato accompaniment, not merely the same old dauphinois. The style continues into the desserts which are modern dishes such as strawberry gratin, a pancake stuffed with Grand Marnier soufflé, pear crème brûlée with a pear sorbet. A new policy has limited the number of people seated at any one time. It is hoped that this will reduce comments on the long waiting time on busy nights. The wine list contains some six dozen bins with a handful from outside France. The selection is very canny indeed, using makers who produce upfront flavours that remind one that France still has an eminent position difficult to challenge: Guigal in the Rhône, Bossard in Muscadet, Rolly Gassmann in Alsace, Lafarge in Mâcon, Jayer in Burgundy. It shows the importance of picking the right shipper. Prices are not excessive. House French from £7. CELLARMAN'S CHOICE : Mâcon-Lugny les Charmes 1987, £11.25; Ch. Millet, Graves 1982, £16.35. Cigarettes, cigars and matches are not sold to customers, nor ashtrays put on the tables. This has reduced the amount of smoking, without affronting the last-ditch resisters.

CHEF: Erik Michel   PROPRIETORS: Erik and Karen Michel
OPEN: Tue to Sun, exc Sat L and Sun D
MEALS: 12.30 to 2, 7.30 to 9.15 (9.45 Sat)
PRICES: Set L £15 (£23) to £17.50 (£25), Set D £22 (£30) to £27.50 (£36)
CARDS: Access, Amex, Diners, Visa
SEATS: 60. Children welcome

---

**RIPPONDEN  West Yorkshire**                                    map 5

## Over the Bridge

Millfold, Ripponden HX6 4DJ                              COOKING 2
HALIFAX (0422) 823722                                      COST £29

The pleasing site in the centre of the village and the handsome conversion of what must have been a weaving shed or weavers' cottages makes for a successful restaurant. Customers pass from a comfortable sitting-out room on the first floor to a well-appointed dining-room below, softened by a multitude of plants. The set-price menu affords sufficient choice of dishes that shows a modern fondness for fruit: banana with scallops, golden plum in soup, orange with meats. There are also some unlikely combinations, such as the whisky with fromage blanc that accompanied a salmon and parsley terrine; it worked very well. Traditional dishes are also updated with a guinea-fowl with claret and smoked bacon that might double for coq au vin – save for the scattering of orange peel. Service is most amenable, despite some reserve. The wine list, about 100-strong, is not excessively priced. House wine £7 and £8.

CHEFS: Sue Tyer and Lindsay Barratt   PROPRIETORS: Ian H Beaumont
OPEN: Mon to Sat, D only
CLOSED: bank hols
MEALS: 7.30 to 9.30
PRICES: Set D £18 (£24)
CARDS: Access, Amex, Visa
SEATS: 48. Private parties: 25 main room. Car-park, 50 places. No children under 12. Wheelchair access (1 step)

---

*Several sharp operators have tried to extort money from restaurateurs on the promise of an entry in a guide book that has never appeared. The* Good Food Guide *makes no charge for inclusion and does not offer certificates of any kind.*

---

## ROADE Northamptonshire — map 3

# *Roadhouse Restaurant*

16–18 High Street, Roade, NN7 2NW  
ROADE (0604) 863372

COOKING 3  
COST £17–£26

This former pub is just off the main Northampton to Milton Keynes road, near junction 15 of the M1. Mr Kewley observes that many country restaurants suffer 'folie de grandeur' and hopes to approach his quite ambitious but understated style of cooking with an eye to protecting the pockets of his local customers while providing himself with a fair living. A reasonable attitude that has nice spin-offs like their not encouraging tipping beyond the prices posted. People like the lack of pretension in the newly decorated pink rooms and the relaxed service. The menu offers seven things in each course and they smack of genuine cooking: gratin of scallops, prawns and salmon; feuilleté of asparagus with a beurre blanc; casserole of rabbit with bacon, mushrooms and mustard; or fillets of red snapper stuffed with sorrel and in a green sauce. Substantial and comforting cooking that may go to some less familiar combinations as in a salad of quails' eggs, bacon, croûtons and rollmops. Pastry has been praised in the game pâté in light pastry with a piquant fruit sauce and the melt-in-the-mouth mince pies. Wine service is as low key as the restaurant; the list, however, is a well-chosen short run of a little bit of everything at prices far short of greedy. House wines are a choice of four from £7.20. CELLARMAN'S CHOICE : Brown Brothers Cabernet Sauvignon/Shiraz 1984, £12; Côteaux du Languedoc, Abbaye de Valmagne 1986, £8.50; Reuilly 1987, Lafond £11.50.

CHEF: Christopher Kewley  PROPRIETORS: Christopher and Susan Kewley  
OPEN: Tue to Sat, exc Sat L  
MEALS: 12.30 to 1.45, 7 to 12  
PRICES: £17 (£22), Set L £12 (£17). Service inc  
CARDS: Access, Visa  
SEATS: 32. Private parties: 40 main room. Car-park, 15 places. Children's helpings. Smart dress preferred. Wheelchair access

## ROBERTSBRIDGE East Sussex — map 3

# *Olivers*

Cripps Corner, Robertsbridge TN32 5RY  
STAPLECROSS (058 083) 387

COOKING 1  
COST £16–£24

The Olivers are having to work hard to establish themselves, but, judging from several glowing accounts of meals, they should do well. Inside, the simple dining-room is brightly lit and has an informal, sometimes intimate atmosphere. Gary Oliver cooks a modern Anglo-French menu with a choice of eight dishes at each course and particularly strong suits in seasonal game and fish: examples have been wild boar pâté, bavarois of salmon and cucumber with a dill jelly, and suprême of guinea-fowl with wild mushrooms and pine nuts. Only occasionally, these are let down by badly judged timing. Vegetables, such as a tartlet of creamed courgettes, roast potatoes in a fresh tomato sauce, *al dente* green beans bundled up with an onion leaf, show the degree of care. The kitchen's self-sufficiency stretches from bread and home-made sausages to well executed desserts like a smooth chocolate mousse moulded in a spiral and set in a wafer-thin chocolate basket. Service, largely by Mrs Oliver, is attentive without being over-zealous. A very short, and French, wine list. House Léonce Bocquet, £5.25. CELLARMAN'S CHOICE : Pouilly Fumé 1987, Dagueneau, £11.50; Savigny-lès-Beaune 1986, Jean Claude Boisset, £10.95.

CHEF: Gary Oliver   PROPRIETORS: Albert and Gary Oliver
OPEN: Wed to Sun
CLOSED: first 3 weeks Jan
MEALS: 12 to 1.45, 7 to 9.45
PRICES: £16 (£20), Set L and D £12 (£16). Service inc
CARDS: Access, Visa
SEATS: 36. Private parties: 45 main room, 18 private room. Car-park, 20 places. No children under 5. Music

---

## ROCHDALE   Greater Manchester                                        map 5

## *One Eleven*

111 Yorkshire Street, Rochdale OL16 1YJ                    COOKING 1
ROCHDALE (0706) 344901                                     COST £23

Arriving at this simple but seemly restaurant is made no easier by a one-way system and minimal frontage. Then come stairs to a bar on a landing. The menu has met with approval for pure bistro food such as a crab gratin or fillet steak with an enriched red wine and cream sauce. Many things have a cream-based sauce. The price is not excessive. The wine list is also short and simple. House Côtes du Rhône, Muscadet or Niersteiner is £5.95.

CHEF/PROPRIETOR: Catherine Adamson
OPEN: Thur to Sat D; Mon to Wed D by arrangement
MEALS: 7.30 to 9.30
PRICES: Set D £13.50 (£19)
CARDS: Access, Amex, Diners, Visa
SEATS: 30. Private parties: 30 main room. Children restricted. Smart dress preferred. Music. Air-conditioned

---

## ROCHFORD   Essex                                                      map 3

## ▲ *Renoufs*

1 South Street, Rochford SS4 1BL                          COOKING 1
SOUTHEND (0702) 544393                                    COST £17–£32

The punters continue to be drawn, to both the restaurant and the luxury hotel two minutes' walk away. Neither, however, attracts much correspondence with the *Guide*. This may be because the menu and style of cooking appeal to different groups than our readers: very traditional, very pressed duck, very seven-sorts-of-fish offered in prime condition year in year out. Local supporters who do read the *Guide* aver that when Derek Renouf is on form and on duty, the cooking is very professional. Although no more than 12 years old, his restaurant might have been conceived in the 1950s. The wine list is long, made longer by various 'special collections' of DRC, Krug, Duboeuf and more, interrupting the main flow. There are several claret off-vintages for first-growth bargain drinking, and regions outside France, for example Germany and California, are given passing mention. As a list, it has a miscellaneous air. House Bordeaux, £7.40. CELLARMAN'S CHOICE : Ch. Respide Medeville, Graves 1983, £17.55; Domaine de Justices Bordeaux 1985, £9.80. Wine, coffee and service are included on the higher priced set menu.

CHEF/PROPRIETOR: Derek Renouf
OPEN: all week D, Sun and Mon L
CLOSED: first 3 weeks in Jan, last week June, first week July
MEALS: 12 to 1.45, 7 to 8.30 (9.30 Fri and Sat)
PRICES: £20 (£27), Set L and D £12 (£17) to £21 (£21). Service inc
CARDS: Access, Amex, Diners, Visa
SEATS: 100. Private parties: 70 main room. Vegetarian meals. Children welcome. Wheelchair access (also WC). Music. Air-conditioned
ACCOMMODATION: 24 rooms, all with bath/shower. Rooms for disabled. B&B £48 to £65. Baby facilities. Pets welcome. Garden. Air-conditioning. TV. Phone

---

**ROCKLEY**  Wiltshire                                              map 2

## *Loaves and Fishes*

Rockley Chapel, Rockley SN8 1RT                          COOKING **2**
MARLBOROUGH (0672) 53737                                 COST  £20−£25

'Dine we must, and we may as well dine elegantly as well as wholesomely,' said Mrs Beeton, as quoted on the menu. Here the elegance is marked by a certain eccentricity, for there cannot be many restaurants in a converted chapel: the kitchen in one aisle, the tables in the other, many small alcoves and levels, many objects and curiosities displayed to amuse, instruct and divert. By contrast, the cooking is straightforward: a set price, a choice of three first courses, three desserts or cheese, but no choice of main course. Such a policy may not always satisfy customers and there have been occasional disappointments. Nonetheless, a Sunday lunch of chicken and tarragon soup, roast leg of lamb with an onion cream sauce and fresh cream toffee meringue with butterscotch sauce would be ample reward for a morning's walking. Unlicensed, with a 50p per bottle corkage charge to parties of six or more. Coffee continues to give trouble.

CHEF: Angela Rawson  PROPRIETORS: Angela Rawson and Nikki Kedge
OPEN: Wed to Sat D, and Sun L
MEALS: 12.30 to 1, 7.30 to 8.30
PRICES: Set D £18 (£21), Set Sun L £17 (£20). Unlicensed, but bring your own: corkage 50p per bottle for parties over 6
SEATS: 28. Private parties: 10 main room. Car-park, 10 places. Children's helpings. Wheelchair access (also WC). Music

---

*All letters to the* Guide *are acknowledged with an update on latest sales, closures, chef changes and so on.*

---

## *Old Manor House* ▮

21 Palmerston Street, Romsey SO5 18GF                      COOKING **3**
ROMSEY (0794) 517353                                           COST £17−£41

It is encouraging when the warmth of personality of the chef/patron suffuses
the whole restaurant with a sense of enthusiasm. How much better than the
(largely metropolitan) chefs who mince across the rickety stage of press and
glossy magazines, venting spleen on their customers (unless rich), convinced of
their own creative spark − that will hiss like a damp lucifer in the perspective
of the years. The Old Manor House and Mauro Bregoli are an entity: his
energies − shooting, fishing, smoking, curing, pickling, gathering and making
− keep it afloat and personify it to a large band of regulars. There may be a
certain lack of hot-house sophistication, but the produce is good and the
cooking is vigorous. 'Mr Bregoli provides not only a pleasant ambience but
quite excellent service. When you consider how much we pay for eating out
these days, I resent the stress elsewhere of trying to live up to the chef, the
management and the waiters. The staff here give the impression that they are
delighted to see you. Looking at the rest of the dining-room, I have noticed that
all the other guests seem to be relaxed, happy and contented.' Another reader,
who lunches there, comments that 'it is the best value we know, the staff, the
cooking, the setting, the lot.' The style is not so traditional as these remarks
might imply: courgette flowers stuffed with shellfish; foie gras cooked with
apples and calvados; red mullet with carrot, saffron and cream sauce; tortelloni
of wild mushrooms; monkfish with rosemary butter; grilled venison with a
confit of onions and spiced fruit are modern dishes, even if fillet with
Roquefort, duck with blackcurrants and the 'wickedly indulgent' desserts are
less so. Whatever the style, there are few criticisms of the execution right from
the assertive amuse-gueules offered in the bar through to the cheeses from
Olivier, which are impressive for range and condition. The wine list is certainly
good on range: clarets and burgundies are encyclopaedic, Rhône, Alsace and
Italy are very well represented. Age has its say, and there are enough half-
bottles and reasonably priced things to assuage the thirst of the less
extravagant. House French, £7. CELLARMAN'S CHOICE : Bandol, Mas de la
Rouvière 1985, £12.50; Sauvignon de St-Bris 1987, Luc Sorin, £10.50. The
restaurant is in a beamed cottage of a building (old is an understatement −
Romsey, after all, has graffiti from the thirteenth century in King John's
Hunting Box). Some have regretted the unfortunate conjunction of house, car-
park and supermarket as diminishing the sense of good living.

CHEF/PROPRIETOR: Mauro Bregoli
OPEN: Tue to Sun, exc Sun D
CLOSED: Christmas to New Year, last 3 weeks Aug
MEALS: 12 to 2, 7 to 9.30
PRICES: Set L £10.50 (£17) to £18.50 (£25), Set D £27.50 (£34)
CARDS: Access, Visa
SEATS: 45. 6 tables outside. Private parties: 12 main room, 24 private room. Car-park, 12
places. Children welcome. Smart dress preferred. No cigars/pipes in dining-room

ROXWELL  Essex                                                  map 3

## *Farmhouse Feast*

The Street, Roxwell CM1 4PB
ROXWELL (024 548) 583                                    COOKING 1
6m W of Chelmsford                                        COST £25

A half-timbered house next to the Chequers in the centre of a village enmeshed in the tentacles of Bungalonia. The inside has bungalow tendencies itself, is not especially comfortable, but has a fair view of the kitchen. Diners will not want for attention as the menu (and formula) is explained. Then, in principle, you do the work while the kitchen does the main course. A set price brings a self-help pair of first courses, a tureen of soup left on the table, said main course (from meat or four vegetarian choices), finishing with help-yourself cheese and puddings. Cooking is moderate, quantities are substantial, the style is British: from liver pâté to brisket in a mushroom, onion and stout sauce to kiwi-fruit Pavlova made with good meringue. The breast of chicken stuffed with apple and kiwi-fruit with a goats' cheese sauce sounds even more British (modern this time) but, surprisingly, it tasted good, though the kiwi was undetectable. The wine list is short and cheap. House wines are Italian and French, £6.50 a litre. CELLARMAN'S CHOICE : Oppenheimer Krotenbrunneu Auslese, £7.10.

CHEFS: Juliet Upson, Allan Green, Peter Spence and John Wealleans
PROPRIETORS: Rosemary and Juliet Upson
OPEN: Tue to Sat D, Wed to Fri L
CLOSED: 2 weeks June, first week Jan
MEALS: 12 to 1.30, 7.30 to 9.30
PRICES: Set L and D £15.95 (£21). Service 10%
SEATS: 86. Private parties: 24 main room, 12, 16 and 30 private rooms. Vegetarian meals. Children's helpings. No smoking. Wheelchair access. Air-conditioned. Partly self-service

RUGBY  Warwickshire                                            map 5

## ▲ *Grosvenor Hotel*

Clifton Rd, Rugby CV21 3QQ                              COOKING 1
RUGBY (0788) 535686                                    COST £15–£30

'Asparagus and bean ragout cascading from a puff pastry pillow' sounds more like the inebriated guest in Room 9 than a vegetarian item on the menu but that is the sort of language this hotel goes in for. Similarly alarming images are ushered up by 'Best end of black-faced lamb with redcurrant glazed courgettes'. One report this year has protested that Richard Johnson is getting culinarily above himself and not sticking to the last of good, sensible cooking. Service, too, can be chaotic. However, in this popular hotel, others have found very sound cooking of grills and the occasional fish as well as 'breast of free-range chicken filled with lobster and garden herbs presented sliced on cassis sauce'. The wine list is short and sweet, with good wines not expensively priced. House French, £6.95.

*Report forms are at the back of the book; write a letter if you prefer.*

CHEF: Richard Johnson   PROPRIETORS: J. Hall and J. Hawes
OPEN: all week, exc Sat L
MEALS: 12 to 2, 7 to 10
PRICES: £18 (£25), Set L £8.95 (£15)
CARDS: Access, Amex, Diners, Visa
SEATS: 42. Private parties: 40 private room. Car-park, 18 places. Children welcome. Smart dress preferred. No pipes in dining-room. Music
ACCOMMODATION: 16 rooms, all with bath/shower. B&B £49.50 to £65. Baby facilities. Pets welcome. Afternoon teas. Garden. TV. Phone

---

**RYE   East Sussex**                                                            map 0

## Chilka House

Black Boy, 4 High Street, Rye TN31 7JE                    COOKING 1
RYE (0797) 226402                                          COST £13–£32

A. K. Ghoshal has transferred from Brighton to the unlikely oak-panelled setting of The Black Boy Tea Rooms. The menu explains that Chilka is India's biggest inland lake, with a 'rich variety of aquatic fauna'. The connection, or distant leap rather, is to fish and seafood curries on the menu: from mild to very hot prawn and king prawn; halibut and salmon either with fresh coconut or sweet-and-sour. Chicken, lamb and vegetables ring the changes: kofta is breadcrumbs, carrot and beetroot, and there is mushroom and cashew nut mix. 'Nan is absolutely scrummy.' There are lassi and lager to drink as well as wine. House wine is £6.95. CELLARMAN'S CHOICE : Ch. Fleur Cardinale, St-Emilion Grand Cru 1983, £14.95; Pouilly Blanc Fumé, Les Griottes 1985, Jean Pabiot, £13.95.

CHEF/PROPRIETOR: A. K. Ghoshal
OPEN: Wed to Sat, D only
CLOSED: 21 Dec to 4 Jan; Feb
MEALS: 6.30 to 10.30
PRICES: £17 (£26), Set D £8 (£13) to £20 (£27)
CARDS: Access, Amex, Diners, Visa
SEATS: 32. Private parties: 32 main room. Vegetarian meals. Children welcome. Smart dress preferred. Wheelchair access. Music

## Landgate Bistro

5–6 Landgate, Rye TN31 7LH                                COOKING 3
RYE (0797) 222829                                         COST £22

'A popular place for celebration dinners, after exams and so on,' is the opinion of one Sussex woman who, with many others, has taken this unpretentious but effective restaurant to her heart. Certainly the food carries the message; the china and incidentals are of the simple sort. The menu, which changes with the seasons, offers eight dishes at each course plus a couple of fish. Three choices stand out as constants: squid stewed with white wine, garlic and tomato; a 'very fishy stew' that has four or five fish types, poached in stock and served with croûtons and a rouille, and pigeon breasts with a simple red wine sauce. Vegetables, charged separately, are cooked well. Chocolate puddings receive much praise and a compote of rhubarb was distinguished by its excellent timing and rather nouvelle arrangement – at odds with the rest of the meal. In short, a restaurant that cares about its ingredients and offers honest food at very fair prices. The wine list is in the same vein: an excellent range at giveaway prices. Everything is nicely chosen and contributes to the heartfelt song: 'Now this proves you do not need to bankrupt your clients.' House French, £5.50. CELLARMAN'S CHOICE : Ch. La Tour de By 1985, £11.20.

CHEF: Toni Ferguson-Lees    PROPRIETORS: Nick Parkin and Toni Ferguson-Lees
OPEN: Tue to Sat, D only
MEALS: 7 to 9.30
PRICES: £13 (£18). Service inc
CARDS: Access, Amex, Diners, Visa
SEATS: 34. Children's helpings. Music

---

**SAFFRON WALDEN  Essex**                                              map 3

## Old Hoops

15 King Street, Saffron Walden CB10 1HE                       COOKING 1
SAFFRON WALDEN (0799) 22813                                  COST £10–£38

The menu of the Morrisons' restaurant, up a flight of stairs in a former pub near the market, promises what the cooking delivers: eclectic home-and-dinner-party cooking at reasonable prices. There is no lack of boldness or invention, however, with a range of ambitious dishes: poached egg on a pastry tartlet filled with prawns masked with tomato mayonnaise and garnished with smoked salmon; venison in a raspberry sauce; a tulip-shaped biscuit with strawberry and passion-fruit sorbets. But the unambitious dishes seem to work best – for example a satisfying meal of chicken and bacon pie, escalope of pork with apple, and banana cream with custard. The atmosphere is informal, although the decoration has recently been smartened up and linen tablecloths have appeared. A short European wine list has house Bouchard at £6.25.

CHEF: Ray Morrison   PROPRIETORS: Don Irwin and Ray Morrison
OPEN: Tue to Sat
CLOSED: 2 weeks in summer
MEALS: 12 to 2.30, 7 to 10.30
PRICES: £14 (£22), Set L £5 (£10) to £20 (£26), Set D £10 (£16) to £25 (£32)
CARDS: Access, Amex, Diners, Visa
SEATS: 40. Private parties: 40 main room. Children's helpings. Music

---

**ST KEVERNE  Cornwall**                                                map 1

## Laden Table

2 Commercial Road, St Keverne TR12 6LY                        COOKING 2
ST KEVERNE (0326) 280090                                          COST £28

Tony Gulliford rightly protested at our dismissal of the grandeur of St Keverne church in the last *Guide*: a fine church indeed, a centre of Celtic evangelism in pre-Saxon Cornwall and, later, of Cornubian protest at the exactions of Westminster. The Laden Table protests not, groans rather, under the yoke of

Gulliford, a cook of long standing. Salmon in pastry with ginger and currants and aïoli of great savour accompanying a first course of prawns may proclaim his affinity to the Hole in the Wall and Anglo-French provincial cooking of past decades, but his generosity and directness suits the locale of three converted cottages far down the Cornish peninsula. Hospitality also: after 'helping other customers to start their car, he entertained us until 2.30am'. Opening times are sometimes erratic. The Christopher Piper wine list makes a decent choice at fair prices over four dozen bins. House Duboeuf, £5.75.

CHEF/PROPRIETOR: Tony Gulliford
OPEN: Tue to Sat, D only, Mon June to Sept
MEALS: 7.30 to 9.30
PRICES: Set D £17.50 (£23)
SEATS: 30. Private parties: 12 main room. Children welcome. No cigars/pipes in dining-room

---

**ST KEYNE  Cornwall**                                                     map 1

## ▲ *Well House* ♥

St Keyne PL14 4RN
LISKEARD (0579) 42001                                         COOKING 3
on B3254, 3m S of Liskeard                                    COST £20–£36

Pass St Keyne's Well on the way to the house: its water was thought good for the eyes. The hotel itself was built for a tea planter late in Victoria's reign. By no means an architectural masterpiece, although civilised by wisteria and climbing plants of impressive size, it has been constantly improved inside and out by Nicholas Wainford. It seems to be one of those places that people remember fondly: perhaps the tranquillity allows them to rediscover themselves, encouraged by the warmth of the welcome and the quality of the cooking. There are few complaints. The restaurant is not at all a country-house melange of nostalgia and fine fabrics: its cool colouring and careful detail impart a sense of space where others might seek to enclose, and that matches the up-to-date cooking. David Pope, a chef who passed through the Capital Hotel and Gidleigh Park on his way to Cornwall, has continued to improve and extend his range. The monthly menus are set-price, lunch especially reasonable, and offer half a dozen choices at each course, as well as cheese and coffee. There are echoes of the modern combinations now found throughout the land in dishes such as fresh pasta with salmon in a basil and pine kernel sauce; foie gras and calf's liver with lentils and shallots; roast squab (French) with broad beans, sage and girolles in a game stock sauce; panaché of veal sweetbread, fillet and kidney with a timbale of spinach and smoked bacon and a coriander sauce; gratin of peaches or a tuile basket filled with white chocolate ice-cream topped with marinated strawberries and served on a glazed sabayon. Some elements sound outré, while others may indicate that the peasant revolution (lentils, cabbage and root vegetables) has reached the far west, but David Pope mobilises the flavours with greater brio than at the outset of his career here, and the experience on the plate does seem to mirror the menu description – that this is by no means always the case elsewhere can be mournfully attested to by many readers. Details continue to be well thought out, the cheeseboard is extending its range, the breads and butter are excellent, petits fours and coffee as they should be. Service is quiet and concerned. Some have feared that Nicholas Wainford seems too worried, that smiles need coaxing, but it is the furrowed brow of care, not petulance. The wine list is very good on clarets and is not expensive. Apart from a nice run of German bottles, there is very little from outside France. Mr Wainford knows about what he holds and his guidance is rewarding. Note that Domaine de Trévallon 1984 lurks at the end of a French country wine section and is half the price of any of the clarets of similar stature. One recent change is that Mr Wainford has banished children under eight from the dining-room. He still welcomes dogs (not, we are sure, in the restaurant). Perhaps his experience has taught him to prefer four legs to two; perhaps children remind his guests too fretfully of what they wish to escape – or seek to conceive. There is a social theory of the English country-house hotel that awaits composition. House French is £6.50.

CELLARMAN'S CHOICE : Mâcon-Lugny les Genièvres 1987, Louis Latour, £11.95; Ch. d'Angludet 1983, £16.15.

CHEF: David Pope    PROPRIETOR: Nicholas Wainford
OPEN: Tue to Sat
MEALS: 12.30 to 2, 7.30 to 9
PRICES: Set L £15 (£20), Set D £24 (£30)
CARDS: Access, Amex, Visa
SEATS: 36. 5 tables outside. Private parties: 40 main room. Car-park, 24 places. No children under 8. Smart dress preferred. Wheelchair access (1 step)
ACCOMMODATION: 7 rooms, all with bath/shower. B&B £42.50 to £85. Deposit: £25 Baby facilities. Pets welcome. Afternoon teas. Garden. Swimming-pool. Tennis. TV. Phone. Scenic [GHG]

---

**ST LEONARD'S**  East Sussex                                                      map 3

## Röser's

64 Eversfield Place
St Leonard's-on-Sea TN37 6DB                                    COOKING 2
HASTINGS (0424) 712218                                          COST £19–£32

On the seafront, flanked by a pizzeria, boarding-houses, hotels and holiday flats, the bow window of Röser's affords its customers a view while protecting them from unseemly curiosity by much net curtaining. The restaurant is by no means restful in its decoration; its walls seem in danger of collapse from the weight of suspended ornament and eyes may glaze from encounter with too many patterns, too many designs. Gerald Röser's cooking is professional in approach, with an over-emphasis on display and an elaboration of tastes, quantities and techniques that may dismay the less voracious diner. His materials, however, are first rate, especially some of the fish. A warm seafood salad of mussels, scallops, sole, langoustines and salmon drew especial praise for its determined shopping and accurate cooking. Much of the style of the place is mid-Channel, but there are hints of Mr Röser's own background in the Schwarzwalder schinken and the German-style lemon and vanilla cheese gateau. Potatoes have been well received, though vegetables have often been under-cooked. One reader successfully asked for them to be better done: this may have more general application as a means of avoiding our current besotted dishing up of raw vegetables. Service is efficient, if occasionally pressing; but not pressing enough against the cigar-smoker who brought a neighbour's early dinner to abrupt end by lighting up at 8.30. The wine list is long and good on French and German wines, shorter on the New World. House wine is French, £6.50. CELLARMAN'S CHOICE : Mâcon-Lugny Les Charmes, £9.50; Sancerre, Domaine Saget 1987, £10.95.

CHEF: Gerald Röser  PROPRIETORS: Gerald and Jenny Röser
OPEN: Mon to Sat, exc Sat L
MEALS: 12 to 2, 7 to 10
PRICES: £18 (£27). Set L £15 (£19). Service 10%
CARDS: Access, Amex, Diners, Visa
SEATS: 50. Private parties: 20 main room, 40 private room. Children welcome. Wheelchair access (2 steps). Music

---

ST MARGARET'S AT CLIFFE  Kent                                              map 3

## ▲ Wallett's Court

West Cliffe
St Margaret's at Cliffe CT15 6EW                                    COOKING 2
DOVER (0304) 852424                                                COST £19–£32

The transition from a glorified bed and breakfast plus dining-room to a small country hotel with restaurant continues. So far, it has been made smoothly, without wrecking the charm of the largely seventeenth-century manor house whose cellars date from Domesday. This year, the Oakleys have built a new kitchen to cope with added tables and a private function room. Meals, however, follow the same set-price structure and modern Anglo-French tone. The menu – three courses during the week and five courses on Saturdays – stresses game and local fish. 'Real food with taste, not just a pretty picture, is what people are demanding,' chef/proprietor Chris Oakley writes firmly. Reports suggest that the rough edges are being honed all the time. A game terrine served with marigold jelly, a salad centred on pigeon marinated in port and medallions of venison in a red wine and shallot sauce are typical of the dishes using local game. Fish – halibut, monkfish, salmon steaks and the like – is usually given simpler treatment. There are good vegetables, soups and mid-meal sorbets too. Puddings are displayed before you choose. There is a very short wine list. House French, £7. CELLARMAN'S CHOICE : Ch. La Croix 1979, Pomerol, £22; Pouilly-Fuissé 1985, André Morey, £15. See under West Cliffe in *The Good Hotel Guide*.

CHEF: Chris Oakley  PROPRIETORS: Chris and Lea Oakley
OPEN: Mon to Sat, D only
MEALS: 7 to 9
PRICES: Set D £14 (£19) to £21 (£27)
CARD: Access
SEATS: 30. Private parties: 30 main room. Car-park, 26 places. Children's helpings
ACCOMMODATION: 12 rooms, all with bath/shower. Rooms for disabled. B&B £32.50 to £60. Baby facilities. Garden. Snooker. TV. Scenic. Doors close at midnight. Confirm by 4
[GHG]

map 1

## ▲ *Rising Sun*

The Square, St Mawes TR2 5DJ          COOKING 3
ST MAWES (0326) 270233               COST £11–£23

The hotel, conveniently close to a large car park, looks out over the Fal estuary.
Though close to Truro and Falmouth, the crow arrives sooner than the driver,
so St Mawes has been spared some of the excesses of holiday traffic. The
building has undergone much refurbishment since the new owners took over.
A fine conservatory affords drinkers in the bar a better view, denied to
restaurant diners. Pastel colours, comfortable chairs and good lighting go to
make a friendly room in which to eat. The set-price menu of six dishes in each
course concentrates on fish. The fact that Roger Jones learned his craft from
Franco Taruschio gives it a slightly Italian hue. It changes from day to day.
Comments from diners have been that the simpler the food, the better do the
flavours of superb materials shine through. Scallops in a light butter sauce
were in perfect balance, while a melange of John Dory and monkfish was very
good but slightly masked, not complemented, by the smoked bacon and pine
kernels. Meat quality has also been endorsed. Although the restaurant seems to
have sorted out most of its suppliers, the cheese continues to be lacklustre.
Desserts are not a let-down: a piercing key lime pie on good pastry; a chocolate
mousse with rum that was as rich as it should be. Bread is made on the
premises, in several interesting varieties and of good quality – well matched
by the butter. Service has not always lived up to the food; perhaps it gains in
assurance as the holiday season wears on. The wine list is mostly from St
Austell Brewery, a good vintner/brewer. It canters over familiar ground, not
ignoring half-bottles, offering fair quality at not outrageous prices. Bar meals
are an independent activity, supervised by Roger Jones, also well reported.
House red and white, £5.95. CELLARMAN'S CHOICE : Bourgogne Aligoté 1986,
£8.85; Viña Ardanza 1981, £12.65.

CHEF: Roger Jones  PROPRIETORS: R.J. Milan and F.N.B. Atherley
OPEN: all week
MEALS: 12 to 2, 7 to 9.30
PRICES: Set L £8.50 (£11), Set D £16 (£19). Snacks from £1. Service inc
CARDS: Access, Amex, Diners, Visa
SEATS: 46. 12 tables outside. Private parties: 50 main room. Car-park, 6 places. No children
under 10. No smoking. Wheelchair access (also WC)
ACCOMMODATION: 12 rooms, 10 with bath/shower. B&B £35 to £70. Deposit: £20. No
children under 10. Pets welcome. Afternoon teas. TV. Phone. Scenic. Doors close at 11.30.
Confirm 7 days before

The Good Food Guide *does not issue certificates of approval and does not allow
restaurateurs to refer to* Guide *recommendations in their promotion. If you see such
references, please tell us where, when and what you saw.*

The Guide *relies on feedback from its readers. Especially welcome are reports on new
restaurants appearing in the book for the first time.*

**SALISBURY  Wiltshire**  map 2

## Harper's

7 Ox Row, The Market Square
Salisbury SP1 1EU
SALISBURY (0722) 333118

COOKING 1
COST £9–£20

Salisbury market fairly bustles. No matter how fast the traffic moves on the ring road, there is still a degree of continuity with the country town it once was. Where better to observe it than from this upstairs restaurant that provides genuine food at wholesome prices, amiably served? A good market-town eating house not overburdened by ideas above its station: main dishes might include grilled loin of pork with Cumberland sauce; chicken in a tarragon cream sauce, pan-fried haddock. Vegetarians are well catered for. A decent wine list which is also inexpensive. House French (red) and German (white), £6, or Bergerac, £7.50. CELLARMAN'S CHOICE : Wynn's Coonawarra Chardonnay 1987, £12; Ch. Musar 1980, £10.50.

CHEFS: Adrian Harper and Julie West   PROPRIETORS: Adrian and Ann Harper
OPEN: Mon to Sat
CLOSED: 25 and 26 Dec
MEALS: 12 to 2, 6.30 to 10 (10.30 Sat)
PRICES: £12 (£17), Set L £4.50 (£9) to £5.75 (£10), Set D £10 (£15). Snacks from £1.30
CARDS: Access, Diners, Visa
SEATS: 60. Private parties: 60 main room. Car-park. Vegetarian meals. Children's helpings. Music. Air-conditioned

---

**SCARBOROUGH  North Yorkshire**  map 6A

## Lanterna

33 Queen Street, Scarborough YO11 1HQ
SCARBOROUGH (0723) 363616

COOKING 1
COST £24

*Plus ça change* at the Lanterna, where owners and staff have remained the same for 16 years. Loyal regulars go for the reliable run-down of chicken (principessa, pizzaiola); veal (milanese, alla crema); steak (Diane, au poivre) and freshly cooked vegetables. There are pasta and fish dishes as well, plus home-made lemon sorbet or zabaglione to finish. House Italian is £7 a litre. CELLARMAN'S CHOICE: Barbera d'Asti 1985, £7.50; Cortese del Piemonte, £6.50.

CHEF: G. Arecco   PROPRIETORS: Mr and Mrs G. Arecco
OPEN: Tue to Sat, D only
MEALS: 7 to 9.30
PRICES: £13 (£20)
CARD: Visa
SEATS: 36. Private parties: 36 main room. Vegetarian meals. No children under 5. Wheelchair access. Music

---

*County Round-ups listing additional restaurants that may be worth a visit are at the back of the* Guide, *after the Irish section. Reports on Round-up entries are welcome.*

## SCUNTHORPE Humberside      map 6

# *Giovanni's*

| 44 Oswald Road, Scunthorpe DN15 7PQ | COOKING 1 |
| --- | --- |
| SCUNTHORPE (0724) 281169 | COST £16 |

Giovanni's is a pizzeria as much as a restaurant, providing unpretentious, often anglicised but honest cooking. Here, consistency goes beyond the wide choice of pastas and pizzas, which include folded calzone and fusilli Etna, to some excellent sauces – a thick tomato purée for aubergine Parmesan and a tangy, honeyed glaze for spare ribs – and changing blackboard dishes which include lobster and Dover sole. There is a basic wine list with a litre of house Italian red or white at £5.60.

CHEF: Piero Catalano    PROPRIETORS: Giovanni and Angela Catalano
OPEN: Mon to Sat
MEALS: 12 to 2, 6 to 11.30
PRICES: £10 (£13). Service inc
CARDS: Access, Visa
SEATS: 90. 6 tables outside. Private parties: 100 main room. Car-park, 10 places. Vegetarian meals. Children's helpings. Wheelchair access (also WC). Music

## SEAFORD East Sussex      map 3

# *Quincy's*

| 42 High Street, Seaford BN25 1PL | COOKING 2 |
| --- | --- |
| SEAFORD (0323) 895490 | COST £19–£30 |

Why so many restaurants should take the name of Quincy (given its rarity in other walks of life) is not clear. No party has discovered the reason for this latest, and welcome, addition to the roll in a quiet, perhaps moribund, Sussex resort. Occupying a bow-windowed former shop, Ian and Dawn Dowding have put up their brass plate after his long spell as chef at the Hungry Monk in Jevington (see entry). In a cottage pair of rooms, on crisp cloths, with windows viewing the street before and the garden behind, meals are served from a set-price menu offering eight dishes at each stage (with supplements more in evidence than they need be). The restaurant can be close packed on busy nights yet Sussex (or Seaford) reserve tends to keep the noise level to a murmur between parties rather than a Home Counties bray, or even a north country frankness – not helped one evening by *Jesu, joy of man's desiring* on the Muzak machine. The cooking stirs memories of the Hungry Monk: slightly complicated, not light, not as unpleasing to eat as it sometimes might sound. That restaurant first encapsulated a specifically English country approach to eating out; it also willed to the world banoffi pie (or so mythology would have it), a classic of British cooking, entailing a murderous attack on condensed milk. Fillet steak with ham and Gruyère in puff pastry at Quincy's has some of the overtones. But finesse and exact flavours are also within the repertoire, as in leg of lamb with garlic and cumin; although salmon and halibut with pesto in filo pastry, sauced with a hollandaise, was not worth the complication, especially as the pesto was undetectable save as a texture. Vegetarians are catered for with lots of mushrooms; bread is good; coffee meagre. Summer pudding is excellent; hot puddings are there too; and Strawberry Gluttony is a symphonic indulgence of the berry. A short wine list has a Quincy and a Breaky Bottom. House Lamblin, £5.25. CELLARMAN'S CHOICE : Ch. St-Cristoly 1986, £8.90; Mâcon-Lugny, Domaine du Prieuré 1988, £9.95.

CHEF: Ian Dowding   PROPRIETORS: Ian and Dawn Dowding
OPEN: Tue to Sat, D only
CLOSED: first 2 weeks Sept
MEALS: 7.15 to 10
PRICES: Set D £12.95 (£19) to £18.95 (£25)
CARDS: Access, Visa
SEATS: 32. Private parties: 12 and 20 main rooms. Vegetarian meals. Children's helpings on request. No children under 5. Smart dress preferred. No-smoking area. Music

---

SEAVIEW  Isle of Wight                                              map 2

## ▲ Seaview Hotel

The High Street, Seaview PO34 5EX                        COOKING 1
SEAVIEW (0983) 612711                                    COST £13−£23

A stone's throw from the sea, this orderly, comfortable, family-run hotel would be at home in a Jane Austen novel. The menu concentrates on seafood – lobster, crab, mussels, sea bass – but medallions of pork in cream and garlic sauce, chicken in Stilton sauce and sliced goose breast salad have all been enjoyed. Commitment to local ingredients extends to island asparagus and biscuits made with stoneground flour from Calbourne Mill, served with the cheese. Three daily vegetables are fresh and well presented. Chocolate ice-cream was too rich and sweet even for one 10-year-old, who was placated with peach sorbet in a brandy-snap basket with raspberries. There has been recent fluctuation in standards, not every visit has been a success. Smoking has been banned in the dining-room, but there is an elegant lounge for after-dinner coffee. House claret from Corney & Barrow, £5.99; Loron Blanc de Blancs, £5.99. CELLARMAN'S CHOICE : Ch. Labegorce Zédé 1984, £11.

CHEF: Charles Bartlett, Nicola Hayward and Steven King   PROPRIETORS: Nicola and Nicholas Hayward
OPEN: all week, exc Sun D
MEALS: 12 to 1.45, 7.30 to 9.30
PRICES: £13 (£19), Set Sun L £7.50 (£13), Snacks from £1.10
CARDS: Access, Amex, Visa
SEATS: 30. 10 tables outside. Private parties: 30 main room, 20 private room. Car-park, 12 places. Children's helpings. No children under 3. Smart dress preferred. No smoking
ACCOMMODATION: 16 rooms, all with bath/shower. B&B £27 to £46. Baby facilities. Pets welcome. Afternoon teas. Fishing. TV. Scenic. Doors close at 12. Confirm booking one week ahead [GHG]

---

CELLARMAN'S CHOICE : *A wine recommended by the restaurateur, normally more expensive than the house wine.*

# Arcadia

560 Langsett Road, Hillsborough
Sheffield S6 2lX                                                   COOKING  1
SHEFFIELD (0742) 323382                                            COST  £15−£24

Despite its down-at-heel surroundings towards the shabby side of town,
Arcadia is attired inside in chic salmon pink with dashes of polished wood and
white linen. Ceiling fans whirr idly. The menu is, to say the least, a bit of a
mixture, both of cooking methods and cultural influences. European dishes −
lamb with mint sauce; Bratwurst with potato cake; monkfish 'osso bucco' with
saffron risotto − line up with offerings from Asia and the Americas: chicken
yakitori; venison chilli con carne with tortilla chips, sour cream and avocado.
Desserts likewise come from just about everywhere: cappuccino ice-cream cake
with boysenberry sauce; black bottom pie; mango sorbet with passion-fruit
sauce. The menu changes monthly and is priced for two courses plus coffee;
puddings are extra. The wine list is as fairly priced as the food and offers a nice
eclectic selection from the world. CELLARMAN'S CHOICE : Eden Valley
Gewürztraminer 1987, £8.75; Lebanese Ch. Musar Lebanon 1979 Hochar, £8.75.

CHEF: Rex Barker   PROPRIETORS: Finalbox Ltd
OPEN: Tue to Sat, exc Sat L
MEALS: 12 to 2.30, 7 to 10
PRICES: £11 (£15), Set D £12.25 (£16) to £16.25 (£20)
CARDS: Access, Amex, Diners, Visa
SEATS: 36. Private parties: 12 main room. Wheelchair access (also WC). Music

# Greenhead House

84 Burncross Road, Chapeltown
Sheffield S30 4SF                                                  COOKING  2
SHEFFIELD (0742) 469004                                           COST  £23−£31

The Allens combine professionalism with a family feel in this smart stone
cottage just on the outskirts of Sheffield. He cooks impressively, she serves
graciously. The pattern is a monthly-changing menu of four courses: one of
them a no-choice (but usually vegetable) soup; the others of four alternatives.
Inspiration is often French, sometimes contemporary, as in a terrine of
monkfish and salmon served with a sauce of tomato and cream, infused with
herbs from the garden; and sometimes more traditional, as in a salad of duck
confit, although it is yanked up to date with a splash of raspberry vinegar
dressing. Sometimes the ideas are quite fresh, as in fillets of brill cooked in a
paper bag with virgin olive oil and bay leaf, and served with a warm fondue of
orange and lemon. Cheeses are British. The wine list, like the menu, takes time
out to explain itself. The house wine policy is stated as: 'We will not buy
ordinary table wines, but from time to time select good quality appellation
wines which we think give good value.' Indeed they do. Côtes du Ventoux
1986 and Touraine Sauvignon Blanc 1987 are a little over £8. Bin-ends are well
worth looking at. CELLARMAN'S CHOICE : Langlois-Château Saumur 1987,
£11.75; Ch de Terrefort-Quancard 1985, £12.

CHEFS: Neil Allen and Christine Roberts   PROPRIETORS: Neil and Anne Allen
OPEN: Tue to Sat, D only
CLOSED: last 2 weeks Apr, first 2 weeks Sept, 24 Dec to 31 Dec
MEALS: 7.15 to 9
PRICES: Set D £19.75 (£23) to £22 (£26). Service inc
CARDS: Amex, Visa
SEATS: 32. Private parties: 32 main room. Car-park, 14 places. Children welcome.
Wheelchair access

## Nirmal's

| 193 Glossop Road, Sheffield S10 2GW | COOKING 1 |
|---|---|
| SHEFFIELD (0742) 724054 | COST £15–£23 |

A green neon sign lights the way at night to this corner restaurant. Narrow
arched windows are curtained in pink to match the tablecloths. Regulars are
warmly welcomed back by Nirmal Gupta, one of the few female Asian chefs in
the country, who continues to produce reliable Indian home cooking. Besides
the range of tandooris, bhunas and kormas, there's a daily list of specials.
Spinach dishes are well reported and a vegetarian set menu is offered in
response to growing demand. New dishes appear now and then: curried
parsnips are a recent arrival. House wine is Californian, £7.50 a litre, or there's
Kingfisher, Tiger or Grolsch beer.

CHEF: Nirmal Gupta   PROPRIETOR: P.L. Gupta
OPEN: all week, exc Sun L
MEALS: 12 to 2.30, 6 to 12 (1am Fri and Sat)
PRICES: £11 (£19), Set L £11 (£15) to £13 (£17), Set D £11 (£15) to £13 (£17). Service 10%
CARDS: Access, Amex, Visa
SEATS: 90. Private parties: 30 main room, 60 private room. Vegetarian meals. Children
welcome. Wheelchair access (also WC). Music

---

**SHEPTON MALLET**  Somerset                                              map 2

## Blostin's

| 29 Waterloo Road | |
|---|---|
| Shepton Mallet BA4 5HH | COOKING 2 |
| SHEPTON MALLET (0749) 3648 | COST £13–£23 |

'I have never had a boring meal here' avers one regular visitor to this small,
busy restaurant. Fish and seafood figure prominently on Nick Reed's ever-
more-ambitious menu: braised squid with fennel and Pastis sauce; baked
salmon with sorrel sauce; fish soup with rouille and croûtons. Much of the
produce is local, including the herbs used in chicken with chive and tarragon
sauce or rack of lamb with garlic and rosemary; Gressingham ducks from
Yeovil come braised with mushrooms, bacon and burgundy and there are
Somerset cheeses and wines. For dessert, meringue swans are set afloat in a
'lake' of strawberry coulis and there are tempting home-made ice-creams and
sorbets. The wine list is short, the prices not high. House French is £5.25.
CELLARMAN'S CHOICE : Clos du Val Sauvignon Blanc 1985, £10.25; Hunter
Valley Centenary Cabernet-Shiraz 1987, £6.95.

CHEF: Nick Reed  PROPRIETORS: Nick and Lynne Reed
OPEN: Tue to Sat, D only (L by arrangement)
MEALS: 7 to 9.30 (10 Sat)
PRICES: £16 (£19), Set L £8.95 (£13), Set D £11.50 (£15) to £12.50 (£16). Service inc
CARDS: Access, Visa
SEATS: 32. Private parties: 30 main room. Children's helpings. Wheelchair access. Music

---

**SHINFIELD  Berkshire**                                                     map 2

## L'Ortolan ♥

The Old Vicarage, Church Lane
Shinfield RG2 9BY                                                    COOKING 5
READING (0734) 883783                                             COST £34–£72

This bunting's cage is a Regency red-brick vicarage. The motorway is not far
distant, reached by the A33 and occasionally visible on winter nights. In
summer, the foliage of the quiet garden gives the illusion of enclosure. This
may be viewed while dining in the conservatory, one of two spaces devoted to
eating in the warmly decorated house. Customers are well cosseted; there are
the trappings of a good and expensive restaurant. John Burton-Race, his wife
Christine, who supervises front-of-house, and his team in the kitchen headed
by sous-chef Nigel Marriage, have pursued for another year their ambition to
serve food as good as any in the country. To this end, there is a new pastry
section to the kitchen. There are also manifold improvements to decorations
and table furnishings. John Burton-Race's style is complicated and his culinary
background that of *haute cuisine*. A dish, therefore, will appear constructed from
many too many elements, yet the overall message is one of harmony. Flavours
are muted: not lacklustre, but not handled boldly. This is the *haute cuisine* way:
food needs to be eaten with some concentration. There are fortunately few
reports of over-reductions or conflicting tastes from extraneous ingredients that
are used by chefs anxious to impart panache. Dishes are of immense
sophistication. Morels are stuffed with a light chicken mixture, then poached
before serving with a little asparagus and a sherry sauce mounted with a little
cream. Sauce and mushroom balance and complement, asparagus refreshes.
The whole is a delight of eye, aroma and taste: simple, yet long in preparation
and high in skill. A lobster salad is dressed on mixed leaves with slices of
truffle, a thin oil dressing coloured and flavoured by cooking the crustacean's
shell and debris, and cubes of tomato tasting stronger than any tomato eaten
that month. The lobster was cooked and seasoned with exactness. 'A breast of
guinea-fowl, surrounded by wild mushrooms accompanied by an individual
pot of extremely hot potato covering chopped meat from the leg of the bird and
topped with a sheet of filo pastry, was absolutely superb.' Other main courses
range over breast of pheasant with a pig's trotter ballotine, veal kidney with an
Hermitage sauce, and rabbit wrapped in a cabbage leaf and light pastry, to give
only abbreviated descriptions. There is a large choice of French cheeses and one
or two hot goats' cheese concoctions as a matter of course. Momentum is not
lost at dessert stage: hot soufflés, gratins of fruits under sugar cages, first-class
tarts and modern French novelties, such as *cristalline de pommes*, appear with

445

ease. 'Raspberry soufflé was outstanding.' A 'lime cork with caramel' (to translate the menu) turned out to be a two-inch upright tube of zebra-striped chocolate. The base was a sponge, then the first inch was filled with a chocolate mousse, the second with a lime one. It was surrounded by a light caramel sauce and topped by a stiff lime glaze and candied lime peel. A masterpiece of wit and construction – and taste too, if you care for lime and chocolate together. Toppings and tailings to the meal are what you might expect: a small plate of fishy delicacies with the aperitif, followed by some sauté foie gras on a brioche slice; a masterful pirate's chest filled with sweetmeats as well as fine petits fours with coffee. Butter is the best French, French bread is bought in and it shows. The service continues to give trouble. On good days it is grand and happy, but on bad, it hustles and hurries, apparently driven by demons – possibly Mr Burton-Race in the kitchen. Wine service is half good, half bad. One young French waiter knew so little he could not state the geographical provenance of a bottle, only that 'it's very nice'. Staff would do well to concentrate on dispelling the slight unease present on flustered days. The menu and daily specials offer a great number of choices at an all-in price, but there are regrettably too many surcharges. Inflation has a high rate in Shinfield, yet, in common with other restaurateurs of his stamp and ability, Mr Burton-Race would claim his real profit is no greater than many places of humbler mien. So long as restaurants do not dissemble their charges, one should not deny the right to ask them – not for this food at any rate. The wine list is as resolutely French as its service. Thirty red Burgundies back to 1959 and 40 clarets to 1961 form the backbone to a frame of Provence, Rhône, Alsace and Loire. A page of country wines, including a Thouarsais and a Brezeme 1983 from the Drôme, precedes the main list. Prices are not low, but the 300 or so bottles come from such estimable sources as Reid Wines and Domaine Direct. Half-bottles are plentiful. The red Burgundies make an intoxicating read. House wines: Bourgogne Rouge 1985, Mongeard-Mugneret, £15.95; Chardonnay 1987, William Fèvre, £15.25. CELLARMAN'S CHOICE : Clos du Marquis, £21.95.

CHEF: John Burton-Race  PROPRIETORS: John and Christine Burton-Race
OPEN: Tue to Sun, exc Sun D
CLOSED: last 2 weeks of Feb and last 2 weeks Aug
MEALS: 12.15 to 2.15, 7.15 to 10.30
PRICES: Set L £23 (£34) to £38.50 (£51), Set D £37 (£49) to £45 (£60)
CARDS: Access, Visa
SEATS: 60. Private parties: 40 main room, 32 private room. Car-park, 15 places. Children's helpings. Wheelchair access (2 steps; also WC)

---

**SHIPDHAM  Norfolk**                                                            map 6

## ▲ Shipdham Place

| Church Close, Shipdham IP25 7LX | COOKING 1 |
| DEREHAM (0362) 820303 | COST £12–£29 |

New owners Tina and Alan Poulton are operating this handsome Georgian rectory at a lower key than when it was an outpost of London life under the de Blanks. The emphasis is on relaxed comfort; 'placid' is how one report described it. There is a shorter and much cheaper lunchtime menu, but the dinner, which changes daily, is a three-course affair, with a trio of choices at each main stage, at a set price. It can be expanded to five courses for another £2, which offers the chance of a sorbet or a salad and a selection of cheese that may improve as business increases. Tina Poulton is in charge of the kitchen and produces honest food, such as mushroom tartlets (that could have been better seasoned); medallions of beef with a good home-made horseradish cream and excellent vegetables; and a hazelnut mousse that carried the taste it should, even if overly firm. The wine list is full of enthusiastic notes that may cause argument, but it is sensibly priced. It produced a good *cru* bourgeois, Ch. Lestruelle 1985 in fine condition, that eased the passage to sleep of one traveller. House French, £4.95. CELLARMAN'S CHOICE : Vouvray, Domaine de Vaufuget 1988, £8.95; Malesan 1985, Bordeaux £8.25.

CHEF: Tina Poulton    PROPRIETORS: Tina and Alan Poulton
OPEN: all week
MEALS: 12 to 1.45, 7.30 to 9.30
PRICES: Set L £7.50 (£12) to £9.95 (£15), Set D £16.50 (£22) to £18.50 (£24). Service inc
CARDS: Access, Visa
SEATS: 40. Private parties: 30 main room, 16 and 30 private rooms. Car-park, 25 places. Children welcome. No smoking in dining-room
ACCOMMODATION: 8 rooms, all with bath/shower. B&B £30 to £77. Deposit: £10. Baby facilities. Pets welcome. Afternoon teas. Garden. Phone. Scenic. Doors close at midnight. Confirm by 5

---

**SHIPTON GORGE** Dorset                                                          map 2

## ▲ *Innsacre Farmhouse Hotel*

Shipton Gorge, Bridport DT6 4LJ                                        COOKING 1
BRIDPORT (0308) 56137                                                  COST £13–£24

This has the air of the true farmhouse: pigs in sties, geese, an orchard full of apple trees, a long, low, untidy building filled with unmatched furniture. It is reached by turning on to the most westerly road signed to Shipton Gorge on the highway from Dorchester to Bridport. The cooking has had very mixed reports. Insufficient restraint in the flavouring has led to clashes between sauce and sauced, and there have been strident, discordant vegetables; enthusiasm can outrun skill. Among the good dishes have been an excellent lemon meringue pie; gutsy mayonnaise with crudités to start; roast beef; and a pleasing timbale of sea bream with saffron sauce. The place is genial, though the Muzak is dreadful; the daytime food is reasonably priced. Wheelchair access was praised by one reader. House French is £6.50. CELLARMAN'S CHOICE : Eldridge Pope's fine Chairman's Claret 1987, £13.50, and Chairman's Burgundy 1987, £11.50.

---

*'All the desserts had been bought in. I asked about them and the chicken (Kiev was from Alveston Kitchens) and P. informed me that he doesn't cook at weekends because he is too busy. The sad thing is that this is true – people were queuing.'* On dining in Somerset

*All entries in the* Guide *are rewritten every year, not least because restaurant standards fluctuate. Don't trust an out-of-date* Guide.

---

CHEFS: Andrew Brine, Simon Wass and Gina Wass   PROPRIETORS: J.H. and H.M. Smith
OPEN: all week
MEALS: 12 to 2, 7.15 to 10.30
PRICES: Set L £9.50 (£13) to £16.75 (£20), Set D £16.75 (£20). Snacks from £1.75.
Service inc
CARDS: Access, Amex, Diners, Visa
SEATS: 42. 4 tables outside. Private parties: 60 main room. Car-park, 40 places. Vegetarian
meals. Children's helpings. No cigars/pipes in dining-room. Wheelchair access
(also WC). Music
ACCOMMODATION: 7 rooms, 5 with bath/shower. B&B £32 to £52. Baby facilities. Pets
welcome. Afternoon teas. Garden. TV. Scenic [GHG]

---

**SHIPTON-UNDER-WYCHWOOD   Oxfordshire** map 2

# ▲ Lamb Inn

Shipton-under-Wychwood OX7 6DQ                                    COOKING 1
SHIPTON (0993) 830465                                            COST £14–£24

The village has elements of the picturesque: Cotswold stone, manor, cricket
ground, spired church. At one end, keeping the air of a sprawling pub, the
Lamb has the traditional touches – beams, stone walls, polished floors and oak
furniture – and an atmosphere helped by locals coming to drink and eat bar
meals. In the small, relaxed dining-room, there is some good straightforward
English cooking under chef George Benham: salmon kedgeree, Loch Fyne
kippers and fry-ups at breakfast time; roast beef, exactly as it was asked for,
with crisp Yorkshire pudding and a good range of sound basic vegetables for
Sunday lunch; unfussy poached haddock with cheese sauce; crisply roasted
duck with green figs and a light treacle tart. Fancier dishes have not invariably
worked as well. In the bar, decorated with old harvest photos, there are good
reasonably priced buffet lunches in the summer, presided over by the chef in
whites. House French, £6.

CHEF: George Benham   PROPRIETORS: Hugh and Lynne Wainwright
OPEN: Mon to Sat D, Sun L
CLOSED: Mon in winter
MEALS: 12.30 to 1.45, 7.30 to 9
PRICES: Set Sun L £8.50 (£14), Set D £14 (£20). Minimum £8.50. Licensed, also bring your
own: corkage £3.50
CARDS: Access, Amex, Diners, Visa
SEATS: 30. 8 tables outside. Private parties: 36 main room. Car-park, 30 places. No children
under 14. Wheelchair access (1 step)
ACCOMMODATION: 5 rooms, all with bath/shower. B&B £30 to £48. Deposit: £10. No
children under 14. Garden. TV. Confirm by 6

---

*This year, in quoting prices for three-course meals at the top of each entry (by the word
'Cost'), we have put a more pessimistic complexion on the upper price by inflating it by 20
per cent. The aim is to prepare the reader for any inflation during the life of the Guide and
also reflect the price of a meal taken without constant attention to the likely size of the bill.
The prices quoted in smaller print below the text remain, as in previous editions, strict
computer calculations of an average three-course meal, the price in brackets reflecting an
average meal with coffee, service and half a bottle of house wine per person.*

**SHOTLEY BRIDGE** Co Durham        map 7

## Manor House Inn

Carterway Heads, Shotley Bridge DH8 9LX      COOKING 2
EDMUNDBYERS (0207) 55268        COST £11–£19

The Pellys' old stone coaching-inn stands just off the A68, about five miles north of Castleside, with magnificent views west over the Derwent valley and reservoir. At the end of 1988, the cosy pub area finally emerged from the builders' rubble and began to serve excellent bar food – quiche made with puff pastry and a cream filling, for instance. Six months later, as the *Guide* goes to press, the restaurant has opened to promising first reports. The simple decorations, with rough honey-coloured walls and carpet, beams and large new windows to open up the views over the moors, reflects the down-to-earth approach of the Pelly sisters to cooking. 'We spend little time creating extravagant sauces and we avoid bizarre marriages of flavours in an attempt to be different. The main ingredient of a dish should always be prominent with secondary flavours added to enhance rather than smother.' Dishes are not always as simple as this might suggest. For example, wild local salmon is wrapped with a layer of spinach mousse in filo pastry and served with fresh spinach puréed with fish stock and cream. Elsewhere on the short menu, Mediterranean and eastern flavours come through: there is beef satay and spiced lamb with aubergine and sultanas. A local monastery provides different lettuce varieties, baby vegetables – leeks the size of spring onions, carrots the length of a thumb joint – and fresh herbs. Cheese savouries, bread, good puddings and macaroons served with coffee are home made. There is a sensibly short wine list with some good growers. Prices are not excessive. House French is £4.25. CELLARMAN'S CHOICE : Mâcon-Lugny 1988, Mathelin, £8.50; Chiroubles 1987, Loron, £10.70. Real ale from Wards.

CHEFS: Jane and Elizabeth Pelly    PROPRIETORS: Anthony, Jane and Elizabeth Pelly
OPEN: all week, exc Sat L and Sun D
MEALS: 12 to 2.30, 7.30 to 10.30
PRICES: £13 (£16), Set L £9 (£11). Service inc
SEATS: 40. Private parties: 30 main room. Car-park, 30 places. Vegetarian meals. No children under 12, exc Sun L. Wheelchair access (1 step; also WC)

**SISSINGHURST** Kent        map 3

## Rankins

The Street, Sissinghurst TN17 2JH      COOKING 2
CRANBROOK (0580) 713964        COST £20–£31

'I have been three times and may well become a regular' is the comment of one who appreciated the cheerful attentions of the staff in this small village restaurant. Hugh Rankin works alone in the kitchen; the short working week, by restaurant standards, is so that he can 'recharge'. Sunday lunch is pitched to the traditional roast beef brigade who may be less well served than by the more imaginative dinner menus – the puddings nearly outnumber first courses and main dishes combined. A meal of moules marinière, noisettes of lamb with a sauce of mint, tarragon and orange, and coffee fudge pudding, a hot steamed pudding served with extensive cream, was good enough for one London emigré who nonetheless wondered if Kentish tastebuds were more sensitive to nuances of flavourings and seasonings than his. London life is also speedier and trimmings and extras, by dint of competitive pressure, come thicker and faster. All are agreed, however, that the Rankins' hearts are in the right place. A very short wine list, continuously updated on a micro, gives quite sufficient quality at fair prices. House French is £6.20. CELLARMAN'S CHOICE : Brouilly, Ch. de la Chaize 1985, £11.60; Muscadet-sur-lie, Ch. de la Jannière 1987, £7.50. Smokers are asked not to indulge until coffee is served. What happens to latecomers is not stated.

CHEF: Hugh Rankin   PROPRIETORS: Hugh and Leonora Rankin
OPEN: Wed to Sat D, Sun L
MEALS: 12.30 to 1.30, 7.30 to 9
PRICES: Set Sun L £13.50 (£20), Set D £16 (£22) to £20 (£26)
CARDS: Access, Visa
SEATS: 30. Private parties: 10 main room; 24 private room. Children's helpings (Sun L only). No children under 8. Smart dress preferred. Music

---

**SLAIDBURN  Lancashire**                                                        map 5

# ▲ *Parrock Head Farm*

Slaidburn BB7 3AH                                                    COOKING 1
SLAIDBURN (020 06) 614                                                 COST £23

A mile or so north-west of Slaidburn, towards the Forest of Bowland, this carefully converted seventeenth-century farmhouse is tricky to find, situated as it is among sheep pastures and off a small unclassified road. Once safely there, however, visitors can relax and rain-soaked walkers can dry off by the log fire before dinner. The menu changes nightly and has a nouvelle slant, with coulis and colourful sauces much in evidence. There are four or five choices per course. Among those on offer recently have been curried parsnip soup, haddock with a cream and dill sauce, roast loin of Bowland lamb with rosemary and walnut sauce. Fresh seasonal vegetables might include swede or cabbage with red pepper. Sweets take in fruit salad in a biscuit basket with raspberry sauce, and mango parfait. A short wine list is organised by weight (reds) and sweetness (whites). Prices are not demanding. House French is £5.50. CELLARMAN'S CHOICE : Pinot Grigio, Tiefenbrunner 1987, £9.20; Chablis Vaillons, Moillard 1986, £14.50.

CHEFS: Vicky Umbers, Stephen Kerfoot and Deborah Wareing   PROPRIETORS: Vicky and Richard Umbers
OPEN: all week, D only
CLOSED: mid-Dec to mid-Feb
MEALS: 7 to 8.15
PRICES: £13 (£19), Snacks from £1.30
CARDS: Access, Amex
SEATS: 32. Car-park, 20 places. Children's helpings. No smoking. Wheelchair access
ACCOMMODATION: 9 rooms, all with bath/shower. Rooms for disabled. B&B £28 to £42. Garden. Fishing. Golf. TV. Phone. Scenic. Doors close at 11.30 [GHG]

SOLIHULL   West Midlands                                       map 5

# Liaison

| 761 Old Lode Lane, Solihull BG2 8JE | COOKING 2 |
| 021-743 3993 | COST £25–£38 |

An earlier edition of this *Guide* called the cooking at this small restaurant, tucked away in a suburban shopping parade off the road to Birmingham Airport, 'intuitive'. The menu reads as that epithet may imply: a variation on the theme of nouvelle cuisine. The language is accurate in neither French nor the English translations; the combinations of ingredients are surprising. On offer early in 1989 were: 'a light whipped mousse of smoked salmon dusted with a passion-fruit dressing and surrounded by slivers of marinated wild salmon'; 'escalopes of wild salmon served on a slightly minted sauce with a cone of fresh raspberries'; 'a galaxy of seafruits and shell-fish resting together on a light seabank of pastry'; 'a duo of boned quail roasted with garlic and shallots, their juices sweetened by berries'. The descriptions sometimes mask perfectly sensible compositions, but the cooking has not had quite so much praise this year. 'The vegetables were insipid, pastel-coloured purées; sauces were astringent and cornfloury.' Nor have there been contradictions of long-standing complaints of slow service and an excess of cigarette smoke. The wine list is all French bar a trio of Germans. There are only six half-bottles, of little interest. Prices are fairly high, especially for the best of the 1982 clarets that are some way from being drinkable. One reader took exception to the substitution of a 1983 Hugel Gewürztraminer by a 1986 – 'just the same, just as good, never any different' – and at no reduction in price. There are four French house wines, from £7.25 to £8.45. CELLARMAN'S CHOICE: Mâcon-Clessé 1985, Thévenet, £13.45; Ch. du Puy, Montagne St-Emilion 1985, £12.75.

CHEF: Patricia Plunkett   PROPRIETORS: Patricia Plunkett and Ank Van Der Tuin
OPEN: Tue to Sat, D only
CLOSED: 2 weeks at Christmas, Aug
MEALS: 7 to 10
PRICES: £23 (£31), Set D £18.95 (£25)
CARDS: Access, Amex, Diners, Visa
SEATS: 34. Private parties: 40 main room. Car-park, 15 places. Children welcome. No pipes in dining-room. Wheelchair access. Music

SOUTH GODSTONE   Surrey                                        map 3

# La Bonne Auberge ♥

| Tilburstow Hill, South Godstone RH9 8JY | COOKING 3 |
| SOUTH GODSTONE (0342) 893184 | COST £18–£43 |

This preternaturally stockbrokerish house is on the old road to East Grinstead south of Godstone. It has been in French ownership for nigh on 30 years. Recently, local people have claimed this as one of the best kitchens from Edenbridge to Tunbridge Wells, after a patch of preciousness. Flavourings on the *carte* (the meal price is determined by the choice of main course) include saffron, ginger, mango chutney, green peppercorns and orange, figs, coriander, paprika. The tendency, therefore, is modern but the kitchen seems to be able to treat these tastes with lightness and discretion as well as to handle traditional fare such as a Sunday roast lunch. At one meal, scallops with ginger and orange were lightly cooked, the sweetness of the fish in balance with blanched spring onions and given gentle point by the flavoured cream sauce. A sauté of monkfish was given bite with a bed of braised chicory and unctuousness with a good butter sauce. A fine slice of turbot was laid on thin strips of courgettes and accompanied by a restrained yet garlicky olive oil and diced tomato. The simplicity of this made it memorable. Pudding was a small apple charlotte, the fruit quite tart, accompanied by a good caramel sauce. This was as good as it sounds. The service and welcome matched it; the ancillaries of bread and such did not. The custom here is to serve a free bonne bouche while you think about dessert: in this instance, a couple of choux puffs with cream and an intense strawberry coulis. The wine list is largely French, modestly priced and well chosen, clarets particularly. Comments are given for every bottle, though the observation that Chablis is 'an often neglected part of the Côte Chalonnaise' must have been a slip of the Amstrad. House French is £6.90.

CHEF: Olivier Hubert PROPRIETOR: Antoine L.S. Jalley
OPEN: Tue to Sun, exc Sun D
MEALS: 12 to 2, 7 to 10
PRICES: Set L £15 (£18) to £20 (£24), Set D £25 (£28) to £32 (£36). Minimum £15. Service inc
CARDS: Access, Amex, Visa
SEATS: 48. 4 tables outside. Private parties: 80 main room, 3 private room. Car-park, 70 places. Children's helpings. Smart dress preferred. Wheelchair access. Music

**SOUTH MOLTON Devon** map 1

## ▲ *Whitechapel Manor* 🍷

COUNTY RESTAURANT OF THE YEAR

South Molton EX36 3EG COOKING 3
SOUTH MOLTON (076 95) 2554 and 3377 COST £24–£40

'It is a long time since I have felt such enthusiasm for a hotel; I think a lot of the charm derives from the Shaplands themselves. John's Devonshire burr puts you at ease immediately and Pat's quiet, efficient, confident manner just convinces you that everything will run on oiled wheels without strife or unnecessary fussing.' Add to that a French chef who can cook and is supplied proper materials to cook with, and a house that is a joy to breathe, eat and sleep in, and you have potential bliss. Whitechapel Manor is in the middle of nowhere, with barely a settlement attached. North of South Molton, it is reached from the last roundabout (for the time being) of the North Devon Link Road but maps are almost a requisite. Surrounding countryside, at first low key, develops into the foothills of Exmoor with villages, churches and valleys enough to refresh the urbane as much as evening dinner will delight the epicene. Although showing a muted, English face to the world, protected by some fine gate-piers and handsome terraced gardens, the house is remarkable within. The passage of seventeenth-century screens is almost eclipsed by the country classical panelling in reception rooms and bedrooms. These latter have been converted to guest use with great skill and none of the current excess of country-housery. The dining-room occupies one wing and will be too small once the hotel is running at full steam. For now, it is quiet and cool, with comfortable chairs, French china and a pale yellow and blue colour scheme. Service is formal and correct, but not by a professional brigade: it is provided by John Shapland himself, sometimes his family, at other times by young women. The cooking team is French, headed by Thierry Lepretre-Granet. The style will be familiar to those who visit top-flight English country hotels: French techniques, an English mélange of flavours (not only drawing on classical repertoire), quite elaborate presentation, good materials. These come from the Shaplands' own agricultural connection: excellent meats, good cream, first-rate butter. Unexpectedly, the Franco-British cheeseboard is from London suppliers; one would hope it could be superseded by entirely local produce.

The food here has occasionally faltered through insufficient courage in seasoning but it can be bold as well as subtle. An inspection revealed first courses of scallops cooked under pastry in a light stock with carrot and leek julienne and a flavouring of chervil, parsley and tarragon, and salmon marinated in a slightly sweet cure, served with a walnut oil-dressed salad and perfumed with leaf coriander. Each of these impressed by their refinement. Main dishes provided more robust tastes, from a Meaux mustard sauce with a fine piece of beef, to rosemary and garlic with a loin of Shetland lamb. Fish cookery is not ignored. An exceptional lobster à la nage with spring vegetables, and a John Dory filleted, layered with fennel, then steamed and served with tomato and a sorrel sauce have been warmly praised for the accuracy of cooking, the delicacy of the juice served with the lobster and the unseasonal intensity of the tomato with the Dory. Vegetables come as an integral part of the dish itself, often framed by some sort of pastry. Potatoes, alas, do not seem viewed with favour, but you can put in a special request for them. Among the desserts, warm apple tart with a calvados sorbet, yoghurt mousse with strawberries, bananas and a caramel sauce, passion-fruit mousse with its sauce, have all been mentioned. Exactly what happens should the proprietors lose their chef is a conundrum to be faced at many such places. The conviction with which the whole operation is pursued should encourage us to think they would be successful in finding another as satisfactory. Credit is nonetheless due to owners who provide the frame in which cooking skills can be shown. The wine list has a lot from Reid Wines and Eldridge Pope: largely French, not long, short on detail, but having good bottles. The pricing to the last penny seems to indicate that a computer is doing the VAT calculation. House claret is £9.50, Muscadet, £7.85. CELLARMAN'S CHOICE : Nelson Chardonnay 1987, Redwood Valley, £16.90; Auxey-Duresses Les Ecusseaux 1982, Ampeau, £23.

---

CHEF: Thierry Lepretre-Granet   PROPRIETORS: John and Patricia Shapland
OPEN: all week
MEALS: 12 to 2, 7 to 9
PRICES: Set L £17.50 (£24), Set D £25.50 (£33)
CARDS: Access, Visa
SEATS: 20. Car-park, 40 places. No children under 10 (D only). No smoking in dining-room
ACCOMMODATION: 10 rooms, all with bath/shower. B&B £49.50 to £78.75. Deposit: 20%.
Afternoon teas. Garden. TV. Phone. Scenic. Doors close at midnight [GHG]

---

*Report forms are at the back of the book; write a letter if you prefer.*

---

## SOUTHAMPTON  Hampshire                                        map 2

# Kuti's

| 70 London Road, Southampton SO1 2AJ | COOKING 1 |
| SOUTHAMPTON (0703) 221585 and 333473 | COST £10–£22 |

This is an Indian restaurant in the mould of the late 1980s: decorated in grey
and pink and with a menu drawing from all the regions. Thus, recommended
dishes include Gujerati thali and southern bhel puri as well as straightforward
chicken curry. Bengali cookery, as in a Bangla fish curry, also features strongly.
Kurgee lamb, a spiced whole leg of lamb, needs a day's notice. Ingredients are
carefully bought. The set-price lunchtime buffet, offering as much as you can
eat, is good value at £6.50 and especially popular. Service is quick. On some
evenings, there's live sitar music. House German is £5.40. CELLARMAN'S
CHOICE : Veena, Indian wine, £6.95.

CHEFS: Anjab Ali and K. Miah    PROPRIETOR: Kuti Miah
OPEN: all week
CLOSED: 25 Dec
MEALS: 12 to 2.15, 6 to 11.30
PRICES: £11 (£18), Set L £6.50 (£10) to £12 (£16). Service 10%
CARDS: Access, Amex, Visa
SEATS: 66. Private parties: 30 main room. Car-park, 10 places. Vegetarian meals. Children
welcome. Smart dress preferred. Wheelchair access (also WC). Music. Air-conditioned

## SOUTHEND-ON-SEA  Essex                                        map 3

# Alvaro's

| 32–34 St Helens Road, Westcliff-on-Sea | |
| Southend SS0 7LB | COOKING 1 |
| SOUTHEND (0702) 335840 | COST £30 |

Only the brightly painted ceramic cockerels, plates and copper ornaments
arranged around the rooms hint at the earthy Portuguese dishes to be found
alongside Southend steak-house fare. There are rustic soups, fresh sardines
grilled on a bed of peppers and a rich fish casserole as well as some new dishes
like a cataplana of clams, salt cod and cured ham and fillets of sole fried in the
Madeiran way with bananas. Many customers, however, still happily stick
with the steaks, roast duck in orange sauce and flambé desserts. Service is
politely old fashioned and without pretension. The wine list has as many
Portuguese as other wines, none highly priced and some worth pursuing such
as the Douro, Mesão Frio Reserva 1980. There are some extras tucked away for
the truly curious. House Chamusca, £6.25 a litre. CELLARMAN'S CHOICE :
Quinta do Crasto Vinho Verde, £8.95; Dão white, São Domingos 1985, £8.25.
Other Portuguese drinks: lager, aguardente (brandy) and mineral waters are
stocked, as well as vintage Port itself.

*See the inside of the front cover for an explanation of the new 1 to 5 rating system
recognising cooking standards.*

CHEF: José Rodrigues   PROPRIETORS: Alvaro, Joyce and José Rodrigues
OPEN: Tue to Sun, exc Sat and Sun L
MEALS: 12 to 2, 7 to 10.30 (6.30 to 10 Sun)
PRICES: £16 (£25). Service 10%
CARDS: Access, Visa
SEATS: 60. Children's helpings. Smart dress preferred. Wheelchair access. Music

## Slassor's

145 Eastern Esplanade
Southend SS1 2YD                                         COOKING 1
SOUTHEND (0702) 614880                                   COST £17

The seafront restaurant is low-key, but in a town with few good eating places
other than fish and chip shops, it is usually crowded: 'Please book at
lunchtime.' The dining-room looks out over the grey Thames, so the menu
highlights fish bought locally or at Billingsgate. The best is written on the
blackboard: smoked haddock with cream and fresh tomatoes; a fish soup of
queen scallops and prawns; whole filleted sea-bream with prawns and a
cheese sauce. These are very reasonably priced. Other recommendations have
included tomato soup, moules and Dover sole in a cream sauce, or more
powerfully flavoured game and meat dishes with wine and fruit sauces. 'Sweet
thoughts' for rounding off include sundaes and meringues. Take your own
wine and pay a small corkage, or take beer.

CHEF: Leslie Slassor   PROPRIETORS: Margaret and Leslie Slassor
OPEN: Mon to Sat, exc Mon L
MEALS: 12 to 2, 7 to 9.30
PRICES: £12 (£14). Unlicensed, but bring your own: corkage 75p
CARDS: Access, Visa
SEATS: 22. Private parties: 30 main room. Children's helpings. Music

---

**SOUTHSEA  Hampshire**                                  map 2

## Bistro Montparnasse

103 Palmerston Road, Southsea PO5 3PS                    COOKING 1
PORTSMOUTH (0705) 816754                                 COST £26

Not so much a bistro, more a good local restaurant trying hard to serve
reasonably priced French food. Found at the end of a pedestrianised shopping
street, it is nothing grand. There is nothing wildly original in the menu either,
but it is built on good seasonal ingredients. Changing monthly, with half a
dozen choices at each stage, it puts the emphasis firmly on locally caught
seafood: in April, crab used as a base for soup, scallops baked with garlic and
parsley stuffing, lobster grilled as a main course. Herbs, wine and cream are
often used to finish fish dishes. Game is as strong as meat – rabbit casserole,
game terrine – and there are good home-made desserts: St-Emilion au
chocolat, caramelised almond ice-cream. Cheeses seem to be carefully bought,
including unpasteurised French and farmhouse British. The house Duboeuf is
£4.45 a carafe. CELLARMAN'S CHOICE : Chablis *premier cru*, Montmains 1985,
£18.60; Côtes du Rhône-Villages, Sainte Anne 1985, £9.40.

455

CHEF: Marc Hull   PROPRIETORS: Paul and Claire Rawson
OPEN: Mon to Sat, D only
CLOSED: first 2 weeks Jan
MEALS: 7 to 10
PRICES: £15 (£22). Service 10% for parties of 10 or more
CARDS: Access, Amex, Diners, Visa
SEATS: 42. Private parties: 20 main room. Children welcome. Wheelchair access. Music

---

**SOUTHWOLD Suffolk**                                                    map 6

## ▲ *Crown* ▮

90 High Street, Southwold IP18 6DP                               COOKING  1
SOUTHWOLD (0502) 722275                                        COST  £13−£23

As Adnams, the brewers and wine merchants, seem set to take over the town of
Southwold, their first venture in diversification, this Georgian hotel, done out
so tastefully, falters. Perhaps the pressures of opening a second hotel, the Swan
(see below), are too much. Anyway, from serving adventurous food – rabbit,
hare, goose and pigeon – the kitchen has progressed to chicken, veal and steak.
From cooking in a variety of styles, it has put everything 'with plums or
apricots' or marmalade. The recommendations are very few, some of the fresh
fish being acceptable. The place is crowded, the customers may get bad-
tempered although the staff do well, and travellers may prefer a less socially
pretentious ambience. The wine list, as it should be, is a treasure trove at very
advantageous prices. Read the notes and drink whatever falls within your
elected price range. This part is as a hotel/pub should be; the other has just
missed an important signpost. Let us hope it finds the right road soon. House
wines and Cruover machine selections are too many and too fast-changing to
mention, but start at £5. CELLARMAN'S CHOICE : Cloudy Bay Sauvignon Blanc
1988, £12.50; Côtes du Rhône, Ch. du Grand Moulas 1987, £6.35. Children are
welcome and the musical nights are good fun.

---

CHEF: Jason Wright   PROPRIETORS: Adnams plc
OPEN: all week
MEALS: 12.30 to 2, 7.30 to 9.45
PRICES: £9 (£13), Set L £10.50 (£14) to £12.50 (£17), Set D £13 (£17) to £15 (£19). Snacks
from £1.30
CARDS: Access, Amex, Visa
SEATS: 79. 4 tables outside. Private parties: 20 and 50 private rooms. Car-park, 18 places.
Children's helpings. No smoking in dining-room
ACCOMMODATION: 12 rooms, all with bath/shower. B&B £25.50 to £41. Afternoon teas.
Fishing. Golf. TV. Phone. Scenic. Doors close at 11.30

---

*On 6 May 1990 all London telephone numbers will change, the 01- prefix being replaced
by either 071- or 081-. See the front of the* Guide *for a list of which numbers will take
which prefix.*

*'This was one of their Gastronomic Evenings – these tend to be about as attractive to me as
revolving restaurants – both to be avoided at all costs, I've learned, over the years.'* On
inspecting in Hampshire

---

## ▲ *Swan Hotel*

Market Place, Southwold IP18 6EG — COOKING 2
LOWESTOFT (0502) 722186 — COST £15–£30

As Simon Loftus and Adnams take over the commissariat of Southwold, so the Swan, for long a large and bustling seaside hotel, falls to the combined assault of modern chef, wine merchant and interior designer. It's far too soon to say how it will progress, though an early meal detected a certain schizophrenia arising from a desire to please the old clientele, who may like roast lamb and mint sauce, and to attract the new, whose tastes may run more to steamed sea bass with lemon-grass. One or two items were properly cooked. The wine list, so far, is shorter and more expensive than the wine merchant connection would anticipate. The next twelvemonth will see if a style develops. House wine, £6.15.

CHEF: Peter Cuffe PROPRIETORS: Sole Bay Hotels
OPEN: all week
MEALS: 12 to 2, 7 to 9.30
PRICES: Set L £10.50 (£15) to £16.50 (£21) Set D £13.50 (£18) to £19.50 (£25)
CARDS: Access, Amex, Visa
SEATS: 96. Private parties: 80 main room, 50 and 80 private rooms. Car-park, 50 places. Children's helpings. Smart dress preferred. No smoking. Wheelchair access (also WC)
ACCOMMODATION: 45 rooms, all with bath/shower. B&B £32 to £68. Deposit £10. Garden. TV. Phone. Confirm within 7 days of booking. Doors close at midnight

**SPARK BRIDGE Cumbria** — map 7

## ▲ *Bridgefield House* 🍷

Spark Bridge, Ulverston LA12 8DA
LOWICK BRIDGE (022 985) 239
4m N of Ulverston, off A5084 on back road leading to Coniston — COOKING 3 — COST £28

Rosemary Glister's imaginative six-course dinners continue to win praise. The hotel, beautifully furnished, warm and elegant, is set on the edge of the River Crake. Everything is meticulously prepared for one sitting at 8 sharp, and Mrs Glister has little patience with people who miss the 7.30 deadline and still expect to eat on time. The menu offers three first courses and desserts, but no choice for the main course. In between come soup, sorbet and savoury. Flavours are mixed with flair: game terrine with rhubarb chutney; salmon poached in white wine with fresh ginger and dry vermouth; pork fillet and sliced plums with a rosemary cream dressing. Good puddings – banana and malt whisky burnt cream, blueberry crumble flan – and extras such as passion-fruit and kiwi sorbet, lambs' kidneys in madeira on toast. Vegetables, often from the garden, get special treatment: salsify roasted in oatmeal; broad beans with hazelnuts and sieved duck eggs. House wine is Californian, £4.84; there is an extensive list with plenty to choose from under £10, and, for example, the scarce Chave Hermitage 1984, £25.96, still a bargain at more than twice that. CELLARMAN'S CHOICE: Rioja, Contino Reserva 1982, £10.45; Sauvignon Blanc, Delegats 1987, £10.53.

CHEF: Rosemary Glister    PROPRIETORS: D. K. and Rosemary Glister
OPEN: all week, D only
MEALS: 7.30 for 8
PRICES: Set D £18.50 (£23)
CARD: Access
SEATS: 20. Private parties: 24 main room. Car-park, 10 places. Children's helpings. Smart dress preferred. No smoking. One sitting
ACCOMMODATION: 5 rooms, all with bath/shower. B&B £30 to £60. Baby facilities. Pets welcome. Garden. Scenic. Confirm by 3 [GHG]

---

**STADDLEBRIDGE   North Yorkshire**                                             map 7

# ▲ McCoy's

The Tontine, Staddlebridge DL6 3JB                                    COOKING 3
EAST HARLSEY (060 982) 671                                        COST £21–£43

In effect, the house and giant stable stand on a traffic island. Signs announce only the Tontine, not McCoy's – the name of the occupying family and the restaurant. The place has a fabled reputation, the three brothers have a gift for hospitality and skill in making people happy. There are three elements to the Tontine: the bedrooms, comfortable and warm; the restaurant, expensive, with fancy cooking amid parasols and sounds of yesteryear; the downstairs bistro, cheaper, where the music is loud rock. The restaurant looks as if it had been furnished from a second-hand dealer but hangs together by the unifying threads of parasols, candlelight, log fires and table linen. At night the lighting is dim, the music narcotic. Good, really, because the effect may look frayed by day or, as one more robust letter had it, 'it is worn out; large holes in the settees.' Who cares? The most unlikely people come here, are seduced by its open warmth and love it. The cooking, like the decoration, anticipated public taste. Whether it has been caught up or even overtaken by its pupil may be a question to resolve at leisure. The food does not shy away from luxury. A meal began with carpaccio, sliced thicker than in Lombardy but well dressed with olive oil, lemon and chopped garlic; and foie gras fried crisp yet yielding and bloody inside, served with a thin madeira sauce and grapes. The balance of sauce and meat, sweetness and salt was well judged. The main courses were breast of guinea-fowl, again sauced lightly with sherry and stock, accompanied by a parcel of spinach leaf enveloping wild rice, pine kernels and grapes; fillet of lamb baked a little too long, sliced on to a sauce of foie gras, with an artichoke heart stuffed with wild mushrooms and a pastry boat filled with red pepper custard. Good vegetables came with this. Desserts were an excellent strawberry cream slice (made with crème pâtissière, not just Chantilly) and a huge raspberry charlotte. This may appear to be heart-stopping stuff, and is very messy in overall conception sometimes. But it is executed with such brio that objections are few. House wine is £7.95. The good-sized wine list is now arranged by type rather than geographical origin. Breakfasts, it was suggested, are among the best in the land. The bistro does not do foie gras so often, but the food is still good – better than at many a bistro – carefully cooked and fresh. One reader protested at the *Guide* calling the décor 'dingy' last year. Perhaps dark-coloured would be more accurate. Further, it is given interest by the plasterwork and the original fireplace. A long menu takes in prawn cocktail, steak, duck breast and Pacific prawns but does them well, with not a hint of needless adornment. The bistro is open all week and residents of the hotel have reported that, on Sunday and Monday nights when the restaurant is closed, dishes from its menu have been cooked for them in the bistro kitchen. The wine list is short and sharp. House wine is £7.95.

CHEFS: Tom and Eugene McCoy  PROPRIETORS: Peter, Thomas and Eugene McCoy
OPEN: restaurant Tue to Sat D; bistro all week
CLOSED: 25 and 26 Dec, 1 Jan
MEALS: 12 to 2 (bistro), 7 to 10 (bistro and restaurant)
PRICES: restaurant £24 (£36), bistro £14 (£21)
CARDS: Amex, Access, Diners, Visa
SEATS: 115. Private parties: 70 main room (restaurant), 60 (bistro), 25 private room. Car-park, 60 places. Vegetarian meals. Children welcome. Music. Air-conditioned
ACCOMMODATION: 6 rooms, all with bath/shower. B&B £59 to £75. Baby facilities. Pets welcome. Garden. Air-conditioning. TV. Phone. Scenic. Doors close at 2am [GHG]

---

**STAFFORD  Staffordshire**　　　　　　　　　　　　　　　　map 5

# Curry Kuteer

31 Greengate Street, Stafford ST16 2HY　　　　　　　　COOKING 1
STAFFORD (0785) 53279　　　　　　　　　　　　　　　　COST £8–£25

The Kuteer, 20 years old and set neatly on the edge of the River Sow near the city centre, has had an extravagant facelift to outshine all comers. An ornate goldfish pond and waterfall now divide a plant-filled lounge and a chandeliered main dining-room. Diners are led from one to the other by a waiter across a small bridge. Despite this disruption and the new emphasis on design, the cooking on which the restaurant built its reputation has remained as consistent as ever. The menu has been expanded to include thalis and specialities such as a tandoori chicken in a minced meat sauce. Recommended dishes include a king prawn rogan josh, karahi chicken, dhal soup and sheek kebab. There are Indian puddings and fruit fritters to finish. Service is unobtrusive and excellent. House Spanish, £5.90.

CHEF: Mohammed Rashid  PROPRIETOR: Shah A. Quayum
OPEN: all week
MEALS: 12 to 2, 6 to 12
PRICES: £8 (£14), Set L £3.40 (£8), Set D £10.95 (£16) to £16 (£21)
CARDS: Access, Amex, Diners, Visa
SEATS: 85. Private parties: 50 main room, 60 private room. Car-park, 8 places. Vegetarian meals. Children's helpings. No children under 4. Smart dress preferred. Wheelchair access (2 steps). Music

---

*The 1991* Guide *will be published before Christmas 1990. Reports on meals are most welcome at any time of the year, but are extremely valuable in the spring. Send them to* **The Good Food Guide,** FREEPOST, *2 Marylebone Road, London NW1 1YN. No stamp is needed if posted in the UK.*

**STAMFORD** Lincolnshire                                      map 6

## ▲ George █

71 St Martin's, Stamford PE9 2LB                          COOKING **2**
STAMFORD (0780) 55171                                       COST £30

Not many hotels have fourteenth-century screens on view in the gentlemen's
lavatory. The George boasts examples of many periods of architectural history:
a splendid building in a matchless town where, in 1712, it was observed that
most notable houses were built by 'innkeepers and tradesmen'. Its sign – a
gantry or gallows – bestrides the entry of the Great North Road to the town
proper. 'Where else can you get such roasts as most Continentals have never
dreamed of, or red mullet like food for the Gods?' was the remark of a more
recent visitor. The George is all things to traveller, resident, wedding parties
and more. A courtyard for al fresco meals, a formal dining-room of old-
fashioned panelling and heraldry, a place for bar food or the more casual meal
on the move. Chris Pitman has been cooking here a long while and if
occasionally there are complaints, they are outnumbered by expressions of
pleased surprise. The restaurant continues to offer roast sirloin and other meats
off the wagon but has a *carte* that reflects modern tendencies: home-made
ravioli of salmon and scallops in a truffle sauce; Stilton terrine on a port sauce;
veal cutlet with wild mushrooms or pigeon with caramelised onions and a
cassis sauce. There is a decidedly Italian accent to the cheaper and simpler food
in the Garden Lounge but there are other styles too: three Lincolnshire
sausages in a mushroom and red wine sauce or stir-fried vegetables in a black-
bean sauce. Italy is the hallmark of the wines in this lower-priced restaurant: a
wide selection of old- and new-style bottles from all regions (except Piedmont)
that can be tried by the glass as well as in larger measure (a glass is enough of
the raisiny-sweet Bukkaram, a dessert Muscat from De Bartolini Sicily, £1.80).
The main restaurant's list is impressive: very well chosen from most significant
zones, although the emphasis remains French. The notes are intelligent. Many
of the classic (and currently fashionable) properties are there: Henri Goyard,
Marcel Vincent, Leflaive, Dagueneau, Rolly Gassmann, Torres, Stag's Leap,
Michel Gros, Rousseau and more. The pricing policy (a fixed profit, not
percentage mark-up) is generous and sane. A 1961 Ch. Pichon-Longueville-
Baron is only £60, which is worth a long detour. The rubric about tipping,
however, is anything but clear: 'VAT and Service are included in our prices.
Gratuities are at the discretion of the guest.' What's that supposed to mean? But
good sense prevails: the Garden Lounge has been declared a smoke-free zone.
House Liliano Chianti, £6.95. CELLARMAN'S CHOICE : Matua Valley Sauvignon
Blanc 1988, £12.75, Cuvaison Zinfandel 1985, £14.45.

---

*Consumers' Association is planning a* Vegetarian Good Food Guide, *to cafés and
restaurants offering at least one vegetarian main course. Please send reports and
recommendations to* The Vegetarian Good Food Guide, FREEPOST, *2 Marylebone
Road, London NW1 1YN.*

*All letters to the* Guide *are acknowledged with an update on latest sales, closures, chef
changes and so on.*

---

CHEF: Chris Pitman   PROPRIETORS: Poste Hotels Ltd
OPEN: all week
MEALS: 12.30 to 2.30, 7.30 to 10.30
PRICES: £17 (£25), Snacks from £2.45. Cover 60p. Service inc
CARDS: Access, Amex, Visa
SEATS: 85. 20 tables outside. Private parties: 90 main room, 16, 22 and 30 private rooms.
Car-park, 150 places. Vegetarian meals. Children's helpings. Smart dress preferred. No
smoking in Garden Lounge. Wheelchair access (also WC)
ACCOMMODATION: 47 rooms, all with bath/shower. B&B £62.50 to £120. Baby facilities.
Pets welcome. Afternoon teas. Garden. TV. Phone. Scenic. Confirm by 6 [GHG]

---

**STOKE-BY-NAYLAND** Suffolk                                          map 3

# ▲ *Angel Inn*

Stoke-by-Nayland, CO6 4SA                                      COOKING 2
COLCHESTER (0206) 263245                                     COST £15−£28

At an inn within a group of picturesque, renovated cottages, is pub food at its
best: a short selection of daily dishes, carefully made with first-rate
ingredients. Expect to wait since everything is cooked to order. Steak and
kidney pudding and herby lamb casserole have proved reliable, but it is in the
more adventurous dishes, such as cheese and ham croquettes in a cream and
mustard sauce flecked with diced red tomato, a good ballotine of duckling in a
caramelised orange sauce and fish en croûte with lobster sauce that the flair of
the kitchen has shown. Fish is more often served plainly: salmon or plaice
grilled, fresh crab dressed in the shell with its claws to one side. Vegetables,
salads and puddings are also above the usual. Meals can be had in a small
group of open-plan, beamed lounge bars with solid armchairs at tables,
comfortable sofas and a few good pieces of furniture; in the dining-room
proper there is a full restaurant service with a more expensive menu but the
same emphasis on fish. All reporters stress the value and enjoyment of the bar
− both surroundings and service. This is not to say the restaurant should be
avoided, but it is more expensive and the printed menu is not as out of the
ordinary as the bar can be. The restaurant wine list is short, good and
excellently priced. Hardly one choice could raise serious objection. House wine
in the restaurant is £5.50.

CHEF: Mark Johnson   PROPRIETORS: Richard Wright and Peter Smith
OPEN: Tue to Sun, exc Tue L and Sun D
CLOSED: 25 and 26 Dec
MEALS: 12.30 to 2 (1.30 Sun), 7.30 to 9
PRICES: £17 (£23), Set Sun L £9.50 (£15)
CARDS: Access, Amex, Diners, Visa
SEATS: 40. Private parties: 26 main room. Car-park, 20 places. Vegetarian meals. Children
welcome. Wheelchair access (also WC)
ACCOMMODATION: 6 rooms, all with bath/shower. Rooms for disabled. B&B £30 to £40.
Garden. TV. Phone. Doors close at 11.30

---

*County Round-ups listing additional restaurants that may be worth a visit are at the back
of the* Guide, *after the Irish section. Reports on Round-up entries are welcome.*

**STON EASTON** Somerset                                               map 2

# ▲ *Ston Easton Park* ♟

Ston Easton BA3 4DF                                                  COOKING 2
CHEWTON MENDIP (076 121) 631                                        COST £23−£41

The bare, severe façade of this grey Palladian mansion completed in 1791 is
relieved only by four pillars surrounding the entrance and a couple of garlands.
But the interior is lavish in the extreme. Further contrast is encountered when
the diner progresses to the dining-room, which is light and summery, almost
casual, with bamboo chairs and pastel-green panelling. The menu, too, strikes
a fresh note, moving with the times. Two years ago there were serving domes
and four-course dinners featuring 30 dishes. Now there are six dishes per
course, and not one that doesn't sound enticing: scallops with lentils and
coriander; ravioli of lobster and basil on a light cognac cream; medallions of
venison marinated in apricot brandy with honey-roast shallots. The one fixture
throughout the years is Tulip Ston Easton Park. There is something of an
imbalance between the generosity with nibbles, amuse-gueule and petits fours
on the one hand, and the paucity of vegetables and salad greens on the other,
but at least ostentatious luxury ingredients and flowery treatments are
conspicuous by their absence. Three cheers. Such a pity, then, that our
inspector dined on the chef's night off. This is a perennial problem, especially
in country-house hotels that serve meals seven days a week. The chef has to
have time off, but restaurants don't tell which days when people book. Unless
there is a strong back-up team, things can go badly wrong. On better nights,
the cooking is accurate and satisfactory, the service pleasing. Meals have begun
on a light note of layered avocado and lobster with a good oil dressing,
proceeded to salmon with a spinach and sorrel sauce that gained body from the
one and accent from the other, and took in a vegetarian dish of a filo tart case
filled with a macédoine of fresh vegetables, wild mushrooms and a tomato
cream sauce. The end, blackberry and apple crumble, is as British as the stark
contrast of geometric box and luxuriant plasterwork that pleased the Palladian
architect and his patron. The wine list is a good collection of older vintages in
claret, with some elderly burgundies for good measure. It does not take too
highfalutin' a line about prices, either, the spread being much fairer than in
many palaces of this character. It is a nice list but does not indulge in many
discoveries. House wine, £9. CELLARMAN'S CHOICE : House Champagne Rosé
Brut 1982, £27; Robson Hunter Valley Chardonnay, 1987, £18.50; Ch. Respide
1981, Graves, £17. The menu states 'no service charge included or gratuity
expected'. To encourage appetite, there is bicycle hire. To assuage hunger, there
are munificent luncheon picnic hampers.

---

*'The "pool" of brown sauce was said to be three-pepper. Asked head waiter if "three"
meant green, red and yellow. He said "Yes, but if you mix them all up that's what you get
– brown."'* On dining in Hampshire

*All entries in the* Guide *are rewritten every year, not least because restaurant standards
fluctuate. Don't trust an out-of-date* Guide.

---

CHEF: Mark Harrington   PROPRIETORS: Peter and Christine Smedley
OPEN: all week
MEALS: 12.30 to 2, 7.30 to 9.30 (10 Fri and Sat)
PRICES: Set L £18.50 (£23) to £19.50 (£24), Set D £29.50 (£34)
CARDS: Access, Amex, Diners, Visa
SEATS: 40. 8 tables outside. Private parties: 40 main room, 14 and 22 private rooms.
Car-park, 40 places. Vegetarian meals. Children's helpings. No children under 12.
Smart dress preferred. No cigars/pipes in dining-room. Wheelchair access
ACCOMMODATION: 20 rooms, all with bath/shower. B&B £60 to £260. No children under
12. Pets welcome. Afternoon teas. Garden. Snooker. TV. Phone. Scenic. Doors close at
midnight. Confirm by 6 [GHG]

---

**STONHAM** Suffolk                                                    map 3

## ▲ *Mr Underhill's* ♥

Stonham IP14 5DW
STOWMARKET (0449) 711206                                    COOKING 3
on A140, 300 yards S of junction with A1120          COST £26−£41

'The changing view over the valley can quickly fill with mist and just as
quickly clear again,' as the contented diner sits in this heavily beamed room,
coloured red on red and hung with enjoyable pictures. The dinner menu is a set
price, three or four courses long, arranged in advance of arrival. 'I find a set
meal of what your host can do well far preferable to a choice of eight poorly
cooked items,' was the response of one visitor. Because of the element of
consultation, Christopher Bradley may actually find himself cooking a full
menu range on a busy Saturday night. The deliberation imposed by the
formula finds echoes in the service, solicitous and concerned, by Judy Bradley.
Memories of one meal earlier in the year were crowned by a pair of overlapping
slabs of smoked salmon hiding a filling of smoked scallops on a chive sauce
with an accompaniment of diced cucumber. The elegance of this dish, the
happy choice of flavours, made it exceptional. If style could be detected from
that menu, it would be a sweet tooth: a duck with honey in the sauce and a
butterscotch rather than dark caramel to go with poached pear for dessert. Both
needed astringency. Other meals reported have not borne this out so forcefully.
All are united on the quality of cheeses, a wide range from Britain and France,
'including a chèvre so delicious it was a shame to have to hand it round.' The
wine list is the product of careful thought, containing some excellent
Australasian and French country wines as well as the classics. House wines
from £7.95. CELLARMAN'S CHOICE : Wirra-Wirra Church Block (Cabernet/
Shiraz/Merlot) 1985, McLaren Vale, £10.95; Rully Blanc 1986, Guyot, £14.50.

---

CHEF: Christopher Bradley   PROPRIETORS: Christopher and Judy Bradley
OPEN: Tue to Sat, D only
MEALS: 7.30 to 8.45
PRICES: Set D £18.45 (£26) to £25.50 (£34). Licensed, also bring your own: corkage £5
CARDS: Access, Amex, Visa
SEATS: 30. Private parties: 30 main room, 16 private room. Car-park, 12 places. Vegetarian
meals. Smoking after meal. Wheelchair access (also WC)
ACCOMMODATION: 1 room, with bath/shower. B&B £40. Garden. Scenic. Confirm by noon

STONOR Oxfordshire                                                                    map 2

## *Stonor Arms*

Stonor RG9 6HE                                                                  COOKING **3**
TURVILLE HEATH (049 163) 345                                          COST £19–£38

Stonor is a hamlet strung along the B480, leading north out of Henley-on-Thames, with two points of interest. Stonor Park, a Tudor manor house with a medieval chapel and magnificent deer park, is open to the public. So is the Stonor Arms, a recently renovated, plain eighteenth-century former pub of white-painted brick with wooden shutters, that trades on two levels. Rather sophisticated bar food is served in the old conservatory: fish soup with water biscuits and rouille; a bowl of ratatouille with garlic bread; cold Cornish lobster with mayonnaise. The room is a scaled-down, less formal, less expensive version of the restaurant, which in turn is a pair of contrasting dining-rooms. One is dark and formal, with oil paintings in large gilt frames; the new conservatory, with canvas, bamboo chairs and a penchant for pink, juts into the garden. The Frosts came from Cromlix House (see Kinbuck, Scotland) and have brought a modern British bias to the food, which runs the gamut from a humble casserole of pulses to morel mushrooms and smoked bacon in a pastry case with a cream and truffle sauce. Ingredients are first rate, presentation is attractive, execution is professional, and the taste combinations are thoughtfully matched: poached turbot is served with a leek and lobster cake; shelled mussels and thick scallops with their coral are fried and served on a wreath of varied, rough-cut lettuce dressed with nut oil. Beef is well hung and game is local. The details are just as impressive: home-made chutney for a chicken and pistachio terrine; oatcakes and herb biscuits with cheese; starter nibbles, bread and petits fours. Puddings are the kind that 'all adult schoolchildren yearn for', from rhubarb crumble to rice pudding with raspberry jam, to steamed white chocolate pudding with a white chocolate sauce. The wine list includes a few surprises – 1972 and 1974 clarets and a Rhône section depending on English bottlings – but it covers a fair area and the few United States and Australian bottles are good. House Chilean (white), £7.77 and Languedoc (red), £7.30. CELLARMAN'S CHOICE : Silver Oaks Cellars, Cabernet-Sauvignon 1983, Alexander Valley, £26; Montrose Chardonnay 1986, Mudgee, £12.45.

CHEF: Stephen Frost   PROPRIETORS: Granville Jackson Associates
OPEN: bar all week, restaurant all week, exc Sun D
MEALS: 12 to 1.45, 7 to 9.30
PRICES: £14 (£19), Set L £17.95 (£24) to £21.95 (£28), Set D £24.75 (£31) to £25.75 (£32)
CARDS: Access, Amex, Visa
SEATS: 40. 3 tables outside. Private parties: 22 main room. Car-park, 30 places. Children's helpings. Smart dress preferred (restaurant). Wheelchair access. Music

*'At dinner the Irish lad kept muttering to himself – not to the customers, to himself. The daughter is a rather unhappy soul, you feel she must have a secret sorrow. It must be waiting on the customers.'* A reader

**STONY STRATFORD  Buckinghamshire**                                    map 2

# Stratfords

7 St Paul's Court, 118 High Street
Stony Stratford MK1 1LA                                    COOKING 1
MILTON KEYNES (0908) 566577                                COST £17–£29

This converted chapel to what was a small public school founded by a
Reverend Sankey in the 1860s has had a chequered history. The school lasted
30 years and was replaced briefly by a cigar factory. In turn there came an
orphanage, then a Roman Catholic school before its rescue from dilapidation,
and dedication to Bacchic rites. Encaustic tiles, wood panelling, high vaults
and the occasional screen and bench leave one no illusions as to its earlier lives.
Commercial pressures being what they are in Milton Keynes, Michael Roberts
and Linda Membride strive to offer fair value. A four-course lunch is £10.50;
dinner is not priced unrealistically (determined by the choice of main course).
The style is up to the minute: rolls of thin-cut celeriac around Chinese
vegetables with a coriander sauce; a goats' cheese soufflé; fillet of lamb with a
crab flan and a curry sabayon (it sounds familiar...); halibut with fresh coconut
and peppers and a tomato sauce. Puddings are quite fancy too, for instance, a
pear poached with lemon, popped into a pastry case, with a ginger butterscotch
sauce and a lime custard – phew! Execution sounds better on paper than is the
result on the plate. The wine list offers excellent value, some nice Loires and
Rhônes from Robin Yapp, and a decent choice from the New World. House
wines include a 1986 Gewürztraminer at £6.50. CELLARMAN'S CHOICE : Fleurie
'La Madone' 1987, Duboeuf, £13.15; Chablis 1985, Leonce Bocquet, £12.

CHEFS/PROPRIETORS: Michael Roberts and Linda Membride
OPEN: Mon to Sat, exc Mon and Sat L
CLOSED: first 2 weeks Jan
MEALS: 12 to 2, 7.30 to 9.30 (10 Sat)
PRICES: Set L £10.50 (£17) to £17.50 (£24), Set D £14.50 (£21) to £17.50 (£24)
CARDS: Access, Amex, Visa
SEATS: 70. Private parties: 70 main room. Car-park, 20 places. No children under 6.
Wheelchair access. Music

**STORRINGTON  West Sussex**                                            map 2

# ▲ Abingworth Hall

Thakeham Road, Storrington RH20 3EF                        COOKING 2
WEST CHILTINGTON (07983) 2257 and 3636                     COST £19–£36

The hall, built in 1910, has all the trappings: decorative lake, rhododendrons,
heli-pad, tennis court and heated outdoor pool, all looking as spruce as if they
had just come back from the dry cleaner's. Inside, the decoration seems to have
been chosen by someone without any strong views on the matter. 'The prints
and paintings on the walls are utterly forgettable.'. But, 'atmosphere, décor and
staff are more comfortable and more ordinary than the hotel's posh amenities
would lead one to expect.' We treat that as a compliment. The menu is full of
dishes that were on every fashionable menu a while back. The *carte* has a choice
of six items per course, the four-course set menu has two. Every main dish

comes with a sauce – brandy and cherry with grilled breast of duck, white wine and sorrel with salmon – and standard items run from melon with Parma ham through bacon and Roquefort salad to rum baba. Ingredients are good, treatment is unpretentious, and timing is right; these are the important things. Well flavoured, silky-textured gravlax; pink, soft, delicately flavoured calf's liver are dishes that win praise. Bread, brioche, ice-cream, sorbet and preserves are all made on the premises. Five dozen bottles on the wine list are well described, but there are no risks taken: Bulgaria is the only non-West European country represented. Some growers, however – Comte Lafon, Michel Juillot and Trimbach - are names to conjure with. House French is £6.80.

CELLARMAN'S CHOICE : Chablis 1986, Jean Durup, £16.80; Ch. Lynch Bages 1978, Pauillac, £38.

CHEF: Peter Cannon   PROPRIETORS: Philip and Pauline Bulman
OPEN: all week
MEALS: 12.30 to 2, 7.15 to 9
PRICES: £21 (£29), Set L £14 (£19), Set D £24 (£30), Snacks from £1.25
CARDS: Amex, Access, Carte Blanche, Diners, Visa
SEATS: 50. 4 tables outside. Private parties: 16 main room. Car-park, 40 places. Smart dress preferred. Wheelchair access (4 steps; also WC). Music
ACCOMMODATION: 21 rooms, all with bath/shower. Rooms for disabled. B&B £52 to £72. Deposit: £10. No children under 10. Garden. Swimming-pool. Tennis. Golf. TV. Phone. Scenic. Doors close at 11 [GHG]

---

## ▲ *Manleys*

| Manleys Hill, Storrington RH20 4BT | COOKING 3 |
|---|---|
| STORRINGTON (0903) 742331 | COST £22–£48 |

Karl Löderer has kept this Queen Anne house with views over the Sussex Downs high in readers' estimation for several years. It is a very pukka restaurant: monogrammed napkins and German crockery, domes and well-upholstered chairs sitting elegantly in a pair of interconnecting rooms, served by young men in dinner jackets. The cooking is quite classic French, with a certain Central European twist evinced in some of the game dishes and desserts. The fish cookery is also very good, perhaps taking advantage of the south coast ports – yet there is small evidence of 'market cookery'. There is a short set-price menu at lunchtimes; otherwise the choice is from the *carte*, save on Fridays when there may be a five-course *menu gourmand*. This last takes in examples of the style: a coarse duck terrine with pistachio nuts served with a high-tasting aspic; foie gras de canard with brioche and precisely cooked and dressed green beans; salmon and scallops served with a fine shellfish sauce; Romney Marsh lamb wrapped in spinach leaves with a simple *jus*; orange and passion-fruit soufflé encased in a thin pancake surrounded by a piquant orange sauce. It is quite substantial food, though no longer as cream-laden as once it was. Portions are generous and the style means that people remember the first courses more vividly than the next, simply because the edge of hunger has been dulled so decisively. The kitchen seems able to keep flavours separate and eloquent, even though many of the dishes are mixtures of prime ingredients. The climax of the meal may be reserved for the final course. It should be the prime British exponent of the salzburger Nockerln but the other delights, for example, hot caramel soufflé or pancakes filled with Grand Marnier cream may prove too great a distraction. The wine list has always been a good one with a fair range of French (and some German) bottles. House wine is £9.80.

CELLARMAN'S CHOICE : Ch. Villegeorge 1979, £14.50; Montagny *premier cru*, Les Coères 1986, £12.95. For a long while, Karl Löderer has refused to include VAT in his prices. At last, as we go to press, the practice is changing.

CHEF/PROPRIETOR: Karl Löderer
OPEN: Tue to Sun, exc Sun D
CLOSED: first 2 weeks Jan, last week Aug, first week Sept
MEALS: 12 to 2, 7 to 9.15 (10 Sat)
PRICES: £25 (£40), Set L £14.50 (£22) to £17 (£27). Service inc
CARDS: Access, Amex, Diners, Visa
SEATS: 48. Private parties: 36 main room, 22 private room. Car-park. Children's helpings on request. No children under 7. Smart dress preferred. No cigars/pipes in dining-room. Wheelchair access (also WC)
ACCOMMODATION: 1 double room, with bath/shower. B&B £75. No children. TV. Phone. Scenic

---

**STOURPORT-ON-SEVERN  Hereford & Worcester**                    map 5

## Severn Tandoori

| | |
|---|---|
| 11 Bridge Street | |
| Stourport-on-Severn DY13 8UX | COOKING 1 |
| STOURPORT (029 93) 3090 | COST £18 |

New wallpaper, new light fittings, new menu: the Severn Tandoori keeps on its toes and produces tandoori, masala and karahi (skillet) dishes of a quality that pleases visitors and regulars alike in surroundings that are comfortable and bright. Rogan josh is also new to the range. Drink lassi. No teas are listed, to the incomprehension of some. House Spanish wine, £5.90.

CHEF: A. Audud   PROPRIETORS: S.A. Quayum, M. Miah, A. Audud, Z. Ali and M. Meah
OPEN: all week
MEALS: 12 to 2.30, 6 to 11.30
PRICES: £9 (£15)
CARDS: Access, Amex, Diners, Visa
SEATS: 70. Private parties: 70 main room, 70 private room. Vegetarian meals. Children's helpings (weekend D only). No children under 4. Wheelchair access (also WC). Music

---

**STRATFORD UPON AVON  Warwickshire**                    map 2

## ▲ Shepherd's,
## Stratford House Hotel

| | |
|---|---|
| Sheep Street | |
| Stratford upon Avon CV37 6EF | COOKING 2 |
| STRATFORD UPON AVON (0789) 68233 | COST £18–£26 |

The thought of Cairo's Shepheard's Hotel, rather than sheep, may have been in mind while this conservatory, reached by a passage to one side of the hotel, was in the making: there are ceiling fans and bamboo chairs, not wattle hurdles and country smocking. Stratford gets no easier to eat in after a trip to the theatre, making Shakespeare a surprisingly uncivilised experience. However, Sylvia Adcock hopes to alleviate Saturday famine by accepting post-performance bookings for that night only. The short menu cooked by Jonathan George ranges from the modish – hot kebab of fruits with home-made vanilla ice-cream – to the predictable – Cornish crab with avocado. Ingredients are fresh, tastes clean. Flaked chicken with mango and a curried mayonnaise, and a rack of lamb with a herb crust and a mint cream sauce have both pleased. One mixed report praised 'the truly excellent starters, puddings and salmon,' but was irked at 'canteen-standard beef and lamb'. The short wine list has the admirable policy of a low fixed mark-up, and there is now a fixed-price lunch on Sundays.

CHEF: Jonathan George   PROPRIETOR: Sylvia Adcock
OPEN: Tue to Sun, exc Sun D
MEALS: 12 to 2, 6 to 9.30
PRICES: £15 (£22), Set Sun L £12.50 (£18). Minimum £8.50
CARDS: Access, Amex, Diners, Visa
SEATS: 40. 3 tables outside. Private parties: 40 main room, 10 private room. Children welcome. Wheelchair access (3 steps)
ACCOMMODATION: 10 rooms, all with bath/shower. B&B £35 to £60. Deposit: £20. No children under 5. Afternoon teas. TV. Phone. Doors close at 12. Confirm by 4

## Sir Toby's

8 Church Street
Stratford upon Avon CV37 6HB                          COOKING 1
STRATFORD UPON AVON (0789) 68822                       COST £24

'The place to go to be cosseted after so much pain and melancholia…' Post-*Hamlet* tristesse, as it happens, not despair at the general standard of Stratford's eating places. Although this modest little one is handy for the theatre and open early enough for a pre-theatre supper, Sir Toby might have said more than 'a plague o' these pickle herring' as he contemplated savoury prawn and avocado ice-cream, vegetable tagliatelle with coconut cream sauce, and caramelised and brandied iced grapes. Wise theatre-goers might prefer to opt for home-made soup, grilled lamb or beef, and ices. Reasonably priced wines; house Bulgarian Cabernet Sauvignon and Chardonnay, £4.95. Friendly service.

CHEF: Joanna Watkins   PROPRIETORS: Carl and Joanna Watkins
OPEN: Mon to Sat, D only (L by arrangement)
MEALS: 5.30 to 9.30
PRICES: £15 (£20)
CARDS: Access, Amex, Visa
SEATS: 40. 4 tables outside. Private parties: 34 main room, 20 private room. Vegetarian meals. Children's helpings. Wheelchair access (1 step; also WC). Music. Air-conditioned

---

'*Petits fours would not be served with the coffee as the washer-up lady who made them had had her finger removed – this we were told in graphic detail whilst we ate.*' On dining in Gloucestershire

# Oakes

169 Slad Road, Stroud GL5 1RG
STROUD (0453) 759950                                               COOKING 4
on B4070, m from Stroud                                          COST £16–£37

Slad is as uninspired a suburb as any spawned by small industrial towns in the
deep valleys of the north. It is surprising to find a restaurant of this calibre here.
The stone house, flat Gothic, is set back from the road; it was a girls' school.
Inside, the surfaces have not been dressed up: bare floors, bare tables, Persian
rugs, table mats. The trappings of stardom are set aside for more homely
virtues: warm welcome, quiet attention, a low-key English approach that is
comforting to the newcomer and has the edge over hysterical self-promotion.
The food is less modest. Chris Oakes cooks a menu as modern and ambitious as
any. The readers' verdict is almost wholly unanimous. This is a pleasant
restaurant with very good food. Rather than a *carte*, at dinner there are two set-
price menus, each containing an alternative for each course. Menus may be
mixed if so desired. This rather muddling approach is made simpler at lunch by
a single menu with two choices per course. The dishes sound more complicated
than they are, but a 'garnish' seems integral to the initial conception. People
have liked a grilled fillet of cod with a breadcrumb and horseradish topping,
accompanied by fine scallops dressed with hazelnut oil, and a 'moist and
puddingy' hot rhubarb soufflé with a honey cream. Puff pastry at Oakes has
been invariably light and good and the fresh pasta has also drawn praise: for
example, a ravioli of crab of outstanding vigour (though vitiated at the end by
too clashing a series of sauces and accompaniments). Chris Oakes' fish cookery
seems especially inventive and enjoyable. Criticisms that surface are twofold:
one is that the experience does not live up to the reputation – hardly the Oakes'
fault – and secondly, that there have been days of wild overseasoning and lack
of clarity in the composition of contrasting flavours, particularly in the sauces.
The wine list is composed from the stock of David Baillie Vintners of Exeter. It
contains some 60 bottles, ranging the world, of modern and good material: the
core, predictably, is Bordeaux and burgundy. It is not expensive. House French
is £6.30. CELLARMAN'S CHOICE : Rosemount Chardonnay 1988, £9.75;
Brouilly, Thévenin 1987, £10.

CHEF: Christopher Oakes   PROPRIETORS: Christopher and Caroline Oakes, and Nowell
and Jean Scott
OPEN: Tue to Sun, exc Sun D
MEALS: 12.30 to 2, 7.30 to 9.30
PRICES: Set L £12.50 (£16) to £28 (£31), Set Sun L £15.50 (£19), Set D £24 (£27) to £28
(£31). Service inc
CARDS: Access, Visa
SEATS: 30. Private parties: 30 main room. Car-park, 12 places. Children's helpings.
Wheelchair access

*'Throughout the evening – a Saturday – a slightly bizarre Mancunian, in dinner jacket
and fez, hovered above, asking at intervals if we would "like a bit o' magic"!'*  On dining
in Lancashire

# The Three Lions ▮

Stuckton Road, Stuckton SP6 2HF
FORDINGBRIDGE (0425) 52489                                    COOKING 3
3/4m off A338 at Fordingbridge                               COST £21–£31

Some measure of fame is coming to the Wadsacks. They have worked, over 10 years, to convert this pub to a restaurant, concentrating their resources on the cooking, not the table linen. It might be a cross between pub and Gasthaus – you could certainly eat off the floor, so clean is it. A profusion of plants, flowers, brass, copper, wall-hangings and Scandinavian fabrics soften the edges. The blackboard menu is long, yet inspires confidence. Its prices are affordable and it changes at every meal. Cooking may have a German or Scandinavian bias, but the curries are a favourite at lunchtime and the fish is worth travelling for. The use of a steam oven guarantees that this is very directly cooked – vegetables too. A lunch of evident Germano-philes started with sweet-cured herrings, took in three neatly trimmed pieces of skate with black butter, some excellent sauerkraut, Bratwurst better than in its country of origin, vegetables that included a celeriac purée enlivened by the zest of a lemon, a first-class apple strudel and a very rich chocolate pot. What is also worth noting is the enthusiasm of correspondents; perhaps it is the unexpected nature of it all. At lunchtime, the bar snacks are as surprising as the full meal: where else could you get a fast plate of brains in black butter or half a dozen oysters rounded off by a fine duck-liver pâté made by the publican? Service is looked after by June Wadsack: it can be brisk, it is always effective. Karl-Hermann Wadsack has been seen emerging from his kitchen in short trousers and long socks, a touching faith in English summers. Mrs Wadsack also has charge of the wine list. This is very good with excellent representation of burgundy and Bordeaux, fewer – though thoughtfully chosen – Germans and Alsaces than might have been expected, a page of dessert wines, always some delectable bin-ends, lots of half bottles and no greedy prices. House wines are French and German at £6.95. CELLARMAN'S CHOICE : Gigondas Dom. St-Gayan 1984, Meffre, £13.50; Gewürztraminer, Fleur de Guebwiller 1985, Domaines Schlumberger, £17.50.

CHEF: Karl-Hermann Wadsack    PROPRIETORS: Karl-Hermann and June Wadsack
OPEN: Tue to Sun, exc Sun D
CLOSED: 4 weeks Feb, 2 weeks July to Aug, 2 weeks Oct
MEALS: 12.15 to 1.30 (1.45 Sun), 7.15 to 9 (9.30 Sat)
PRICES: L £14 (£21), D £17 (£26). Service 10%
CARDS: Access, Visa
SEATS: 55. Private parties: 50 main room. Car-park, 40 places. No children under 14.
Wheelchair access (also WC). Air-conditioned

*All letters to the* Guide *are acknowledged with an update on latest sales, closures, chef changes and so on.*

*If you see a certificate in a restaurant bearing the words 'Good Food and Wine Guide', the claim is false – see the Introduction. Please write and tell us the name and address of the restaurant.*

STURMINSTER NEWTON  Dorset                                        map 2

## ▲ *Plumber Manor*

Sturminster Newton DT10 2AF                                    COOKING  2
STURMINSTER NEWTON (0258) 72507                             COST  £20−£29

This Jacobean country house is not a large hotel: it combines style with
intimacy. The dining-room is in pale greens and blues with a white ceiling.
The atmosphere is family. Richard Prideaux-Brune presides, and local serving
girls tend to look vaguely worried about their guests. There are two set menus
of three courses, each with a small supplement for a fourth (fish) course: The
cooking combines French classics − chateaubriand with béarnaise sauce, sole
Véronique − with beef Wellington and English puddings. The repertoire is
fairly constant, and the old-fashioned air extends through presentation and
portions, right down to garnishing with cherry tomatoes, sprigs of parsley, and
rounds of fine flaky pastry. Flavours are strong rather than subtle. Warm
mousseline of roughly shredded crab is freshly baked with cream and sherry.
Pink best-end of lamb comes with a tartlet on onion purée and mint, and a
sticky, strong, acid-sweet sauce made from stock, wine and redcurrant jelly.
Eighty largely French wines are supported by almost half as many half-bottles,
and there is choice under £10.

CHEFS: Brian Prideaux-Brune and Mrs Baker   PROPRIETORS: Richard Prideaux-Brune,
Alison Prideaux-Brune and Brian Prideaux-Brune
OPEN: all week D only, L for parties by arrangement
MEALS: 7.30 to 9.30
PRICES: Set D £16.50 (£20) to £20 (£24). Service inc
SEATS: 60. Private parties: 40 main room, 12 and 22 private rooms. Car-park, 20 places.
Vegetarian meals. Children welcome. Smart dress preferred. No cigars/pipes in dining-
room. Wheelchair access
ACCOMMODATION: 12 rooms, all with bath/shower. Rooms for disabled. B&B £50 to £90.
No children under 12. Garden. TV. Phone. Scenic [GHG]

SUDBURY  Suffolk                                                  map 3

## *Mabey's Brasserie*

47 Gainsborough Street
Sudbury CO10 7SS                                               COOKING  3
SUDBURY (0787) 74298                                           COST  £20

The Fords left their Sudbury bistro for a brasserie in Colchester (see entry) and
now Robert Mabey has converted their bistro into a brasserie − a brasserie,
however, working bistro hours. Mabey's previous role (for he is Connaught-
trained) was chef at Hintlesham Hall (see Hintlesham). He should therefore
bring to the task considerable skill and experience in haute cuisine. Its
translation into cheaper eating, offering a fast-changing menu on a blackboard
has sometimes faltered. The tight-packed booths of the dining-room offer
privacy, and a view of Mabey, baseball-capped, behind the kitchen counter,
but make it difficult for some to see the blackboard. One meal took in noodles
in garlic, tarragon and mushroom sauce; roast giant prawns with a Chinese
dipping sauce; game stew (mainly venison) with croûtons; a rack of

lamb cooked exactly; lime crème brûlée and roasted bananas in a caramel sauce with almonds. The servings are generous: steaks fill the plate. Chips are thick-cut and fried with the skins left on. Reporters have found the food too rich – a fault rarely met in a brasserie. As Robert Mabey himself points out, where a small place can work on a cash margin rather than a big kitchen's percentage mark-up (on lobster as well as on tomatoes), bargains and generosity should abound. The wine list is short but, as it draws mainly on Lay & Wheeler, the bottles are nicely chosen and none too dear. House Plaimont Côtes de Gascogne is £5.95 (red) and £6.50 (white).

CHEF: Robert Mabey    PROPRIETORS: Robert Mabey and Johanna Cheesman
OPEN: Mon to Sat
MEALS: 12 to 2, 7 to 10
PRICES: £11 (£17)
CARDS: Access, Visa
SEATS: 35. Private parties: 40 main room. Vegetarian meals. Children's helpings.
Wheelchair access (2 steps)

---

## SURBITON  Surrey                                                                   map 3

# Chez Max

| 85 Maple Road, Surbiton KT6 4AW | COOKING 3 |
| 01-399 2365 | COST £23–£32 |

South-western Surbiton is not often a gourmet's paradise, nor is it a restaurateur's. So there must be some satisfaction in the survival of Max Markarian's restaurant, at sufficiently high margins of profit to pay for refurbishment and with no sign of his losing his stamina. A *prix fixe* menu with plenty of choice at lunchtime is replaced in the evening by a *carte* of half a dozen alternatives at each stage. The cooking is up to date: marinated raw salmon with spinach leaves and a yoghurt dressing; steamed crab in cabbage leaves with garlic and lemon sauce; breast of duck with strawberry and honey vinaigrette; guinea-fowl with lime and grape sauce; many fruity (exotic, of course) desserts. It is also competent and enjoyable, although not exactly breaking into inspiration or adventurous shopping. The wine list is succinct to a fault, and French. Of the four red 'Rhônes' one is Piat de Beaujolais, another is Moulin-à-Vent. Clarets make the biggest splash, in age, in price, in range. House French, £8.50. CELLARMAN'S CHOICE : Savennières, Clos du Papillon 1987, £15; Ch. Bellevue Lugagnac 1983, £12.50.

CHEF: Max Markarian    PROPRIETORS: Mr and Mrs M. Markarian
OPEN: Tue to Sat, exc Sat L
MEALS: 12.30 to 2, 7.30 to 10
PRICES: £19 (£27), Set L £16.50 (£23). Minimum £12.50. Service 12.5%
CARDS: Access, Amex, Diners, Visa
SEATS: 32. Private parties: 32 main room. No children under 7. No pipes in dining-room.
Wheelchair access (also WC)

---

*County Round-ups listing additional restaurants that may be worth a visit are at the back of the* Guide, *after the Irish section. Reports on Round-up entries are welcome.*

---

SUTTON  Surrey                                                        map 3

## *Partners 23*

23 Stonecot Hill, Sutton SM3 9HB
01-644 7743                                                     COOKING 3
on the A24, near Woodstock pub                          COST £20–£40

This small restaurant occupies a unit in a dull shopping parade on a windswept
suburban hillock. People from the surrounding districts keep it in business and
it does not compromise on ingredients or menu. The service is more personal
and friendly than in smart-set central locations. For some, this is almost a
drawback but for the majority, the 'performance' surrounding explication of
the cheese basket, full of Anglo-French produce from a supplier in Oxted, is a
necessary, and cathartic, part of the ritual. The set-price evening menu,
supplemented by daily extras at lunchtime, is something in the same vein but
less expensive. There are half-a-dozen choices at each course. The style is
'modern' Franglais, mobilising components that 20 years ago would have
seemed remarkable (luxuries for caliphs indeed) but now, alas, are two a
penny: filo baskets filled with haddock and quails' eggs; quail with oyster
mushrooms; guinea-fowl stuffed with foie gras; rabbit with pine kernels. It is
not all luxury, for the other side of the shopping list has rabbit, lambs' tongues,
lentils, monkfish. The cooking is praised by many, found heavy by a few – in
part because the quantities are generous, in part because of all the butter used
in the preparation and sauces. Flavours are not always as piercing as they
might be. There is an acceptable, almost wholly French, wine list. House
French wines, five in all, are £7.95. CELLARMAN'S CHOICE : St-Romain 1985,
Guyot, £19.65; Chassagne Montrachet, *premier cru*, Clos Maltroye, 1983, £24.25.

CHEFS: P.T. McEntire, Rebecca Jones, Karen MacDonald and Mathew Bickerton
PROPRIETORS: Andrew Thomason and Tim McEntire
OPEN: Tue to Sat, exc Sat L
CLOSED: Christmas to New Year
MEALS: 12.30 to 2, 7.30 to 9.30
PRICES: Set L £14.25 (£20) to £17.75 (£24), Set D £25.95 (£33). Licensed, also bring your
own: corkage £7.95
CARDS: Access, Amex, Diners, Visa
SEATS: 34. Private parties: 36 main room. No children under 10. Wheelchair access.
Air-conditioned

SUTTON COLDFIELD  West Midlands                                     map 5

## ▲ *New Hall* ▼

Walmley Road, Sutton Coldfield B76 8QX                         COOKING 2
021-378 2442                                                   COST £21–£42

'The oldest inhabited moated house in England.' The oldest moat maybe, the
house not so likely. It is now a country conference hotel owned by Thistle, with
a country club coming on stream. The business is Business, with enough staff
to justify its formal opening by the Secretary of State for Employment. The
cooking has been entrusted to Allan Garth, once at Gravetye Manor, an
exponent of modern British cooking. Reports tell of a long menu with some

emphasis on fish and some nice ideas: salad of roast monkfish tail; home-smoked salmon; home-cured beef; paupiettes of leek and Gorgonzola; ragout of lobster; brill with scallops on a basil butter sauce; noodles with aubergines, basil and a white wine cream sauce. Nothing to shock a fairly conservative audience, but not without attractions. Execution tends to the light flavoured, if not bland, though a dish of rabbit with wild mushrooms and hazelnuts was good enough to convince of real talent in the kitchen if business considerations do not crowd it out. The wine list is long, with a good range from all producing countries. House French, £9.45 and £9.75. CELLARMAN'S CHOICE : Domaine de Trévallon, Coteaux des Baux 1986, £16.50; Nautilus Hawkes Bay Sauvignon Blanc 1986, £14.50.

CHEFS: Allan Garth and Nigel Hitches   PROPRIETORS: Thistle Country House Hotels
OPEN: all week, exc Sat L
CLOSED: 1 Jan
MEALS: 12.30 to 2 (2.15 Sun), 7 to 10 (9.30 Sun)
PRICES: £25 (£35), Set L £12.50 (£21) to £15 (£24), Set D £19.50 (£29)
CARDS: Access, Amex, Carte Blanche, Diners, Visa
SEATS: 60. Private parties: 10 main room, 8,10 and 40 private rooms. Car-park, 80 places.
Vegetarian meals. Children's helpings. Smart dress preferred at D. No-smoking area.
Wheelchair access (also WC)
ACCOMMODATION: 64 rooms, all with bath/shower. Rooms for disabled. B&B £75 to £90. No children under 7. Baby facilities. Afternoon teas. Garden. TV. Phone. Scenic. Confirm by 6

---

**TAPLOW  Buckinghamshire**                                                   map 2

## ▲ *Cliveden*

Taplow SL6 0JF                                                        COOKING 3
BURNHAM (062 86) 68561                                                COST £31–£56

There probably is no grander hotel restaurant, even as the conversion of English, Welsh and Scottish mansions continues apace. The level of conviction arises from the conjunction of the National Trust and John Tham's Blakeney Hotels. Only the former could deliver a mature and maintained 376 acres of grounds (including some wonderful statuary); only the latter could convert (and now build anew) such unashamedly luxurious accommodation. Although diners themselves may be viewed as part of England's heritage, with visitors pressing their noses to the windows, it is an experience that may justify the very large bills. People speak highly of the service and the cosseting – not just the feather-bedding of millionaires from abroad, but a genuine interest in everybody's welfare. The cooking would have to be brilliant indeed to keep up with the surroundings. Reports have been reassuring that the food is rarely unsatisfactory. It achieves a degree of competence within an orthodox framework: cream of courgette soup; a salad of avocado, smoked chicken and quails' eggs dressed with walnut oil; medallions of monkfish with a mustard, dill and cucumber sauce; ragout of sole and shellfish with water asparagus; noisettes of lamb with a sorrel and mint sauce; a good cheeseboard, French and British; and a simple dessert of fresh fruit salad was a meal that pleased immensely. Others have commented on the menu being too short and unenterprising with only a few dishes having a memorable intensity, for example, quails' eggs with wild mushrooms. The wine list is anything but small and anything but cheap. In fact it is difficult to afford except in these flamboyant circumstances. Fortunately the house wines, a Côtes du Ventoux and a Bordeaux Sauvignon, are not so dear at £9. Tips or a service charge are 'neither included nor expected'. There is still a £3 surcharge added to every bill on behalf of the National Trust. It is difficult to stomach this item on an account for several hundred pounds, but somehow the inevitable questions are countered. However much we may carp, in the never-never world of five-stars, Cliveden is competitive. Living like a lord, away from noise and smoke, is a better deal in the country than the same role-play in the West End. That lords may need to earn more in a day than many bring home in a fortnight is by the way, or at least another question, as is whether the National Trust is right to countenance such behaviour.

CHEFS: Ron Maxfield and Michael Womersley    PROPRIETORS: Blakeney Hotels Ltd
OPEN: all week
MEALS: 12.30 to 2, 7.30 to 9.30
PRICES: £40 (£47), Set L £25.80 (£31) to £27.80 (£33), Set D £39.80 (£45). Service inc
CARDS: Access, Amex, Diners, Visa
SEATS: 49. Private parties: 110 main room, 30 private room. Car-park, 100 places.
Children's helpings. Smart dress preferred. Wheelchair access (also WC)
ACCOMMODATION: 25 rooms, all with bath/shower. Rooms for disabled. Lift. B&B £130 to
£375. Deposit: £130. Baby facilities. Pets welcome. Swimming-pool. Sauna. Tennis.
Fishing. Snooker. TV. Phone. Scenic

---

TAUNTON  Somerset                                                    map 2

## ▲ *Castle Hotel* ▮

Castle Green, Taunton TA1 1NF                               COOKING 4
TAUNTON (0823) 272671                                       COST £13–£58

Plumb centre of Taunton and overlooking a car-park, this is a town hotel in the best sense of the word. It may be expensive, but it takes in a wide band of customers. Have tea in the Rose Room some day. At one with this aspect are the traditional English lunch menus offered by Gary Rhodes in the restaurant and the fairly priced Sunday lunches. The *carte* or the set dinner menu are of a fancier bent: fresh crab bisque with three shellfish ravioli; confit of duck on marinated butter beans and endives; foie gras terrine with a warm artichoke and baby leek salad; best end of lamb on pommes Anna with grilled aubergine and a confit of garlic; venison topped with a wild mushroom mousse on potato cakes and served with its own sauce. This chef moves with the times. The customers like it, just as they like the complimentary gazpacho to start off their meal, and the varieties of breads. They do not like the small portions or the occasionally remorseless delays. Gary Rhodes's sauces are often marked out for praise, as in a Sunday lunch of warm fillets of lemon sole with asparagus tips and a mussel orange sauce, followed by an escalope of salmon on pale green noodles with an oyster champagne sauce accompanied by vegetables on a side plate, and finishing with the 'bountiful and varied' cheese trolley and walnut bread. (Our correspondent was evidently anxious for fish.) Although the Castle is strongly about luxury, from the new chairs in the dining-room to the redecorated front hall, it should be credited with a desire to spread its charms as widely as possible. People remark on the usually affable and courteous welcome. The wine list is large and exhaustingly laid out. It starts with 23 house wines from £5.50 to £8.50, another mark of social conscience. It also tells you (in the computer code) the supplier of every bottle (Corbar is Corney & Barrow). Averys of Bristol is the source of many of the older Bordeaux and burgundies but selection is more catholic than that implies: good ranges from Germany, the United States and Australia, as well as a group of Greek bottles and half a dozen from Somerset. Half-bottles are very generously supplied. The choice from the French regions – Loire, Rhône, the south-west – is not as imaginative as the rest of the list. CELLARMAN'S CHOICE : Ch. Léoville-Barton, St Julien 1978, £35; Beaune, Vignes Franches 1982, Louis Latour, £18.10. The Chapmans write that a 'service charge is neither included nor anticipated as service is our business.'

CHEF: Gary Rhodes   PROPRIETORS: The Chapman family
OPEN: all week
MEALS: 12.30 to 2, 7.30 to 9 (9.30 Fri and Sat)
PRICES: £39 (£48), Set L £10.50 (£13), Set D £21 (£24). Service inc
CARDS: Access, Amex, Diners, Visa
SEATS: 110. Private parties: 65 main room, 50 and 110 private rooms. Car-park, 40 places. Children's helpings (with prior notice). No cigars/pipes in dining-room. Smart dress preferred. Wheelchair access (also WC)
ACCOMMODATION: 35 rooms, all with bath/shower. Lift. B&B £66 to £95. Baby facilities. Afternoon teas. Garden. TV. Phone. Doors close at midnight. Confirm by 6 [GHG]

---

TETBURY  Gloucestershire                                    map 2

## ▲ Calcot Manor

Beverston, Tetbury GL8 8YJ
LEIGHTERTON (066 689) 391                          COOKING 3
on A4135, 3m W of Tetbury                         COST £19–£47

We self-deprecating British often come across some rural scene, some romantic ruin, in France or Italy and gaze wonderingly at it. 'This could never be in Warwickshire,' we say. But drive out of Tetbury to the high road leading from Bath to Stroud. At Beverstone, mildly overgrown, is a complex of buildings: ruined castle, church, farm and magnificent columned barn as romantic as any in the recesses of Lot et Garonne. Not far from this group is Calcot Manor, itself interesting: a grange of the Cistercian abbey of Kingswood with its surviving tithe barn. The Ball family have steadily converted it to a comfortable and graceful country-house hotel – complete with whirlpool baths and four-poster beds. Ramon Farthing continues to cook in a fiercely modern style that draws compliments from many but with a few suggestions that the food is too elaborate for the tastes to shine through. A milk chocolate sauce with a kumquat soufflé overlays the fresh citrus tang; a caramel and almond ice-cream with fresh peaches and raspberries served in April looked impressive but those fruits are seasonal far from these shores. Other practices of ancienne nouvelle cuisine are noted – much flourishing of silver domes and 'spartan nouvelle' vegetables among them. This would not deny that Ramon Farthing is very accomplished. Whole scallops in cream with spinach and lamb's lettuce, flavoured with a bacon and tomato sauce, was as good to eat as to look at, and another scallop dish, served warm with a marinated rainbow trout, baby leeks and a carrot and orange sauce, was extremely harmonious. Main courses have also had good notices: a duck served with braised onion and beetroot sitting on a fine grenadine sauce, and a fine piece of salmon with a thyme cream sauce and shredded peppers are fairly typical examples. Some have reported a clash of components: a loin of smoked veal that was crowded out by a chocolate mint sauce is an instance. Cheeses are a fair British selection and home-made biscuits and the bread basket have been well praised. The hotel, and its kitchen, may be the sort of place that excites strong opinion: too glossy lifestyle magazine for some, a tasteful and seemly way of conducting things for others. House French is £7.50. CELLARMAN'S CHOICE : Ch. de la Rivière 1979, Fronsac, £21.50; Clos du Château Bourgogne Chardonnay 1984, £21.85.

CHEF: Ramon Farthing   PROPRIETORS: Brian and Barbara Ball
OPEN: all week, exc Sun D
MEALS: 12.15 to 1.45, 7.30 to 9.30
PRICES: Set L £15 (£19) to £25 (£29), Set D from £25 (£29) to £35 (£39), Snacks from £2.50 (residents only). Service inc
CARDS: Access, Amex, Diners, Visa
SEATS: 45. 6 tables outside. Private parties: 48 main room, 12 private room. Car-park, 75 places. Vegetarian meals. Children's helpings (L only). Smart dress preferred. No smoking in dining-room. Wheelchair access (also WC)
ACCOMMODATION: 13 rooms, all with bath/shower. Rooms for disabled. B&B £60 to £110. No children under 12. Afternoon teas. Garden. Swimming-pool. TV. Phone. Scenic. Doors close at midnight. Confirm by 6 [GHG]

---

THORNBURY  Avon                                                        map 2

## ▲ *Thornbury Castle* 🍷

Castle Street, Thornbury BS12 1HH                              COOKING 3
THORNBURY (0454) 418511                                     COST £18–£37

It was bad luck the Dukes of Buckingham kept getting their heads chopped off. Had they lived, Thornbury might have been completed. As it is, this is England's finest lived-in ruin. The magnificent conversion from restaurant to hotel, initiated by Kenneth Bell, has made it a magnet to international and business clients. Nonetheless, the restaurant itself has retained a local following, and the welcome to passing travellers – like the reader on his way to Wales for a weekend with the in-laws – is warm and fortifying for the rigours ahead. The luxury and service of the hotel lend it a slight impersonality (some would call it professionalism) which makes it difficult for the restaurant to keep up. It does try, and there are few complaints. The materials are good, the cooking has many solid virtues, quantities are generous. Also detected, however, is a slight imprecision in flavours, occasional bad timing and inconsistency in seasoning. The smoked salmon has been especially remarked for its quality; other good reports have been on a salmis of pigeon breast with a port and currant sauce; a hearty fish soup Nîmoise, though underseasoned; a piquant tomato sauce with red mullet; a turbot with sweet peppers and thyme that was generous and perfectly timed; excellent beef and lamb and a fruity kumquat sauce with tasty though too-fat duck. Vegetables are not a strong point and the desserts seem more traditional than the preceding courses, as do the petits fours. A fine range of English unpasteurised cheeses includes Double and Single Gloucesters and Hurston Dunlop, made by David Bone (*aet.* 74) from his house cow at Wiveliscombe in Somerset. Service is extremely skilled, and there seems a real desire to please. Lunch is good value. There is talk of a live guitarist wandering from table to table – perhaps this is only on fiesta nights. Any restaurant that offers Domaine de Trévallon as a house wine at £8.90 must be singular and worth cultivating. Maurice Taylor's wine list is an amazing treasure trove, all at very fair prices. London hotels, with which he may be fairly compared, should take a lesson from him. There are two pages of wines under £12; there are plenty of half-bottles, old and new; and there are the treasures of the Proprietor's Reserve, some of which may be fairly speculative very old English bottlings, but all of which would stir an adventurer's heart. Some sections are deceptive: red burgundies, for instance, do not offer as wide a range of modern wines as might be expected; but this is more than made up by the Rhônes, the New World, Spanish and Italian choices. Memories of lists of the Bell era, replete with old Averys bottlings, half-bottles and other gems, will return to some people. House white wine is the Thornbury Castle Müller-Thurgau at £7.85. CELLARMAN'S CHOICE : Rosemount Fumé Blanc 1987, £11.40; Ch. Musar 1979, £11.30.

CHEFS: Colin Hingston and John Barber   PROPRIETOR: Maurice Taylor
OPEN: all week
MEALS: 12 to 2, 7 to 9.30 (9 Sun)
PRICES: Set L £12.50 (£18) to £15.50 (£21), Set D £21.50 (£27) to £25.50 (£31). Service inc
CARDS: Access, Amex, Carte Blanche, Diners, Visa
SEATS: 60. Private parties: 25 main room. Car-park, 30 places. Vegetarian meals. No children under 12. Smart dress preferred. Wheelchair access
ACCOMMODATION: 18 rooms, all with bath/shower. B&B £64 to £85. No children under 12. No smoking in dining-room. Garden. TV. Phone. Scenic [GHG]

---

**THORNTON CLEVELEYS  Lancashire**                                    map 5

## ▲ *Victorian House*

Trunnah Road
Thornton Cleveleys FY5 4HF                                    COOKING 2
CLEVELEYS (0253) 860619                                        COST £26

Thornton Cleveleys is a twin settlement, with an umbilical dual-carriageway. The restaurant is at the Thornton end, opposite the church. It was once a convent, its grounds long since consigned to the purgatory of suburbia. M. and Mme. Guérin, he French, she English, have worked in Paris for many years (as well as Staffordshire) so 'the antimacassar tendency of this theatrically Victorian production appears mellowed by the French connection.' Dinner starts well with good bread. It goes on to a fixed-price menu of four courses (second course soup or sorbet) with a wide choice, including a vegetarian dish, for instance roast brown rice and hazelnut pâté with 'an exquisite nutty cream sauce'. Although there have been ups and downs reported, the cooking is generous without excess: chicken livers with Noilly Prat and cream; mackerel marinated in Muscadet; gratin of eggs with mushroom and leeks; lamb with mustard; chicken with claret and honey; pork with onion cream sauce. A besetting problem is excess salt. Some of the flavourings are approximate, or so amalgamated as to be indiscernible. Desserts have included hot steam puddings (pistachio and pineapple), so the French does not totally crowd out the Victorian. Cheeses are British. The wine list is French and excellent value. The choice is careful and interesting (more detail would help), extending to a few good vins de pays. Champagne is not expensive at all. House French, £6.90. CELLARMAN'S CHOICE : Menetou-Salon, le Petit Clos 1986, £11.50; Côtes de Buzet, Ch. de Gueuze 1982, £9.70.

CHEF: Didier Guérin   PROPRIETORS: Louise and Didier Guérin
OPEN: all week, D only
CLOSED: last week Jan, first week Feb
MEALS: 7 to 9.30
PRICES: Set D £14.50 (£22). Service inc
CARD: Access, Visa
SEATS: 40. 4 tables outside. Private parties: 40 main room. Car-park, 20 places. Vegetarian meals. No children under 6. Smart dress preferred. Music
ACCOMMODATION: 3 rooms, all with bath/shower. B&B £35 to £50. Deposit: £10. No children under 6. Pets welcome. Garden. TV. Phone. Scenic. Confirm by 6

---

**THORNTON-LE-FYLDE  Lancashire**                                    map 5

## ▲ *River House* ♥

Skippool Creek
Thornton-le-Fylde FY5 5LF                                    COOKING 3
POULTON-LE-FYLDE (0253) 883497                               COST £36

Here is a restaurant of long service: its first entry in the *Guide*, under the Scotts' ownership, was in 1961. It is a Victorian house by the side of one of the creeks to the River Wyre. Among the masts and hulls of the yachts are waders and waterfowl. Our inspectors saw two herons and a great-crested grebe before dinner. Perhaps binoculars on the table is excessive, but there may be temptation. Within, in dining-rooms, bar or conservatory/verandah, the decorative atmosphere is still Victorian, with the warm comfort of a private home. The *carte* is quite long – a dozen items for each course – but bears the qualifying message that 'in view of the chaotic supply situation in fresh foods, on occasion, some items on this menu may not be available'. The same chaos is said to obtain on the wine list. This smacks of inefficiency, who knows where? The menu mixes the old and the new: roast lamb and mint sauce and an assiette gourmande des viandes with a tarragon sauce; beluga caviare with soufflé suissesse. This marriage seems very successful. The menu is also high on protein: substantial dishes, no stinting on the meats or fish. An inspection yielded a good, rich soufflé suissesse and a salmon angélique (volatile supply lines had caused absence of the usual turbot included in this latter dish) that was pieces of fish baked with cream, dill and cucumber. The main course of assiette gourmande consisted of large quantities of beef, lamb and veal on a tarragon sauce. The meats were good, the modes of cooking varied enough to keep interest alive and the sauce strong without intrusion. Pigeon breasts with a madeira sauce was equally good, though the sauce might have been lighter, the service a little more refined. Excellent vegetables were followed by a triune dessert: three ramekins of crème brûlée, rhubarb compote and home-made yoghurt. Each satisfactory, not improved by their combining. Good cafetière coffee and trimmings before and after the meal. The wine list may be good but shows little sign of letting on. Though bins are described with sparse detail, the facts, emerging by catechism or demonstration, are often impressive: a good, well-chosen collection from many regions, many countries. However, some of the staff know little more than the colour, so it helps neither the unsure nor the curious. Wine service, by contrast, causes the reds to be properly decanted and the whites properly cooled even if the glasses are not kept full – but that, for many of us, is a good thing. In 1961, chicken River House was ten shillings and sixpence (52p). This was roasted 'with mushrooms and onion stuffing, apricot, stuffed bacon rolls and grapes'. In 1989, breast of chicken 'taken off the bone, stuffed with a farce of walnuts, cheese, lemon and herbs, served with a chicken sauce and pilaff rice' was £11.50. 'Oh! happy days.' The Scotts have always been animal lovers: in 1973 it was Schnauzers, in 1989 it was a labrador and cats. House Spanish is £10. CELLARMAN'S CHOICE : Ch. Figeac 1982, £51.80; Cloudy Bay Chardonnay, 1987, £20.50.

CHEFS/PROPRIETORS: Bill and Carole Scott
OPEN: Mon to Sat, exc Sat L
MEALS: 12 to 2, 7.30 to 9.30
PRICES: £25 (£30). Licensed, also bring your own: corkage £5
CARDS: Access, Amex
SEATS: 45. Private parties: 45 main room. Car-park, 20 places. Children's helpings. Wheelchair access. Music
ACCOMMODATION: 4 rooms, 1 with bath/shower. B&B £55 to £80. Baby facilities. Pets welcome. Garden. TV. Phone. Scenic. Confirm by 6

---

**THRESHFIELD  North Yorkshire**  map 7

## Old Hall

| Threshfield BD23 5HB | COOKING 1 |
| SKIPTON (0756) 752441 | COST £18 |

In a short space of time, new owners have re-established Old Hall into a very pleasant, thriving and bustling pub serving excellent beer (Timothy Taylors) and good food in hyper-English pub surroundings. The menu, however, chalked up on a board, reads like a geography lesson and underlines how multi-cultural Britain is best seen in pubs and bistros, not high-class restaurants. Clams cataplana, pork vindaloo and Indonesian lamb might rub along with Roman chicken and Chinese red mullet. Flavours are not skimped, nor are quantities. Puddings do not get the plaudits of the savoury dishes. House wine, £6.

CHEFS: Carl Gilbert and Rachel Mawer   PROPRIETOR: Ian Taylor
OPEN: all week, exc Mon in winter
MEALS: 11.30 to 2, 6.30 to 9.30
PRICES: £10 (£15). Snacks from £1.10
SEATS: 40. 4 tables outside. Private parties: 35 main room. Car-park, 30 places. Children's helpings. Wheelchair access (also WC). Music

---

*Preliminary test of a good restaurant: order fresh orange juice and see what you get.*

---

TICKHILL   South Yorkshire                                              map 5

# Forge

1 Sunderland Street, Tickhill DN11 9PT                      COOKING 1
DONCASTER (0302) 744122                                         COST £29

Reactions to Helen Taylor's lavishly elaborate, one might almost say baroque,
style of cooking can vary. For some the complexity, the array of vegetables and
the garnishes spilling over the plate are too much. Dishes often astound by the
argument of flavours: poached pear hollowed out and filled with pigeon and
walnut salad and a thin lining of Stilton mousse topped with tarragon cream;
monkfish pieces coated in coconut in a filo pastry case with a mild fruity curry
sauce; medallions of pork on fresh pineapple with a cream curry sauce and
mango jelly. One customer has described it as French nouvelle for
Yorkshiremen. But the bookings are for months ahead; the cooking, the
ingredients and the generosity carry the day. By contrast with the gastronomic
opulence, the setting is restrained, rather like a cellar kitchen in a large house.
There is a certain amount of shunting about to accommodate two sittings on
busy nights, but none of it is bad mannered and the clientele happily complies.
The wine list is short and sensible. House French, £5.40, and German, £7.20.
CELLARMAN'S CHOICE : Morgon 1987, Louis Tête £9.90. Coffee is taken
upstairs in the lounge.

CHEF: Helen Taylor   PROPRIETORS: Helen and Howard Taylor
OPEN: Tue to Sat, D only
MEALS: 7 to 9.30
PRICES: Set D £19.50 (£24)
SEATS: 38. Children welcome. No cigars/pipes in dining-room. Music. Air-conditioned

TIDEFORD   Cornwall                                                    map 1

# Heskyn Mill

Tideford PL12 5JS                                             COOKING 1
LANDRAKE (075 538) 481                                           COST £25

The old mill wheel is still there, though no longer working. Inside the cottage
are beams low enough to pose a threat to tall diners, comfortable sofas and an
open fire. 'Our local suppliers are being more consistent and adventurous.
Also, our customers seem more willing to experiment,' say the Edens who use
as much Cornish fish, shellfish, meat and game as they can. Besides the regular
carte, they offer a list of specials which changes every four to five weeks, and
daily dishes such as a salad of queen scallops. The kitchen produces eventful
combinations: pheasant breast stuffed with garlic and cream cheese; rack of
lamb with cranberries and satsumas; John Dory with lime and tarragon. But
the style of the actual cooking is much older-fashioned than these sound. Duck
with juniper berry sauce has been praised and home-made ice-creams are the
favourite dessert. The wine list is very satisfactory, addressing the New World
as well as the Old. House French, from Lamblin, £5.95. CELLARMAN'S CHOICE :
Senorio de los Llanos, Valdepeñas 1975, £9.25; Wyndham Estate Oak-Matured
Chardonnay 1987, £9.75.

CHEFS: K. Williams and F.A. Eden   PROPRIETORS: F. and S.M.L Eden
OPEN: Tue to Sat
MEALS: 12 to 1.45, 7 to 10
PRICES: £15 (£21), Snacks from £1.65
CARDS: Amex, Visa
SEATS: 60. 6 tables outside. Private parties: 50 main room. Car-park, 25 places. Children's
helpings. Music

---

**TORQUAY  Devon**                                                                      map 1

# ▲ *Mulberry Room*

| 1 Scarborough Road, Torquay TQ2 5UJ | COOKING 2 |
|---|---|
| TORQUAY (0803) 213639 | COST £8–£20 |

Hardly a stone's throw from Remy Bopp (see entry below), Lesley Cooper
operates this café/restaurant/guest-house on a corner in Torquay's hotel
district. She attracts holidaymakers through her doors by dint of good cooking
and good value, but more important, perhaps, is that locals appreciate the
worth of what she is doing. This is café cooking as it was always meant to be,
served in surroundings as pretty as a tea room, with imagination thrown in.
The blackboard shows the soups, the pâtés, the savoury tarts and nut rissoles,
along with a roast chicken, a Torbay sole or a lamb casserole; the table in the
first room displays the lemon meringue pie, trifle, walnut and carrot cake,
meringues and soft fruit and other good cakes and sweets. The scale of
generosity is remarkable, the touches of invention laudable. Sunday lunch is
a fixture and excellent value for a roast with trimmings. The wine list is short
and very cheap. House wine is £5. CELLARMAN'S CHOICE : Sancerre Rosé
1986, £8; Domaine de Gaillat, Graves 1978, £10.50. Lesley Cooper's honey is
also very good.

---

CHEF/PROPRIETOR: Lesley Cooper
OPEN: Wed to Sun L, and Sat D
MEALS: 12.15 to 2.30, 7.30 to 9.30
PRICES: £7 (£10), Set L £5.75 (£8) to £6.75 (£9), Set D £13 (£16) to £14 (£17). Snacks from
£1.50. Service inc
SEATS: 30. 2 tables outside. Private parties: 40 main room. Vegetarian meals. Children's
helpings. Wheelchair access (also WC). Music
ACCOMMODATION: 3 rooms. B&B £10.50 to £19. Deposit: 10%. Afternoon teas. TV. Doors
close at 9. Confirm by 7

---

# *Remy's*

| 3 Croft Road, Torquay TQ2 5VN | COOKING 2 |
|---|---|
| TORQUAY (0803) 292359 | COST £24 |

The restaurant quarter of Torquay seems to lie just behind Belgrave Road; two
restaurants in this *Guide* are but 20 yards from each other – leaving a desert the
size of the Gobi beyond the oasis. Remy Bopp first came to England nearly 20
years ago and Torquay was his destination. A stint in the north ended with his
return to the seaside, tending a simple and genuine French restaurant that
continues to garner its tithe of warm approval each year. There is to be more

comfort in 1990 with a new bar to sit out in. A set-price menu brings a choice six or eight dishes in each course, modern restaurant fare rather than French bourgeois: fresh pasta and smoked salmon; sweetbreads in shortcrust with a calvados sauce; best end of lamb with basil and tomato; guinea-fowl with a truffle sauce. Cheeses are good, thanks to Vin Sullivan's Devon arm, and fish comes fresh from Brixham. As M. Bopp himself observes, 'I make everything on the premises, keep the prices reasonable, use fresh ingredients and give customers a few hours of happiness.' Mme Bopp contributes to that happiness with tactful and careful attention to the service. The wine list kicks off with a range of Alsaces (M. Bopp's native province), then covers the rest of France, quickly but in keeping with the style of the place. House Duboeuf, £5.85. CELLARMAN'S CHOICE : Crémant d'Alsace, £16; Riesling d'Alsace 1986, Gisselbrecht, £9.85.

CHEF/PROPRIETOR: Remy Bopp
OPEN: Tue to Sat, D only
CLOSED: 2 weeks Aug
MEALS: 7.15 to 9.30
PRICES: Set D £15.85 (£20). Service inc
CARDS: Amex, Visa
SEATS: 40. Private parties: 38 main room, 38 private room. Children's helpings. Smart dress preferred. Music

---

**TRESCO  Isles of Scilly**　　　　　　　　　　　　　　　map 1

## ▲ *New Inn*

Tresco TR24 0QQ　　　　　　　　　　　　　　　COOKING 1
SCILLONIA (0720) 22844　　　　　　　　　　　　　COST £13−£22

The Isles of Scilly are goals for themselves, not objects of gastronomic pilgrimage. However, the New Inn offers cooking of an imagination and freshness well above the norm, particularly the fish. At lunch there are decent snacks at the bar but evening set dinners encompass greater variety and invention than may be expected. The wine list, too, is longer than the situation may demand. House wine is £5.25.

CHEF: Graham Stone　PROPRIETORS: Christopher and Lesley Hopkins
OPEN: all week, D only
CLOSED: 2 weeks Dec
MEALS: 7.30 to 8.30 (6.30 to 8 Fri in summer)
PRICES: Set D £9.50 (£13) to £13.50 (£18), Snacks from £1
SEATS: 36. Private parties: 20 main room, 12 private room. Vegetarian meals. No children under 10
ACCOMMODATION: 12 rooms, 10 with bath/shower. B&B mid-Oct to mid-Apr £16.85; D,B&B mid-Apr to mid-Oct from £35. Deposit: £30. Baby facilities. Afternoon teas. Garden. Swimming-pool. Phone. Scenic [GHG]

---

*The text of entries is based on unsolicited reports sent in by readers, backed up by inspections conducted anonymously. The factual details under the text are from questionnaires the* Guide *sends to all restaurants that feature in the book.*

---

**TRURO Cornwall** map 1

## ▲ *Alverton Manor*

Tregolls Road, Truro TR1 1XQ              COOKING 3
TRURO (0872) 76633              COST £13–£37

The name, the scale, the large gardens on the outskirts of Truro might indicate a country-house operation, but the Costelloes, who have spent great sums converting this Victorian former bishop's residence, then convent, seem to have their eyes fixed on the business potential of Cornwall's capital – a town with a high incidence of estate agents and developers. Although decorated with lavishness, there is an impersonality, a lack of gracious public rooms and an excess of Muzak (*Swan Lake* at dinner *and* breakfast ad nauseam, although an electric piano has also been reported) and fax machines. This tilt to efficiency rather than warmth comes over when booking a room. You are informed that the full charge will be debited to your credit card account should you cancel at short notice and the room not be relet. Such practice is dubious: the nature of the contract on reserving a table or a room entitles the supplier of the service to compensation for loss of profit, not the whole cost. After all, the sheets won't need washing, nor the room need cleaning.

Chef Alan Vickops has been with the venture since its inception. Just as the place is the grandest in the county, his cooking is in the most obviously metropolitan style (of about five years ago). This may involve some *nouvelle* silliness: vast plates, silver domes, menus that read 'a symphony of Cornish crab and Scottish smoked salmon' and 'scallop mousse draped with chive sauce'. He is also keen on raspberry butter sauce. In 1988 it appeared with red mullet and ginger; more recently with a breast of chicken poached with citrus zests. Surprisingly, it met with approval on both occasions. Last year's fashion also was evident in the free granita after the first course: reporters have found it too sweet, and often more sorbet than flaky granita. Set aside these potential irritants – which may not be so to some – and the kitchen does produce reliable food which the restaurant staff, mostly young and Cornish, deliver amiably and without airs and graces. Some good dishes have been red mullet with scallops in saffron cream sauce; scallop mousse; a fish soup looking like a fish stew; cannons of lamb, in pastry, with a rosemary sauce; marquise au chocolat; coconut pie with a mango coulis. In general, dishes have impressed by their appearance and execution. The wine list has shown occasional failures of management. Prefaced by a disclaimer about years (if you can't get continuity, don't stock it, or change the list), many wines have been out of stock, including the house red without, amazingly, a substitute being offered. Some of the prices are stellar – or lunar, depending on your point of view – but there are some interesting bottles, for example the Australians from Peter Lehmann and Mount Helen. House French, £7.75. CELLARMAN'S CHOICE : Ch. Latour (no, not that one – a Bordeaux Supérieur) 1984, £12.75; Peter Lehmann Dry Semillon 1988, £11.75. Tips are 'not expected'.

---

*'We brought one home (a breast of pigeon) and had it cold for lunch the following day; it was even better than when hot!'* On dining in Lancashire

CHEF: Alan Vickops   PROPRIETORS: Mr and Mrs J.J. Costelloe
OPEN: all week
MEALS: 12.15 to 1.45, 7.15 to 9.45
PRICES: £23 (£31), Set L £7.95 (£13), Set D £11.55 (£17). Service inc
CARDS: Access, Amex, Diners, Visa
SEATS: 50. 3 tables outside. Private parties: 35 main room, 25 and 35 private rooms. Car-park, 70 places. Children's helpings (Sun L only). No children under 12. Smart dress preferred. Wheelchair access (also WC). Music
ACCOMMODATION: 25 rooms, all with bath/shower. Rooms for disabled. Lift. B&B £63 to £85. No children under 12. Afternoon teas. Garden. Snooker. TV. Phone. Scenic [GHG]

## Le Provençal

| 15 Kenwyn Street, Truro TR1 3BU | COOKING 1 |
|---|---|
| TRURO (0872) 72546 | COST £34 |

Mike Berriman's small cottage of a restaurant might confirm the Mediterranean view of Cornwall – that the whitewash and flowers are justified by the weather – by intention if not fact. His cooking, if not wholly Mediterranean itself, is best seen through the medium of fish or lamb, which serves to foster the illusion. The food can be direct and enjoyable. Dinners have included steamed sea bass with ginger and lemon; fish soup with cumin; a Provençal fish soup; lamb steak with flageolets; duck with blackcurrants. Life often seems too much for the organisation of the restaurant, so not all tales are of joy: incompetence and shortcuts have also figured. The wine list was being altered at the time of writing, so no details are available.

CHEF/PROPRIETOR: Mike Berriman
OPEN: Mon to Sat D (L by arrangement only)
MEALS: 7 to 10.30
PRICES: £22 (£28)
SEATS: 20. Private parties: 15 main room. Children's helpings. Wheelchair access (1 step)

---

| TUNBRIDGE WELLS   Kent | map 3 |
|---|---|

## Cheevers

| 56 High Street, Tunbridge Wells TN1 1XF | COOKING 3 |
|---|---|
| TUNBRIDGE WELLS (0892) 545524 | COST £21–£28 |

The decoration is a careful blend of old and new, with a sleek modern interior behind original frontage on the hilly High Street. Likewise, the food is a balance of the traditional and fashionable, with local produce to the fore in a short menu that rings the changes from day to day. A few favourites, like the crab mousse wrapped in spinach or the parfait of two chocolates, are fixtures, and guinea-fowl, salmon, loin of veal and free-range chicken make frequent appearances with different sauces. Otherwise, well-reported dishes have come and gone: rack of lamb roasted rare in a mint and almond crust with a well-reduced, shiny sauce; mussels, once in ravioli and another time in fennel soup; a white chicken sausage with apple. Flavours are kept uncluttered and are sometimes earthy, as in a salad of leaves, lentils and gammon. The firmly British style is followed through in plainly cooked vegetables, English cheeses, a hot walnut and ginger pudding, even a kir made with English white wine and locally made raspberry liqueur. Curiously, given all this, bread and coffee are disappointing. Smokers are politely discouraged and tips are not expected. The wines number around 50 and are French, bar half a dozen. The choice is an intelligent one and the prices fair. There are a couple of whites from Penshurst. House French is £5.75. CELLARMAN'S CHOICE : Vouvray Domaine de L'Epinay 1986, £10.75; Ch. l'Etoile, Graves 1982, £14.50.

CHEF: T.J. Cheevers   PROPRIETORS: T.J. Cheevers, M.J. Miles and P.D. Tambini
OPEN: Tue to Sat
MEALS: 12.30 to 2, 7.30 to 10.30
PRICES: £15 (£21), Set D £18 (£23)
CARDS: Access, Visa
SEATS: 36. Private parties: 36 main room. Children welcome. No cigars/pipes in dining-room. Wheelchair access

## Sankey's Seafood at the Gate

The Gate, 39 Mount Ephraim
Tunbridge Wells TN4 8AA                                            COOKING 1
TUNBRIDGE WELLS (0892) 511422                                        COST £29

Easily found in the town centre, Sankey's is run by a man with a passion for fish, bought as fresh as possible every day. The menu changes all the time according to availability and ranges from fat Cornish cock crabs, Helford oysters, Loch Fyne salmon and other natives to exotica such as sweet and meaty Cuban rock lobsters, soft-shelled crabs from Florida or tilapia from Jamaica. The food is served on plain wooden tables and comes with French bread to mop up the juices and sauces as well as either vegetables or a choice of salad. The style of cooking varies from bouillabaisse, paella, and a Portuguese treatment for clams, to an avocado bake for crabs. The timing and sauces may go wrong with these complicated ideas and the simpler dishes, such as salads or plainly grilled or poached fish, get the greatest praise. The intention is to create space for upstairs dining and downstairs drinking and snacking. The wine list on the back of the big menu is great fun and good, with useful glasses and half-bottles. House French from £6 and some nice Belgian beer and French cider, to say nothing of English wine.

CHEF: Eleuterio Lizzi   PROPRIETOR: Guy Sankey
OPEN: Mon to Sat
MEALS: 12 to 2, 7 to 10
PRICES: £20 (£24), Snacks £2.50. Service inc
CARDS: Access, Amex, Visa
SEATS: 60. 6 tables outside. Private parties: 8 main room, 30 private room. Children's helpings on request. No cigars/pipes in dining-room

*If you see a certificate in a restaurant bearing the words 'Diploma of Merit. The Good Food Guide (United Kingdom)', the claim is false (and the restaurant may be in contempt of court in displaying it) – see the Introduction. Please write and tell us the name and address of the restaurant.*

# Thackeray's House ♥

85 London Road
Tunbridge Wells TN1 1EA
TUNBRIDGE WELLS (0892) 511921

COOKING **3**
COST £20–£46

This small detached house, once home to England's greatest novelist (a worthy debating point), cooks less conservatively than the Conservative club it neighbours. Bruce Wass was first noticed when he was chef at Odins, now some years past, but he came to Kent with London values and has never ignored what goes on in the world beyond. That said, he has a ferocious sense of the right and proper in materials: 'I have never cooked fish that has been frozen', he once wrote, 'nor used salmon that was farmed.' Some pride, then, in bearing the fruit of Devon holidays home to the South-East in his subsequent use of Ann Petch's pork, bacon, Shetland lamb and sausages. The restaurant is serious in the nicest sense: everything home made; a thoughtful menu; formal service without pomposity. The use of small rooms makes the restaurant intimate, but the decoration stops short of claustrophobic. Dishes that have pleased include croustade of Arbroath smokies and crab; chicken boudin with a hot onion marmalade; saddle of venison with pear and juniper; mutton with port, juniper and orange; coconut parfait with exotic fruit. Bread, brioche and pastry work is first-class. Some of the dishes tend to be complicated. There are occasional gourmet evenings and Mr Wass' social conscience (for prices are not low) is eased by the existence of Downstairs at Thackeray's where simpler food is cooked. Downstairs may be a cheaper version, but there are witnesses that it's not worse: 'scallops from Glenborrodale – small but perfect, served at their simple best; honey roast duck with lemon sauce brought back fond memories of Provence; date, ginger and toffee pudding' met all expectations. The shoppers of the South-East should note it. The wine list shows the same devotion to careful buying. Mr Wass comments that his Australian section is reduced, 'because I no longer feel they offer the value they did. I have yet to taste an American wine that I can list with confidence.' Others may disagree. The choice of growers is sensitive: this is an example to many others that if you have so few wines you have to get it right. The longest section is claret, and there are a very fair number of halves, some of them dessert wines. Prices are quite high. House Côtes de Gascogne, £8.90. CELLARMAN'S CHOICE : Ch. de L'Estagnol 1986, Rodet, £10.45; Mâcon-Peronne 1987, Daniel Rousset, £12.75. 'We do not expect any tips.'

CHEFS: Bruce Wass and Nigel Ramsbottom    PROPRIETOR: Bruce Wass
OPEN: Tue to Sat
CLOSED: 1 week at Christmas
MEALS: 12.30 to 2.30, 7 to 10
PRICES: Set L £13.90 (£20) to £16.75 (£23), Set D £24 (£30) to £32 (£38). Service inc
CARDS: Access, Visa
SEATS: 35. Private parties: 40 main room. Children's helpings. No cigars/pipes in
dining-room

'The tables are rather close and you could hear the man at the next table whistling. Yes, whistling.'    On dining in Lancashire

map 3

## Cézanne

68 Richmond Road, Twickenham TW1 3BE                    COOKING 3
01-892 3526                                             COST £26

In a shopping parade on the main road between Richmond and Twickenham, the restaurant – it may be tritely observed – is done out in Impressionist colours. The simplicity of it all disappoints lovers of the plush: 'the food was very good but the white cloths, white china – all in a good state – lacked any luxury'. Others will huzzah and hope time and money was spent on the cooking. 'I like this rather plain little restaurant very much. My lunch was scallops on a tagliatelle of courgettes and chives in a creamy sauce; saddle of hare delicately sliced and arranged in a flower with a good side dish of vegetables; and banana and sesame in a perfect filo container with a rich caramel sauce.' Good cooking, nice ideas, but nothing flash, with prices kept within reason, seem to be the consistent message. Most complaints surround not the quiet (yet here and there slow) charm of the service but the impossibility of discovering what is on for lunch. 'They do not have a set menu,' says one; 'You have to ask about the set menu,' says another. A third had an excellent time, but few of the dishes were from the menu. Perhaps it has depended on the state of business, but the doubt has now been resolved and there is no set lunch. Flavours are direct, but rarely impossible to perceive (as with the sesame and banana). 'Given a carpet on the floor and less sepulchral music, this would be really good.' There is an interesting short wine list from good suppliers at fair prices. House wines, £7. CELLARMAN'S CHOICE : Savennières, Ch. du Chamboureau 1985, £10; Wente Brothers Cabernet Sauvignon 1985, £10.

CHEF: Tim Jefferson   PROPRIETORS: Tim and Philippa Jefferson
OPEN: Mon to Sat, exc Sat L
CLOSED: bank hols
MEALS: 12.30 to 2, 7 to 10.30 (11 Fri and Sat)
PRICES: £15 (£22)
CARDS: Access, Amex, Visa
SEATS: 38. Private parties: 40 main room. Vegetarian meals. Children's helpings. Wheelchair access. Music

## McClements

12 The Green, Twickenham TW2 5AA                       COOKING 3
01-755 0176                                            COST £35

The small house is by the village pump on the Green – though whether Twickenham has exchanged gossip there since the days of Pope, Walpole and Lady Suffolk must be questionable. Tattle at McClements, however, will be all films and television. Like the kitchen, the restaurant is small, though in parts elegant. Size may cause problems from smokers. Reports would lead one to believe this is a fish restaurant as John McClements seems to have real talent in this direction: sea urchin soufflé; oysters wrapped in spinach, with sevruga caviare; bouillabaisse in an idiosyncratic version; scallops grilled with smoky bacon; ravioli filled with oysters, mussels and crab in a lobster sauce. Other mentions are of a lobster salad with pickled vegetables and tiny raviolis of goats' cheese and a dessert of a chocolate mille-feuille – the pastry substituted by thin chocolate wafers. Service has always been formal: a tray is borne to the table, the plates lifted from it with decorum. Where problems have arisen it has been from delays. The wine list includes a decent number of halves. House wines from Berry Bros & Rudd, £7.50.

CHEF/PROPRIETOR: John McClements
OPEN: Tue to Sat, exc Sat L
MEALS: noon to 2.30, 7 to 10.30
PRICES: Set L £15 (£23), Set D £21 (£29). Service 10%. Licensed, also bring your own: corkage £5
CARDS: Access, Amex, Visa
SEATS: 24. Private parties: 20 main room, 15 private room. No children under 3. Wheelchair access (also WC). Music

---

ULLSWATER  Cumbria                                                           map 7

## ▲ *Sharrow Bay* ♟

Howtown Road, Ullswater CA10 2LZ
POOLEY BRIDGE (08536) 301/483
2m from Pooley Bridge on E side of lake,                          COOKING 3
signposted Howtown and Martindale                             COST £19–£43

The acme of British catering; the charm of this lakeside villa is best appreciated lying in bed listening to torrents streaming down the hillside, and the susurration of waterfowl. The enthusiasm for the well-being of guests is disconcerting for a nation so subdued as the British. It may be noticed in the small sitting-rooms where you gather for sherry and a read of the menu. Sitting at quite close quarters, the conversation is *sotto voce* at the most. Enter Francis Coulson or Brian Sack and smiles appear, enthusiasm waxes, anticipation is brought to a point. The rest of the staff are of like mind. This is one of the few places where the morning greeting of the chambermaid is as fervent, articulate and genuine as that of the owners themselves. Families with young children have difficulty visiting Sharrow; the house is so full of ornament that a hasty movement – even well-meaning – may precipitate disaster. One forgives their exclusion, for once. Take your drink for long enough to read the menu carefully. Its form is arresting: a quarto sheet covered edge to edge with duplicated typing. Dinner and lunch (the latter cheaper, with a simpler menu) both offer a choice of first course, followed by a fish dish and a sorbet common to everyone in the dining-room, then choice of main course and dessert. As you progress through a dog-leg from lounge to dining-room, the cold desserts are laid out before you and interpreted by a skilful guide. The scope of the options is grand: from foie gras of duck on toasted brioche with a citrus accompaniment to fresh orange, melon and grapefruit cocktail; from best end of lamb in puff pastry with spinach and herbs to mushroom omelette; from fresh strawberry coconut meringue gateau to sherry trifle. The English grand hotel tradition flashes past you as decisions are made – so too, does the speculation that a dinner made up of the three simpler dishes listed above would tend towards the expensive at the set price of £31.50. The menu is large: 14 first courses, nine meat and fish dishes, and a dozen sweet things. It has the depth of business to be able to change daily. This year's crop of letters is unstinting in its praise: the strength of the restaurant is that people enjoy it so much, the solicitude is so evident, the view over the water so breathtaking, that the occasional fussiness of the cooking or the infrequent lapse is overlooked. Breakfasts are cooked by the master himself and teas are in the country tradition of self-sufficiency and the home-made, magnificent both. You can stay in the main villa or in Bank House a mile away. The annexe provides its own breakfasts in a room worth visiting for the architecturally magpie tendencies of its builder. The wine list is long and supplied by Youdell of Kendal. It is not invariably expensive; there is a proper showing of halves; it goes beyond France; there are some interesting bottles, for instance Blagny, Château de Blagny 1985 from Latour; but there is still an unhealthy reliance on big firms like Cordier, Bouchard and Louis Latour. House wines: non-vintage St-Emilion and Mâcon Blanc Villages at £9.50. CELLARMAN'S CHOICE : Beaune Vignes Franches 1978, Louis Latour, £27.60; Perrier-Jouët, Grand Brut, N.V., £25.50.

CHEFS: Francis Coulson, Johnnie Martin, Colin Akrigg, Philip Wilson, Alison Kennedy and Timothy Ford   PROPRIETORS: Francis Coulson and Brian Sack
OPEN: all week
MEALS: 1 to 1.45, 8 to 8.45
PRICES: Set L £14.50 (£19) to £21.50 (£26), Set D £31.50 (£36). Service inc
SEATS: 65. Private parties: 10 main room. Car-park, 30 places. No children under 13. Smart dress preferred. No smoking. Wheelchair access
ACCOMMODATION: 30 rooms, 26 with bath/shower. Rooms for disabled. D, B&B £68 to £136. No children under 13. Afternoon teas. Garden. TV. Phone. Scenic. Doors close at 12. Confirm by noon [GHG]

---

ULVERSTON   Cumbria                                               map 7

## Bay Horse Inn and Bistro

Canal Foot, Ulverston LA12 9EL                          COOKING 3
ULVERSTON (0229) 53972                                 COST £16–£26

Pass through the purgatory of Glaxo and its factory, get off the Barrow to Greenodd road, and you will achieve the heaven of the shore of Morecambe Bay with a view to Arnside Knott. The Bay Horse is a pub full of equine artefacts and, if you wish, bar billiards. The restaurant occupies a verandah, glassed in, only feet from the high-water mark. This is a John Tovey enterprise, Robert Lyons being the chef and resident director. Trademark of the Tovey scheme may be bobotie, a South African dish, found here as well as at the Miller Howe Kaff (see entry, Windermere). The Bay Horse version of this spiced lamb and almond first course has less lamb but the macaroni is wonderfully buttery. The real signs of Tovey origins, however, are the imaginative combination of ingredients, the excellent ways with vegetables and the refusal, flights of fancy notwithstanding, to ignore plain yet creative cookery. At Sunday lunch, for instance, for not much more than £10.50, guests may be regaled with a sugar-baked Waberthwaite ham or lamb baked in hay. Wilder combinations are kept in their place. The Horse has not adopted the Miller Howe formula of one-time, no-choice theatre. A *carte* is available at dinner, supplemented by a short and cheap table d'hôte at lunch. People seem willing to return time and again to try such dishes as smoked salmon and asparagus in egg custard, moules marinière, mango and lime soup with almonds or broccoli, cheese and fennel soup (they are strong on soups here). Then for the main dish there might be sweetbreads with tongue and chanterelles in a marsala sauce, salmon with vermouth and cream, wild rabbit with coriander and onion purée with a damson cheese tartlet, or pork on a fresh asparagus purée with cream and apples. Four or five vegetables along with this, then on through profiteroles with fresh peach cream and butterscotch, banana baked with apricot, vanilla, rum and raisins or an Irish coffee meringue. Coffee is good and comes without charge. For those who suspect this style of being a touch coarse and the flavours too varied to blend well, there are staunch defenders, prepared to vouchsafe comparability with any French or French-style cooking in the capital. The wine list is short, from Mitchell's of Lancaster, but includes some acceptable bottles at fair prices. In this second year, partitions have been torn down so that every diner may have the benefit of the view – in the daytime at least. House Orlando is £8 for red, £8.75 for white. CELLARMAN'S CHOICE : Montana Sauvignon Blanc 1988, £9.25; Montana Cabernet Sauvignon 1986, £9.25.

---

CHEF: Robert Lyons   PROPRIETORS: Robert Lyons and John Tovey
OPEN: Tue to Sun, exc Sun D
MEALS: 12 to 1.15, 7 to 9
PRICES: £16 (£22), Set L £10.50 (£16). Minimum £7.50. Service 10%
CARD: Access
SEATS: 30. 3 tables outside. Private parties: 20 main room. No children under 12. Smart dress preferred. No smoking. Wheelchair access (1 step; also WC). Music. Air-conditioned

---

**UNDERBARROW Cumbria**                                               map 7

## ▲ *Tullythwaite House*

| Underbarrow LA8 8BB | COOKING 2 |
|---|---|
| CROSWAITE (044 88) 397 | COST £18−£29 |

One doesn't know who might once have stumped up the slippery path from the iron gate to the arched front door: imagination says a poet, or at least a watercolourist, though an honest farmer is more likely. Dinner is served at one sitting, sometimes at 7 for 7.30 and sometimes at 7.30 for 8, attended by Michael Greenwood – both punctilious and measured. The menu is a short four-course matter at a set price, a choice of three first courses reducing to single alternatives thereafter. The emphasis of flavour is towards the sharp and tangy; thus, where fruit is used, it is to point up, not, as so often the case, to sweeten. Reports have continued to arrive approving dishes such as ballotine of duck with spiced plum sauce; Dover sole with two pepper sauces; pheasant with cranberries and oranges; and terrine of prunes with port and chocolate and English vanilla sauce (custard?). The short wine list has become less short. House French, £5.45. See under Greenriggs in *The Good Hotel Guide*.

---

*Report forms are at the back of the book; write a letter if you prefer.*

---

CHEF: Janet Greenwood  PROPRIETORS: Michael and Janet Greenwood
OPEN: Wed to Sat D, Sun L
CLOSED: Feb
MEALS: 12.30 to 2.30, 7 or 7.30 for 7.30 or 8
PRICES: Set L £11.95 (£18), Set D £17.95 (£24)
CARDS: Access, Visa
SEATS: 16. Private parties: 16 main room. Car-park, 14 places. No children under 12. Smart
dress preferred. No smoking. One sitting
ACCOMMODATION: 3 rooms, all with bath/shower. B&B £40 to £65. No children under 12.
Garden. TV. Scenic. Doors close at 11. Confirm by 4 [GHG]

---

**UPPINGHAM  Leicestershire**                                                    map 6

## ▲ *Lake Isle* ▮

16 High Street East, Uppingham LE15 9PZ                          COOKING 1
UPPINGHAM (0572) 822951                                            COST £13–£29

The High Street shop frontage sports curtains in the evening; the entrance itself
is gained via a passage two doors up. From small beginnings, it has become a
full-blown hotel. A breakfast of fresh orange juice, melon with green figs, herb
omelette and grilled kidneys Dijonnaise was celebrated by one reader as a fair
start to any day. The restaurant, predominantly green with pine furniture and
fittings and bentwood chairs, offers a *prix fixe* menu of three or four courses with
a couple of alternatives at each. The menu and style are resolutely French:
saucisson de venaison Lyonnaise; suprême de pintade au Porto avec groseilles;
roulade de porc aux épinards; sauce au poivre rose; délice de flétan avec soles
au laitue, sauce au safran – although none of the foregoing would be found so
expressed in France itself. The bread that comes, Lakeland style, with knife and
board is universally praised and the soups, though salty, have pleased for a
robust texture and flavour. Robust and genuine, too, was chicken-liver pâté
although constructions of fish in terrine have not been so welcomed – nor fish
in general on some days. Ice-creams have a good flavour and other puddings
are substantial and rich. Coffee is often poor. The glory of the restaurant is the
wine list. It considers the pocket, it helps the drinker of half-bottles, it has a
good range and it has bottles you might not otherwise buy. The difficulty is
choosing something. House French, £6.50. CELLARMAN'S CHOICE : Montagny
*premier cru* Ch. de la Guiche, André Goichot, 1986, £11.50; Lirac Rouge Ch. de
Segries 1986, Peloux, £7.75.

---

CHEFS: David Whitfield and Liam Tinney  PROPRIETORS: David and Claire Whitfield
OPEN: all week, exc Mon L and Sun D
MEALS: 12.30 to 2, 7.30 to 9.30 (10 Sat)
PRICES: Set L £9 (£13) to £11.50 (£16), Set D £15 (£20) to £18.50 (£24)
CARDS: Access, Amex, Diners, Visa
SEATS: 35. Private parties: 40 main room, 12 private room. Children's helpings.
Wheelchair access
ACCOMMODATION: 10 rooms, all with bath/shower. B&B £32 to £55. Pets welcome. TV.
Phone. Doors close at midnight [GHG]

---

*'On our third time of asking for the bill, we were told, ''That's the third time you've asked
for the bill.'' Yes, and the first time was an hour ago.'*  On dining in London

---

## ▲ *Spindlewood Hotel*

Wallcrouch, Wadhurst TN5 7JG
TICEHURST (0580) 200430
on B2099, between Wadhurst and                    COOKING 1
Ticehurst                                         COST £21–£30

'We are 2 miles south-east of Wadhurst on the B2099 between Wadhurst and
Ticehurst. If possible can you include this in the address, as several people
drive on from Wadhurst for a mile or so, think they have missed us, and return
– and hence arrive late and bemused.' Certainly. This Victorian country house,
formerly a nursing home, is set in five acres of grounds. Inside are pictures and
stuffed toys for sale; in winter it can appear gloomy, but a generous choice of
dishes is compensation. Boned quail is stuffed with plum, baked in filo pastry
with a plum and calvados sauce; ox-tail soup is home made; roast veal
sweetbreads are served with Yorkshire pudding in a mustard sauce. Fish
depends on the market and is treated well: sole and salmon mousse comes in a
shellfish bisque. Among the orange and caramel floating islands, and the
steamed chocolate sponge with vanilla and chocolate sauces, are savouries to
finish. The family serves. There is room for a trio of English wines in a 60-
bottle, largely French list. House wine is £5.95. CELLARMAN'S CHOICE :
Pouilly-Fumé, La Tuilerie 1987, £13.70; Mercurey, Champs Martin 1984,
Michel Juillot, £17.50. It is a good, usually reliable place for family gatherings.

CHEF: Harvey Lee Aram    PROPRIETOR: R. V. Fitzsimmons
OPEN: all week
CLOSED: 4 days at Christmas
MEALS: 12.15 to 1.30, 7.15 to 9
PRICES: £15 (£21), Set L and D £17.85 (£23) to £19.50 (£25)
CARDS: Access, Amex, Visa
SEATS: 40. Private parties: 50 main room, 18 private room. Car-park, 60 places. Vegetarian
meals. Children's helpings. No cigars/pipes in dining-room. Music
ACCOMMODATION: 9 rooms, all with bath/shower. B&B £42 to £70. Deposit: £20. Baby
facilities. Garden. TV. Phone. Doors close at midnight. Confirm by 6

## *Mary's*

Manor House, Walberswick IP18 6UG                  COOKING 1
SOUTHWOLD (0502) 723243                            COST £12–£17

Mary may be the name, but the menu claims to be 'Felicity's Fare': indication of
the passage of time and ownership from Mary Allen (once in this *Guide*) to
Felicity and Rob Jelliff. The first years of transition were uneasy, judging by
our post, but now this restaurant, never apparently less than two-thirds full,
seems back on form. The decoration – fishing nets and nautical items – might
be a subject for Ardizzone drawings, and the cooking takes a maritime view of
the stove: fresh dabs, plaice and slip soles; fried cod, prawn omelette and
home-smoked cod roe. Good soups, good pâté, good casseroles and 'fabulous'
pecan pie have been commented on. Only open weekends in the off-season;

snacks and specials at lunch and tea; a short set-price daily menu in the evening is the arrangement of trade. The wines are Adnams and not at all expensive. The choices are decent ones, but vintages are not given for the fastest movers. House French is £4.85. CELLARMAN'S CHOICE : Côtes du Rhône, Vignerons de Vacqueyras, £6.25; Pulham Vineyards Magdalen Rivaner, £8.

CHEFS: Felicity Jelliff and Joanne Connolly   PROPRIETORS: Felicity and Rob Jelliff
OPEN: Tue to Sun L, Fri and Sat D
CLOSED: Mon to Thu Nov to Easter, Jan
MEALS: 12 to 2, 7.15 to 9
PRICES: £8 (£12), Set D £10.75 (£14), Snacks from 95p
SEATS: 45. 10 tables outside. Private parties: 25 main room, 20 and 25 private rooms.
Car-park, 20 places. Vegetarian meals. Children's helpings. No smoking in dining-room.
Wheelchair access (2 steps; also WC). Music

---

## WATERHOUSES  Staffordshire                              map 5

## ▲ Old Beams

| Waterhouses ST10 3HW | COOKING 3 |
|---|---|
| WATERHOUSES (0538) 308254 | COST £17–£38 |

Once a tavern on the drovers' road from Leek to Ashbourne, Old Beams has spread its accommodation to either side of the road with an increase in bedrooms for guests. They, and non-residents, dine in either a conservatory extension, with murals of fantasy, or the smaller dining-room in the house itself. Nigel Wallis cooks a serious menu, which includes set-price lunches and dinners. Ann Wallis is a solicitous and effective hostess. A dinner as reported began with oysters in watercress sauce and a tart of mushrooms with slices of pigeon breast; was punctuated by a guava sorbet, compliments of the house; went on to fallow deer cooked with wild mushrooms and a game sauce, served with a good array of vegetables, then a finish of hazelnut and cinnamon vacherin and a cheeseboard of mixed origin that did credit to supplies in this part of the country. Other accounts have concurred in thinking the cooking reliable and genuine. One person objected more strongly to the cabaret of cats in the dining-room than the piano that is sometimes played, and there have been observations of a certain complacency engendered by local success. The wine list does credit to the classic regions, as well as Spain and the United States. It does not, however, explore many of the by-ways that may still offer fine drinking for less than £10. House burgundy is from £10.35 to £10.85.
CELLARMAN'S CHOICE : Chassagne-Montrachet Rouge, Clos de la Boudriotte 1983, Ramonet, £20.75; Alsace Riesling 1982, Zind Humbrecht, £13.80.

CHEF: Nigel J. Wallis   PROPRIETORS: Nigel J. and Ann Wallis
OPEN: Tue to Sun, exc Sat L and Sun D
MEALS: 12 to 2, 7 to 10
PRICES: £23 (£32), Set L £10.25 (£17) to £12.50 (£19), Set D £17.50 (£24)
CARDS: Access, Amex, Diners, Visa
SEATS: 50. Car-park, 18 places. No children under 4. No smoking in dining-room.
Wheelchair access (also WC). Music
ACCOMMODATION: 6 rooms, all with bath/shower. Rooms for disabled. B&B £47.50 to £65.
Garden. Tennis. TV. Phone. Scenic. Doors close at 12 [GHG]

**WATH-IN-NIDDERDALE** North Yorkshire          map 7

## ▲ *Sportsman's Arms*

Wath-in-Nidderdale HG3 5PP          COOKING **2**
HARROGATE (0423) 711306          COST £12–£31

Wath-in-Nidderdale is farming country; Pateley Bridge, nearby, is tripperish. Small wonder, then, that this inn does good business and need not go far for its materials. Although the pub side persists, the restaurant is the more important element and continues to offer generous, well cooked and nicely imaginative food serviced by an impressive team who know their job and make the wanderer feel at home – even when surrounded by conversations of winter holidays, metropolitan shopping and international business that may preoccupy many of the customers. The dining-room has not pursued the country pub image, taking in spot lighting, wicker chairs and giant modern restaurant plates. The cooking has gone that way too: quite a lot of fruit in some of the recipes, excellent local (and French) cheeses – mark especially the Cotherstone and Coverdale – and more fruit, as well as a pineapple and Tia Maria gratin, at pudding time. An inspection revealed a potential for too much butter in some of the cooking but mainly a warmth and generosity of approach that might typify the epithet 'Yorkshire'. A rack of lamb, taken off the bone, cooked as ordered and served with a julienne of beetroot and gherkin, roast cloves of garlic and a nice reduction of the pan juices was spot on, as were the vegetables left in dishes on the table – for once large enough to hold everything supplied. Venison, not gamey enough to be wild, was produced in a sauce made from the wine in which it had been cooked, mushrooms and herbs. It neither outfaced by its quantity, nor overpowered with heavy-handed seasoning or flavouring. The wine list is adequate, reasonable and improving. The notes are helpful and there are some nice bottles; a few more good halves would not come amiss, though it should be conceded that that's easier said than done, and Mr Carter has not stinted where halves are easily available. House French is £5.95. CELLARMAN'S CHOICE : Pouilly Fumé, Les Loges 1987, Saget, £11.60; Volnay 1982, Louis Latour, £19.50. The £14.20 dinner includes a half-bottle of wine. Tipping is 'not encouraged'.

CHEF/PROPRIETOR: J.R. Carter
OPEN: all week, exc Sun D
MEALS: 12 to 1.45, 7 to 10
PRICES: £19 (£26), Set L £8.50 (£12) to £9.50 (£13), Set D £8.90 (£13) to £14.20 (£14.20)
CARDS: Access, Amex, Diners, Visa
SEATS: 45. 6 tables outside. Private parties: 60 main room. Car-park, 50 places. Vegetarian meals. Children's helpings. Wheelchair access (also WC)
ACCOMMODATION: 6 rooms, 2 with bath/shower. B&B £27 to £40. Baby facilities. Pets welcome. Garden. Fishing. TV. Scenic

*The 1991* Guide *will be published before Christmas 1990. Reports on meals are most welcome at any time of the year, but are extremely valuable in the spring. Send them to* The Good Food Guide, FREEPOST, *2 Marylebone Road, London NW1 1YN. No stamp is needed if posted in the UK.*

## ▲ *Well House*

High Street, Watlington OX9 5PZ                                    COOKING 1
WATLINGTON (049 161) 3333                                       COST £18−£30

A handsome late-medieval merchant's house, likened by some to a coaching-inn, and converted to a small hotel and restaurant. The cooking is quite adventurous, although ensuring satisfaction of English tastes with desserts fitted to an older last. Accompaniments such as blackcurrants and pink peppercorns with fillet steak; curry with exotic fruits and cashew nuts on saffron rice; oyster mushrooms with medallions of veal poached in stock, are hardly traditional England. The wine list is very decent as Alan Crawford is an enthusiast. House French, £6. CELLARMAN'S CHOICE : Ch. Bel Chanteau 1985, St-Emilion, £10.15; Pouilly-Vinzelles 1983, Mesnard, £13.90.

CHEFS: Patricia Crawford and Debbie Nunn    PROPRIETORS: Patricia and Alan Crawford
OPEN: Tue to Sat, exc Sat L and Sun D
MEALS: 12.30 to 2.15, 7.30 to 9.30 (10 Sat)
PRICES: £18 (£25), Set L and D £13.80 (£18), Snacks from £3. Service inc
CARDS: Access, Amex, Diners, Visa
SEATS: 40. Private parties: 50 main room, 10 private room. Car-park, 15 places. Children's helpings (Sun L only). Smart dress preferred. Wheelchair access
ACCOMMODATION: 9 rooms, all with bath/shower. Rooms for disabled. B&B £35 to £53.50. Baby facilities. TV. Phone. Scenic. Doors close at 11. Confirm by 6

## *Moorings*

6 Freeman Street
Wells-next-the-Sea NR23 1BA                                       COOKING 3
FAKENHAM (0328) 710949                                           COST £15−£20

'Please warn your readers that we are a "Restaurant du Quartier" rather than a High Temple of Food.' It seems doubtful that the warning is necessary since customers almost invariably relish the quayside atmosphere, the warm welcome for children and the pleasantly relaxed service of the Phillips' easy-going approach. If there are complaints − for example, that the chatter from the open kitchen was at times overpowering − they do not seem to seriously detract from the pleasure of Carla Phillips' spirited cooking and many customers return so often that they become friends. Dishes change erratically in response to their popularity and the availability of ingredients, especially the local fish that has gradually become the most important element of the menu. 'You can come back a week later and the menu has changed completely. Or you can return after two months and the previous menu, which you found a trifle lacking, is repeated verbatim.' But there is usually plenty of choice among the dozen dishes per course and a consistent simplicity, flair and respect for local raw materials in the descriptions of leisurely meals: an outstanding smoked fish mousse, juicy home-cured gravlax, sweet pickled herrings with cream and dill, local housewife's brawn with a salad of pickled peppers, Dover sole fried in olive oil, plump local cockles under a herby breadcrumb topping and very garlicky fresh cod done like stockfish. Each crisp vegetable has a different sauce or finish: basil for green beans, a caramel glaze for carrots, mustard sauce for leeks, and breadcrumbs for cauliflower. Puddings are a balanced choice and British cheeses include Mattsel, a local goats'. Service, which could sometimes be poor, has picked up considerably with the arrival of some older staff. Bernard Phillips gives helpful advice on wine. House wine is £5.50 and CELLARMAN'S CHOICE : is Matua Valley Reserve Sauvignon Blanc 1988, £15.

CHEFS: Carla Phillips and Jane Lee    PROPRIETORS: Bernard and Carla Phillips
OPEN: all week, exc Wed and Thurs L and Tue and Wed D
CLOSED: 4 to 22 June, 29 Nov to 14 Dec, 24 to 27 Dec
MEALS: 12.30 to 2, 7.30 to 9
PRICES: £11 (£16), Set L £9.75 (£15), Set D £11.75 (£17). Service 10%. Licensed, also bring your own: corkage £2.75
SEATS: 44. Private parties: 44 main room. Vegetarian meals. Children's helpings. Wheelchair access (also WC)

---

**WEOBLEY   Hereford & Worcester**                                         map 2

## ▲ Jule's Cafe

Portland Street, Weobley HR4 8SB                          COOKING 1
WEOBLEY (0544) 318206                                    COST £17−£23

A fine timbered building houses this welcoming French-style bistro, where patron-chef Julian Whitmarsh is always happy to talk food. Jule's is open for lunchtime snacks and afternoon teas, but the serious business of the day starts at 7.30pm when an eclectic three-course menu takes the floor. The French influence is obvious, but there's also more than a suspicion of traditional British, a good helping of Middle Eastern and even a discreet hint of Scandinavian. A typical choice might include grilled avocado with tahini sauce and prawns, or sweet marinated herring with a walnut and horseradish sauce to start; a Provençal beef dish flavoured with orange and juniper, or a Gascon loin of pork, stuffed with prunes and sage and baked in red wine with brown lentils for main courses. Vegetarians are not forgotten and there are further wholefood undertones in details like a wholemeal pastry for deep-fried crab pasties. Puddings are chocolaty or fruity, with four sorts of home-made sorbet. Twenty plus wines on the list, the house wine at £5.75.

CHEFS/PROPRIETORS: Julian and Juliet Whitmarsh
OPEN: Tue to Sun
MEALS: 12 to 2, 7.30 to 10.30
PRICES: £12 (£17), Set D £13.95 (£19), Snacks from 95p
CARDS: Access, Visa
SEATS: 36. Private parties: 30 main room. Vegetarian meals. Children's helpings. Wheelchair access
ACCOMMODATION: 3 rooms. B&B £15 to £25. Afternoon teas. Scenic. Doors close at 1am. Confirm by 6

---

*The Guide relies on feedback from its readers. Especially welcome are reports on new restaurants appearing in the book for the first time.*

WEST BAY  Dorset                                    map 2

# Riverside Café
# and Restaurant

West Bay, Bridport DT6 4EZ                    COOKING 1
BRIDPORT (0308) 22011                         COST £12–£19

The waterfront off-shoot of Bridport is West Bay. Dorset manages to capture the
best and the worst of the English seaside: West Bay includes some of the latter.
However, as intrepid holidaymakers seek stamps for postcards to home-tied
toilers, they might aim for the sub-post office that is also the Riverside Café and
Restaurant. The exterior may be unprepossessing but inside is spotlessly clean
and there are no odours of stale fat – such as can linger over whole districts of
England at five o'clock on a Friday afternoon. The Watsons have been here for
two decades cooking the freshest of fish every season. Its value is remarkable,
waitress service is charming – though it's self-service if not booked, and there
is a table reservation charge – and its local fame is deserved. The best, but not
the only thing to look for, is the list of daily specials. On one July day,
promenaders of the Dorset strand could have supped on baked red mullet, hake
with a provençale sauce or a baked brill sufficient for two or three people.
Lobster, crab and mussels are often available. Finish with summer pudding or
raspberries and clotted cream. 'A fish soup of exquisite form and substance
with prawns, squid, monkfish and more besides, with a bowl of hot croûtons;
then grilled John Dory with a slightly spicy coating to permeate and add to the
flavour, with new potatoes and a small salad. It's not Mosimann-by-the-sea,
but you can see into the kitchen and know there are no short cuts.' Three dozen
decent bottles constitute a sensible and intelligent wine list. House wine is
£6.75. CELLARMAN'S CHOICE : Savennières, Clos du Papillon 1987, £9.75;
Cooks Dry Red, Hawkes Bay, £6.25.

CHEF: Janet Watson  PROPRIETORS: Janet and Arthur Watson
OPEN: all week
CLOSED: Nov to end Feb
MEALS: 10 to 8 (8.30 Sat)
PRICES: £9 (£16), Set L £6.50 (£12). Table reservation charge
CARDS: Access, Carte Blanche, Diners, Visa
SEATS: 80. 10 tables outside. Private parties: 70 main room. Children's helpings.
Wheelchair access (also WC). Music

WEST BEXINGTON  Dorset                              map 2

# ▲ Manor Hotel

Beach Road, West Bexington DT2 9DF            COOKING 1
BURTON BRADSTOCK (0308) 897616                COST £15–£25

The old house sits atop the village with a view down to the sea, and a large new
conservatory takes advantage of the setting. There is a three-course set-price
menu at lunch and dinner in the restaurant as well as lighter, cheaper food in
the Cellar Bar. The area is popular for family holidays and the Manor does not
side step its responsibilities on that score. The menu, therefore, has something

for everyone but reporters continue to compliment it for its generosity (some would say excess) and its fair prices, even if occasionally the sauce outweighs the sauced. Vegetarians are catered for; non-smokers are protected; the fish comes from good sources. The menu does not change substantially from year to year. The wine list, with a lot but not all from Eldridge Pope, is well up to the job. House French is £5.65. CELLARMAN'S CHOICE : Fleurie, Domaine Jacquet 1987, Aujoux, £9.95; Montagny *premier cru* 1986, Cave des Vignerons de Buxy, £12.95.

CHEF: Clive Jobson    PROPRIETORS: Richard and Jayne Childs
OPEN: all week
MEALS: 12 to 2, 7 to 10 (10.30 Sat)
PRICES: Set L £10 (£15) to £12.50 (£18), Set D £14.95 (£21)
CARDS: Access, Amex, Visa
SEATS: 65. 18 tables outside. Private parties: 65 main room, 20 and 50 private rooms. Carpark, 50 places. Vegetarian meals. Children's helpings. Music
ACCOMMODATION: 10 rooms, all with bath/shower. B&B £27 to £50. Deposit: £10. Baby facilities. Garden. TV. Scenic. Doors close at midnight. Confirm by 6

---

**WEST MERSEA  Essex**                                                      map 3

## ▲ *Le Champenois, Blackwater Hotel*

20–22 Church Street
West Mersea CO5 8QH                                          COOKING 2
COLCHESTER (0206) 383338                                   COST £12–£25

'South Essex French' is a cultural sub-group yet to be investigated but here is its paradigm. The menu, virtually unchanging from year to year, runs to snails, frogs' legs, mussels, king prawns, duck with cherries, guinea-fowl with marsala and dishes with cream-based sauces. True French would have six dishes, not a dozen, and might have skate, choucroûte, jambon de Bayonne and other *simple* dishes that could be supported by a small kitchen without pretence. Décor as well is authentic: Tudor beams in a brick Victorian building and checks everywhere. This is a very popular restaurant and some speak highly of its standards, others less highly. There are English roasts at lunchtime. Otherwise the star dishes are mushrooms with cream, onion and garlic; vegetable mousse; warm potato salad with chives and lightly smoked marinated herring; calves' kidneys dijonnaise; herbed rack of lamb; chocolate mousse and a whole array of puddings. French cheeses are often in good condition. The wine list consists of an album of labels, about 60, mainly French, not dear. House Duboeuf is £6.30. CELLARMAN'S CHOICE : Touraine Sauvignon Blanc 1987, Oisly et Thésée £7.95; Châteauneuf-du-Pape, Clos St-Jean 1981, £16.40. No tips are expected.

---

*On 6 May 1990 all London telephone numbers will change, the 01- prefix being replaced by either 071- or 081-. See the front of the* Guide *for a list of which numbers will take which prefix.*

CHEF: R. Roudesli PROPRIETOR: M. Chapleo
OPEN: all week, exc Tue L and Sun D
CLOSED: 3 weeks in Jan
MEALS: 12 to 2, 7 to 10
PRICES: £16 (£21), Set L £7.90 (£12) to £9.50 (£14)
CARDS: Access, Amex
SEATS: 46. 3 tables outside. Private parties: 55 main room, 25 private room. Car-park,
20 places. Children's helpings. Smart dress preferred. Wheelchair access (also WC)
ACCOMMODATION: 7 rooms, 4 with bath/shower. B&B £21 to £46. Deposit: £10. Baby
facilities. Pets welcome. Afternoon teas. Garden. TV. Scenic. Doors close at 1am.
Confirm by 9

---

## WEYBRIDGE  Surrey                                                    map 3

# Colony

| | |
|---|---|
| 3 Balfour Road, Weybridge KT13 8HE | COOKING 1 |
| WEYBRIDGE (0932) 842766 | COST £19–£34 |

The continuity of staff adds both confidence and cheer to a visit to this stylish
oriental restaurant where the fish dishes are the best offering. Lobster served on
a bed of soft noodles, deftly handled to keep fingers cleaner than sometimes,
with a chicken stock and white wine sauce as a simple yet flavoursome
accompaniment; deep-fried squid with a very light batter; bass steamed with
ginger and spring onion, with a modicum of soy sauce are but some of those
mentioned. The best results often seem to come from prearranged meals. House
wine, £7.

---

CHEF: Kam Yau Pang PROPRIETOR: Michael Tse
OPEN: all week
MEALS: 12 to 2.30, 6 to 11 (11.30 Fri and Sat)
PRICES: £11 (£21), Set L and D £12.50 (£19) to £17 (£28). Minimum £12.50. Service 12.5%
CARDS: Access, Amex, Diners, Visa
SEATS: 80. Private parties: 70 main room, 20 private room. Children welcome. Music.
Air-conditioned

---

## WEYMOUTH  Dorset                                                    map 2

# Perry's

| | |
|---|---|
| The Harbourside, 4 Trinity Road | |
| Weymouth DT4 8TJ | COOKING 1 |
| WEYMOUTH (0305) 785799 | COST £18 |

No sooner did it open in 1987 than reports began to flow in, recounting an
unpretentious restaurant serving fresh, locally caught, plainly cooked fish. The
brief menu includes meat and vegetarian dishes and the blackboard lists most
main courses by the names of the day's catch: perhaps brill, plaice, sea bass,
lemon and Dover sole. Barbara Perry buys from several quarters to remain
independent of suppliers. 'The flat fish we grill whole on the bone unless
people particularly want it filleted. The larger fish we bake in the oven quite
simply with fresh herbs.' Only occasionally do sauces appear – beurre noir for

skate, a very creditable portugaise for monkfish. Vegetables, steamed and served al dente, are appropriate. First courses, which have included lobster soup, crab cocktail and sweet scallops, 'prised open with difficulty that very morning' and fried simply in butter, are as good. Servings are ample. Traditional English puddings, such as apple and almond tart or a Bakewell tart with almond nibs on top of layered crème pâtissière and raspberry jam, are acceptable. A cheerful wine list, with house wine at £6.25 a litre.

CHEFS: Barbara Perry, Justin Davis and Lloyd Rimmer   PROPRIETORS: Barbara, Stewart and Graham Perry, and Julia Buckley
OPEN: all week, exc Sun L
MEALS: 12 to 2.30, 7.30 to 10.30 (7 to 10.30 in summer)
PRICES: £10 (£15)
CARDS: Access, Visa
SEATS: 42. 3 tables outside. Private parties: 30 main room. Vegetarian meals. Children's helpings. Wheelchair access (2 steps). Music

---

**WHITBY North Yorkshire**                                                                    map 6A

# Magpie Café

| 14 Pier Road, Whitby YO21 3JN | COOKING 1 |
|---|---|
| WHITBY (0947) 602058 | COST £10–£23 |

This café is still synonymous with cheap eating in Whitby. Go early if you want a ringside seat overlooking the fish quay, harbour and parish church with its 199 steps. Local fish and chips top the bill (look for knock-down prices in season) and there are good crab starters and salmon, crab or lobster salads. To finish, there's a choice of 30 home-made sweets; among these, the daily special might be bread-and-butter pudding or lemon teacup soufflé. The café caters for difficult diets too, by offering fat-, dairy- and gluten-free dishes. Children not only get mini-meals, but also high chairs and a box of toys to investigate should boredom strike. Most customers prefer pots of strong tea, but the house wines (half-bottles) are French (red), £3 and Californian, Italian and German (white), £3.45. CELLARMAN'S CHOICE : Muscadet, £4.60; Chablis, £10.50.

CHEF: Ian Robson   PROPRIETORS: Sheila and Ian McKenzie
OPEN: all week
CLOSED: end Oct to week before Easter
MEALS: 11.30 to 6.30
PRICES: £13 (£19), Set L (served all day) £5.90 (£10) to £9 (£14)
SEATS: 100. Private parties: 50 main room. Vegetarian meals. Children's helpings. No-smoking tables

# Trenchers

| New Quay Road, Whitby YO21 1DH | COOKING 1 |
|---|---|
| WHITBY (0947) 603212 | COST £8–£18 |

Whitby's charm, despite the souvenir shops, is that of a working port. At night, as the pubs are closing, fishing boats in the narrow river harbour light up and chug slowly out to sea. Trencher's, on the New Quay, may look like an anonymous pizzeria with little sense of place, but in fact it is one of the best places to eat local fish and enjoy the atmosphere. Down one side runs a long bar where the fish are freshly battered and fried; alternatively, there is poached cod, fresh local crab, salmon and lobster or daily specials. Children are made welcome and puddings are tailored to suit them. Be prepared to queue and remember the relatively early closing. House wine from £7.50 a litre.

CHEFS: Tim Lawrence and Gary Moutrey    PROPRIETOR: Terry Foster
OPEN: all week
CLOSED: Christmas to mid-Mar
MEALS: 11 to 9
PRICES: £11 (£15), Set L £3.95 (£8) to £5.95 (£10), Set D £3.95 (£8) to £9.25 (£14), Snacks from 50p. Service inc
SEATS: 150. Private parties: 150 main room. Vegetarian meals. Children's helpings. Wheelchair access. Music

---

**WHITLEY BAY  Tyne & Wear**                                          map 7

## Le Provençale

183 Park View, Whitley Bay NE26 3RE                    COOKING 2
091-251 3567                                           COST £16–£31

This must be the only hermaphrodite Provençal outside classical myth, but the links with Mediterranean culture are tenuous in a cheerful and hospitable restaurant that remains the toast of Whitley Bay. The long menu at dinner constitutes excellent value, only surpassed by the reasonable prices at lunchtime and the set price of the popular special nights held on Mondays and Thursdays. The restaurant has expanded, and opened a sitting area and bar upstairs. The menu's strengths lie in its range of steaks and fresh fish. The wine list is a good canter through some perfectly decent bottles at fair prices. House French, £6 a litre.

CHEF: Michael Guijarro    PROPRIETORS: Mr and Mrs M. Guijarro
OPEN: Mon to Sat, exc Mon and Wed L
CLOSED: 1 week in summer
MEALS: 12 to 2, 7.30 to 9.45 (10.15 Sat)
PRICES: £20 (£26), L £10 (£16), Set D Mon to Thur £11.95 (£17)
CARDS: Access, Amex, Diners, Visa
SEATS: 26. Private parties: 26 main room. Children's helpings (L only). No children under 7. Music

---

**WICKHAM  Hampshire**                                                map 2

## ▲ Old House

The Square, Wickham PO17 5JG                           COOKING 2
WICKHAM (0329) 833049                                  COST £31

The Old House stands in the village square and was probably the first building in Wickham to be designed in early Georgian style. What was once a timber-framed outhouse and stables is now the dining-room, which has doors opening on to the garden. The experience of eating here remains rewarding under the eye of the Skipwiths. The brief menu describes itself as 'regional French'. A meal could commence with snail soup or pheasant terrine, leading on to bacon-wrapped quails with red wine and cassis sauce, pot-roast rabbit or monkfish glazed with mustard. French apple tart or fresh orange jelly with chocolate mousse draw matters to a conclusion. The wine list is compact but includes a handful of clarets imported directly by Richard and Annie Skipwith, particularly Ch. Virmon, St-Emilion which, in 1985 vintage, is CELLARMAN'S CHOICE at £20.75. Ch. Bagnols 1983, also St-Emilion, is £12.25. House Muscadet and Côtes du Rhône are £8.

CHEF: Nicholas Harman   PROPRIETORS: Richard and Annie Skipwith
OPEN: Mon to Sat, exc Mon L and Sat L
CLOSED: 2 weeks July to Aug, 10 days at Christmas, 2 weeks at Easter
MEALS: 12 to 1.45, 7 to 9.30
PRICES: £19 (£26). Service inc
CARDS: Access, Amex, Diners, Visa
SEATS: 35. Private parties: 35 main room, 14 private room. Car-park, 12 places. Children's helpings. No cigars/pipes in dining-room. Wheelchair access (also WC)
ACCOMMODATION: 12 rooms, all with bath/shower. B&B £60 to £80. Baby facilities. Garden. TV. Phone. Scenic. Doors close at midnight [GHG]

**WILLERBY  Humberside**                                              map 6

# ▲ Restaurant Lafite, Willerby Manor Hotel

Well Lane, Willerby HU10 6ER                                   COOKING 1
HULL (0482) 652616                                          COST £13−£30

The spacious dining-room, which overlooks lawned gardens, has an elegant air, and service tends towards the formal without being pretentious. Set meals of four courses are priced according to the choice of main dish, a selection which might include best end of lamb wrapped in filo with an orange and port sauce, medallions of venison with claret sauce, and baby turbot bamboo-steamed with butter sauce. The quality of the meats is good and sauces are stock-based and well reduced. Starters, such as mussel stew and smoked salmon mousse, are followed by home-made soup or a sorbet. For dessert, coffee gateau with mint cream sauce has been liked. House French, £6.95; others worth exploring.

CHEF: Robert Steel   PROPRIETORS: Willerby Manor Hotels Ltd and J. Townend & Sons Ltd
OPEN: all week, exc Sat L and Sun D
MEALS: 12 to 1.45, 7 to 9.30
PRICES: £17 (£25), Set L £7.95 (£13) to £9 (£14), Set D £9 (£14) to £19.95 (£25)
CARDS: Access, Amex, Visa
SEATS: 85. Private parties: 70 main room, 400 private room. Car-park, 250 places. Children's helpings. Smart dress preferred. Music (weekends)
ACCOMMODATION: 41 rooms, all with bath/shower. B&B £51 to £62. Children welcome. Baby facilities. Afternoon teas. Garden. Air-conditioning. TV. Phone. Scenic. Confirm by 6

*See the inside of the front cover for an explanation of the new 1 to 5 rating system recognising cooking standards.*

**WILLINGTON  Co Durham**                                    map 7

## *Stile*

97 High Street, Willington DL15 0PE                          COOKING 1
BISHOP AUCKLAND (0388) 746615                          COST £17–£23

A converted cottage with not one, but two conservatories imparting light, air
and space to a pair of dining-rooms that may serve as a beacon in a benighted
area. Mike Boustred is an amiable host, enthusiastic and thoughtful. The menu
is long, almost too long given that the daily specials number more than a dozen
and the *carte* is not yet broached. This may lead to unevenness in materials.
Nonetheless, the beef is consistently praised and a refugee from Durham was
more than happy with his thick celery soup, grouse in red wine, and orange
pancakes. Vegetables there are in lashings. A shorter menu might also
encourage greater concentration of sauces. Puddings are also enjoyed: there is
often a hot traditional item (apple and almond or chocolate and orange) and
English sweet-teeth are encouraged by hot bananas and hot blueberries as
well. Vegetarians are well catered for, with at least three main dishes to choose
from every day. The wine list is not expensive. House French is £5.25.
CELLARMAN'S CHOICE : Chardonnay 1987, Vin de Pays du Jardin de la France,
£7.50; Prince de la Rivière 1982, Fronsac, £11.

CHEF: Jenny James   PROPRIETORS: Mike Boustred and Jenny James
OPEN: Tue to Sun, D only
MEALS: 7 to 9.45
PRICES: £14 (£19), Set D £12.50 (£17)
CARDS: Access, Visa
SEATS: 50. Private parties: 34 main room, 18 private room. Car-park, 14 places. Vegetarian
meals. Children's helpings on request. No smoking. Wheelchair access (2 steps). Music

---

**WILLITON  Somerset**                                       map 1

## ▲ *White House Hotel* ❡

Williton TA4 4QW                                             COOKING 3
WILLITON (0984) 32306                                        COST £35

Long service is always an achievement in itself and Dick and Kay Smith have
gained more than their majority in this relaxed Georgian hotel-restaurant that
feels most un-Georgian within and is filled with good furniture, objects and
pictures. Good value is a marked quality of their accommodation, which
absorbs children more willingly than most, and a fervent advocacy of local
materials is a hallmark of the cooking. The short set-price daily menus always
start with soup, then offer a choice of four in each of three subsequent courses
plus a consistently good board of local cheeses (where better to sample them?).
The cooking has been thought, in repeated *Guide* entries, as French provincial;
one should stress the mediating effect of British taste. Where else are you
served baked avocado with prawns, or with smoked pork, or with crab?
Certainly not in Franche-Comté. The cooking is very assured: soufflés
suissesses as light as can be, given a little sweetness by a wreath of small
prawns; well chosen duck with caramelised apples given edge by balsamic

vinegar; superlative vegetables; desserts that do not descend to mere registers of fruit and ice-cream; very fine accessories such as tiny pissaladières for amuse-gueule, first rate bread, olives brought back from Spanish holidays. The wine list, buttressed by a fine collection of marcs and armagnac, is not over-priced. There are some good old clarets and longer runs of Rhône and Provençal (Bandol) vintages than are usually found on restaurant or merchant lists, two Hermitages from 1976 (one a Chave), for example. Prices on some of the Rhônes have actually been reduced. The collection as a whole shows discrimination and careful purchasing over a number of years that has borne fruit for contemporary drinking. New World wines are being given their first outing in 1989. House wines, £10 (red) and £9 (white). CELLARMAN'S CHOICE : João Pires Dry Muscat 1988, £8; Hermitage Blanc, Chevalier de Sterimberg 1979, Jaboulet, half-bottles, £10.

CHEFS/PROPRIETORS: Dick and Kay Smith
OPEN: all week, D only
CLOSED: Nov to mid-May
MEALS: 7.30 to 8.30
PRICES: Set D £21 (£29)
SEATS: 26. Private parties: 20 main room. Car-park, 17 places. Children's helpings. Wheelchair access
ACCOMMODATION: 13 rooms, 10 with bath/shower. Rooms for disabled. B&B £23 to £46. Deposit: £25. Baby facilities. Pets welcome. TV. Doors close at midnight. Confirm by 7 [GHG]

---

**WINCHCOMBE  Gloucestershire**                                    map 2

## *Corner Cupboard Dining Room*

Corner Cupboard Inn, Gloucester Street
Winchcombe GL54 5LX                                    COOKING 2
WINCHCOMBE (0242) 602303                               COST £25

'More like a cave' is one comment on this long room to one side of the Corner Cupboard Inn – itself a buttressed, mullion-windowed Cotswold picture-postcard of a building with a pretty garden at the back. The cave has a wooden floor, an enormous fireplace and many naive drawings and prints on the wall. It looks as friendly as it feels. Christine Randle might be said to have come out of the shadow of her predecessors, Christopher and Joanna Wickens, now in Northleach (see entry, Wickens) and produces food in the same genre as those years but with a character of her own. The pottery on the tables and the slow but amiable service (often by the cook herself) identify this as a country restaurant, but one which offers good value for an adventurous menu. Christine Randle is largely self-taught, so many of the dishes will be recognised from books and other restaurants, notably the Roux brothers, Pool Court and Sharrow Bay. Although some experiments, like a sirloin stuffed with ham and Gruyère in a mustard sauce, are not successful, pigeon breasts wrapped in cabbage, a spinach soup, or loin of pork rolled in bacon (keen on stuffing and rolling here) and sticky date pudding are warmly applauded. The bread, from a baker in Gotherington, is also good. The wine list, compiled by

Michael Elliot of the Corner Cupboard Inn, is short and to the point (though some details are lacking); its prices are not excessive. House French red is £6.50; white, £6.25. CELLARMAN'S CHOICE : Châteauneuf-du-Pape 1986, £12.50; Puligny-Montrachet 1984, £14.95.

CHEF/PROPRIETOR: Christine Randle
OPEN: Tue to Sat, D only
MEALS: 7.30 to 9
PRICES: Set D £15.95 (£21)
SEATS: 18. Private parties: 18 main room. Car-park, 15 places. No children under 10. No smoking. Wheelchair access (1 step; also WC). Music

---

**WINCHESTER  Hampshire**                                              map 2

## Brann's ♥

9 Great Minster Street, The Square
Winchester SO23 9HA                                          COOKING 2
WINCHESTER (0962) 64004                                  COST £15–£32

Opposite the museum, itself part of the cathedral square, is this converted brick property: a wine bar on the ground floor and restaurant above. Winchester is now in the thick of the south-east's resurgence. Hemmed in by expressways, the sky a perpetual cast of purple-orange, it is difficult to imagine the town as a once gentle domain of close, college and county. Brann's might be thought well tuned to the new world of property, estate agents and service industry. Nicholas Ruthven-Stewart moved here from a successful stint at Fifehead Manor, Middle Wallop. He cooks a modern-sounding range of dishes, from pheasant with lentils to a spinach and basil roulade with red pepper sauce. Some dishes have received much approval; among them, monkfish with a shellfish sauce, breast of chicken with lemon, tarragon and Pernod and a toffee sponge 'shot with thin strips of orange peel with a butterscotch sauce – calorific but one of the best puddings I've eaten'. This may be balanced against a meal that started with a superannuated fish sausage on a sauce proclaimed saffron but nigh innocent of this delicacy, and continued with a pheasant of unbearable tastelessness improved neither by its sauce nor its vegetable accompaniment. A kitchen, then, of variable consistency. There is service in the wine bar, which is less oppressively vacuous in decoration than the room upstairs, and people in wheelchairs can have the full dinner menu. The bar also has the enlightened provision of a separate room for non-smokers. The wine list is good, wide-ranging and thoughtful. House French is £6.40.
CELLARMAN'S CHOICE : Babich Sauvignon Blanc, Hawkes Bay 1987, £11.50; Ch. Vignelaure 1981, Georges Brunet, £11.95.

CHEF: Nicholas Ruthven-Stuart    PROPRIETORS: David and Barbara Brann
OPEN: Mon to Sat
MEALS: 12 to 2.30, 7 to 10.30
PRICES: Set L £10 (£15) to £12.50 (£18), Set D £19 (£24) to £21.50 (£27). Minimum £10
CARDS: Access, Amex, Visa
SEATS: 50. Private parties: 24 main room. Vegetarian meals. Children's helpings. No-smoking area. Wheelchair access (also WC)

# ▲ *Miller Howe* ♥

Rayrigg Road, Windermere LA23 1EY
WINDERMERE (096 62) 2536                                          COOKING 4
on A592 between Windermere and Bowness                              COST £42

Guides stand or fall by their opinion of Miller Howe, and John Tovey's creation
has had such an effect on the tilt of country-house cooking, especially in the
north, that its assessment is bound to reflect on the aspirations and success of
many individual businesses, not only those with formal links with Miller
Howe: the Bay Horse at Ulverston, Uplands at Cartmel and the Miller Howe
Kaff in Windermere itself (see entries). Arguments pro and con the formula of a
set meal served to a dining-room of several parties who are sent to table at the
same time (two sittings on Saturday) have surfaced from year to year. If that is
not enough, the particular pitch and style of Miller Howe cooking, which
explores different taste combinations, especially of sweet and savoury, almost
to the death; which places a great many apparently conflicting flavours on one
plate and yet also has that British virtue/sin of lavish simplicity, for example at
the pudding stage, has been emulated in a thousand kitchens (domestic and
professional), sometimes with alarming results. Apart from some fulminous
letters, the chorus of praise has been as strong as ever. 'Quite the nicest small
hotel we know.' 'The quality and originality of the food was the best I have
ever experienced here.'

   Comments on meals served over a winter weekend include the following: a
'delicious' cream of sweetcorn and red pepper soup with diced fennel (the soup
comes second in the procession of courses); a 'five star' escalope of salmon
served with a Noilly Prat and chive sauce; a 'perfect, *not* pink' breast of duck
roasted and served on a fresh cherry purée and onion sauce with a rich gravy; a
raspberry crème brûlée which could have had a fruitier tang; and a warm
lemon and lime steamed sponge with a vanilla custard that beat the lot. The
complexity (some would say messiness) is seen in a roast marinated guinea
-fowl served with a calvados and apple purée, a prune and bacon roll and a port
and green peppercorn gravy with swede and horseradish, beetroot and orange,
leeks in white wine and three other vegetables, each in minute quantity. As
was observed, 'accompaniments sound rather too diverse but fitted well,
though the peppercorns may have been excessive; the vegetables were good,
fresh and lightly cooked.' This is a grand venture that is brought off
successfully, uncommonly frequently. Individualists may object: some may
find the Saturday night regimentation too great; others fume as the whole room
waits for the cycle of service to stop and start again; others find the self-
consciousness too much, so that even the Divine gifts of a setting on a slight rise
on the edge of Windermere with views of fells and sunsets may seem part of the
Tovey magic; and others may question whether the food would not be just as
good if the kitchen brigade pulled their socks up and had a menu with choices
as any other self-respecting restaurant manages to do. No matter, aficionados
remain loyal. It should also be noted that the price for the meal itself (even
though service is added automatically) is by no means high by national
standards. The wine list is sometimes criticised for high mark-ups but is
distinguished by many New World bottles that come more reasonably than

famous names. The enthusiasm of a vegetarian who was unable to follow the
system was, unsurprisingly, muted.

CHEF: Gaulton Blackiston   PROPRIETOR: John J. Tovey
OPEN: all week, D only
CLOSED: Dec to Feb
MEALS: 8.30 (7 and 9.30 Sat)
PRICES: Set D £26 (£35). Service 12.5%
CARDS: Access, Amex, Diners, Visa
SEATS: 70. Private parties: 30 main room. Car-park, 40 places. Vegetarian meals. No
children under 12. Smart dress preferred. No smoking. Music. Air-conditioned. One sitting
ACCOMMODATION: 13 rooms, all with bath/shower. B&B £85 to £160. No children under
12. Pets welcome. Afternoon teas. Garden. Fishing. Golf. Air-conditioning. Phone. Scenic.
Doors close at 11. Confirm by 6 [GHG]

## Miller Howe Kaff

Lakeland Plastics, Station Precinct
Windermere LA23 1BQ
WINDERMERE (096 62) 2255                                   COOKING 2
behind Windermere station                                  COST £16

The Kaff – Miller Howe on the cheap – is part of the Lakeland Plastics
complex. This was refurbished and redesigned at the end of 1988, affording the
Kaff more space and room for an open kitchen. Food, therefore, is no longer
shipped down from above; but cooked on the premises. Third chef Ian Dutton
comes over from Miller Howe every day to help William Tully. The bargain is
palpable: bobotie (see also the Bay Horse Inn, Ulverston) or Cumberland
sausage with apple sauce and date and onion chutney at prices below the fast-
food offerings of motorway service stations. These are served with a salad, the
ingredients of which would be remarkable anywhere. Such is the Kaff's
popularity that the wait can be long. There are daily specials on the blackboard
and vegetarians are not forgotten. A daily pudding is buttressed by cherry, fruit
or ginger cake and shortbread – all, of course, made here or at Miller Howe.
Customers are strange creatures and there are some who express surprise that
this is not as good as Miller Howe itself; that there are no truffles included in
the price of the coffee, at 60p, for instance. In reality, it is more difficult to run
a good cheap place than a good expensive one and, perversely, trickier to
satisfy the clientele. House white and red, £5.90. Wines of the week are also
on the blackboard.

CHEFS: William Tully and Ian Dutton   PROPRIETOR: John J. Tovey
OPEN: Mon to Sat, daytime only
MEALS: 10 to 4
PRICES: £8 (£13). Minimum £3. 1.20pm to 2pm
SEATS: 28. Private parties: 28 main room. Car-park, 60 places. Vegetarian meals. Children
welcome. No smoking. Wheelchair access. Self-service

*The* Guide *office can quickly spot when a restaurateur is encouraging customers to write
recommending inclusion. Such reports do not further a restaurant's cause. Please tell us if a
restaurateur invites you to write to the* Guide.

## Roger's ▼

| 4 High Street, Windermere LA23 1AF | COOKING 3 |
|---|---|
| WINDERMERE (096 62) 4954 | COST £26 |

The Pergl-Wilsons' small restaurant has become a Windermere fixture. Dark décor, tightly packed tables and the nuisance of nearby smokers may not do justice to the simple inventiveness of the menu. The arrangement is one often found in the north: first courses, then a single soup, followed by main course and dessert. The range of choices is enviable: on a spring night, from Californian asparagus with a red pepper and basil sauce or chicken livers with morels in flaky pastry, to saddle of hare with grapes and port or suckling pig with an apricot stuffing. The menu does not promise more than it can deliver and there is directness to the saucing and the components used in their making. Cheeses are usually British − half a dozen or more − and there are hot puddings, such as almond and Amaretto with a butterscotch sauce. Readers confirm that the restaurant remains consistent. The wine list is as thoughtful as the menu: Rhônes and Loires shipped by Yapp Brothers, a Pouilly Vinzelles 1986 (£14.50) from Mathias, and a Contino Reserva Rioja 1981 (£9.95) are to be recommended, though Mouton Cadet not so much. The House French is from Cordier, £6.50. CELLARMAN'S CHOICE : Ch. Malescot-St-Exupéry 1978, £33.50; Meursault, Louis Latour 1985, £18.95.

CHEF: Roger Pergl-Wilson  PROPRIETORS: Roger and Alena Pergl-Wilson
OPEN: Mon to Sat D, Tue to Fri L by arrangement
MEALS: 12.30 to 1.30, 7 to 10
PRICES: £14 (£22)
CARDS: Access, Amex, Diners, Visa
SEATS: 42. Private parties: 28 main room, 18 private room. Children's helpings. Wheelchair access. Music

---

WINTERINGHAM  Humberside                                          map 6

## ▲ Winteringham Fields

COUNTY OF THE YEAR RESTAURANT

| Winteringham DN15 9PF | COOKING 4 |
|---|---|
| SCUNTHORPE (0724) 733096 | COST £16−£31 |

The conversion of what was an old farmhouse, remembered by one impressed diner as once 'neglected and hanging in cobwebs' is not designer-country-style but rather Swiss and relaxed: dark furnishings and carpets; warm, soft-coloured wallpapers. The dining-room is well dressed without pretension, having no domes but good cutlery. The food, offered on a short *carte* of maybe five dishes in each course, supplemented by two or three daily specials, is none too heavy. Vegetable terrine with a carrot coulis and a tomato sorbet; cassolette of lobster, scallops and turned vegetables in a Monbazillac sauce; monkfish steamed and served on a bed of shallots and green olives are not dishes that sink the frame, but they do ignite both appetite and appreciation. The range of the cooking takes in oft-met luxuries, but has in addition nice ideas: a dish of sauerkraut with shellfish; a 'cannelloni' of aubergine stuffed with smoked duck and Brie that melted into a duck stock glaze, 'using the bread to soak this up was a treat'; ravioli of lobster with a basil sauce. Execution, too, has met

509

expectations: calf's liver quite *à point*; vegetables lightly steamed and as fresh as can be, as the Schwabs develop their gardening skills; turbot steamed to catch the melting texture before toughening, moist yet never wet. The large cheese trolley proclaims its 30 occupants to be French, but English, Welsh and Swiss interlopers have been espied. Condition: good. Ice-creams have been mentioned, as have hot pears with an almond sauce accompanied by ice-cream as a chaudfroid; and an orange ice-cream with a Cointreau sauce has had a credit too. If capable of further consumption, selection from four desserts seems the most popular choice. M. Schwab has just employed a chef-pâtissier to reinforce his bread and pastrymaking skills. 'It is a welcome oasis in a rather dreary part of England. On a cold winter night, there was a roaring fire to greet us and attentive staff to look after our needs.' As the east wind keens off the North Sea, not stopped by wold, not stopping till dale, to so convert necessity to joy is pleasure indeed. The wine list, not long, not much outside France, is still said to be improving but leaves room for further betterment. House Bergerac, £7.50. CELLARMAN'S CHOICE : Châteauneuf-du-Pape, Domaine du Vieux Télégraphe 1984, £14; Tokay Gris d'Alsace 1985, Muré £10.

CHEFS: Germain Schwab, Christian Sirurguet and Mark Midwinter
PROPRIETORS: Annie and Germain Schwab
OPEN: Mon to Sat, exc Sat to Mon L
CLOSED: 3 weeks from mid-Jan
MEALS: 11.30 to 2.30, 7 to 10
PRICES: £20 (£26), Set L £12 (£16), Set D £20 (£24). Service inc
CARDS: Access, Visa
SEATS: 40. Private parties: 14 main room, 10 private room. Car-park, 16 places. Children welcome. Smart dress preferred. Wheelchair access (1 step; also WC). Music. Air-conditioned
ACCOMMODATION: 4 rooms, all with bath/shower. B&B £45 to £70. No children under 12. Afternoon teas. Garden. TV. Phone. Scenic. Doors close at midnight. Confirm by 6

---

## WITHERSLACK  Cumbria                                            map 7

## ▲ *Old Vicarage* ♥

Witherslack LA11 6RS
WITHERSLACK (044 852) 381                                    COOKING 3
off A590                                                        COST £29

An inspector speaks of the reverence with which meals are approached and the hushed tones of the dining-room: appropriate for a former vicarage. The decoration pursues the image: house plants, Liberty prints, ornate wallpapers, large mirrors. This is tempered by a cottagey feel to some of the bedrooms and the unexpected bamboo and cane in the bar. The purchase of a damson orchard next door has given the Burrington-Browns and the Reeves another five bedrooms, an all-weather tennis-court and damson wine to serve their guests. In a valley between Whitbarrow Scar and Cartmel Fell, this south Lakelands hotel has attracted its usual crop of warm comment. Breakfasts are adequate for the most fastidious giants. Dinner is at 7.30 for 8. In regional style it is no-choice and five courses long, starting with a made dish of fish or vegetable, then a soup, with bread, a roast, a hot and/or cold pudding and finishing with cheese. This unvarying formula appears to please many: it has the advantage of simplicity, leaving the kitchen to concentrate on excellence, and it gives good value. As the owners themselves comment, 'This places a much stricter discipline on the preparation; a mistake for one is a mistake for all.' People do approve the purity of taste in the first courses, for example, avocado in tarragon cream or mousseline of sole with a dill hollandaise. The intense soups – tomato and basil or cucumber and dill are two – are more common than the insipid lettuce, watercress, lemon and mint affair served one evening. The meats are very fine: a whole goose carved for a Christmas gathering; Gressingham duck that redefined the bird for one reader; spring lamb with all the flavour of the fells; good beef. Sauces may be relishes or more complex affairs such as chicken roasted with almonds and madeira sauce. Vegetables are treated carefully: often plain, always fresh, sometimes as a composition – leeks stir fried with red pepper and pine kernels. The puddings get accolades even though the traditional ones, for instance, a Bakewell tart, seem heavy on the sugar to some people. Cheeses, always British, mainly north western, are properly cared for and described.

Over the years, the wine cellar has matured and developed. Prices are not excessive. A few of the older, finer clarets have become bargains, but newer purchases reflect market prices more closely, reasonably enough. The accent is French and the only regions with depth are the classic ones, but there are many well-chosen bottles among the Australian, Spanish and Italian sections. No house wine, but four or more bottles are offered by the glass and the proprietors will suggest something reasonable from the list, perhaps the Colombard Domaine du Compte 1987, Vin de Pays des Landes, at £8.15. CELLARMAN'S CHOICE : Bourgogne Chardonnay, Les Setilles 1987, Leflaive, £14.80; Volnay 1983, Michel Lafarge, £25.35. The restaurant is open to persuasion about admitting young children and service is personal and amenable. 'After a lovely stuffed pear to begin, roast guinea-fowl with a Cumberland sauce, then a chocolate roulade with strawberries, Mr Reeve, who seemed to be managing single handed, was kindness itself when our friends' car would not start. He came out and cleaned the plugs before, admitting defeat, he telephoned the garage.' Try that in London.

CHEFS/PROPRIETORS: Roger and Jill Burrington-Brown, Irene and Stanley Reeve
OPEN: all week, D only
CLOSED: 1 week at Christmas
MEALS: 7.30 for 8
PRICES: Set D £19.50 (£24)
CARDS: Access, Amex, Diners, Visa
SEATS: 35. Private parties: 18 main room. Car-park, 25 places. Children's helpings. No smoking in dining-room. Music. One sitting
ACCOMMODATION: 13 rooms, all with bath/shower. Rooms for disabled. B&B £40 to £63. Children under 10 by arrangement. Garden. Tennis. TV. Phone. Scenic. Doors close at 12
[GHG]

*If you see a certificate in a restaurant bearing the words 'Good Food Guide (International)', the claim is false (and the restaurant may be in contempt of court in displaying it) – see the Introduction. Please write and tell us the name and address of the restaurant.*

## WITHYPOOL  Somerset                                              map 1

## ▲ *Royal Oak*

Withypool TA24 7QP                                          COOKING 1
EXFORD (064 383) 506 and 507                             COST £18−£39

The village inn of Withypool is complete with inglenook and beams aplenty −
a candidate for a holiday snap. Food is cooked for both the bar and the
restaurant and each may have its supporters. The restaurant manages good
vegetables, a decent light and foamy cucumber soup and sauces with veal and
plaice that would improve any specimen of chop or fillet. Its cheeseboard,
prime examples of Sharpham, Ashprington, Tornegus, Colford Blue and
Exmoor, would put many an importer's selection to shame. The bar food
includes Ann Petch's Heal Farm sausages and more of those cheeses. Pound for
pound, the bar may win. The wine list, if not its service, is couth and
intelligent. House French, £6.50. CELLARMAN'S CHOICE : Brouilly, Ch. des
Tours 1987, £12.05; St Véran 1986, Duboeuf, £11.85.

CHEF: Joanna Lomasney   PROPRIETOR: M.J. Bradley
OPEN: all week
CLOSED: 25 and 26 Dec
MEALS: 12 to 2 (1.30 Sun), 7 to 9
PRICES: £21 (£33), L £12 (£18), Set D £14.50 (£21) to £19.50 (£26), Snacks from £3.50
CARDS: Access, Amex, Visa, Diners
SEATS: 32. 2 tables outside. Private parties: 18 main room. Car-park, 20 places. Vegetarian
meals. Children's helpings. No children under 10. Smart dress preferred
ACCOMMODATION: 8 rooms, 6 with bath/shower. B&B £25 to £56. Deposit: £20. No
children under 10. Pets welcome. Afternoon teas. Fishing. TV. Phone. Doors close at
midnight. Confirm by 6

## WOBURN  Bedfordshire                                            map 3

## *Paris House*

COUNTY
OF THE
YEAR
RESTAURANT

Woburn MK17 9QP
WOBURN (0525) 290692
off A4012, 1m SE of Woburn in Abbey grounds              COOKING 3
                                                         COST £18−£41

Alone amid the Woburn parkland, it might be a Highland shooting-lodge were
it not for the softness of landscape and the fact the house was transported lock,
stock and barrel from the Paris Exhibition of 1878. There is a choice of set-price
menus, and cooking by all accounts is steady and satisfying. The style is
aggressively French, down to the curt and unintelligible menus, and has
moved towards dishes such as crispy duck on a bed of noodles with ginger, and
sea bass with aubergines and tomatoes, all flavours that stand up for
themselves, if boldly handled, and don't merely smother with unctuous
stealth. There is a fair amount of richness here, rarely cut by adequate
vegetables: 'two baby carrots and one broccoli spear could have been crisp and
lacked company. Red cabbage seemed a strange bedfellow.' Its charms seem
strongest to regular visitors: a meal of délice of wild salmon with asparagus,
followed by ribs of beef chasseur and a large hot soufflé au Grand Marnier

pleased greatly a man who commonly insists on the famous raspberry soufflé. The edge to the cooking may sometimes be dulled as on some days Peter Chandler acts more as maître d'hôtel than as chef de cuisine. The only comments on wines are that they remain dear; we have not received a list. CELLARMAN'S CHOICE : Pouilly Fumé 1987, Daguenau £19.50; Pinot Noir d'Alsace 1985, Zind-Humbrecht £19.

CHEF/PROPRIETOR: Peter Chandler
OPEN: Tue to Sun, exc Sun D
CLOSED: Feb
MEALS: 12 to 2, 7 to 10
PRICES: Set L £14.50 (£18) to £23 (£28), Set D £23 (£28) to £29 (£34). Minimum £14.50
CARDS: Access, Amex, Diners, Visa
SEATS: 52. 3 tables outside. Private parties: 45 main room, 40 private room. Car-park, 20 places. Children's helpings. No children under 12 at D. Smart dress preferred. No cigars/pipes in dining-room

---

**WOODBRIDGE Suffolk**                                                  map 3

# Wine Bar ▼

17 Thoroughfare, Woodbridge IP12 1AA                      COOKING 2
WOODBRIDGE (039 43) 2557                                         COST £18

Sally O'Gorman is a talented cook working within a format that offers reasonably priced and imaginative food. Any wine bar that can offer a sauté of duck liver on toast with an orange and cinnamon sauce, followed by grilled slip sole with an anchovy and red pepper compote, with a final flourish of prune and port ice-cream, on a high street in Suffolk, is remarkable indeed. Just occasionally reality does not live up to the promise of the menu's ingredients, and customer/staff relations are not invariably of the happiest. Often there is no written bill, the total merely being stated: this can be disconcerting. The wine list is in the best wine bar tradition: it eschews the expensive and ransacks the world for an intelligent selection of more than five dozen, not overpriced and plenty by the glass. House French from Perpignan, £5.30. CELLARMAN'S CHOICE : Ch. St Christophe 1981, St-Emilion, £12.50; Cape Mentelle Semillon-Sauvignon 1988, £12.40.

CHEF: Sally O'Gorman    PROPRIETORS: Sally O'Gorman and Richard Lane
OPEN: Tue to Sat
CLOSED: 25 and 26 Dec
MEALS: 12 to 2.30, 7 to 11
PRICES: £10 (£15)
SEATS: 50. No children under 14. Music

---

*The 1991* Guide *will be published before Christmas 1990. Reports on meals are most welcome at any time of the year, but are extremely valuable in the spring. Send them to* The Good Food Guide, FREEPOST, *2 Marylebone Road, London NW1 1YN. No stamp is needed if posted in the UK.*

## WOODFORD  Greater Manchester  map 5

# Three Gates

547 Chester Road, Woodford
Bramhall SK7 1PR
061-440 8715 and 439 7824

COOKING 2
COST £15–£30

The plain, rectangular dining-room of this restaurant, beside the church on the Bramhall to Wilmslow road, manages to be comfortable and pleasant with nary a hint of ostentation. The style of cooking is much-garnished modern British with some original combinations of flavour. Pork with pear is unexpectedly successful, the intensity of the sauce bolstered by Poire Williams. However, local lamb in red wine with roulade of salmon is as unsatisfactory as it sounds, each component well executed but offering nothing to the other. Other dishes, for example, tarts filled with broccoli or chestnut soufflé, display good baking skills but poor flavour assessment of the broccoli and the chestnuts, or of the much too strong pimento chutney that comes with them. Besides the *carte* there is a specials board of half a dozen first and main courses, which might offer eggs poached in vermouth cream or river and sea fish in filo on a lime and dill yoghurt cream. Desserts are praised: egg custard brûlée on a base of apples and raisins poached with Amaretto lurks beneath a superb crisp crust; sticky toffee pudding has been 'out of this world'. Yet again an urge to decorate, a desire for variety, contribute elements to the plate that only detract from the impact of the centrepiece. Good coffee comes with home-made petits fours. House French, £6.25.

CHEFS: Gary Jenkins and Andrew Stocks  PROPRIETORS: Neil and Sylvia Tate
OPEN: Mon to Sat, exc Sat L
MEALS: 12 to 2, 7 to 10
PRICES: £17 (£25), Set L £10.95 (£15). Service 10%
CARDS: Access, Amex, Diners, Visa
SEATS: 46. Private parties: 46 main room. Car-park, 16 places. Children welcome.
Wheelchair access (2 steps; also WC). Music. Air-conditioned

## WOODSTOCK  Oxfordshire  map 2

# ▲ Feathers Hotel

Market Street, Woodstock OX7 1SX
WOODSTOCK (0993) 812291

COOKING 1
COST £18–£37

Well placed on the main square of Woodstock, the Feathers is in a seventeenth-century house with an unimposing white frontage. Inside, Gordon Campbell-Gray has managed to keep an uncontrived country feel, with antique furnishings throughout and, in colder spells, log fires. Lunch is a set-price menu, but dinner is now entirely à la carte, with a choice of some eight first and main courses. The former focus on soups with paired flavourings – tomato and smoked bacon, or pea and pear, for example – and salads; the latter give a broader choice of meat, game or fish, often served with light, contrasting sauces. Most dishes have an uncluttered modern feel, more British than French, witness fresh asparagus and duck liver salad with walnut oil dressing, and pan-fried duck in a sage and apple flavoured cream sauce. Reports suggest that standards are still inconsistent, but there have been enthusiastic recommendations of the smoked goose salad with a honey dressing, venison casserole, well-timed roast lamb and rich banana and butterscotch cream. House French, £8.50.

CHEF: Sonya Kidney  PROPRIETOR: Gordon Campbell-Gray
OPEN: all week
MEALS: 12.30 to 2.15, 7.30 to 9.45
PRICES: £21 (£31), Set L £12.50 (£18) to £13.50 (£19)
CARDS: Access, Amex, Diners, Visa
SEATS: 40. Private parties: 36 main room, 40 private room. Children's helpings. No cigars/pipes in dining-room. Wheelchair access. Music
ACCOMMODATION: 15 rooms, 13 with bath/shower. B&B £50 to £105. Baby facilities. Pets welcome. Afternoon teas. Garden. TV. Phone. Doors close at 11.30 [GHG]

---

**WOOLER** Northumberland                                            map 7

## ▲ *Ryecroft Hotel*

Wooler NE71 6AB                                                COOKING 1
WOOLER (0668) 81459                                          COST £11−£23

The year since the last *Guide* has been one of major alterations at Ryecroft: bedrooms have been redecorated, bathrooms built and a conservatory extension for lunches and teas added to the bar. There has also been a change in the kitchen with Michael Ord replaced by Paul Hibbin, who has come via the Roux brothers and Whitstable. Reports have usually been positive, suggesting that the daily five-course set menu has so far kept to the pattern of straightforward, homely cooking combining British and continental ideas. Starters have included marinated prawns, leek and Stilton soup, moules marinière; main courses a venison and steak pudding, lemony chicken with coriander, salmon with hollandaise. Puddings are creamy and traditional. A very short wine list offers some perfectly decent day-to-day drinking at very fair prices. House Bulgarian is £5.25. CELLARMAN'S CHOICE : Penfold's Dalwood Shiraz Cabernet 1984, £6.95; Sancerre, Domaine des Cotelins 1985, £8.75.

CHEFS: Pat McKechnie and Paul Hibbin  PROPRIETORS: Pat and David McKechnie
OPEN: all week, exc Sun L
CLOSED: first 2 weeks Nov, 24 Dec to 1 Jan
MEALS: 12.30 to 1.30, 7 to 8.30
PRICES: Set L £7 (£11), Set D £15 (£19)
CARDS: Access, Visa
SEATS: 50. Private parties: 30 main room, 20 private room. Car-park, 20 places. Children's helpings. No smoking in dining-room
ACCOMMODATION: 9 rooms. B&B £21 to £52. Deposit: £5. Baby facilities. Pets welcome. Afternoon teas. Garden. Phone. Scenic. Doors close at midnight. Confirm by 6 [GHG]

---

*'It did me the world of good to go to a fish and chip shop for lunch – a plate of cod and chips followed by spotted Dick and custard was the best value-for-money meal I've had for years.'* On dining in Essex

---

**WOOLHOPE** Hereford & Worcester　　　　　　　　　　map 2

## ▲ *Butchers Arms*

Woolhope HR1 4RF
FOWNHOPE (043 277) 281　　　　　　　　　　　　　COOKING **2**
off B4224, 7m SE of Hereford　　　　　　　　　　　　COST £20

'Very English, very Herefordshire' was one comment on this half-timbered pub-restaurant that once doubled as a pub and butcher's shop. Doubtless the stock was grazed on the green hills around. It is sad that Mary Bailey, partner and cook, died in the past year. Julie Squire, her successor in the kitchen, has continued the tradition of good pub food – such as rabbit and bacon pie cooked in Herefordshire cider – and offers a restaurant menu in the same vein but with slightly greater elaboration. Fillet of spring lamb is well hung, stuffed with a gutsy gammon and garlic mousse and apricots and served on a simple redcurrant sauce. The flavours are strong and harmonious. There is no great pretension, but no mincing or posing either. Vegetarians are treated fairly in bar and restaurant: lasagne, mushroom biriani, spinach and goats' cheese strudel are a sample of what's on offer. Desserts are largely ice-cream based, some being bought in, and a frozen ginger-and-coffee meringue cake would please many who hanker for a creamy and substantial end to the meal. Coffee is Rombouts. The wine list is short. The beer and cider is good. House French is £5.35 a litre. CELLARMAN'S CHOICE : English Three Choirs Medium Dry 1986, £5.95.

---

CHEF: Julie Squire　PROPRIETOR: Bill Griffiths
OPEN: all week
MEALS: 11.30 to 2.15 (12 to 1.45 Sun), 7 to 10 (9 Sun)
PRICES: £11 (£17), Snacks from £1.95. Minimum £6.35
SEATS: 70 bar, 26 dining-room. 7 tables outside. Private parties: 26 main room. Car-park, 80 places. Vegetarian meals. No children under 14. No cigars/pipes in dining-room. Music
ACCOMMODATION: 3 rooms. B&B £20.50 to £33. TV. Scenic. Doors close at 11.30

---

**WOOLLEY GREEN** Wiltshire　　　　　　　　　　　　map 2

## ▲ *Woolley Grange*

Woolley Green
Bradford-on-Avon BA15 1TX
BRADFORD-ON-AVON (022 16) 4705 and 4773　　　　COOKING **3**
signposted 1m from Bradford on Bath Road　　　　COST £19–£48

Jack Woolley may once have dreamed that Grey Gables would be as good as this new hotel and restaurant intends to be. The stone-built seventeenth-century manor house sits just outside Bradford-on-Avon, itself one of the gems of this region: Anglo-Saxon church, tithe barn, houses of clothiers all competing for the eye's attention. The Grange has been done up in grand style by the Chapmans, the decoration being as cheerful and light as the architecture will allow. The presence of a conservatory, with cane furniture and views over the gardens, gives some variety to an evening's visit. Anand Sastry has come to cook at Woolley Grange, almost like a meteor. First reports have been impressed by his modishness, accuracy and skill. Fresh tagliatelle with oysters: a nage of langoustines and scallops with leaf coriander; beef with wild mushrooms (some buttons, too); fillet of veal topped with parsley and a nest of carrots are some of the things that have caused a Wiltshire stir. It should come as no surprise that Anand Sastry worked at Harvey's and Inigo Jones in London and Raymond Blanc's Manoir in Great Milton (see entries). The borrowings are extensive. The execution, so far, appears satisfactory, the sauces light but well flavoured, the materials of high quality. Much is grown in the Grange's gardens. The service is pressing; the bread is not good; the style a little over-ambitious. But in these early days some hurry may be justifiable. The wine list has special sections on Pomerol and Gevrey-Chambertin. This affords some variety and interest. The range is otherwise very adequate, with some good and fashionable labels. Prices are not excessive. House Duboeuf is £9. CELLARMAN'S CHOICE : Ch. Bertineau 1983, Lalande de Pomerol, £12.70; Irongate Hawkes Bay Chardonnay 1986, £19.25. Children are looked after, even to a supervised playroom and nursery where they can have meals. At the bottom of the bills is the note 'we neither make nor expect a service charge'.

CHEF: Anand Sastry   PROPRIETORS: Nigel and Heather Chapman
OPEN: all week
MEALS: 12.30 to 2, 7 to 9.45
PRICES: £33 (£40), Set L £14.50 (£19), Set D £19.50 (£24). Service inc
CARDS: Access, Amex, Diners, Visa
SEATS: 56. 8 tables outside. Private parties: 16 main room, 16 private room. Car-park, 40 places. Vegetarian meals. Children's helpings. Wheelchair access (1 step; also WC)
ACCOMMODATION: 15 rooms, all with bath/shower. Rooms for disabled. B&B £67.50 to £135. Baby facilities. Pets welcome. Afternoon teas. Garden. Swimming-pool. Tennis. Snooker. TV. Phone. Scenic [GHG]

---

WOOTTON  Isle of Wight                                                    map 2

## ▲ Lugleys

Staplers Road
Wootton Common PO33 4RW                                      COOKING 3
NEWPORT (0983) 882202                                           COST £30

Angela Hewitt denies professional status and attitude. 'I tend to cook how I feel,' she writes. And she cooks everything, alone. The food is 'truly very good, marvellous', according to one reporter. How she feels must be brimming with confidence and flair. Not that the inside of the tiny restaurant would lead to that conclusion. Sixteen seats and 15 varieties of chair; old-master posters trimmed and put into jumble sale frames; the place has an air of relaxed ease with the world. Through the windows (clean but cracked) watch 'Charolais knee deep in flower-spangled grass' beyond a garden. The solo cooking knows its limitations, 'I cannot be as fancy as I would like,' but Ms Hewitt also understands her materials: fish from boats nearby; meat from Quantock Veal (not as intensively reared as the Dutch) and Heal Farm in north Devon; grouse from Harrods. One London visitor likened her direct yet sensitive style to Sally Clarke's (see entry, London). A meal taken in the summer began with goats' cheese in a filo-like parcel on a sesame salad. The pastry (as in other dishes) excelled, the cheese had melted to the right degree and was not too high in flavour, the baby cos lettuce leaves were well dressed with sesame oil. Also a chilled green and red pepper soup: the red puréed with chicken stock, the green a thicker purée cupped in a lettuce leaf and floated on the bowl. A pear sorbet, perhaps with a touch of vanilla, was fresh and unexpected. Roundels of Soay lamb, not trimmed enough of their fat, sat on a fragrant, herby tomato sauce, accompanied by robust brown lentils. Opposite, a fine lobster was served with a coconut sauce: shocking to some but convincing to two waverers. Broad beans, with two other vegetables, had been skinned, the mark of true leguminous devotion. Desserts were a rhubarb crème brûlée and a lemon chiffon pie with peach confit. The first was correct, the second was foaming creamy lemon piled into a fragile tuile-like case with peaches lying alongside. That same evening one could have been served free-range eggs baked with rocket, rose-petal ice-cream, and more. The bread was good, the coffee was hot, service came with a smile, so what matters the lack of matching furniture? The china was pretty and everything shone with cleanliness. Lunches are served by arrangement, teas and snacks in the season. House wines, maybe a Vouvray or a claret, from £7.25.

CHEF/PROPRIETOR: Angela Hewitt
OPEN: Mon to Sat, D only (L by arrangement)
CLOSED: 2 weeks May and Nov
MEALS: 7 to 9.30 (10 in summer)
PRICES: £18 (£25). Minimum £9.95
SEATS: 16. 5 tables outside. Private parties: 16 main room. Car-park, 12 places. No children under 12. No cigars in dining-room
ACCOMMODATION: 2 rooms. B&B £18 to £35. No children under 12. Afternoon teas. TV. Confirm by noon 1 day before

---

**WORCESTER  Hereford & Worcester**                                     map 2

## Brown's

24 Quay Street, Worcester WR1 2JN                          COOKING 2
WORCESTER (0905) 26263                                    COST £19–£35

The Severn washes its way past the front door of this converted cornmill, and diners, as they meander through the set courses, can observe the river's progress the while. A bustling, informal brasserie atmosphere somewhat belies the menu, which is elegant and fairly pricey (and smoked salmon or fillet of beef costs extra). Roast duck with blackberry and apple sauce has been praised, likewise lamb and kidney provençale 'enriched with much garlic'. Out of half a dozen dishes per course, options to start may include a daily soup, sauté of squid with fresh ginger or croustade of wild mushrooms. Main courses are mostly roasts or grills – be it venison, calf's liver or langoustine and bacon kebabs – eye-catchingly presented and thoughtfully sauced. There are additional daily fish dishes and vegetables are a strong point, organic in the main and cooked 'simply – but no worse for it'. Salads have multitudinous components; puddings are mousses, ices, sorbets and meringues. Children are evidently poorly controlled in Worcester: Brown's raised the minimum age from 5 to 10 a couple of years ago, thus making many family outings, even for Sunday lunch, impossible. The wine list is almost exclusively French, although

there is a page of fine German hocks and moselles. There are few bargains.
House French is £6.95 or £7.95. CELLARMAN'S CHOICE : Ch. Haut-Marbuzet,
1984, £18.95; Chablis *premier cru* Vau de Vey 1985, Durup, £23.

CHEFS: W. R. Tansley and S. Meredith    PROPRIETORS: R. and P. M. Tansley
OPEN: all week, exc Sat L and Sun D
CLOSED: bank hols and 1 week at Christmas
MEALS: 12.30 to 1.45 (2 Sun), 7.30 to 9.30
PRICES: Set L £13 (£19) to £16 (£22), Set D £23 (£29). Service 10%
CARDS: Access, Amex, Diners, Visa
SEATS: 80. Private parties: 80 main room. No children under 10. Wheelchair access
(also WC)

---

**WRIGHTINGTON** Lancashire                                    map 5

# High Moor

Highmoor Lane, Wrightington WN6 9PS                    COOKING 2
APPLEY BRIDGE (025 75) 2364                            COST £13–£34

Now in its seventh year, High Moor has won a loyal local clientele. It is also not
far from the M6: turn left at junction 27 and head for Wrightington. No doubt
much of the draw is its period charm, with plenty of seventeenth-century
beams and a large open fire, but this is to do the kitchen down. Reports show
that regulars also return for the reliable cooking, traditionally rooted but given
a clear style by showy modern flourishes described in detail on the menu.
Thus, first courses may range from a duck-liver terrine with Cumberland sauce
to a lobster and asparagus salad with Champagne vinegar dressing; main
courses from roast guinea-fowl with potato and turnip cake to beef fillet filled
with Indonesian spiced sweetbreads. All appear to be well executed.
Puddings, which have their own menu, are similarly bold and free with
flavours, as in a Southern Comfort cheesecake finished off with maple syrup
and flambé bananas. Sunday lunches from a set-price, four-course menu built
around traditional roasts start at less than half the cost of à la carte meals, and so
are especially popular – book well ahead. House French, £7.50 (white), £11.50
(red). CELLARMAN'S CHOICE : Bianco di Custoza 1987, £9.50.

CHEF: James Sines    PROPRIETOR: John Nelson
OPEN: Tue to Sun, exc Sat L and Sun D
MEALS: 12 to 2, 7 to 10
PRICES: £20 (£28), Set L £8 (£13) to £16 (£22). Service 10%
CARDS: Access, Amex, Diners, Visa
SEATS: 95. Private parties: 80 main room. Car-park, 35 places. Children welcome.
Wheelchair access. Music. Air-conditioned

---

*Consumers' Association is planning a* Vegetarian Good Food Guide, *to cafés and
restaurants offering at least one vegetarian main course. Please send reports and
recommendations to* The Vegetarian Good Food Guide, FREEPOST, *2 Marylebone
Road, London NW1 1YN.*

*'We were not made to feel inferior because of our working dress as low-budget touring
actors in T-shirts and dilapidated trainers.'*  On dining in Strathclyde

---

## Laburnum House

Wylam NE41 8AJ | COOKING **2**
WYLAM (0661) 852185 | COST £12−£25

Even the *Guide* occasionally gets it wrong, and last year Laburnum House suffered from assorted crossed wires. Now it's time to put the record straight. The detached, stone building dates back to 1716 and is one of the oldest houses in the village. For many years it was a general store and the outside still looks shop-like, with windows flanking the central door. Furnishings and table settings are basic, for the money and care are lavished on the food, which achieves high standards. The blackboard menu offers bags of choice from a list of modern French dishes. Beginnings range from tomato and orange soup, through chicken liver terrine with Cumberland sauce, to crab pâté in puff pastry with chive cream. Main courses, prettily presented and accompanied by crisp vegetables, could be Tyne wild salmon in filo or wood pigeon in red wine. A summer meal that began with asparagus with a lemon butter and an avocado cascading with a mixture of shellfish also took in lemon sole with giant prawns and a sandwich of puff pastry with a filling of mussels, scallops, prawns and crab claws on a tomato sauce that cut some of the richness. Generosity was almost to a fault. For those with room for dessert, the owner's mother makes a mean brown-bread ice-cream. The wine list is short and innocent of vintages, but the sources are good. House wine from Viénot is £5.75.

CHEF: Kenn Elliott  PROPRIETORS: Rowan Mahon and Kenn Elliott
OPEN: Tue to Sat, exc Sat L
MEALS: 12 to 1.30, 6.30 to 10
PRICES: £17 (£21), Set L from £8 (£12), Set D £9.50 (£13). Service inc
CARDS: Access, Amex, Diners, Visa
SEATS: 40. Private parties: 40 main room. Children's helpings. Wheelchair access (1 step; also WC). Music

## Jennings

16 Damgate Street
Wymondham NR18 0BQ | COOKING **2**
WYMONDHAM (0953) 603533 | COST £14−£30

Jennings takes over where Adlard's left off. The two small rooms of the one-time butcher's shop retain their chintz: not in the lap of luxury, but decent settings on well-spaced tables. Both David's cooking and Sarah's warm welcome and proper service have caused visitors to exclaim their support for the new occupants. The style is not so assured as the Adlards' − pastry, for example, may range from good to indifferent in a single meal and sauces may tend to the sweet and simple on occasion − but flavours and techniques have been exact. A fine fillet with peppercorn sauce; salmon on a bed of field mushrooms; fricassee of seafish; pigeon breasts with celeriac; lobster and salmon mousse; almond and Amaretto ice-cream; a lemon and lime tart with a glazed top; and a well-risen though light-flavoured hot rum and praline soufflé are all applauded. Cheese, coffee, bread and ancillaries have also been cared for. The menus offer a range of options, from a short 'supper' menu, through to a full four-course dinner at more than double the price. The wine list of under four dozen bins shows enterprise and reasonable prices. House wines, £5.80.

CHEF: David Jennings  PROPRIETORS: David and Sarah Jennings
OPEN: Tue to Sat, D only
MEALS: 7.30 to 9.30
PRICES: Set D £9.50 (£14) to £21 (£25). Service inc
CARDS: Access, Amex, Visa
SEATS: 28. Private parties: 18 main room, 12 private room. Children's helpings. Music. Air-conditioned

---

YATTENDON  Berkshire                                          map 2

## ▲ *Royal Oak* ♥

The Square, Yattendon RG16 0UF                      COOKING 3
HERMITAGE (0635) 201325                                 COST £48

Take a map and good glasses if you seek this village in the dark. The motorway keeps bringing more people, yet this part of Berkshire provides barely the infrastructure of directions and signposts to carry the traffic surely to its destination. Yattendon is picturesque and the Royal Oak is dead centre. The Smiths have created a multi-faceted business: pub, country hotel and swish restaurant. The enterprise expands as they develop the Beetle and Wedge (see entry, Goring). The most praiseworthy aspect is the elevation of the pub food to the level of the restaurant. You have to book your table in both sections, and the kitchen takes equal care with orders from either. In truth, the financial reward of accepting simpler surroundings and less luxurious food (though there are many dishes that figure on both menus) seems persuasive. A chef that has worked in both the Greenhouse and Langan's Brasserie might be expected to broaden the definition of restaurateuring. He should be supported. However, the fairly high prices of the restaurant might reasonably lead one to expect a more decisive break from pub habits. Yet an order for fresh orange juice was filled out of a bottle, with some resentment at the suggestion that it should rather be squeezed. And the waitresses are none too free with their 'sirs' and 'madams' (rather a lot of 'you') and seem only to warm to their task as the evening progresses. The house, decorated in rich creams, is Home Counties writ large. At one meal, the cooking was surprisingly approximate, with some sense that the restaurant merely pandered to the expectations of the clientèle. The menu included wild mushrooms in four of its 16 choices. Trendy, yes, but lacking in flavour or the skill to put that flavour into relief. A cheese soufflé was badly undercooked yet had a leather-like top; a chive sauce swamped good John Dory with the taste of raw onion; a vast collection of vegetables had no connection with the ingredients of the main course; a signature dessert of plums, pancake and a fine vanilla ice-cream had no valid relationship between pancake (only one) and fruit; the amuse-gueule were crude and the bread poor. The coffee was excellent. Balance that with much praise from others for memorable John Dory served with langoustines, good hollandaise with asparagus and artichoke hearts stuffed with mushrooms, or a salad of foie gras with wild mushrooms. The wine list is long, good, French and expensive. Half-bottles barely exist but you may have half a bottle for a small surcharge on the half-price. House wines Cabernet 1986 and Sauvignon 1988 de Touraine, £7.50. CELLARMAN'S CHOICE : Mâcon, La Roche Vineuse 1987, Lacharme, £15; Châteauneuf-du-Pape, Vieux Télégraphe 1986, £19.50.

CHEF: Richard Smith    PROPRIETORS: Richard and Kate Smith
OPEN: all week (Sun D bar meals only)
MEALS: 12 to 2, 7.30 to 10
PRICES: £29 (£40)
CARDS: Access, Amex, Visa
SEATS: 30. 10 tables outside. Private parties: 30 main room, 8 private room. Car-park, 35 places. Children's helpings. No cigars/pipes in dining-room. Wheelchair access
ACCOMMODATION: 5 rooms, all with bath/shower. B&B from £48 to £58. Baby facilities. Pets by arrangement. Afternoon teas. Garden. TV. Phone. Scenic. Doors close at 11. Confirm day before [GHG]

---

**YORK** North Yorkshire                                                    map 5

## Kites ♥

13 Grape Lane, York YO1 2HU                              COOKING 2
YORK (0904) 641750                                          COST £18

Variously described as 'a bistro with food for enthusiasts' and 'having the feeling of a workers' vegetarian co-operative', Kites is up some poky stairs on the second and third floors, five minutes' walk from the Minster. Students come in term time, tourists in the vac. Painted red floorboards and a couple of kites hanging from the ceiling are the nearest things to frills. Table settings are simple; 'cutlery is not the nickable kind,' reception is a warm smile, no pre-dinner drinks. The long menu – there are 10 main courses, two of them vegetarian, plus fondues and salads – changes twice a year. The eclectic style reflects Boo Orman's enthusiasms and her travel destinations. Eggs crusader follows a medieval recipe. Masaman pork is a Thai dish with coconut milk, roasted peanuts, lemon-grass and spices. Local pigeon features, too, wrapped in smoked bacon and charcoal-grilled, and cheeses are from Coverdale, Wensleydale and Swaledale. Soups and sauces owe their success to good stocks and oriental flavours are impressive. Kites enters the *Guide* because it offers good value for money. Service is informal and friendly. The short wine list is an object lesson in how to pick interesting, flavoursome wines and sell them at prices anybody should be happy to pay. House south-western French wines are £5.95. CELLARMAN'S CHOICE : Delegats Hawkes Bay, Sauvignon Blanc 1987, £10.95; Raimat Abadia 1985, £8.75. They do alcohol-free cocktails, too.

---

*Several sharp operators have tried to extort money from restaurateurs on the promise of an entry in a guide book that has never appeared.* The Good Food Guide *makes no charge for inclusion and does not offer certificates of any kind.*

---

CHEFS: Mark Ball and Darren Allen    PROPRIETOR: Boo Orman
OPEN: Mon to Sat, D only and Sat L
MEALS: 12 to 2, 6.30 to 10.30 (6 to 11 Sat); 7 (6.30 Sat) in winter
PRICES: £10 (£15)
CARDS: Access, Amex, Diners, Visa
SEATS: 48. Private parties: 30 main room. Vegetarian meals. Children's helpings.
No-smoking main dining-room only. Music

## McCoy's at York

17 Skeldergate, York YO1 1DH                    COOKING 2
YORK (0904) 612191                               COST £24

Extending themselves southwards, the McCoy brothers have settled on the
burgeoning service and tourist economy of York as suitable for their inimitable
mixture of good cooking, friendliness and fun as practised at Staddlebridge
(see entry). Eugene McCoy, cook at the bistro at the Tontine, makes regular
appearances at this riverside warehouse conversion in York. Much of the
culinary formula, as well as the young and happy service, is well known: up to
four soups, dishes such as chicken JoJo, and prices that are far from cheap.
There is also an emphasis on fish – the whole lemon sole, pan-fried and
exquisitely fresh, 'the largest lemon sole of my experience', figuring here as
further north. The cooking ranges from good, when using palpably fresh
ingredients, to just above 'bistro' levels. However, the jam roly-poly was a
masterpiece at the end of one meal. The wines are interestingly chosen, though
not cheap, on a short list. House wine is £6.50.

CHEF: Eugene McCoy and D. Lockwood    PROPRIETORS: Peter, Thomas and Eugene McCoy
OPEN: all week
MEALS: 12 to 2.15, 7 to 10.30
PRICES: £14 (£20). Snacks from £1.60
CARDS: Access, Amex, Diners, Visa
SEATS: 100. Private parties: 100 main room. Vegetarian meals. Children's helpings.
Wheelchair access. Music. Air-conditioned

## ▲ Middlethorpe Hall ♥

Bishopthorpe Road, York YO2 1QP                 COOKING 2
YORK (0904) 641241                               COST £17–£42

This is one of the most impressive, even palatial, country- house hotels,
looking over York's racecourse on one side, manicured and exquisite lawns on
the other. The grandeur of the main rooms, and their sympathetic restoration,
makes it very enjoyable to visit and to dine in. The esprit de corps of the staff is
also good; they make every customer feel important without unnecessary
servility. The scale of the operation has led to the conversion of the stable court
to many bedrooms and the pursuit of conference business. These new rooms,
although generously decorated and provisioned, feel more like a hotel than a
country house; their subservience to the house itself, reinforced by the walk
across for dinner, is a little too redolent of peasants and squires of old. At
Middlethorpe once lodged, for a few short years after her elopement, Lady

Mary Wortley Montagu, the eighteenth-century propagandist for smallpox inoculation, traveller to Turkey and blue-stocking. Her biographer observes that she selected the house for economy: it was close enough to York that 'it would allow their friends to come for short afternoon visits instead of dinner'. The big question today is whether to visit Middlethorpe for dinner or for the experience of sleeping in one of the great rooms. Some diners have certainly been satisfied. A wedding breakfast of Stilton and celery mousse, saddle of lamb with chestnut stuffing, fresh fruit in a brandy snap basket with an orange and Pernod sorbet and a selection of cheese met every desideratum of one reader: 'Table settings very fine; lovely flowers on tables; wonderful bread rolls and good butter; fresh tasting mousse; fine tasting lamb with an intense sauce, even if the vegetables were none too imaginative; an outstanding dessert' – cleansing, deep-flavoured, harmoniously composed. This has not always been the experience of more casual visitors who have found the food often lacklustre and lacking any flavour of consequence, particularly when the price is borne in mind. The wine list is extensive and expensive. It has many qualities: lots of half-bottles; some very good growers; good representation of Loire, Rhône and south-western French wines in addition to the classic regions; up-to-date, informed choice of other countries' products. It is unfortunate that some are much more expensive that they need be. Seven house wines are shared by the Historic House Hotels group: Bordeaux, £8.50. CELLARMAN'S CHOICE : Bouzy Rouge 1983, Barancourt, £15; Domaine les Bastides, Coteaux d'Aix en Provence, 1983, £11.85.

CHEF: Kevin Francksen  PROPRIETORS: Historic House Hotels Ltd
OPEN: all week
MEALS: 12.30 to 1.45, 7.30 to 9.45
PRICES: £26 (£35), Set L £12.90 (£17) to £14.90 (£19), Set D £20.50 (£25) to £23.90 (£28). Service inc
CARDS: Access, Amex, Diners, Visa
SEATS: 60. Private parties: 40 main room, 14, 20 and 40 private rooms. Car-park, 70 places. Vegetarian meals. No children under 8. Smart dress preferred
ACCOMMODATION: 31 rooms, all with bath/shower. Lift. B&B £83 to £126. No children under 8. Afternoon teas. Garden. TV. Phone. Scenic [GHG]

## 19 Grape Lane

| | |
|---|---|
| 19 Grape Lane, York YO1 2HU | COOKING 2 |
| YORK (0904) 636366 | COST £14–£31 |

York has not in the past been a place for restaurants, though beauty should reap its fair reward in life's pleasures. Things are changing, evidently. This restaurant off Peter Gate in a cobbled lane, dotted with panders to the art of shopping, occupies two floors of a small house. Tables are close fitted, but the atmosphere is smart and the decoration cool. There was a false but impressive start in 1988 when business began with Aidan McCormack at the stoves. He is now cooking at Hartwell House (see entry, Aylesbury) and his place has been taken by Michael Fraser. The menus stay the same in conception: a short-choice, set-price at lunch and dinner and a *carte* of half-a-dozen items in each course. The range of the menus is less refined: breast of chicken with leeks rather than stuffed with mango, coated with coconut served with a curry sauce, but none the worse for that (even if their prices have advanced by 25 per cent). Reports speak of careful cooking and of pleasing taste: a cauliflower soup that was comforting if bland; a sauté of pork in an irreproachable cream and mustard sauce with accurately cooked vegetables and boulangère potatoes; and an orange yoghurt mousse with bramble coulis 'delicious in both taste and design'. The wine list is thoughtful and is widening its French horizons to the New World, including Chile. There is an odd trio of 1973 clarets which may or may not be a good thing but prices are firm yet not too high. House French is £7.75. CELLARMAN'S CHOICE : Mâcon-Clessé 1985, £11.95. Penfolds Dalwood Shirez/Cabernet 1984, 11.95. After-theatre suppers can be had by arrangement.

CHEFS: Michael Fraser and Trajan Drew    PROPRIETORS: Gordon Alexander and Carolyn Alexander
OPEN: Tue to Sat
CLOSED: 2 weeks Jan and Oct
MEALS: 12.30 to 1.45, 7.30 to 10.30
PRICES: £18 (£26), Set L £8.50 (£14), Set D £16.50 (£22)
SEATS: 34. Private parties: 25 main room. Children welcome. Wheelchair access (1 step). Music

# Scotland

---

**ABERDEEN  Grampian** map 8

## *Silver Darling*

Pocra Quay, Footdee, Aberdeen AB2 1DQ
ABERDEEN (0224) 576229

COOKING **2**
COST £15–£32

The room sizzles to the smells of the barbecue; at the end of the North Pier you might almost be out at sea. Immediately next door stands the pilot roundhouse surmounted by a light tower. An unlikely venue, therefore, for Provençal grilling of fish and shellfish, or Breton mouclades or the savours of basil and garlic. Didier Dejean has continued to receive praise for his cooking and the young team at the front of house for its relaxed approach to eating – which may be otherwise described as casual and slow, depending on the reporter. House burgundy is £6.75.

CHEF: Didier Dejean   PROPRIETORS: Didier Dejean, Norman Faulks and Catherine Wood
OPEN: all week, exc Sat L and Sun L
MEALS: 12 to 2, 7 to 10
PRICES: £20 (£27), Set L £9.20 (£15) to £11.50 (£17)
CARDS: Access, Amex, Visa
SEATS: 35. Private parties: 35 main room. Car-park. Children welcome. Wheelchair access (1 step; also WC). Music

---

**ABERFELDY  Tayside** map 8

## ▲ *Atkins at Farleyer House*

*COUNTY OF THE YEAR RESTAURANT*

Aberfeldy, PH15 2JE
ABERFELDY (0887) 20332
from Aberfeldy take B846 to Kinloch
Rannoch for 2m

COOKING **3**
COST £21–£38

Farleyer House is almost in the dead centre of Scotland. It might be thought that the Atkins' move from the dead centre of metroland (the Old Plow at Speen, which featured in the *Guide*) would be traumatic. It does not seem so. The house, surrounded by forest and glen, is Scottish austere but has a pleasing balance to its façade. Inside, the main sitting-rooms act as frames to good pictures and antiques and the dining-room is more sober. Not so the cooking. Frances Atkins is not one to present simple food: grilled fillet of halibut rolled in herbs and brioche crumbs, on a bed of dauphinois potatoes with a light Pinot noir sauce offends every presumption about fish cookery. However, these things do seem to work, perhaps because her touch is quite light and she has a good sense for materials. She also varies her approach. Not the whole meal is complex. Thus while the main course may be a plate containing a whole quail baked in a salt crust, a breast of pigeon and a leg of duck stuffed with oatmeal, all served with port, raspberries and apple, the first courses may be as simple as a slice of minted pea tart, the pastry crisp and buttery, the peas enshrined in a light mint aspic, or a chilled lemon balm and apple soup of good distinct flavours, though vitiated by ice cubes and a blob of cream. Desserts play with as many soft fruits as do southern restaurants blessed with easy marketing, and a fair hand is displayed with ice-creams and sorbets. Hot soufflés – for instance an apricot soufflé with a warm pistachio sauce – have also been praised. Petits fours and coffee in the lounges are a pleasure, helped by the informed attentions of Gerald Atkins, whose wine list is a good start in a country thick with impressive tomes. The price spread is nicely wide, with no insistence on Bordeaux and burgundy at three-figure prices. House French is £8.50.

CHEF: Frances Atkins PROPRIETORS: Gerald and Frances Atkins
OPEN: all week
MEALS: 12.30 to 1.30, 7.30 to 8.45
PRICES: Set L £15 (£21), Set D £25 (£32)
CARDS: Amex, Visa
SEATS: 30. Private parties: 30 main room, 12 private room. Car-park, 14 places. No children under 10. Smart dress preferred. Wheelchair access (also WC). Music
ACCOMMODATION: 12 rooms, all with bath/shower. B&B £65 to £150. Deposit: £25 per person per day. No children under 10. Garden. Fishing. Golf. TV. Phone. Scenic. Doors close at midnight. Confirm 48 hours ahead

**ABERFOYLE Central** map 8

## *Braeval Old Mill* 🍷

By Aberfoyle, Stirling FK8 3UY
ABERFOYLE (087 72) 711 COOKING **2**
on A81, 1m from Aberfoyle COST £15–£28

A wood-burning stove and its chimneypiece divide the dining-room into two. Dashes of citrus yellow in cushions and napkins have been used to enliven the greystone, flag-floored interior of this completely renovated old watermill. Set Sunday lunches are good value. Fiona Nairn's service transmits her enthusiasm, while in the kitchen Nick Nairn's cooking mingles classic dishes – medallions of pork in cider sauce; fillet of beef with Roquefort – with newer ideas: seafood fricassee with vegetables, saffron and chives; breast of chicken with a ham and garlic mousse. Satisfied reports praise such dishes as warm monkfish salad; Loch Tay salmon baked in filo pastry; pigeon breasts with madeira sauce. Desserts include honey and whisky ice-cream and fresh strawberries with sablés. Cheeses are served with oatcakes, and coffee comes with tablet – not a panacea for over-indulgence, but a type of Scottish fudge. The wine list is very extensive with fine judgement as to growers, be they Burgundian or Californian. The vintages are mainly young but that keeps the prices keen, and everyone is helping by their vinification of lighter wines, anyway. A good range of house wines from £5.50. CELLARMAN'S CHOICE: Mâcon Viré 1987, Bonhomme, £12.75; Mercurey 1985, Michel Juillot, £15.95.

CHEF: Nick Nairn   PROPRIETORS: Nick and Fiona Nairn
OPEN: Tue to Sun, D only, and Sun L
CLOSED: 3 weeks Jan to Feb, 1 week May, 1 week Nov
MEALS: 12 to 1.30, 7 to 9.30
PRICES: £17 (£23), Set Sun L £10.95 (£15)
CARDS: Access, Amex, Visa
SEATS: 34. Private parties: 34 main room. Car-park, 16 places. No children under 10. No cigars/pipes in dining-room. Smart dress preferred. Wheelchair access (1 step; also WC)

---

ACHILTIBUIE  Highland                                                      map 8

# ▲ *Summer Isles Hotel* 🍾

Achiltibuie, IV26 2YG                                          COOKING 2
ACHILTIBUIE (085 482) 282                                      COST £29

Twenty-five miles down a single-track road from Ullapool, this hotel – its roof patterned by solar panels, looking as if it were a secret-service watching post – sits amid transparently beautiful scenery. Reports from those who venture this far north are that the cooking continues to improve. Where could one be closer to the source? Vegetables and fruit are grown in the garden or in the hydroponicum that Mr Irvine senior, once owner of the hotel, still maintains for early and rapid cropping; fish comes from loch and sea so fresh it arrives barely in time for dinner; game is from the hills around. Dinner is five courses and coffee with choice only of puddings. As few will drive out only for the meal, the lack of choice is more bearable. Set price it may be, but the kitchen doesn't stint on the lobster or the salmon. A 1989 meal began with onion, cider and apple soup served with great buckwheat and caraway loaves. Next came a crab salad with two sorts of (hydroponic) lettuce and chervil, young spinach and spring onion, which was outstanding for its simple purity. The meat course of sirloin was not as flavourful as might have been hoped, helped along though it was by a garlic and ginger sauce. Puddings were an average Pavlova and a surprisingly good moist cake of fruit, walnuts and dried apple. Cheese – Highland ewe's, cow's and a Cheddar – came with such outstanding Stilton-and-almond biscuits that it was hardly needed. Service was both pleasant and meticulous. Mark Irvine is especially solicitous of the wines and does things properly. The list is well judged and evenly priced for this style of place: strongest, of course, on France but with a few less conventional choices. There will be something for everyone, though not much below 10 – that is the cost of buying mainly French. House French is 5.50. CELLARMAN'S CHOICE : Rioja Muga 1973, £14; Gewürztraminer 1985, Keuntz-Bas, £12.50.

---

CHEF: Chris Firth-Bernard   PROPRIETORS: Mark and Geraldine Irvine
OPEN: all week, D only
CLOSED: mid-Oct to Easter
MEALS: 8
PRICES: Set D £21 (£24). Service inc
SEATS: 28. Private parties: 8 main room. Car-park, 24 places. No children under 8. No smoking. One sitting
ACCOMMODATION: 13 rooms, 12 with bath/shower. B&B £30 to £62. No children under 8. Pets welcome. Afternoon teas. Fishing. Scenic. Doors close at 10.30. Confirm by 6 [GHG]

## ANSTRUTHER Fife

map 8

# Cellar ♀

24 East Green, Anstruther KY10 3AA
ANSTRUTHER (0333) 310378

COUNTY
OF THE
YEAR
RESTAURANT

COOKING 3
COST £16–£34

'Peter Jukes continues to do good things with fish. His policy is simple – buy the best of the day's catch, and don't destroy its flavour by over elaborate saucing. If he were ever to delete his crayfish and mussel bisque from the menu he would risk a rebellion by an army of clients who drive miles to dine here. His treatment of halibut, turbot, sole and monkfish is exemplary and for non-fishy types, rosettes of lamb with rosemary or good fillet of Scotch beef are available. The wine list is bettered by few in the area. This is a place rich in atmosphere where the philosophy is keep it simple, serve it fresh and don't mess it about.' So writes one man of Fife, happy to support this low-profile fish restaurant that is, perhaps, better known to those in the region than gastro-tourists from the south. The wine list is exceptional for its white wines, with strong showings in Alsace, Chablis and Chardonnays from the New World. The prices are very keen. House wine, £7.50.

CHEF: Peter Jukes  PROPRIETORS: Peter and Vivien Jukes
OPEN: Mon to Sat, exc Mon L (Tue to Sat in winter)
CLOSED: 2 weeks Christmas and New Year, 1 week May
MEALS: 12.30 to 1.30, 7 to 9.30
PRICES: £10 (£16), Set D £18.95 (£25) to £22.50 (£28)
CARDS: Access, Amex, Visa
SEATS: 32. Private parties: 32 main room. Children's helpings (L only). No smoking. Wheelchair access (also WC). Music

## ARISAIG Highland

map 8

# ▲ Arisaig Hotel

Arisaig PH39 4NH
ARISAIG (068 75) 210 and 240

COOKING 1
COST £11–£28

Close to the water's edge, the hotel is an inn built in the eighteenth century, with views of Muck, Eigg and Rhum to tantalise and beguile. It has, under the jovial (oft-kilted) hospitality of the Stewarts, retained some aspects of an inn, from waitresses calling 'Room 3' when your table is ready, to the comment of one Lowland visitor: 'The air and the peace soon closed the eyes, shutting out the woodchip décor.' The food (bar lunches, more formal dinners) is resplendently simple and to be applauded for the quality of the fish and shellfish. The deep-fried king prawn tails may sound like scampi but are not like that at all, and 'worth the journey' to one less taken by location than others. Fine locally smoked produce, from Macdonald, is also worth seeking out. The hot puddings, generous and genuine, are another feature to praise: pineapple upside-down cake and pear and orange crumble are two we've heard of. The wine list is not expensive. House French from Moreau, 6.95 per litre.
CELLARMAN'S CHOICE : Australian Orlando Cabernet-Sauvignon and Chardonnay, both 1987 and both £7.50.

CHEFS: Janice and Gordon Stewart   PROPRIETORS: Mr and Mrs George William Stewart and Gordon Stewart
OPEN: all week
MEALS: 12.30 to 2, 7.30 to 8.30
PRICES: £13 (£19), Set L £6 (£11) to £12 (£18), Set D £17 (£23), Snacks from £1
SEATS: 50. Private parties: 12 main room. Car-park, 60 places. Children's helpings. No smoking
ACCOMMODATION: 15 rooms, 6 with bath/shower. B&B £24.50 to £49. Baby facilities. Pets (dogs) welcome. Afternoon teas. Phone. Scenic [GHG]

---

## ▲ *Arisaig House*

Beasdale, by Arisaig PH39 4NR
ARISAIG (068 75) 622                                                    COOKING 2
on A830, 3m E of Arisaig                                          COST £24−£37

No disputing the quality of the hotel, a Relais & Châteaux member. The Smithers are in tight control and housekeeping is faultless. The house and grounds, too, are in a matchless setting, some three miles on the Fort William side of Arisaig. Views of the Morven hills across the water, the meadows by the glen and the towering hills behind are a tonic worth a long drive (or a request stop at Beasdale). The house was designed by Philip Webb, who had great skill in domesticating the forbidding and a fine ability to create internal spaces much lighter than expected. The public rooms, although refitted in the 1930s after a severe fire, are especially soothing. The dining-room exhibits decorative schizophrenia between the art deco of the framework and the Augustan mahogany and silver, but it is grand enough for the food of elegant simplicity served therein at formal dinners with a set-price menu of relatively few choices: a dish of smoked pigeon, venison and duck; a plate of smoked salmon and oysters; a bowl of cauliflower cream soup with little seasoning; chateaubriand béarnaise and a halibut steak on tomato sauce; some slight elaboration in the vegetables, turnip diced with a béchamel, potatoes sauté with bacon, plain mange-tout; greater choice with the puddings – international style – fruits, puff pastry, cream; good coffee, good yet simple petits fours. Such food will give much pleasure, so long as it is done with total conviction and ineffable skill. Service is willing, as it is throughout the hotel, although it may not inevitably be perfect in its knowledge. The wine list is not encyclopaedic but the bottles are of good pedigree and fancy prices. House wines from £10. 'We do not charge for service.'

---

CHEF: David Wilkinson   PROPRIETORS: Ruth and John Smither
OPEN: all week
CLOSED: end Oct to Easter
MEALS: 1 to 2, 7.30 to 8.30
PRICES: L £11 (£20), Set D £27.50 (£33)
CARDS: Access, Visa
SEATS: 30. Private parties: 8 main room. Car-park, 16 places. No children under 10. No smoking in dining-room. Wheelchair access
ACCOMMODATION: 14 rooms, all with bath/shower. D, B&B £66 to £165. Deposit: £50. No children under 10. Afternoon teas. Garden. Snooker. TV. Phone. Scenic. Confirm by 4.30 [GHG]

## AUCHMITHIE Tayside

map 8

# *But'n'ben*

Auchmithie, by Arbroath DD11 5SQ
ARBROATH (0241) 77223                         COOKING 1
3m NE of Arbroath, off A92                      COST £17

This former fisherman's cottage, white-painted, with quarry-tiled floor and
splashes of colour from pictures for sale on the walls, has pine tables and a
bustle of tearoom/café/restaurant in the kitchen. 'Village mums come in for an
afternoon cuppie and a gossip before school-children come home; local
businessmen have lunch; families have high teas; and there are slightly more
formal evening dinners with tables dressed in linen and lace. The principles on
which we run our restaurant is to provide a welcoming, cosy and friendly
atmosphere for everyone.' Such incontrovertible good sense, voiced by the
owner herself, must gain applause. There are those that find the surroundings
less seemly than they expect but the food is very honest and rooted in the
locality. Fish comes from Arbroath, game from a nearby shoot, smokies from
someone who does them properly – naturally. Specialities are self-evident,
given the place: shellfish, salmon, game and soft fruit in season. All baking,
including bread, is done on the premises, and the jam is home made too. This
sounds twee, but the place receives warm support as genuine and warm-
hearted (and very fairly priced). House French, £5.50. CELLARMAN'S CHOICE :
Chablis, Thomas Bassot, £13.80; Sancerre, Laporte, £10.60.

CHEFS: Margaret and Angus Horn   PROPRIETORS: Margaret, Iain and Angus Horn
OPEN: Mon to Sun, exc Tue L and D, Sun D
MEALS: 12 to 2.30, 4 to 6, 7.30 to 9.30
PRICES: £9 (£14), Snacks from £2.80
CARD: Visa
SEATS: 34. 2 tables outside. Private parties: 34 main room. Car-park, 10 places. Vegetarian
meals. Children's helpings. Wheelchair access (also WC)

## AUCHTERARDER Tayside

map 8

# ▲ *Auchterarder House*

Auchterarder PH3 1DZ
AUCHTERARDER (076 46) 3646/7                    COOKING 1
on B8062, NE of Auchterarder                    COST £24–£60

A new chef at this giant of a house in full Scottish baronial style has caused a
retreat from the full-blown sillinesses of yesteryear. Cooking is luxurious,
bland and still expensive. Some of it has pleased immensely: a puff pastry case
filled with scallops and spinach; lamb with a Dubonnet and red wine sauce.
But it is simpler, even though cool – perhaps on account of the distance from
kitchen to dining-room is one suggestion. On one occasion, the staff were
unable to identify any of the cheeses on offer, something of a record. The wine
list was still undergoing revision well into the season. It is to be hoped that
such revision will remove two 'vintages' of Beaujolais Nouveau, the older £1
more than the younger: this must be a unique feature. House Loron is £8.50.

One reporter's wife was at boarding-school here, before its conversion. However, she found that much of the plumbing in the Ladies was as her classmates had left it. She spent the whole evening rushing from room to room in an ecstasy (or horror) of recognition.

CHEF: John Colin Bussey  PROPRIETOR: Ian Brown
OPEN: all week
MEALS: times by arrangement
PRICES: Set L £17.50 (£24) to £31.50 (£39), Set D £25 (£32) to £40 (£49)
CARDS: Access, Amex, Carte Blanche, Diners, Visa
SEATS: 25. Private parties: 60 main room. Car-park, 40 places. No children under 12. Smart dress preferred. Wheelchair access
ACCOMMODATION: 11 rooms, all with bath/shower. Rooms for disabled. B&B £70 to £100. Deposit: 10%. Baby facilities. Pets welcome. Afternoon teas. Garden. Fishing. Golf. TV. Phone. Scenic. Doors close at midnight

---

**AYR  Strathclyde**                                                                 map 8

## Fouter's Bistro

2A Academy Street, Ayr KA7 1XE                                    COOKING 1
AYR (0292) 261391                                                        COST £14–£29

The burghers of Ayr, hardly spoiled for choice when it comes to eating out, have pounced eagerly on Fouter's cellar bistro. The latest introduction is a set-price 'Brasserie' menu, available every night except Saturday, offering two simple courses cooked in French style – soup, pâté or salad, followed by moules marinière, vegetarian lasagne or steak and chips – for 7.50. Details can be unreliable, and if lured on to the *carte*, the bill rises substantially. There is a small choice of fresh market fish every day: coquilles St Jacques and salmon trout have both been good. Puddings are feasts of cream and booze. House wine, £7.95. The wine list, done with Whighams of Ayr, is not cheap by Scottish standards but offers a fair range.

CHEF: Andrew Gilligan  PROPRIETORS: Laurie and Fran Black
OPEN: Tue to Sun, exc Sun L
CLOSED: 25 to 27 Dec, 1 to 3 Jan
MEALS: 12 to 2, 6.30 to 10.30 (7 to 10 Sun)
PRICES: £17 (£24), Set L £7.25 (£14) to £7.95 (£14), Set D £7.50 (£14) to £9.75 (£16)
CARDS: Access, Amex, Carte Blanche, Diners, Visa
SEATS: 39. Private parties: 39 main room. Vegetarian meals. Children's helpings. No-smoking area. Music. Air-conditioned

---

**BALLATER  Grampian**                                                          map 8

## ▲ Green Inn

9 Victoria Road, Ballater AB3 5QQ                                 COOKING 2
BALLATER (033 97) 55701                                             COST £23

Deceptively unprepossessing outside, friendly and warm inside, the Hamiltons' restaurant is opposite the church, overlooking the green. Aiming to provide good but not elaborate meals as an alternative to the pricier eating places nearby, the kitchen concentrates on local beef, venison (both fresh and smoked), seafood and, following the purchase of a small farm, home-grown fruit and vegetables. Enterprising plans are afoot to extend the range and quality of produce by starting an Aberdeen Angus beef herd and a small milk-sheep flock to produce yoghurt and cheese for the restaurant. Meanwhile, old favourites like the smoked salmon and venison platter are as good as ever. Other well-reported dishes have been pork loin in wine sauce, haddock and prawns in a cream sauce, salmon with a herby mayonnaise and the freshly cooked selection of vegetables that accompanies main dishes. Leave space for crumbles, ice-creams and other home-made puddings. The wine list is short and to the point. House French is £5.95. CELLARMAN'S CHOICE : Brown Brothers dry Muscat Blanc 1987, £9.75; CVNE Imperial Reserva 1978, £9.95.

CHEFS: A.C.S. Hamilton   PROPRIETORS: Mr and Mrs A.C.S. Hamilton and Anne Howden
OPEN: all week
CLOSED: Nov to Feb
MEALS: 12.30 to 2, 7 to 9.30
PRICES: £12 (£19), Snacks from 95p
CARDS: Access, Visa
SEATS: 30. 2 tables outside. Private parties: 28 main room. Vegetarian meals. Children's helpings. Wheelchair access. Music. Air-conditioned
ACCOMMODATION: 3 rooms, all with bath/shower. B&B £17.50 to £30. Deposit: £10 Baby facilities. Pets welcome. Air-conditioning. TV. Scenic. Doors close at 11.30. Confirm by 5

---

## ▲ The Oaks, Craigendarroch Hotel and Country Club

Braemar Road, Ballater AB3 5XA
BALLATER (033 97) 55858                                        COOKING 4
on A93, 1m W of Ballater                                       COST £13–£37

Craigendarroch grows: the Lochnagar Restaurant opened in May 1989, offering simpler and faster food to hotel residents, time-share owners and members of the country club. The Oaks, however, is where the action lies. All cooking on this extensive site is under Bill Gibb, British Transport Hotels trained, much bemedalled, a Scot who prefers to till his native soil. The old house has been extended sympathetically so the visitor little realises the scale of the operation. Within, all is new country house style – instant age – but with a striking dining-room that celebrates the Auld Alliance in its use of fabric for wall coverings. Scotland is taken seriously. Each week there is a 'Taste of Scotland' menu, with bagpipes and a whisky nosing. Bill Gibb is assiduous in developing local supplies, even naming the varieties of potatoes he uses, but does not ignore the outside world: French leaves, tropical fruits and nouvelle cuisine are quite in evidence in dishes such as a rendezvous of fish, a quail consommé with Chinese vegetables and poached quail eggs, and a beef fillet on a bed of wild mushrooms with tarragon butter and a madeira sauce. The level of thought is high: lobster bisque gains an extra dimension from asparagus and elaboration from a trimming of quenelles of fish and diced red peppers; beef and venison are partnered on the same plate, each with its own sauce; a parfait is made with nectarines and curaçao. Often there are two sauces dividing the plate, making for dramatic arrangement. Pork gets blueberries and apple, the venison and beef get juniper and mustard. Berries figure strongly. There is a longish *carte*, bolstered by a nightly set-price gourmet menu. Strong points that have been remarked are the light yet intense sauces, the presentation and the clarity of tastes in sorbets and desserts. Service is proper. The approach to running a restaurant is sanity itself: children are welcomed, smoking is forbidden in the dining room, tipping is discouraged (even by a note on the menu). Yet the prices remain fairer than those of many regional competitors. Tipping is not the essential that proprietors would have us believe: just pay the staff a living wage. Fairness also shines through the wine list, which offers excellent growers and makers at far from greedy mark-ups. There is not a lot below 10 but you get a good bottle. Greater choice of Australasian and Californian wines might allow more excitement at the lower end of the range. House French is £7.50.

CHEF: Bill Gibb   PROPRIETORS: Craigendarroch Ltd
OPEN: all week
MEALS: 12.30 to 2, 7.30 to 10
PRICES: £20 (£29), Set L £8.95 (£13), Set D £18.95 (£23) and £27.50 (£31). Snacks from £1
CARDS: Access, Amex, Diners, Visa
SEATS: Oaks 54; Lochnagar 100. Private parties: 12 main room, 120 private room. Car-park, 100 places. No children under 8. Smart dress preferred. No smoking. Wheelchair access (also WC)
ACCOMMODATION: 50 rooms, all with bath/shower. Rooms for disabled. Lift. B&B £69.50 to £95. Baby facilities. Afternoon teas. Garden. Swimming-pool. Sauna. Tennis. Fishing. Golf. Snooker. TV. Phone. Scenic. Doors close at 12. Confirm by 6 [GHG]

## ▲ *Tullich Lodge*

Ballater AB3 5SB
BALLATER (03397) 55406                                   COOKING 2
on A93, 1m E of Ballater                                 COST £10–£25

In his annual letter to the *Guide*, Neil Bannister commented, 'She used to say "and put some parsley in the boot" as we came over to see her. What more apt title for the memoirs of another inn holder?' This kitchen's relation to crops and seasons, to growing and gathering is as close as that of Mr Bannister's friend. 'If we want basil in the winter, I make pesto' was his comment on the efflorescence of hot-house, year-round herbs – tasting of nothing, costing a lot. The epitome of Scottish baronial, the Lodge does not open until April 'as the drive is too steep and usually ice-bound'. However, a traveller who got there early in the year and found 'snow outside, warm inside' was impervious to the weather, so cosseted was he by food, drink and comfort. That comfort is homely rather than stately, idiosyncratic rather than formulaic. The cooking of set meals (variation can be arranged) is refreshingly direct: one *carte* in May read: spinach soup; fillet of plaice with vegetables and seaweed and a white wine sauce; braised ox-tails with vegetables and potatoes; rum and almond gateau or Scottish cheeses; coffee. Terrine of pheasant with pickled damsons; spinach soup; fillets of sole stuffed with vegetables; apple and redcurrant ice and cream read another menu that pleased one party mightily. Approval is not always universal: the slight unevenness of appointments, the ups and downs of a kitchen will have their effect. The wine list is a good one of 50 bottles, wholly French save three Germans, with half a dozen half-bottles. There are some interesting growers, prices are not out of the way, though some white wines sound too old. The organic Languedoc Domaine d'Ormessan is but £7, while house Muscadet is £8 and house claret £7. CELLARMAN'S CHOICE : Meursault Rouge 1985, Latour Giraud, 16; Mâcon-Villages 1983, Leroy, £12.

CHEFS: Neil Bannister and Steven Lawson    PROPRIETORS: Hector Macdonald and Neil Bannister
OPEN: all week
CLOSED: mid-Dec to end Mar
MEALS: 1, 7.30 to 9
PRICES: Set L £6 (£10), Set D £17 (£21). Service inc
CARDS: Access, Amex, Diners
SEATS: 26. Private parties: 10 main room. Car-park. Vegetarian meals. Children's helpings (L only). Smart dress preferred. No smoking in dining-room. Wheelchair access (also WC)
ACCOMMODATION: 10 rooms, all with bath/shower. B&B £72 to £144. Baby facilities. Pets welcome. Garden. TV. Phone. Scenic

---

**BLAIRGOWRIE  Tayside**                                                    map 8

## ▲ *Kinloch House Hotel*

Blairgowrie, PH10 6SG
ESSENDY (025 084) 237                                          COOKING 2
on A923, 3m W of Blairgowrie                                  COST £7–£24

Rhododendrons hug the drive, a view of water and a fine-proportioned house; all set off by grazing beasts. 'Charolais' said one; 'Highland', observed another. Calf also figures on the menu, cooked eight ways at dinner. The menu is a long one, combining a permanent set of specialities and a changing repertoire of more adventurous cooking (often at a supplement). People speak well of it: reliable (not always the vegetables) and not so expensive as the formal surroundings might imply. Mr Shentall wears a kilt for serving dinner and seems none too pleased with customers who omit to dress with uniform of jacket and tie. If you look the part, the welcome will be extremely affable. Game and seafood appear to be the best things to order. The wine list has many fair clarets back to 1970; the burgundies are less good; the ports are worth a look. They play fair with halves. Lunch may be something in the bar rather than full-scale dining, but is very palatable and quite sufficient. Tipping is 'not encouraged'. House French £5.95. CELLARMAN'S CHOICE : Ch. Beaumont, Haut-Médoc 1982, £12.25.

CHEF: Bill McNicoll    PROPRIETOR: David and Sarah Shentall
OPEN: all week
MEALS: 12.30 to 2, 7 to 9.15
PRICES: £8 (£12), Set L from £4.50 (£7), Set D £17.50 (£20). Service inc
CARDS: Access, Amex, Diners, Visa
SEATS: 60. Private parties: 30 main room; 25,30 private rooms. Car-park, 40 places. No children under 7. Jacket and tie. No smoking in dining-room. Wheelchair access (also WC)
ACCOMMODATION: 21 rooms, all with bath/shower. Rooms for disabled. B&B £38.50 to £68. No children under 7. Baby facilities. Pets welcome. Garden. Fishing. Phone. Scenic. Doors close at 12. Confirm by 6 [GHG]

## CAIRNDOW  Strathclyde                                           map 8

# Loch Fyne Oyster Bar

Clachan Farm, Cairndow PA26 8BH                          COOKING 3
CAIRNDOW (049 96) 217 and 264                            COST £16

'The *Guide* statement that this is an indoor picnic spot speaks volumes for the
arrogant snobbery, but oh-so-British attitude that décor is more important than
decent nosh. Actually this is a very acceptable, roomy eating place. It gives the
lie to most British caterers who will tell you that oysters etc. and other good fish
"will not sell". It was packed at Saturday and Tuesday lunchtime by people
smashing food and wine to pieces, which is just how a restaurant should be.'
Food with a view is the unique selling point of this recently extended loch-side
restaurant next door to its own smokery. Sit outside and catch your breath at
the scenery as you eat, or perch on stools at the new bar inside, where oysters
can be gulped at the counter. All the fish is local and the menu covers smoked
fish – salmon, mackerel, mussels – seafood platters and a handful of hot
dishes, including poached Finnan haddock and Loch Fyne kippers. And, of
course, there are oysters from beds at the head of the loch, served on crushed ice
and seaweed. Smoked venison or venison sausages are other possibilities, and
to finish there are Scottish cheeses with oatcakes. The short wine list includes
such wise choices as La Guita Manzanilla and Barancourt Brut Champagne,
with, by the glass (from £1.10), Hardy's Chardonnay 1987 (£8.86) and Alsace
Pinot Blanc 1988, Ribeauvillé Co-op (£7.25); also 10 beers and two single
malts. House French white, £4.90.

CHEF: Greta Cameron   PROPRIETORS: Loch Fyne Oysters Ltd
OPEN: all week
MEALS: 10 to 9
PRICES: Set L and D £2.75 (£6) to £8.95 (£14)
CARDS: Access, Amex, Diners, Visa
SEATS: 80. 6 tables outside. Private parties: 55 main room. Car-park, 80 places. Children's
helpings. Wheelchair access (also WC)

## CANONBIE  Dumfries & Galloway                                   map 8

# ▲ Riverside Inn ♥

Canonbie DG14 0UX                                        COOKING 2
CANONBIE (038 73) 71512 and 71295                        COST £11–£25

Such is the reputation of the inn that, despite its quiet setting, well off the main
road at the end of a village on the River Esk, it is always busy. It dates from the
turn of the century. The dining-room has a relaxed country feel: the polished
oak tables are made from sewing machine treadles and the chairs are wheel-
backed. Even at lunchtime, when meals are ordered from the bar, there are
some interesting dishes – rillettes of pigeon and pork, poached wild salmon
with watercress sauce, cider roast ham with Cumberland sauce. Simpler
snacks, too, are lifted well above the ordinary by the quality of produce and
careful cooking. Take the chips, for example, 'hand cut, drained and dried,
crisp; they rustled like daffodils in the breeze.' In the evening, the cooking

changes gear for set-price, four-course menus full of imagination. Flavours and textures are carefully thought through around the central ingredient: roast saddle of lamb, for example, served with onion and flageolet cream sauce, bacon and parsley pudding and gravy with a hint of orange, or rabbit casserole in cider served with smoked bacon and a mustard cream. Other ideas are less British in inspiration – monkfish tails cooked with a salpicon of tomato and red peppers, roast farm duck served with burgundy and mushroom sauce – but local produce is always to the fore. The selection of four vegetables is planned with as much care as main dishes: there have been parsnip croquettes, cauliflower in a mild mustard sauce, sprouts with walnuts, deep-fried courgettes in beer batter. Finally comes a range of farmhouse British cheeses – changing all the time – and puddings mixing the sticky and fruity. Service is personalised, but tipping is 'discouraged'. The wine list gives a more than adequate spread at decent prices. The burgundies are a little too weighted to Mommessin and Latour but to compensate there is Viña Arana 1980 from Rioja Alta at £8.70 and CVNE's Imperial Gran Reserva 1976 at £9.90. Wines of the month vary, from £4.25 to £5.25, but own-label house wines are £5.95.

CHEFS/PROPRIETORS: Robert and Susan Phillips
OPEN: Mon to Sat
CLOSED: 2 weeks Feb and Nov
MEALS: 12 to 2, 7.30 to 8.30
PRICES: Bar L £8 (£11), Set D £17 (£21)
CARDS: Access, Visa
SEATS: 28. 4 tables outside. Private parties: 28 main room. Car-park, 25 places. Children's helpings. No smoking. Wheelchair access (also WC)
ACCOMMODATION: 6 rooms, all with bath/shower. Rooms for disabled. B&B £40 to £50. Deposit: £15. Garden. Fishing. TV. Scenic. Doors close at 11. Confirm by 5 [GHG]

---

**CRINAN Strathclyde** map 8

## ▲ *Lock 16, Crinan Hotel*

Crinan PA31 8SR COOKING 1
CRINAN (054 683) 261 COST £19–£37

Nick Ryan is doing for prawns what Clive Davidson does for salmon and beef (see Champany Inn, Linlithgow); this is a formula restaurant that repeats night after night to a satisfied public. There is a set menu that has as its centrepiece jumbo prawns Corryvreckan, sizzling in copper pans with tropical fruit. As they arrive at table the room relaxes, jackets come off, the world tucks in. This shellfish is fresh. What happens after the ecological disaster is a scenario to write tomorrow. House French is £8.75; white wines are the thing at Lock 16. One of the chief attractions is the view and the tables are so angled that all can see the sunset.

---

*'The staff, which seems to consist mostly of young Australians, are friendly but pretty casual. It is unusual perhaps, on choosing a Burgundy, to be told, ''That will put some colour in your cheeks.'' However, my younger colleague told me I was merely carping in an old-fashioned way.'* On eating out in Wales

CHEF: Nick Ryan   PROPRIETORS: Nick and Frances Ryan
OPEN: all week
MEALS: 12.30 to 2, 7 to 9
PRICES: £12 (£19), Set D £22.50 (£31)
CARDS: Access, Visa
SEATS: 24. Private parties: 24 main room. Car-park, 30 places. Vegetarian meals. Children welcome. Smart dress preferred. Wheelchair access (also WC)
ACCOMMODATION: 22 rooms, all with bath/shower. Rooms for disabled. Lift. B&B £37.50 to £65. Deposit: £20 per person. Baby facilities. Pets welcome. Afternoon teas. Garden. Fishing. Phone. Scenic. Doors close at midnight. Confirm by 6

---

**CUPAR  Fife**                                                    map 8

## Ostlers Close

25 Bonnygate, Cupar KY15 4BU                          COOKING 3
CUPAR (0334) 55574                                        COST £30

This small restaurant has attracted a consistent post-bag since the last *Guide* for its continued emphasis on fish and game in a modern manner: crab in a dill mayonnaise; lobster langoustines and scallops with a curry vermouth sauce; wood-pigeon with sloe gin and blackcurrants, or casseroled with pleurottes. Some have said the high point is at the pudding stage, for instance a 'scintillating' strawberry shortcake and good sticky toffee pudding. One reader summed up: 'Does the size and simple décor put people off? Meat and game courses all good and distinct. Vegetables and salads first rate.' Service is cheerful and talkative. A fairly priced wine list strays occasionally outside France, even to Austria. House French from Loron, £6.15. CELLARMAN'S CHOICE: Mount Pleasant Chardonnay 1985, £14.15; Ch. Tahblik Shiraz 1986, £9.15.

CHEF: James Graham   PROPRIETORS: Amanda and James Graham
OPEN: Tue to Sat, and Mon D (bookings only)
MEALS: 12.15 to 2, 7 to 9.30
PRICES: £19 (£25). Service 10%. Minimum 10
CARDS: Access, Visa
SEATS: 28. Private parties: 20 main room. No children under 8. No smoking during meals. Wheelchair access (1 step; also WC)

---

**DRUMNADROCHIT  Highland**                                map 8

## ▲ Polmaily House Hotel

Drumnadrochit IV3 6XT                                COOKING 2
DRUMNADROCHIT (045 62) 343                         COST £18–£29

This Edwardian house is away from the village on the Glen Urquhart road. Compared to the palatial offerings of Inverlochy (see Fort William) its comforts seem more like those of home: the occasional frayed stair carpet can give confidence to some. Alison Parsons has moved from a short *carte* to a set-price menu with no more than three choices, sometimes none if you opt for the five-course extravaganza. The philosophy of 'the best fresh produce cooked to order' shows in regional dishes: Scottish smoked cheese soufflé; Orkney king scallop baked in filo pastry; medallions of venison with blackcurrant. The menu may also extend to the Anglo-French provincial style: pork rillettes with prunes, salmon with an excellent sorrel butter sauce. Vegetables have often been praised and are grown in the Parsons' own garden if possible: a carrot and parsnip purée was reported to have an 'amazingly heady parsnip flavour'. Ice-cream, too, is home made and there are sometimes some good traditional puddings. The wine list is a good one, not so long as to outface the diner, but with a fair selection of good growers (Grippat, Magenta, Millérioux), some nice bourgeois châteaux, a nod to new wine countries and sufficient halves. Bin-ends are worth a close read. House white Bordeaux, £5.65 and claret, £5.95. CELLARMAN'S CHOICE : Costeggiola Soave Classico, Guerrieri Rizzardi 1987, £7.35; Savigny-lès-Beaune, Simon Bize 1985, £16.70.

CHEFS: Alison Parsons and Barbara Drury   PROPRIETORS: Alison and Nick Parsons
OPEN: all week, D only
CLOSED: mid-Oct to end Mar
MEALS: 7.30 to 9.30
PRICES: £17 (£21), Set D £13.50 (£18) to £17.50 (£24). Service inc
CARDS: Access, Visa
SEATS: 30. Private parties: 12 main room. Car-park, 20 places. Children's meals by arrangement. No smoking in dining-room. Wheelchair access
ACCOMMODATION: 9 rooms, 7 with bath/shower. B&B £30 to £70. Deposit: £25. Baby facilities. Garden. Swimming-pool. Tennis. Fishing. Scenic. Doors close at midnight. Confirm by 4 [GHG]

---

**DRYBRIDGE  Grampian**                                                     map 8

## *The Old Monastery* ♚

Drybridge AB5 2JB
BUCKIE (0542) 32660
2m S of junction of A98                                        COOKING 1
and A942                                                       COST £23

Whatever happens, don't take the turn to Drybridge village itself. The monks who used this as a retreat from Fort William were anxious for isolation and a view of the Spey entering the Moray Firth: 'flat with lots of white surf.' Drink in the Cloisters Bar; dine in the Chapel Restaurant; read a menu and wine list written as reverently as any monkish devotional tract. Douglas Gray cooks a more ambitious menu than the location might lead one to expect. It takes traditional form: onion soup; game pâté with a game relish; madeira sauce with pheasant; orange with duck; coffee choux buns topped, croquembouche style, with an Amaretto toffee; bavarois and roulade. The Grays still nurse ambitions to supply vegetables from their own garden. The wine list may concentrate on France and Germany, but has some cheaper Spanish, Italian and Bulgarian bottles. It also has some excellent growers: Jayer, Saget, Dagueneau and François Roussier from Savennières. Prices are fair and there are lots of halves. House wines from £5.95. CELLARMAN'S CHOICE : White Rioja, Marqués de Cáceres 1986, £7.90; Ch. la Rabionne, Fronsac 1978, £9.80.

CHEF: **Douglas Gray**   PROPRIETORS: **Douglas and Maureen Gray**
OPEN: **Tue to Sat**
CLOSED: 3 weeks Jan, 2 weeks Nov
MEALS: 12 to 2, 7 to 9.30 (10 Sat)
PRICES: £13 (£19)
CARDS: Access, Amex, Diners, Visa
SEATS: 45. 2 tables outside. Private parties: 45 main room. Car-park, 28 places. Children's
helpings. No children under £8. No smoking in dining-room

---

**DUNKELD** Tayside                                                        map 8

## Kinnaird House

Kinnaird Estate, By Dunkeld PH8 0LB
BALLINLUIG (079 682) 440                                    COOKING 3
on B898, NW of Dunkeld                                     COST £18–£40

John Webber once cooked at Gidleigh Park and Cliveden. He was a golden boy
of nouvelle cuisine in the provinces. Some time has elapsed before his
reappearance on Tayside in this sumptuous restaurant which opened as we
went to press. A meal taken in the nick of time confirms he has ambition and
there is much possibility he will realise it. The cooking displayed finesse and
generosity, with technique in the foreground (though not displacing taste) in
such dishes as fillet of pork with a spinach forcemeat on a vermouth and
allspice cream sauce, and ragout of lobster, sole and salmon topped with a
cheese and herb crust with a strong savour of tarragon. Any veering to the over-
generous may have been prompted by excitement at the sight of customers. The
menu gives wider choice at both lunch and dinner than many places in the
Scottish countryside. Also, the wine list is a good selection from all countries at
prices that are cheaper than the food price might lead one to expect. House
wine is £8. Rooms are intended but work is not yet initiated.

CHEF: John Webber   PROPRIETORS: Kinnaird House Estate
OPEN: Tue to Sun, exc Sun D
CLOSED: 25 Dec D
MEALS: 12.30 to 2, 7.30 to 9.15
PRICES: Set L £12 (£18) to £26 (£33), Set D £22.50 (£29) to £26 (£33)
SEATS: 35. Private parties: 25 main room, 25 private room. Car-park. No children under 12.
No smoking. Wheelchair access (also WC)

---

**DUNVEGAN** Isle of Skye                                           map 8

## Three Chimneys

Colbost, Dunvegan IV51 9SY
GLENDALE (047 081) 258                                      COOKING 2
on B884, 4m W of Dunvegan                                  COST £28

The 'remote north-west of Skye' is not now so unpopulated; there are various
crafts outlets, a toy museum, even a piping centre if you are enthralled by drone
and chanter. The Three Chimneys is a stone crofter's cottage on a single-track
road overlooking Loch Dunvegan, its two low-beamed dining-rooms simply

decorated and cheered by flowers and candles. The Spears firmly proclaim that theirs is that rare bird in the north, a serious restaurant rather than a hotel dining-room with a limited set menu. The definition 'restaurant' extends to the mood as much as the food. The feeling of a hotel dining-room is quite at odds with the bustle, friendly bustle at that, of a restaurant in full cry. Certainly the prevailing view seems to be that this is set to become *the* place to eat on the island. The Spears go to considerable lengths to provide fresh and, as far as possible, local food: Skye oysters at a price low enough to cause apoplexy in St James's, smoked salmon from North Uist, shark from the west, and soft fruit from nearby Glendale; the ice-cream is Nardini's, from Largs. The dinner menu – there is a simpler, lighter one at lunchtime – offers eight or so first courses, a dozen main courses, and various homely puddings. Shirley Spear's cooking might be identified as traditional Scots with fanciful garnishes, although her own menu descriptions are more fulsome. If your tastes are simple, stick to the home-made soups, 'exceptional' local langoustines in the shell, a grilled steak or wild salmon with lime, vermouth and dill cream. The more optimistically adventurous might try leek and hazelnut crowdie cream roulade with blackcurrant sauce, Highland lamb hot-pot with parsley dumplings ('we enrich the gravy with a little wine and gooseberry-mint jelly'), aubergine, apricot and sweet almond pancakes (one of the two vegetarian dishes, the other being vegan) or halibut fillet with strawberry and black peppercorn sauce. Eddie Spear serves, and the pace can seem too leisurely if you have a ferry to catch. There is a tiny wine shop and off-licence next door – malts a speciality. Mr Spear's choice of wines is good – not a long list, but some excellent bottles at acceptable prices. House Provençal Ch. de Fonscolombe, £6.75.

CELLARMAN'S CHOICE : Alsace Riesling 1987, Blanck, £8.50.

---

CHEF: Shirley Spear   PROPRIETORS: Eddie and Shirley Spear
OPEN: Mon to Sat, plus Sun D July, Aug, bank hols
CLOSED: mid-Oct to end Mar
MEALS: 12.30 to 2, 7 to 9
PRICES: £16 (£23). Minimum £1.50 L, £10 D
CARDS: Access, Visa
SEATS: 35. 2 tables outside. Private parties: 24 main room. Car-park, 30 places. Vegetarian meals. Children welcome. Music

---

**DUROR   Strathclyde**                                                           map 8

## ▲ *Stewart Hotel*

Duror, Appin PA38 4BW
APPIN (063 174) 268 and 220                                              COOKING 1
6m SW of Ballachulish, on A828                                        COST £22–£30

Two generations of Lacys run this former sporting-lodge with large extension for bedrooms. Views, of course, are very fine. Wayne Smith, who is chef, comes from Australia and perhaps has the enthusiasm of that country for very modern styles of cooking. Yet he tempers it with a restraint imposed by the nature of his materials and allows it free rein only in the arrangement of the food. The short set-price menu, offering two alternatives at each course, is very fresh in its pleasing simplicity: squid sauté with herbs; courgette and rosemary soup; rack of lamb with tomato and garlic; pancakes with a calvados sabayon. There is often a hot or warm pudding, although not of the steamed British variety. The wine list is short but not tinged with avarice. House wine is 6.80.

CELLARMAN'S CHOICE : Ch. Labégorce-Zédé, Margaux 1984, £11.90; Ch. Rieussec, Sauternes 1986, £27.

CHEFS: Wayne Smith, Donald Joyce and Dennis Lacy   PROPRIETORS: Michael and Dennis Lacy
OPEN: all week, D only
CLOSED: 2 Nov to end Mar, exc Christmas and 31 Dec
MEALS: 7 to 9.30
PRICES: Set D £17 (£22) to £20 (£25)
CARDS: Access, Amex, Diners, Visa
SEATS: 32. Car-park, 30 places. No children under 7. Smart dress preferred. No smoking. Wheelchair access (1 step). Music
ACCOMMODATION: 20 rooms, all with bath/shower. B&B £35 to £45. Deposit: 20%. Baby facilities. Pets welcome. Afternoon teas. Garden. Sauna. TV. Phone. Scenic. Doors close at 1am. Confirm by 6.30

---

**EDDLESTON  Borders**                                                    map 8

## Champany at the Horseshoe Inn ▮

COUNTY OF THE YEAR RESTAURANT

Eddleston EH45 8QP                                              COOKING 2
EDDLESTON (072 13) 225 and 306                            COST £15−£36

The long low inn was known for its draught beers, homely pub food and horseshoe-shaped windows until Clive and Anne Davidson, owners of Champany at Linlithgow (see entry), bought it as the first of a chain to be run as a joint venture with Scottish & Newcastle Breweries. Now it has been remodelled precisely on the winning formula of its parent steak-house − perhaps the best in Britain − with a stylish main restaurant and a cheaper Chop & Ale House done out in countrified style and serving burgers, chicken, scampi and the superb-quality steaks on which Champany originally made its name. A small back bar serves a fine malt whisky. In the main restaurant, textures livened by royal blues and gold, there are various architectural fittings, familiar from Linlithgow: a sea-water pool for lobsters and crayfish, a shucking table for oysters from Loch Fyne and a dressy American-style salad counter. The *carte* is straightforward, based on prime raw ingredients cooked very simply − seafood and salmon done seven different ways for first courses, charcoal-grilled lamb and beef, steamed lobster or salmon again for main courses, all served with salads. And three set menus follow along the same lines. There is no doubting the quality of ingredients, especially the steaks, which are always perfectly matured, tender and flavoursome, but as yet the kitchen has not found its mark. Sauté potatoes have come swimming in oil, lobster has been over-generously mayonnaised, salads and dressings have been tired and ice-creams hard and granular. Even the chips have been clumsy. This may reflect teething problems and the early lack of turnover, but comments about a soulless, commercial feel quite unlike that of the original Champany do not seem to bode well. The wine list is offspring Champany: same format, fewer wines, different wines on occasion, different prices too (perhaps reflecting the vintage of the list, not the bottle). It must be the most tiring list of all to look through, page after page is turned only to find perhaps one wine, perhaps none for some regions. Not many bottles are under £20 and the canny diner must on occasion throw the whole thing on the floor in irritated frustration. The bottles, however, are impeccable; the service correct. House wine is £8.50.

CELLARMAN'S CHOICE : Hautes Côtes de Nuits 1977, Guy Doufouleur, £16.50.

CHEF: Stephen Worth  PROPRIETORS: Champany Ltd
OPEN: Tue to Sat, exc Sat L
MEALS: 12.30 to 2, 7.15 to 10
PRICES: £18 (£26), Set L £9.50 (£15), Set D £15 (£20) to £25 (£30) Minimum £8.50.
Service inc
CARDS: Access, Amex, Diners, Visa
SEATS: 45. 4 tables outside. Private parties: 45 main room. Car-park, 60 places. No children under 8. Smart dress preferred. Wheelchair access (2 steps, also WC)

---

**EDINBURGH  Lothian**                                                  map 8

## *Chinese Home Cooking*

21 Argyle Place, EH9 1JJ                                    COOKING 1
031-229 4404                                                 COST £6–£10

The name is accurate. Situated in Edinburgh's bed-sitter land, the restaurant may provide true home-from-home comforts for many, and enjoyment for many others. The food is inexpensive, there's no corkage on wine or other drinks brought into the unlicensed premises, and the cooking is straight-forward and decent.

CHEF/PROPRIETOR: Steven Chan
OPEN: all week, D only
MEALS: 5.30 to 11
PRICES: £7 (£8), Set D £5 (£6). Unlicensed, but bring your own: no corkage
SEATS: 40. Private parties: 30 main room. Children welcome. No smoking

## *Indian Cavalry Club*

3 Atholl Place, EH3 8HP                                     COOKING 2
031-228 3282                                                 COST £10–£29

The Indian new wave came to Edinburgh and prospered. This stylish restaurant, hung with swathes of calico, the staff in militarist uniform, has opened a basement Tiffin Room for snacks and lighter meals to supplement the restaurant on the ground floor. One person observed that standards don't slip because Shahid Chowdhury always seems to be present. The cooking is light in touch and the spicing is not too aggressive. It might be thought a compromise with western tastes but in fact it reflects sophisticated preferences in northern India. House wine is £5.90.

---

*'Even after two attempts, no dice: closed. The tone on the phone is amateurish: "We felt too tired to do lunch after last night's dinner".'*  On trying to inspect in Norfolk

---

CHEF: Bilquis Chowdhury   PROPRIETORS: Shahid and Bilquis Chowdhury
OPEN: all week
MEALS: 12 to 2.30, 5.30 to 11.30
PRICES: £12 (£20), Set L £4.95 (£10) to £9 (£14), Set D £8.95 (£14) to £17.95 (£24). Snacks
from £1.65. Minimum £3.50
CARDS: Access, Amex, Diners, Visa
SEATS: 63. 16 tables outside. Private parties: 70 main room, 30 and 30 private rooms.
Vegetarian meals. Children's helpings (weekends only). Smart dress preferred.
No-smoking area. Wheelchair access (2 steps, also WC)

## Kalpna

| | |
|---|---|
| 2–3 St Patrick Square, EH8 9ES | COOKING 1 |
| 031-667 9890 | COST £7–£16 |

The owners chose their elephant logo to demonstrate that there's no need to eat
meat to be big, strong and intelligent. The restaurant, opposite the Odeon
cinema, specialises in Gujerati vegetarian food, with a few South Indian dishes
to give contrast. The manager and head chef have been in residence for nine
years, and regulars praise their consistent creativity. There are half a dozen or
so starters, including rice pancakes and poori in tamarind sauce, then a choice
of set thalis or main dishes. Specialities include mushroom masala flavoured
with coconut and coriander, and makhani sabzi, vegetables in a sweet-and-
sour ginger sauce. Other dishes feature aubergine, lentils, okra or spinach, all
flavoured with freshly ground spices. There are six rices and six breads – and
even the desserts have a vegetarian slant with carrot-based halva and seero for
vegans, made from wholemeal wheat, sugar, fresh ginger, raisins and cashews.
House French is £5.50.

CHEF: Ajay Bharatdwaj   PROPRIETORS: Mr M.E. Jogee, Mrs Mehta, Mr E. Barton and Ajay
Bharatdwaj
OPEN: Mon to Sat
MEALS: 12 to 2, 5.30 to 11.30
PRICES: £6 (£11), Set L £3 (£7) to £4.50 (£9), Set D £5.50 (£10) to £7.50 (£13). Service 10%
CARDS: Access, Visa
SEATS: 60. Private parties: 40 main room, 30 private room. Vegetarian meals. Children's
helpings. No smoking. Wheelchair access. Music

## Kelly's

| | |
|---|---|
| 46 West Richmond Street, EH8 9DZ | COOKING 1 |
| 031-668 3847 | COST £12–£31 |

On a wide street between the University and the Salisbury Crags is found this
most pleasant, simple restaurant occupying a single room, once a bakery, in a
row of slightly forbidding houses. There are very reasonable set-price menus at
lunchtime and a set-price dinner menu (that often sports a couple of dishes
carrying supplements) with always one vegetarian main course and five or six
other choices. A meal of smoked haddock tartlet in a cheese sauce, poached
trout in a wine and dill sauce and shortbread with grapes covered in a wine
and grape juice glaze is not untypical. There is a fair amount of cheese in the

recipes and not a little cream. A nice neighbourhood restaurant, pleasantly appointed and very amiably serviced. The wine list is intelligent and succinct: nor are its ransoms outrageous. Try Ch. Mayragues 1987, a Gaillac made by a Scot with a French wife and domicile. House French vin de pays from Sichel, £5.80. CELLARMAN'S CHOICE : Muscadet, Fief de la Brie 1988, £7.20; Côtes du Rhône, Ch. du Grand Moulas 1988, Ryckwaert, £7.50.

CHEFS: Jacqué Kelly and Vivian Grant   PROPRIETORS: Jacqué and Jeff Kelly
OPEN: Tue to Sat, exc Sat L
MEALS: 12 to 2, 6.45 to 9.45
PRICES: Set L £6.50 (£12) to £10 (£16), Set D £15 (£21) to £20 (£26)
CARDS: Access, Amex, Visa
SEATS: 32. Private parties: 28 main room. Vegetarian meals. Children's helpings. No smoking till 9pm. Wheelchair access (1 step; also WC). Music

## Loon Fung

| 2 Warriston Place, EH3 5LE | COOKING 1 |
|---|---|
| 031-556 1781 | COST £7–£23 |

There's good, fresh-cooked Cantonese food to be had here, hence the queues on Saturday nights. Behind the smoked plate-glass window, the restaurant is plainly decorated in cream and brown. Look out for the fresh fish of the day and other chef specials. There are 16 dim-sum and upwards of 100 dishes: beef in ginger sauce; crispy lemon duck; generously topped prawn toasts; carefully caramelised Szechuan beef, specked with chilli. Order with caution as portions are large. House wine is £6.50 a litre.

CHEF: Tin Fat Siu   PROPRIETORS: Tin Fat Siu and Sammy Tam
OPEN: all week, exc Sat L and Sun L
CLOSED: 25 Dec, Chinese New Year
MEALS: noon (2 Sat and Sun) to midnight (1am Fri and Sat)
PRICES: £9 (£18), Set L £4 (£7), Set D £8.50 (£14) to £13.50 (£19). Service 10%
CARDS: Access, Amex, Visa
SEATS: 75. 14 tables outside. Private parties: 30 main room, 45 private room. Children welcome. Music

## Marché Noir ♥

| 2–4 Eyre Place, EH3 5EP | COOKING 1 |
|---|---|
| 031-558 1608 | COST £12–£28 |

On the edge of Edinburgh's new town, this returns to the listings under its new owners as a moderately, though not cheaply, priced (especially in Southern eyes) French restaurant. French, that is, with qualifications: 'Our basic style is French provincial with nouvelle touches. However, we also use Polish, Hungarian, Vietnamese and traditional British recipes and techniques.' So writes Mark-Damien Budworth. It might stand as an *echt*-statement of British cookery. An inspector, commenting on the resolutely French language titles on the menus says: 'A rather beany, vaguely saffron-flavoured veg soup is not pistou. Generous, very fresh pieces of monkfish were fine, but plenty of beurre on top of blanc (thickened cream) do not constitute beurre blanc. And an attractive, cinnamony, open tart of apple and raisins is not apfelstrudel.' The service is very pleasant at all times: 'that wonderful Edinburgh desire to please a customer, so refreshing to a Londoner'. Lunches are half the price. The wine list is unexpectedly long, having caught the Scottish sickness of encyclopedism. But the bottles are first-rate, most interestingly chosen and annotated and at exceptionally fair prices: Jurançon, Clos Guirouilh 1984, £8; Ch. Lagrange 1970, £25; Hardy's Eileen Hardy Malbec/Cabernet Sauvignon 1984, £12. House French is £6. CELLARMAN'S CHOICE : Gewürztraminer, Zinnkoepflé 1986 Muré, £11; St-Aubin *premier cru* le Charmois 1984, Clerget, £12.

CHEFS: Laurent de la Torre and James Davie   PROPRIETORS: Mark-Damien Budworth and Malcolm Duck
OPEN: all week, exc Sat L
CLOSED: 1 week Jan
MEALS: 12 to 2.30, 7 to 10 (10.30 during Festival)
PRICES: Set L £8 (£12), Set D £12 (£17) to £17.50 (£23)
CARDS: Access, Visa
SEATS: 45. Private parties: 45 main room. Vegetarian meals. Children's helpings. No cigars/pipes in dining-room. Wheelchair access (1 step). Music

# Martin's

70 Rose Street, North Lane, EH2 3DX                    COOKING 2
031-225 3106                                           COST £13−£34

'Impossible to find', Martin's is hidden away in a back lane between Castle Street and Frederick Street on the north side of Rose Street. Outside is grim, but all within is light and bright. It's an incongruous setting for a restaurant that provokes enthusiastic reports. The food is 'nouvellish, but not affected'. Dishes are becoming more elaborate and there's an increasingly green-conscious use of organic vegetables and free-range chicken. Fish is a speciality: warmed monkfish salad; filo parcels with langoustine and gurnard in an 'interesting and well-balanced' watercress and ginger sauce have been relished recently. For pudding there are home-made ice-creams and sorbets plus chocolate marquise or 'excellent' apple and hazelnut strudel. House French is £6.75. CELLARMAN'S CHOICE : Mâcon-Vire, Domaine de Roally 1987, £12.75; Marqués de Murrieta Gran Reserva 1976, £18.95.

CHEFS: David McCrae, Andrew Porteous and Forbes Scott   PROPRIETORS: Martin and Gay Irons
OPEN: Tue to Sat, exc Sat L
CLOSED: 2 weeks from 25 Dec
MEALS: 12 to 2, 7 to 10 (10.30 Fri and Sat)
PRICES: £19 (£28), Set L £7.95 (£13). Service of 10% for parties of 6 or more
CARDS: Access, Amex, Diners, Visa
SEATS: 28. Private parties: 34 main room, 10 private room. No smoking in dining-room. Wheelchair access (2 steps)

*See the inside of the front cover for an explanation of the new 1 to 5 rating system recognising cooking standards.*

# Pierre Victoire

10 Victoria Street, EH1 2HG
031-225 1721

COOKING 2
COST £8–£18

As we went to press, Pierre Levicky was trying out a second venture at 8 Union Street (clearly with one eye on the Festival) and autumn 1989 plans were fluid, though this branch seems set to continue. Certainly, to cram 50 people in where 30 seems a crowd, have a chaotic-looking kitchen on view, employ young French waiting staff understanding little English, persist in carrying rubbish bags through the restaurant while people are eating, is to court discontent. That tales of woe have equalled plaudits must indicate that sometimes it has been too busy –'virtually under siege'– too crowded for everything to work as it should. That Pierre Victoire transcends disaster is due to sensational value, good fresh food and much goodwill. A London visitor and three friends between them sampled every item on the menu and drank two bottles (Champagne and house red), four liqueurs, coffee and mineral water. Their bill was £43.50. 'Service was friendly and efficient. The restaurant was packed, including a family party of 12. They could do with bigger premises and more attention to detail but (the Champagne was amazing at the price), I'd go back any day. How do they do it?' The converted coffee-bar in a roughcast arched vault, with unmatched tables and café chairs, is on the slope down to the Grassmarket: convenient, therefore, for a tourist's inspection of the old town. Set lunch of three courses with a couple of choices at each stage is exceptional value. The evenings bring a short *carte*. Successes have included a game and mushroom soup of real stock, little cream and good fungal aroma, moules marinière properly cleaned and cooked, a pink roast leg of lamb with cassis and orange sauce that was not as sweet as is usual in England, chicken with lemon and ginger, and salmon steak with smoked salmon. Pâtés are good; desserts less so. Pierre Levicky was also, in summer 1989, about to employ a pastry chef: many would say not before time. The wine list is short and French, with three featured halves. Most customers seem to drink house wine. House French, £4.90. CELLARMAN'S CHOICE : St-Emilion, Ch. Plaisance 1983, £8.90; Côtes de Nuits-Villages 1982, £8.60.

CHEF/PROPRIETOR: Pierre Levicky
OPEN: all week
MEALS: 11am to 1am
PRICES: £10 (£13), Set L £4.60 (£8), Set D £7.40 (£11) to £12 (£15). Service inc
CARDS: Access, Visa
SEATS: 65. Private parties: 65 main room. Children's helpings. Wheelchair access (1 step).
Music

---

'We seem to be so health conscious that restaurateurs are avoiding the use of salt, butter, cream and seasonings which bring out the flavour of food. Even herbs seem to be less used and are being replaced by trendy leaves of various colours. If this continues, the Guide will be left to compare brands of Edwina's approved nutrition pills, and what a dull life it will be! Will you kindly organise a campaign to ''get the flavour back into cooking''. It will be very popular.' From a reporter in West Midlands

---

# ▲ *Pompadour Room, Caledonian Hotel*

| | |
|---|---|
| Princes Street, EH1 2AB | COOKING 3 |
| 031-225 2433 | COST £21–£55 |

At these prices the food should be good; and indeed this old railway hotel, where Jeff Bland has been chef for two years or more, is producing some very fine cooking. In an ornate French-style dining-room, whose very curlicues must have suggested its name, the customer at least gets a good acreage of carpet for the money; conversations need not be overheard. A lot of the food circulates on trolleys. Even the breads, and there may be six sorts, have their own trolley. The staff are of long service, attentive and competent, though wine service has shown defects. The dinner *carte* comes dear and ranges through modern repertoires. Not a lot is simple, though few dishes attain the inordinate complexity of 'steamed fillet of sole wrapped with scampi, mousse of sole and pan-fried fillets of sole, surrounded by salmon sauce garnished with cucumber and snails' eggs.' The best bet is the set-price lunch menu. This changes weekly, offers a few choices and proved faultless in a meal of filo pastry vegetable parcels in cream sauce; a casserole of game in a well-concentrated sauce giving it power and substance; good vegetables; a handsome selection from the sweets trolley; a vast cheese trolley and good coffee and petits fours. Further traffic congestion comes from the trolley bearing the roast joint of the day. The owners, Norfolk Capital Hotels, seem to allow their chefs time to develop their talents. Billesley Manor near Stratford-upon-Avon (see Billesley) is a case in point and the Caledonian appears to be another. The wine list is extensive and mostly pricey, although one bargain of a young vintage port has been reported. The large dining-room is divided equally between smokers and non-smokers. All may listen to the piano.

CHEF: Jeff Bland   PROPRIETORS: Norfolk Capital Hotels
OPEN: all week, exc Sat L and Sun L
MEALS: 12.30 to 2, 7.30 to 10.30 (7 to 10 Sun)
PRICES: £34 (£46), Set L £14.50 (£21)
CARDS: Access, Amex, Diners, Visa
SEATS: 45. Car-park, 150 places. Children welcome. Smart dress preferred at D. Wheelchair access (also WC). Music at D
ACCOMMODATION: 237 rooms, all with bath/shower. Rooms for disabled. Lift. B&B £98.50 to £133.50. Deposit: 1 night. Baby facilities. Afternoon teas. TV. Phone. Confirm by 6

# *Shamiana*

| | |
|---|---|
| 14 Brougham Street, EH3 9JH | COOKING 2 |
| 031-228 2265 and 229 5578 | COST £22 |

The Shamiana is reckoned by some as the best Indian in town. Its clean crisp décor, with patterned grey and white tiles on the floor and arrangements of fresh flowers, is supposed to be reminiscent of Moghul interiors, and there is a rare emphasis on both quality and authenticity. If something is not quite as it should be, which does happen, Khalil Mansoori, the proprietor who also runs front of house, attends to it at once. The menu is not as long as some, but there is still plenty of choice: five starters, four tandoor dishes, eight curries including parsee lamb with dried apricots and herby chicken with poppyseeds, melon and crushed aniseed, and eight kashmiri and other specialities. Rice is aromatic, breads are fresh and moist. Vegetable dishes are relatively expensive, but worth it for the distinct flavours. There's a cleverly constructed wine list matching bottles to dishes, or lagers. House French, £5.95. Booking is almost essential and service can be slow, making the 12.5 per cent service charge seem rather high.

CHEF: K. Mansoori   PROPRIETORS: M.E. Jogee and K. Mansoori
OPEN: all week, exc Sat L and Sun L
CLOSED: 25 Dec, 1 Jan
MEALS: 12 to 2, 6 to 11.30
PRICES: £10 (£18). Service 12.5%
CARDS: Access, Amex, Diners, Visa
SEATS: 42. Private parties: 18 main room. Vegetarian meals. Children's helpings. No cigars/pipes in dining-room. Wheelchair access (1 step). Music

## Szechuan House

95 Gilmore Place, EH3 9NU                          COOKING 1
031-229 4655                                     COST £10-£20

This modest converted shop, decorated with Chinese lanterns, is the main contender north of the border for commitment to Szechuan food. Thanks to Chao-Gang Liu's background in Szechuan, there has been no accommodating dilution for western tastes. Among the spicier dishes are steamed lamb and beef, shredded pork in fish flavour, and sliced beef in hot soup, obviously as effective in keeping out the Edinburgh cold as they are in combating humidity in China. The duck is smoked on the premises, in a wok over burning leaves, and served with Chinese bread sauce. Seafood and vegetarian dishes lead the field, although vegetarian chicken implies an identity crisis. Great Wall is £7.30 a bottle, house French is £5.40.

CHEF: Chao-Gang Liu   PROPRIETORS: Hsueh-Fen and Chao-Gang Liu
OPEN: all week, D only
MEALS: 5.30pm to 2am (3am Fri and Sat)
PRICES: £11 (£17), Set D £7.30 (£10) to £9.20 (£12). Service inc
CARDS: Access, Visa
SEATS: 40. Private parties: 24 main room, 12 private room, Vegetarian meals. Children welcome. Music

## Verandah Tandoori

17 Dalry Road, EH11 2BQ                             COOKING 1
031-337 5828                                     COST £10-£18

In Edinburgh's Haymarket near the station, Wali Uddin's restaurant, done out in browns of wood, cane and wicker, continues to pick up awards and favourable reviews from local critics. The menu is not oppressively long and lays greater emphasis on northern India and Bangladesh than the south. Vegetarians are well catered for. Specialities include the cool lamb pasanda, the hot king prawn pathia, and the positively mild korma badarmi. A greater effort to match wine to the food has been made this year with an intelligent new list, though you may still have mango lassi or Grolsch lager. House French, £4.25.

CHEFS: Wali T. Uddin and Kaisar Miah   PROPRIETORS: Wali T.Uddin, Kaisar Miah, Foysol Choudhury and Nurjahan Uddin
OPEN: all week
MEALS: 12 to 2, 5 to 11.45
PRICES: £10 (£18), Set L and D for 2 £15.55 (£20) to £22.55 (£28)
CARDS: Access, Amex, Carte Blanche, Diners, Visa
SEATS: 44. Private parties: 60 main room. Vegetarian meals. Children's helpings (L only). Wheelchair access (1 step). Music. Air-conditioned

## Vintners Room

87 Giles Street, Leith, EH6 6BZ                                  COOKING 2
031-554 6767                                                     COST £14–£29

The vaults where once lived and traded the wine merchants of Leith resound again to the clink of glasses: 'ethnic restaurants and nouvelle cuisine are Leith's lot'. In fact, quarters at this address are also occupied by Wines from Paris, a first-rate new-wave merchant, and the Malt Whisky Association. The restaurant has scope to expand from its core of a fine plastered room, ornate enough for any wine merchant, into a many-faceted business, perhaps even restoring the vaults below to human life and voice. A stranger, knowing not the Cummings, remarked the food was redolent of the 1970s. Those who recall the cooking at the Hole in the Wall in Bath before the Cummings sold it will recognise the style. They need not dismiss it. A fine fish soup with trimmings – lighter than the concoctions of most restaurants, 'about the only coq au vin I'd have trusted anywhere', calf's brains with black butter, salmon in pastry with ginger and currants, monkfish au poivre are some dishes reported. At its best, this is food that ignores fashions. As yet, there are too many practical things going on to ensure consistency. The wine list, with an early strong showing of Rhônes and Loires from Robin Yapp, may also develop. Tipping is 'optional but disliked'.

CHEFS: William Marsden and Tim Cumming   PROPRIETORS: Tim and Sue Cumming
OPEN: all week, exc Sat L and Sun D
CLOSED: 1 week Christmas
MEALS: 12 to 2.30, 6.30 to 10
PRICES: £17 (£24), Set L £7.50 (£14) to £10.50 (£17). Service 10%
CARDS: Access, Diners, Visa
SEATS: 65. Private parties: 40 main room. Car-park, 10 places. Children's helpings. No smoking. Wheelchair access (2 steps, also WC). Air-conditioned

## Waterfront Wine Bar

1C Dock Place, Leith EH6 6LU                                     COOKING 1
031-554 7427                                                     COST £16

In the summer, even with outside tables, it can be packed to the gills; in the winter, full without congestion. Some people are firm advocates of certain items of the repertoire: pigeon breasts with cherry sauce; char-grilled steaks (order medium if you want them rare); duck with ginger; Italian brown bread.

Others are more dismissive, especially of the service 'which tends to disappear after the main course is served'. The wines are not expensive. House French, £5.20. CELLARMAN'S CHOICE : Portuguese Garrafeira 1970, Barrocão, £7.20; Wyndham Chardonnay Bin 222 1987, £6.80.

CHEFS: Helen Ruthven, Robin Bowie and Paul Mcleman  PROPRIETORS: Helen and Ian Ruthven, Sarah Reid and Robin Bowie
OPEN: Mon to Sat
MEALS: 12 to 2.30 (3 Sat), 6 to 9.30 (10 Fri and Sat)
PRICES: £8 (£13)
SEATS: 150. 13 tables outside. Private parties: 26 main room, 15 and 40 private rooms. Vegetarian meals. No children under 5. Wheelchair access (also WC). Music

---

**ELIE  Fife**                                                                    map 8

## *Bouquet Garni*

| 51 High Street, Elie KY9 1BZ | COOKING 3 |
| ELIE (0333) 330374 | COST £18–£26 |

Elie is a small holiday and fishing town and there, in a very small restaurant owned by a family involved in fisheries and fishmongering, cooks Walter McCrindle. He has outside interests too. After training at the Malmaison in Glasgow (a sound base in classical cooking), he now spends his days as a lecturer in catering. The restaurant reflects a professional background: the food it serves, mainly fish, is complex, up to date and assured. 'The quality of the ingredients is flawless and the imagination in the kitchen would rival London counterparts,' writes one 'dazed' reporter. A small but willing team, in a dining-room pleasantly but not extravagantly appointed, serve some impressive dishes in a deliberate way: lobster and scampi soup; a trio of fish with crayfish and saffron sauce; halibut with scallops, mussels, prawns and crayfish on wild rice; lemon sole stuffed with salmon mousse on a carrot and ginger sauce. Meat gets a look-in, a couple of dishes on a menu that is fairly long for such a tiny place. Presentation is considered and handsome; quantities are generous. Apart from the Scottish cheeses, reporters have waxed eloquent on shortbread layered with a 90° proof Glayva cream, topped with a fine butterscotch sauce. This is very fine cookery that may strike some as over-elaborate in its mixing of species and ingredients but which does seem to put flavour first. The wine list may be short, but it is very reasonable and the growers are good. House Bordeaux is £5.95.

CHEF: Walter McCrindle  PROPRIETORS: A.T. Keracher and Walter McCrindle
OPEN: Tue to Sat, D only
MEALS: 7.30 to 10
PRICES: £16 (£22), Set D £14.50 (£18). Service inc
CARDS: Access, Visa
SEATS: 22. Private parties: 20 main room. Children's helpings. No children under 12. No cigars/pipes in dining-room. Wheelchair access. Music

---

*'I can confirm that Tokyo has to be the most expensive city in the world to dine in. Dinner for 10 cost £3,300 and for 17 approximately £4,800.'*  A senior inspector

---

ERISKA **Strathclyde**                                                    map 8

## ▲ *Isle of Eriska Hotel*

Eriska PA37 1SD
LEDAIG (063 172) 371                                          COOKING **2**
off A828, 12m N of Oban                                    COST £11−£43

The Buchanan-Smiths' towered and turreted greystone hall presides over its
own isolated private island off the west coast. The menu continues to operate to
a six-course formula. Deep-fried Brie and then minted pea soup might precede
a handsome roast − pork, perhaps, or turkey − carved at the table. A daily fish
dish is also offered. Following on are desserts, then mushrooms on toast or
another savoury and, finally, cheese. Vegetables come from the garden, milk
and cream from the resident Jerseys, eggs from local hens. 'It is a place to gather
one's strength for the rougher edges of life beyond the island,' writes one well-
rested reporter. The young staff, taking their cue from the owners, 'chat without
being familiar and have a sense of service'. Diners, however, should not relax
so much that they neglect to don smart dress for dinner. Children are given
high tea at 6pm. The wine list is dominated by France and, within that ambit,
by famous names: Latour, Chapoutier, Ch. de Nozet, Viénot, Trimbach. It
covers the country in that mode, not cheaply, and is best for bourgeois châteaux
from Bordeaux. There are a handful of Germans, Australasians, and Stags Leap
Californians.

CHEFS: Vilas Roberts   PROPRIETORS: Robin and Sheena Buchanan-Smith
OPEN: all week
CLOSED: Dec to Mar
MEALS: 12.45 to 1.30, 7.30 to 8.30
PRICES: Set L £5.75 (£11) to £9.65 (£15), Set D £28.75 (£36)
SEATS: 40. Private parties: 10 main room, 12 private room. Car-park, 50 places. Children's
helpings. Children restricted. Smart dress preferred. Wheelchair access (also WC)
ACCOMMODATION: 16 rooms, all with bath/shower. Rooms for disabled. B&B £93.15 to
£103.50. Deposit: £50. Baby facilities. Garden. Tennis. Fishing. TV. Phone. Scenic. Confirm
by 4 [GHG]

FORT WILLIAM **Highland**                                          map 8

## ▲ *Factor's House*

Torlundy, Fort William PH33 6SN
FORT WILLIAM (0397) 5767                                      COOKING **2**
3m N of Fort William on A82                                    COST £29

The house, sheltering below Ben Nevis at the gates of the Inverlochy Castle
estate − 'good views while eating' − might be Scandinavian for its wealth of
natural-finish joinery. Peter Hobbs is the son of Grete Hobbs of Inverlochy
Castle and, though experienced in the ways of international hotel-keeping, has
opted for a simpler style here. He describes it himself as 'a guest-house with
restaurant'. Guests are offered a wealth of diversions other than food, from the
hotel's own sailing-boat to all manner of Scottish field sports. The dining-room
and other public spaces have been redecorated this year (using the same
designer as the Castle), but the arrangement of the blackboard menu in the

lounge remains as before. Choice is small but it changes daily, and offers more than simple home cooking. First courses normally include a soup, perhaps chicken broth, and a couple of other dishes, for instance warm poached egg salad or fresh noodles with sweetbreads and tomato sauce. Main courses often include steak, perhaps with a choron sauce or a savoury butter, and often too a pie (rabbit or venison), and there is also a fish dish, perhaps trout in oatmeal or salmon with a beurre blanc. Puddings are simple: rum and currant flan; Atholl brose; butterscotch ice-cream. The emphasis is on first-class ingredients. Two dozen and odd wines from Corney & Barrow and Justerini & Brooks give a metropolitan feel to the list. Prices throughout the enterprise, which is conducted with much relaxed skill, are reasonable. It might be thought an overflow operation to the Castle, but not a bit of it. The Factor's House is not just a poor relation. 'You could change for dinner but a couple of Italians, looking for ghosts in Scottish castles, turned up on spec at 8pm in jeans (Italian, though) and were welcomed.'

CHEF: Steven Doole    PROPRIETOR: Peter Hobbs
OPEN: Tue to Sun D only (plus L for residents)
CLOSED: mid-Dec to mid-Jan
MEALS: 7.30 to 9.30
PRICES: Set D £17.50 (£24)
CARDS: Access, Amex, Diners, Visa
SEATS: 24. Private parties: 24 main room. Car-park, 16 places. Children's helpings. No children under 8. Wheelchair access (also WC)
ACCOMMODATION: 7 rooms, all with bath/shower. Rooms for disabled. B&B £40.25 to £69. Deposit: £50. No children under 8. Garden. Tennis. Fishing. Golf. TV. Phone. Scenic. Doors close at 12.30. Confirm by 6 [GHG]

---

## ▲ Inverlochy Castle ♥

Fort William PH33 6SN
FORT WILLIAM (0397) 2177                          COOKING 4
3m N of Fort William on A82                       COST £30–£53

On reading reports sent in over the year, the term 'obsessive' springs to mind: so many staff, such constant attention, so many greetings, such endless cleaning and purpose. Yet there is a glint of steel: the sherry glasses too large? whip them away to re-pour; a hint of delay as if for a tip? 'What are you doing here, sunshine?' The steel is not only bared to the staff: 'Any reservation not cancelled within six full weeks of arrival date is liable to be charged for, unless accommodation is re-let to another client.' The point of this is, how warm is the hospitality? Readers are in two minds. They do concur, however, in praising the efficiency and in approving the cooking. It centres on a set-price dinner of five courses, in a setting of polished wood, crystal and silver most of us dream of but do not experience – some, though, like the foursome observed dropping out of the sky on to the front lawn, have helicopters to facilitate weekly sampling. There are three or four choices of first and main courses and dessert, two soups (one thick, one thin) and a good Scottish cheeseboard. The menu construction is very skilled: two fish, one meat at first; one fish, two meat at third – it sounds simple but the balance is impeccably maintained. Occasionally, there is an extra (grouse) at an extra price. At £38, couldn't that be thrown in? The food does not often suffer from over-refinement – a summer meal included lentil soup and a well-flavoured woodpigeon consommé – although moules marinière was executed with more finesse than brio, when the latter is desirable. An inspection meal this year, however, did reveal a slight insipidity in veal of evanescent taste and a dish of scallops deprived of their corals (perhaps for the American clientele). But the skill, for instance in a tart of pineapple with a rum and raisin ice-cream, is readily available. 'Orange soufflé was sufficient – for four – offputting.' The wine list is another Scottish encyclopaedia of claret and burgundy, at prices that are not as high as the setting may lead to expect. Australia is more generously dealt with than California and there are some very aristocratic Italians. Half-bottles there are in abundance, and selection as a whole is not so fancy that there is nothing worth trying under £15 or £20. The stumbling block for many of our readers is the price: say £250 for dinner, bed and breakfast for two. At that it needs to be perfect. On the credit side, young children are welcomed to the hotel (if they share their parent's bedroom), though not to dinner; and tipping is discouraged.

CHEF: Graham Newbould   PROPRIETOR: Grete Hobbs
OPEN: all week
CLOSED: mid-Nov to mid-Mar
MEALS: 12.30 to 1.45, 7.30 to 9
PRICES: Set L £24 (£30) to £28 (£34), Set D £38 (£44)
CARDS: Access, Visa
SEATS: 36. Private parties: 18 main room. Car-park. No children under 10. Smart dress preferred. No smoking
ACCOMMODATION: 16 rooms, all with bath/shower. B&B £121 to £165. Deposit: 50%. Afternoon teas. Garden. Tennis. Fishing. Snooker. TV. Phone. Scenic. Doors close at midnight [GHG]

---

| GLASGOW Strathclyde | map 8 |
| --- | --- |

## Café Gandolfi

| 64 Albion Street, G1 1NY | COOKING 2 |
| --- | --- |
| 041-552 6813 | COST £16 |

Artful, modernist furniture gives a very Glasgow feel to this spacious brasserie, but food and atmosphere conjure up continental cafés, with staff both 'friendly and civilised'. At the core of the menu are smart modern snacks – light and healthy – some of which double as first or main courses. Goats' cheese salad, gravlax, baked red peppers, pastrami on rye and Finnan haddock with potatoes are examples. These are well done; the goats' cheese salad, for example, has two large ovals of ripe cheese laid on a salad with lots of walnuts, fresh basil and tomatoes. Dishes of the day can be more substantial and occasionally clumsy – 'untidy noisettes of lamb, underseasoned, with traffic-light pepper sauces and four mange-tout were messy to look at but tasted fine.' Drinks include Traquair House ale, a good range of teas and coffees and home-made lemonade. Only six wines, sensibly chosen, of which two are organic. The João Pires Dry Muscat is 'divinely light, clean and dry'.

CHEFS: Margaret Clarence and Andrew Bickerstaff   PROPRIETOR: Iain M. MacKenzie
OPEN: Mon to Sat
CLOSED: bank hols
MEALS: 9.30am to 11.30pm
PRICES: £9 (£13), Snacks from £1.30. Service of 10% for parties of 6 or more
SEATS: 60. Private parties: 12 main room. Vegetarian meals. Children's helpings. No
children after 8pm. Wheelchair access (2 steps). Music

## Loon Fung

| | |
|---|---|
| 417 Sauchiehall Street, G2 3LG | COOKING 1 |
| 041-332 1240 and 1477 | COST £9–£32 |

'Ideal for a simple meal in unfussy surroundings,' writes a reporter, pleasantly
soothed after dinner in this spacious restaurant. There's a page of dim-sum,
such as meat and nut dumpling and wafer-wrapped prawn, besides many
other dishes: Szechuan king prawns; crunchy stuffed duck; baked oysters with
roast belly pork; sizzling steak and lamb. Special set vegetarian meals are £9;
other set dinners are from £13. House Italian is £7, but China tea is free.

CHEF: M. Kan   PROPRIETOR: P.W. Cheng
OPEN: all week
MEALS: 12 to 11.30
PRICES: £13 (£23), Set L £4.50 (£9), Set D £9 (£14) to £21 (£27), Snacks from £1.40.
Licensed, also bring your own: corkage £2
CARDS: Access, Amex, Diners, Visa
SEATS: 200. Private parties: 200 main room. Vegetarian meals. Children's helpings. Smart
dress preferred. Wheelchair access (1 step; also WC). Music. Air-conditioned

## October ♥

| | |
|---|---|
| 128 Drymen Road, Bearsden, G61 3RB | COOKING 3 |
| 041-942 7272 | COST £11–£28 |

'We do not have the truffle and foie gras fraternity here,' writes Ferrier
Richardson, describing his refurbished restaurant in Glasgow. In truth, the
setting is now seductive, as well as offering space for a larger kitchen brigade
and opportunity for more of the trimmings associated with today's fine eating:
amuse-gueule, petits fours and the like. One correspondent described it for us:
'fresh modern décor, predominantly white with soft blue touches, the new bar
area littered with huge comfortable blue-edged cream cushions, now a
welcome oasis. Tall pale modish vases with dried flowers in the corners, huge
mirrored walls at side and back enhance the feeling of spaciousness. The
service and ambience is cool with intermittent periods of brio and animation.
The seating is now actually comfortable, with blue velvet banquettes against
the wall.' There is a large *carte*, at prices that would make a southerner blush
but maybe a northerner blench, and a shorter selection at two set prices for
lunchtime. This is equally reasonable. The repertoire is very modern; it has left
the old sweet/sour dialectic far behind and nods towards the peasant (tripe
with onions and tarragon) and the oriental, especially Japanese (stir-fried
monkfish and scallops with boiled rice and chilli sauce). A winter meal that

included Camembert wrapped in crisp filo pastry, a broccoli soup, a slightly dry turkey escalope fried with Gruyère and smoked ham, classic filet mignon with a red wine sauce (superbly done) and a duo of sorbets (lemon and redcurrant) that provided the right uplift at the end, was wholly liked, particularly for the pointed seasoning of the sauces and the quality of the accompanying vegetables. There has been comment on tables too close together to avoid cigar drift (that well-known restaurant meteorological condition) and on smelly wine glasses, but the general verdict is that the refurbishment has done Mr Richardson good and that improvements to the aim of occasionally misdirected darts of taste or execution should make this a very satisfactory place. The wine list is as modern as the cooking, working hard for worldwide coverage in 50 bottles. He makes a fair fist of it, with some interesting choices at decent prices: Peter Lehmann's wines from Barossa Valley, Prince Poniatowski's Vouvray demi-sec, Baron d'Ardeuil's Côtes de Buzet. Offering only one half-bottle of red wine is not very helpful. House Loire from Rémy Pannier, £7.50. CELLARMAN'S CHOICE : Peter Lehmann Dry Semillon 1988, £9.95; Bandol Rouge, Mas de la Rouvière 1983, Bunan, £12.95.

CHEF: Ferrier Richardson    PROPRIETORS: Premiere Cuisine Ltd
OPEN: Mon to Sat
CLOSED: 1 week at Easter, first 2 weeks Aug
MEALS: 12 to 2, 7 to 10
PRICES: £16 (£23), Set L £6.75 (£11) to £8.75 (£13). Service inc
CARDS: Access, Visa
SEATS: 48. Private parties: 52 main room. Children welcome. Wheelchair access (also WC). Music. Air-conditioned

## ▲ One Devonshire Gardens

| 1 Devonshire Gardens, G12 0UX | COOKING 2 |
|---|---|
| 041-339 2001 | COST £25–£40 |

'Cosseting' might be one description of the approach in this small, very luxurious hotel that aims for country-house style in an urban environment. The food and the service reflect this and the short fixed-price menu at dinner (with a soup course coming second) reads as a pleasing light variation on some of the more elaborate Scottish baronial piles. Steamed mussels with garlic, tomato and herbs; a warm mousseline of sweet peppers; salad of duck and asparagus with citrus fruits and pine nuts; fillet of beef teriyaki and often mixed fish dishes – a 'medley' or two fillets – are some of the pointers. The tone of the restaurant is subdued. The wine list from Corney & Barrow has nothing much from beyond France but an up-market selection from within its borders. House wines are from £11.50. CELLARMAN'S CHOICE : Ch. Bertin 1985 Montagne St-Emilion, £15.75; Vacquéyras 1985, Jaboulet, £14.30.

*'Once the long alley is safely negotiated, one has to pass the bar and dare to refuse drinks; this is the first and last sight of anyone possibly having a management function. Dinner is a set price £17 for a menu that if not hewn in stone, is at least heat-sealed and unchanged by the season.'* On dining in Buckinghamshire

CHEF: Jim Kerr   PROPRIETOR: Ken McCulloch
OPEN: all week, exc Sat L
CLOSED: 25 Dec, 1 Jan
MEALS: 12 to 2, 7 to 10
PRICES: £15 (£25), Set D £24 (£33)
CARDS: Access, Amex, Carte Blanche, Diners, Visa
SEATS: 48. Private parties: 36 main room, 16 private room. Car-park, 12 places. Children's helpings on request. Smart dress preferred. Music
ACCOMMODATION: 8 rooms, all with bath/shower. B&B £85.50 to £112. Baby facilities. TV. Phone. Confirm 24 hours before [GHG]

## Peter Jackson at the Colonial ♥

25 High Street, G1 1LX                                    COOKING 3
041-552 1923                                             COST £10–£40

Peter Jackson explains that his restaurant has had a complete refurbishment – not before time, according to reporters unanimously unimpressed with the previous décor. Perhaps the surroundings will do justice to the food, which continues to draw good reports. The cooking has led the field in exploring modern combinations, though success of chicken breast stuffed with exotic fruit, rolled in coconut and then shallow fried must be moot. Materials and their supply occupy much of the chef's attention – organically grown vegetables are the norm – and yield dividends in superlative pheasant and the rich flavour of the smoked goose used in a winter salad. The menu is a short *carte*, with all fish offered either as a first or a main course, and a no-choice 'Taste of Scotland' menu of five courses. Each menu has suggestions for wine and specific recommendations from Peter Jackson himself. Customers may leave the choice to Mr Jackson, who will concoct a surprise menu at a single price. This is consistently popular. The 'Taste of Scotland' description is a notion, not a reality: aubergines, pears in March, even lentils are hardly Scottish. At lunch there are two short menus, 'Business' and 'Executive', that constitute remarkable value. They put this restaurant on a par with the best Chinese places for social utility and adaptability. Service continues to be fair and well-informed. One party gave their order to Peter Jackson himself. 'We unashamedly indicated envisaging a reasonably modest bill and together planned the fare. This is a good restaurant for taking recommendations from the chef!' The wine list is a good one, though prices are somewhat higher than may be necessary, and lesser whites are kept too long. Aspects of it are worth travelling for: a range of clarets back to Ch. Ausone 1928, an extensive choice of halves, and some good dessert wines, including Tokays. House Bouchard red and Listel white are £6.75.

CHEF/PROPRIETOR: Peter Jackson
OPEN: Mon to Sat, exc Sat L and Mon D
MEALS: 12 to 2.30, 6 to 10.30
PRICES: £25 (£33), Set L £5.85 (£10) to £9.95 (£15), Set D £16 (£21) to £24 (£30)
CARDS: Access, Amex, Diners, Visa
SEATS: 40. Private parties: 40 main room. Children welcome. Wheelchair access

## Rogano

| 11 Exchange Place, G1 3AN | COOKING 3 |
| 041-248 4055 | COST £38 |

'If this is mass catering, give me more,' wrote a contented soul, referring to our scathing comments in the last *Guide*. Indeed, the tone of reports has been uniformly positive, save for a short period at the start of the season. The regime in this place, redolent of the 1930s yet up to date in its cooking and natural approach to people and their wants, has not changed. William Simpson's cooking, and particularly his buying, have been exemplary. A meal that began well with oysters and fish soup (with an excellent rouille), moved up a notch with the grilled lobster; suffered a barely perceptible blip with smoked salmon mousse wrapped in fillets of sole where, as so often, the taste of smoked outgunned all others; but resumed an upward course with vegetables (not always thought a strong point), syrup sponge with Amaretti cream and a strawberry shortcake. Debate has been occasioned by desserts. Service throughout was matchless in tone and performance. Fish is not compulsory: there is a vegetarian main course and three or four meat dishes. Rogano succeeds in being all things to all people with Café Rogano and snacks at the bar, where value is good and service is willing. Dishes will be 'adapted' for vegetarians. The wine list is not cheap but offers a good range, including three Sancerres and good Loire house wine from Rémy Pannier at £7.95. Wine service has been especially marked out as exemplifying the Rogano touch with people. CELLARMAN'S CHOICE : Sancerre, Le Grand Chémarin 1987, £15.25; Gewürztraminer, Les Sorcières 1986, Dopff & Irion £14.95. 'Credit card slips are totalled.'

CHEF: William Alexander Simpson   PROPRIETORS: Alloa Brewery
OPEN: Mon to Sat
MEALS: 12 to 2.30, 7 to 10.30
PRICES: £21 (£32). Snacks from £2.50. Service 10%
CARDS: Access, Amex, Diners, Visa
SEATS: 100. Private parties: 25 main room, 14 private room. Vegetarian meals. Children welcome. Music. Air-conditioned

## Ubiquitous Chip ▮

| 12 Ashton Lane, G12 8SJ | COOKING 2 |
| 041-334 5007 | COST £28 |

A party of foraging English were attracted by the informality. A table in the courtyard took advantage of the summer heat. Greenery hangs in profusion. The Ubiquitous Chip has a long history. Its first few years in the early 1970s were unlicensed, which some would find hard to believe. The intentions were to be a reaction to the standard, the packaged, the 'chips with everything' approach; to promote Scottish materials, Scottish culture, robust and individual cooking. These values persist even as Ron Clydesdale trades without his former partner, Ian Brydon, now living in France. The menu still reads like a manifesto and the four corners of Scotland are ransacked for the larder. Those English, to revert to the beginning, were impressed by the quality of the fish – Ayr-landed cod was cooked with precision and was as fresh as could be – and were particularly taken by the ragout of ox-tail's slow cooking, careful butchery and a melding of flavours to the right degree of richness. Some dishes are cooked in a French (provincial) way; some lean on Scots practice as with the haunch of venison and Cumberland sauce; and some reflect modern tastes as in turbot with a pine kernel and green peppercorn crust and a red wine sauce. Not everything is correct: a bread-and-butter pudding was too solid, though an oatmeal ice-cream was thought brilliant; clapshot (mixed purée of potato and swede) was too thin; cheeses looked a bit glum. A scholar who marked his assessment concluded 'the meal ranged from quite good (Beta, just a couple of items) to good (Alpha Beta, for most of it) to very good for one or two'. The service is relaxed and talkative, though crises may occur, and the sommelière has been praised for her guidance and advice. The wine list (and wine shop) has put behind it any dim memory of those unlicensed beginnings. From clarets to malt whisky it is a remarkable choice. Australasia, the United States, Spain, Portugal and Italy are given their due, as are half-bottles. The prices are very generous. With mark-ups so low, it is small surprise that the French vins du pays form a small part of the collection. If you can afford burgundy, why bother with the Hérault? Nonetheless, magnums of Domaine de Trévallon are the same price as single bottles in London.

CHEF/PROPRIETOR: Ron Clydesdale
OPEN: Mon to Sat
MEALS: 12 to 2.30, 5.30 to 11
PRICES: £16 (£23). Service inc
CARDS: Access, Amex, Diners, Visa
SEATS: 100. 12 tables outside. Private parties: 60 main room, 40 private room. Vegetarian meals. Children's helpings. Wheelchair access (also WC)

---

**GULLANE** Lothian                                                                                              map 8

## *La Potinière* ▮

Main Street, Gullane EH31 2AA                                                    COOKING 4
GULLANE (0620) 843214                                                            COST £16–£28

The recipe for happiness in catering practised here is this: lunch five times a week and dinner once, no choice and a set price for the customers, who all sit down at the same time. The Browns have brought the formula to a high pitch of achievement. Externals are without pretension: it might be a garage on the main street of this small golfing resort. The austerity is lifted within by good linen, fabrics, cutlery and glassware. Nonetheless, at full bore, the acoustics give cutlery meeting crockery the racket of the school dining-hall. The progression of a summer meal was from carrot and orange soup on a fine stock base, through tricorns of smoked salmon in filo pastry sitting on a spinach and basil sauce, to a main dish of pigeon breast on a bed of lentils with chanterelles and a cream sauce arranged on one side of a large platter with gratin potatoes on the other, then Brie with an apple and oatmeal biscuits before a soufflé glacé praliné. A repertoire that some discount as repetitious, as well as cream-laden, is in fact evolving. Cream seems less emphasised this year, new dishes have involved Far Eastern flavours, even curry; and novelties such as lamb noisettes with a madeira sauce look set to be incorporated into the structure. In the event, because getting a table is so difficult (but try ringing for cancellations), it is unlikely you will eat here more than a few times a year – and where is monotony then? As Hilary Brown does all the cooking, so her husband does the serving. This matches the kitchen for pace and is gentle in technique and manner. The deep love and thought that has gone into the cooking – the correct amount of basil to balance the spinach and the nugget of tomato found at the bottom of the courgette timbale – are matched in David Brown's wine list. This marvel is difficult to better for range and price, though like the cooking, it seems mainly French. In fact, other countries are represented in the cellar though not yet on the list. David Brown is an encyclopaedist; who else collects 11 Gewürztraminers and 14 Chablis? Even a Chablisien would not have so many. Many local customers leave the choice to him, in advance, thus ensuring the bottle will be opened and decanted in good time. It is not easy to criticise a place that succeeds so transparently in giving pleasure while not seeking to capitalise on its gift for short-term gain. 'Tips are discouraged but are seldom offered as we have no staff.'

CHEF: Hilary Brown   PROPRIETORS: David and Hilary Brown
OPEN: all week L, exc Wed and Sat; Sat D
CLOSED: 1 week June, Oct
MEALS: 1, 8
PRICES: Set L £12.50 (£16) to £13.50 (£17), Set D £19.50 (£23)
SEATS: 32. Private parties: 30 main room. Car-park, 10 places. Children welcome. No smoking during meal. Wheelchair access. One sitting

---

HADDINGTON  Lothian                                                      map 8

## ▲ Browns Hotel

1 West Road, Haddington EH41 3RD                              COOKING  1
HADDINGTON (062 082) 2254                                    COST £15–£26

It's seductive, this resplendent Georgian-style hotel, with unimpeded views over the Lammermuir hills. 'We only meant to have dinner here once, but ended up eating on all three nights of our stay because the first was so very good with such generous portions.' Among the dishes which beguiled that reporter were: 'light but hot red pepper soup; boeuf en croûte, succulent and tender; vegetables more like a delicious, hot crispy salad; apricot tart, a triumph.' Colin Brown cooks a French menu with tartan edgings: scallops with fresh mango and grilled magret of duck with blackcurrants are just as likely to be there as Cullen skink or roast venison haunch. Breakfasts of kippers and creamy scrambled eggs are excellent. The wine list gets to a half-century, with a couple of New Zealanders and Australians to add variety to the French. The prices are very fair. House French is £5.25 (white), £5.75 (red). CELLARMAN'S CHOICE : Ch. Romefort, Haut Médoc 1981, £9.40; Mâcon-Villages 1987, Duboeuf, £9.20.

---

*If you see a certificate in a restaurant bearing the words 'Diploma of Merit. The Good Food Guide (United Kingdom)', the claim is false (and the restaurant may be in contempt of court in displaying it) – see the Introduction. Please write and tell us the name and address of the restaurant.*

---

CHEF: Colin Brown   PROPRIETORS: Colin Brown and Alexander McCallum
OPEN: all week, D only, and Sun L
MEALS: 1 to 3, 7.30 to 9
PRICES: Set L £10.75 (£15) to £12.50 (£17), Set D £17.50 (£22)
CARDS: Access, Amex, Visa
SEATS: 38. Private parties: 38 main room. Car-park, 10 places. Vegetarian meals. Children's helpings. Wheelchair access (also WC)
ACCOMMODATION: 6 rooms, 5 with bath/shower. B&B £39.50 to £52.50. Deposit: £10. Baby facilities. Garden. TV. Phone. Scenic. Doors close at midnight. Confirm by 6

---

## HAWICK  Borders                                                    map 8

## Old Forge ▼

Newmill-on-Teviot, nr Hawick, TD9 OJU
TEVIOTDALE (045 085) 298                                    COOKING 1
4m S of Hawick, on A7                                       COST £13–£18

Readers can remember bringing their ponies to be shod on the anvil that is still in the fireplace. This quiet country inn is popular with locals both for the good and cheap wines offered by Bill Irving and for Margaret Irving's adventurous cooking. Dinner consists of three or four courses at a set price. 'The Guinea Pig Menu', running parallel to the usual short choice, appeals to people willing to try new dishes in the repertoire. It has proved a great success. Soups are ever popular; chestnut, orange and mushroom is the latest one recommended. Beginnings may include hummus and pitta, 'imaginative enough in Edinburgh, picture it in Newmill'. Steak, kidney and oyster pudding in a lemon and parsley crust coming to table in a napkin wrapping; stuffed aubergine with apricots and hazelnuts, 'deliciously exotic'; home-made wholemeal bread; sticky toffee pudding; black-coffee water-ice with cream and chocolate flake have all been mentioned. Some hanker for straighter, more obviously local food, but not everyone can be pleased all the time. Bill Irving started five years ago with 16 wines; his list is now respectable in length and excellent in choice. No doctrinaire sticking to France, but excellent Italians and Australasians at prices that bring good wine within the reach of everyone. House wines, £6.95. CELLARMAN'S CHOICE : Cloudy Bay Chardonnay 1987, £15.95; Ch. Notton, Margaux 1973, £9.95.

---

CHEF: Margaret Irving   PROPRIETORS: Bill and Margaret Irving
OPEN: Tue to Sat, D only
CLOSED: first 2 weeks May, first 2 weeks Nov
MEALS: 7 to 9.30
PRICES: Set D £9.95 (£13) to £11.95 (£15). Service inc
CARDS: Access, Amex, Visa
SEATS: 28. Private parties: 30 main room. Car-park, 10 places. Vegetarian meals. Children's helpings. Wheelchair access

---

*On 6 May 1990 all London telephone numbers will change, the 01- prefix being replaced by either 071- or 081-. See the front of the Guide for a list of which numbers will take which prefix.*

# ▲ Culloden House

Inverness IV1 2NZ
INVERNESS (0463) 790461                                          COOKING 2
off A96, 3m E of Inverness                                     COST £25–£39

Although built in 1772, the house claims Bonnie Prince Charlie as a celebrated visitor (the night before he lost the cup-tie at home in 1746). It can only be described as grand: a Georgian pile with two flanking service wings. The inside, Adamesque, continues the theme of space and luxury. Jacuzzis have got as far as the bathrooms. The dining-room is almost a columned hall, with dark green walls and white plasterwork. Candlelight, fresh flowers, polished tables, good silver and glass are all of a piece, magnificently topped off by the laird himself, Ian McKenzie, appearing in full kilt for the evening session. Lunch is served à la carte, but dinner is a five-course meal at a single price. Opinions of visitors are firm that the cooking is of high standard, though locals talk of inconsistency. One inspector was bowled over by the ability to marry the most disparate of flavours. The hallmark is the thoroughgoing use of fruit in every possible dish. 'Sliced avocado draped with smoked salmon served with a light orange dressing'; redcurrants with a game terrine; a very superior Cullen skink was innocent of it but was quickly followed by an orange and passion-fruit sorbet; fillet of beef had a deep and rich pickled walnut sauce that was sweetened with grapes and apple; only the venison was not so treated, for that had a cream spinach sauce and ceps and chanterelles, but the duck that night came with blackberries and pears. Desserts, after a selection of 10 or so Scottish cheeses ('blue-veined Scottish ewe's cheese is Stilton dressed up as lamb,' complained one), are a galaxy of fruits yet again – the sideboard has pouring jugs of raspberry and strawberry coulis next to the cream. The chef, Michael Simpson, comes from Gleneagles, and his wife is the pastry-cook; the restaurant manager has joined from Sutherland's in London. There is a very long and superior wine list. At an inspection meal in the summer, the wine prices were observed to be very high and about one-third of the less expensive clarets were out of stock. However, prices are not really out of the way for this style of place and the range is acceptable. House claret is £8.50 from Louis Vialard of Ch. Cissac; the white is a burgundy from Bacheroy-Josselin at £12.90.

CHEF: Michael Simpson   PROPRIETORS: Ian and Marjory McKenzie
OPEN: all week
MEALS: 12.30 to 2, 7 to 9
PRICES: L £17 (£25), Set D £25.50 (£33)
CARDS: Access, Amex, Diners, Visa
SEATS: 50. 3 tables outside. Private parties: 50 main room, 25 private room. Car-park, 50 places. Vegetarian meals. Children's helpings. Smart dress preferred. No smoking
ACCOMMODATION: 20 rooms, all with bath/shower. B&B £75 to £140. Deposit: £75. Pets welcome. Afternoon teas. Garden. Sauna. Tennis. Snooker. TV. Phone. Scenic. Doors close at midnight

*See the back of the* Guide *for an index of restaurants listed.*

# ▲ *Ardsheal House*

Kentallen PA38 4BX COOKING 2
DUROR (063 174) 227 COST £10−£31

This long, accumulative house is separated from Loch Linnhe only by
greensward. Views of the loch are frequent as the intrepid drive more than a
mile down the rough track that marks the approach. On a fine day, the views
are breathtaking. The owners, Jane and Robert Taylor, are American, although
Jane Taylor has been seen wearing a tartan skirt. They conduct their hotel with
bonhomie and enthusiasm. Their chef, Christopher Bussey, has been replaced
but reports continue to be favourable. There is a new conservatory annexe to
the dining-room, affording more light than formerly. Lunch is a simpler affair
than dinner − which evidently is the centrepiece of the kitchen's efforts. This is
served to diners seated at the same time. There are six courses at a single price,
with simple alternatives at the first, third and fifth stage. The second course
is soup. It is interesting to speculate when and why soup was delegated
from first to second course. It never used to be so. Or is the made dish, now
served first, really the hors d'oeuvre − that is, the preliminary, the nineteenth-
century version of the amuse-gueule? Sometimes the whole ordering of British
country-house dinners seems to be the result of some Lake District hotelier's
whim. The process of dinner was likened by one reporter to a conveyor belt,
but it must always seem so when the whole room marches in step. Others have
commented on the relaxed, leisurely pace of it all. Dishes such as the twice-
baked garlic and goat cheese soufflé (a popular house standard); collops of
monkfish with soy and fresh ginger sauce; salmon en croûte with fennel and
Pernod sauce; and hot lemon soufflé may be met on the menu. The sauces tend
to the surprising: herbed Champagne and yoghurt, whisky sauce with duck,
snail egg sauce with scallops. Cheeses are good, though they come twice: once
with a salad after the main course, again with fruit as a dessert. The wine list is
skilled in the selection and fair in price. The eight châteaux from Bordeaux that
start the list, priced from £8.50 to £13, are a good sign of care and involvement.
House Bouchard, £6.50. CELLARMAN'S CHOICE : Ch. les Videaux, Côtes de
Blaye 1985, £9.50; Menetou-Salon, Morogue 1987, £10.

CHEF: Graeme Cockburn  PROPRIETORS: Jane and Robert Taylor
OPEN: all week
CLOSED: 1 Nov to Easter
MEALS: 12.30 to 2, 8.30
PRICES: Set L £6.50 (£10) to £10.50 (£14), Set D £25 (£28). Service inc
SEATS: 40. Private parties: 38 main room. Car-park, 20 places. Children's helpings. Smart
dress preferred. No smoking in dining-room. Wheelchair access (also WC). Music. One
sitting at D
ACCOMMODATION: 13 rooms, all with bath/shower. B&B £50 to £86. Baby facilities. Pets
welcome. Afternoon teas. Garden. Tennis. Snooker. Scenic. Doors close at midnight.
Confirm by 5.30 [GHG]

---

*If you see a certificate in a restaurant bearing the words 'European Good Food Guide
(UK)', the claim is false (and the restaurant may be in contempt of court in displaying it) −
see the Introduction. Please write and tell us the name and address of the restaurant.*

---

map 8

## ▲ *Taychreggan Hotel*

Kilchrenan PA35 1HQ                                    COOKING 1
KILCHRENAN (086 63) 211                          COST £9–£28

The house was originally a drovers' inn, perched idyllically on the shore of
Loch Awe, the largest freshwater loch in Scotland, described by Boswell on his
Johnsonian tour as 'the pretty wide lake'. Needless to say, pride of place is
given to the 'Dr Johnson suite' in the hotel. Comfortably decorated and
furnished, the hotel has a courtyard outside for summer eating, while in the
dining-room, tall windows look out towards the loch. Lunches are from a cold
table, but dinners are substantial five-course affairs suitable for those who have
been for long walks. Reports find little to fault with the cooking or short menu,
three or four choices for each principal course. Grilled fillet of halibut with sea
urchin sauce; braised hare with Guinness and wild mushrooms; pressed calf's
liver with port wine jelly have been examples. Continental ideas, such as
carpaccio, prawns provençale and ceviche of scallops still highlight local
produce. A home-made ice-cream always appears among desserts. New owners
John and Monika Tyrrell (Gail Struthers continues from the previous régime)
seem to have upheld the good practices of the Taylors. A chivalrously priced
wine list of 60-odd has a few 1966 clarets worth trying, burgundies from Sapin,
Bouchard and Labouré Roi outnumbering the others and a handful from
outside France. House Labouré-Roi, £8.

CHEF: Gail Struthers   PROPRIETORS: John and Monika Tyrrell
OPEN: all week
CLOSED: 23 Oct to week before Easter
MEALS: 12 to 2.30, 7 to 9
PRICES: Bar L £7 (£9), Set D £17 (£23)
CARDS: Access, Amex, Diners, Visa
SEATS: 36. 6 tables outside. Car-park, 25 places. Children's helpings. Smart dress preferred.
Wheelchair access (also WC)
ACCOMMODATION: 17 rooms, 15 with bath/shower. B&B £35 to £70. Baby facilities. Pets
welcome. Afternoon teas. Garden. Fishing. Golf. Snooker. Phone. Scenic. Doors close at
midnight. Confirm by 6 [GHG]

---

KILFINAN  Strathclyde                                  map 8

## ▲ *Kilfinan Hotel*

Kilfinan PA21 2AP                                      COOKING 1
KILFINAN (070 082) 201                            COST £21–£28

'I was astonished to find a superb meal in a warm, spotlessly clean dining-
room with a wood fire in the grate.' Quite where this reporter did expect to find
such a meal was not made clear, but enthusiasm for everything from venison
marinated in red wine and juniper berries right down to the 'well-trained
service' is evident. The old coaching-inn next to the church of St Finan is a
sporting hotel in the sense of offering fishing, stalking and shooting. The food
has a bias to local produce, plain cooking and red-blooded appetites. Dinner is
four courses, one of them soup. Loch Fyne scallops are cooked in vermouth and

cream, roast rib of beef comes with Yorkshire pudding, and strawberry shortcake brings up the rear. Mark-ups on the 40-bottle French wine list are not greedy. House Loire is £5.50. CELLARMAN'S CHOICE : Ch. Méaume 1983, £9.20; Pouilly-Vinzelles 1986, Geisweiler, £9.55.

CHEF: David Kinnear  PROPRIETOR: N.K.S. Wills
OPEN: all week
MEALS: 12 to 2, 7.30 to 9.30
PRICES: £17 (£23), Set D £17 (£21) to £19 (£23), Snacks from £2.20
CARDS: Access, Amex, Diners, Visa
SEATS: 24. 2 tables outside. Private parties: 50 main room. Car-park, 20 places. Children's helpings. Smart dress preferred. Wheelchair access (also WC). Music
ACCOMMODATION: 11 rooms, 10 with bath/shower. B&B £38 to £56. Deposit: 10%. Baby facilities. Pets welcome. Afternoon teas. Garden. Fishing. TV. Phone. Scenic. Doors close at 11. Confirm 7 days before [GHG]

---

**KILLIECRANKIE Tayside**　　　　　　　　　　　　　　　　　　map 8

## ▲ *Killiecrankie Hotel*

Killiecrankie PH16 5LG　　　　　　　　　　　　　　　　　　COOKING 2
PITLOCHRY (0796) 3220　　　　　　　　　　　　　　　　　　COST £11–£23

In the autumn of 1988, the Hattersley Smiths retired from this unassuming country hotel, a rambling white-washed house set in lovely country overlooking the River Garry. First reports of meals under the new proprietors, Colin and Carole Anderson, augur well, as does their declared intent 'to run a two-star hotel at three-star standards with one-star prices'. For the time being at least, most things continue as before. The plain cream dining-room could do with a lick of paint, but the kitchen team of four works wonders to produce very good lunches – pâtés and salads, poached salmon, home-made ice-creams and meringues – and set-price (with frequent supplements) four-course dinners. The style is a mixture of old-fashioned roasts, newly landed grilled fish and Angus steaks, with a few more ambitious ideas, even if they may arrive 'garnished to death'. On an April menu, rock turbot was served with a lemon and dill mousse, and sauté of kidneys Turbigo in a choux bun. Service by local lasses is thoughtful. The Justerini & Brooks-supplied wine list is relevant and by no means overpriced, although one person detected a rise from one ownership to the other. House wines from £4.50. CELLARMAN'S CHOICE : Chablis, Domaine Ste-Claire, 1987, Brocard, £11.50; Ch. Labégorce-Zédé 1984, £10.15.

---

*This year, in quoting prices for three-course meals at the top of each entry (by the word 'Cost'), we have put a more pessimistic complexion on the upper price by inflating it by 20 per cent. The aim is to prepare the reader for any inflation during the life of the* Guide *and also reflect the price of a meal taken without constant attention to the likely size of the bill. The prices quoted in smaller print below the text remain, as in previous editions, strict computer calculations of an average three-course meal, the price in brackets reflecting an average meal with coffee, service and half a bottle of house wine per person.*

CHEFS: Paul Booth and Brian McGill    PROPRIETORS: Colin and Carole Anderson
OPEN: all week
CLOSED: end Nov to mid-Feb
MEALS: 12.30 to 2, 7 to 8.30 (bar meals to 10)
PRICES: Bar L £8 (£11), Bar D £10 (£13), Set D £15 (£19)
CARDS: Access, Visa
SEATS: 70. Private parties: 20 main room. Car-park, 30 places. Vegetarian meals. Children's helpings (D only). No children under 5. No smoking in dining-room. Wheelchair access (also WC)
ACCOMMODATION: 12 rooms, 8 with bath/shower. Rooms for disabled. B&B £21.15 to £42.30. Deposit: £15. Pets welcome. Afternoon teas. Garden. Scenic. Doors close at midnight. Confirm by 6

---

**KILMELFORD  Strathclyde**                                            map 8

# ▲ *Cuilfail Hotel*

Kilmelford PA34 4XA                                            COOKING 2
KILMELFORD (085 22) 274                                      COST £10–£23

The surprise of one correspondent on driving to this hotel for lunch in the bar was the magnificence of the parsnip and nutmeg soup with Granary bread, followed by the clootie dumpling and a chocolate sundae. The hotel postcard immortalises the facade with the letters making up its name across the main gable all wonky and askew. This may exemplify the homely generosity of a kitchen that cooks a good-value dinner (of a relatively stable repertoire), offers a genuine vegetarian alternative, and those excellent bar lunches as well as genuine food in an evening bistro. Cooking is straightforward, relishing the Scottish connection, though what kiwi-fruit with smoked venison does for Scotland, no one can tell. The salmon with orange hollandaise and the prawns in a vol-au-vent are outstanding in their succulence. Strangely, the vegetables accompanying one meal were lacklustre for a vegetarian cook, except for the oatmeal-dusted turnips. Pastry is not a forte – or rather, the hand is *too* forte. But taste is put before most other values and at these prices it should be warmly applauded. A St Bernard and a golden labrador are in residence. There are a couple of dozen wines and house French is £4.95.

---

CHEF: Hilary McFadyen    PROPRIETORS: Mr and Mrs J. McFadyen
OPEN: all week
CLOSED: Jan and Feb
MEALS: 12 to 2, 6.30 to 9
PRICES: £6 (£10), Set D £12.50 (£17) to £14.50 (£19)
CARDS: Access, Visa
SEATS: 70. 4 tables outside. Private parties: 28 main room. Car-park, 20 places. Vegetarian meals. Children's helpings. No smoking in dining-room. Wheelchair access. Music
ACCOMMODATION: 12 rooms, 7 with bath/shower. B&B £18 to £42. Deposit: 30%. Afternoon teas. Garden. Fishing. Scenic. Doors close at midnight. Confirm by 6.30

---

*All details are as accurate as possible at the time of going to press, but chefs and owners often change, and it is wise to check by telephone before making a special journey. Many readers have been disappointed when set-price bargain meals are no longer available. Ask when booking.*

---

map 8

## ▲ *Cromlix House* ♟

Kinbuck FK15 9JT                                        COOKING 4
DUNBLANE (0786) 822125                                   COST  £10−£44

Readers of *Watership Down* should visit the grounds of Cromlix. 'I have not seen so many rabbits for years, thousands of them; and red squirrels, pheasants, and grouse, you name it.' The 'grounds' cover 5,000 acres. You may also see Jacob sheep, raised for the larder (house speciality: smoked Jacob lamb) or clipped for their wool (another house speciality: Jacob knitwear). Cromlix is a shooting-lodge in rolling wooded country just north of Dunblane. It is large, imposing, solid, handsome, but not pretty. Inside is a large comfortable private home, family antiques scattered around, a fine series of public rooms, including three dining-rooms and a refurbished conservatory in which to savour hail and frost from heated haven. Cromlix has always been upper-crust, in price as well as style, but there is a vocal lobby to push its claims: worth every penny, ineffably comfortable and nicely considerate (pre-dinner canapés are brought round to the bedrooms as you change) and, of course, good cooking. The form this takes is a five- to seven- course menu at a set price. A menu is *conseillé*, as they say in France, but alternatives are listed below the main form, giving perhaps three choices at each point. Witness is unanimous that, although there is the capacity and willingness to cook or arrange dinner according to the whim of the consumer, 'you get Brownie points for electing the chef's choice for the night'. The style of cooking is tilted towards the autarchy of a northern estate, with the tastes and decorative flourishes of metropolitan life. Not everything is home reared or shot: Norfolk duck, foie gras and a few southern vegetables, but no excess of tropical fruits or imported delicacies. An inspection meal bore out the letters and comments of others: a square of pastry is set on top of a tomato and onion fondue and covered with four split heads of asparagus, the whole surrounded by a sorrel sauce; then a roundel of perfect salmon supporting a salmon mousse decorated with pieces of lobster and a vegetable julienne with a chervil sauce. 'This was one of the best things I have eaten for some time.' The subsequent sorbet, 'fruits of the forest' was, perhaps, blackberry and raspberry − in any event, a strange glass-covered forest they must have come from in June. On to guinea-fowl stuffed with foie gras that yielded less flavour and delight than the spinach mousse contained within a leaf wrapping that came with it − a masterpiece of timing and lightness that revealed new sides to the taste of spinach. There were good young vegetables and fashionable lentils. Summer pudding was the dessert: bready and thus 'lots of pudding, not much summer'. It was voted a palpable hit by one half of the table, a near miss by the other. The last course of Scottish cheese was good but not perfect, coming with a nice home-made roll as well as oatmeal biscuits. Coffee and petits fours were excellent and generous. Altogether, then, fine cooking, good ideas and no excess. The service is exemplary even if less informed than it might be − it is not good enough to know nothing of the plate you are carrying. It is interesting that most reporters feel they have had value for money: the place therefore convinces; no mean achievement at this cost. 'Most' is said advisedly. There are some who still find the cooking overly complex to allow the ingredients to shine. Disappointment cuts deeper when the ambition is so high. The wine list does make an effort to moderate the cost. Although replete with clarets and burgundies at elevated prices (the petits-châteaux an honorable exception), there is a section of varietals (many from the Ardèche) available by the glass for taking through the meal. These have helpful notes too. Then there are plenty of American, Australian and other wines in the medium-price bracket as well as half-bottles. There are areas where the merchant is preferred over the wine itself, Beaujolais comes almost without exception from Marc Dudet (Duboeuf in another guise) not from the other many excellent individual producers in the region. House wine is from £7.50. CELLARMAN'S CHOICE : Rioja Reserva 904 1973, £15.50; Ch. Tahblik Marsanne 1984, £10.50.

CHEF: Mark Salter    PROPRIETOR: The Hon. Ronald Eden
OPEN: all week
CLOSED: 2 weeks Feb
MEALS: 12 to 2.30, 7 to 10
PRICES: Set L £5 (£10) to £19 (£24), Set D £15 (£21) to £30 (£37)
CARDS: Access, Amex, Diners, Visa
SEATS: 60. 4 tables outside. Private parties: 30 main room, 12, 16 and 24 private rooms. Car-park, 30 places. Children's helpings. Children restricted. No smoking. Wheelchair access (also WC)
ACCOMMODATION: 14 rooms, all with bath/shower. B&B £75 to £110. Deposit: 50%. Baby facilities. Pets welcome. Afternoon teas. Garden. Tennis. Fishing. TV. Phone. Scenic. Doors close at midnight [GHG]

---

KINGUSSIE  Highland                                                     map 8

## ▲ The Cross ▮

25–27 High Street, Kingussie PH21 1HX                        COOKING 3
KINGUSSIE (0540) 2762                                        COST £21–£32

Close to a pedestrian crossing on the main street is a converted shop. Behind its windows is Ruth and Tony Hadley's unlikely restaurant with rooms: a personal enterprise in a country where almost all good restaurants are 'personal' in such a way. The benefits are many: customers appreciate the devotion and attention, 'The Cross was our favourite in a Scottish tour ...'; the food and wine receive consistent care and a high level of explication; the lack of overheads is reflected in modest charges (though less modest than last year). The demerits are when the customer takes against the recipe: there are no staff, no emollience of luxury to soften the impact. Aspects of the Cross are distinctive: shabbiness (though the dining-room has received a welcome facelift); decorative mismatches; personal intensity. 'It took me nearly an hour of pleasant conversation to have a starter, drink, order food and wine – wine service is an integral part of eating here, not pretentious, just indulged because it is enjoyable.' Others may question 'the confidential approach to service at close range'. No one, however, disputes the value of the four-course weekday dinner menu or the seven-course Saturday extravaganza. Ruth Hadley cooks beautifully. The table settings do her justice. The wines are a joy. The approach is one of calm simplicity: there are mousses, there are terrines, but for the most part ingredients work alone – assisted by sauces, but uncluttered by much pastry work, stuffings or fandango. The extent of the repertoire is not so wide as to amaze: mountain hare and venison Francatelli are often cooked, but here so well – in the latter case, definitively – that no one could cavil. Often, restaurants with fine cellars and cooks who eschew elaboration, foster good cheeseboards. No reports ignore the one at the Cross (even if only reflecting on the condition of its covering cloth). Valiant efforts of supply, loving explanation (even annotation) and good condition all contribute to a first-rate six-cheese selection. A meal as reported may serve as typical: pigeon and mushroom charlotte was a cabbage-wrapped parcel of pigeon-breast and onion and mushroom, while an alternative first course of mousseline of scallops with an egg and cream sauce (suffused by scallop flavour) might be called 'delicate' by some, 'bland' by the coarse-natured, certainly 'technical perfection' by all. Onion and cider soup came second, with no choice offered. Soups are invariably good, if our reports say true. Main courses were slices of river and sea trout with a chive butter sauce (once more described as 'bland' by one who sought more upstanding flavours) or a wild duck of perfect crispness and delectable texture with a piquant blackcurrant sauce. Vegetables are normally al dente and simple. The cheeseboard that night was made up of two French, one Irish, one Scottish and an English. The other last course was a 'brandy alexander' ice-cream. Ices often figure as a possibility, their flavour extracted from many sources: wild hawthorns one night. To go with all this (and the good bread) is a wine list invariably well served and always competitively priced according to a fixed mark-up. The half-bottle range is remarkable. The clarets show commendable discretion in holding back good châteaux not yet ready for drinking; there are some nice French regional choices – five red Chinons, a couple of Cahors bottles; the Australasians show discernment, especially the David Hohnens from Cloudy Bay; the Spanish whites include some rarely encountered novelties and, finally, the choice of dessert wines is enough to make the most savoury tooth order a second pudding. No house wine as such, but four or five are suggested each month as particularly good value. CELLARMAN'S CHOICE : Domaine du Tariquet, Cuvée Bois, Côtes de Gascogne 1987, £7.70; Buzet, Cuvée Napoléon 1985, £7.45. 'We do not levy a service charge, nor do we solicit tips.' Smoking in the coffee lounge only.

CHEF: Ruth Hadley    PROPRIETORS: Tony and Ruth Hadley
OPEN: Tue to Sat, D only
CLOSED: 3 weeks May, first 3 weeks Dec
MEALS: 6.30 to 9.30
PRICES: Set D £18.50 (£21) to £25 (£27)
SEATS: 24. Private parties: 18 main room. No children under 12. No smoking in dining-room. Wheelchair access
ACCOMMODATION: 3 rooms, all with bath/shower. D, B&B £42 to £96. Deposit: £20. No children under 12. Fishing. Golf

*'On this particular night the oven stopped working and the glass entrance door shattered. Despite occasioning, not unreasonably, a little delay, it says much for the service that the staff remained unflustered and good humoured, with jokes about Manuel of Fawlty Towers, etc. They coped well and were very attentive. One other diner's meal was returned because it was not hot enough, and was quickly replaced with a totally recooked dish. It is in these extremities that one can best test the quality of the management and they came through very well.'* On eating in Berkshire

KINROSS Tayside                                         map 8

## ▲ *Croft Bank House Hotel*

Station Road, Kinross KY13 7TG
KINROSS (0577) 63819                          COOKING 2
off M90 at Junction 6                            COST £28

The charitable would say all the money's been put into the dining-rooms – not the ancillary offices. The house is a late-Victorian detached villa sitting firmly on Station Road, just off the motorway, 'but you can see the hills'. Bill Kerr has worked in the area for several years but the menu shows every sign of an openness to modern tastes, even at their most bizarre: veal fillet topped with asparagus, crayfish tail and Gruyère cheese with a light cream, pink peppercorn sauce. Bill Kerr is quite keen on pastry domes – on a sauté of mushrooms and garlic with cream and bacon as well as on a voluptuous shellfish bisque that stinted not on the raw materials. A device perhaps, but one which pleases. Sauces tend towards the buttery-creamy but the handling of the technical side is reliable: a breast of chicken stuffed with apricots and leeks perfumed by an Alsace wine was a good balance of fruit and savoury tastes. Beef and fish are supplied generously from sound sources. Desserts stray not far from the cream and the booze, but a sauté of apples with a hot caramel sauce was what was required. House wine is £6.50.

CHEF: Bill Kerr    PROPRIETORS: Bill and Diane Kerr
OPEN: Tue to Sun
CLOSED: 2 weeks Oct
MEALS: 12 to 2, 7 to 9
PRICES: £17 (£23)
CARDS: Access, Visa
SEATS: 44. Private parties: 18 main room, 50 private room. Car-park, 25 places. Children's helpings. Smart dress preferred. Wheelchair access (2 steps). Music
ACCOMMODATION: 4 rooms, all with bath/shower. B&B £30 to £40. TV. Doors close at 11. Confirm 1 day ahead

LINLITHGOW Lothian                                      map 8

## *Champany Inn* ▮

Champany Corner, Linlithgow EH49 7LU
PHILPSTOUN (050 683) 4532 and 4388
2m NE of Linlithgow at junction of          COOKING 3
A904 and A803                                    COST £44

Here are the virtues of simplicity and single-mindedness brought to high perfection. There is much that is American about Champany's character, and the analogy of *Dallas* may be otiose but have some point: where else would a piercing blue carpet have the name repeated a hundred times as the sole ornament? Rugged masonry is placed cheek by jowl with luxurious joinery. Dining at Champany is a participatory event, where maximum variety is gained from a minimum range. Lobsters are fished for, beef is eyed, (organic) vegetables chosen from a basket, salads fetched and carried, cheese scooped. Champany specialises: salmon (farmed), lobster and beef. Lamb and poultry get a look in, as does caviare. The simplicity is carried over to cheese: Stilton. The race is on to produce the best. With beef, at least, success seems to have come. By dint of long hanging, quick passage through a marinade, then charcoal-grilling, a superlative product is achieved. Were it not, the pack of cards would collapse, leaving but a series of gimmicks. American, French, English travellers: they taste and seem convinced. The cooking achieves that crust of successfully grilled meat, that delicate contrast of textures; the hanging enhances the flavour – 'how few young chefs in restaurants really like meat with taste.' As amateurs may know, maturing one's own meat at home doesn't really work. The process must be started higher up the chain of supply. Clive Davidson knows what he's about. At the end of the meal the same cast of mind has left its stamp: the simple things are done brilliantly. Elderflower, mango and strawberry are ice-cream flavours mentioned; crème brûlée, 'the best'; soft fruits; not a lot more. The wine list is an ample companion, the sommelier an excellent guide. It is true to form that the restaurant has developed its own varietal blends to suit its style of cooking and then had the patience to wait five years for maturity. The strength is in burgundies, white and red, with clarets a strong second. For a palate that likes ripe meat, there are few older vintages of Pinot noir or Chardonnay. Other regions of France get short shrift, including the Rhône where the names are not exciting. Other countries fare better. Half-bottles are a treat. House wines are £8.50. CELLARMAN'S CHOICE : Hautes Côtes de Beaune 1985, Michel Plait, £13. As the *Guide* went to press, the Davidsons had recently reopened their former premises in Edinburgh's Grassmarket, still called The Beehive.

CHEFS: David Gibson and Clive Davidson    PROPRIETORS: Clive and Anne Davidson
OPEN: Mon to Sat, exc Sat L
CLOSED: 3 weeks from 24 Dec
MEALS: 12.30 to 2, 7.15 to 10
PRICES: £25 (£37). Minimum £9.50. Service 10%
CARDS: Access, Amex, Diners, Visa
SEATS: 50. 13 tables outside. Private parties: 50 main room. Car-park, 100 places. No children under 8. Smart dress preferred. Wheelchair access

---

**MELROSE** Borders                                                          map 8

## *Marmion's Brasserie* ▼

| Buccleuch Street, Melrose TD6 9LB | COOKING 1 |
|---|---|
| MELROSE (089 682) 2245 | COST £6–£16 |

After visiting the abbey, lunch may stir recall of the immured Constance, abandoned lover of Lord Marmion, in Scott's tale – or simply appetite for a cosmopolitan choice in this bustling place where many customers seem to be regular visitors and there is a sense of coming and going unlikely in a Border town. The dishes may be elaborate: calf's liver in a Grand Marnier and cream sauce with oranges and pine nuts, though sometimes the simpler brasserie manner may prevail, as in moules marinière. Short cuts are hinted at in some reports. The very short wine list is very good, from Edinburgh's Wines from Paris. House wines from Guy Saget, £4.95. CELLARMAN'S CHOICE : La Vieille

Ferme, Côtes de Lubéron 1988, £6.50; Victoria Gardens Estate Chardonnay/ Colombard 1987, 7.95.

CHEF: Seoras Lindsey  PROPRIETORS: Ian and Sheila Robson
OPEN: Mon to Sat
MEALS: 12 to 2, 6.30 to 10
PRICES: L £5 (£6), D £9 (£13), Snacks from £2.30
CARD: Access
SEATS: 60. Private parties: 60 main room. Children's helpings. No pipes in dining-room. Wheelchair access (1 step; also WC). Music. Air-conditioned

---

**MOFFAT** Dumfries & Galloway                                           map 8

# ▲ Beechwood Country House Hotel

Moffat DG10 9RS                                                    COOKING **2**
MOFFAT (0683) 20210                                               COST £13–£22

After three years' absence from the *Guide* and several changes of hands, this greystone country house has settled down under the new owners, Paul and Carolyne Gardener. The solid Victorian building is peaceful against a backdrop of 12 acres of beech trees, has magnificent views over the Annan valley and market town of Moffat yet also has idiosyncrasies, such as 'the illuminated AA sign fixed on to a superb mature fir tree in the front garden and the Viennese marches and polkas wafting out of the kitchen door'. Lunch is light but in the evening Carl Shaw cooks a five-course dinner, rounded out by canapés in front of the sitting-room fire and petits fours. The menu changes daily and is limited to perhaps three dishes at each course – but nonetheless there is real variety. Undoubtedly, the kitchen is still finding its feet and occasionally flavours have gone awry, but the determination to build dishes around the best produce and to work towards a self-sufficient kitchen is already evident. First courses tend to be the most elaborate, for example, a generous portion of frogs' legs in a sharp Champagne and mushroom vinaigrette. These contrast with plainer main course meat dishes such as roast saddle of venison with a black cherry sauce; lamb cutlets with a herb crust and mint sauce; roast breast of duck with honey and clove sauce; all served with unadorned, slightly crunchy vegetables. At the final stages, there has been a visually impressive fruit salad in a convoluted biscuit basket; chocolate chestnut terrine with cocoa-dusted crème anglaise and well-kept local Lockerbie and Orkney smoked Cheddar on the cheeseboard. Breakfasts show care, too; in season, chanterelles from the beech woods are served with scrambled eggs. You may catch Carl Shaw serving at the end of his stint at the stove, or relaxing with guests in the bar after dinner; it's a friendly place. A short wine list is of mixed quality and gives a nod to countries outside France. Two halves of Mercurey 1986 are cheaper than a whole: doubtless the mathematics will be checked one quiet day after the season. House Vaucluse, £5.95.

---

*'The chef spent most of the evening at the bar – his pupils, he claimed, did not need supervision.'* On dining in Avon

---

CHEF: Carl Shaw PROPRIETORS: Paul and Carolyne Gardener
OPEN: all week
MEALS: 12 to 2, 7.30 to 9.30
PRICES: Set L £7.50 (£13), Set D £14.95 (£18). Service inc
CARDS: Access, Amex, Visa
SEATS: 26. Private parties: 30 main room. Car-park, 12 places. Children's helpings. No smoking in dining-room
ACCOMMODATION: 7 rooms, all with bath/shower. B&B £36.85 to £57.70. Baby facilities. Pets welcome. Afternoon teas. Garden. TV. Phone. Scenic. Doors close at midnight

**MUIR OF ORD Highland** map 8

## ▲ *Dower House* 🍷

Highfield, Muir of Ord IV6 7XN COOKING 2
MUIR OF ORD (0463) 870090 COST £29

Robyn and Mena Aitcheson established a reputation at Le Chardon in Cromarty, where restaurants are few. They have not moved many miles towards Inverness, to settle at this pleasant eighteenth-century house in a few acres just outside the village on the Dingwall road. Here, with rooms to supplement the income, they have set up a small restaurant. The style is emphatically modern: veal cooked in herbs and cream, with red peppers running through it, topped with a hint of paprika and perhaps curry powder; pigeon breasts cooked pink in a chocolate sauce with raspberries. Fish appears regularly: a salad of turbot with a home-grown salad of leaves and herbs, and fresh langoustines with a warm sea-vegetable vinaigrette are two dishes that have been mentioned. Cheese concentrates on a few varieties served well, so as not to risk the lengthy supply lines involved in maintaining an elaborate board. Puddings such as pancakes (a golden colour from the free-range eggs) with black cherries, the sauce given punch with orange juice and kirsch and the balance maintained by cooling ice-cream, have obviously pleased frames hungry after a day on the foreshore. Children are welcome, but the very young are soundly confined to high tea at 5.30pm. Dinner is at the same time for all. Early reports indicate that the settling in period is not yet over, but things are promising, none the less. The wine list offers the best French bottles to the front with a couple of pages of other countries – these are interestingly chosen, by no means the hackneyed token New-Worlders that often crop up. There are no bargains, nor are there ransoms. House French from Bouchard, £7.20.

CHEF: Robyn Aitchison PROPRIETORS: Robyn and Mena Aitchison
OPEN: all week, D only
MEALS: 7.30 for 8
PRICES: Set D £18 (£24)
CARDS: Access, Amex, Visa
SEATS: 20. 3 tables outside. Private parties: 30 main room, 8 and 10 private rooms. Car-park, 40 places. Vegetarian meals. Children's helpings. No children under 4. No smoking. Wheelchair access (also WC). One sitting
ACCOMMODATION: 5 rooms, all with bath/shower. Rooms for disabled. B&B £35 to £ 70. Deposit: 20%. Baby facilities. Garden. Fishing. Golf. TV. Phone. Scenic. Confirm by 6

*The* Guide *always appreciates hearing about changes of chef or owner.*

---

NEWTONMORE  Highland                                        map 8

## ▲ *Ard-Na-Coille Hotel*

---

Kingussie Road, Newtonmore PH20 1AY                COOKING 2
NEWTONMORE (054 03) 3214                             COST  £28

The proprietors have taken refuge from academic life in this white house surrounded by trees. Exposure to the ruder shocks of catering have neither denatured them nor rendered less pleasant their welcome and enthusiasm. Refurbishment, which is needed, continues piecemeal; meanwhile, the no-choice four-course dinners cooked by Barry Cottam, and the wine list that may accompany them, are worth a visit. Diners speak of simple, almost to the point of evanescent, service and cooking that never sinks to pretension and has an accurate and direct approach of much delight. Tomato soup with basil and mint; fillet of halibut with a light curry sauce; breast of pheasant with an aromatic ceps sauce; good cheese; simple vegetables and desserts: these are dishes reported from a meal early in the year. A special lunch of fresh asparagus soup, cold salmon, home-made bread and salad made the visit of another party. The wine list, by all reports, is sensational in range and value. House wine, £7.

---

CHEF: Barry Cottam   PROPRIETORS: Barry Cottam and Nancy Ferrier
OPEN: all week, D only
CLOSED: Nov and Dec
MEALS: 7.45
PRICES: Set D £17.50 (£23)
SEATS: 18. Private parties: 18 main room. Car-park, 20 places. Children's helpings on request. No smoking. One sitting
ACCOMMODATION: 9 rooms, 7 with bath/shower. B&B £22.50 to £40. Baby facilities. Garden. Doors close at 11.30. Confirm by 4 [GHG]

---

NORTH BERWICK  Lothian                                      map 8

## *Harding's* ♟

---

2 Station Road, North Berwick EH39 4AU             COOKING 2
NORTH BERWICK (0620) 4737                        COST  £11−£22

Just by the station buffers, and looking rather like a white-painted shack, inside, Harding's is light, spacious and convivial. The clientele is a mix of locals and visitors fresh off the train from Edinburgh. Local game, fish and fruits are employed as and when they appear, and the blackboard menu changes daily to take account of this. The food looks broadly nouvelle with good marks for presentation and ample portions. First courses might include carrot and celery soup or an avocado salad; main courses have flavourful sauces: beef fillet with horseradish and tarragon; partridge with sherry; salmon and turbot with chive and saffron. Puddings can be elaborately prettified: a baked filo parcel came filled with strawberries and brown sugar on a liqueur muscat sauce. This is the place for carefully selected Australian wines which change as vintages change or rarities come to hand. House Australian Cabernet Sauvignon/Malbec 1987 and Semillon Chenin 1987, both from Hill-Smith, are £5.30. CELLARMAN'S CHOICE : Balgownie Chardonnay 1986, £15.50; the scarce Cloudy Bay Sauvignon Blanc 1988, £14.20.

CHEF/PROPRIETOR: Christopher Harding
OPEN: Tue to Sat, exc Tue D
MEALS: 12 to 2, 7.30 to 9
PRICES: £7 (£11), Set D £13.50 (£18)
SEATS: 25. Private parties: 25 main room. Car-park, 3 places. Children's helpings. No
smoking. Wheelchair access (also WC). Music

---

## OBAN  Strathclyde                                               map 8

## ▲ *Knipoch Hotel* ▮

Oban PA34 4QT
KILNINVER (085 26) 251                                            COOKING 2
on A16, 6m S of Oban                                              COST £17–£38

Magnificent views over the loch are to be had from the front rooms of this
whitewashed Georgian hotel, once the local tax collector's house. Despite
setting and price, it is neither self-conscious nor fussy. But the stripped-pine
floor and Persian rugs in the sitting-room and a dining-room struck one
reporter as less than handsome. The five-course menu changes nightly and
offers no choice, save a brief list of 'alternative dishes' – pâté, steak. The Craigs
make much use of local fish and have taken to smoking halibut as well as
salmon on the premises. Only wild fish are used (apart from farmed mussels)
for smoking, since experiments performed *en famille* demonstrated that 'tasters
could immediately differentiate between farmed and wild fish, regardless of
methods of processing – wet and dry brining, marinating etc. – it was as if the
curing/smoking concentrates the flavours and accentuates the differences rather
than masking them.' Menus feature Scottish produce: cock-a-leekie soup;
Aberdeen Angus fillet; Oban halibut with two sauces; Sound of Luing
scallops. Another family enthusiasm is pickling of all sorts; look out for good
relishes with the terrines and cold meats. Cheese is served with walnut bread.
There are 10 house wines from £5.80 and the wine list begins to be
encyclopaedic. The spread is very complete, including Eastern Europe as well
as New Zealand, and the notes are extensive. It is a list that improves every
year. CELLARMAN'S CHOICE : from the house wines might be Chianti Classico
Riserva 1981, Antinori, £9.90; Fitou 1985, £5.80. Mr Craig is an enthusiast of
Romantic music and malt whisky. This must be a potent late-night cocktail.
See under Knipoch in *The Good Hotel Guide.*

CHEFS: Colin and Jenny Craig   PROPRIETORS: The Craig family
OPEN: all week
CLOSED: 14 Nov to 14 Feb
MEALS: 12.30 to 1.30, 7.30 to 9
PRICES: Set L £12.50 (£17), Set D £26 (£32)
CARDS: Access, Amex, Diners, Visa
SEATS: 46. Private parties: 24 main room. Car-park, 40 places. Children's helpings
ACCOMMODATION: 18 rooms, all with bath/shower. B&B £46 to £92. Deposit: £50. Baby
facilities. Afternoon teas. Garden. TV. Phone. Scenic. Doors close at 11. Confirm by 6 [GHG]

---

*The* Guide *relies on feedback from its readers. Especially welcome are reports on new
restaurants appearing in the book for the first time.*

---

## ▲ *Peat Inn* 🍾

Peat Inn KY15 5LH                                          COOKING 5
PEAT INN (033 484) 206                                  COST £17−£38

The fruits of fame and glory are visible at Peat Inn, settlement and hostelry
both, at the intersection of roads from Crail, Elie and Cupar. Some raise
eyebrows as they pass from the granite outside to the luxury of fabric and
carpet, especially in the glorious bedrooms of the new-built Residence, that
envelops within. Others breathe a sigh of content at the prospect of comfort at
last − at prices that will shock no one who has seen the scale of provision. The
development of Peat Inn has also been likened to those French country
restaurants that refurbish each time a star or point is awarded. There comes a
moment when the inside, the trappings, the ambition even, seem to vault
beyond the humble shell. The first thing to strike any traveller is an
'overwhelming' welcome. After many years in the business, the Wilsons have
not lost their warmth, nor enthusiasm. Their staff follow suit. The lunch menu
is a set-price, four-courser with no choice. Its value is palpable, its freshness
without question. At night there is a long tasting meal of six courses (for the
whole table only) and a *carte* of perhaps eight dishes at each stage. Reports
concentrate on fish dishes. Not that the venison liver in a red wine reduction,
pigeon with a pigeon charlotte, or saddle of hare on a bed of spinach should be
ignored. Veal, white meats, butcher's meats (save beef) are not the things to go
for. Some of the current repertoire is becoming famous: flan of Arbroath
smokies with lemon sauce, a mousse rather than a tart; sole mousse with
hollandaise sauce; a whole lobster with a Barsac sauce, the spiciness lifting the
sweetness and enhancing the round flavour of the shellfish; and a fine Fish
Market selection of turbot, sole and monkfish baked in milk, with pieces of
salmon, crayfish and lobster laid across the top and a splendid chive cream
sauce: this excelled for variety of texture as much as sweetness of flavour.
Desserts may sound simple but obviously stunned a party of eight returning
graduates of St Andrews. David Wilson adheres to a way of cooking more
elaborate than self-taught super dinner-parties. There are plenty of references
to international tendencies, fashionable components. Yet he does keep direct
roots to Fife, to Scotland, to appetites that need satisfaction, not mere titillation
with truffles or caviare. The wine list is beyond reproach. Pink sheets for red,
white for white, this model of clarity divides France by regions and quarters,
and the rest of the world by grape types. The range is immense, the sporadic
notes are illuminating, the choice of growers and vintages informed and
searching, the prices eminently fair. From such an enthusiast, you might expect
bottle-age in the reds − not just 1945 Pétrus and Latour, but 1975 Riojas and
1980 California Cabernet Sauvignons. An unexpected delight is to be able to
contemplate Trimbach's Clos Ste-Hune 1976, Mme Fourlinnie's Bonnezeaux
Ch des Gauliers 1962, Robert Ampeau's Meursault Les Perrières 1976 and a
trio of 1976 Germans, all of them under £28. Country-house hoteliers from the
south of England, were they to survey all that was on offer here at the prices
charged, should blush. Tips 'are not asked for nor expected.'

CHEF: David Wilson    PROPRIETORS: David and Patricia Wilson
OPEN: Tue to Sat
CLOSED: 2 weeks Jan and Nov
MEALS: 1, 7 to 9.30
PRICES: £23 (£26), Set L £13.50 (£17), Set D £29 (£32). Service inc
CARDS: Amex, Access, Diners, Visa
SEATS: 48. Private parties: 24 main room, 12 private room. Car-park, 24 places. Children's
helpings. No smoking during meals. Wheelchair access (also WC). One sitting L only
ACCOMMODATION: 8 rooms, all with bath/shower. Rooms for disabled. B&B £75 to £92. No
children under 12. Garden. Fishing. Golf. TV. Phone. Scenic. Confirm by 4 [GHG]

---

**PEEBLES  Borders**                                                                      map 8

## ▲ *Cringletie House*

Eddleston, Peebles EH45 8PL
EDDLESTON (072 13) 233                                                    COOKING 2
on A703, 2m N of Peebles                                               COST £10–£29

Visitors to this splendid red-stone pile, barnacled with turrets and
commanding sweeping views in every direction, need fear no hint of austerity.
The interior is comfortably furnished and Stanley and Aileen Maguire are
'exceptional hosts', according to one regular, who describes this secluded hotel
as 'a warm and welcoming establishment'. The Maguires' two elder sons, Paul
and Simon, have joined the operation and one reader concluded, after a two-
day stay, that the hotel is in good form. The menu, served in the high-ceilinged,
dark green-and-white dining-room, changes daily. Sauces rule: whisky sauce
for kidneys; lychee sauce for duckling; seafood and garlic sauces for salmon.
There have been imaginative first courses: stuffed aubergine with tomato and
cinnamon; savoury stuffed apple with mint cream. Fruit and vegetables come
from the walled kitchen garden and there are mousses, gateaux and sometimes
summer pudding to round off. The wine list runs to a hundred bins and ranges
over the world, with a slight emphasis on clarets and a fair showing of hocks
and moselles. Prices are fair. House French is £6.90. CELLARMAN'S CHOICE :
Hautes Côtes de Beaune 1983, £10.75; Savennières, Clos du Papillon
1987, £9.50.

---

CHEFS: Aileen Maguire and Sheila McKellar    PROPRIETORS: Mr and Mrs Stanley Maguire
OPEN: all week
CLOSED: Jan and Feb
MEALS: 1 to 1.45, 7.30 to 8.30
PRICES: Set L £4.50 (£10) to £9 (£15), Set Sun L £11.50 (£16), Set D £18 (£24)
CARDS: Access, Visa
SEATS: 56. Private parties: 30 main room. Car-park, 40 places. Vegetarian meals. Children's
helpings. No smoking in dining-room
ACCOMMODATION: 13 rooms, all with bath/shower. Lift. B&B £32.50 to £65. Baby facilities.
Pets welcome. Afternoon teas. Garden. Tennis. TV. Phone. Scenic. Doors close at 11.
Confirm by 5 [GHG]

---

*'This was one of their Gastronomic Evenings – these tend to be about as attractive to me as
revolving restaurants – both to be avoided at all costs, I've learned, over the years.'* On
inspecting in Hampshire

---

## PERTH  Tayside                                                map 8

# Timothy's

24 St John Street, Perth PH1 5SP                    COOKING 1
PERTH (0738) 26641                                  COST £5–£15

Athole and Caroline Laing's restaurant celebrated its twenty-first birthday last
year with a major refurbishment. Otherwise, everything has stayed the same,
including the reliable cooking and warm welcome for both adults and children
– toys provided. More Danish in form than content, the menu is built around 20
*snitter*, or appetisers, and the same number of *smørrebrød*, adapted to take on
board all kinds of surprising ingredients and named after them rather
punningly. Roaming Dane, for example, combines home-cooked ham with
curried banana; Red Dragon offers prawns, sesame and sweet-and-sour
chicken. These are supplemented by soups, plainer cold platters and salads.
Ingredients are fresh and good. Celebrations and birthdays are always made a
fuss of at Timothy's, part of the personal attention from proprietors who make
it a point of pride that one or the other is always on hand. The fondue
bourguignonne, something special for a major event, provides six sauces and
green salads as well as half a pound of beef. There are home-made sundaes for
dessert, and Scandinavian and old-fashioned English puddings. The small,
constantly changing wine list has an emphasis on French bottles, or there is a
choice of lagers, beers and iced akvavits. House French is £5.60.

CHEF: Caroline Laing  PROPRIETORS: Caroline and Athole Laing
OPEN: Tue to Sat
CLOSED: 3 weeks in summer
MEALS: 12 to 2.30, 7 to 10.15
PRICES: £9 (£15). Snacks 95p. Cover 25p D only. Minimum £5 after 9.30pm
CARD: Access
SEATS: 54. Private parties: 20 main room. Vegetarian meals. Children's helpings.
Wheelchair access. Music. Air-conditioned

## PORT APPIN  Strathclyde                                      map 8

# ▲ Airds Hotel ▮

Port Appin PA38 4DF                                 COOKING 3
APPIN (063 173) 236                                 COST £16–£38

The Allens' homely hotel is now a member of the Relais & Châteaux group but
loyal regulars remark that nothing has really changed, apart from the
redecoration of the public rooms. The refurbishment and maintenance is a
constant process: 'We thought we were the first users of our bedroom, but
found it had been done up last year.' The dining-room has been re-dressed, 'a
spectacular gilt mirror creating lightness in the hall … and lots of new prints
and new curtains in the lounge.' 'We appreciate their vigilance on high
standards,' runs one report. 'Betty is the most modest of chefs, and Eric is
untiringly helpful, with a word for everyone.' The Allens write that they try to
provide quietly formal service with traditional Highland hospitality and that
their son, Graeme, has joined the kitchen after three years in London. The
setting is on their side: from the dining-room there are views over the

shimmering water of the loch and mountains beyond. Reports concentrate on the quality of the food and cooking, which shows great care with local produce and vegetables and herbs grown in the garden. Bread for all the meals is baked early each morning and croissants have been added for breakfast. The daily set-price menu, which runs from first course through soup and the main dish to cheese or pudding, takes an uncluttered approach; the kichen appears mindful that people are staying for days, its duty then is not to overburden them. Smooth chicken-liver terrine with toasted brioche, game salads, Loch Linnhe prawns with herb mayonnaise and others are followed by creamy vegetable soups. But this restraint should not be interpreted as lack of technique. The sauces for main dishes, varying from tarragon cream for brill and a red wine reduction flavoured with juniper for hare, and occasionally more glamorous dishes like a mousseline of scallops with a Barsac cream sauce, show an assured hand. The quality and cooking of the vegetables are invariably commented upon too: superb new potatoes, lightly cooked spiced cabbage, parsnip purée. Puddings have often included an alcoholic ice-cream, such as raspberry with Drambuie, an orange terrine and lemon tart. Smoking is politely opposed in the dining-room. The wine list, a massy tome, could be criticised for a handful of typing errors, but the cellar is beyond reproach. Such collections excite regret that more than one bottle may not be consumed at a time – well, not many more … The urge for comparison and evaluation must be great, the more so when the prices are so fair: bargains they are not, but nor are they capricious or grasping. The strength lies in the clarets, above all, but most countries get a showing with good, if few, bottles. Half-bottles there are aplenty: always a problem for hotels catering for couples. House Bordeaux £9.

CHEFS: Graeme Allen, Moira Thompson and Betty Allen   PROPRIETORS: Eric and Betty Allen
OPEN: all week
MEALS: 12.30 to 1.30, 8 to 8.30
PRICES: Set L £10 (£18) to £12 (£20), Set D £25 (£32)
SEATS: 40. Private parties: 40 main room, 8 private room. Car-park, 30 places. Children's helpings. No children under 6. Smart dress preferred. No smoking in dining-room. Wheelchair access
ACCOMMODATION: 14 rooms, all with bath/shower. B&B £50 to £90. Deposit: £50. No children under 6. Afternoon teas. Garden. TV. Phone. Scenic. Doors close at 11.45. Confirm by 4 [GHG]

---

**PORTPATRICK   Dumfries & Galloway**                                        map 8

## ▲ *Knockinaam Lodge*

Portpatrick DG9 9AD                                                    COOKING 3
PORTPATRICK (077 681) 471                                       COST £20–£35

The track runs three miles out of Portpatrick, reputed embarkation point of St Patrick, the first of many to take the packet-boat thence. At the end of it, in a cove and hollow, lies this former sporting-lodge, now a most professional hotel and restaurant filled with good pictures, decorated with taste and discretion. The view from the dining-room across the sea to Ireland is sensational. The hotel has had its ups and downs since first coming to prominence 20 years ago in the hands of a French couple. It has been owned by the Frichots, Anglo-Seychellois with experience in continental hotels, for the last five years. There has been a steady affirmation of the skill of their management and the success of the kitchen brigade, all French bar one, headed by Daniel Galmiche. The main effort is dinner, a four-course meal with but one choice between fish and meat for the main course. Refreshingly for the northern regions, there is no second course of soup nor a large cheeseboard afterwards. There are two first courses, one of which is usually fish. The style of cooking is decidedly modern, without excess of artifice nor wild combinations of flavours but with plenty of artistry and taste. Fish has been repeatedly approved, be it humble varieties such as ling, cooked with lentils à l'ancienne or dearer varieties as in a warm salad of langoustine with strawberry vinaigrette, or courgette flowers stuffed with a mousseline of sea bass. The skills extend to vegetable cookery, a plate of steamed vegetables served with vanilla and coriander being especially remembered, though some find the quantities too reminiscent of nouvelle cuisine – in fact, they seem well judged throughout the meal. Meat has also been mentioned: from venison, cooked sweet-and-sour, to lamb en croûte with a herb sauce (though the truffles – like golf balls – that were there on presentation seemed absent when the dish was eaten). Puddings may be extremely beautiful to the eye, modern to the taste – redcurrant parfait – or traditional as the tarte Tatin of either apple or pear. Small wonder, from accumulated comment, that M. Frichot takes Knockinaam seriously – so should we – as well as having pride in their twice-daily bake, their croissants and their fresh luxuries brought in from Paris. The wine list is fairly dear and largely French, though there is one unexpected English bottle. House French, £9. CELLARMAN'S CHOICE : Mercurey, Ch. de Chamirey 1985, £15; Pernand Vergelesses, Les Vergelesses 1982, £17.50.

CHEF: Daniel Galmiche   PROPRIETORS: Marcel and Corinna Frichot
OPEN: all week
CLOSED: Jan to Easter
MEALS: 12.30 to 2, 7.30 to 9
PRICES: £13 (£20), Set D £24 (£29). Service inc
CARDS: Access, Amex, Diners, Visa
SEATS: 28. Private parties: 40 main room. Car-park, 25 places. No children under 12. Smart dress preferred. No smoking in dining-room. Wheelchair access (1 step; also WC)
ACCOMMODATION: 10 rooms, all with bath/shower. B&B £53 to £106. Deposit: £100. Baby facilities. Pets welcome. Afternoon teas. Garden. TV. Phone. Scenic. Doors close at midnight [GHG]

SCARISTA   Isle of Harris                                          map 8

## ▲ Scarista House

Scarista, Isle of Harris, PA85 3HX
SCARISTA (085 985) 238                                    COOKING 1
on A859, 15m SW of Tarbert                                 COST £25

The Johnsons still own this exposed manse though there is no sign that their virtual sabbatical is over. A slightly doctrinaire approach to running hotels makes this a great place for like minds but not so friendly to those who disagree. Dinner at 8pm is a simple three-course affair, with cheese, dessert and coffee, no choice. Although much was made in Alison Johnson's memoirs of the inspirational aspect of cooking – waiting until the last minute for materials to arrive, cooking what comes naturally from the far north – menus seems to include rather a lot of avocado, pineapple, rice, red peppers, melon and ices. The wine list is intelligent, from Justerini, Adnams and Yapp. House Corbières, £4.

CHEFS: Alison Johnson, Morag Macleod and Lena Maclennan  PROPRIETORS: Andrew and Alison Johnson
OPEN: Mon to Sat, D only
CLOSED: Nov to Mar
MEALS: 8
PRICES: Set D £17 (£21)
SEATS: 20. Private parties: 8 main room. Car-park, 10 places. Vegetarian meals. Children's helpings. No children under 8. No smoking. Wheelchair access One sitting
ACCOMMODATION: 7 rooms, all with bath/shower. B&B £45 to £60. Deposit: £40. No children under 8. Pets welcome. Garden. Phone. Scenic. Confirm by 6 [GHG]

---

SCONE  Tayside                                                        map 8

## ▲ Murrayshall Hotel

Scone PH2 7PH                                                    COOKING 4
SCONE (0738) 51171                                            COST £18–£38

Three hundred acres of parkland surround this hotel two miles north east of Perth (take the road to Coupar Angus). In Scottish style, this land is devoted to golf, one third the avowed activities of Murrayshall. Bruce Sangster's cooking in the constantly refurbished restaurant is of more significance for the purposes of this *Guide*, and seems to give as much satisfaction as a well-mown fairway in July. There were reflections in reports for the last edition that, although execution was fine, the level of invention was no higher than at many similar places. Reports in the past year would seem to gainsay that, or at least hint that success on the plate outweighs any thought of *déjà vu* on the menu. The standard *prix fixe* dinner menu, offering four courses and coffee with a choice of two in each course, is the subject of all the comment. There are cheaper offerings at lunchtime and a golfing style of eating (lighter and faster) available in the clubhouse. A dinner of a warm salad of pigeon with walnut oil dressing or a roulade of smoked salmon and sole mousse; pea and lettuce soup perfumed with curry or grilled goats' cheese; roast guinea-fowl on rösti potato with a madeira sauce or veal fillet with langoustines and a brandy sauce; ending with bread-and-butter pudding or hazelnut parfait, pleased two inspectors mightily. The list does indeed read like a thousand others but in truth had few errors (oversalted mousse, no perceptible curry seasoning, impossibly fancy bread-and-butter pudding – what an abused simplicity this has become), and many countervailing qualities (the carefully considered vegetables, the delectable complementary bonne bouche of liver pâté with rowan jelly and the fine condition of the guinea-fowl, 'the best I've ever tasted'). High skill, then, in the service of very good (usually local) materials. There are gourmet evenings, with guest chefs; the service is just so; and the wine list has bottles to do justice to the food. It gets called the Cellar Book, just as the very first course may be termed, 'A little tasting whilst the finishing touches are being made to your first course'. There is a fair spread to the cellar, but it is never cheap. There is a tendency to use only one or two sources in a region – for instance Beaujolais from Loron or Rhône from Jaboulet – which reduces the apparent choice. Alsace belies that comment, however – and in Germany no shippers are listed at all. There are only house wines under £10, and not much under £15. Six House French from £7.95. CELLARMAN'S CHOICE : Berberana Rioja Gran Reserva 1975, £14.75; Sauvignon de St-Bris 1987, Auffray, £15.

CHEF: Bruce Sangster   PROPRIETORS: Macolsen Ltd
OPEN: all week
MEALS: 12 to 1.45, 7 to 9.30
PRICES: Set L £12.75 (£18) to £15 (£21), Set D £25.90 (£32)
CARDS: Access, Amex, Diners, Visa
SEATS: 60. Private parties: 20 main room, 70 private room. Car-park. Children welcome. Smart dress preferred. No smoking in dining-room. Wheelchair access. Music
ACCOMMODATION: 19 rooms, all with bath/shower. B&B £57.50 to £105. Deposit: 10%. No children under 12. Pets welcome. Afternoon teas. Garden. Tennis. Golf. TV. Phone. Scenic. Confirm by 6

---

**SLEAT   Isle of Skye**                                                          map 8

## ▲ *Kinloch Lodge* ☂

Isle Ornsay, Sleat IV43 8QY
ISLE ORNSAY (047 13) 214 and 333
1m off A851 between Broadford and                                COOKING  1
Armadale                                                              COST  £35

The storms and tempests of early 1989 caused much damage at this former shooting-lodge but it has been repaired by the Macdonalds, who play host for nine months of the year to a succession of guests, many of whom have been coming for the past 16 years. Some there are who, while recognising the nobility, miss the grandeur of other less relaxed, more hide-bound establishments. This does not always lead to satisfaction at the prices. Reports of the cooking are not uniform, a note of perfunctoriness having crept in. It certainly makes no claims to haute cuisine, rather to the dinner party style of cooking. A daily menu offers two choices at each principal course and then a long tail to the meal of good cheeses, a fine dessert and coffee. A meal might consist of a very spicy tomato soup given smooth unction by an avocado cream; then a fillet of hake rolled in oatmeal with marvellous fresh flakes of fish with a mild tartare sauce; good vegetables; a very dinner-party sweet of a blackcurrant and lemon suédoise with vanilla meringues (hazelnut meringue with coffee-butter cream was raved about too). When it works, it works well; if it does not, then it may seem a sore trial to palate and purse. The wine list is long and good. Excellent Californians and Australians are more than mere postscript to the long sections of claret and burgundy, better value as well. Although 'bargain' is not the description, there is consideration for those who don't want to spend more than £15 and there are half-bottles as well. House Bordeaux, £7. There is no service charge and tipping is 'actively discouraged'.

CHEFS: Lady Macdonald and Peter Macpherson   PROPRIETORS: Lord and Lady Macdonald
OPEN: all week, D only
CLOSED: 1 Dec to mid-Mar
MEALS: 8
PRICES: Set D £25 (£29). Service inc
CARDS: Access, Visa
SEATS: 25. Private parties: 8 main room. Car-park, 25 places. No children under 10.
One sitting
ACCOMMODATION: 10 rooms, 9 with bath/shower. B&B £40 to £80. Deposit: £50. Baby
facilities. Pets welcome. Afternoon teas. Garden. Fishing. Scenic. Confirm by 3

---

**STEWARTON  Strathclyde**                                               map 8

# ▲ *Chapeltoun House* ♟

Stewarton KA3 3ED
STEWARTON (0560) 82696
2m from Stewarton, on B769 towards                          COOKING **2**
Irvine                                                       COST  £20–£34

Chapeltoun was built in 1900 by an industrialist's family, and is now a small
country-house hotel with 20 acres of private gardens in which to wander.
When it is cool, fires burn indoors, in a house of formal mien, a little heavily
furnished. The two adjoining dining-rooms are oak-panelled and decorated in
shades of plum, with uncovered polished wood tables and crisp napkins. The
four-course set menu is carefully executed by George McIvor. For the first
course, marinated scallops on a tomato mousse have been good, while the
second course of soup or fish has produced a delicate and perfectly rolled
smoked haddock and brill roulade on a leek sauce. Main courses include a
vegetarian dish alongside saddle of rabbit in thyme-scented sauce; fillet of veal
with cashew nuts on a Tia Maria cream sauce; or steaks plain or sauced.
Creamy desserts on a self-service basis let the side down somewhat,
particularly when disfigured by a ham-fisted previous diner. Excellent coffee
and petits fours. The staff are pleasant, though long waits at untended bars may
give rise to insecurity, and shyness may be interpreted as indifference. The
Muzak can, self-confessedly, be 'dreadful'. The wine list is quite long, 10 per
cent of it outside France and Germany. There are some very good wines,
nonetheless, and the prices are fair. Oddities include a Ch. Branaire 1920 and a
Ch. Lagrange 1923, but there is good representation of the 1970s in claret and a
sufficient number of half-bottles. House French, four of them, from £7.80 to £9.
CELLARMAN'S CHOICE : St-Aubin 1980, Loron, £13.30; Torres Viña Esmeralda
1987, £10.

---

*The 1991 Guide will be published before Christmas 1990. Reports on meals are most
welcome at any time of the year, but are extremely valuable in the spring. Send them to*
The Good Food Guide, FREEPOST, 2 Marylebone Road, London NW1 1YN. *No stamp
is needed if posted in the UK.*

---

CHEF: George McIvor   PROPRIETORS: Colin and Graeme McKenzie
OPEN: all week
MEALS: 12 to 2, 7 to 9.15
PRICES: £19 (£28), Set L £14.50 (£20), Set D £21.50 (£28)
CARDS: Access, Amex, Visa
SEATS: 55. Private parties: 35 main room, 20 and 55 private rooms. Car-park, 50 places.
Vegetarian meals. No children under 12. Smart dress preferred. No smoking. Wheelchair
access (3 steps; also WC)
ACCOMMODATION: 8 rooms, all with bath/shower. B&B £65 to £99. No children under 12.
Pets welcome. Afternoon teas. Garden. Fishing. TV. Phone. Scenic. Doors close at midnight.
Confirm by 1pm [GHG]

---

**SWINTON  Borders**                                                      map 8

# ▲ Four Seasons, Wheatsheaf Hotel

Swinton TD11 3JJ                                                 COOKING 2
SWINTON (089 086) 257                                               COST £24

Swinton is north of the giant castle keep of Norham, guarding the English
border, and south of the River Blackadder: a fine sandwich. One can find
sandwiches at the Wheatsheaf Hotel, indeed, 'the best pub food on the
borders,' says one enthusiast – but better by far to order something more
adventurous or to book one of the few tables in the hotel's restaurant. Alan
Reid has proved himself a natural cook of great skill. The food that has
especially pleased has been the salmon, venison and beef, available in
profusion – some of the fish even landed by the chef himself. The poached
salmon steak with a hollandaise 'was the best I can remember for years:
generous middle cut, firm, moist, large flakes of rich solid salmon. The
hollandaise was fluffy, eggy, lemony, buttery,' wrote one happy diner.
Superlatives appear elsewhere. A beginning of warm salad of duck with
avocado was favourably compared to many a fancy French holiday meal. A
happy place, well served. The wine list is as reasonably priced as the food. Its
range is short but adequate and many of the growers are good ones. House
French is £4.95. CELLARMAN'S CHOICE : Contino Reserva 1982, CVNE £11.45;
Mâcon-Lugny 1988, Mathelin, £7.90.

---

CHEFS: Alan Reid and George Robertson   PROPRIETORS: Alan and Julie Reid
OPEN: Tue to Sun
MEALS: 11.45 to 2, 7 to 10
PRICES: £13 (£20). Snacks from £2.25
CARDS: Access, Visa
SEATS: 20. Private parties: 20 main room, 28 private room. Vegetarian meals. Children's
helpings. Smart dress preferred. No cigars/pipes in dining-room. Wheelchair access (1 step
also WC)
ACCOMMODATION: 3 rooms. B&B £19 to £30. Baby facilities. Pets welcome. Garden. TV.
Scenic. Doors close at midnight

---

*'While I feel happy and privileged to eat an artistic creation, I do not see why I should leave
a restaurant feeling inadequately fed having paid a food bill of £58 plus service.'* On
dining in London

---

SCOTLAND

TIRORAN  Isle of Mull                                    map 8

## ▲ *Tiroran House*

Tiroran, Mull, PA69 6ES                              COOKING 2
TIRORAN (068 15) 232                                    COST £29

'We approached it by yacht and anchored in Loch Scridain just below before
wandering up to the house through the gardens: an amazing way to go and
have a first-class dinner.' Whether by yacht or by ferry, water must be crossed
to arrive at this sporting-lodge with views of land and sea. The atmosphere is
house-party: the single time of eating sees to that. The cooking is Anglo-
Scottish, using good ingredients with sufficient invention to keep interest
alive. The three-course meal plus cheese and coffee has no choice at its centre –
often a roast or a large piece of salmon – but first courses include a nicely
judged Stilton soup or sweetbreads in puff pastry on a beurre blanc and
desserts often include an English Guards pudding, gooseberry tart, treacle tart
or syllabub as well as blackcurrant délices or lime soufflés. Cheeses are good
and local; fudge comes with coffee. Packed lunches are a pride and joy. The
wine list is fairly priced and includes a good range, much from Corney &
Barrow. Would that all hotels could operate on such modest margins. 'No
gratuities are expected or accepted.'

CHEF: Sue Blockey   PROPRIETORS: Wing Commander and Mrs Blockey
OPEN: all week, D only (L residents only)
CLOSED: mid-Oct to early May
MEALS: 7
PRICES: Set D £20 (£24). Service inc
SEATS: 20. Private parties: 8 main room. Car-park, 20 places. No children under 10. Smart
dress preferred. No smoking. One sitting
ACCOMMODATION: 9 rooms, all with bath/shower. B&B £38 to £77. Deposit: £25. No
children under 10. Pets welcome. Garden. Fishing. Scenic [GHG]

ULLAPOOL  Highland                                      map 8

## ▲ *Altnaharrie Inn* ♥

Ullapool IV26 2SS                                    COOKING 4
DUNDONNELL (085 483) 230                                COST £48

'When walking up the hill behind the Inn, we met a couple who asked,
"What's the hotel like?" "The best in Scotland," I replied, without hesitation.
A more considered response may have qualified my reply, but the answer
reflects my feelings.' Perhaps that is all we need to write about this former
drovers' inn reached by ferry from Ullapool. 'On arrival in Ullapool, please
telephone, but please keep your luggage in the car until we are able to direct
you to the appropriate place at which to meet the ferry.' Once embarked, the car
left behind, no cares or woes encumber the traveller in the anticipation of Gunn
Eriksen's matchless cooking. One top-league restaurateur, brought back to
earth as he motored south, was moved to reflect that of all the dishes cooked
during his week-long stay only one did not excel his own achievement: praise
indeed. Each night brings forth a five-course dinner for a single sitting. Soup is
the invariable prelude, then two substantial courses (often reversing the usual

order of fish and meat), cheeses (including Philippe Olivier imports) followed by desserts, usually three, all of which you are encouraged to sample, all 'as pretty as Ascot hats'. Much has already been made of Ms Eriksen's capacity to build on what is around her: nettles, hawthorn or samphire, fish from the sea – 'the finest fish cook in Britain' – or deer or game from the hills about. She gets good practice: her repertoire is wide but well tried. An inspection meal yielded a nettle and Brie soup with both flavours clearly distinguishable; an asparagus mousse in filo pastry with a lemony hollandaise of luxury and attack; a plate of sole, turbot and a pastry purse of prawns with a Champagne butter sauce and a Champagne and cress sauce that was 'a triumph', followed by cheeses and desserts. Two sauces may be a trademark: the lobster served with a white wine sauce, and a sauce of roes and corals 'as bright as Cardinal-polished tiles, had such intense flavours that you felt sad at finishing it'. Service from Fred Brown and one or two helpers is expert and informed. Breakfasts are memorable. 'They have a knack of rubbing off the rough edges of austerity.' Of course there will always be those who find it claustrophobic. The restaurant holds as many as occupy the bedrooms. The menu is recited to you; some colloquy between tables is inevitable. But these facts must be apparent as foot is laid on outward ferry deck. The wine list is long enough for everyone. It is French, save for a few hocks and Mosels. There are some nice clarets and some good wholes and halves of red burgundy. White burgundy fares less well. Regional wines don't get much of a look-in. The house is a non-smoking one, by popular demand, it is inferred. 'A non-tipping policy applies.'

CHEF: Gunn Eriksen    PROPRIETORS: Fred Brown and Gunn Eriksen
OPEN: all week, D only
CLOSED: late Oct to Easter
MEALS: 7.45
PRICES: Set D £35 (£40). Service inc
SEATS: 14. Private parties: 14 main room. Car-park, 20 places. Vegetarian meals. Children's helpings. No children under 10. No smoking. One sitting
ACCOMMODATION: 7 rooms, all with bath/shower. D, B&B £79 to £95. Deposit: £75. No children under 10. Garden. Fishing. Scenic. Confirm by 4 [GHG]

## ▲ *Morefield Motel*

| Ullapool IV26 2TH | COOKING 1 |
|---|---|
| ULLAPOOL (0854) 2161 | COST £23 |

The connections of the proprietors, once scallop-divers, with the fishermen ensure supplies of fresh fish to this 'Tartan-Spanish' restaurant and lounge bar (different menus in each) and motel outside the town. The restaurant is the place to be – the bar, though cheaper, 'indulging in the oral plate syndrome, i.e. piled high with lots of stuff you haven't asked for'. Grilled fish is the thing to eat. House wine, £5.50.

CHEF: Elise Ann Ross  PROPRIETORS: David Smyrl and David Courtney Marsh
OPEN: all week
MEALS: 12 to 2, 6 to 9.30
PRICES: £16 (£19)
CARDS: Access, Amex, Visa
SEATS: 106. 6 tables outside. Private parties: 40 main room. Car-park, 35 places. Children's
helpings. Separate smoking area. Wheelchair access (also WC). Music
ACCOMMODATION: 11 rooms, all with bath/shower. Rooms for disabled. B&B £15 to £30.
Deposit: 10%. Baby facilities. Afternoon teas. Scenic. Doors close at midnight. Confirm by 6

---

**WALLS** Shetland                                                          map 8

## ▲ *Burrastow House*

Walls, ZE2 9PB
WALLS (059 571) 307                                                  COOKING 2
3m W of Walls                                                   COST £10−£22

Remote even by Shetland standards, but easy to find, this eighteenth-century
house 'with Victorian baronial accretions' stands on a promontory facing the
island of Vaila, and has been taken over by Ann Prior and Bo Simmons. The
hallmark is informality: shelves stuffed with natural history books, children
welcomed, an antediluvian dumb waiter, and occasional bursts of pop music
from the kitchen where the proprietors take turns at cooking. Their resources
are local: salmon from the nearby smokery; home-grown vegetables and herbs;
Shetland lamb; lobsters from the voe; milk and cheese from the ewe tethered in
the front garden. Yet in cooking, Russian, German, Mediterranean and Middle
Eastern influences jostle with English and Scottish. 'We like mutton reestit
soup, a very strongly flavoured Scotch broth with salted mutton;' 'salmon steak
was deliciously moist and well complemented by a purée of local nettles and
sheep's milk cheese.' Also commended: sole with saffron and pistachio;
marinated fish salad; hot crab ramekins; Scottish cheeses; apple and
boysenberry flan; breakfast muesli and kippers. The wine list may be short but
it's very reasonable and the holdings of organic wines are increasing. Orkney
Raven Ale is available on draught. House wine is £5. CELLARMAN'S CHOICE :
Muscadet, 'Le Master' 1987, £8.30; Ch. de Prade, Bordeaux 1986, £8 (organic).
This is a place to watch otters.

---

CHEFS/PROPRIETORS: Bo Simmons and Ann Prior
OPEN: all week, exc Tue (residents only), L by arrangement Oct to Apr
CLOSED: Feb
MEALS: 12.30 to 2.30, 7.30 to 9
PRICES: L £7 (£10), Set D £15 (£18). Service inc
SEATS: 20. Private parties: 16 main room. Car-park, 5 places. Vegetarian meals. Children's
helpings on request. No smoking. Music
ACCOMMODATION: 3 rooms, 2 with bath/shower. B&B £32.50 to £55. Baby facilities. Pets
welcome. Afternoon teas. Garden. Fishing. Scenic. Confirm by 6

---

*'The waitress, when told of our disappointment at the meal, said she was sorry but the
owner/chef had gone to Twickenham on Saturday, got drunk and had fallen down some
stairs and injured his leg.'*  On dining in Avon

## ▲ *Knockie Lodge*

Whitebridge, IV1 2UP
GORTHLECK (045 63) 276                                      COOKING **2**
on B862, 8m N of Fort Augustus                          COST  £10–£28

The view is the thing, and it's there in abundance at Knockie Lodge, once the resort of shooters, with new panoramas opening up from the 1989 additions of reading-room and billiard room. The light bar lunches are almost as great a feature as the set dinner menu in a restaurant that will not hold many more than residents. Travellers should note. Chris Freeman cooks four courses before cheese and coffee; there is no choice until an alternative is offered for pudding; soup comes second. The centrepiece is not merely roast meat but perhaps quail with spinach and grapes or fillet of lamb with apricot sauce. The cooking is the reverse of elaborate but meals have been balanced exercises in careful timing, careful buying and careful cooking. It is not as easy as it may seem to get enough ripe avocados to serve a roomful of guests; nor to time and cook glazed onions so successfully. Coffee and tablet (the Scottish version of fudge) good; decaffeinated not so good. House wine from Loron, £6.

CHEF: Chris Freeman    PROPRIETORS: Brenda and Ian Milward
OPEN: all week
CLOSED: end Oct to end Apr
MEALS: 12.30 to 1.30, 8
PRICES: Set L £6 (£10), to £10.50 (£15), Set D £18 (£23)
CARDS: Access, Amex, Visa
SEATS: 22. Private parties: 12 main room. Car-park, 30 places. No children under 10. No smoking in dining-room. Smart dress preferred. One sitting at D
ACCOMMODATION: 10 rooms, all with bath/shower. D,B&B £48 to £64. Deposit: £50. No children under 10. Pets welcome. Garden. Fishing. Snooker. Scenic [GHG]

# Wales

## Hive on the Quay

Cadwgan Place, Aberaeron SA46 0BT      COOKING 1
ABERAERON (0545) 570445      COST £17

The Holgates' summertime café/restaurant overlooking the harbour started 15 years ago as a tea-shop and ice-cream parlour, but it now serves buffet lunches and, in the high season of July and August, straight dinners. The name comes from the family honey farm which once occupied the premises; there are still some observation hives on show and the honey itself, now made elsewhere, appears in jars for sale and in tea-time cakes and biscuits. The café proper, which has a conservatory extension, has a family atmosphere and looks into the busy kitchen. Dishes are chalked up on blackboards: for lunch, soup, soused mackerel, good savoury and fruit pies, ploughman's lunch and special children's dishes. The pies, served cold, have a rich shortcrust pastry and fillings like layered sausage meat, shredded onion and apple. Ploughman's lunch is with organic farmhouse Cheddar and good local bread. Dinners are smarter, with waitress service, but dishes still have a Welsh ring, as in grilled mackerel stuffed with cockles and wrapped in bacon, baked ham with parsley sauce, cawl, fresh crab salad and, of course, potato cakes. House Bulgarian is £4.60 and there are two organically produced French wines at £5.70 and £6.75. Children are asked to buy their Comets from the kiosk '*as they leave*'.

CHEF: John Bromley    PROPRIETORS: Margaret and Sarah Holgate
OPEN: all week L, plus D July and Aug
CLOSED: end Sept to Spring bank hol
MEALS: 12 to 2, 6 to 9
PRICES: £10 (£14). Snacks from 80p. Service 10% at D
SEATS: 55. 2 tables outside. Vegetarian meals. Children's helpings. Wheelchair access. Self-service at L

*This year, in quoting prices for three-course meals at the top of each entry (by the word 'Cost'), we have put a more pessimistic complexion on the upper price by inflating it by 20 per cent. The aim is to prepare the reader for any inflation during the life of the* Guide *and also reflect the price of a meal taken without constant attention to the likely size of the bill. The prices quoted in smaller print below the text remain, as in previous editions, strict computer calculations of an average three-course meal, the price in brackets reflecting an average meal with coffee, service and half a bottle of house wine per person.*

# Old Coffee Shop

| | |
|---|---|
| 13 New Street, Aberdovey LL35 0EH | COOKING 1 |
| ABERDOVEY (065 472) 652 | COST £10 |

The all-day café, open on Sunday as well, is deservedly popular with visitors and locals alike. It is not large, so competition for seats may be fierce in high season. 'Baking better than any west of Offa's Dyke' may be a large claim, but it has been made. It is honest cooking, daily cooking, reasonably priced cooking, taking in cottage pie, braised pheasant, plaice and prawns, waffles and cakes. It may not be haute cuisine, but that's not what eating is all about. Sunday lunch is the traditional roast.

CHEFS: Susan Griffiths  PROPRIETORS: Alan and Susan Griffiths
OPEN: Tue to Sun, daytime only
MEALS: 10 to 5.30 (L 12 to 3)
PRICES: £7 (£8), Snacks from £1.20. Unlicensed, but bring your own: corkage £1.50
SEATS: 30. Private parties: 30 main room. Vegetarian meals. Children's helpings. No-smoking area

# ▲ Penhelig Arms Hotel ♥

| | |
|---|---|
| Aberdovey LL35 0LT | COOKING 1 |
| ABERDOVEY (065 472) 215 | COST £8–£20 |

The Hughes have moved a hundred yards down the road from the Maybank Hotel (which featured in the *Guide*) to afford themselves more scope in this harbourside inn. Ignore, if you can, the fixtures and fittings until the proprietors have had time to settle in. In the daytime there is good, freshly prepared bar food and on Sunday a set lunch. At night Sally Hughes offers a short menu at a set price. It is strong on fish and shellfish, some caught in the Dovey estuary, the rest bought at Penmaenmawr. It is also simple and direct. A salad of succulent mushrooms, just cooked, in a garlic and curry mayonnaise was exactly that. A soup of carrot, tomato and lemon was not over-creamed and allowed the three tastes to proclaim themselves. A lack of finish may be outweighed by wholly good intentions and excellent produce. The wine list, under Robert Hughes' care, is a gem of intelligent choice allied to generous pricing. The properties offered are excellent and fashionable. There are 12 house wines, starting at £5.95. CELLARMAN'S CHOICE : Saumur-Champigny, Ch. Targe 1986, Pisani, £8.50; Ch. Lynch-Bages, 1978, £29; Gewürztraminer 1987, Rolly Gassmann, £9.25.

CHEF: Sally Hughes  PROPRIETORS: Robert and Sally Hughes
OPEN: all week
MEALS: 12 to 2, 7 to 9
PRICES: L alc £7 (£8), Set Sun L £6.50 (£10), Set D £12.95 (£17). Service inc set
CARDS: Access, Visa
SEATS: 42. Private parties: 24 main room. Car-park, 12 places. Children's helpings. Music
ACCOMMODATION: 12 rooms, all with bath/shower. B&B £24 to £56. Deposit: £10. Pets welcome. Afternoon teas. TV. Scenic. Doors close at midnight. Confirm by 6

ABERSOCH  Gwynedd                                                          map 4

## ▲ *Porth Tocyn Hotel* ♥

| Abersoch LL53 7BU | COOKING 2 |
| ABERSOCH (075 881) 3303 | COST £13−£25 |

Still a family-run hotel after more than 30 years, Porth Tocyn is roundly praised for magnificent views over Cardigan Bay and a straightforward approach to good food. In part, this reflects the Fletcher-Brewers' awareness that they cannot afford self-indulgence. 'The high-handed dismissal of the provincial dining public by so-called mega-chefs seems to us to signify an intolerant arrogance.' So, although the daily five-course set dinner menu offers limited choice, it is tailored to suit diverse tastes, mixing the conventional and the adventurous. Sauces are often fruity, but not always in the nouvelle style − rosemary, port and bramble sauce for April lamb, lemon and mint for grilled plaice, fresh slivered apricot mixed with smoked goose in a salad. Accompanying vegetables are good and so are puddings and savouries. At lunchtime there are informal soups, salads and sandwiches, and on Sunday a buffet. The wine list is very adequate, taking in a fair range of Old and New World wines. Prices are not give-away. House French, £7.50. There are often some nice bin-ends and plenty of half-bottles. The approach here to the service charge is one we would endorse. To quote: 'This is not sought after at all. Service charges should be non-events in any decent establishment. Just tell your readers not to pay anything on principle unless they really want to. Sometimes people do feel in this mood. Even I do sometimes if I have had an exceptional time and good value for money.'

CHEF: E.L. Fletcher-Brewer    PROPRIETORS: The Fletcher-Brewer family and Sue Bower
OPEN: all week
MEALS: 12.30 to 2, 7.30 to 9.30
PRICES: Set Sun L £9.50 (£13), Set D £12.35 (£16) to £17.30 (£21), Snacks from £1.25
CARD: Access
SEATS: 60. 12 tables outside. Private parties: 60 main room. Car-park, 60 places. Children's helpings (with prior notice). No children under 7 at D. Smart dress preferred. Wheelchair access (1 step; also WC)
ACCOMMODATION: 17 rooms, all with bath/shower. Rooms for disabled. B&B £29.75 to £47.50. Deposit: £40. Baby facilities. Pets welcome. Afternoon teas. Garden. Swimming-pool. Tennis. TV. Phone. Scenic. Doors close at midnight [GHG]

## ▲ *Riverside Hotel*

| Abersoch LL53 7HW | COOKING 1 |
| ABERSOCH (075 881) 2419 and 2818 | COST £24 |

The original hotel, harbour to one side, River Soch to the other, has spawned a long extension ending in a glasshouse. It is family-run and caters for families (for example, high teas for young children). Good-value and honest cooking seem to be its hallmarks. The short set-price dinner menu, changing from day to day, may include spicy tomato soup, fillet of beef with a peppered cream sauce, and pecan tart. Then, adding lustre and adventure, it may offer more elaborate affairs such as a courgette mousse and saffron sauce or breast of duck with kumquats and coriander. Home-made bread and ice-cream reveal the wish to be genuine. Reports stress the relaxing feel of the place, service being friendly yet effective in the hybrid country-cosy, stripped-pine, pizzeria-looking restaurant. Occasionally dishes are produced lacking some essential of their description on the menu, but the wholesomeness of the cooking still shines through. Bar lunches are served from noon to 2pm. The short wine list is not exorbitant, with house French at £5. CELLARMAN'S CHOICE : Berberana Gran Reserva Rioja 1978, £13.20; Mâcon-Villages Blanc 1987, Antonin Rodet, £10.10.

CHEF: Wendy Bakewell    PROPRIETORS: John and Wendy Bakewell
OPEN: all week
CLOSED: Nov to Mar
MEALS: 12 to 2, 7.30 to 9.30
PRICES: Set D £15.95 (£20), L Snacks from £2
CARDS: Access, Visa
SEATS: 34. Private parties: 34 main room. Car-park, 30 places. Vegetarian meals L, by arrangement at D. No children under 5. Smart dress preferred. No smoking in dining-room. Music
ACCOMMODATION: 12 rooms, all with bath/shower. B&B £27.50 to £55. Deposit: £30. Baby facilities. Afternoon teas. Garden. Swimming-pool. Fishing. TV. Phone. Scenic. Doors close at 12. Confirm by 4

---

## ABERYSTWYTH  Dyfed                                                    map 4

## Gannets

| | |
|---|---|
| 7 St James' Square, Aberystwyth SY23 1DU | COOKING 1 |
| ABERYSTWYTH (0970) 617164 | COST £8–£16 |

A cheerful, basic bistro, near the University and castle, where business people and academics rub shoulders with families and tourists to eat from a menu of 10 or so first courses and twice as many main dishes. The style is of roasts, grills and hearty pies, and the emphasis is strong on freshness and local produce. Most of the meat and poultry comes from Dilys Mildon's family farm nearby, as do organic root vegetables. A local game farm supplies fur and feather, while seafood is landed on the quay only 150 metres from the restaurant. Thus the menu is studded with Welsh lamb pie, pheasant in burgundy sauce, smoked Welsh trout and the like. Desserts have featured crisp-cum-gooey hazelnut meringue and peach and papaya sorbet. House Italian £5.40 a litre.

CHEF: David Mildon    PROPRIETORS: David and Dilys Mildon
OPEN: Mon to Sat
MEALS: 12 to 2, 6 to 9.30
PRICES: L £5 (£8), D £9 (£13). Service inc
CARDS: Access, Visa
SEATS: 40. Private parties: 40 main room. Vegetarian meals. Children's helpings. Wheelchair access. Music

---

*If you see a certificate in a restaurant bearing the words 'Good Food and Wine Guide', the claim is false – see the Introduction. Please write and tell us the name and address of the restaurant.*

---

map 4

# ▲ *Ye Olde Bulls Head Inn* ♥

Castle Street, Beaumaris
Anglesey LL58 8AP                                    COOKING 3
BEAUMARIS (0248) 810329                              COST £24

Despite continuing alterations, Keith Rothwell and David Robertson's seventeenth-century coaching-inn has kept to the high standards of their first two years. Most of the renovation is on the hotel side (heating and bathrooms for all the bedrooms) and both bars, decorated with antique weaponry and serving good ales, and beamed attic dining-room, once the saddle room, remain unchanged save for new china and cutlery and improvements of detail. Glowing accounts of meals emphasise the local produce, both meat and fish, as much as the descriptions on the menu. This is divided into two parts: half a dozen first and main courses, largely meat and poultry, and another three or four fish or game dishes for each course, which are added daily. The cooking style is straightforward, a mixture of new and old which avoids a stylised feel, and portions are generous. Slightly pink pan-fried calf's liver in an intensely flavoured truffle sauce, guinea-fowl stuffed with hazelnut mousseline and finished with an orange and tarragon sauce, baby monkfish in a rich cream sauce and monkfish tart with wild mushrooms are among recommended dishes. Many other fish are simply grilled or served in salads. Cheese and puddings both have their own menus, which are justified. The cheeses are largely well-kept Welsh. Desserts have included an exquisite pairing of chocolate marquise and orange soufflé in a sharp orange sauce and a more modern blackcurrant tartlet in papaya sauce. Coffee and petits fours do not disappoint either. Service is variously described as excellent, amiable and effective. The wine list is distinguished by its lack of greed and short selection of clarets. At lower prices (but not lower margins) there are also some fine choices from elsewhere in France and the rest of the world. House Bordeaux is £7.50. CELLARMAN'S CHOICE : Ch. de Pez, St Estèphe 1970, £27.95; Gewürztraminer, Réserve Personnelle 1985, Trimbach, £15.95.

CHEF: Keith Rothwell    PROPRIETORS: Rothwell and Robertson Ltd
OPEN: all week
MEALS: 12 to 2.30, 7.30 to 9.30
PRICES: £13 (£20), Snacks from £1.10
CARDS: Access, Visa
SEATS: 70. Private parties: 70 main room, 40 private room. Car-park, 15 places. Children's helpings. No children under 7
ACCOMMODATION: 11 rooms, all with bath/shower. B&B £29.50 to £49.50. Baby facilities. Phone. Scenic. Doors close at 1am. Confirm by 6

---

*'We seem to be so health conscious that restaurateurs are avoiding the use of salt, butter, cream and seasonings which bring out the flavour of food. Even herbs seem to be less used and are being replaced by trendy leaves of various colours. If this continues, the Guide will be left to compare brands of Edwina's approved nutrition pills, and what a dull life it will be! Will you kindly organise a campaign to "get the flavour back into cooking". It will be very popular.'* From a reporter in West Midlands

BRECHFA  Dyfed                                                                          map 4

## ▲ *Ty Mawr* ♥

Brechfa SA32 7RA
BRECHFA (026 789) 332                                                      COOKING 1
on B4301, 6m from A40                                                 COST  £12–£23

The massed forces of the Flaherty family make this old farmhouse, with many
beams and stone walls, hum for visitors and customers alike. To keep all of
themselves busy, they bake bread and cook dishes for shops and retailers
outside Brechfa as well as running the hotel. There is a definite tendency
towards vegetarian and organic foods, although the menu does not
immediately show it, nor has anyone commented that quantities are tempered
with a view to helping achieve weight loss. The menu, priced according to
which main dish is chosen, does not change a great deal from month to month
and popular home-made gravlax, mushrooms in garlic butter, piperade
basquaise and bobotie are still on offer. Puddings are a high point, especially
meringue. Service is cheerful, the sense of the place is family rather than formal
– tipping is not encouraged. The wine list is improving. There are some nice
organic wines, from Musso in Burgundy and Eugène Meyer in Alsace, for
example. The spread, for so short a list, is fair and the prices very reasonable
indeed. House French, £5.95.

CHEFS: Alan and Timothy Flaherty  PROPRIETORS: The Flaherty family
OPEN: all week, D only, and Sun L
MEALS: 12 to 2, 7 to 9.30
PRICES: Set Sun L £8.75 (£12), Set D £12.50 (£16) to £16 (£19). Service inc
CARDS: Access, Visa
SEATS: 60. Private parties: 30 main room. Car-park, 60 places. Vegetarian meals. Children's
helpings. Smart dress preferred. No-smoking area
ACCOMMODATION: 5 rooms, all with bath/shower. B&B £40 to £50. Baby facilities. Pets
welcome. Afternoon teas. Garden. Scenic. Doors close at 11.30. Confirm by 2 [GHG]

BROAD HAVEN  Dyfed                                                                 map 4

## ▲ *Druidstone Hotel*

Broad Haven SA62 3NE                                                      COOKING 1
BROAD HAVEN (0437) 781221                                               COST  £18

Perched above the sea, down a concealed turning that takes you over two
cattle-grids, the Druidstone has views over an unspoiled coastline and out to
sea. 'The cellar bar spills easily on to the terrace with the best view in the
world, looking down on to a wonderful beach.' The atmosphere, described in
one report as 'an ambience of charming, well-spoken hippies, sometimes laid
back to the point of being casual,' and the homespun décor are those of a family
home; dogs wander in and out, children are more than welcomed at mealtimes
and accommodation may seem basic. Likewise, the food seems an extension of
home cooking, with no pretence to sophistication, but fresh ingredients and
inventive flair. Local fish offers some of the best choices – seafood quiches or
sea bass with fresh herbs and vermouth – or there are old-fashioned pies,
roasts and a good choice of vegan and vegetarian dishes. Exotica, such as

Chinese yellow-bean soup and falafel, appear on the bar menu. Wear warm clothes in winter. This is a family hotel; go not for restful cosseting, but for activities, good value and fun. Children are done proud: 'The children's meal at 6.30 was freshly cooked and did not involve chips, baked beans, hamburgers or fish fingers. It can be done!' House Duboeuf is £5.

CHEFS/PROPRIETORS: Rod and Jane Bell
OPEN: all week, exc Sun D
MEALS: 12.30 to 2.30 (1 to 2 Sun), 7.30 to 10
PRICES: £11 (£15), Snacks from £1.10
CARDS: Amex, Visa
SEATS: 40. 8 tables outside. Private parties: 36 main room, 12 private room. Car-park, 40 places. Vegetarian meals. Children's helpings. Wheelchair access (also WC)
ACCOMMODATION: 9 rooms. Rooms for disabled. B&B £19.50 to £39. Deposit: £15. Baby facilities. Pets welcome. Afternoon teas. Garden. Scenic. Doors close at midnight

---

## CAERNARFON  Gwynedd

map 4

# Y Bistro Bach

| 4 Y Maes, Caernarfon LL55 2NF | COOKING 1 |
| CAERNARFON (0286) 673075 | COST £14 |

Danny and Nerys Roberts started this small offshoot of Y Bistro (see Llanberis) when that restaurant did not attract enough call for full lunches. Bach is an altogether more informal operation, but the dozen or so dishes are cheap, excellent and firmly promote Welsh cooking and produce. Glamorgan or lamb sausages, baked leek and ham with cheese sauce, and bread-and-cheese lunches with Welsh farmhouse cheese are the order of the day. Salads and teatime cakes are made at Y Bistro and brought down. There is a simple choice of wines, beer, teas and soft drinks. House wines are £5.75

CHEFS: Nerys Roberts, Graham Ward and Terry Brady   PROPRIETORS: Danny and Nerys Roberts
OPEN: all week, exc Sun and Mon to Thur D in winter
MEALS: 12 to 3, 6 to 8.30
PRICES: £7 (£12)
CARDS: Access, Visa
SEATS: 60. Private parties: 20 main room. Vegetarian meals. Children welcome

---

## CARDIFF  South Glamorgan

map 4

# Armless Dragon

COUNTY
OF THE
YEAR
RESTAURANT

| 97 Wyvern Road, Cathays, Cardiff CF2 4BG | COOKING 1 |
| CARDIFF (0222) 382357 | COST £23 |

The Dragon is close to the Sherman Theatre in a modest inner-city area transformed by the growth of the University. Dress is apparently informal. 'We once asked a man in a singlet to put his shirt on.' Flavours are robust, with influences from Wales to the Far East. From the short menu, on which daily specials outweigh the fixed dishes, the fish dishes stand out. These are never fixed. Whatever is available that day is offered one of five ways: grilled, poached, baked with garlic and tomato, bonne femme or fried with a spicy Caribbean sauce. Sewin and hake are local; shark is from the North Cornish coast. The daily dishes are more adventurous, as in an octopus salad with grilled red pepper and chickpeas or a crab soup with lemon-grass. Meat is also carefully treated; boudin blanc and potted venison are both home made. So, too, are the satisfying puddings, which range from trifles and chocolate ganache to healthy Hunza apricots with cashew-nut cream. House French, £4.90. CELLARMAN'S CHOICE : Ch. Malescasse 1978, £11.50; Thomas Mitchell Fumé Blanc, £9.50.

CHEFS: Mark Sharples, David Richards and Debbie Coleman   PROPRIETORS: Mark Sharples and David Richards
OPEN: Mon to Sat, exc Sat L
CLOSED: bank hol Mons, Christmas to New Year
MEALS: 12.30 to 2.15, 7.30 to 10.30 (11 Sat)
PRICES: £14 (£19)
CARDS: Access, Amex, Diners, Visa
SEATS: 50. Private parties: 50 main room. Vegetarian meals. Children welcome. Wheelchair access. Music

## Bo Zan

| 78 Albany Road, Roath, Cardiff CF2 3RS | COOKING 2 |
| CARDIFF (0222) 493617 | COST £15−£24 |

Cardiff is well served for Chinese food of various kinds, but the Bo Zan, unpromisingly flanked by a handbag shop and a video shop in a suburban street, stands out for its Szechuan specialities − nearly half the dishes on the menu are marked by an asterisk to show hot, spicy seasoning − and plain approach to cooking. The décor is quietly Chinese, with the odd print and umbrella. Service can be cool, even temperamental − one waitress refused to take an order from two customers who took too long to make up their minds − but the food carries all before it. Unglutinous sauces allow colours, flavours and textures to come through in such dishes as sizzling scallops and prawns, ma po do fu (minced beef with bean curd in hot sauce), aromatic duck with hoisin sauce, sea-spiced chicken and kunpo chicken with hot chilli and bamboo shoots. One fried rice dish comes in lotus leaves in an aromatic pouch studded with pork, prawns and onions. House French is £5.50; sake is also available.

CHEF: Kim-Lam Fung   PROPRIETORS: Kim-Lam and Emma Fung
OPEN: all week, exc Sun L and Mon L
MEALS: 12 to 1.45, 6 to 11.30 (11.45 Sat)
PRICES: £12 (£19), Set D £10 (£15) to £14.75 (£20)
CARDS: Access, Amex, Diners, Visa
SEATS: 60. Private parties: 35 main room, 25 private room. Vegetarian meals. Children's helpings L and early D. Wheelchair access (1 step). Music

*If you see a certificate in a restaurant bearing the words 'European Good Food Guide (UK)', the claim is false (and the restaurant may be in contempt of court in displaying it) − see the Introduction. Please write and tell us the name and address of the restaurant.*

## La Brasserie

| | |
|---|---|
| 60 St Mary Street, Cardiff CF1 2AT | COOKING 1 |
| CARDIFF (0222) 372164 | COST £10–£22 |

The French side of the coin (see Champers, below, for the Spanish) may be noisy but the value is not disputed by people in Cardiff. The wines are even served properly and the staff know about what they are serving. House wine is £4.95. The same firm has opened Le Monde upstairs – see entry.

CHEF: Franco Peligno  PROPRIETOR: Benigno Martinez
OPEN: Mon to Sat
MEALS: 12 to 2.30, 7 to 12.15am
PRICES: £11 (£17), Set D £5.75 (£10) to £12.95 (£18)
CARDS: Access, Amex, Diners, Visa
SEATS: 75. Private parties: 75 main room. Children welcome. Music

## Le Cassoulet

| | |
|---|---|
| 5 Romilly Crescent, Canton | |
| Cardiff CF1 9NP | COOKING 2 |
| CARDIFF (0222) 221905 | COST £24 |

A stylish new frontage now keeps Welsh draughts at bay and the set lunch has gone, but otherwise there are no changes of great moment. Most important, cassoulet remains. This robust pièce de résistance from Toulouse is about the only distinctly regional dish on a generally provincial French menu that takes in poached eggs in pastry with béarnaise sauce; salmon marinated in sugar, salt, brandy and dill, served with a lemon and chive flavoured cream; poached brill and sole on a beurre blanc; and breast of chicken in a Pernod sauce. Cheeses, all French, have been in good condition and generously served. 'Good, honest, not overcomplicated cooking.' The fish is of the highest quality. Otherwise it is left to the wines, from Gaillac and Côtes de Buzet, and the armagnac to evoke the south-west. House French, £5.25.

CHEF: Gilbert Viader  PROPRIETORS: Gilbert and Claire Viader
OPEN: Tue to Sat, exc Sat L
MEALS: 12 to 2, 7 to 10
PRICES: £15 (£20)
CARDS: Access, Visa
SEATS: 35. Private parties: 35 main room. Children welcome. Wheelchair access. Music

## Champers

| | |
|---|---|
| 61 St Mary Street, Cardiff CF1 1FE | COOKING 1 |
| CARDIFF (0222) 373363 | COST £9–£23 |

Next door to its partner, La Brasserie, Champers stresses the Spanish side of the firm's activities. Local people are grateful for the desire to give good value and the large number of customers who ensure rapid turnover of food. 'I have never seen a limp piece of lettuce.' Once you learn the hybrid system of serve yourself and waiter service, everything goes swimmingly. House wine is £4.95.

CHEFS: Paul Griffiths and Paul Howell    PROPRIETOR: Benigno Martinez
OPEN: all week, exc Sun L
MEALS: 12 to 2.30, 7 to 12.15am
PRICES: £12 (£17), Set D £5.75 (£9) to £15.95 (£19). Service inc
CARDS: Access, Amex, Diners, Visa
SEATS: 70. Private parties: 6 main room, 70 private room. Children welcome. Music

## La Chaumière

44 Cardiff Road Llandaff
Cardiff CF5 2DP                                            COOKING 1
CARDIFF (0222) 555319                                     COST £11–£22

Green and white painted brick walls, colour prints of cats, and pendulous
globes of dried flowers set the attractive tone for this small, welcoming
restaurant over a betting shop not far from Llandaff cathedral. The menu
changes monthly; the style is franglais. The techniques seem fairly basic but it
pleases many, as does the atmosphere of hospitality. Recommendations have
included: mousseline of salmon in spinach sauce; steak in Stilton sauce with a
filo pastry shell; roast duck with lentils. Sweets are fun: hot chocolate fondue
comes with fresh fruit slices for dipping. The service is friendly but not always
knowledgeable. The wine list has no vintage dates (Puligny-Montrachet and
Piesporter get the same treatment) because, goes the explanation, 'each
delivery can mean a different vintage'. House Minervois and Muscadet, £6.

CHEF: Kay Morgan    PROPRIETORS: Cliff and Kay Morgan
OPEN: Tue to Sun, exc Sat L and Sun D
CLOSED: first 2 weeks Jan
MEALS: 12.30 to 2, 7.30 to 10
PRICES: £16 (£22), Set L £6.95 (£11) to £7.95 (£13). Service inc set L only, alc 10%
CARDS: Access, Amex, Diners
SEATS: 36. Private parties: 44 main room. Car-park, 36 places. Children's helpings

## De Courcey's

Tyla Morris House Pentyrch
Cardiff CF4 8QN                                            COOKING 1
CARDIFF (0222) 892232                                     COST £19–£30

After a false start as The Hamilton, the curious wooden house – imported from
Scandinavia in 1892 and reconstructed – was reopened as an ambitiously
upmarket French restaurant by the Thielmanns late in 1988. Thilo Thielmann
was a Holiday Inn manager for many years and the new decorations bear a
familiar stamp of luxury. There are showy touches in the menu and cooking
too. Noisettes of lamb are 'in harmony' with bacon, mushrooms and cherry
tomatoes while a coconut half filled with crab meat, prawns and grated coconut
covered with Marie Rose sauce is served on a gold-rimmed black plate.
However, gutsier ideas among the seven choices for each course include a
ratatouille terrine, mackerel marinated in white wine and apple juice, beer
braised beef topped with horseradish dumplings. There has been evidence of
skill, but it remains to be seen whether it develops uniformly. There is a short

wine list with none too many facts for some of the wines. House wine, £7.25. Sunday lunch is half price for children under 10.

CHEF: David Leeworthy    PROPRIETORS: Thilo and Patricia Thielmann
OPEN: all week, exc Fri L and Sat L, Sun D
MEALS: 12 to 2, 7.30 to 10
PRICES: Set L £13.50 (£19), Set D £19.50 (£25)
CARDS: Access, Amex, Diners, Visa
SEATS: 50. 5 tables outside. Private parties: 50 main room, 14 private room. Car-park, 30 places. Vegetarian meals. Children welcome. Smart dress preferred. Wheelchair access (3 steps). Music

## Gibsons

8 Romilly Crescent Canton
Cardiff CF1 9NR                                            COOKING 2
CARDIFF (0222) 341264                                      COST £15–£31

The departure of chef Andrew Canning from this long-established family concern has meant that Irene Canning spends more time in the kitchen and the restaurant is closed all day on Tuesday. Nonetheless, Gibsons is probably at the top of the list with serious diners in Cardiff for birthdays and celebrations, and the set lunches and five-course dinners are excellent value for money. Alongside classic French filets mignon and crêpes de fruits de mer are Welsh sea trout and lamb, not to mention heartier rustic dishes: ragout of kid provençale; mushroom and black-eyed pea Stroganoff. Puddings sound moreish, in the mould of coffee meringues with cream and Tia Maria; mocha and walnut ice-cream; steamed treacle pudding. The wine list may be short, but it gives liquid food for thought at not too high a price, though too many 1984s are still in evidence. House French is £6.80 a litre. CELLARMAN'S CHOICE : Haute Côtes de Beaune Tasteviné 1985, £10.35; Crustaces d'Alsace 1985, Dopff & Irion, £7.50.

CHEFS: Irene Canning, Matthew Canning and John Khalid    PROPRIETOR: Irene Canning
OPEN: Mon to Sun, exc Tue L and Sun, Mon and Tue D
MEALS: 12.30 to 3, 7.30 to 9.30
PRICES: £17 (£24), Set L £8.95 (£15) to £10.50 (£16), Set D £18.50 (£26)
CARDS: Access, Amex, Diners, Visa
SEATS: 38. Private parties: 12 main room. Car-park, 5 places. Vegetarian meals. Children's helpings

## Le Gourmet Enchanté

Wesley Lane, off Charles Street
Cardiff CF1 4EH                                            COOKING 1
CARDIFF (0222) 394767                                      COST £15–£29

In the shell of an Iranian restaurant, French cooking now goes on. Perhaps the Arabian nights atmosphere provides the enchantment for the gourmet. Welcome is conspicuously pleasant and the cooking appears to tread safe but not tedious French bounds, with the likes of mussels in filo with beurre blanc; artichoke mousse; smoked goose breast; kebab of monkfish; guinea-fowl with juniper sauce. There is a very short wine list with house wine at £5.95.

CHEF: Yvon Dumas   PROPRIETORS: Selbrook Ltd
OPEN: Mon to Sat, exc Sat L
CLOSED: bank hols and 25 Dec
MEALS: 12 to 2.15, 7 to 10.15
PRICES: £17 (£24), Set L £10 (£15) to £14 (£19)
CARDS: Access, Amex, Diners, Visa
SEATS: 42. Private parties: 50 main room, 25 private room. Children's helpings Wheelchair access (3 steps). Music. Air-conditioned

## Happy Gathering

233 Cowbridge Road East Canton
Cardiff CF1 9AL                                           COOKING 1
CARDIFF (0222) 397531                                     COST £11–£26

Here be dragons, rampaging in red and gold round the walls of this sizeable Cantonese restaurant. The Happy Gathering can pull the crowds to fill its enormous dining-room, even if it never quite achieves the heights of taste and quality. The menu offers a plenitude of set dinners plus pages of dishes such as Peking duck, seafood and cashew nuts in a bird's nest, and pork in satay sauce. Dim-sum are available every day until 7pm, with over 20 steamed and deep-fried delicacies ranging from prawn-stuffed duck webs to glutinous rice in lotus leaf. House French, £6.

CHEF: Kin Kwun Chan   PROPRIETOR: Sui Sang Chan
OPEN: all week
MEALS: noon to 11.45
PRICES: £13 (£21), Set L and D £7 (£11) to £18.50 (£22)
CARDS: Access, Amex, Diners, Visa
SEATS: 250. Private parties: 180 main room, 40 private room. Children welcome. Music. Air-conditioned

## Indian Ocean

290 North Road Gabalfa
Cardiff CF4 3BN                                           COOKING 1
CARDIFF (0222) 621152 and 621349                          COST £13–£19

Despite its unprepossessing location next to a flyover, this is a restaurant aiming for an upmarket, sophisticated ambience. Accordingly, there is glass-and-marble décor, formal service and a list of cocktails with names like 'elephant's trunk' and 'raj rascal'. The menu is fairly standard new-wave, with a range of tandoori dishes – including trout and quail – vegetarian thali and half a dozen specialities like bateer-e-khas, dryish spiced quail, or lamb chop bahar, cooked in fresh herbs and spices. The cooking is well above average. King prawn sukka is large slices of fresh prawns in thick, spicy sauce with spinach and tomato; lamb pasanda, made with slices of good quality lean lamb, comes in a mild creamy sauce. The nans and pilau rice have also impressed. House French is £4.95.

*Report forms are at the back of the book; write a letter if you prefer.*

CHEF: Abdul Kadir   PROPRIETOR: Abdul Muhim
OPEN: all week
CLOSED: Christmas Day
MEALS: 12.15 to 2.30, 6.15 to 11.30
PRICES: £10 (£16), Set L and D £10 (£13) to £12.50 (£16)
CARDS: Access, Amex, Diners, Visa
SEATS: 60. Private parties: 50 main room, 8 private room. Vegetarian meals. Children
welcome. Smart dress preferred. Wheelchair access (1 step; also WC). Music.
Air-conditioned

## Le Monde

60 St Mary Street, Cardiff CF1 1FE                    COOKING 1
CARDIFF (0222) 387376                                  COST £26

The latest addition to Benigno Martinez's cluster of informal eating places: a
fish restaurant found up a long flight of stairs by La Brasserie (see entry). It is
now thought by some to be the most popular, full every night of the week with
queuing for up to two hours at the weekends. In atmosphere and approach it is
broadly similar to the wine bar and brasserie downstairs: there is sawdust on
the floor, the charcoal grill in the kitchen is in view of the restaurant and the
wine list is an edited version of that downstairs. At the core of the menu is fish,
sold by the pound to be cooked on the grill, and prime cuts of meat, backed up
by a handful of fishy first courses, such as a soup potent with olive oil, peppers,
garlic, onion and tomato.

CHEF: Earl Smikle   PROPRIETOR: Benigno Martinez
OPEN: Mon to Sat
CLOSED: 25 Dec, 1 Jan
MEALS: 12 to 3, 7 to 12.30
PRICES: £17 (£22)
CARDS: Access, Amex, Diners, Visa
SEATS: 86. Private parties: 80 main room. No children under 10. Smart dress preferred.
Music. Air-conditioned

## Noble House

9–10 St David's House
Wood Street, Cardiff CF1 1ER                            COOKING 2
CARDIFF (0222) 388430                                   COST £17–£37

The Noble House may be 'the best Chinese restaurant in Cardiff', according to
one reader. It has the edge on others for service and setting, with its plush
décor. Spicy Szechuan prawns, sweet-and-sour pork, satay and spring rolls
have all been well liked recently. There are plenty of vegetarian dishes,
including several with a tofu base, as well as sizzling chicken, lamb and squid
and paper-wrapped prawns and aromatic duck. Sunday lunch is a buffet.
House French, £5.90. Private party rooms were expected to be open in the
summer of 1989 as the *Guide* went to press.

*See the inside of the front cover for an explanation of the new 1 to 5 rating system
recognising cooking standards.*

CHEF: K.M. Chung    PROPRIETORS: Charlen Ltd
OPEN: all week
MEALS: 12 to 2.30 (2.45 Sun), 6 to 11.30 (6.30 to 11 Sun)
PRICES: £13 (£22), Set L and D £12 (£17) to £25 (£31). Service 10%
CARDS: Access, Amex, Diners
SEATS: 80. Private parties: 80 main room. Vegetarian meals. Children's helpings (Sun only). Wheelchair access (also WC). Music. Self-service Sun buffet

## Salvatore

14 Romilly Crescent Canton
Cardiff CF1 9NR                                                          COOKING 1
CARDIFF (0222) 372768                                                       COST £35

Italian restaurants are now in a minority in Cardiff, so Salvatore's offers a useful alternative to exotic or French cuisine. At lunchtime it is a popular meeting place for business people. Mario Colayera, the long-time chef/proprietor, died in spring 1989, but his wife Elizabeth has taken over the running of the restaurant and there have been few changes. The menu remains strongly anglicised in conception and, some regret, in execution: dishes like roast duck with an apple and orange sauce, and calf's liver and onions are Italian in name but not, apparently, in character. But pasta is home made, there are daily specials such as crespella and marinated anchovies, and there have been good reports of dishes such as breast of veal stuffed with pork and spinach, and chicken with tarragon. The real attraction seems to be the range of fresh fish bought at Ashton fish market and displayed at the beginning of the meal to help customers choose. Again, it often has little or no association with Italian cooking – dressed crab, laverbread and cockles and tropical fish seem to appear as often as fritto misto – but does that matter in the end? More to the point, it is fresh and well cooked, usually plainly. There are a few Italian wines and more French. House Italian, £6.50. CELLARMAN'S CHOICE : Brunello di Montalcino 1983, Villa Banfi, £16.95.

CHEF: Robert Deacon    PROPRIETOR: Elizabeth Talfan Colayera
OPEN: Tue to Sat, exc Sat L
CLOSED: 2 weeks in summer
MEALS: 12.30 to 2, 7.30 to 10
PRICES: £19 (£29)
CARDS: Access, Amex, Diners, Visa
SEATS: 50. Private parties: 50 main room. Children's helpings. Wheelchair access. Music

## Tandoori Ghor

134 Whitchurch Road, Cardiff CF4 3LJ                                  COOKING 2
CARDIFF (0222) 615746                                                COST £13−£19

'The kitchen is wide open to the dining-room so that you can see the chef at work; the menu offers an interesting choice with emphasis on unusual tandoori dishes.' Thus wrote an enthusiastic visitor about the restaurant which was once a Greek taverna and still shows Artexed signs of its previous occupants. Shamsul Khan, the chef, is an engineer from Bangladesh. His style of cooking leans towards Burmese spicing and avoids the use of artificial colouring for marinated meats. Recommendations have come for the vegetable samosas, not stuffed with potato as is so often the case, with a very fine yoghurt ginger, garlic and mint dressing. Using filo pastry instead of the authentic Indian wrapping may be another sign of the previous occupants. Rice cookery, too, appears most skilled and chicken tikka masala was 'moist, tender, highly spiced and creamy'. One reader regretted that more use was not made of fresh coriander, funugreek and Indian parsley. Sweets are bought in; coffee is good even if the UHT cream is an abomination. House wine, £4.50.

CHEF: Shamsul Khan    PROPRIETORS: Shamsul and Tahmina Khan
OPEN: Mon to Sat D and Sun L
CLOSED: 25 and 26 Dec
MEALS: 12 to 3, 6 to 12 (1am Fri and Sat)
PRICES: £8 (£16), Set L £9 (£13). Minimum £4
CARDS: Access, Amex, Diners, Visa
SEATS: 40. Private parties: 50 main room. Vegetarian meals. Children's helpings.
No-smoking area. Wheelchair access (1 step; also WC). Music

---

CARMARTHEN  Dyfed                                          map 4

## ▲ Four Seasons, Cwmtwrch Farm Hotel

Nantgaredig, Carmarthen SA32 7NY
NANTGAREDIG (026 788) 238                              COOKING 1
on B4310, m N of A40, 5m E of Carmarthen         COST £15−£22

One set of outbuildings is bedrooms, another is a restaurant and kitchen, around about are 30 acres of farmland. Stone floors, stone walls, exposed beams and a wide conservatory impose a peaceful rurality and give views to the hillside. Aga cookery by Jenny Willmott and her daughter Emma has been epitomised as 'perfectly simple and simply perfect'. A short menu features sewin and lamb alongside the pâtés, avocado, Parma ham, and halibut and prawns in a cheese sauce that would sit more happily in a suburb further east. A short but helpful wine list includes house wine from the Bordelais at £5. Note that the telephone number will change to (0267 290) 238 in winter 1989.

CHEFS: Jenny and Emma Willmott    PROPRIETORS: Bill and Jenny Willmott
OPEN: Mon to Sat, D only
CLOSED: 2 weeks Mar
MEALS: 7.30 to 9.30
PRICES: Set D £11.50 (£15) to £13.50 (£18), Snacks from £2
SEATS: 52. 3 tables outside. Private parties: 42 main room, 10 and 42 private rooms. Car-park, 20 places. Vegetarian meals. Children's helpings (early). No children Sat D.
Wheelchair access (also WC)
ACCOMMODATION: 6 rooms, all with bath/shower. Rooms for disabled. B&B £20 to £38.
Deposit: £10. Baby facilities. Pets welcome. Afternoon teas. Garden. Air-conditioning.
Scenic

---

'Why is restaurant X in the Guide? This place is about design, not food. I liked the wood best.'  On dining in London

---

## Basil's Brasserie

| 2 Eastgate, Cowbridge CF7 7DG | COOKING 1 |
|---|---|
| COWBRIDGE (044 63) 3738 | COST £22 |

'At Basil's you can taste the difference,' according to their till print-out, but it's too soon to say with confidence how much things have altered under the new ownership of Alain Dubois of Bistro Twenty One, Bristol (see entry) and Philippe Harding. The style stays the same as hitherto, with food ordered at the bar and served by waitresses; nor does the essence of the extremely long, international menu appear to have changed. This free-ranging approach is very popular though its culinary success is less obvious: 'Sewin with bacon was served still crimped in a foil parcel … a difficult undertaking to unwrap but the result was worth it;' 'deep-fried potatoes with skins on were cooked to perfection;' 'excellent salad with mustardy dressing' are be balanced by 'steak with laverbread and pepper sauce (that) was chewy, with far too much pepper in the sauce, disappointing;' 'raspberry sorbet had run out so I was offered blackcurrant straight from the plastic tub into my glass, not very special;' and, 'an enterprising menu is perhaps more ambitious than the kitchen can support, the style is let down on the plate.' Puddings are only moderate, though there are lots of them. There is a short wine list with house French at £5.50.

CHEF: Dewi Morgan   PROPRIETORS: Alain Dubois and Philippe Harding
OPEN: Tue to Sun, exc Sun D
MEALS: 12 to 2 (2.30 Sun), 7 to 10
PRICES: £12 (£18)
CARDS: Access, Visa
SEATS: 80. Private parties: 28 main room. Car-park, 7 places. Vegetarian meals. Children's helpings. Wheelchair access (3 steps)

## Mulligan's

| Stalling Down, Cowbridge CF7 7DT | COOKING 1 |
|---|---|
| COWBRIDGE (044 63) 2221 | COST £28 |

Inland location and roadside setting may not seem promising for a British fish restaurant. Yet in this whitewashed house in a fork of the A48, you may get the best fish available in South Wales, driven up from Port Talbot fish market and Charles Sadler, supplier at Penarth. Book a table for the restaurant upstairs, alternatively sit downstairs, where there are no reservations, or go to the take-away window, which offers good battered cod, hake, skate or plaice and chips. Lobster, served three ways, and a much-praised fish soup are other specialities on the restaurant menu. The atmosphere is controlled but bustling, with service by busy young men in dark green aprons. House Duboeuf, £5.90.

CHEF: Tim Trezise   PROPRIETORS: Mr and Mrs G.A. Villa
OPEN: all week
MEALS: 12 to 2.15, 6.30 to 10.30
PRICES: £17 (£23)
CARDS: Access, Visa
SEATS: 120. Car-park, 20 places. Children's helpings. Wheelchair access (2 steps). Music

## DINAS MAWDDWY  Gwynedd

map 4

# *Old Station Coffee Shop*

Dinas Mawddwy SY20 9LS
DINAS MAWDDWY (065 04) 338

COOKING 1
COST £7

Eileen Minter's converted station house serves filling snacks rather than meals, but it is an invaluable little eating-place in a badly served area. The mainstays here are various wholemeal quiches, pizza with fresh herbs, filled jacket potatoes, various vegetable soups – parsnip and apple, for example – and a range of salads which come with a bowl of home-made mayonnaise. There is almost as wide a choice of home-baked biscuits and cakes, some of them Welsh, others in the wholefood vein, which can be eaten there or bought to take home. Portions are generous and prices very reasonable. There is a range of teas, coffees, and wine by the glass.

CHEF/PROPRIETOR: Eileen M.A. Minter
OPEN: all week, daytime only
CLOSED: mid-Nov to mid-Mar
MEALS: 9.30 to 5
PRICES: £4 (£6), Snacks from 35p. Service inc
SEATS: 36. 9 tables outside. Private parties: 16 main room. Car-park. Vegetarian meals. Children's helpings. No smoking. Wheelchair access (also WC). Self-service

## DOLGELLAU  Gwynedd

map 4

# ▲ *Abergwynant Hall*

Penmaenpool, Dolgellau LL40 1YF
DOLGELLAU (0341) 422238
on A493, 3m W of Dolgellau

COOKING 1
COST £13–£31

The warm crimson and green décor creates a comfortable country-home atmosphere in this solid granite house which dates from the 1860s. Diners in the conservatory at the back can glimpse a natural lake among trees in the large grounds. Despite a few hitches with the service, the overall impression is that the kitchen is still striving hard to use top-quality, fresh ingredients to good effect. Recent dishes include pink trout fillet poached in white wine on a red pepper sauce, and cassoulet of game. Fillet of beef with onions and mushrooms in a red wine sauce is tender and well-flavoured. A vegetarian main course is always on offer. A short dessert selection includes dark chocolate cups with nutty hazelnut mousse on pale green minted cream; alternatively choose from Welsh cheese or Stilton. House wine, £6.50, and there's an additional list of 60-plus, mostly under £10.

*'This restaurant changed hands approximately three weeks ago and appears to have taken a conscious decision to head for the lower end of the market. To quote the manager/owner, "We don't want to bother with these soufflé and mousse things."'* On dining in West Yorkshire

CHEF: Peter Roberts  PROPRIETORS: Mary and Jonathan Saddington
OPEN: Tue to Sat, D only and Sun L
MEALS: 12.30 to 2.30, 7 to 9.30
PRICES: Set Sun L £8.50 (£13), Set D £15.50 (£21) to £20.50 (£26)
CARD: Access
SEATS: 60. Private parties: 30 main room, 30 private room. Car-park, 12 places. Children's helpings. No smoking in dining-room. Wheelchair access (also WC)
ACCOMMODATION: 5 rooms, all with bath/shower. B&B £30 to £55. Deposit: 10%. Baby facilities. Afternoon teas. Garden. Swimming-pool. Fishing. Golf. Snooker. Scenic. Doors close at 11. Confirm by 6

## Dylanwad Da

| | |
|---|---|
| 2 Smithfield Street, Dolgellau LL40 1BS | COOKING 2 |
| DOLGELLAU (0341) 422870 | COST £19 |

Rechristened 'A Good Influence' by its new owner, a young Welshman called Dylan Rowlands (formerly at Abergwynant Hall, above), this friendly and informal restaurant is said by enthusiastic customers to live up to its name through the food. The dinner menu may not make a great impression of Welshness, and the inherited décor is ordinary pine bistro, but the cooking carries all before it and the friendly bilingual staff bend over backwards to be helpful. 'We were unable to find fault with any of the intriguing dishes that we sampled,' concluded one report. Another dinner in May was excellent, if almost too rich and filling. A first-course crab tartlet was a large tender pastry shell with a creamy, tasty filling and a bubbling topping of Welsh Cheddar cheese; a main course of spiced lamb looked like a plate of brown stew, but the combination of banana and pineapple in the mildly curried sauce was delicious; other dishes of chicken tagliatelle and breast of chicken with leek and Pernod sauce turned out to be equally good. Home-made cognac and honey ice-cream, steamed chocolate pudding and chilled orange and Cointreau custard have won special commendation for the desserts. There is quiet piped music in the background and smoking is discouraged. The wine list is as good value as the food. House French, from £5.60.

CHEF/PROPRIETOR: Dylan Rowlands
OPEN: D only; all week in summer, Tue to Sat in mid-season, Thur to Sat in winter
MEALS: 7 to 9.30
PRICES: £11 (£16)
SEATS: 30. Private parties: 30 main room. Vegetarian meals. Children's helpings. Music

## ▲ George III Hotel

| | |
|---|---|
| Penmaenpool, Dolgellau LL40 1YD | |
| DOLGELLAU (0341) 422525 | COOKING 1 |
| on A4935 2m W of Dolgellau | COST £11−£24 |

Newly decked out in Sanderson fabrics, this hotel serves food in the restaurant, the Welsh Dresser Bar and the Cellar Bar. 'Spend here your measure of time and treasure, and taste the treats of Penmaenpool,' wrote Gerard Manley Hopkins, quoted proudly in the brochure. The chief virtue is being open almost every day of the year, 'most unusual in these parts', commented one Merioneth resident. Sunday lunch is an especial bargain, the only lunch served in the restaurant itself, but bar food is ample and also good value. Dinner in the restaurant is more expensive and covers a much wider range. It has been criticised for inconsistency, but it is *there*. A fair wine list, showing fondness for Roederer Champagnes, Heemskirk Cabernet Sauvignon from Tasmania and Pierre Ponnelle burgundies. Parents should note that, due to pressure from the town's constabulary to enforce the law to the letter, children under 14 may not enter the bar, but may consume their bar lunches in the restaurant. House wine, £6.25. See under Penmaenpool in *The Good Hotel Guide*.

CHEF: David Collett  PROPRIETOR: Gail Hall
OPEN: Mon to Sat, D only and Sun L
CLOSED: Christmas and New Year
MEALS: 12.30 to 2, 7.15 to 8.45
PRICES: £14 (£20), Set L £6 (£11), Snacks from £1. Minimum £6. Service 10%
CARDS: Access, Amex, Visa
SEATS: 46. 15 tables outside. Private parties: 20 main room. Car-park, 100 places.
Children's helpings. Smart dress preferred. Wheelchair access (1 step; also WC)
ACCOMMODATION: 12 rooms, 10 with bath/shower. Rooms for disabled. B&B to £35.
Deposit: £20. Baby facilities. Pets welcome. Garden. Fishing. TV. Phone. Scenic. Doors
close at 11.30. Confirm by 6 [GHG]

---

**GLANWYDDEN** Gwynedd                                           map 4

# *Queen's Head*

| Glanwydden LL31 9JP | COOKING 1 |
| LLANDUDNO (0492) 46570 | COST £20 |

Here, in a village inn with pews, settles and stools squeezed in around dark polished tables and with flowers and stuffed animals for decoration, is pub cooking as it should be. Unpretentious, ranging from open prawn sandwiches and crab or lobster salads to Sunday roasts and daily specials like chicken and leek pie, the food is largely based on fresh and local produce. Prize-winning Conway mussels, sauté in garlic butter and topped with smoked cheese, remain a favourite, but look to the blackboard for the best choices. There are well over a dozen home-made puddings, including lethal chocolate and brandy or orange and Grand Marnier trifles, treacle tart and fruit crumbles. House wine from £6.25 a litre. CELLARMAN'S CHOICE : Chardonnay 1987, Vin de Pays d'Oc, Duboeuf, £7.25; Ch. Dantugnac 1985, Dulong, £5.45.

CHEFS: Robert F.W. Cureton and Bryn Powell  PROPRIETOR: Robert F.W. Cureton
OPEN: all week
MEALS: 12 to 2.15, 7 (6.30 Sat) to 11 (9 Sat and Sun)
PRICES: £12 (£17), Snacks from £1.10
CARDS: Access, Visa
SEATS: 120. 12 tables outside. Private parties: 26 main room. Car-park, 25 places. No
children under 14. Music

---

'*I hung back to talk a little with the owners, and try to figure out why the place seems so . . . well . . . unprofessional. It's because it is unprofessional.*' On inspecting in the Scottish Highlands

## ▲ *Castle Cottage*

Pen Llech, Harlech LL46 2YL
HARLECH (0766) 780479

COOKING 2
COST £15–£20

An inspector commented after dining in sight of Edward I's masterpiece of a castle, 'The food would go down well in any part of Britain. In this part of Wales it is truly outstanding.' Low-beamed, with floral curtains and pink tablecloths, the dining-room of this small restaurant with rooms sets a deceptively cottagey mood. But the menu, for set-price dinners only, is more sophisticated than homely, more French than British. Jim Yuill, chef and proprietor, is proud of reliance on fresh and often local ingredients, and reports on the cooking have been unanimously good. For the first course, there have been stuffed crêpes, gratin of local sea bass, pâtés, roulades, grilled goats' cheese and the like. Main dishes, mainly meat and poultry, often come traditionally sauced: cream and dill for salmon or a fricassee of monkfish and prawns, vermouth and orange for duck, red wine for beef. The home-made ice-cream apparently stands out among the desserts and lives up to its reputation. For those who stay overnight, reveille is accompanied by a proper breakfast. There is a nice, short wine list, half of it French, the other half from round the world. Prices are very fair. There are 10 Italians that would fit every bill. House French is £5.50. CELLARMAN'S CHOICE : Côtes de Thongue, Cuvée de l'Arjolles 1986, £8.50; Gattinara 1980, Umberto Fiore, £9.75.

CHEF: Jim Yuill   PROPRIETORS: Jim and Betty Yuill
OPEN: all week, D only
MEALS: 7 to 9.30
PRICES: Set D £10.50 (£15) to £12.50 (£17)
CARDS: Access, Visa
SEATS: 34. 4 tables outside. Private parties: 40 main room. Children's helpings. No smoking in dining-room. Wheelchair access. Music
ACCOMMODATION: 6 rooms, 4 with bath/shower. B&B £15 to £32. Deposit: 25%. Baby facilities. Pets welcome. Scenic. Doors close at midnight

## ▲ *The Cemlyn* ❦

High Street, Harlech LL46 2YA
HARLECH (0766) 780425

COOKING 3
COST £19–£26

Some restaurateurs are their best apologists and Ken Goody, burly, bearded, cheerful and generous, is one of those. 'I get a little weary of pompous menus – everything stuffed, wrapped, laid on and covered with something else. We simply offer good sauces plus a simple individual onion quiche with our lamb, or a pastry case of oyster mushrooms with a steak, for example. There is only me cooking, so I'm forced to keep things simple (and that shows up any flaw in the raw materials). So often when I eat out, everything seems to taste the same and one only knows one has reached the pudding because it is sweet.' This would not be quoted if it did not have the concurrence of many other, disinterested, reporters. When the 1989 season opened, this restaurant that looks out over Tremadoc Bay (the no-smoking room has the best view), 'was packed with people like us, locals who enjoy it as the best in Gwynedd. He *is* good, you know, constantly worried that things aren't good enough – but pear and parsley soup (far too much, as usual) flavoured delicately with curry, was delicious, as was the home-made roll and Welsh butter. Gressingham duck, crispy and crunchy, honey and orangey skin, carrots in Martini went beautifully with it, and five other clean-tasting vegetables. Some good, not expensive wines. I was seduced by a butterscotch and dried fruit pudding with toffee sauce and am still groaning happily.' Correspondents are impressed by how well the whole experience hangs together but there is quite a lot of food, and it will take four hours to do the meal justice. Indeed, it may take as long as that just to absorb the walls of pictures and the bric-à-brac (lots of frogs). The cooking has little side to it, the menu reads straightforwardly and frankly. There is a soup to begin, perhaps gazpacho, or cream of pea (with an alternative, for instance artichoke vinaigrette), then a second course that may involve shellfish (crab mayonnaise, scallops and salmon thermidor), or a warm quail salad or home-cured gravlax. The main course does seem simple on the surface but is redeemed by accurate cooking, generosity, and at least one well-chosen accompaniment (that duck, for instance, came with a sage, apple and onion purée and glazed peaches). Vegetables are plentiful and desserts are quite substantial – ice-creams rather than sorbets (with sauces too), a mousse in a pie, some good double cream as well as crème fraîche. Cheeses are British, not just Welsh. The wine list seems to continue this ability to offer good things without charging the universe. It is not very long, but every section (and it goes to Australia, the United States, Chile and Bulgaria) has something that could be strongly recommended: the Recioto della Valpolicella 1982; the Brezème 1983; the halves of Ch. Rieussec 1983 and Don Zoilo fino. There are six house wines, from £6 to £7. CELLARMAN'S CHOICE : Alsace Riesling Réserve 1984, Rolly Gassmann, £11; Bourgogne Passe-tout-grains 1986, Henri Jayer, £11.

CHEF/PROPRIETOR: Ken Goody
OPEN: all week, D only
CLOSED: Jan to Easter
MEALS: 7 to 9.30
PRICES: Set D £13 (£19) to £16 (£22)
CARDS: Access, Visa
SEATS: 36. 3 tables outside. Private parties: 40 main room, 10 private room. Children's helpings. No smoking in 1 dining-room. Wheelchair access (also WC)
ACCOMMODATION: 2 rooms, 1 with bath/shower. B&B £18 to £30. No children under 8. Golf. TV. Scenic. Doors close at midnight. Confirm by 6

---

**HAVERFORDWEST Dyfed**                                          map 4

## Jemima's

Nash Grove, Freystrop
Haverfordwest SA62 4HB
HAVERFORDWEST (0437) 891109                        COOKING 1
S of Haverfordwest, on the Burton road                    COST £22

They have been known to cook duck here, although the comments of customers must be predictable. Indeed, duck terrine has been praised as well as breast of duck with a blackcurrant sauce. A very short menu in this not very beautiful building on what is known as Puddleduck Hill, keeps options open by having one-third of its first courses as 'mixed hors d'oeuvre'. The approach and service are as fresh and natural as the food: a watercress and sorrel soup tasted as it ought, vegetables and herbs come from the garden, the fish is worth its catching. A short wine list offers a Gevrey Chambertin at £14 'for those with money as well as taste'. House Duboeuf is £5.50. CELLARMAN'S CHOICE : Peter Lehmann Shiraz-Cabernet 1984, £7; João Pires Dry Muscat 1987, £6.70.

CHEF: Ann Owston   PROPRIETORS: Ann Owston, Wendy and April Connelly
OPEN: Tue to Sat, D only
MEALS: 7 to 9
PRICES: Set D £12.50 (£18)
CARD: Access
SEATS: 20. Private parties: 26 main room. Car-park, 10 places. Children welcome. No smoking in dining-room

## ▲ *Sutton Lodge*

| Portfield Gate, Haverfordwest SA62 3LN | COOKING 1 |
| HAVERFORDWEST (0437) 68548 | COST £22 |

This early-nineteenth-century country house, a mile west of Haverfordwest, had a brief spell as a health farm before turning into a seven-bedroom hotel and restaurant at the end of 1988. The original kitchen, dominated by a restored, unused cooking range, is the current dining-room, but a new kitchen and larger dining-room are under construction. At the time of writing, a stop-gap operation was under way, with a no-choice four-course menu for £13.50. Preferences are stated when booking, and no offence is taken if a table is cancelled because the food does not appeal. Local produce – Ramsey Island crab, fresh sewin wrapped in filo pastry, smoked Welsh cheeses and meats – is interwoven with gazpacho, smoked duck confit, and Bakewell tart with blackcurrant crème anglaise, to produce a fabric that is simple, honest and unostentatious. The relaxed air of homely comfort can be deceptive: the place is properly run. There is a minimal wine list. House Duboeuf, £5.15.

CHEF: Stanford Moseley   PROPRIETORS: Stapal Hotels Ltd
OPEN: all week, D only
CLOSED: Jan
MEALS: 6.30 to 9
PRICES: Set D £13.50 (£18)
CARDS: Access, Amex
SEATS: 12. Private parties: 10 main room. Car-park, 10 places. No children under 12. Music
ACCOMMODATION: 6 rooms, all with bath/shower. B&B £27.50 to £50. No children under 12. Pets welcome. TV. Scenic

*Consumers' Association is planning a* Vegetarian Good Food Guide, *to cafés and restaurants offering at least one vegetarian main course. Please send reports and recommendations to* The Vegetarian Good Food Guide, FREEPOST, *2 Marylebone Road, London NW1 1YN.*

LALESTON  Mid Glamorgan                                    map 4

# Great House

High Street, Laleston CF32 0HP                   COOKING  1
BRIDGEND (0656) 57644                           COST  £12−£30

Restaurants, as this one, that leave envelopes addressed to this and other
guides in their reception areas for merry customers to inform us of their jolly
nights out, tend to spoil the system. We sent an inspector. Through the self-
satisfaction, sexism and moderate taste, she descried a place that may do at a
pinch in the district. The cooking is that restaurant-sub-culture version of
modern European, often described fulsomely on the menu: deep-fried avocado
with a light garlic dressing; melon and kiwi cocktail with a strawberry coulis;
or finely chopped leg of lamb mixed with blackcurrants and wrapped in filo,
then baked before serving on a blackcurrant sauce. Some positive attributes,
though, are identified: a remarkable conversion of a fine house; a willing staff;
good value, especially at lunch and in the coffee-shop; decent coffee; main
courses of stir-fried pork in cream and herbs and fried plaice rolled in oats and
sesame seed that had no hint of greasiness; and a fair wine list. Signs there are,
though, of over-selling and compromise. 'One of only two restaurants I know
in south Wales where evening dress is the norm!' House wine is French, £5.20.
CELLARMAN'S CHOICE : House claret, £9; house Champagne, £11.50.

CHEFS: Barry Bingham, Steven Mudd and Norma Bond   PROPRIETORS: Stephen and
Norma Bond
OPEN: Mon to Sat, exc Sat L
MEALS: 12 to 2, 6.30 to 9.30 (9.45 Sat)
PRICES: £19 (£25), Set L £7.95 (£12) and £8.95 (£13), Set D £12.95 (£18), Snacks from £2
CARDS: Access, Diners, Visa
SEATS: 120. 3 tables outside. Private parties: 80 main room, 40 private room. Car-park, 30
places. Children's helpings. Wheelchair access (2 steps; also WC). Music

LLANBERIS  Gwynedd                                         map 4

# Y Bistro

43−45 High Street, Llanberis LL55 4EU           COOKING  2
LLANBERIS (0286) 871278                         COST  £20−£28

The modest shop-front entrance is deceptive; inside is large enough to lose a
few armchairs. The atmosphere is homely and relaxed, the food loyally Welsh,
reflecting the surroundings − the edge of Snowdonia National Park in a former
slate-mining area. It also reflects the conviction of Nerys Roberts 'to promote
and use local Welsh produce and adapt old recipes, ie local meat, game and
fish, Welsh cheeses, Snowdon pudding etc.' This does not mean a diet of leeks
and laverbread; instead chicken breast comes with Pencarreg cheese, and
spring lamb is a feature. Vegetarian dishes are prepared on request (clearly
stated on the menu), and fish varies with the market, but pan-fried oyster
mushrooms with asparagus sauce, and foil-baked Dover sole with lovage,
indicate the style. Perhaps some indication of the Welsh attitude to puddings
can be gained from the description by one reporter of a sponge as 'nicely
heavy'. Welsh wine is conspicuous by its absence from the 60-bottle list, but

there is an English wine, and good choice at reasonable prices throughout. House Vaucluse is £5.75. CELLARMAN'S CHOICE : Montana Chardonnay 1987, £11.55; Szegedi Cabernet 1985, £8.70. See also Y Bistro Bach, Caernarfon.

CHEF: Nerys Roberts   PROPRIETORS: Danny and Nerys Roberts
OPEN: Tue to Sat, D only
CLOSED: Christmas week
MEALS: 7 to 9.30
PRICES: Set D £15.75 (£20) to £18 (£23). Licensed, also bring your own: corkage £2
CARDS: Access, Visa
SEATS: 48. Private parties: 36 main room, 20 private room. Vegetarian meals. Children welcome. Smart dress preferred. Wheelchair access (2 steps). Music. Air-conditioned

---

**LLANDDERFEL  Gwynedd**                                           map 4

# ▲ *Palé Hall*

Llandderfel LL23 7PS                                          COOKING 1
LLANDDERFEL (067 83) 285                                      COST £18−£37

There can't be many hotels where the bar is constructed from marble fireplaces torn out of the bedrooms in the course of refurbishment. Palé Hall, at the end of a long and rutted drive on the banks of the Dee as it emerges from its mountain fastness of Lake Bala, is the place to see one. For all that, the architecture – late-Victorian that has crypto-Lutyensesque touches and some superb interiors – is magnificent. New ownership has brought a friendliness and warmth previously lacking, as well as real flowers and a better sense of sympathetic furnishing and ornament. The Hall also sports an amazing round bath with a gold-plated phoenix for taps. The cooking does not quite match the supercharged environment. It is never incompetent but it is low-key. An inspection meal of mushrooms in garlic and white wine sauce; breast of chicken stuffed with a duxelles and a sherry cream sauce; and strawberry Pavlova certainly pleased, even if it did not excite. It may be a reflection on the customers as much as on the kitchen that in the same week (in May) blackberries could serve as an accompaniment to chicken-liver pâté and to a fan of melon. The wine list ranges over the world, with not many halves (but too many aged whites). Almost the most interesting selections are in fact the house Bordeaux, organic both, Ch. La Gorre 1987 (white) and Ch. St Jean d'Aumières Coteaux de Languedoc (red), each at £7.50.

CHEF: Bryn Roberts   PROPRIETORS: Timothy and Jain Ovens
OPEN: all week
MEALS: 12 to 2, 7 to 9.30
PRICES: £21 (£31), Set L £12.50 (£18), Set D £21 (£27). Licensed, also bring your own: corkage £4
CARDS: Access, Amex, Diners, Visa
SEATS: 50. Private parties: 50 main room, 24 and 45 private rooms. Car-park, 150 places. Vegetarian meals. No smoking in dining-room. Wheelchair access
ACCOMMODATION: 17 rooms, all with bath/shower. Lift. B&B £88 to £120. Deposit: £20. Afternoon teas. Garden. Sauna. Fishing. TV. Phone. Scenic. Doors close at 12.30am

---

*'There is a choice of wines: red or white. Clearly the proprietors know their limitations.'*  On dining in Hereford & Worcester

---

LLANDEILO  Dyfed                                                      map 4

## Millers Braseria

Old School, Carmarthen Street Llandeilo
SA19 6AN                                              COOKING  1
LLANDEILO (0558) 822159                               COST  £24

In Wales there is a school of thought that spells brasserie the Italian way. It
does not seem to denote a difference in style – British all the way – but this
happy place produces good fish, properly cooked asparagus, and pheasant eggs
for an egg mayonnaise with a difference. The romantic might think that the egg
were the harvest of woodland wanders; doubtless the game-bird hatchery is
the true source. House wine is £4.95. Coffee is unlimited.

CHEFS: James Thomas and Sian Jones   PROPRIETORS: James and Shann Thomas
OPEN: Tue to Sun, D only
MEALS: 6.30 to 10.30
PRICES: £15 (£20). Snacks from £3.95
CARD: Access
SEATS: 50. Private parties: 50 main room. Car-park, 8 places. Children's helpings on
request. Smart dress preferred. No-smoking area. Wheelchair access (1 step, also WC).
Music

---

LLANDEWI SKIRRID  Gwent                                               map 4

## Walnut Tree Inn 🍾

Llandewi Skirrid NP7 8AW
ABERGAVENNY (0873) 2797                               COOKING  4
on B4521, 2m NE of Abergavenny                        COST  £40

*(COUNTY OF THE YEAR RESTAURANT)*

Any restaurant that persists as long as the Walnut Tree will garner a variety of
opinions and wise observations on whether it is on the up or the down of a
cycle of culinary invention. In reality, consistency is its finest achievement,
closely followed by its redefinition of pub food. Year in, year out, the
Taruschios delegate little, take few holidays and please vast numbers of
customers. Debate centres on the lack of silver cutlery, silver service and silver
tongues. The majority are simply grateful that so masterful a cook is prepared to
continue plying his trade in so accessible a fashion. It may be crowded, it may
be noisy, the colour schemes may not be the product of ineffable taste, but the
service is kindly and informed, the building as clean as a new pin, the food
brilliant and the wine list as good to drink from as it is to read – Bill Baker's
comments are sharp. Popularity and choice are the keys to a long menu of more
than 30 dishes, with fresh foods that reflect the seasons as much as the locality.
Franco Taruschio's cooking may have an Italian cast (with a certain Thai and
Far Eastern tilt as well), but he has adopted local suppliers and specialities:
Glamorgan sausages are there as well as bresaola. It is a restaurant that has
drawn people back over a period of more than two decades. One inspector
wrote, 'There were one or two quite subtle changes to the menu. Scallops
lightly flavoured with garlic was particularly enjoyable, the crispy crab
pancake was bigger than usual and full of flavour. The fresh salmon in garlic
butter was cooked and flavoured to perfection and the papillote of turbot and

salmon, placed in layers in a wrapping of lettuce leaves and then lightly poached – also a new addition to the menu – was superbly cooked and presented. Once again, my faith is restored.' Meals can encompass a great range of skills and experience: trenette con pesto are folds of very narrow pasta with a central mound of pesto eloquent of basil and olive oil; Thai pork appetisers are three little cups of lettuce leaves filled with spiced minced pork – redolent of haggis to one Scot; the brodetto is a 'huge sizzling and steaming mixture of fish and shellfish in an earthenware dish with an appetising smell of garlic, tomato and fish.' After a meal that sounds as good as this, the chef can then produce a cassata pronounced 'the best item on the menu'. Other puddings are equally praised, for instance a fruit terrine of oranges, strawberries and mango set in a jelly with balls of mango sorbet and an orange coulis. As one reporter remarked, 'Nothing oversweet, everything light, fresh and real.' Some find flavourings too muted on occasion or the style of cooking less elaborate (and thus less worthy of accolade) than haute cuisine. Ignore this; the Taruschios are angels. The wine list is a cracker: mature burgundies, clarets and Rhônes, a fine slate of Italians old and new, many imported only by the Taruschios, all at sensible prices. Good bottles and interesting ideas leap out from every page. Half-bottles are not forgotten though, perforce, are less exciting save for a few mature clarets. Some have hoped that storage of old bottles may become more controlled after seeing 1961s in racks in the restaurant itself. Others would like better glasses. House Italian is £7.50 a litre. Some strangers have felt they are treated with more indifference than those who have been before.

CHEF: Franco Taruschio  PROPRIETORS: Franco and Ann Taruschio
OPEN: Tue to Sat
CLOSED: 2 weeks Feb
MEALS: 12 to 2.30, 7.15 to 10
PRICES: £25 (£33). Cover £1
SEATS: 80. 5 tables outside. Private parties: 30 main room. Car-park, 60 places. Children's helpings. Wheelchair access (also WC). Air-conditioned

---

**LLANDRILLO  Clwyd**                                                                                 map 4

## ▲ Tyddyn Llan

Llandrillo LL21 0ST
LLANDRILLO (049 084) 264
on B4401 at end of village; turn off                                    COOKING 2
A5 at Corwen                                                            COST £15–£26

Were it not for the bedrooms, places like this would have a struggle, amidst mountain, lake and rushing torrent, to generate sufficient income, however reasonable their charges. Bridget Kindred has handed over most of the cooking to David Barratt, but the style remains the same: a *prix fixe* dinner menu of four or five choices, and a cheaper Sunday lunch. Hot spiced crab with fresh ginger; oysters baked with cream and Parmesan; sauté of lambs' kidneys and liver with Marsala; Gressingham duck glazed with honey and peppercorns and served with cognac and orange sauce; an excellent though small choice of British farmhouse cheeses and a strawberry and raspberry soufflé have been judged very enjoyable, the more so for the relaxed pace and easy manners of

Peter Kindred. Fires burn much of the time, endless outdoor pursuits beckon, the narrow winding roads make return home unenviable; much better to stay. The wine list numbers more than 80 bins and is by no means confined to France, nor even Europe. House wines, from £6.50. CELLARMAN'S CHOICE : Pouilly Vinzelles 1986, Bouchard, £13.25; Valpolicella Superiore 1984, Bolla, £10.35.

CHEFS: David Barratt and Bridget Kindred   PROPRIETORS: Peter and Bridget Kindred
OPEN: all week D, Sun L, L snacks Wed to Sat
CLOSED: Mon and Tue, Nov to Mar (exc residents)
MEALS: 12.30 to 2, 7 to 9.30
PRICES: Set Sun L £10 (£15), Set D £14 (£20) to £15.50 (£22)
CARDS: Access, Visa
SEATS: 35. Private parties: 45 main room. Car-park, 25 places. Vegetarian meals. Children's helpings. Smart dress preferred. Wheelchair access. Music
ACCOMMODATION: 9 rooms, all with bath/shower. B&B £33.75 to £60. Deposit: 10%. Baby facilities. Afternoon teas. Garden. Fishing. Phone. Scenic. Doors close at midnight. Confirm by 6 [GHG]

---

**LLANDUDNO  Gwynedd**                                                                      map 4

## ▲ *Bodysgallen Hall* ♥

Deganwy, Llandudno LL30 1RS
DEGANWY (0492) 84466
from A55 join new A470 and follow                                          COOKING 3
Llandudno signposts; hotel 1m on R                                         COST £15–£31

The stairs in the tower at the centre of the hall begin Victorian and get progressively older: six centuries in six floors. From the top, Conwy castle and the Telford and Stephenson bridges waltz in unlikely harmony. Around the base, terraces of gardens and restored parkland are themselves worth the visit. For a hotel owned by a group with an eye to conferences and overseas markets, Bodysgallen retains strong ties of affection and esteem among local supporters. 'After 40 meals, I consider the past *Guide* rating too low,' remarked one of these. The staff are singled out for their willingness and smartness, even if the occasional tyro is silent or nervous. Martin James's cooking has continued in the vein that was established many years ago – itself a tribute to sensitive management. Local suppliers are nurtured, yet supplemented by outside reinforcements, and the cooking is an exemplar of the British tendency. All this is done at a price, Sunday lunch in particular, not often matched by similar places across the border. From a more than adequate range of dishes in a fixed-price menu, the style is seen. Leek and potato soup with a julienne of chicken and thyme; a salad of cold roast quail with a mushroom mousse with a herb yoghurt dressing; fillet of salmon topped with laver-bread with a white wine sauce; veal with a brandy and mixed peppercorn sauce; mille-feuille of hot spiced mango. Occasional comments have rated the presentation higher than the flavour. The wine list is strongest in claret (including a range of Gruaud Larose back to 1962) but is fairly evenly spread, taking in countries other than France in its 250 bins: it does its job well. There is a Welsh wine, Croffta. The Jean Léon Cabernet Sauvignon from Penedès 1979 will out-perform any of the French bottles at the same price (and more). They have a good range of dessert

617

wines, including the rarely met Ch. de la Roulerie 1984 from the little-known appellation Coteaux du Layon Chaume, a slightly lower ranking AOC to Quarts de Chaume and Bonnezeaux. House Bordeaux £8.70. CELLARMAN'S CHOICE : Cassis, clos Ste-Magdeleine 1985, £15.25; Savigny-lès-Beaune *premier cru* 1984, Vollet, £28.05.

CHEF: Martin James  PROPRIETORS: Historic House Hotels
OPEN: all week
MEALS: 12.30 to 2, 7.30 to 9.45
PRICES: Set L £10.50 (£15) to £13.75 (£18), Set D £21.50 (£26) Service inc
CARDS: Access, Amex, Diners, Visa
SEATS: 62. Private parties: 48 main room, 2 private room. Car-park, 50 places. No children under 8. Smart dress preferred. No cigars/pipes in dining-room. Wheelchair access. Music
ACCOMMODATION: 28 rooms, all with bath/shower. Rooms for disabled. B&B £68 to £103. No children under 8. Pets welcome. Afternoon teas. Garden. Tennis. TV. Phone. Scenic. Confirm by 5 [GHG]

## *Craigside Manor*

Colwyn Road, Little Orme
Llandudno LL30 3AL                                                COOKING 1
LLANDUDNO (0492) 45943                                          COST £11–£28

Once a convent, always with glorious views of the sunset across Llandudno Bay, now a restaurant with bar and function suite – whose disco beat may intrude on the pleasure of those eating downstairs. The conversion is in public-house style. Food in the bar is as popular as it is in the restaurant, better value and more quickly served. The restaurant appears to have been through so uneven a patch that the presence of David Harding, who made his reputation at Bodysgallen Hall close by, has been queried. Some good and straightforward Sunday lunches have been noted, also individual dishes such as a warm salad of duck and chicken livers with quail eggs and bacon, scallops on a bed of mange-tout and asparagus, and monkfish in garlic sauce. Depressing, though, have been veal that would do the poorest trattoria discredit; commercial ice-cream; and insufficient wines kept ready for service. The service, too, has reflected the slowness of the kitchen. So, although still a place to find an adequate meal, it is by no means the automatic choice in Llandudno. The wine list covers a fair range, burgundies largely by Louis Jadot. There is a special selection of medium-priced bottles from Bulgaria, Australia, Portugal and the Rhône. House French, £5.95. CELLARMAN'S CHOICE : Ch. Guibeau, Puisseguin-St-Emilion 1985, £12.50.

CHEF: David Harding  PROPRIETORS: Mr and Mrs Ward
OPEN: all week, exc Sun D
MEALS: 12 to 2, 7.30 to 9.45 (10 Sat)
PRICES: £19 (£23), Set L £7.95 (£11). Service inc
CARDS: Access, Amex, Diners, Visa
SEATS: 60. Private parties: 20 main room, 120 private room. Car-park, 120 places. Vegetarian meals. Children's helpings. Smart dress preferred. Wheelchair access (3 steps; also WC). Music

▲ *This symbol means accommodation is available.*

## ▲ St Tudno Hotel

North Parade, Llandudno LL30 2LP          COOKING 1
LLANDUDNO (0492) 74411          COST £17–£40

From the outside, this is a classic seaside hotel on the main promenade. Once you have left behind the sea air and the gulls, much of the hotel's Victorianism drops away. No more so than in the dining-room, decorated in cool shades of green, like a trompe-l'oeil conservatory with hanging plants, cane chairs and trellis wallpaper to match. The cooking is a blend of the old and new with a Welsh streak in both produce and ideas: Anglesey scallops and oysters, locally smoked meats and traditional roasts, as many as nine Welsh farmhouse cheeses. Apart from this, dishes have a modern feel and are deliberately being pushed in a healthy direction. Fillet of sole is steamed and served on a fresh red and yellow pepper sauce, beef is filled with pine kernels and finished with a tomato and yoghurt sauce, medallions of lamb come with a crab timbale. Desserts are, by contrast, usually rich and creamy. One reader likened the procedure for booking to that of immigration: 'More bother than the Canadian authorities.' The wine list is of decent length and mainly French. CELLARMAN'S CHOICE : Mâcon Chameroy 1986, Latour £12; Bourgogne Rouge, Champs Perdrix 1985, £11.50.

CHEF: John Gabbatt    PROPRIETORS: Martin and Janette Bland
OPEN: all week
CLOSED: Christmas and New Year
MEALS: 12.30 to 1.45, 6.45 to 9.30 (9 Sun)
PRICES: £23 (£33), Set Sun L £10.25 (£17), Set D £17.50 (£25)
CARDS: Access, Amex, Visa
SEATS: 60. Private parties: 45 main room. Car-park, 4 places. Vegetarian meals. Children's helpings. No children under 5. Smart dress preferred. No smoking. Wheelchair access. Air-conditioned
ACCOMMODATION: 21 rooms, all with bath/shower. Lift. B&B £49 to £70. Deposit: £25. Baby facilities. Afternoon teas. Swimming-pool. TV. Phone. Scenic. Doors close at midnight. Confirm by 2 [GHG]

---

LLANGOLLEN Clwyd          map 4

## Caesar's

Deeside Lane, Llangollen LL20 8PN          COOKING 1
LLANGOLLEN (0978) 860133          COST £22

Hard by the falls on the River Dee, which provide a soothing view and mellifluous backdrop of sound in the small and cosy, but not overcrowded restaurant. Comments on the food are consistently keen: 'salmon terrine set off visually and by taste with two sauces (beurre blanc and watercress)'; 'chicken with garlic, crisp on the outside, tender and juicy inside with a well-reduced sauce'; 'chocolate pudding the best I've had'. Service can be patchy. House French is £5.45. CELLARMAN'S CHOICE : Ch. Thieuley, Cépage Sauvignon, 1987, £8.95; Penedès 1975, Ferret i Mateau, £9.50.

---

*See the back of the* Guide *for an index of restaurants listed.*

---

CHEFS: R.J. Hendey, J. Robbins and S. Plevin   PROPRIETORS: G. Hughes, B.P. Hughes and R.J. Hendey
OPEN: all week, D only
MEALS: 6.30 to 9.30
PRICES: Set D £14.95 (£18). Service inc
CARDS: Access, Visa
SEATS: 28. Private parties: 28 main room. Children's helpings. Wheelchair access. Music

## ▲ Gales ❢

| 18 Bridge Street, Llangollen LL20 8PF | COOKING 1 |
| LLANGOLLEN (0978) 860089 | COST £14 |

A background buzz of Welsh in this wine bar-cum-bed-and-breakfast proves beyond doubt that locals eat here. The bedrooms have been comfortably refurbished and the pictures by local artists that line the oak-panelled walls downstairs are for sale – to buyers who can lay their hands on a cool thousand. The food, however, is far more affordable, with a top main dish price of around a fiver. On the blackboard are salads, cold dishes and hot specials – perhaps Italian minced beef with a cheese and pasta topping – all keeping up to standard. Desserts are home made: chocolate mint cheesecake, for example. There is a list of 90 wines as well as a dozen by the glass, spread among all major producing regions. They are very fairly priced. The star, however, is a 'fine wine list', the biggest sections being claret and port, where some very interesting bottles are offered at no more than retail rates: from a Ch. Pape-Clément 1961 to a Salon le Mesnil Champagne 1976 vintage. You can buy for consumption on or off the premises. House French is £5.25. CELLARMAN'S CHOICE : Bourgogne Rosé 1987, Luc Sorin, £7.85; Nobilo Sauvignon Blanc Fumé, Hawkes Bay 1986, £9.40.

CHEF: Gillie Gale, Maggie Gosling and Jennifer Johnson   PROPRIETORS: Richard and Gillie Gale
OPEN: Tue to Sun, exc Sun D, Mon June and July
CLOSED: Sun and Mon Aug to May
MEALS: 12 to 2, 6 to 10.15
PRICES: £7 (£12)
SEATS: 70. Private parties: 70 main room, 25 private room. Children's helpings. Wheelchair access. Music
ACCOMMODATION: 8 rooms, all with bath/shower. B&B £25 to £39.50. Deposit: £10. Baby facilities. Pets welcome. TV. Phone. Scenic. Confirm by 7

| LLANRWST  Gwynedd | map 4 |

## ▲ Meadowsweet Hotel ▮

| Station Road, Llanrwst LL26 0DS | COOKING 2 |
| LLANRWST (0492) 640732 | COST £31 |

A late-Victorian house at the road's edge, looking across the River Conwy to virgin hills beyond. It is occasionally described by correspondents as 'guest-housey' but that would ignore the sophisticated cooking and the air of clean comfort to public rooms and accommodation. There is a set lunch menu in high season, but year-round efforts are concentrated on a daily set-price dinner with three or four choices at each stage. The cooking does seem very accomplished in a modern idiom. Gravlax, salade tiède of pigeon with pine kernels, salmon with chive hollandaise, chicken with ceps and cream have a hackneyed ring, but they are cooked with an assurance that raises them above the ruck: an intense meat glaze with local lamb; and desserts of further strength in flavour and invention. The place can be full to exclusion at Eisteddfod time but it is encouraging that even at the end of the season, a wet weekend in October, efforts in presentation and marketing do not relax and a meal then was of 'a depth of flavour rarely experienced elsewhere'. The wine list is very long indeed, giving useful vintage notes from Lay & Wheeler's price list, and covers most countries substantially, catching breath only when arriving in California. There are few bargains, indeed margins are a fraction higher than among competitors. But the recompense is encyclopaedism: it has to be there (for the last four or five vintages at least), if only you can find it. House French, £6.95 a litre. CELLARMAN'S CHOICE : Côtes du Rhône Parallèle 45 1985, Jaboulet, £10.25; Sancerre, Dom. de la Mercy Dieu 1988, Reverdy, £13.50. The drawback with Meadowsweet, over three years now, is the service. Either the wires are stretched too taut and things take too long, or the youngsters brought in are inadequate to the task. Breakfast was served amiably enough but, 'I have seen smarter and better in a Clacton boarding-house.'

CHEF: John Evans   PROPRIETORS: John and Joy Evans
OPEN: all week, D only
MEALS: 6.30 to 9.30
PRICES: Set D £17.75 (£26)
CARD: Access, Amex, Visa
SEATS: 36. Private parties: 50 main room. Car-park, 10 places. Children's helpings. Smart dress preferred. No smoking in dining-room. Wheelchair access. Music
ACCOMMODATION: 10 rooms, all with bath/shower. B&B £28 to £38. Deposit: £5. Baby facilities. Pets welcome. TV. Phone. Scenic. Doors close at midnight. Confirm by 6.30
[GHG]

---

LLANWRTYD WELLS  Powys                                             map 4

## ▲ Llwynderw Hotel

Abergwesyn, Llanwrtyd Wells LD5 4TW                    COOKING 3
LLANWRTYD WELLS (059 13) 238                              COST £29

Four miles to the north of Llanwrtyd Wells, in the midst of unspoiled moorland, stands this austere eighteenth-century-fronted house, run as a hotel these 20 years past. The land once belonged to the Cistercian monks of Strata Florida over the mountains towards Aberystwyth. Even today, sheep provide the loudest sound on the hillsides. Michael Yates' kitchen offers dinner with an occasional alternative first course and a trio of desserts, but no choice apart from that. The cooking is not elaborate but it is harmonious. People are well satisfied – their tongues loosened by the hospitality, and the fact the owner may be eating with them. The centrepiece is often a roast: duck, beef or guinea-fowl, with all the trimmings. A salad affords a break after the main course, cheese (farmhouse Cheddar or Stilton) comes next, and dessert arrives with the coffee: memories of times past. The dining-room is formal and impressive, but the welcome is warm-hearted. The wine list is largely French with some Germans and Spanish Riojas. There are some 80 bins, not excessively priced, with some curious off-years in claret magnums (often a bargain hunter's delight), these having sketchy detail as to makers and growers. A £10 set lunch is available by arrangement. In the past year bedrooms and bathrooms have been upgraded.

CHEF: Valentin Bayona  PROPRIETOR: Michael Yates
OPEN: all week, D only
CLOSED: 1 Nov to 15 Mar
MEALS: 8
PRICES: Set D £19 (£24)
SEATS: 24. Car-park, 12 places. No children under 10. One sitting
ACCOMMODATION: 12 rooms, all with bath/shower. D, B&B £55 to £95. No children under 10. Pets by arrangement. Afternoon teas. Garden. Fishing. Golf. Scenic. Doors close at 11.30

---

MACHYNLLETH  Powys                                                     map 4

## ▲ Ynyshir Hall

Eglwysfach, Machynlleth SY20 8TA                        COOKING 1
GLANDYFI (065 474) 209                                  COST £10–£23

'The setting is beautiful. The meal was very good. Guests who have seen five different owners say the beauty of the place still draws them back and all owners have had culinary skills.' The regime of the Allisons and David Dressler in the kitchen is of longer duration than some have been. Even so, rumours of departure surround them, too. The cooking is simple but uses what is to hand to good effect; main courses are on the lines of roast lamb with rosemary and garlic, grilled trout, swordfish pie, roast quail with chestnut and grape stuffing. The wine list is short and largely bereft of half-bottles. House wine is £5.50.

CHEF: David Dressler  PROPRIETORS: Jane and Richard Allison
OPEN: all week
MEALS: 12 to 1, 6.30 to 8
PRICES: Set L £6 (£10) to £8 (£12), Set D £13 (£17) to £15 (£19). Service inc
CARDS: Access, Amex, Diners, Visa
SEATS: 24. Private parties: 30 main room. Car-park, 15 places. Children's helpings on request. No smoking in dining-room
ACCOMMODATION: 9 rooms, all with bath/shower. B&B £29 to £52. Deposit: 10%. Baby facilities. Pets welcome. Afternoon teas. Garden. Fishing. TV. Phone. Scenic. Doors close at 11.30

---

*If you see a certificate in a restaurant bearing the words 'The Good Food and Restaurant Guide', the claim is false – see the Introduction. Please write and tell us the name and address of the restaurant.*

*'The staff, which seems to consist mostly of young Australians, are friendly but pretty casual. It is unusual perhaps, on choosing a Burgundy, to be told, ''That will put some colour in your cheeks.'' However, my younger colleague told me I was merely carping in an old-fashioned way.'*  On eating out in Wales

---

**MATHRY Dyfed**                                          map 4

## Ann FitzGerald's Farmhouse Kitchen

*(COUNTY OF THE YEAR RESTAURANT badge)*

Mawbs Fawr, Mathry SA62 5JB                    COOKING 2
CRESGOCH (034 83) 347                          COST £11−£23

Do not miss the signpost; proceed with determination; the pot-holed track *will* end in your destination. The farm looks derelict. It is not. The FitzGeralds have several arms to their business: they feed people in the restaurant, lunch and dinner, they supply take-aways to holidaymakers, and they bake, at least three times a day. The bread, therefore, is good. The unsalted butter is too. Not many places make the disarming admission that the cooking is 'of the old school with no regard to calorie control. Portions are big and the use of butter, heavy cream, wine, cognac, madeira, Champagne, etc. is profligate.' In this case the assertion seems accurate. In simple terms, the food is much better than the location might imply: it is generous; it has gusto; it is made with many home-grown vegetables and herbs, good meats, good game and excellent fish. The menu is large, again taking the location into account, and takes care of vegetarians. At lunch there is an abbreviated choice and on Sundays there is a roast. One reported meal yielded sole and crab mousseline with a prawn sauce and an escalope of salmon baked with a chive sauce. The eaters, evidently from the fishless interior, followed up with baked sea bass with a red pepper sauce, stuffed with a slightly dry salmon mousse; and a salmon steak with a Champagne and dill sauce. In all these the sauces were old-fashioned and full of flavour; so was the thick caramel with the apple tart and the rhubarb fool. Cafetière coffee was good, fudge excellent. There is no wine list, but customers can bring their own and it will be served decently.

CHEFS: Lionel and Ann FitzGerald    PROPRIETOR: Ann FitzGerald
OPEN: all week
CLOSED: L Christmas to Easter
MEALS: 12 to 3, 6.30 to 9
PRICES: £17 (£19), Set L £10 (£11), Set D £14 (£15). Unlicensed, but bring your own: no corkage
SEATS: 30. 4 tables outside. Private parties: 40 main room. Car-park, 40 places. Vegetarian meals. Children's helpings. No children under 9. Wheelchair access. Music

**NEWPORT Dyfed**                                         map 4

## ▲ Cnapan ▼

East Street, Newport SA42 0WF
NEWPORT (0239) 820575                          COOKING 2
nr Fishguard                                   COST £23

This is very much a family business. As the Coopers and the Lloyds put it, 'we are a country house which has a restaurant.' Upstairs are five bedrooms. Downstairs, Eluned Lloyd and Judi Cooper, mother and daughter, do nearly all the cooking, serving lunches and teas with a distinctly Welsh flavour − cawl, onion tart, chicken and ham pie, griddle and apple cakes − and dinners which are more deliberately cosmopolitan, designed to please both local customers and holidaymakers. Nonetheless, all food keeps the feel of good home cooking. There are at least half a dozen choices for each course: main dishes range from the Mediterranean and spicy, gingery pork or cod portugaise, for example, to more local ideas like trout stuffed with apple and fennel, poacher's pie and lamb fillet in a creamy red wine and redcurrant sauce. Fillet steak and vegetarian dishes are always available. To finish, there are local Welsh cheeses – there are some 35 made in Dyfed – and an old-fashioned pudding of the day among other choices. Thirty-odd wines are very reasonably priced and yet well chosen. It would actually be difficult to fault any of the bottles, including two organic Rhônes from René Fabre. House Coteaux de l'Ardèche, £4.95.

CELLARMAN'S CHOICE : Hautes Côtes de Beaune Tasteviné 1985, Caves des Hautes Côtes, £9.50; Tokay d'Alsace 1986, Eugene Meyer (organic), £8.50.

CHEFS: Eluned Lloyd and Judi Cooper    PROPRIETORS: Eluned and John Lloyd, Judi and Michael Cooper
OPEN: all week, exc Tue (Fri and Sat D and Sun L only, Nov to Mar)
CLOSED: Feb
MEALS: 12.30 to 2.30, 7.30 to 9
PRICES: £14 (£19)
CARDS: Access, Visa
SEATS: 34. 4 tables outside. Private parties: 36 main room. Car-park, 6 places. Vegetarian meals. Children's helpings. Wheelchair access (also WC)
ACCOMMODATION: 5 rooms, all with bath/shower. B&B £19.50 to £29. Deposit: 10%. Baby facilities. Afternoon teas. TV. Scenic. Doors close at midnight. Confirm by 5 [GHG]

---

**NORTHOP  Clwyd**                                                      map 4

## ▲ *Soughton Hall*

Northop CH7 6AB
NORTHOP (0352 86) 207 and 484                              COOKING 2
off A5119, Northop to Mold                                  COST £20–£37

The building, remodelled by Charles Barry and reflecting the oriental travels of its then owner, William Bankes, is sensational. When approached by the avenue of limes leading to its main front, the great illuminated windows lend something of the air of a Victorian waterworks, a palace of industry, but that is soon dispelled on crossing the threshold. The Rodenhurst family have worked hard at restoring their acquisition and seem determined to make it a premier, and paying, example of the British heritage culture in action: stately first floor dining-room (with good ceiling paintings), Welsh harpist playing of an evening, waitresses in long beribboned gowns. Chef Malcolm Warham used to work at Eastwell Manor in Kent and his style, shown on both a set-price short menu (with too many supplements) which is changed regularly and a longer *carte*, is modern. Dishes such as a terrine of salmon, wood mushrooms and spinach with a tomato coulis; a salad of langoustines, quail and apple; grilled salmon with a beurre noisette; collops of monkfish with a ragout of spinach and mussels on a sesame, chive and tomato dressing, might indicate some of his preferences. A good sorbet is served as automatic second course. Vegetables are satisfactory and puddings include versions of British traditionals. Lemon curd tartlet comes with a chocolate feathering, a raspberry sauce, slices of grapefruit, orange and mango. Elaborate does not necessarily mean better. One reader, satisfied enough, wishes the kitchen would moderate its ambition. The wine list accords with the intentions of the hotel: quite long, quite well chosen, not cheap. It recognises many countries outside France. House Duboeuf is £7.95. CELLARMAN'S CHOICE : Savigny-lès-Beaune 1983, Louis Latour, £22.50; Montana Marlborough Chardonnay 1988, £14.95.

CHEF: Malcolm William Warham  PROPRIETORS: John and Rosemary Rodenhurst
OPEN: all week exc Mon L, Sat L, Sun D
MEALS: 12 to 2, 7 to 9.30 (10 Sat)
PRICES: Set L £14 (£20) to £16.50 (£23), Set D £18.50 (£25) to £24.50 (£31)
CARDS: Access, Amex, Visa
SEATS: 50. Private parties: 50 main room, 20 private room. Car-park, 50 places. No children under 10. Smart dress preferred. No smoking
ACCOMMODATION: 12 rooms, all with bath/shower. B&B £80 to £100. Deposit: 25%. No children under 10. Afternoon teas. Garden. Tennis. Snooker. TV. Phone. Scenic

---

**PONTFAEN** Dyfed                                                      map 4

# ▲ *Tregynon Country Farm Hotel*

Pontfaen SA65 9TU
NEWPORT (0239) 820531
from junction of B4313/B4329, take B3413 towards          COOKING 1
Fishguard. Take first R, and R again for ¹/₂m               COST £18

The enterprise began as a flight from city life. Today, the Heard family care for temporary fugitives in an isolated farmhouse (it is essential to ring for details). Caring bulks large in their view: every sort of diet is provided for, smokers are reminded that their pollution includes 70 toxic substances, food is organically produced whenever possible and often from the farm itself. Cooking is mainly for residents but others may book, though prior consultation about the menu is advised. A simple and inexpensive daily menu is composed (made more difficult for the kitchen by the variety of ailments and allergies that may afflict residents), with several of the main courses at supplements from £1 to £2.50. The cooking is robust and well handled: good soups, good vegetables, a light vegetarian dish of stuffed aubergine with a red wine sauce, a decent chicken cooked with orange and almond. Chocolate chip ice-cream is first class. This is a place with a mission, deservedly attracting many disciples. Children eat earlier, at 6pm. The wine list of three dozen items is both nicely chosen and very fairly priced. Its notes are extremely detailed. House wine is £5.50 and there are Ruddles, Newquay Steam Bitter and other beers in bottle or can. So far, Peter Heard has not explored many organic wines now available. Doubtless that will come.

---

*If you see a certificate in a restaurant bearing the words 'Good Food Guide Top Restaurants', the claim is false (and the restaurant may be in contempt of court in displaying it) – see the Introduction. Please write and tell us the name and address of the restaurant.*

---

CHEF: Sheila Heard   PROPRIETORS: Peter and Sheila Heard
OPEN: all week, D only
MEALS: 7.30 to 8.45
PRICES: Set D £10 (£15)
SEATS: 28. Private parties: 16 main room. Car-park. Vegetarian meals. Children restricted after 7.30pm. Music
ACCOMMODATION: 8 rooms, all with bath/shower. Rooms for disabled. B&B £34. Deposit: 25%. Baby facilities. Afternoon teas. Garden. TV. Scenic. Confirm by noon

---

## PONTYPRIDD   Mid Glamorgan                                    map 4

# John & Maria's

| 1–3 Broadway, Pontypridd CF37 1BA | COOKING 1 |
| PONTYPRIDD (0443) 402977 | COST £19 |

Should Wales and Italy ever meet on the rugby pitch, John & Maria's could face an awkward clash of loyalties. Flags and team photos of both countries, not to mention straw-wrapped Chianti flasks and scenic Italian posters, decorate this café/restaurant opposite the station. Service is cheerful and informal; pasta, ace; veal, steaks and grilled halibut, recommended; vegetables not. Chips with everything. Minestrone, ice-cream and sherry trifle are all 'own make'. Packed, and especially good value, at lunchtimes. House wine, £5.50 a litre.
CELLARMAN'S CHOICE : Corvo di Salaparuta red and white, £6.80.

CHEF: Maria Orsi   PROPRIETORS: The Orsi family
OPEN: Mon to Sat
CLOSED: bank hols, 25 and 26 Dec
MEALS: 11.30 to 3, 5.30 to 10 (9.30 Mon and Tue)
PRICES: £11 (£16)
CARDS: Access, Visa
SEATS: 120. Private parties: 35 main room, 12 and 20 private rooms. Vegetarian meals. Children's helpings on request. Music

---

## PORTHGAIN   Dyfed                                             map 4

# Harbour Lights

| Porthgain SA62 5BW | COOKING 3 |
| CROESGOGH (034 83) 549 | COST £14–£24 |

Porthgain is at the end of a road leading to the sea. The village of whitewashed houses is remarkable for its ruined stone-crushing works; it is a detour from any road to anywhere. This does not affect the success of Harbour Lights, full much of the summer season. The restaurant, with bare brick, small tables and mixed crockery has as direct and down-to-earth an approach to surroundings as the cooks have to the food. 'Exceptional value'; 'if you had any doubts about this, don't'; 'a gem of a place,' are just a few comments of those who have made the journey. The cooking makes no bones about pretension: minestrone soup; laverbread with a cheese sauce; crab Mornay; brill with a butter sauce; sticky toffee pudding have all come in for praise. The materials are gloriously fresh and the flavours direct and piercing. The wine list is a very careful and intelligent choice from all around the world simply arranged by grape variety. Equal attention is given to vegetarian, carnivorous, and piscivorous dishes. House French Gamay (£6.25) and Sauvignon Blanc (£6.50).

CHEF/PROPRIETOR: Anne Marie Davies
OPEN: all week, exc Sun D
CLOSED: Jan and Feb
MEALS: 12 to 3, 7 to 9.30
PRICES: Set L £10 (£14), Set D £15 (£20)
CARD: Access
SEATS: 40. 6 tables outside. Private parties: 30 main room. Car-park, 100 places. Vegetarian meals. Children's helpings. Wheelchair access (1 step). Music

---

PORTMEIRION  Gwynedd                                           map 4

## ▲ Portmeirion Hotel

Portmeirion LL48 6ET
PORTHMADOG (0766) 770228                          COOKING 1
A487, signposted at Minffordd                      COST £15−£26

The focal point of Sir Clough Williams-Ellis' fantasy village is set on a beautiful, secluded peninsula overlooking a wide sweep of sandy estuary, towards Cardigan Bay. The hotel reopened in 1988, having been gutted by fire in 1981. It has been rebuilt and decorated in 1920s style with lavish use of gilt mirrors, marble-effect columns and oriental glitz which seems perfectly in keeping with the extravagances of the village, though some might find it verging on the vulgar. Fourteen bedrooms are in the main house, 20 in the village. The set menu at £16.50 offers good value and uses plenty of fresh local produce: best end of Welsh lamb with brioche and herb crust; poached fillet of Welsh salmon with prawns, white wine and mushrooms; local salmon, scallops and prawns in a herb sauce. Portions are generous (sometimes served on Portmeirion pottery) and vegetables carefully cooked, but service can be inexperienced and uncommunicative. Desserts are duller than the sweet wines to drink with them: strawberries and cream; Cornflake-based chocolate and apricot torte; coffee and brandy cream. Self-service coffee. House French, £9 a litre. CELLARMAN'S CHOICE : Brown Brothers Cabernet Sauvignon, Koombahla vineyard 1985, £11.50; Mâcon-Lugny Les Genièvres 1986, Louis Latour, £11.50.

CHEF: Hefin Williams   PROPRIETORS: Portmeirion Ltd
OPEN: all week, exc Mon L
CLOSED: 3 weeks end Jan
MEALS: 12 to 1.45, 7 to 9.30 (9 Sun, Nov to Feb)
PRICES: Set L £10 (£15) to £12 (£17), Set D £16.50 (£22)
CARDS: Access, Amex, Diners, Visa
SEATS: 120. 8 tables outside. Private parties: 100 main room, 8 and 30 private rooms. Car-park, 100 places. Children's helpings (to 8pm). No children under 8 (after 8pm). Smart dress preferred. No smoking. Wheelchair access (also WC). Music
ACCOMMODATION: 34 rooms, all with bath/shower. B&B £45 to £100. Deposit: £20. No children under 8 (in main house). Garden. Swimming-pool. Tennis. Fishing. TV. Phone. Scenic. Confirm by 6 [GHG]

# ▲ *Plas Bodegroes* ♟

Pwllheli LL53 5TH
PWLLHELI (0758) 612363 and 612510                                    COOKING 4
on A497, 1m W of Pwllheli                                              COST £21–£26

The woodland setting seems all Welsh myth; the eighteenth-century
architecture all seemliness and comfort. This restaurant with rooms gathers
plaudits the year through. One English visitor put it telescopically: 'intelligent
modern cooking; friendly yet businesslike; obviously going places; wine list
astoundingly cheap; relaxing place to stay; real comfort and gastronomy.' The
menu is imbued with a very strong sense of place. As an inspector remarked, 'If
hotels and restaurants in Wales can suffer from long and difficult supply lines,
the special quality of the produce from smaller farms and smallholdings can be
an alternative answer, making the isolation a virtue.' There is a five-course
menu with three or four dishes at each stage. This may be treated à la carte, or a
five-course choice can be taken at a single price. On Tuesdays, only residents
are served, from a shorter menu. The cooking is sophisticated in a way that can
surprise those used to the more robust approach of North Wales. Soups,
pungent and eloquent, have included fresh vegetable with lots of asparagus
tops, and a crab bisque 'both delicate and creamy' that included a parcel of claw
meat wrapped in a spinach leaf and little pieces of smoked chicken to provide a
counterpoint of flavour. Crab has also been used to fill a courgette flower served
with a shellfish sauce and to accompany a scallop mousse, served with
laverbread. Two visiting restaurateurs were given turbot and skate, the first
steamed, with a tarragon mousse and shellfish sauce, the second braised, with a
vermouth and chive butter sauce; 'both perfect, fresh, moist, just cooked, two
sublime sauces. No restaurant in our experience has bettered these dishes.'
Although the fish may provide the clearest regional bias, the meat and poultry
is also locally reared: from quail (no longer French) to beef. Cheese, too, is
largely from the Principality. Chris Chown reports improvements to his cellar
arrangements that enables him to store and mature cheese direct from the
farms. Desserts have less of a Welsh tinge. Not that they aren't good. There is
often something in chocolate; truffle cake is well reported. Just as often might
be a sandwich of fruit with cinnamon biscuits – strawberries, apple and
rhubarb, plums and lychees are some of the combinations reported – each with
a complementary sauce (passion-fruit, mint custard, liqueur cream). The
cooking seems poised and the technique almost invariably faultless – just as
co-owner Gunna a Trodni's hospitality impresses by its warmth and efficacy.
Wines have increased in number with improvements in cellarage. There is a
basic collection of four dozen bottles supplemented by a like number of more
rapidly changing fine wines. As the house works to a mark-up of a single lump
sum plus a very small percentage, bargains abound. The emphasis remains
French, but changes may occur in the future. The list of clarets alone should
afford delight to any visitor. Half-bottles are strongly in evidence. House
French, £6. CELLARMAN'S CHOICE : St-Aubin 1986, Henri Prudhon, £14; Ch.
Notton, Margaux 1985, £11.50; Delegat's Sauvignon Blanc 1987, £11. Tips are
'accepted but not expected.'

CHEF: Christopher Chown   PROPRIETORS: Christopher Chown and Gunna a Trodni
OPEN: all week D, exc Tue (residents only)
CLOSED: 3 Jan to 13 Feb
MEALS: 12.30 to 1.30, 7 to 9
PRICES: £16 (£21), Set D £17.50 (£22). Minimum £12. Service inc
CARDS: Access, Visa
SEATS: 45. 5 tables outside. Private parties: 60 main room. Car-park, 25 places. Children's
helpings. No smoking in dining-room. Wheelchair access (1 step; also WC). Music
ACCOMMODATION: 5 rooms, all with bath/shower. B&B £30 to £70, D, B&B £45 to £100.
Deposit: 10%. Baby facilities. Pets welcome. Garden. TV. Phone. Scenic. Confirm by 6
[GHG]

---

**REYNOLDSTON   West Glamorgan**     map 4

## ▲ Fairyhill

Reynoldston SA3 1BS     COOKING 1
GOWER (0792) 390139     COST £15−£29

The Gower peninsula is paradise: Fairyhill is plumb centre. Although there are
few lanes, a map is desirable. The house is north of the village, Georgian, and
set in 24 acres, which John Frayne still enjoys landscaping with more
mechanical help than Capability Brown ever had. This is no upmarket
conversion: the description given by readers is more often 'plain French-style
hotel' or 'bed-and-breakfast' than 'English country house'. The food meets
with more approval than the rooms and Kate Cole produces a modern
repertoire on a short menu that exceeds many in the district for sophistication
and skill, offering foie gras and wild mushrooms as well as local materials like
cockles and laverbread. Quite disconcertingly, once the Fraynes have taken
orders and set people eating, they themselves sit down to dinner. Although it's
fun in grand hotels to play at spotting the management among the customers, it
is more worrying when they are in close proximity. But complaint is by no
means the dominant tone: a foie gras terrine with muscat jelly, a guinea-fowl
with wild mushrooms, cockles fried in batter, good vegetables and an array of
old-fashioned creamy sweet dishes on the sideboard have elicited praise. Not
so runny béarnaise, stodgy puddings and a poor leek soup − in Wales, too. The
wine list is arranged by type rather than region and offers a short but
interesting range from places beyond France. House Bulgarian, £5.50.

CHEF: Kate Cole   PROPRIETORS: John and Midge Frayne
OPEN: Mon to Sat D, Sun L (and Sun D Easter to Sept)
MEALS: 12.30 to 1.30, 7.30 to 9.30
PRICES: £18 (£24), Set Sun L £10.50 (£15)
CARDS: Access, Visa
SEATS: 60. Private parties: 40 main room, 20 private room. Car-park, 60 places. Vegetarian
meals. Children's helpings (L only). Smart dress preferred. Wheelchair access
(also WC). Music
ACCOMMODATION: 11 rooms, all with bath/shower. B&B £49 to £59. Deposit: 20%. Pets
welcome. Garden. Sauna. Fishing. TV. Phone. Scenic. Confirm by 2 [GHG]

---

*The* Guide *relies on feedback from its readers. Especially welcome are reports on new
restaurants appearing in the book for the first time.*

## ▲ *Llyndir Hall*

| Llyndir Lane, Rossett, LL12 0AY | COOKING 2 |
|---|---|
| ROSSETT (0244) 571648 | COST £14–£35 |

This small, early-nineteenth-century house equidistant from Wrexham and Chester is pitching for the burgeoning economy of Cheshire, as Home Counties as any part of Herts or Essex. The two young chefs, each from famous places, are cooking modern luxury food with some, though not total, success. A pleasant dining-room on two levels, the lower opening into a conservatory giving on to the garden and lawns, is elegant enough and the service suave enough for the potential range of custom. The food can also be suave and assured, witness a very fine fish terrine without claggy padding of nameless mousseline and excellently prepared marinated salmon, tasting admirably fresh, served with a salad dressed with a confident vinaigrette. Meat cookery has shown less competence in timing, though the dark reduction served with medallions of beef with roasted shallots and chestnuts, and the stock and pan juices that came with a best end of lamb with sweetbreads and morels, have been praised. Good Welsh cheeses; a fair hand with ice-cream; weakish coffee; expensive glasses of Champagne. Perhaps with business and pressure, the talent that is latent will shine through to lift this from mere competent luxury to very good. At present it comes quite dear. The wine list is of medium length with no surprises. House French, £7.50 and £7.75.

CHEFS: Kevin Ley and Stuart Maynard  PROPRIETORS: Elegant Hotels Ltd
OPEN: all week
CLOSED: 25 Dec D
MEALS: 12 to 2, 7 to 9.30
PRICES: £21 (£29), Set L £9 (£14) to £11.50 (£17), Set D £17.50 (£23)
CARDS: Access, Amex, Diners, Visa
SEATS: 50. Private parties: 30 main room. Car-park, 70 places. Children's helpings.
No children under 5 at D. Smart dress preferred. No cigars/pipes in dining-room.
Wheelchair access
ACCOMMODATION: 8 rooms, all with bath/shower. B&B £55 to £82. Deposit: £25. Baby facilities. Afternoon teas. Garden. TV. Phone. Scenic

## *Bardells*

| St Bride's-super-Ely CF5 6EZ | COOKING 1 |
|---|---|
| PETERSTON-SUPER-ELY (0446) 760534 | COST £15–£25 |

The Budgens seem a cheerful family, most of them involved in some way in this home-turned-restaurant. The name is in honour of Mr Pickwick's landlady. June Budgen's cooking is unaffected and satisfactory: a large helping of prawns lightly tossed in garlic butter; a well-judged watercress soup; a chicken breast with Pernod; a fillet of sewin with lime butter, all pleased their recipients. The tranquil surroundings and affable service do the kitchen justice. There is a short wine list as reasonably priced as the food. House wines, £5.50 and £5.75.

CHEFS: Jane and Lucy Budgen   PROPRIETOR: Jane Budgen
OPEN: Tue to Sat, D only and Sun L (other days by arrangement)
MEALS: 12.30 to 1.30, 7.30 to 9
PRICES: Set Sun L £11 (£15), Set D £16 (£21)
CARDS: Access, Diners, Visa
SEATS: 24. 2 tables outside. Private parties: 24 main room. Car-Park, 20 places. Children's helpings on request. No smoking. Music

---

**SWANSEA West Glamorgan** map 4

# Annie's

56 St Helen's Road, Swansea SA1 4BE COOKING 1
SWANSEA (0792) 655603 COST £14–£24

Ann Gwilym's restaurant has a loyal clientele. 'We eat here fairly often and are never disappointed. Fresh food. Unusual dishes changed fairly frequently and depending on market supplies. Informal atmosphere – you don't have to be in a hurry.' The atmosphere is set as much by the stripped pine décor, friendly service and tasteful background music – jazz and classical – as by the relaxed pace. Downstairs there is a café-bar serving a small clutch of daily dishes. Upstairs, in the main dining-room, the short set and à la carte menus have an Anglo-French domestic feel and certain threads of continuity run through the seasonal changes: pâtés, imaginative first-course salads and modern fruity poultry or game dishes are balanced against traditional steaks and fish in butter or wine sauces. Thus, for example, poached salmon has been served variously with dill, laverbread, twinned saffron and watercress sauces, and crevettes. Some dishes have been described as only adequate, but salmon croquettes, with a light and creamy filling in a crisp crumb coating, and a surprisingly uncloying chicken with tropical fruit in a white port sauce have been praised. The wine list, from Lay & Wheeler, is pitched exactly to the market: very decent bottles, but listed without vintages. House French, £5.60. CELLARMAN'S CHOICE : Syrah d'Ardèche, Guyot, £7.80; Sauvignon du Haut-Poitou, £7.20.

CHEFS: Ann Gwilym and Stephane Rivier   PROPRIETOR: Ann Gwilym
OPEN: Tue to Sat, D only (plus Mon in summer)
MEALS: 7 to 10.30
PRICES: £15 (£20), Set D £10.80 (£14). Service inc
CARDS: Access, Visa
SEATS: 56. Private parties: 34 main room, 22 private room. Children's helpings on request. Music

---

# La Braseria

28 Wind Street, Swansea SA1 1D2 COOKING 1
SWANSEA (0792) 469683 COST £18

Part of a group with La Brasserie and Champers in Cardiff (see entries) and sharing a simple, good-value, fresh approach to wine bar and grill-room cooking. Serve yourself some salad, point to what you want and it will be brought to your table when it's been cooked. Wines continue the policy of fair pricing. La Braseria has an Hispano-French tilt rather than the Italian of its name. House wine, £4.85 (white), £4.95 (red).

CHEF: M. Tercero    PROPRIETORS: Benigno Martinez and M. Tercero
OPEN: Mon to Sat
MEALS: 12 to 2.30, 7 to 12
PRICES: £9 (£15)
CARDS: Access, Amex, Diners, Visa
SEATS: 200. Private parties: 100 private room. Children welcome. Wheelchair access (also WC). Music. Self-service salad bar

## Green Dragon Bistro

| Green Dragon Lane, Swansea SA1 1DG | COOKING 2 |
| SWANSEA (0792) 641437 | COST £20 |

Found down a narrow lane off Wind Street in the city centre, this lunchtime bistro is unimposing from the outside and none too elegant inside. But the kitchen, under chef/proprietor Kate Taylor, goes from strength to strength. Although normally serving only lunch, Kate Taylor has introduced new monthly French regional evenings, with *prix fixe* three-course dinners. These have proved a great success. The style of the daily menu is also solidly provincial French, with a few modern and Welsh dishes − a starter of bacon, laverbread and cockles, for example − thrown in for good measure. There is a surprisingly wide choice of around a dozen starters, which may also be taken as main courses with a supplementary charge, and an equal number of more substantial main courses. Local fish is particularly well represented. Recommendations include seafood soup and aïoli, salmon terrine and salad, marinated mackerel and fresh tartare sauce. Meats range from slowly braised cassoulet to roast rack of local lamb with tarragon, or more personal ideas such as smoked goose breast with walnuts. Everything is remarkably good value. Dinner is by arrangement. The wine list is nicely chosen and fairly priced. House Pascal Frères, from the Rhône, £6.75. CELLARMAN'S CHOICE : Rioja, Marqués de Cáceres, white 1987, £7, red 1985, £7.50.

CHEF/PROPRIETOR: Kate Taylor
OPEN: Mon to Sat, L only
MEALS: 12 to 3
PRICES: £12 (£17)
CARDS: Access, Amex, Diners, Visa
SEATS: 50. Private parties: 100 main room. Children's helpings. Wheelchair access (1 step; also WC). Music

## Happy Wok

| 22A St Helen's Road, Swansea SA1 4AP | COOKING 1 |
| SWANSEA (0792) 466702 and 460063 | COST £8−£23 |

Happy for diners, that is, though it should perhaps be taken more seriously than the name implies. The restaurant takes refreshing cognizance of being in Wales, using more seafood than most Glamorgan eating places and substituting lamb for duck in 'Peking Duck'. The interior is stylish and the service affable. Sizzling dishes make a strong appearance.

CHEFS: C.C. Yuen and K.W. Yuen  PROPRIETORS: I.M. Diu, K.W. Yuen and C
OPEN: all week
CLOSED: 4 days at Christmas
MEALS: 12 to 2.30, 6.30 to 11.30
PRICES: Set L £3.50 (£8), Set D £10.50 (£16) to £13.50 (£19). Minimum £5
CARDS: Access, Amex, Diners, Visa
SEATS: 55. Private parties: 60 main room. Children welcome. Music. Air-conditioned

## Roots

2 Woodville Road, Mumbles
Swansea SA3 4AD                                           COOKING 1
SWANSEA (0792) 366006                                      COST £16

Vegetarian restaurants are not easily found in the area and this relatively new
one avoids many of the usual wholefood clichés. Mushroom and Brie crêpes,
Stilton and celery pâté with well-garlicked bread, melon with grapes and port
are good examples from the frequently changing menu. Other dishes – stir-
fries, curries, tacos and veggieburgers – are more obvious. All the vegetables
used are organically grown and vegan meals are always available. Desserts are
more luscious than healthy: peach cake with cream, French apple tart, fruit and
brandy crêpes and so on. In the evening, the tables are candlelit to lift the
stripped pine interior. There is a variety of teas and coffee but no licence, so
take your own wine.

CHEF: Judith Rees  PROPRIETORS: Judith Rees and Heather Tull
OPEN: Mon to Sat, exc Mon D and Tue D
MEALS: 12 to 2.30, 6.30 to 9
PRICES: £9 (£13), Snacks from £1.45. Unlicensed, but bring your own: corkage 50p per
bottle
SEATS: 38. 1 table outside. Private parties: 50 main room. Vegetarian meals. Children's
helpings. No-smoking area. Wheelchair access (1 step). Music

TALSARNAU  Gwynedd                                          map 4

## ▲ Hotel Maes-y-Neuadd

Talsarnau LL47 6YA
HARLECH (0766) 780200                                     COOKING 3
off B4573, 1m S of Talsarnau                              COST £14–£30

The house is not peculiarly beautiful – handsome and solid would be more
accurate – but the meadow from which it takes its name is idyllically disposed
half-way down a mountain, surrounded by black Welsh cattle munching
buttercups, looking across the water to the Lleyn peninsula. Car drivers of the
intrepid sort will enjoy the steep ascent to the estate. Inside is pleasant, with no
excess of elegance, some good art on the walls and lighting for once bright
enough to see what is on the plate in the dining-room, likened by one to a good
French place: comfortable chairs and exquisite place settings. Correspondents
have repeatedly stressed their joy and surprise at the quality of Trevor
Pharoah's cooking, to say nothing of the effective service and warm welcome
by the Horsfalls and the Slatters. The restaurant operates seven days a week,

with exceptionally good-value Sunday lunches, but as usual, the centre of culinary ambition is the four-course dinner (second course soup or salad) with a longer menu than is usual in country hotels. 'We weren't expecting much but, my goodness, we couldn't wait, every night.' Trevor Pharoah served some of his training at the Dorchester, so that when he is described as cooking in the 'modern British' style, warning cones start flying. Accounts of his repertoire, however, should reassure the wary that the best of Mosimann has been translated to Wales, not the crazy excesses of some 'modern Britons' layering blue cheese with prawns, tropical fruit and perhaps a bit of Bombay pickle. His cooking is, in fact, quite restrained. An inspection meal yielded these comments: 'steamed scallops with artichoke and pickled samphire were timed right, wonderfully fresh, with clear tastes from the component parts brought together by a light buttery sauce. Then was served a carrot and orange soup which got its effect from good stock, lots of carrot, a modicum of cream and a careful orange counterpoint. With it came the most impressive array of fresh breads: wholemeal, walnut, cheese and wholemeal, Melba toasts, bread twists and whorls. Good bread, good soup equals good meal.' The Gressingham duck, not, for once, too undercooked, came on a galette of woven celeriac strips. The sauce was described as a marmalade, with pickled kumquats. The fight-off of sweet and sour was not overstated but cut through the duck to the right degree. Then came a cheeseboard, all Welsh, 'the best I have yet been offered.' Quantities had been finely judged to leave space for an exemplary hot chocolate fudge pudding. Others speak of the fine quality of the sorbets. 'The food calls up the adjectives clean, fresh, light, clear; and the service, discreet, restrained, professional.' If that isn't enough, the breakfast is good. The wine list is a fine, but not great, broad selection more than adequate to its task. It is not especially cheap. House French from £6.05. CELLARMAN'S CHOICE : Montagny 1986, Ponsot £15.50; René Barbier Penedés Cabernet Sauvignon 1985, £13.25. Alas, children under seven are not welcome.

CHEF: Trevor Pharoah    PROPRIETORS: Michael and June Slatter, Malcolm and Olive Horsfall
OPEN: all week
CLOSED: 2 Jan to 2 Feb
MEALS: 12.15 to 1.45, 7.30 to 9
PRICES: Set L £9.95 (£14) to £12 (£17), Set D £18.50 (£24) to £21 (£25)
CARDS: Access, Visa, Amex, Diners
SEATS: 36. Private parties: 50 main room; 14 private room. Car-park, 50 places. Vegetarian meals. Children's helpings. No children under 7. No smoking in dining-room. Wheelchair access
ACCOMMODATION: 15 rooms, all with bath/shower. Room for disabled. B&B £36 to £90. Deposit: £20. No children under 7. Pets welcome. Afternoon teas. Garden. TV. Phone. Scenic. Doors close at 11. Confirm by 5 [GHG]

---

*'Service was excellent but the first thing the girl said was, ''I apologise for the shouting from the kitchen. I'm afraid it's inevitable.'' In fact we heard no shouting till later but we felt all was not right because although we got there soon after 1pm and ordered pretty sharpish, our main courses weren't served till 2.30pm and we didn't leave till about 4. I know it's nice to linger over Sunday lunch – but even so.'* On lunching in Oxfordshire

## TALYLLYN  Gwynedd                                           map 4

## ▲ *Minffordd Hotel*

Talyllyn LL36 9AJ
CORRIS (065 473) 665                                    COOKING 2
at junction of A487 and B4405                              COST £20

This hotel succeeds in its aims, providing relaxation, invigoration and
sustenance. The presence of so many holidaymakers from large urban centres
may encourage a togetherness that appeals to like minds, but there are few
other humans to converse with for many miles. The son of the owners,
Jonathan Pickles, cooks a short set-price meal, offering a couple of choices as
main courses and a few more on either side. Value continues to be high. Soups
are often good, the fish fresh and the puddings have that British affection for
simple luxury. Cheese could be more exciting, for Wales is an epicentre of the
new-wave cheesemakers. Service in the small dining-room, as in the rest of the
hotel, is whole-hearted and genial. The short wine list offers as fair value as the
food. House French is £5.50. CELLARMAN'S CHOICE : Ch. du Roy, Pomerol
1983, £11.95; Chablis *premier cru*, Montmains 1987, Durup, £13.65. Service,
according to the menu, is 'free' and 'willingly given', so no tipping. The Pickles
have published a grand little historical pamphlet describing their house. It was
Temperance until 1966. Michael Faraday stayed here in 1815: he was 'much
gratified', but nearly lost his life by losing his way on a climb of Cader Idris.
Conditions are not so dangerous for modern guests, but the gratification
continues.

CHEF: Jonathan Pickles    PROPRIETORS: Bernard and Jessica Pickles
OPEN: Tue to Sat, D only
CLOSED: Jan and Feb
MEALS: 7.30 to 8.30
PRICES: Set D £14 (£17). Service inc
CARDS: Access, Diners, Visa
SEATS: 28. Private parties: 28 main room. Car-park, 12 places. Children's helpings. No
children under 3. Smart dress preferred. No smoking in dining-room. Wheelchair access
ACCOMMODATION: 7 rooms, all with bath/shower. D, B&B £38 to £66. Deposit: 10%. No
children under 3. Garden. Phone. Scenic. Doors close at 11. Confirm by 6 [GHG]

## THREE COCKS  Powys                                         map 4

## ▲ *Three Cocks Hotel*

Three Cocks LD3 0SL
GLASBURY (049 74) 215                                  COOKING 2
on A438, between Brecon and Hay-on-Wye              COST £20–£29

This solid, stone-built inn could easily pass as an *auberge*, and the food likewise
would feel at home on the other side of the Channel. Reports have arrived of
delicate and aromatic shellfish soup with tangy rouille, a simple and elegant
brill on a bed of curly endive, and splendid kidney vol-au-vent moated by a
mustard sauce. The proprietor's wife is Belgian and her touch shows in a
profuse deployment of cream. The set-price menu starts with soup and runs
through three courses and coffee. The sweet nouvelle saucing that creeps in

from time to time is not to everyone's taste, nor are the tiny parcels of vegetables and the misjudgements with salt that keep cropping up. Desserts pass muster. The wine list is a good short one. House French Duboeuf is £6.50. CELLARMAN'S CHOICE : Croffta, Müller-Thurgau 1984, £9.50; Ch. Phélan-Ségur, St-Estèphe 1978, £27.

CHEF: M.E. Winstone    PROPRIETORS: Mr and Mrs M.E. Winstone
OPEN: all week, exc Sun L and Tue
CLOSED: Dec and Jan
MEALS: 12 to 1.30, 7 to 9
PRICES: £20 (£24), Set L and D £17 (£20), Snacks from £1.25. Service inc
CARDS: Access, Visa
SEATS: 35. Private parties: 35 main room. Car-park, 30 places. Children welcome. Smart dress preferred. Music
ACCOMMODATION: 7 rooms, all with bath/shower. B&B £25 to £46. Baby facilities. Garden. Scenic. Doors close at midnight. Confirm by 5 [GHG]

---

**TREARDDUR BAY  Gwynedd**                                                    map 4

## Bay Leaf

Lôn Sant ffraid, Trearddur
Bay, Anglesey LL65 2YR                                          COOKING 1
TREARDDUR BAY (0407) 860415                                        COST £20

Half of Trearddur Bay's GNP is earned in the month of August. No wonder, then, that the Bay Leaf shifts from five nights a week to seven when the children are let out from school. This was discovered by one reader on a stroll round the bay. She couldn't believe her luck. It is not a vegetarian restaurant, but that way of life and style of cooking seems closest to the ideals of the owners and, at least, some of the staff. One waiter in particular, 'seemed to act as quality control' in his advice to enquiring diners. There appears a delight in food – three colours of peppercorn in the mills; elaborate fruit garnishes to vegetarian main courses – that is infectious, even if quantities may be daunting. Meat eaters will get five vegetables with their main course. Recommended vegetarian dishes have included good soups; buckwheat pancake stuffed with nuts, sweetcorn and mushrooms, garnished with stuffed olives, orange twist and toasted almonds; mushrooms in garlic; cashew nut and mushrooms au poivre and a cashew nut and mushroom bake. The cornucopia of food is never-ending, and coffee cups are refilled at no extra cost. A short wine list covers diabetic and low-alcohol labels and some organics. Dress rules are not imposed but, despite the holiday spirit, 'shorts and scruffy jeans are frowned on.' House French wine, £5.50.

CHEFS: Anthony Pierce and Rita Radcliffe    PROPRIETOR: Anthony Pierce
OPEN: Tue to Sat D; all week D Aug
MEALS: 7 to 10.30
PRICES: £12 (£17)
CARDS: Access, Diners, Visa
SEATS: 34. Private parties: 24 main room. Car-park, 18 places. Vegetarian meals. Children's helpings. Wheelchair access (also WC). Music

---

**TREFRIW  Gwynedd** map 4

## *Chandler's*

| | |
|---|---|
| Trefriw LL27 0JH | COOKING **2** |
| LLANRWST (0492) 640991 | COST £24 |

The village was once a port for barges carrying slate down river to Conwy. This was indeed the village chandlery. Now it looks a little like a schoolroom, because of the desks. Readers of modern whodunnits may recognise the village as the birthplace of Brother Cadfael, Ellis Peters' monk sleuth. Chandlers is a surprise for the area and deserves more recognition. There is a spirit to please and a willingness to try. The menu is kept short and varies only in detail over periods: veal, sirloin steak, lamb, chicken, duck or quail, fresh fish of the day. A passing customer was surprised and delighted by the zing of the lamb, roast with a mustard glaze, and the fresh moistness of the large fillet of sewin. Vegetables are good. A vegetarian dish is always available; the bread is good and home baked. The urge to incorporate the greengrocer's shop in simple things like salads, and as trimmings to this and that, might be moderated. There is a totally un-doctrinaire wine list: short, inexpensive, a little light on detail, with some excellent 'specials' on a fast-changing supplement. House French, £5.85. CELLARMAN'S CHOICE : Rothbury Estate, Syrah 1986, £9.85; Rioja Gran Reserva 1978, £10.95. Bottled beer (from Kenya, Israel, West Germany, Brazil) is a speciality. The coffe is unlimited.

CHEF: Adam Rattenbury  PROPRIETORS: Adam and Penny Rattenbury and Tim Kirton
OPEN: Tue to Sat, D only
MEALS: 7 to 10
PRICES: £14 (£20)
CARDS: Access, Visa
SEATS: 36. Private parties: 36 main room. Car-park, 10 places. Vegetarian meals. Children welcome. No smoking. Music

---

**TRELLECH  Gwent** map 4

## *Village Green*

| | |
|---|---|
| Trellech NP6 4PA | COOKING **1** |
| MONMOUTH (0600) 860119 | COST £16−£30 |

Once the Crown Inn, now a restaurant and brasserie (where there is a daily developing blackboard menu), this provides rough and ready, and fairly approximate, modern cooking. Just as the marcher Earls of Gloucester brought French habits to the happily Welsh population (leaving a motte and bailey castle as their relict), so now the French influence is represented by Raymond Blanc's tartare of salmon. A John Dory with ginger and chive butter sauce showed that the daily fish dish can be satisfactory, and other good reports have come in for baked cod in a cream sauce, pastry and an admirable end-of-meal tart cascading with fresh fruits. House wine from Duboeuf, £5.95.

---

*'I have the distinct impression that this is not a normal hotel at all but a place that arranges indecent private parties.'*  On inspecting in Devon

---

CHEF: Colin Sparks  PROPRIETORS: Bob and Jane Evans
OPEN: Tue to Sat
MEALS: 12 to 2, 7 to 9.45
PRICES: £18 (£25), Set L £10.50 (£16)
SEATS: 52. Private parties: 10 main room, 18 and 16 private rooms. Car-park, 14 places. Vegetarian meals. Children's helpings on request. No children under 5. Smart dress preferred. No pipes in dining-room. Wheelchair access (1 step, also WC)

---

**WOLF'S CASTLE  Dyfed**                                                     map 4

# ▲ *Stone Hall*

Welsh Hook, Wolf's Castle SA26 5NS
LETTERSTON (0348) 840212                                       COOKING 2
W of A40 between Letterston and Wolf's Castle            COST £16–£22

The unlikely combination of a house going back to the times of Welsh princes, waitresses dressed in traditional Welsh costume, a menu written in French and a dining-room seemingly displaced from south Brittany, shows the abiding charm of the French restaurant experience. There is no regional affiliation in the menu; it is more the moules farcies, salade composée au fromage de chèvre, escargots, truite Dugléré, canard à la vallée d'Auge, nougat glacé sort of Frenchness. But readers report that the food tastes genuine nonetheless. The fish, in any event, is Fishguard, and brill steamed with fennel, and monkfish on a bed of leeks, pleased one inspector. Vegetables are *not* French: three sorts of potatoes, carrots and a ratatouille are hardly Gallic accompaniments for fish. Desserts seem keen on chocolate. Service is halting but friendly and the wine list is simple and French (plus four Germans). House Touraine, Gamay and Sauvignon, £6.90. CELLARMAN'S CHOICE : Juliénas 1986, René Monnet, £9.80; Chablis 1986, Jean-Marc Brocard, £13.60.

---

CHEFS: Martine Watson, Lionel Balland and Denise Andry  PROPRIETORS: Alan and Martine Watson
OPEN: all week, D only Apr to Oct, Tue to Sun D Nov to Mar
MEALS: 7.30 to 9.30
PRICES: £12 (£18), Set D £10.50 (£16) to £11.50 (£17)
CARDS: Access, Amex, Visa
SEATS: 34. Private parties: 45 main room, 30 private room. Car-park, 50 places. Children's helpings
ACCOMMODATION: 5 rooms, all with bath/shower. B&B £28 to £39.50. Deposit: £20 Baby facilities. Garden. TV. Scenic

---

# ▲ *Wolfscastle Country Hotel*

Wolf's Castle, SA62 5LZ                                           COOKING 1
TREFFGARNE (043 787) 225                                         COST £23

A stern stone house on the road from Haverfordwest to Fishguard. The name is more romantic than the building, but the surrounding countryside is magnificent. Visitors have been warmer about the food than the hotel side of things, and have praised the kitchen for 'honest intentions, with good ingredients and no short cuts'. This may still result in a prawn and salmon salad served in a glass, cocktail style, and garnished with a side salad of undressed radish, tomato and lettuce; but it can also rise to a tress of salmon and monkfish in a good creamy saffron sauce. A plain grilled Dover sole, in exemplary condition, was also handled very well. Puddings include favourites, such as bread-and-butter pudding and the Roux brothers' lemon tart, and some well-liked, well-made mousses and parfaits: apricot and brandy mousse, and blackcurrant parfait with custard and blackcurrant sauce, are among those noticed. There is often, if not always, a vegetarian dish among the 10 options in each course. Fish, surprisingly for the location if not the region, is not a strong suit: normally only one fish main course is to be found. The wine list is arranged somewhat haphazardly, for instance, a Rioja appears under 'Burgundy and districts'. There are some fair wines at fair prices. House French is £6 a litre. CELLARMAN'S CHOICE : Mâcon-Lugny les Charmes 1987, £8.50; Pinot Noir, Bourgogne, Faiveley 1985, £12.50.

CHEFS: Alex George and Steve Brown  PROPRIETOR: Andrew Maxwell Stirling
OPEN: all week, D only, and Sun L
MEALS: 12 to 2, 7 to 9.30
PRICES: £14 (£19)
CARDS: Access, Amex, Visa
SEATS: 60. 6 tables outside. Private parties: 50 main room, 150 private room. Car-park, 60 places. Children's helpings. Smart dress preferred. Music. Air-conditioned
ACCOMMODATION: 15 rooms, all with bath/shower. B&B £25 to £40. Deposit: 15%. Children welcome. Pets welcome. Tennis. TV. Phone. Doors close at 12. Confirm by 6

---

**WREXHAM** Clwyd                                                    map 4

## ▲ Llwyn Onn Hall Hotel

Cefn Road, Wrexham LL13 9TT                          COOKING 2
WREXHAM (0978) 261225                                COST £12–£25

Recommendations have come in steadily since this seventeenth-century Welsh manor-house was converted into a hotel in 1985. It is traditional without being imposing, with swagged curtains and plenty of fresh flowers in the dining-room. Both menus – a short daily table d'hôte and an à la carte which changes every six weeks – offer restrained, yet carefully detailed, dishes; among first courses, 'excellent' chunky lobster and pimento terrine wrapped in spinach, other liver pâtés or terrines with home-made brioche and a compôte or chutney to offset them. Main dishes such as lemon sole with lobster sauce; chicken with Dubonnet and grape sauce, veal with wild mushrooms and brandy may be occasionally drowned by their sauce but smoked trout in a cream and chive sauce or sauté chicken breast with apple and mustard sauce, have worked well. Vegetables are plain and desserts are largely modern French ideas along the lines of a white and dark chocolate terrine with a vanilla sauce. Good strong coffee can be taken on the columned verandah. The wine list is short. House French is £5.85. CELLARMAN'S CHOICE : Côtes du Rhône, Ch. du Grand Moulas 1987, £6.85; Chablis, Domaine de Valéry 1987, £15.15. 'Tips are not asked for or expected.'

CHEFS: Gareth Jones and Stephen Rawlinson    PROPRIETORS: Roger and Vanessa Graham-Palmer
OPEN: all week
MEALS: 12 to 2, 7.30 to 9.30
PRICES: £16 (£21), Set L £8.95 (£12), Set D £12.50 (£16). Snacks from £1.50. Service inc
CARDS: Access, Amex, Diners, Visa
SEATS: 60. 5 tables outside. Private parties: 60 main room, 12 private room. Car-park. Children's helpings (Sun L only). Wheelchair access (also WC)
ACCOMMODATION: 13 rooms, all with bath/shower. B&B £46 to £58. Baby facilities. Afternoon teas. Garden. TV. Phone. Scenic. Doors close at 11. Confirm by 6

# Isle of Man

## *La Rosette*

Main Road, Ballasalla
BALLASALLA (0624) 822940

COOKING 1
COST £30

Drinks may be sipped in a new upstairs sitting-room looking over Ballasalla village. In common with a number of Isle of Man restaurants, La Rosette maintains a menu of great length, including fillet steak five ways and eight to 10 varieties of vegetable for every table. It's a wonder there are so many sorts available year round. Addressing a captive audience, development can become arrested. Nonetheless, approvals come in, mentioning the warm welcome from Rosa Phillips and the general desire to please. The length of the menu continues into dessert when no fewer than four hot puddings are offered. A short wine list is firmly based in France, but customers are graciously allowed to bring their own bottles. House wine is £6.95. CELLARMAN'S CHOICE : Morgon, Ch. Gaillard 1986, Mathelin, £12; Pouilly Fumé, Les Foltières 1987, £14.50.

CHEF: Robert Phillips  PROPRIETORS: Robert and Rosa Phillips
OPEN: Mon to Sat, exc Mon L
MEALS: 12 to 2.30, 7 to 10.30
PRICES: £18 (£25). Cover 85p. Licensed, also bring your own: corkage £3
CARDS: Access, Visa
SEATS: 47. Private parties: 24 main room, 8 and 15 private rooms. Children's helpings.
Music

## *Rafters*

9 Duke Street, Douglas
MANX (0624) 72344

COOKING 1
COST £14

The top floor of a department store on the Isle of Man may not seem the most propitious locale for a good meal but Stephen Whitehead, who has the concession, is determined to attract a loyal following for his daytime restaurant. The name reflects the attic site, full of light and beams. Soups, crab in generous quantity, children's menus, all-day breakfasts and 'gorgeous meringues' are a real bonus to a Douglas visit or shopping trip. The cooking is honest and fresh.

Weight-watchers and vegetarians are well catered for. House wines at £5.50 vary as to what was last bought.

CHEF/PROPRIETOR: Stephen John Whitehead
OPEN: Mon to Sat, daytime only
MEALS: 10 to 5.30 (L 12 to 2.30)
PRICES: £9 (£12), Snacks from £1.20. Service inc
CARD: Diners
SEATS: 60. Vegetarian meals. Children's helpings. Wheelchair access (also WC). Music

---

**ONCHAN  Isle of Man**                                                  map 4

## Boncompte's

King Edward Road, Onchan                                  COOKING 1
DOUGLAS (0624) 75626                                      COST £14–£32

If the island is England-in-aspic, then Boncompte's long menu will remind visitors of styles that are not so often found on the mainland. The view over the bay alone is worth the visit, though this place has long been popular with visiting business-people and locals alike. The set-price lunch menu is a fixture and the dinner *carte* offers fresh shellfish as well as the more expected flambé dishes and steaks. The sweets trolley – a juggernaut of whipped cream and calories – is reputedly the only one on the island: they know the route to a businessman's heart. House French is from £6.90. CELLARMAN'S CHOICE : Ch. Castéra, 1983, £9.50; Rioja Gran Reserva 1981, Faustino, £9.50.

CHEF: Jaime Boncompte   PROPRIETORS: Jaime and Jill Boncompte
OPEN: Mon to Sat, exc Sat L
CLOSED: 3 weeks Mar
MEALS: 12 to 2, 7.30 to 9.30
PRICES: £18 (£27), Set L £9 (£14)
CARDS: Access, Diners, Visa
SEATS: 85. Private parties: 85 main room. Car-park, 20 places. Vegetarian meals. Children's helpings. No pipes in dining-room. Wheelchair access (also WC). Music

# Channel Islands

map 1

## *Granite Corner*

Rozel Harbour, Rozel                                                    COOKING 2
JERSEY (0534) 63590                                                       COST £35

Eating on the Channel Islands is not an easy matter. Some of the hotels produce a fair table for residents, but many of the restaurants operate on a lowest-common-denominator principle that is inimical to good food. Granite Corner is in fact French: 'the only French restaurant on the island' may seem a strange claim but not far from the truth. Jean-Luc Robin is from Périgord so the shellfish and fish that bulk so large on his menus are supplemented by confits and foie gras (and cheese from St-Malo). It is sad that the hybrid culture of the islands should have borrowed so little from its immediate neighbour – the parallel of the Costa Brava fish bars springs to mind. The restaurant is tiny, in a fisherman's cottage on the harbour and offers a seasonal menu with daily additions. The centrepiece for many visitors will be an assiette de poissons, according to what was bought that day, or the lobster, mayonnaise or enveloped in pastry, that is almost invariably available. The wine list even includes one bottle from Miguel Torres and benefits from the lack of VAT in its prices. Its makers, however, are not as unfamiliar as English drinkers might expect: Delorme, Duboeuf, Saget, Maufoux. CELLARMAN'S CHOICE : Pouilly Fumé, Clos des Berthiers 1988, £12.50; Mercurey, Domaine de la Renarde 1986, £11.

CHEF: Jean-Luc Robin   PROPRIETORS: Jean-Luc and Louise Robin
OPEN: Tue to Sat, D only
CLOSED: Dec, Jan, Feb
MEALS: 7.45 to 9
PRICES: £22 (£29). Service 10%
CARDS: Access, Amex, Diners, Visa
SEATS: 24. Private parties: 24 main room. No children under 12. Smart dress preferred. Music

*All letters to the* Guide *are acknowledged with an update on latest sales, closures, chef changes and so on.*

*County Round-ups listing additional restaurants that may be worth a visit are at the back of the* Guide, *after the Irish section. Reports on Round-up entries are welcome.*

# ▲ *Longueville Manor* ♟

St Saviour                                                                          COOKING 3
JERSEY (0534) 25501                                                        COST £12−£42

This is all about comfort and reassurance, from antique furniture and pretty
bedrooms, via the pool (more a decorative setting for cocktails than a stage for
athletic vigour) to the food. Barry Forster cooks with the confidence you would
expect of someone who has been through the Ritz and Ettington Park with
Michael Quinn. His dishes are up to date without being at the edge of fashion.
Roast fillet of veal and kidney comes with sweetbread ravioli and garlic confit;
lamb is baked in pastry with a filling of rosemary and onion mousse. Herbs are
from the garden, and there is no shortage of local seafood. Jersey lobster and
crab are served simply as a salad with asparagus vinaigrette, for example,
although ravioli of foie gras with black trumpets and Sauternes is doubtless
somebody's idea of heaven. Menus go out of their way to be accommodating.
The tasting menu runs to eight samplers from the *carte*. The four-course
vegetarian menu slots a basil and tomato soup after a green-piece assembly of
asparagus, French bean and mange-tout in vinaigrette, before parcels of fried
leek and Roquefort, with dessert or cheese to finish. Best value, it is agreed,
comes from the fixed-price menus. Lunch can be any two courses or all three;
dinner is four if you count the mid-meal sorbet. The style is creamed pea and
pear soup, steak and oyster pie, curried monkfish and mussel fricassee, sticky
toffee pudding. A handful of relatively inexpensive wines is listed alongside,
presumably designed to allay the indigestion that can be caused by glancing at
prices of classic and venerable French wines on the full list; but these are nicely
balanced by value from Italy and New Zealand. House wines, £5.75.
CELLARMAN'S CHOICE : Ch. Laroque St-Emilion 1985, £14.15; Sauvignon de
St-Bris 1985, Labouré-Roi 1985, £9.75.

CHEF: Barry Forster   PROPRIETORS: The Lewis family and the Dufty family
OPEN: all week
MEALS: 12.30 to 2, 7.30 to 9.30
PRICES: £31 (£35), Set L £9.50 (£12) to £13.50 (£16), Set D £19.50 (£22). Snacks from
£2.75. Service inc
CARDS: Access, Amex, Carte Blanche, Diners, Visa
SEATS: 65. 8 tables outside. Private parties: 75 main room, 16 private room. Car-park,
30 places. Children welcome. Smart dress preferred. Wheelchair access (also WC).
Air-conditioned
ACCOMMODATION: 33 rooms, all with bath/shower. Rooms for disabled. Lift. B&B £59 to
£134. Deposit: £45. No children under 7. Pets welcome. Afternoon teas. Garden.
Swimming-pool. TV. Phone. Scenic [GHG]

# Northern Ireland

---

**BALLYNAHINCH  Co Down** map 9

## *Woodlands*

29 Spa Road, Ballynahinch BT24 8PT COOKING 1
BALLYNAHINCH (0238) 562650 COST £25

Guests study the menu in an ambience of gently faded elegance, seated on sofas by a large open fire in the drawing-room. The eighteenth-century house and grounds, set deep in the quiet of the countryside, reek of charm and character and promote an unhurried mood due partly to the skill of owner David Sandford, who gives a friendly welcome without intruding. The food shows French influences and offers some interesting ideas, even if these don't always succeed. County Down pheasant, although tender, has been overpowered by a spiced orange and blackcurrant jelly; loin of pork with apple and cider sauce has been bland and over-creamy. But rack of lamb has been good and there is a pleasing contrast of texture and flavour in chicken livers with bacon and water-chestnuts. Vegetables are good and varied. A complimentary glass of sweet wine is offered with dessert, and petits fours with coffee. Cheese is not always in the best condition. House French is £6.25.

CHEF: Alison Sandford  PROPRIETORS: Alison and David Sandford
OPEN: Thur to Sat, D only. Private parties at other times
MEALS: 7.30 to 9.30
PRICES: Set D £16.25 (£21)
CARD: Access, Visa
SEATS: 45. Private parties: 45 main room, 14 private room. Car-park, 20 places. Children's helpings. No cigars/pipes in dining-room

---

**BELFAST  Co Antrim** map 9

## *Belle Epoque*

103 Great Victoria Street
Belfast BT2 7AG COOKING 1
BELFAST (0232) 323244 COST £23

Curiously mixed reports come in for Belfast's leading French restaurant, but there is no doubt of its popularity. In part this can be explained by the effective décor, using statuettes, mirrors, prints and murals to create a period ambience which is accentuated by the young French service. Some customers are also impressed by the food: for example, mignon de boeuf with oysters, a fricassee of turbot with mixed vegetables, and assiette de cochonnaille have given pleasurable eating. Equally, there are imaginative vegetarian dishes such as grated celeriac in yoghurt with chopped chives and almonds. Others have felt that dishes lack any real French feel or flavour − a criticism which is understandable given that choices of melon with Malibu-flavoured mayonnaise and a skewer of exotic fruit basted with brandy butter have popped up − and that the relatively high prices are not always justified, given slips like separated and heavy sauces. House wine is £3.95.

CHEFS: Alan Rousse and Chris Fitzgerald  PROPRIETOR: J. Delbart
OPEN: Mon to Sat, D only
CLOSED: 25 and 26 December
MEALS: 6 to 12.30 (11.30 Sat)
PRICES: £13 (£19)
CARDS: Access, Diners, Visa
SEATS: 80. Private parties: 40 main room. Vegetarian meals. Children welcome. Music. Air-conditioned

## Strand

| 12 Stranmillis Road, Belfast BT9 5AA | COOKING 1 |
| BELFAST (0232) 682266 | COST £17 |

Once a corner house, now a casual wine bar and restaurant, the Strand has a mixed clientele which 'goes there for the food or to be seen, not both'. The menu changes slowly, is very long for such a place, and runs to imaginative bistro food such as oysters done in two ways; a marinated skewer of fruit browned under the grill; calf's liver with onion, green pepper and tomato sauce; salmon with leek and spinach sauce. Service is good, friendly and fast. One diner commented, 'Northern Ireland has yet to discover wine service.' House French is £4.45. CELLARMAN'S CHOICE : Côtes du Roussillon, £4.95; Wynn's Coonawarra Cabernet Sauvignon, £10.95.

CHEFS: M. Payne, M. McAuley, Bill Bailey and Gary Ardill  PROPRIETOR: Anne Turkington
OPEN: all week, exc Sun L
MEALS: noon to 11
PRICES: £9 (£14)
CARDS: Access, Amex, Diners, Visa
SEATS: 80. Vegetarian meals. Children welcome. Music. Air-conditioned

---

BELLANALECK  Co Fermanagh                                          map 9

## Sheelin

| Bellanaleck | |
| FLORENCECOURT (036 582) 232 | COOKING 1 |
| 4m from Enniskillen | COST £8−£22 |

The quay on Lough Erne is in walking distance of this thatched cottage of a restaurant − not a common sight in Northern Ireland. It is open most of the week in high season but is a daytime café, save on Fridays and Saturdays, for the rest of the year. The acclaim is especially for the unchanging Saturday night four-course gourmet dinner (choose a main course over the phone when booking the table). Hors d'oeuvre, pancakes, meat and vegetables, then good substantial dessert is the form: the filling of the pancakes sometimes varies. It's still good enough for many to return to time and time again but tedium may set in if intervals are too short. Teas get a mention from local regulars and the bakery that shares the premises is a good one. House French is £4.95.

CHEFS: The Cathcart family   PROPRIETOR: Arthur Cathcart
OPEN: Mon to Sat L, Fri and Sat D (Tue to Sun D June to Aug)
MEALS: 12.30 to 2.30, 7 to 9.30
PRICES: £10 (£14), Set L £5 (£8) to £8 (£12), Set D £10 (£14) to £16 (£18), Snacks from £1.20. Service 10% (D only)
CARDS: Access, Amex, Visa
SEATS: 30. Private parties: 30 main room. Car-park. Children's helpings. Smart dress preferred

---

COLERAINE  Co Derry                                                          map 9

## ▲ Macduff's

112 Killeague Road, Blackhill
Coleraine BT51 4HH                                              COOKING 1
AGHADOWEY (026 585) 433                                         COST £24

'The roseate hues of early dawn, The brightness of the day.' These may be the words with which guests at MacDuff's greet the morning; certainly they were composed by a former resident: Mrs Cecil Alexander, wife of the Archbishop of Armagh, who also turned in 'All things bright and beautiful', 'There is a green hill far away' and 'Once in Royal David's city.' The restaurant in this former rectory is found in the basement; travel from red reception to green dining-room. Cooking is less robust than much found in the province – someone even reflected that portions were small, but he weighed 15 stone and was used to more starch. The menu shows some signs of adding to its range in the last twelvemonth, but the parameters of reasonably predictable fare remain constant, with a welcome edge of spice to dishes like Algerian pepper salad; deep fried scampi with chilli dip and chicken tikka with sambals. Chicken breasts used to be cooked with white wine, cream and leeks: now the recipe has the addition of mango slices and pistachios. Vegetables are grown here and taste fresh – they come plentiful. The Erwins are good hosts, the wine list takes in a half-century of bottles and very few halves. It is a decent selection, largely French, properly served – even if all bar one red burgundy is a Beaujolais. House Duboeuf is £5.80.

CHEF: Alan Wade   PROPRIETORS: Joseph and Margaret Erwin
OPEN: Tue to Sat, D only
MEALS: 7 to 9.30
PRICES: £12 (£20)
SEATS: 34. Private parties: 34 main room; 16 private room. Car-park, 30 places. No children under 10
ACCOMMODATION: 6 rooms, 5 with bath/shower. B&B £25 to £45. No children under 10. Garden. Swimming-pool. TV. Scenic. Doors close at 1am. Confirm by 6

## *Hillside Bar*

| | |
|---|---|
| 21 Main Street, Hillsborough BT26 6AE | COOKING 1 |
| HILLSBOROUGH (0846) 683475 and 682765 | COST £26 |

The inviting Georgian pub does extremely good bar food downstairs; the small upstairs restaurant has a restful atmosphere. The menu has charm, although some find it features too many rich, creamy dishes. Helpings are generous but flavours don't always live up to expectations. One reporter's lamb châteaubriand consisted of 'large quantities of boned gigot, awash with a tasteless wine sauce'. Puddings are more pleasing and cheese is well kept. Service can be slow. House French, £5.95.

CHEFS: Noel Doran and John McAvoy   PROPRIETORS: Harlequin (Hillsborough) Ltd
OPEN: all week, exc Sun D
MEALS: 12 to 3 (12.30 to 2 Sun), 7 to 9.30
PRICES: £16 (£22), Snacks from £1.25
CARDS: Access, Amex, Diners, Visa
SEATS: 46. 4 tables outside. Private parties: 30 main room. Vegetarian meals. Children welcome in dining-room. No-smoking area

## *Iona*

| | |
|---|---|
| 27 Church Road, Holywood BT18 9BU | COOKING 1 |
| HOLYWOOD (023 17) 5655 | COST £17–£25 |

The converted loft, above a shop in one of the main streets leading down to the seafront, is misleadingly low-key. Bare contemporary decoration is broken only by prints and candles in pottery brackets on the walls. Against this setting, Dutch-born Bartjan Brave's careful French *carte*, using such luxurious ingredients as foie gras and smoked salmon, can come as a surprise. But the quality lies largely in the cooking: a light aubergine tartlet with a courgette sauce; tasty fish and vegetable mousse on mixed salad leaves; lemon sole and mussels in a restrained tomato sauce; lamb roast rare with an excellent honey and rosemary sauce. There are nouvelle influences scattered through a menu with a largely classical feel, and game or gourmet vegetarian options. Local fish is a feature too: there have been terrines, soups and shellfish platters, mussels with saffron sauce and brill on a spinach sauce. Service has been described as lacking in polish, but young and friendly. There is live music mid-week.

CHEF/PROPRIETOR: Bartjan Brave
OPEN: Tue to Sat, D only
MEALS: 6.15 to 10.30
PRICES: £15 (£18), Set D £17.45 (£17.45) to £20.45 (£20.45). Service inc. Unlicensed, but bring your own: no corkage
SEATS: 30. 9 tables outside. Private parties: 30 main room. Vegetarian meals. Children's helpings on request. Music

*The* Guide *always appreciates hearing about changes of chef or owner.*

| KILLINCHY   Co Down | map 9 |
|---|---|

## *Nick's*

| | |
|---|---|
| 18 Kilmood Church Road | |
| Killinchy BT23 6SB | COOKING **2** |
| KILLINCHY (0238) 541472 | COST £22 |

This is very much a country operation; signs point the way from Killinchy and you find the restaurant inside a converted church in a small village some three miles from Balloo. Original features like arched windows and a beamed ceiling give character to the split-level dining area, but the atmosphere remains very relaxed and chatty, with chef Nick Price popping in and out of the kitchen. There is much to commend in his food: quality local produce including home-smoked trout, a constantly changing daily menu built around half a dozen main dishes, and careful cooking. Many of the ideas are adventurous without gimmickry, a virtue in a region short on novelty. Take as an example an early spring menu: the *al dente* vegetables in a piquant but not overpowering Thai peanut dressing and the apricot-stuffed leg and breast of duck beautifully offset by a spicy plum sauce, both exotic ideas, were carefully adapted so that they really worked on the plate. More traditional steaks, fish with wine and cream sauces and old-fashioned rich puddings served with clotted cream are equally confident. Finish with Irish coffee or a liqueur from an array of over 25. 'For sale' boards have been up at various times, but disposal was rejected in favour of expansion. A wine bar in Belfast is mooted but we have yet to hear. House wines, £5.

CHEFS: Nick Price and   PROPRIETORS: Nick and Kathy Price Jenny McCrea
OPEN: Tue to Sat, D only
CLOSED: 2 weeks Sept to Oct, one week mid-Mar
MEALS: 7.30 to 10
PRICES: £12 (£18)
CARDS: Access, Diners, Visa
SEATS: 45. 3 tables outside. Private parties: 30 main room. Car-park, 60 places. Children's helpings. Music

| PORTRUSH   Co Antrim | map 9 |
|---|---|

## *Ramore*

| | |
|---|---|
| The Harbour, Portrush BT56 8DQ | COOKING **2** |
| PORTRUSH (0265) 824313 | COST £29 |

In a modern building with fine views of the harbour and West Bay, the restaurant offers dinner only but the downstairs wine bar is open most of the day. George McAlpin carries the standard of *nouvelle cuisine* in Northern Ireland, said to be borne higher since the last *Guide*. The menu is quite ambitious and successful when the raw materials are of sufficient standard: foie gras terrine layered with leeks; a trellis of quail with truffles; a combination of crab and turbot with beurre blanc; veal fillet edged with chicken quenelles and with a vin jaune and morel sauce. Desserts include hot soufflés, a puff pastry enclosing exotic fruits and baked in the oven, as well as a modish 'grand dessert' selection. The wine list includes a handful from outside France, including

Opus One 1983 from Mondavi and Rothschild. Many Drouhin burgundies,
Duboeuf Beaujolais and reasonable prices on the list, but there is a deeply
uninformative selection of half-bottles. House French is £6. CELLARMAN'S
CHOICE : Chablis 1987, Drouhin £12; Ch. Fonsèche Haut Médoc 1985, £10.
Booked up at weekends.

CHEF: George McAlpin   PROPRIETORS: John and Joy Caithness, George McAlpin and Jane
McAlpin
OPEN: Mon to Sat, exc Sun and Mon D
CLOSED: last 2 weeks Jan
MEALS: 12.30 to 2.30, 7 to 10
PRICES: £16 (£24), Snacks from £3.25
SEATS· 55. Private parties: 60 main room. Car-park, 8 places. Children welcome. Music.

# Republic of Ireland

Reporting to the *Guide* of restaurants in the Republic has always been sporadic, coming largely from tourists and therefore concentrated on certain areas. In 1989 our sister organisation, Consumers' Association of Ireland, published for the first time a *Consumer Choice Guide to Restaurants in Ireland*, listing 300 eating places recommended by readers of its magazine, *Consumer Choice*. Anyone planning a lengthy trip to the Republic would find this useful; for readers making a short foray the following list of two dozen restaurants, which appear in the *Consumer Choice* guide and have been endorsed by our Irish inspector and *Guide* readers, may suffice.

All reports received on these restaurants will be photocopied for our colleagues in Dublin, and we look forward to being able to offer improved coverage of the Irish Republic next year.

*Consumer Choice Guide to Restaurants in Ireland* is published by the O'Brien Press and distributed in Great Britain by Hodder & Stoughton. Available in bookshops or from Consumers' Association, PO Box 44, Hertford SG14 1SH, price £4.95.

## Dublin City and County

### Eastern Tandoori
34/35 South William Street
Dublin 2
01-710428/710506

### Ernie's Restaurant
Mulberry Gardens
Donnybrook
Dublin 4
01-693300
(Donnybrook Mews, off Main Street, behind block of shops and pub)

### Kapriol Restaurant
44 Lower Camden Street
Dublin 2
01-751235/985496

### Westbury Hotel (Russell Room)
Off Grafton Street
Dublin 2
01-791122

### Park Restaurant
26 Main Street
Blackrock
Co. Dublin
01-886177

## *King Sitric*

East Pier
Howth
Co. Dublin
01-325235/326729

# East

## *Dunderry Lodge*

Dunderry
Robinstown
Navan
Co. Meath
046-31671
(Between Navan and Athboy)

## *Hunter's Hotel*

Rathnew
Co. Wicklow
0404-40106
(On Greystones–Rathnew road; turn
off N11 at Ashford or Rathnew)

# South East

## *Lacken House*

Dublin Road
Kilkenny
056-61085/56511
(In the city, at start of N10 at Carlow)

## *Neptune Restaurant*

Ballyhack
Co. Wexford
051-89284
(In Ballyhack village, on Waterford
estuary, 19km from New Ross)

## *Cedar Lodge*

Carribbyrne
Newbawn
Co. Wexford
051-28386/28436
(19km west of Wexford, on N25
Wexford–Waterford)

# Cork City and County

## *Arbutus Lodge Restaurant*

Montenotte
Cork
021-501237
(Near St Luke's Cross)

## *Crawford Gallery Cafe*

Emmet Place
Cork
021-274415

## *Billy Mackesy's*

(Bawnleigh House)
Ballinhassig
Co. Cork
021-771333
(On 'back' Kinsale road)

## *Blue Haven Hotel*

Pearse Street
Kinsale
Co. Cork
021-772209

## *Ballymaloe House*

Shanagarry
Midleton
Co. Cork
021-652531
(On L35, 3km outside Cloyne on the
Ballycotton Road)

# South West

## *Doyle's Seafood Restaurant*

John Street
Dingle
Co. Kerry
066-51174

## *The Half Door*

John Street
Dingle
Co. Kerry
066-51600

## Foley's Seafood and Steak Restaurant
23 High Street
Killarney
Co. Kerry
064-31217

## Nick's Restaurant
Main Street
Killorglin
Co. Kerry
066-61219

# West

## The Cloister
Abbey Street
Ennis
Co. Clare
065-29521

## Rosleague Manor Hotel
Letterfrack
Co. Galway
095-41101
(Off main Clifden–Westport road,
11km from Clifden)

# North and North West

## Cellars Restaurant
Clanbrassil Street
Dundalk
Co. Louth
042-33745/35684
(In Backhouse Centre)

## Reveries Restaurant
Rosses Point
Co. Sligo
071-77371

## Knockmuldowney House
Culleenamore
Co. Sligo
071-68122
(5km from Strandhill on
Ballisodare–Strandhill road)

# County round-ups

Last year's innovation of County round-ups was popular with readers and this year we give a revised selection. All the eating places listed below have been recommended by readers but for one reason or another have not graduated to the main listings. They are not places that simply failed at inspection. We hope the list will be especially useful for anyone travelling round the country. All reports on these places would be most welcome.

## England

### Avon

**Bristol** *Anchor* Church Street, Oldbury on Severn (0454 413331). Imaginative pub food.
*Grand City* 5-6 Triangle South (0272 291975). Good Chinese in city centre.
*Millwards* 40 Alfred Place, Kingsdown (0272 245026). Cordon Vert vegetarian food.
*Neil's Bistro* 112 Princess Victoria Street, Clifton (0272 733669). Good bistro food.
*Restaurant du Gourmet* 43 Whiteladies Road, Clifton (0272 736230). Long-established French restaurant.
*Rocinantes* 85 Whiteladies Road (0272 734482). Popular tapas bar.
**Bath** *Circus Restaurant* 34 Brock Street (0225 330208). Comfortable rooms and restaurant near John Wood's Circus.
*Combe Grove Manor* Shafts Road, Monkton Combe (0225 834644). Country house ambience.
*David's* 17 Pulteney Bridge (0225 464636). Food atop the Avon weir.
*Number Five* Argyle Street (0225 444499). French café near Pulteney Bridge.
*Pump Room* Stall Street (0225 444477). Coffee and tea (or waters) in elegance.
*Sally Lunn's* 4 North Parade Passage (0225 461634). Best buns.

### Bedfordshire

**Aspley Guise** *Moore Place* The Square (0908 282000). Gracious dining.
**Broom** *Cock* 23 High Street (0767 314411).
**Dunstable** *Mings* 168 High Street North (0582 662477). Chinese food.
**Houghton Conquest** *Knife and Cleaver* The Grove (0234 740387). Upmarket pub food.

**Leighton Buzzard** *Akash Tandoori* 50 North Street (0525 372316). Tandoori.
**Turvey** *Three Fyshes* Bridge Street (023 064 264). Brewing their own beers.
**Woburn** *Black Horse* Bedford Street (0525 290210). Good pub food.

## Berkshire

**Cookham** *Alfonso's* 19-21 Station Hill Parade (0628 525775). Trattoria loved by locals.
**Hungerford** *Galloping Crayfish* 3 The Courtyard, 24 High Street (0488 84008). Wine bar.
**Maidenhead** *Monkey Island Hotel* Bray on Thames (0628 23400). Table with a view.
**Newbury** *Dew Pond* Kings Clere Road, Old Burghclere, nr Newbury (063 527408). Revamped and improved Chinese restaurant.
**Wargrave** *Warrener* Warren Row, nr Wargrave (0628 822803). Cottage dining in style.
**Windsor** *Hong Kong* 2 Alexandra Road (0753 859979). Good take-away.

## Buckinghamshire

**Amersham** *King's Arms* 3 High Street (0494 726333). Good food in market town hotel.
**Aylesbury** *Bottle and Glass* On the Oxford Road, Gibralter, nr Aylesbury (0296 748488). Fifteenth-century beamed pub.
**Milton Keynes** *Hatton Court Hotel* Bullington End, Hanslope (0908 510044). Gothic revival and jacuzzis.
**Wendover** *Rising Sun* Little Hampden, nr Wendover (0240 28360). Pub food.

## Cambridgeshire

**Cambridge** *Browns* 23 Trumpington Street (0223 461655). For feeding the family.
*Free Press* 7 Prospect Row (0223 68337). Real ale and imaginative pub cooking.
*King's Pantry* 9 Kings Parade (0223 321551). Vegetarian restaurant.
*Old Orleans* Millers Yard, 10–11 Mill Lane (0223 322777). American-style eaterie.
*Peking Restaurant* 21 Burleigh Street (0223 354755). Szechuan and Peking food.
*Waffles* 71 Castle Street (0223 312569). Serves only waffles.
**Huntingdon** *Old Bridge Hotel* 1 High Street (0480 52681). Very good wines.
**Melbourn** *Pink Geranium* Station Road (0763 260215). Rolls-Royces and haute cuisine.
*Sheen Mill* Station Road, nr Royston (0763 261393).
**Peterborough** *Bistro 29* 29 Bridge Street (0733 61996). Very good bistro food.

## Cheshire

**Altrincham** *Hale Wine Bar* 108 Ashley Road, Hale (061-928 2343). Wine bar food.
**Cheadle** *Topkapi* 7A Wilmslow Road (0538 4912915). Turkish foods, meze and kebabs.
**Chester** *Aphrodites* Gamul House, 52 Lower Bridge Street (0244 319811). Greek Cypriot food at reasonable prices.

*La Brasserie* Chester Grosvenor Hotel, Eastgate Street (0244 324024). Stylish 'brasserie' glitz.

*Fourgate's* 126 Foregate Street (0244 315046). Wine bar and restaurant.

*Franc's* 14 Cuppin Street (0244 317952). Young fogeys' French café.

**Knutsford** *Friedlander's* 48 King Street (0565 54677). Traditional German flavours and presentation.

**Macclesfield** *Marco Polo* Lilac Cottage, New Road, Prestbury (0625 829466). Italian restaurant.

**Nantwich** *Churche's Mansion* 150 Hospital Street (0270 625933). Sixteenth-century, eating in style.

## Cleveland

**Guisborough** *King's Head* Newton under Roseberry, nr Great Ayton (0642 722318). Good value, beautiful walks.

**Hartlepool** *Krimo's* 8 The Front, Seaton Carew (0429 266120). Italian restaurant much loved by locals.

**Kirklevington** *Martha's Vineyard* Kirklevington Country Club, Thirck Road (0642 780345). Enterprising bistro.

**Saltburn-by-the-Sea** *Grinkle Park Hotel* Easington (0287 40515). Rooms in a Victorian house.

**Stockton-on-Tees** *Barnacle* 13–15 Dovecot Street (0642 602000). Fish restaurant.

*Waiting Room* 9 Station Road, Eaglescliffe (0642 780465). Home-made café food.

**Yarm** *Santoro* 47 High Street (0642 781305). Italian trattoria.

## Cornwall

**Cawsand** *Karen's Kitchen* Garrett Street (0752 822314). Fish restaurant.

**Falmouth** *Nansidwell Country House* Mawnan, nr Falmouth (0326 250340). Gracious living, fine situation.

*Trengilly Wartha Inn* Nancenoy, Constantine (0326 40332). A young team trying hard.

**Fowey** *Fowey Brasserie* 1 Lostwithiel Street (0726 832649). Fish soup, French cooking.

**Helford** *Shipwright's Arms* Helford village, nr Helston (0326 23235). Fish and shellfish by the water's edge.

**Helston** *New Inn* Manaccan, nr Helston (0326 23323). Good pub cooking.

**Penzance** *Count House* Botallack, St Just (0736 788588). Views of the sunset while eating dinner.

*Ma Cuisine* 5 Alverton Street (0736 63814). A personal, small restaurant.

*Mounts Bay Vineyard* Tolver Water, Long Rock (0736 60774). All-day eating.

## Cumbria

**Bowness-on-Windermere** *Jackson's Bistro* West End, St Martins Place (096 62 6264). Busy holiday restaurant.

**Carlisle** *Skinburness Hotel* Skinburness, Silloth on Solway (0697 332332). Refurbished hotel.

**Cleator** *Shepherd's Arms* Ennerdale Bridge (0946 861249). Small country hotel and pub.

**Cockermouth** *Wythop Mill* Embleton (0596 81394). Restored mill and café-restaurant.

**Kendal** *Greenriggs Country House Hotel* Underbarrow, nr Kendal (0448 8387). Setting and atmosphere.

**Keswick** *Dog & Gun* 2 Lake Road (0596 73463). Cheerful town centre pub.

**Kirkby Lonsdale** *Cobwebs Country House* Leck, Cowan Bridge (0524 272141). Good value.

**Penrith** *The Old Church Hotel* Ullswater, Watermillock (07684 86204). Nice furnishings, careful cooking.

*Leeming Country House* Watermillock (0853 6622). Luxury accommodation.

## Derbyshire

**Chapel-en-le-Frith** *Brief Encounter* The Old Station Master's House, South Station (0298 812030). Ambitious small restaurant.

**Derby** *Boaters Bar and Restaurant* 17 Friargate (0332 40581).

*Sarang* 14 Peartree Road (0332 44815). Indian wholefood and vegetarian.

**Matlock** *Riber Hall* (0629 582795).

## Devon

**Dartmouth** *Ford House* 44 Victoria Road (080 43 4047). Bed and breakfast.

**Doddiscombsleigh** *Nobody Inn* (0647 52394). Very fine wines.

**Exeter** *Agricultural Inn* Brampford Speke (0392 841868). Country pub.

*The Cafe at the Meeting House* 38 South Street (0392 410855). Wholefood.

*Woodhayes* Whimple, nr Exeter (0404 822237). Quiet country house, new owners.

**Honiton** *Combe House* Gittisham, nr Honiton (0404 42756). Beautiful house and setting.

**Ilfracombe** *Whites* 12 Beach Road, Hele Bay (0271 62821). Small seaside restaurant.

**Kingsteignton** *Old Rydon Inn* Rydon Road (06216 54626). Popular pub restaurant.

**Modbury** *Modbury Pippin* 35 Church Street (0548 830765). Small country town restaurant.

**Newton Abbot** *Pizza Cafe* 50 Queen Street (0626 55102). Simple pizzas in market town.

**Okehampton** *Castle Inn* Lydford (0822 82242). Good pub food and rooms.

**Plymouth** *Yang Cheng* Western Approach (0752 660170). Good Cantonese cooking, dim-sum.

**Torquay** *Old Vienna* 6 Lisburne Square (0803 295861). Cooking with Austrian accent.

**Totnes** *Willow* 87 High Street (0803 862605). Vegetarian.

## Dorset

**Blandford Forum** *Marigold Cottage* High Street, Spetisbury, nr Blandford Forum (0258 452468). Lunches and teas.

**Bournemouth** *Coriander* 14 Richmond Hill (0202 22202). Mexican 'brasserie'.

**Dorchester** *Old Bakehouse Hotel* Piddletrenthide (0300 4305). Exotic cooking in English countryside.

**Maiden Newton** *Le Petit Canard* 56 Dorchester Road (0300 20536). Good value small country restaurant.

**Shaftesbury** *Old Bakery* 14 Salisbury Street (0747 52069). English cookery.

**Weymouth** *Hamilton's* 5 Brunswick Terrace (0305 789544). Healthy eating award-winners.

*Sibleys* The Esplanade (0305 782196). Family seaside eating.

# Durham

**Consett** *Pavilion* 2 Station Road (0207 503388). Good service, Cantonese cooking.

**Darlington** *Eastern Bamboo* 194 Northgate (0325 461607). Careful Chinese cooking.

*Hall Garth Country House Hotel* Coatham Mundeville (0325 300400). Ancient house with antiques.

**Durham** *Hallgarth Manor* Pittington (091 3721188). Small country house hotel.

*Rafters* 25A Claypath (0913 842909). Up a floor, good bistro food.

**Neasham** *Newbus Arms Hotel and Restaurant* Neasham, nr Darlington (0325 721071). Bistro and hotel.

**Stanley** *Oak Tree Inn* Tantobie, nr Stanley (0207 235445). Food and wines in former manor-house.

**Teesdale** *Fox and Hounds* Cotherstone, Barnard Castle (0833 50241). Pub food, many beams.

# Essex

**Braintree** *Braintree Chinese* 3 Rayne Road (0376 24319). Reliable.

**Broxted** *Whitehall* (0279 850603). Upmarket hotel, convenient for Stanstead airport.

**Burnham-on-Crouch** *Contented Sole* 80 High Street (0621 782139). Fish, steaks and wine.

**Colchester** *Colne Valley Tandoori* 110 High Street, Earls Colne (0787 223380). Popular curry-house.

**Dedham** *Terrace Restaurant*, Dedham Vale Hotel, Stratford Road (0206 322273). Upmarket.

**Great Yeldham** *White Hart* Poole Street (0787 237250). Beamed pub, extensive grounds.

**Ilford** *Bolaka* 132 Cranbrook Road (01-554 5395). Indian; good service.

**Leigh-on-Sea** *Osborne Bros* Billet Wharf, High Street (0702 77233). Shellfish and jellied eels.

**Westcliff-on-Sea** *Oldham's* 13 West Road (0702 346736). Fish and chips, friendly service.

**Witham** *Crofter's* 25 Maldon Road (0376 511068). Wine-bar-style food.

# Gloucestershire

**Awre** *Red Hart Inn* Newham-on-Severn (0594 510220). Bar meals al fresco.

**Bledington** *Kings Head* The Green, nr Kingham (060 871 365). Specials on the board are best.

**Blockley** *Crown Inn and Hotel* High Street, nr Moreton-in-Marsh (0386 700245). Cracking pub food.

**Charingworth** *Charingworth Manor* nr Chipping Campden (038 678 555).
Luxury, at a price.

**Cheltenham** *Forrest's Wine Bar* 1 Imperial Lane, The Promenade (0242 238001).
Longstanding wine bar.

*Number Twelve* 12 Suffolk Parade (0242 584544). French cooking, modern
touch.

**Chipping Campden** *The Malt House* Broad Campden (0386 840295). Priority to
residents.

**Cirencester** *Shepherds Bistro* Fleece Hotel, Market Place (0285 65807/8/9). Grills
the main attraction.

**Lechlade** *Trout Inn* St Johns Bridge (0367 52313). Riverside garden the hook.

**Little Washbourne** *Hobnails Inn* nr Tewkesbury (024 262 237/458). Soft baps a
speciality.

**Moreton-in-Marsh** *Annie's* 3 Oxford Street (0608 51981). English and French
country cooking.

**Shurdington** *The Greenway* nr Cheltenham (0242 862352). Reliable, good
value.

**Winchcombe** *Wesley House* High Street (0242 602366). Beamed lounge, warm
welcome.

## Greater Manchester

**Chorlton** *Billies* 115 Manchester Road (061-881 9338). Vegetarian and vegan.

**Manchester** *Pizzeria Bella Napoli* 6 Booth Street (061-236 1537). Friendly and
reliable.

*Deansgate Restaurant*, Ramada Renaissance Hotel, Blackfriars Street
(061-835 2555). New large chain hotel restaurant.

*Gaylord*, Amethyst House, Spring Gardens (061-832 6037). Old-style Indian.

*Royal Orchid* 36 Charlotte Street (061-236 5183). Run by owners of Siam Orchid
(see entry).

**Salford** *Salford College of Technology* Frederick Road (061-736 6541). Cheap
dinners, even cheaper lunches.

**Worthington** *Kilhey Court* Chorley Road (0257 423083). Lakeside setting.

## Hampshire

**Beaulieu** *Montagu Arms Hotel* Palace Lane (0590 612324). Rooms and restaurant.

**Crampmoor** *Mandarin Chef* Winchester Road (0794 512170). Chinese
restaurant.

**Hartley Wintney** *Mariners* 48 High Street (025 126 2273). Fish.

**Liphook** *Old Thorns* Longmoor Road (0428 724555). Japanese restaurant.

**Rotherwick** *Tylney Hall Hotel* nr Hook (0256 764881). Large country house
hotel.

**Southampton** *Town House* 59 Oxford Street (0703 220498). Vegetarian meals.

## Hertfordshire

**Barley** *Fox & Hounds* High Street, nr Royston (076 384 459). Pub-brewery, bar
food.

**Burnham Green** *White Horse* 1 White Horse Lane (043879 416). Good pub food.

**Little Wymondley** *Redcoats Farmhouse Hotel* Redcoats Green, nr Hitchin (0438 729500). Welcoming hotel and restaurant.

**Old Hatfield** *The Salisbury Restaurant* 15 The Broadway (070 72 62220). Modern British cooking.

**Ware** *Moynihan* 47 Church Street (0920 463389). Chef/patron cooking.

**Watton-at-Stone** *George and Dragon* High Street (0920 830285). Bar meals.

**Welwyn** *Heath Lodge* Danesbury Park Road (043 871 7064). Luxury country executive and conference hotel and restaurant.

## Hereford & Worcester

**Abberley** *The Elms* Stockton Road, nr Worcester (0299 896666). Hotel with immaculate gardens.

**Broadway** *Goblets Wine Bar*, Lygon Arms, High Street (0386 852255). Wine in touristic luxury.

**Bromsgrove** *Grafton Manor* Grafton Lane (0527 579007). Country house cookery.

**Hereford** *Gaffers* 89 East Street. Wholefood café.

*Governor's Restaurant*, Merton Hotel, 28 Commercial Road (0432 265925). City-centre restaurant and hotel.

**Much Birch** *Old School House* (0981 540006). Guest-house with meals for non-residents.

**Ombersley** *The Venture In* (0905 620552). Pleasant atmosphere.

**Ross-on-Wye** *Meader's* 1 Copse Cross Street (0989 62803). Hungarian.

## Humberside

**Grimsby** *Leon's Family Fish Restaurant* Riverside, 1 Alexandra Road (0472 356282). Fish and chips.

**Hull** *Cerutti's* 10 Nelson Street (0482 28501). Fish restaurant.

**Walkington** *The Manor House* Northlands (0482 881645).Upmarket restaurant with upmarket rooms.

**Willerby** *The Grange Park Hotel* Main Street, nr Beverley (0482 656488). Rooms and restaurant.

## Isle of Wight

**Ventnor** *La Cloche* 10 Pier Street (0983 854562).

## Kent

**Biddenden** *West House Restaurant* 28 High Street (0580 291341). Italian.

**Boughton Monchelsea** *Tanyard Hotel* Wierton Hill (0622 744705). Country hotel and restaurant.

**Canterbury** *George's Brasserie* 71 Castle Street (0227 765658). Reasonably priced French brasserie.

**Eynsford** *Gate House Tea Rooms* Lullingstone Castle. Café.

**Tonbridge** *Office Wine Bar* 163 High Street (0732 353660). Wines and food, on two floors.

**Tunbridge Wells** *Eglantine* 65 High Street (0892 24957). New restaurant, pricey, certainly ambitious.

**Yalding** *Walnut Tree* Yalding Hill (0622 814266). Good wine list.

**Wye** *Wife of Bath* 4 Upper Bridge Street (0233 812540). French provincial cooking.

## Lancashire

**Blackpool** *Robert's Oyster Bar* 92 Promenade (0253 21226). Good oysters and tea.

**Clitheroe** *Brown's Bistro* 10 York Street (0200 26928). Well-liked bistro.

**Crawshawbooth** *Valley Restaurant* 542 Burnley Road (0706 831728). Young people on the up.

**Gressingham** *Mrs Hogg's* nr Hornby (0468 21274). British cooking by a long-standing local favourite.

**Lytham St Anne's** *C'est la Vie*, Dalmeny Hotel, 19–33 South Promenade (0253 712236). Seaside hotel restaurant.

**Preston** *Cayso* 50 St Johns Place (0772 202214). Caribbean cookery.

**Slaidburn** *Hark to Bounty* (02006 246). Pub meals.

**Up Holland** *Le Renoir* Lafford Lane (0695 622105). Haute cuisine and luxury, new chef.

**Whitewell** *Inn at Whitewell* (020 08 222). Fishing, wine merchant, pub, inn and restaurant.

## Leicestershire

**East Langton** *Bell Inn* Main Street (085 884 567). French restaurant in an inn.

**Empingham** *White Horse* Main Street, nr Oakham (078 086 221). Good bar meals.

**Glen Parva** *Manor Restaurant* The Ford, Little Glen Road (0533 774604). Manorial cooking.

**Leicester** *Altro Mondo* 52 Chatham Street (0533 471446). British trattoria.
*Bobby's* 154-156 Belgrave Road (0533 660106). Tandoori café.

**Melton Mowbray** *Stapleford Park* (057 284 522/229). High life with hamburgers.

**Old Dalby** *The Crown Inn* Debdale Hill, Melton Mowbray (0664 823134). A fine country pub with good home cooking.

**Quorn** *Quorn Grange* 88 Wood Lane (0509 412167). Country-house hotel.

**Stretton** *Ram Jam Inn* The Great North Road, Oakham (078 081 776). The best roadhouse, open again after a fire.

**Syston** *La Saison* 72 High Street (0533 606222). French restaurant.

## Lincolnshire

**Barkston** *Barkston House* nr Grantham (0400 50555). Georgian house with modern cooking.

**Burgh le Marsh** *Windmill Restaurant* nr Skegness (0754 810281). Their own windmill provides flour.

**Grantham** *Kings Hotel* 130 North Parade (0476 590800). Town centre hotel.

**Grimsthorpe** *Black Horse Inn* nr Bourne (077 832 247). Georgian coaching-inn and restaurant.

**Horncastle** *Magpies* 73–75 East Street (0658 27004).
*Mantles* The Market Place (0658 26726). Speciality fish restaurant.

**Lincoln** *Brown's Pie Shop* 33 Steep Hill (0522 27330). Pies, pies and more pies.

**Louth** *Mr Chips* 17–21 Aswell Street (0507 603756).
**Northorpe** *Northorpe Hall* nr Gainsborough (0724 763258).

## Merseyside

**Liverpool** *Baltic Fleet* Wapping (051 709 3116). Refurbished pub, good fish.
*Equatorial* 4 Brownlow Hill (051 709 5225). Singaporean cooking.
*Jenny's* Old Ropery, Fenwick Street (051 236 0332). Seafood.
*Orient* 54–54A Berry Street (051 709 2555). Chinese restaurant.
*Tate Gallery Café* The Albert Dock (051 709 3223). Art and coffee.

## Norfolk

**Cromer** *Mirabelle* Station Road, West Runton (0263 75396). Seaside
sophisticates eat here.
**Diss** *Salisbury House* 84 Victoria Road (0379 644738). Restaurant with rooms.
**Framingham Pigot** *Old Feathers* Fox Road (0508 62445). Sophisticated country
cooking.
**Guist** *Tollbridge* Dereham Road (0362 84359). Careful food and presentation.
**King's Lynn** *Peking* 10–12 Railway Road (0553 774115). Szechuan cooking.
**Stow Bardolph** *Hare Arms* (0366 382229). Pub and restaurant.
**Upper Sheringham** *Red Lion* (0263 825408). Good pub, good vegetarian dishes
too.

## North Yorkshire

**Appleton-le-Moors** *Dweldapilton Hall* (0751 5227). Country-house hotel.
**Bainbridge** *Rose and Crown* (0969 50225). Best for bar food.
**Bolton Abbey** *Devonshire Arms* nr Skipton (075 671 441). Delightful
surroundings and restaurant food.
**Burnsall** *Red Lion* nr Skipton (0756 72244). English cooking.
**Fewston** *Swinsty Tea Garden* Fewston House (094 388 637). Vegetarian food on
offer.
**Hawes** *Cockett's* Market Place (09697 312). New ownership getting well
established.
**Harrogate** *Shabab* 1 John Street (0423 500250). Indian: good-value lunch.
**Knaresborough** *4 Park Place* (0423 868002). Small, individual restaurant.
*Bengal Dynasty* 6–8 Bond End (0423 863899). Indian tandoori restaurant.
**Reeth** *Arkleside Hotel* (0748 84200). Personal service, family food.
*Burgoyne Hotel* (0748 84292). Mountainous breakfasts.
**Richmond** *Restaurant on the Green* 5–7 Bridge Street (0748 6229). Coffee house
and restaurant.
**York** *Taylors Tearooms* 46 Stonegate (0904 622865). Coffee house and daytime
restaurant.

## Northamptonshire

**Ashby St Ledgers** *Old Coach House Inn* nr Daventry (0788 890349). Pub
restaurant.
**Burton Latimer** *Water Margin* 26 High Street, nr Kettering (0536 724817).
Cantonese cooking.

**Cogenhoe** *Dunkley's* Castle Ashby station (0604 810546).
**Crick** *Edwards of Crick* The Wharf (0788 822517). Canalside.
**Nassington** *Black Horse Inn* nr Peterborough (0780 782324). Good pub cooking.
**Northampton** *Sun Rise* 18 Kingsley Park Terrace, Kettering Road (0604 711228). Chinese restaurant.
**Stoke Bruerne** *Bruerne's Lock* The Canalside, Towcester (0604 863654). Narrow-boat cooking.

## Northumberland

**Berwick-upon-Tweed** *Scotsgate Tearoom* 1 Sidney Court (0289 308028).
**Corbridge** *Flags 2* 18 Front Street (0434 712536). Good value, jolly atmosphere.
**Morpeth** *Tandoor Mahal* 17 Bridge Street (0670 512420). Indian tandoori.
**Seahouses** *Seafarers* Main Street (0665 720931). Teas.
**Seaton Sluice** *Waterford Arms* Collywellbay Road, Whitley Bay (091 237 0450). Cheerful pub with fine view.
**Stamford** *Masons Arms* Stamford Cott (0665 77275). A terrace on the old north road.

## Nottinghamshire

**Elston** *Coeur de Lion* Elston Towers, Elston, nr Newark (0636 525380). Pastiche Chateau building, French cooking.
**Nottingham** *Chand* 26 Mansfield Road (0602 474103). Basement Indian restaurant.
*Laguna Tandoori* 43 Mount Street (0602 411632).
*Man Ho II* 35–37 Pelham Street, Hockley (0602 474729). Steamed sea bass, crispy lamb, Cantonese/Pekinese cooking.
**Upton** *Cross Keys* Main Street (0636 813269). Good bar food.
**Warsop** *Goff's* Burns Lane (0623 844137). Evident enthusiasm for good food.

## Oxfordshire

**Binfield Heath** *Bottle and Glass* nr Henley-on-Thames (0491 575755). Thatched pub, bar food.
**Burford** *Lamb* Sheep Street (0993 823155). Beautiful high street, a good trip out from Oxford.
**Clanfield** *Plough* Bourton Road (0367 81222). Luxury country cooking.
**Maidensgrove** *Five Horseshoes* nr Henley-on-Thames (0491 641282). Good pub food.
**Oxford** *Browns* 5–9 Woodstock Road (0865 511995). Every undergraduate loves it.
*Michel's Brasserie* 10 Little Clarendon Street (0865 52142).
**Shipton-under-Wychwood** *Shaven Crown* (0993 830330). Magnificent hall roof, good bar food at the back of the courtyard.
**Stanton Harcourt** *Harcourt Arms* (0865 881931). Near Alexander Pope's tower.
**Steeple Aston** *Red Lion* South Street (0869 40225). Village pub with varied food.
**Sutton Courtenay** *Fish Inn* 4 Appleford Road (0235 848242). Pub with chef/proprietor.

**Witney** *Country Pie* 63 Corn Street (0993 703590). Country café restaurant near the centre of town.

## Scilly Isles

**St Martin's** *St Martin's Hotel* (0720 22092). New hotel restaurant.

## Shropshire

**Church Stretton** *Acorn* 26 Sandford Avenue (0694 722495). Wholefood restaurant.

**Diddlebury** *Glebe Farm* nr Craven Arms (0584 76221). Rooms and dinner in Elizabethan farmhouse.

**Ellesmere** *Nightingales* 8 Market Street (0691 622863). Bistro.

**Llanymynech** *Bradford Arms* nr Oswestry (0691 830582). Bar food.

**Norton** *Hundred House Hotel* Shifnal (0952 71353). Good bar food.

**Shrewsbury** *Antonio's* Victorian Arcade, Hills Lane (0743 231244). Trattoria.

*Delanys* St Julians Craft Centre, St Alkmunds Square (0743 60602). Vegetarian restaurant.

*Peach Tree Brasserie* 21 Abbey Foregate (0743 246600). Upmarket bistro facing the abbey.

## Somerset

**Bishops Lydeard** *Kingfishers Catch* Taunton Road (0823 432394). Pretty country pub restaurant.

**Brent Knoll** *Goat House* Bristol Road (0278 760650). Roadside café.

**Doulting** *Brottens Lodge* (0749 88352). Restaurant with rooms.

**Dunster** *The Tea Shoppe* 3 High Street (0643 821304). Good lunches and teas.

**Frome** *The Frome Scene cinema* Christchurch Street West (0373 63549). Mood food for movie buffs.

**Kilve** *Hood Arms* (0278 74210). Good quiche and other bar food: restaurant-style at night.

**Priddy** *The Miners' Arms* nr Wells (0749 870217). Home-grown snails, more restaurant than pub.

**Shepton Mallet** *Bowlish House* Wells Road (0749 2022). Rooms, food and good wine list.

## South Yorkshire

**Barnsley** *Armstrongs* 6 Shambles Street (0226 240113). Nouvelle cuisine, South Yorkshire style.

**Dinnington** *Dinnington Hall Hotel* Falcon Way (0909 569661). Country house rooms.

**Rotherham** *Dragon Pearl* 23 High Street (0709 374994). Cantonese.

**Sheffield** *Bay Tree* 19 Devonshire Street (0742 759254). Vegetarian food, between the University and the city centre.

*Capital* 19 Charles Street (0742 756041). Cantonese.

*Charnwood Hotel* 10 Sharrow Lane (0742 589411). Rooms in converted Georgian house.

*Zing Vaa* 55 The Moor (0742 722432). Chinese.

## Staffordshire

**Lichfield** *Eastern Eye* 19 Bird Street (0543 254399). Indian tandoori.
**Penkridge** *William Harding's House* Mill Street (0785 712955). Enterprising cooking.
**Rugeley** *The Old Farmhouse Restaurant* Armitage (0543 490353). Converted farmhouse near the Trent and Mersey canal.
**Seighford** *Holly Bush* (0785 282280). Good bar food.
**Stone** *La Casserole* 6 Oulton Road (0785 814232). Good-value cooking.
**Swinfen** *Swinfen Hall Hotel* nr Lichfield (0543 481494). Country-house hotel restaurant.

## Suffolk

**Aldeburgh** *Aldeburgh Fish & Chip Shop* 226 High Street (0728 852250). Fresh fish.
**Bradfield Combust** *Bradfield House* Sudbury Road (0284 86301). Atmospheric rooms and restaurant.
**Bury St Edmunds** *Angel Hotel* Angel Hill (0284 753926). Handsome town centre hotel.
**Dunwich** *Ship Inn* St James's Street (0728 73219). Good fresh fish and other bar food.
**Snape** *Golden Key* Priory Road (0728 88510). Pub food.
*Granary Tearooms* Maltings (0728 88302). You can have lobster with your tea.
*Plough and Sail* Maltings (0728 88304). Lobster with your real ale.
**Sudbury** *Friars* 17 Friars Street (0787 72940). French restaurant.
**Walberswick** *Potter's Wheel* Village Green (0502 724468). Shop, gallery and restaurant with a vegetarian bias.
**Yoxford** *Jacey's* Blythburgh House, High Street (0728 77298). Careful cooking, personal attention.

## Surrey

**Addington** *Willow* 88 Selsdon Park Road, South Croydon (01–657 4667). Chinese food.
**Croydon** *Bali Restaurant* 5–6 New Parade, Dorking High Street (0306 886412). Indonesian/Malaysian food.
**Egham** *Next Door* 6 High Street (0784 439496). Suburban café bar.
**Richmond** *Kim's* 12 Red Lion Street (01–948 5777/5779). Singaporean.
*Richmond Brasserie* Tower House, Bridge Street (01–332 2524). Satisfactory brasserie.
**South Croydon** *Kelong* 1B Selsdon Road (01-688 0726). Malaysian/Indonesian.
**Surbiton** *Pattaya* 9 Claremont Road (01-390 3361). Thai.
**Sutton** *Thai Hut* 7 Cheam Road (01-661 9395). Thai.
**West Byfleet** *Chu-Chin-Chow* 63 Old Woking Road (09323 49581). Cantonese food.

## Sussex (East and West)

**Brighton** *Annie's* 41 Middle Street (0273 202051). British bistro.
*Latin in the Lane* 10 Kings Road (0273 28672). Good pasta, cheerful trattoria.
*Melrose* 132 Kings Road (0273 26520). Cypriot café.

*Swans Restaurant* 21 Norfolk Square (0273 721211). Fair English cooking.

**Chichester** *Through the Greenhouse* 23 St Pancras (0243 788814). Theatrical bistro.

**Chilgrove** *White Horse Inn* (024 359 219). Great wine list, new chef.

**Eastbourne** *Bosworth's Wine Bar* 8 Bolton Road (0323 23023). Char-grills and wine.

*Seeracha* 94 Seaside (0323 642867/30502). Thai restaurant.

**Fulking** *Shepherd & Dog* (0791 56382). Bar meals.

**Gatwick** *Gatwick Hilton International* Gatwick Airport (0293 518080). Brunch and airport luxury.

**Little Horsted** *Horsted Place* nr Uckfield (0825 75581). Luxury country house.

**Telham** *Little Hemingfold Farmhouse* nr Battle (0424 64338). Rooms.

**Three Legged Cross** *The Bull* nr Ticehurst (0580 200586). Bar food.

## Tyne & Wear

**Fenham** *Red Herring* 4 Studley Terrace (091-272 3484). Wholefood and a good bread oven.

**Jesmond** *Pizzeria Francesca* 134 Manor House Road (091-281 6586). Pizzas, not pasta.

**Newcastle Upon Tyne** *Fishermans Wharf* 15 The Side (091-232 1057). Fish restaurant.

*Jade Garden* 53 Stowell Street (091-261 5889). Cantonese restaurant.

*New Emperor* Berwick Street (091-222 1333). Late night eating.

*Veggie's* 12 St Mary's Place (091-261 6330). Good vegetarian restaurant.

## Warwickshire

**Alcester** *Rossini* 50 Birmingham Road (0789 762764). International cooking, Italian accents.

**Ansty** *Ansty Hall* Nr Coventry (0203 612222). New country-house conversion of Caroline House.

**Barford** *Glebe Hotel* Church Street, Warwick (0926 624218). Good value in handsome surroundings.

**Leamington Spa** *Poppadums* Bath Street (0926 450986). Indian tandoori restaurant.

**Rugby** *Dilruba* 155 Railway Terrace (0788 542262). Good value Indian restaurant.

**Ryton-on-Dunsmore** *Ryton Gardens* nr Coventry (0203 303517). Wholefood in organic gardening centre.

**Stratford Upon Avon** *Marlowe's* 18 High Street (0789 204999). Fair food in Tudor dining-room.

**Warwick** *Fanshawe's* 22 Market Place (0926 410590). New restaurant on the up.

## West Midlands

**Birmingham** *Gershwin's*, (at Alexandra Theatre) Suffolk Street, Queensway (021-633 4682).

*Casa Paco* 7 Fletchers Walk, Paradise Place (021-233 1533). Good value Spanish.

*Henry Wong* 283 High Street, Harborne (021-427 9799). Massive Cantonese in former bank.

*Nutters* 422 Bearwood Road, Warley (021-420 2528). Vegetarian.
**Oldbury** *Jonathan's Hotel* 16-20 Wolverhampton Road (021-429 3757).
Refurbished with accommodation, Victorian-style.
**Stourbridge** *French Connection* 1&3 Coventry Street (0384 390940). Bistro.
**Sutton Coldfield** *Bobby Browns* Bricebridge Pool, Sutton Park
(021-308 8890). Converted boathouse in parkland.
**Walsgrave** *Hotel Campanile* 4 Wigstone Road, Coventry (0203 622311). Budget
hotel.
**Wolverhampton** *Bilash* 2 Cheapside (0902 27762). Good balti dishes.

## West Yorkshire

**Bradford** *Karachi* 15-17 Neal Street (0274 732015). Good cheap curries from
fresh ingredients.
**Holdsworth** *Holdsworth House* Halifax, (0422 240024). Handsome house,
classical cooking, comfortable rooms.
**Huddersfield** *Golden Cock* Farnley Tyas, (0484 663563). Restaurant in a pub.
*Shabab* 37-39 New Street, (0484 549514). Indian tandoori.
**Ilkley** *Sous le Nez* 19-21 Church Street (0943 600566). Herbivores and
carnivores get equal treatment here.
**Leeds** *Conservatory Cafe Bar* 35A Albion Place, (0532 477320). Agreeable
brasserie atmosphere.
**Milnes Bridge** *La Maison* The Old Vicarage, Manchester Road, Huddersfield
(0484 648099).
**Sowerby Bridge** *Java Restaurant* Wharf Street (0422 831654). Indonesian
restaurant within a pub.
**Thunderbridge** *Woodman Inn and Restaurant* nr Huddersfield
(0484 605778). Good pub food.
**Wentbridge** *Wentbridge House* nr Pontefract (0977 620444). Good-quality
lunches.
**Wetherby** *Wetherbys Restaurant* 16 Bank Street (0937 580153). Converted stone
cottages.

## Wiltshire

**Bradford-on-Avon** *Georgian Wine Lodge* 25 Bridge Street (0221 62268). Wine
bar and restaurant.
**Castle Combe** *Manor House Hotel* nr Chippenham (0249 782206). Teas on the
lawn: picture-postcard village.
**Devizes** *Peking Palace* 2 Northgate Street (0380 2513). Chinese.
**Inglesham** *Inglesham Forge* (0367 52298). Ambitious country restaurant.
**Lacock** *Red Lion* High Street (0249 73456). Pub food and accommodation.
**Marlborough** *Bentley's Wine Bar and Bistro* 7 Kingsbury Street (0672 54776).
**Norton** *Vine Tree* nr Malmesbury (0666 3654). Sophisticated pub.
**Rowde** *George and Dragon* High Street (0380 3053). Bar Food.
**Salisbury** *Lamb* Hindon (0747 89573). Good pub food.
**Warminster** *Chinn's* Celebrated Chophouse, 12-14 Market Place
(0985 212245). Daytime cafe.

# Scotland

**Acharacle** (Highland) *Glencripesdale House* Glencripesdale, Loch Sunart, (0967 85263). Fine seafood in remote and comfortable farmhouse.

**Alloway** (Strathclyde) *Burns Byre* Mount Oliphant (0292 43644). Good lamb, but also good vegetarian.

**Auchterhouse** (Tayside) *Old Mansion House Hotel* By Dundee (0826 26366). Improving cookery in handsome surroundings.

**Busta** (Shetland) *Busta House* Mainland (0806 22506). Comfort, views and fair cooking.

**Callander** (Central) *Roman Camp Hotel* Off Main Street, East End (0877 30003). Elaborate cooking.

**Colonsay** (Strathclyde) *Isle of Colonsay Hotel* (095 12 316). Remote location, genuine cooking.

**Cults** (Grampian) *Faraday's* 2 Kirk Brae, nr Aberdeen (0224 869666). Improving cooking.

**Dumfries** (Dumfries & Galloway) *The Old Bank* 94 Irish Street (0387 53499). Restaurant and coffee shop.

**Dunvegan** (Skye) *Harlosh Hotel* (0470 22367). New management, improving cooking.

**Edinburgh** (Lothian) *Bamboo Garden* 57A Frederick Street (031-225 2382). Chinese.

*The Beehive Inn* 18-22 Grassmarket (031-225 7171). Back in the Champany fold, see main entry under Linlithgow.

*Chans* 1 Forth Street (031-556 7118). Chinese.

*Helios Fountain* 7 Grassmarket (031-229 7884). Wholefood vegetarian.

*Hendersons* 94 Hanover Street (031-225 2131). Bistro.

*Kweilin* 19-21 Dundas Street (031-557 1875). Good Cantonese.

*Singapore Sling* 503 Lawnmarket, Royal Mall (031-226 2826). Malaysian.

*Skippers Bistro* 1A Dock Place, Leith (031-554 1018). Best for fish.

*Viva Mexico* 10 Anchor Close, Cockburn Street (031-226 5145). Mexican.

**Gattonside** (Borders) *Hoebridge Inn* (0896 823082). Good pub food.

**Glasgow** (Strathclyde) *Babbity Bowster* 16-18 Blackfriars Street (041-552 5055). Nice atmosphere, offshore view of French brasserie.

*Balbir's Vegetarian Ashoka* 149 Elderslie Street (041-204 0186). Indian vegetarian.

*Buttery* 652 Argyle Street (041-221 8188). New chef, looking good.

*Gypsy Baron* 28 Cheapside Street (041-221 1727).

*Hanrahan's* 16 Nicholson Street (041-420 1071/1069). New chef, cheerful place.

*The Penguin Café* The Roof Top, Princes Square, 48 Buchanan Street (041-2210 303).

*Rab Ha's* 83 Hutchson Street (041-553 1545). Emphasis squarely on Scottish game, meat and fish.

*Triangle* 37 Queen Street (041-221 8758).

**Heiton** (Borders) *Sunlaws House Hotel* Kelso (0573 35331). Nice house.

**Inverness** (Highland) *Dunain Park* (0463 230512). Hospitable and warm country house.

**Irvine** (Strathclyde) *Hospitality Inn* 46 Annick Road (0294 74272). Prize-winning chef, modern international.

**Kentallen** (Highland) *Holly Tree* (0631 74292). Fine views, originally a railway station.

**Kingussie** (Highland) *The Osprey Hotel* (0540 2510). Small county hotel.

**Kirkcaldy** (Fife) *Harbour Bar* 471 High Street (0592 264270). Good pub food.

**Lanark** (Strathclyde) *La Vigna* 40 Wellgate (0555 4320). Scottish Italian in converted plumber's showroom.

**Moffat** (Dumfries & Galloway) *Well View Hotel* Ballplay Road (0683 20184). Handsome guest house.

**Quothquan** (Strathclyde) *Sheildhill Hotel* nr Biggar (0899 20035). Refurbished, new chef, looking good.

**Scourie** (Highland) *Tigh-Na-Mara* Scourie by Larig, Tarbet (0971 2151). Good fish, honestly cooked.

**St Andrews** (Fife) *The New Balaka* 3 Alexandra Place, Market Street (0334 74825). Indian tandoori.

**St Margaret's Hope** (Orkney) *Creel Restaurant* Front Road (0856 83311). Waterfront restaurant, assured fish cookery.

**Ullapool** (Highland) *Ceilidh Place* 14 West Argyle Street (0854 2103). Mellow paradise for happy holidays.
*Frigate* Shore Street (0854 2488). Quayside cafe and restaurant for fish.
*Turf and Surf* Harbour Lights Hotel, Garve Road (0854 2222). Surf and turf.

**Timsgarry** (Isle of Lewis) *Baile Na Cille* Outer Hebrides (0851 75242). Good food, genuine family atmosphere.

**Weem** (Tayside) *Ailean Chraggan Hotel* by Aberfeldy (0887 20346). Very fresh fish, the hotel kitchen has its own viviers.

# Wales

**Aberdovey** (Gwynedd) *The Maybank Hotel* 4 Penhelig Road, Penhelig (0654 72500). New owners.

**Aberystwyth** (Dyfed) *The Pavilion Restaurant* The Royal Pier (0970 624888). Stylish place, trying hard.

**Betws-y-Coed** (Gwynedd) *Royal Oak Hotel* Holyhead Road (0690 2219). Grill room with river views.

**Bylchau** (Clwyd) *Sportmans Arms* Bryntrillyn, nr Denby (0745 70214). Good food in walker's paradise.

**Borth-y-Gest** (Gwynedd) *Blossoms Restaurant* Ivy Terrace, Portmadoc (0766 513500). Well presented cooking, up-and-coming.

**Caernarfon** (Gwynedd) *Seiont Manor Hotel* Llanrug (0286 76887/77349). A world of luxury.

**Cardiff** (South Glamorgan) *Blas-Ar-Cymru/A Taste of Wales* 48 Crwys Road (0222 382132). Welsh cookery.

*Trillium* 40 City Road (0222 463665). Wide choice of wines, formal cooking.

**Carmarthen** (Dyfed) *Eifiona's Restaurant* 31 Lamnas Street (0267 230883). Sunday lunch is very Welsh.

**Cilgerran** (Dyfed) *Castle Kitchen* High Street (0239 615055). Cottage restaurant.

**Craig-y-Don** (Gwynedd) *Floral Restaurant* Victoria Street, Llandudno (0492 75735). Good, fresh dishes.

**Criccieth** (Gwynedd) *Blue China Tearooms* Lon Felin (0766 523239). Handsome café by the lifeboat station.

**Dinas Cross** (Dyfed) *Freemason's Arms* (03486 243).

*Rose Cottage Restaurant* Newport (0348 6301). On the up.

**Efailwen** (Dyfed) *Cegin Yr Efel Isaf* (0994 7653). Well supported by local residents.

**Erbistock** (Clwyd) *Boat Inn* nr Wrexham (0978 780143). Deeside dining.

**Fishguard** (Dyfed) *Plas Glyn Y Mel* (0348 872296). Large house and gardens, ambitious menu.

**Glynarthen** (Dyfed) *Penbontbren Farm Hotel* nr Cardigan (0239 810248). Country cooking.

**Goodwick** (Dyfed) *Farmhouse Kitchen* Glendower Square, nr Fishguard (0348 873282). Brtish cooking.

**Letterston** (Dyfed) *Something's Cooking* The Square (0348 840621). Fish and chips.

**Llanaber** (Gwynedd) *Llwyndu Farmhouse* nr Barmouth (0341 280144) Farm guest-house above Cardigan Bay, creative cooking.

**Llandudno** (Gwynedd) *Lanterns Restaurant* 7 Church Walk (0492 77924). Good fish soup.

**Llangammarch Wells** (Powys) *The Lake Hotel* (059 12202). Food is improving.

**Miskin** (Mid-Glamorgan) *Miskin Manor Hotel* (0443 224204). Country-house hotel and restaurant.

**Mold** (Clwyd) *The Sybarite* 33 New Street (0352 3814). Sybaritic atmosphere to please all tastes.

**Newport** (Dyfed) *Trewern Arms* Nervern (0239 820395).

**Newport** (Gwent) *Celtic Manor* Coldra Woods (0633 413000). 'Welsh Chef of the Year'.

**Pontfaen** (Dyfed) *Gelli Fawr Country House* Newport, nr Fishguard (0239 820343). Handsome accommodation, impressive new arrival.

**Porthkerry** (South Glamorgan) *Egerton Grey Country House Hotel* (0446 711666). Sumptuous refurbishment.

**Rhyd-Ddu** (Gwynedd) *Cwellyn Arms* Caernarfon (076686 321). Hillwalker's delight.

**Swansea** (West Glamorgan) *Keenans* 82 St Helens Road (0792 644111). New and ambitious restaurant.

*P.A.'s* 95 Newton Road, Mumbles (0792 367723). Coffee shop, bistro, wine bar.

*Rossi Seafood* The Quayside, 3 Victoria Quay (0792 648785). Fish restaurant.

**Trefriw** (Gwynedd) *Hafod House Hotel* (0492 640029). Comfortable rooms, good welcome.

# Isle of Man

**Castletown** *Chablis Cellar* 21 Bank Street (0624 823527). Cheerful quayside restaurant suitable for all ages.
**Douglas** *L'Experience* Summerhill (0624 23103). Improving French bistro.
*Mon Plaisir* Victory Court, Prospect Hill (0624 77299). New and ambitious French restaurant.
**Ramsey** *Grand Island Hotel* Bride Road (0624 812455). Grand in name and intent.
*Harbour Bistro* 5 East Street (0624 814182). Not too expensive.

# Northern Ireland

**Bushmills** *Auberge de Seneirl* 28 Ballyclough Road, Co Antrim (0265 741536). Sophisticated cooking; with accommodation.
**Groomsport** *Red Pepper* Main Street, Co Down (0247 270097). Good sauces, good variety.
**Hillsborough** *Plough Inn* 3 The Square, Co Down (0846 682985). Good high tea.

# Channel Islands

**Rozel Bay** *Apple Cottage* St Martin's, Jersey (0534 61002). Beautiful location, very good lunches.
**Sark** *Aval de Creux Hotel* (0481 832036). Peace, comfort and good cooking.
**St Helier** *La Capannina* 65-67 Halkett Place, Jersey (0534 34602). Enjoyable Italian restaurant.
*O Fado* 20 Esplanade, Jersey (0534 71920). Portuguese food.

# Desperately seeking Flora

**John Beishon**, Director of the Association for Consumer Research, recounts just how hard it is to reconcile a low-fat diet with eating out in Britain today.

Britain has one of the highest levels of heart disease in the world. Recent figures show that 500 people die a day from heart disease and strokes. The tragedy is that so many of these are premature deaths, particularly men dying in their fifties. The cost to individuals, families and the community is enormous, yet much of this disease is avoidable and the greatest villain of the piece is the British diet. There is controversy surrounding many aspects of diet and disease but the one thing virtually all authorities agree on is that high levels of fat consumption, and particularly saturated fats, are the culprits associated with heart disease.

There are encouraging signs that people are changing their home cooking and eating habits but what about eating out? Is the restaurant world taking this issue seriously? Sadly, the answer seems to be that it is not. Restaurants are still serving up dishes overflowing with saturated fats. How many times have you been offered, say, a piece of cheesecake and then encouraged to take thick double cream with it? This will give you, in one helping, more saturated fat than you should eat in several days. Anton Mosimann, formerly of the Dorchester, now cooking at the Belfry, his own club, has for several years tried to encourage chefs to produce less fatty food but seems to have had little success so far. The Belfry is one of the very few restaurants that mark dishes with a symbol to denote low fat content.

With awareness of health growing among consumers, it is time to look at what restaurants are doing, or rather not doing, to help the customer. The problem has been highlighted for us at Consumers' Association because several of our staff have discovered, usually as a result of a screening check, that they have dangerously high levels of cholesterol in their blood and that they must control their diet, mainly in respect of saturated fat intake. The first question to ask is: can you find out what is in the dishes on the menu in the average restaurant? Many people have to avoid certain foods or ingredients because of allergies or specific medical conditions, and they deserve all the help they can get. But the issue of fat is of key importance because the evidence is that nearly all of us eat too much fat, and too much of the wrong kind of fat.

A great deal of progress has been made on informative labelling of food sold in shops. European and international standards require most packaged foods to have full ingredient lists and, increasingly, nutrition information as well. It is all the more ironic that as labelling standards have risen in shops, there are no similar requirements for restaurants to describe their dishes accurately or to common agreed standards, or to tell you what is in them.

I recently found myself in the vulnerable category of male, in my fifties, with a cholesterol level so high that the risk of heart attack was x times the average. Probably at least 10 per cent of British men have this problem and it is literally vital that they do something about it. Like other readers of this *Guide* I enjoy good food and eating out in good restaurants. So can I continue to eat out and survive? The answer is – only with great difficulty. We have not yet done a *Which?* survey of restaurants and how they cater for those on a low-cholesterol diet, but here are the results of my own first experiences.

The excess fat problem arises mainly from eating too much total fat, and particularly too much saturated fat, that is fat from animal as opposed to vegetable sources. My high cholesterol level also means that I should eat fewer high-cholesterol foods. So, no butter, cream, eggs, or cheese (other than cottage cheese) and no fried foods. Lean meat is acceptable in moderation, but I should eat no liver or kidneys, nor, to be strict, any crab or lobster. Sounds dismal? Not really. Virtually all fish is good news, and I can eat most vegetables and fruit, except highly fatty ones like avocados and, sadly, coconut, which is very high in saturated fat. For sauces and dressings, judicious mixtures of olive oil (which is mono-unsaturated) and sunflower, safflower, walnut and similar oils (all poly-unsaturated) are as palatable as, if not better than, mayonnaise.

The first essential was not to eat butter with my bread roll, so I now habitually ask for Flora instead of butter. The first place I tried this resulted in a kindly but bemused waitress saying she would enquire, only to return with the news that, 'Sorry, Flora doesn't work here.' Three of the top restaurants in the *Guide* were unable to produce Flora or any margarine substitute for butter at all. The Savoy River Room, however, responded magnificently with three Flora pots with their foil neatly rolled back like sardine cans. And if the much-maligned British Rail restaurant car can swiftly produce pots of Flora why can't all restaurants? One of the very best restaurants proudly presented me with Flora in a butter dish but then served all the vegetables swimming in butter. Amends were made as they were quickly replaced with a fresh dish and a herb and oil dressing which was, in my view, far tastier than a bland butter coating. Sadly, this was one of only two restaurants I have found that label dishes as being low-fat or low-cholesterol. As usual, the United States are well ahead of us and use a little symbol, a red heart, as a standard indicator of 'heart-healthy' dishes.

It is depressing to find how few waiters and waitresses know what is in the dishes on offer, and menu descriptions are often almost completely uninformative or even misleading. Worse still, a request not to put butter on grilled fish, or seafood with a mixed fish dish, does not always get to the kitchen. One gets the impression that order-takers are trained on customer-care courses to humour these oddball customers and dutifully write down what they say, but not to bother the kitchen with all that nonsense.

Heart disease has now reached epidemic proportions and it is time restaurants took their responsibilities seriously. They must, at the very least, start to give consumers a choice of low-fat dishes, poly-unsaturated fat dressings, and low-cholesterol dishes. Ideally, menus should somewhere list the ingredients of dishes, so that vulnerable customers can check. A recognised symbol is needed to indicate which dishes are low in saturated fats and low in cholesterol. Restaurants should encourage people to choose healthier items. But we need to go further; it is time to stop using so much butter, eggs and cream as easy ways of covering food with bland sauces. More chefs need to be trained to use low-fat alternatives in cooking and to be more aware of the health hazards of different ingredients.

The message is not all doom and gloom; there is no need to deny yourself all butter, eggs and cream, or duck and goose. These high-fat, high-cholesterol dishes can still be eaten but it is important to ensure that your diet is in balance and that these dishes only make up around 30 per cent of your fat intake. To do this however, we do need to know what we are letting ourselves in for when we eat out.

# Food gets prepared; food gets eaten up

The *Guide* often champions the small-scale restaurant that offers a caring, personal approach and committed cooking in the kitchen. **Mary Adlard**, who with her husband, David, runs *Adlard's* in Norwich, charts some of the ups and downs of fulfilling customers' expectations day after day. Their first enterprise was *Adlard's* in Wymondham...

Looking back, I realise that neither David nor I knew what running our own small restaurant would entail. Perhaps nobody ever does. Certainly David, being a very thorough person by nature, had planned and prepared as well as anyone could have done.

Over the years he had accumulated detailed files containing menu ideas, business budgets and brochures on crockery and cutlery. He had built up an extensive collection of lovingly cared for cookery books. He had amassed many expensive copper pans on his meagre salary. He even had some good, solid, secondhand stoves in storage in a garage in London. He had also deliberately spent time in every area of catering, working as a waiter, restaurant manager and in all sections of the kitchen, and he had taken a course to reinforce his tremendous interest in wines. The one thing he had not been able to do was save much money, since, like all chefs, he was very badly paid.

So, no matter how minute the preparations, starting up was bound to be tough. Only by scraping together money from every possible relative and an understanding bank manager could we find enough to buy a small, converted butcher's shop in Wymondham. The dining-room, which we decorated prettily in floral wallpaper with lots of lacy touches, was fine, but our living accommodation upstairs was a nightmare. There were holes in the floorboards, no central heating and our bathroom, which was downstairs, had to double as the Ladies'. Every night at six I'd hurriedly stash away our toothbrushes and half-used bits of soap, then swirl David's scattered whiskers down the plug. Fortunately, a kind neighbour allowed an outhouse attached to his property to be used as the Gents'.

The restaurant had the great advantage of being small enough that we could do everything ourselves. But it was damned hard work. Unable to afford the luxury of a kitchen porter, David cooked everything and then cleaned up while I prepared the vegetables and washed all the glasses by hand. Of course, you quickly discover that the actual time spent cooking is only a percentage of the work. I spent a lot of time in the car picking up supplies from all over the place and then there are the hundred and one other tasks: ordering, typing up the menu, planning for parties, continual updating and printing of the wine list, constant general paperwork, bills and ever-looming VAT returns to complete – not to mention the constant interruption of phone calls, staff tears, the breakdown of the washing machine or perhaps cleaning up vomit after a customer's excesses. I became a very reluctant and unhappy business partner.

One night, six months after we had opened, everything suddenly changed. I will never forget how, at ten past nine on Tuesday, 1 February 1984, David suffered a stroke in the middle of service. He was putting the final touches to a mille-feuille of mussels when suddenly he complained of double vision, started talking gibberish and one whole side of his face went slack. Then he collapsed and lay, unconscious, on the kitchen floor. Miraculously, by the time the ambulance arrived, he had regained consciousness and they had to carry him out – struggling. He probably wanted to finish the dish!

Later we were to find out that one-third of all people who suffer such a stroke die. David was, in this context, very lucky. He suffered no paralysis except for a slight weakness in his left hand, which he can still feel when making bread. He did, however, lose his speech completely. I was worried, sad, lonely and overwhelmed, but through sheer necessity I had to stop moaning and take control of the business immediately. I asked Robert Mabey, a good friend of David's from the *Connaught* days and a brilliant chef who had then just finished his job at *Le Gavroche*, if he might be able to help out. To my relief he was free to come at weekends and, on this basis, kept us and our business alive for the next four months. For this we are forever indebted to him.

The proverbial silver lining to our troubles was the way our relationship flourished. Throughout David's long struggle to regain his speech, he was always cheerful and never felt sorry for himself. I admired him tremendously. Six months later, our wedding in the States coincided with the first birthday of the restaurant opening. It had been a horrendously trying time, but David was very nearly completely fit once more. Since then, he has always worked as hard as he did before the stroke. An average day starts at 9.30 in the morning and finishes at midnight with, at most, an hour and a half off in the afternoon on a good day.

Even now, six years later, I do not find the restaurateur's day easy. I suppose the hardest part is the sheer drudgery and repetitiveness of it all. Food gets prepared; food gets eaten up. The routine is the same, day in, day out, with a great deal of cleaning up before, during and after the cooking. Likewise, running front of house is a five-night-a-week performance, 48 weeks a year, no matter what. Of course, there are aspects I love, especially meeting a great number of interesting people and getting to know some of the customers as friends. But, like anyone else, I get tired, fall sick, have mini-breakdowns when things go wrong and feel like sleeping after I have been up all night with a sick child.

Inevitably, then, the smile is sometimes plastered on with the lipstick. My greatest challenge is not to transmit this to the customers. I feel a responsibility to ensure that our customers' evening meets their expectations and, as the out-front person, you are only too aware that there is much more to this than excellent food. We spend a long time each day setting the tables, bearing in mind what time people are arriving, so that we can fill up various areas of the restaurant to create some atmosphere. I hate it when we get it wrong. Last St Valentine's night, for example, with ten tables of two, the restaurant was painfully quiet and seemed to echo like an empty dance-hall.

Sometimes the disappointments are not our fault. I have noticed since our move from Wymondham to Norwich that a higher degree of comfort and smarter décor lead certain customers to expect perfection in every way, although this does not always fit with the relaxed, friendly, unpretentious atmosphere we try to provide. In any case, you just cannot win with some customers. There are those who, having asked what the chef recommends, reply 'Oh, he'd like to get rid of that, would he?' Cutting cheese is another problem area: the piece you offer is either too big, which is interpreted as the cheese going bad, or too small, in which case the customer may feel cheated. Such incidents become infuriating with time; my patience level is not what it used to be.

The most stressful moments for me come during the pauses between courses. I see people getting fidgety and conversation drying up; they are hoping the arrival of the next course might fuel some dialogue and start to shoot meaningful glances in my direction. I rush into the kitchen to communicate this to David and see that he's working flat out. In my calmer moments I convince myself that, for the money spent, people should take the view that they are having an entire evening out, the table being theirs for the evening. But at the time my blood pressure soars and I hide in the kitchen, unable to face that table until I've brought them some food. I wish everyone understood what cooking to order means.

Combining parenthood and the restaurant business has been an interesting challenge, too. When our daughter, Lucy, was a newborn and I wasn't working, we had a unique schedule built around restaurant hours. I would sleep during the evening and get up at midnight. That was the highlight of our day; we'd spend an hour or two eating and chatting, having a play and cuddle with Lucy, thinking she was the most adorable baby in the world. Once I began work again, she would sit in her bouncy chair in the kitchen during the early evening, taking in the hustle and bustle before I put her to bed.

I often wonder how long one can remain committed to the highest standards before burning out. Now that I am a mother and we can afford to pay more staff, my workload has lessened, but for David it's a different story. I often resent the hours necessary to run the business and wish that he would put Lucy and me first more often, but at the same time I cannot but admire his dedication and standards. For me, this is the vital element that keeps me going. He is good at what he does and that makes me proud of our efforts.

# 'The best coffee is the one you like best' [Claudia Roden]

**Struck by the many complaints the *Guide* receives about coffee in restaurants, a tasting team emerges with five recommendations for restaurateurs.**

Readers reporting to the *Guide* almost invariably comment on the coffee served them in a restaurant. Its quality is evidently less than ideal, yet technology has never made a coffee-maker's life more easy. However, as each new machine is invented, so the desire for profit, the incompetence of the operator and sheer laziness of mind seems to set the potential improvement at nought. Only England could manage, as it did in the 1950s, to pervert the first espresso machines to production of an anaemic and characterless liquid.

To set our minds in train, the *Guide* this year devised a simple coffee tasting, although its execution was far from elementary. The variables in coffee-making that we wished to assess were the choice of bean or blend; the degree of roasting; age and freshness of the coffee itself; its strength; the method of making; the temperature of serving; whether it was served immediately or kept hot for a time; and its suitability for purpose (mid-morning, after-dinner, etc.). In the event we restricted our ambitions to freshness, strength and length of keeping hot.

The tasting consisted of various permutations using two coffee-making techniques found often in restaurants: espresso and cafetière; and using two nationally available coffee brands: Lavazza and Lyons. The panel was of three people.

Of course, the self-evident truth was that people like what they like and there's no persuading them otherwise. Nonetheless the clear winner, out of 12 cups on the table, was newly opened, freshly made half-strength espresso. This underlined a simple message: coffee needs to be fresh in every way; and it benefits from maximum aroma. Espresso made too strong consumes aroma with bitterness – hence the preference for half-strength.

A second conclusion that seemed warranted was that it is more difficult to make a good cup of coffee with a cafetière than with an espresso. The best cup of cafetière came fourth, after three variations of espresso. To work cafetière to its best advantage would seem to require excellent choice of coffee blend and grind, a thing not often allowed for in restaurants where proprietors look too much to costs.

Coffee merchants, like wine and food merchants, are always happy to supply something at rock-bottom price, but it will invariably be rock-bottom quality.

The third conclusion was about bad coffee: the really poor cups at our tasting were all too familiar from misspent evenings. Coffee from a packet of grounds kept open for four days, made in a cafetière and then kept hot for 20 minutes, was 'absolutely anonymous', 'unidentifiable as coffee', 'not even a decent warm drink', 'tea?'. Staleness and the keeping hot turned an anodyne blend (at best) into a caffeine-addict's nightmare. So often, this life-cycle of a coffee-bean is precisely that followed in a British restaurant.

Any reader tempted to ask what all the fuss can possibly be about, in a country where 90 per cent of the coffee drunk is instant, should ponder Ian Henshall's words in a recent article in the *Guardian*. 'The English like their coffee to taste like tea,' he suggested. 'Few coffees taste more like tea than a mild roast Brazil that has either been processed into instant or spent the last couple of months on the supermarket shelf, before being brewed with an eye to economy.' We do not intend to neglect the vocal minority who recognise and enjoy good coffee, nor even their meeker cousins who know when they are being ripped off for 'near-tea.'

Our recommendations to restaurateurs are these, offered to all but the few – sadly, mostly in London or top-flight provincial places – who already provide a good enough cup of coffee to be a fitting climax to a fine meal:

1 Invest in an espresso machine, so that you can offer a choice of coffees, competently made, to accommodate those who like strong dark coffee as well as those who prefer something milder. It need not be expensive, and it is foolproof: two cups ready in under five minutes, and no refills expected, though second cups can of course be provided – and charged for.

2 Whether your other method is cafetière or the caterer's standby, the automatic filter machine (a.k.a. 'pour-on'), follow the instructions in such matters as grind of coffee, jug-warming, and so on, but be generous with the grounds and never, if using a filter, keep the coffee standing for more than 20 minutes. (Cafetière coffee cools too quickly to allow that transgression.)

3 Experiment with blends of coffee, not just brands. Aromatic blends are best for the automatic, and also for espresso, where it is not necessary to use a very dark roast provided you have plenty of aroma, thus avoiding the often-levelled complaint of bitterness.

4 Decaffeinated coffee doesn't come only in sachets of instant, tasting of gravy browning. Consider offering 'real' decaffeinated coffee, freshly made, just like mainstream coffee. So popular has it become that even the West End's most

superior coffee merchant, H. R. Higgins, now lists Columbia coffee beans 'decaffeinated in Switzerland by a water process.'

5  Do not attempt to increase your profits by listing 'coffee and petits fours' at an inflated price. Many people prefer to finish eating with their chosen dessert, rounding off the meal with a good cup of coffee, no more. It is particularly blatant to charge for petits fours at the end of a set meal, which – if the menu-planner has done the job properly – is perfectly balanced without the need for random fillers. Put them on the table, if you must, but make it a generous gesture, not yet another device to pump up the bill.

# What to drink in 1990

No guide such as this can be infallible; poor years can produce bargains and pleasant surprises, good years disappointments. Increasingly, the maker of the wine has as much significance as the vintage, not only as technological development enables the canny and the skilled to overcome, or at least minimise, the vagaries of weather, but also because the best wine-makers are fearful of a universal bland wine being the result of this technology and are therefore even more painstakingly stamping their individuality on their products. Included here, therefore, are *some* names of makers or properties who are thought especially good – often up and coming rather than well established. This list does not attempt to be complete, but when some of these names appear on a wine list, it may be a further sign that the restaurant has interest in recent developments and changing fortunes and thus has used intelligence in purchasing and selection. Countries are listed alphabetically, regions alphabetically within countries. Double starred (**) vintages are especially good; single starred (*) are good.

## Argentina

Drink **whites** as young as possible. **Reds** up to ten years old can be enjoyed.

## Australia

**Whites** Rhine Riesling – **1988, *1987, not much older unless botrytised. Chardonnay and Semillon – **1987, **1986, *1985. Older wines if oak-aged or botrytised (Semillon).

**Reds *1980–1987** Merlot and Pinot Noir mature faster than Cabernet, Shiraz or Cabernet/Shiraz blends.
MAKERS TO WATCH FOR Balgownie, Cape Mentelle, Coldstream Hills, Evans & Tate, Heggies, Tim Knappstein, Lake's Folly, Peter Lehmann, Geoff Merrill, Michelton, Mosswood, Pewsey Vale.

## Bulgaria

**Whites** Drink young. Chardonnay may age the best, back to 1985.

**Reds** Drink young unless Cabernet Sauvignon, then *1985, *1983, *1984. Most Bulgarian reds are released by producers only when ready to drink.

## Chile

**Whites** Drink young.

**Reds** Cabernet Sauvignon ages best; the best vintages are 1981–1985.
MAKERS TO WATCH FOR Canepa, Concha y Toro, Cousiño Macul, Santa Rita,
Miguel Torres, Los Vascos, Undurraga.

## England and Wales

Drink mostly young, no older than 1985.
MAKERS TO WATCH FOR Astley, Barton Manor, Breaky Bottom, Bruisyard,
Chalkhill, Chiltern Valley, Joyous Garde, New Hall, Penshurst, Pulham,
Staplecombe, Three Choirs.

## France

### Alsace

The best recent vintages have been **1985 and *1983. Pinot Blanc drinks best
young. Some Gewürztraminers age well. Muscat is attractive young, more
complex with a few years' bottle age. Riesling and Tokay are good between 4 and
10 years old, even older for Vendange Tardive and Sélection des Grains Nobles
wines. Pinot Noir seldom improves after two years.
MAKERS TO WATCH FOR Blanck, Marc Kreydenweiss, Muré, Ostertag, Rolly
Gassmann, Schlumberger, Zind Humbrecht.

### Beaujolais

**1988 was a fine year, simple Beaujolais or Beaujolais Villages are drinking
well. *Crus* are not all yet ready though many are now made for quicker
maturation. *1987 Villages are fading. 1986 and *1985 are still good for some
*crus*. Older vintages will depend for their success on their makers. Moulin-à-
Vent commonly lasts the longest.
MAKERS TO WATCH FOR Aujas, Belicard, Braillon, Brun, Descombes, Geoffray,
Pâtissier, Pelletier, Sarrau.

### Bergerac

Drink whites and rosés young; simple reds within two years, Côtes de
Bergerac and Pécharmant **1983, *1985 and *1986 (scarce older bottles might be
even better) and sweet Monbazillac five years or older (the best can last 10
years).
PRODUCERS TO WATCH FOR Ch. Court-les-Mûts, Ch. La Jaubertie, Ch. du
Treuil de Nailhac, Ch. La Borderie, Ch. Tiregand.

### Bordeaux

**Reds** The wines of Bordeaux span a giant range from ordinary to superfine.
Many should be drunk quickly, others may keep a century. There are two
broad groupings, although variations within them can be very great.

*Petits châteaux and crus bourgeois* Some properties make wines vastly better than
their humble classification. The districts or appellations include Bordeaux,
Bordeaux Supérieur, Côtes de Bourg, Premières Côtes de Bordeaux or
Premières Côtes de Blaye, properties in the outlying districts of St Emilion and
Pomerol, Fronsac and the Graves.

The best vintage ready for drinking among petits châteaux is *1986. **1985 is drinking well. *1983, and **1982 and 1981 are ready, though 1982 may need more time. 1979 and 1978 are fully ready, though St Emilion and Pomerol wines mature faster than those of the Médoc and the Graves. Some of the especially good bourgeois, noted for instance in the list below, will keep for much longer and may be treated as classed growths.

MAKERS TO WATCH FOR This is a most selective list of some châteaux that always make wine of better quality than their classification implies. It also includes properties that have recently become fashionable or esteemed for serious wine making: d'Angludet, Beaumont, Bourgneuf-Vayron, Chasse-Spleen, Cissac, le Crock, Fonbadet, Fonréaud, Gloria, Labégorce-Zédé, Patache d'Aux, Potensac, Siran.

*Classed growths* (including St Emilion Grand Cru Classé and Pomerol): **1985 is the first year ready to drink for lesser properties and some from St Emilion and Pomerol. 1984 was not a success in St Emilion or Pomerol; other communes are not very attractive yet. *1983 is possible from St Emilion and Pomerol but not for other districts. **1982 is pre-eminent but for the most part not nearly ready except, again, from St Emilion. 1981 is drinkable for St Emilion, Pomerol and lesser properties as well as the softer districts like Graves, St Julien and Margaux. **1979 is a good year for the better châteaux, lesser ones are drying out. **1978 is good. 1977 is best not tried, though the best are cheap and drinkable. 1976 is fruity but may be fading. **1975 is tough for good Médoc and Graves and will not be at their best for some time, if ever, but St Emilions and Pomerols can drink well. 1975 is often a disappointment. Earlier vintages that can be enjoyable are 1971 (better in St Emilion and Pomerol), **1970 (even now, still tough for the very best growths), *1966 (not very fruity but classic), 1964 (very fine in St Emilion), 1962 (can still provide good examples of the best châteaux) and **1961 (be warned that the top ten still have some way to go although us lesser mortals may find them perfect even now). Earlier good years are **1959, 1955, **1953, **1949, **1947 and **1945.

MAKERS TO WATCH FOR These are some of the rising stars; it is an arbitrary list but may still have some use when faced with an unfamiliar wine list: Cantemerle, Domaine de Chevalier, Couhins-Lurton, Dauzac, Issan, la Lagune, le Pin, Plince, St-Pierre, Soutard, Tertre-Rôteboeuf.

**Dry whites** Drink them young (especially Bordeaux Blanc and Entre-Deux-Mers), 1988 or at worst 1987, unless they come from a serious property (mostly in Graves) with a long history of white wine vinification which also includes a proportion (if not the entirety) of Sémillon in the cépage and some ageing in wood. Then, the best of recent vintages are 1987, 1985, 1983. (Top Graves live very much longer).

**Sweet wines** The Premières Côtes de Bordeaux and St-Croix du Mont may be drunk young, from 1987, 1986 and 1985 but only the best St-Croix will improve beyond five years. Sauternes and Barsac should be allowed to mature longer than this (good vintages such as 1985 will benefit from 10 years or more), though *1985 is coming round and the light 1984 is ready now. **1983 is very fine but the best properties need much longer. Earlier vintages are 1981, *1980, 1979, *1976, *1975 (for the best), *1970. Older vintages include: *1969,

\*1967, \*1955, \*\*1945.

MAKERS TO WATCH FOR  Châteaux that have preserved their commitment to great sweet wines include Bastor-Lamontagne, Climens, Coutet, Doisy-Daëne, Guiraud, de Malle, Rabaud-Promis, Rayne-Vigneau, Raymond-Lafon, Rieussec, Sigalas-Rabaud, Suduiraut.

## Burgundy

**Reds**  Vintage recommendations are even less reliable for Burgundy than Bordeaux. The maker and his style are essential for success. These are some of the better recent vintages. Côte de Nuits normally matures better, over a longer cycle, than Côte de Beaune. Drink the simpler wines from \*1987 and \*1986, but avoid the better growths after \*1985 as they are not ready. \*1983 was mixed but some are fine; \*\*1982s are now mature; \*\*1980 was best on the Côte de Nuits; \*\*1978 is still drinking wonderfully for the best growths.

GROWERS WHO HAVE BEEN MAKING THEIR MARK  There are myriad small growers here and this is only a note of a few whose name have caught the British eye of approval in recent years: Robert Ampeau, Simon Bize, Dujac, Jean Grivot, Jayer, Olivier Leflaive, Domaine Parent, Daniel Rion, Armand Rousseau, Jean Trapet, Alain Verdet, Michel Voärick.

**Whites**  Drink Mâcon from the most recent vintage and Mâcon Villages (including the good villages Lugny, Viré, Clessé) from \*\*1987, \*1986, and \*1985. The best of the recent vintages for the Côte d'Or and Chablis are \*1987, \*\*1986, \*\*1985 and \*1983.

CHABLIS GROWERS WHO HAVE BEEN MAKING THEIR MARK  René Dauvissat, Jean Durup, William Fèvre, Alain Geoffroy, Henri Laroche, Louis Michel, Louis Pinson, François Raveneau, Philippe Testut, Robert Vocoret.

## Buzet, Frontonnais, Gaillac  (Reds)

Drink Buzet \*1987, 1986, \*\*1985, 1983, 1982 or 1978. (Drink Frontonnais and Gaillac young.)

NAMES TO WATCH FOR  *Buzet* Ch. des Jonquilles, Ch. de Padère, Ch. Sauvagnères.
*Frontonnais*  Ch. Bellevue-la-Forêt, Ch. Flotis.
*Gaillac*  Domaine Jean Cros, Labarthe, Larroze.

## Cahors

The lighter style drinks young. The more traditional 'black' wines are good from \*1983, \*1982 and \*1978.

NAMES TO WATCH FOR  Ch. du Cayrou, Clos de Gamot, Domaine de Goudou, Domaine de la Pineraie, Domaine de Paillas, Clos Triguedina.

## Champagne

The most common vintage in restaurants this year will be \*1983. The best of earlier vintages are \*\*1982, \*1981, \*\*1979, \*1978, \*1975. Older vintages are an acquired taste.

## Loire

**Dry whites and rosés**  Drink the youngest vintage. \*\*1988 promises well. \*1987 is often too tired in Muscadet. Sancerre sometimes has a longer life than expected, developing depth and fruit, as does Savennières or Vouvray, over five years. Pouilly Fumé, Quincy, Reuilly and Menetou Salon last none too long.

MAKERS AND PROPERTIES TO WATCH FOR Bailly, Bizolière, Bossard, Brédif, Dezat, Huet, Poniatowski, Saget, Sauvion, Vatan.

**Sweet whites** mature as slowly as Sauternes. Young Côteaux du Layon may be drunk from 1986. Best recent vintages for Quarts de Chaume and Bonnezeaux are *1985, *1983, *1982, *1978, *1976.

NAMES TO WATCH FOR Baumard, Belle Rive, Ch. de Fesles, Renou, Soucherie, Moulin Touchais.

**Reds** Many reds should be drunk young, Chinon and Bourgeuil and Cabernets ageing the best. They are most susceptible to bad weather because of their northerly situation. Best recent vintages are *1986, **1985, *1983, *1982.

MAKERS TO WATCH FOR Caslot-Galbrun, Couly-Dutheil, Lamé-Delille-Boucard, Raffault, Roussier.

### Rhône

**Whites** Normally drink young: the best recent vintages are 1988, 1987, 1986, 1985, 1983 and 1978.

**Reds** In the northern Rhône (Crozes Hermitage, Hermitage, Côte Rôtie, St Joseph and Cornas), Crozes Hermitage is the fastest developer (lasting often no more than five years) and Hermitage and Côte Rôtie the slowest. The best recent vintages are *1985, **1983, *1982, *1980, **1978.

MAKERS TO WATCH Chapoutier, Chave, Clape, Grippat, Guigal, Jaboulet, Sorrel.

In the south (Châteauneuf, Gigondas, Lirac, Côtes du Rhône and many wider appellations) the Côtes du Rhône should be drunk quickly from the current vintage, though some will last from *1985. Other good vintages are **1983, *1981, *1980 and **1978. Châteauneuf is the longest lasting, although fine old Gigondas is a pleasure.

NAMES TO WATCH FOR Domaine de Longue-Toque, Ch. de Beaucastel, Les Cailloux, Chante-Perdrix, Roger Sabon, Guigal, Domaine de Mont-Redon, Ch. Rayas, Domaine de Castel-Oualou.

## Germany

Drink basic wines (QbA) young, none earlier than *1987. Earlier vintages that are good for the better wines are **1985 especially in Rheingau, *1983 especially Mosel-Saar-Ruwer, *1981, **1976 (Spätlese or above), *1975 (Spätlese or above). Trockenbeerenauslese and Eiswein should not be drunk from vintages later than 1981 as they are not ready – many will live for decades.

MAKERS TO WATCH FOR Bassermann-Jordan, Deinhard, Diel, Fritz Haag, Lingenfelder, Balthasar Ress, Schloss Vollrads, Scholl & Hillebrand.

## Italy

**Whites** Drink 1988 or 1986 (1987 was disappointing for whites) except for senior Chardonnays, where 1985 is showing well.

**Reds** Tuscan wines had good years in 1986, **1985, *1983, **1982, 1978 and 1975. Chiantis are drinking well from 1985, Chianti Riservas from 1982 and 1983; **1982 is the star year, especially for 'super-Tuscans' from top Chianti producers. Barolos and Barbarescos need time to mature. Younger than 1983 is generally too young. **1982 and **1978 are the best since *1974 and *1971. Lighter reds (Dolcetto, Barbera) from 1987 are pleasant now.

MAKERS WHOSE NAMES SHOULD BE NOTED  Antinori, Ascheri, Conterno, Deltetto, Gaja, Isole e Olena, Jermann, Lageder, Mascarello, Schiopetto, Tiefenbrunner.

## New Zealand

Most New Zealand white wines are made for young drinking, although Chardonnays and Semillons may well last more than four or five years as will late-harvest (sweet) Rieslings and Muscats. Red wines are too recent a development for sound advice, although Cabernet Sauvignon will obviously outlast Merlot and Pinot Noir.

MAKERS TO WATCH FOR  Babich, Cloudy Bay, Delegat's, Esk Valley, Matua Valley, Montana, Nobilo's, Redwood Valley, St Helena, Selaks, Stoneleigh, Villa Maria.

## Portugal

Almost all Portuguese white wines should be drunk young but some reds age well. Older vintages that may be offered from the 1970s are 1971, 1974 and 1978. Most of the 1980s were adequate vintages, 1980, 1982, 1983 and 1985 the best.

MAKERS WORTH LOOKING FOR  Caves Aliançia, Quinta da Aveleda, J M da Fonseca, Adega Cooperativa de Mealhada, João Pires, Caves Velhas, Solar das Bouças, Quinta do Côtto, Caves Sao João. Vintage port works to another cycle. The best year for current drinking is **1966 but much of 1975 is simple and cheap and not a keeper. Some, though not all, ready from *1970, *1963, *1960, **1955, *1948, **1945.

## Spain

**Whites** Drink quickly unless Chardonnay or white Rioja from the best producers.

**Reds** Riojas are not ready (unless not aged in oak – '*sin crianza*') after the *1985 vintage. Earlier vintages are *1983, **1982, *1981, *1980. Simple Riojas, not Reservas or Gran Reservas, are unreliable if earlier than 1980. Many Ribero del Duero wines need up to ten years and Vega Sicilia even longer. 1982 and 1981 are drinking quite well, however.

MAKERS TO WATCH FOR  El Coto, Montecillo, Muga, Chivite, Marqués de Griñon, Raimat, Bodegas Fariña (Toro), Bodegas Los Llanos, Bodegas Ollara, La Rioja Alta.

## United States

### California

**Whites** Drink mostly young, except Chardonnays from **1986 and **1985, and botrytised Rieslings and Gewürztraminers.

**Reds** Drink vintages earlier than 1987. Zinfandel, Merlot and Pinot Noir are often best before 5–8 years. Cabernet Sauvignon keeps well, though old specimens are not common. Best years of the 1980s have been 1986, 1985, 1982, 1980.

MAKERS WHO HAVE RECEIVED ACCLAIM IN RECENT YEARS  Au Bon Climat, Carmenet, Frog's Leap, Iron Horse, Jekel, Matanzas Creek, Ridge, Rutherford Hill, Saintsbury, Trefethen, Mark West, William Wheeler.

# Your rights in restaurants

A restaurant is legally obliged to provide you with a meal and service which are of a reasonable standard, and a failure to do so may give you the right to sue for breach of contract. Having said this, it is important to remember that the reasonableness or otherwise of both the meal and the service must be judged on the type of restaurant in question.

Dining out should be a pleasurable experience. However, it is as well to be aware of your basic legal rights just in case you find yourself in an awkward situation, like one of these:

*You book a table in advance but when you arrive, the manager says there's been a mistake and there's no room.*
When you book, you're making a contract with the restaurant and they must give you a table, in reasonable time. If they don't, they're in breach of contract and you can claim a reasonable sum to cover any expenses you had as a result, eg travelling costs.

*You go into a restaurant and as you sit and look at the menu, you realise the meal is going to be much more expensive than you thought.*
A restaurant must display a menu and a wine list outside, or immediately inside the door – so check the prices before you sit down. Prices shown must be inclusive of VAT. If they aren't, tell the local Trading Standards Officer (see 'The law enforcers').

*The restaurant says it doesn't serve children. Can you insist it does so?*
No – however unfair it may seem. A restaurant can turn away anyone, without giving a reason, except on grounds of sex, race, colour or ethnic origin.

*You only want a cup of coffee but the waiter tells you there's a minimum charge of £3 per person.*
A restaurant must display any minimum charge or cover charge outside or immediately inside the door. If no charge is indicated, tell the local Trading Standards Officer. You do not have to pay the charge if it is not displayed. Under a new Code of Practice (see below) menus are supposed to show cover and minimum charges as prominently as any other charges.

*The bill comes to quite a bit more than you expected and has had 10% service charge added – do you have to pay this?*

As with the minimum charge, the restaurant must display outside or immediately inside the door any service charge to be automatically included in the bill. If it is displayed, you should pay it unless there was something specifically wrong with the service. But if a service charge is not clearly indicated, you don't have to pay – it's up to you whether to tip and, if you do, by how much.

Restaurants are being asked to follow new rules about how to indicate extra charges on their menus. A Code of Practice, introduced in March 1989 under the Consumer Protection Act, says restaurants should include any compulsory service charges *within* the price for each item (rather than adding a percentage to the total bill). This would make it easier for customers to see at a glance how much they'll have to pay. But they only have to do this 'wherever practicable'. The Code also recommends that restaurants do not suggest optional sums for service or other items, so menus and bills should not say 'We suggest you give an optional 10% gratuity'.

It's not yet clear how much impact the Code will have. It is not legally binding, although if the restaurant is prosecuted, the court will take into account whether it has been followed.

*You go into a restaurant because your favourite dish is on the menu. But the waitress says it's 'off' today. Your second choice isn't available either.*

A restaurant doesn't have to be able to serve all items on the menu, although it should have most. If you think the restaurant is genuinely trying to mislead people, tell the local Trading Standards Officer.

*You order 'fresh fruit salad', yet it's obviously out of a tin.*

Under the Trade Descriptions Act, a restaurant must provide food and drink as described on the menu or by the waiter. If you think what you're served doesn't match the description, don't start eating. Complain immediately and ask for something else. You could also tell the local Trading Standards Officer that the restaurant is misleading customers.

*Your fish arrives not properly cooked – it's still cold in the middle.*

Under the Sale of Goods and Services Act (and under common law in Scotland), restaurants must prepare food with reasonable care and skill. If this does not appear to be the case, do not eat the dish you have been served and complain. If you don't manage to get things put right, you can deduct what you think is a fair sum from the bill (see 'Claiming your rights'). Alternatively, make it clear that you are paying 'under protest', so you can claim compensation later.

*You get a nasty stomach upset after eating out at a restaurant. You think the lamb hot-pot was to blame.*

If you think your illness is a result of a restaurant meal, tell your doctor and the local Environmental Health Officer (see 'The law enforcers'). The EHO can investigate the incident and may decide to prosecute; under the Food Act, it's a criminal offence for a restaurant to serve food unfit for human consumption. If it can be proved that the restaurant caused your illness – which can be difficult – it could be fined and made to compensate you. In serious cases, it may be worth getting legal advice about suing the restaurant yourself.

*You're kept waiting an hour before the waiter takes your order. When you complain, the waiter is rude to you.*

A restaurant must give you a reasonable standard of service. If it doesn't, you can refuse to pay all or part of the service charge, even if it's automatically included in the bill.

*The waitress drops a dish and the food goes all over your new suit.*

If it's the restaurant's fault that you've had food or drink spilled on you, you can claim the cost of cleaning. If the article of clothing can't be cleaned, you can claim the cost of a new one.

*You've come out for a leisurely evening but the waiter has different ideas. He whips dishes away before you've finished eating and then presents you with the bill.*

A restaurant must give you reasonable time to finish your meal and have a cup of coffee, bearing in mind the type of restaurant and what time it is. If you think you've been unreasonably rushed, complain and don't pay part or all of the service charge.

*The people on the next table are smoking. The smoke's wafting in your direction and is spoiling your meal. Can you get the manager to tell them to stop?*

The manager can't insist on people not smoking, unless it's specifically a non-smoking restaurant or a non-smoking area. If it is, smokers could be asked to leave if they don't stop. If it's important to you, check beforehand what the smoking arrangements are.

*You're a bit short of cash so you ask if you can pay by credit card. The restaurant says 'no'.*

A restaurant doesn't have to accept payment by credit card – or even by cheque – unless it had agreed to do so beforehand, or there's a sign on the door. So check first.

*You're paying by credit card. When the waiter gives you the voucher to sign you see the total has been left blank, presumably in the hope you'll add something extra for service. Do you have to pay?*

Be careful – you could end up paying for service twice. Check whether service is compulsory and, if it is, whether the charge has already been added to the bill. If it has, then there's no reason why you should add anything extra. We think it's misleading of restaurants to present vouchers in this way when service is already included, although it's not illegal. If the service charge is not compulsory, then it's up to you whether you add any more and, if so, how much.

*You give your coat to the waitress to hang up. By the time you leave, it has disappeared.*

A restaurant must take reasonable care of your belongings if they're in a cloakroom. If it doesn't you can claim compensation for any damage or loss. Notices limiting the restaurant's liability are only valid if they're reasonable and prominently displayed. If there's no cloakroom, make sure you ask staff to put your coat or other belongings in a safe place, otherwise you won't be entitled to any compensation.

## Claiming your rights

1. Try to sort out your problem on the spot. Ask to speak to the manager, explain what the problem is and say what you want done, for instance, a substitute dish provided. Don't be afraid to make a fuss.

2. If you're not able to come to an agreement with the manager, then you have two options: to deduct a suitable amount from the bill (it's then up to the restaurant to sue you for the balance if it doesn't agree); or to make any payment you're not happy about 'under protest' (put this down in writing when you make the payment). That way you can try to claim it back later by suing under the small claims procedure (see below).

3. If you're still not happy, get advice on your legal position. You can get free advice from Citizens' Advice Bureaux, Law Centres and Consumer Advice Centres. The Trading Standards department of the restaurant's local authority may also be able to help. If you go to a solicitor, check first how much it's likely to cost you. Many solicitors offer a half-hour interview for a fixed fee of £5. Or you can join **Which? Personal Service**, which gives advice and help to individual members (write to Which? Personal Service, Consumers' Association, 2 Marylebone Road, London NW1 4DX for details).

4. When you've found out where you stand, write to the restaurant. Tell them what the problem was and what you want done about it.

5. If you have no success, and think you have a strong case, you can sue under the small claims procedure in the county court. In England, Wales and Northern Ireland, the maximum you can claim is £500. You

won't need a solicitor. Just issuing a summons may spur the restaurant into action. In Scotland, claims of under £750 are heard under the small claims procedure of the Sherrif Court.

## The law enforcers

The job of enforcing many of the laws affecting restaurants, and which protect consumers' rights, is done not by the police but by officials employed by the local authority. **Environmental Health Officers** enforce food hygiene laws and regulations. They investigate complains by the public. They make routine visits to restaurants – although they're very overstretched. The Institution of Environmental Health Officers would like all new food premises, such as restaurants setting up in business, to be licensed by their local authority before they start trading. Consumers' Association supports this idea.
**Trading Standards Officers** enforce the law about factual descriptions of goods and services. They will investigate complaints about false or misleading claims made by restaurants, or misleading indications of prices.

If EHOs or TSOs have enough evidence that restaurants have committed a criminal offence, they can prosecute. If found guilty, restaurants can be fined and you could be awarded compensation.

## Restaurants' rights

*You book a table for four at a country restaurant. But the car won't start and you decide not to go.*
If you book a table at a restaurant, you must turn up in reasonable time. If you don't keep your booking, or are very late, you're in breach of contract and the restaurant could sue you for compensation. Let the restaurant know as soon as possible if you can't make it, so the restaurant can reduce its loss by rebooking the table. Some restaurants have started to take customers' credit card numbers when they book and say that if they don't turn up, a charge will be made. As long as they tell you beforehand, restaurants are within their rights to do this. But the charge should only be reasonable compensation for their loss, not a penalty.

*You go out for a meal with relatives but a row develops between feuding members of the family. The manager says the shouting is disturbing other customers and asks you to leave.*
You must behave reasonably in a restaurant, otherwise the restaurant can refuse to serve you and ask you to leave.

*You can't be bothered to change out of your old gardening clothes before going out for Sunday lunch. The manager refuses to give you a table.*

If you are not dressed suitably, the restaurant can refuse to give you a table, even if you've booked.

*You've just had the worst meal of your life – it was inedible. Do you have to pay?*

You must pay the bill unless you have genuine cause for complaint, in which case you can deduct what you think is a fair amount as compensation. Explain exactly why and, if asked, leave your correct name and address. It's then up to the restaurant to sue you to recover the money. Don't be put off by threats to call the police. They have no right to intervene unless you intended to leave without paying for no genuine reason, or if you caused a violent scene, which could be a criminal offence.

Based on an article to appear in *Which?* in November 1989.

# General lists

## The *Guide's* longest-serving restaurants

| | | | |
|---|---|---|---|
| Connaught Hotel, W1 | 37 years | Chez Moi, W11 | 21 years |
| Gay Hussar, W1 | 33 years | Cleeve House, | |
| Porth Tocyn Hotel, | | Bishop's Cleeve, | |
| Abersoch, Gwynedd | 33 years | Gloucestershire | 21 years |
| Gravetye Manor, | | Horn of Plenty, | |
| East Grinstead, West Sussex | 29 years | Gulworthy, Devon | 21 years |
| Sharrow Bay, Ullswater | | Pool Court, | |
| Cumbria | 29 years | Pool in Wharfdale, | |
| Bloom's, EC1 | 27 years | West Yorkshire | 21 years |
| Dundas Arms, Kintbury, | | Rothay Manor, | |
| Berkshire | 27 years | Ambleside, Cumbria | 21 years |
| Box Tree, Ilkley, | | Sundial, Herstmonceux, | |
| West Yorkshire | 25 years | East Sussex | 21 years |
| French Partridge, Horton, | | At the Sign of the Angel, | |
| Northamptonshire | 25 years | Lacock, Wiltshire | 19 years |
| Walnut Tree Inn, | | Chueng Cheng Ku, W1 | 19 years |
| Llandewi Skirrid, Gwent | 25 years | Le Gavroche, W1 | 19 years |
| Butley-Orford Oysterage, | | Summer Isles Hotel, | |
| Orford, Suffolk | 23 years | Achiltibuie, Highland | 19 years |
| Splinters, Christchurch, | | Timothy's, Perth, Tayside | 19 years |
| Dorset | 23 years | | |

## London restaurants open after midnight

These restaurants take last orders after midnight.

China, China, W1 (Fri, Sat only)

Good Food, WC2

Langan's Brasserie, W1 (Sat only)

Maroush, W2

Melati, W1 (Fri, Sat only)

Spices, N16 (Fri, Sat only)

## London restaurants by cuisine

### AFRICAN
Blue Nile, W9

### CHINESE
China, China, W1
Chuen Cheng Ku, W1
Dragon Inn, W2
Dragon's Nest, W1
Forum Court, SE25
Fung Shing, WC2

Golden Chopsticks, SW7
Good Food, WC2
Hung Toa, W2
Jade Garden, W1
Mandarin Kitchen, W2
Ming, W1
New World, W1
Poons, WC2
Si Chuen, W1
Soong Szechuan, NW3
Wong Kei, W1

Zen, SW3
Zen Central, W1
Zen W3, NW3

### GREEK
Beotys, WC2
Kalamaras, W2
Lemonia, NW1
Nontas, NW1

## HUNGARIAN
Gay Hussar, W1

## INDIAN
## TANDOORI
Bombay Brasserie, SW7
Fleet Tandoori, NW3
Fleet Tandoori II, N10
Ganpath, WC1
Gopal's of Soho, W1
Great Nepalese, NW1
Jamdani, W1
Kanishka, W1
Lal Qila, W1
Ragam, W1
Suruchi, N1

## INDIAN
## VEGETARIAN
Mandeer, W1
Rani, N3
Sabras, NW10
Spices, N16
Sree Krishna, SW17

## INDONESIAN
Mandalay, SE10
Melati, W1
Singapore Garden
    Restaurant, NW6

## ITALIAN
Carraro's, SW8
L'Incontro, SW1
Orso, WC2
Pagu Dinai, SW6
Pizzeria Castello, SE1
Pizzeria Condotti, W1
River Café, W6
San Martino, SW3
Santini, SW1

## JAPANESE
Ikkyu, W1
Miyama, W1
Nanten Yakitori Bar, W1
Ninjin, W1
Suntory, SW1
Wakaba, NW3

## JEWISH
Bloom's, E1

## MIDDLE
## EASTERN
Al Hamra, W1
Efes Kebab House, W1
Maroush, W2
Phoenicia, W8
Topkapi, W1

## POLISH
Brewer Street Buttery, W1
Zamoyski, NW3

## PORTUGUESE
Ports, SW3

## SPANISH
Galicia, W10
Guernica, W1
Rebato's, SW8

## SWEDISH
Anna's Place, N1
Garbo's, W1

## THAI
Bahn Thai, W1
Bedlington Café, W4
Blue Elephant, SW6
Bua Luang, SW18
Chiang Mai, W1
Royal Thai Orchids, SW15
Tuk Tuk, N1

# Afternoon teas

These hotels serve afternoon teas to non-residents.

## London
Auberge de Provence, SW1
Capital Hotel, SW3
Connaught, W1
Dukes Hotel, SW1
Four Seasons, Inn on the
    Park, W1
Kingfisher Restaurant,
    Halcyon Hotel, W1
Ninety Park Lane, W1
Nontas, NW1
Oak Room and Terrace
    Garden, Le Meridien
    Piccadilly Hotel, W1
Royal Roof Restaurant,
    Royal Garden Hotel, W8
Savoy, WC2
Le Soufflé, Inter-
    Continental Hotel, W1

## England
Alverton Manor, Truro
Arundell Arms, Lifton
Ashwick House, Dulverton
Beetle & Wedge, Moulsford
Bell, Aston Clinton
Bilbrough Manor, Bilbrough
Billesley Manor, Billesley
Breamish House, Powburn
Brockencote Hall,
    Chaddesley Corbett
Buckland Manor, Buckland
Calcot Manor, Tetbury
Castle Hotel, Taunton
Cedar Restaurant, Evesham
    Hotel, Evesham
Le Champenois, Blackwater
    Hotel, West Mersea
Cleeveway House, Bishop's
    Cleeve

Corse Lawn House Hotel,
    Corse Lawn
Courtyard, Broughton Park
    Hotel, Broughton
Crabwall Manor,
    Mollington
Crown, Southwold
Denbigh Arms, Lutterworth
Dower House, Royal
    Crescent Hotel, Bath
Esseborne Manor,
    Hurstbourne Tarrant
Farlam Hall, Brampton
Feathers Hotel, Woodstock
George, Stamford
George Hotel, Dorchester
Gidleigh Park, Chagford
Great House, Lavenham
Grosvenor House, Rugby
Hartwell House, Aylesbury

Hewitt's, Lynton
Homewood Park, Hinton Charterhouse
Innsacre Farmhouse Hotel, Shipton Gorge
Jule's Café, Weobley
Kirkstone Foot Country House Hotel, Ambleside
Langley Wood, Redlynch
Langley House Hotel, Langley Marsh
Lewtrenchard Manor, Lewdown
Lugley's Wootton
Lygon Arms, Broadway
Mallory Court, Bishop's Tachbrook
Marryat Room, Chewton Glen Hotel, New Milton
Middlethorpe Hall, York
Miller Howe, Windermere
Mill House Hotel, Kingham
Mortons House Hotel, Corfe Castle
Mulberry Room, Torquay
Netherfield Place, Netherfield
New Inn, Tresco
La Noblesse, Hospitality Inn, Brighton
Northcote Manor, Langho
Old Coach House, Barham
Park Cottage, Hopton Castle
Pier at Harwich, Harwich
Priory Hotel, Bath
Queen Anne, Buckland-Tout-Saints Hotel, Kingsbridge
Restaurant Lafite, Willerby
Rising Sun, St Mawes
Rookery Hall, Nantwich
Rothay Manor, Ambleside
Royal Oak, Withypool
Royal Oak, Yattendon
Ryecroft Hotel, Wooler
Seaview Hotel, Seaview
Sharrow Bay, Ullswater
Shepherd's, Stratford-upon-Avon
Shipdham Place, Shipdham
South Lodge, Lower Beeding
Stock Hill House, Gillingham
Ston Easton Park, Ston Easton

Stone Close, Dent
Summer Lodge, Evershot
Swan Hotel, Leighton Buzzard
Teignworthy Hotel, Chagford
La Vielle Auberge, Battle
Vine House, Paulerspury
Wateredge House, Ambleside
Well House, St Keyne
Whipper-in, Oakham
Whitechapel Manor, South Molton
Winteringham Fields, Winteringham
Woolley Grange, Woolley Green

## Scotland

Airds Hotel, Port Appin
Ardsheal House, Kentallen
Arisaig Hotel, Arisaig
Arisaig House, Arisaig
Auchterarder House, Auchterarder
Beechwood Country House, Moffat
Burrastow House, Walls
Chapeltoun House, Stewarton
Crinan Hotel, Crinan
Cringletie House, Peebles
Cromlix House, Kinbuck
Cuilfail Hotel, Kilmelford
Culloden House, Inverness
Inverlochy Castle, Fort William
Kilfinan Hotel, Kilfinan
Killiecrankie Hotel, Killiecrankie
Kinloch Lodge, Sleat
Knipoch Hotel, Oban
Knockinaam Lodge, Portpatrick
Morefield Hotel, Ullapool
Murrayshall Hotel, Scone
Oaks, Craigendarroch Hotel, Ballater
Pompadour Room, Caledonian Hotel, Edinburgh
Stewart Hotel, Duror
Summer Isles Hotel, Achiltibuie

Taychreggan Hotel, Kilchrenan

## Wales

Abergwynant Hall, Dolgellau
Bodysgallen Hall, Llandudno
Cnapan, Newport (Dyfed)
Druidstone Hotel, Broad Haven
Four Seasons, Cwmtwrch Farmhouse Hotel, Carmarthen
Hotel Maes-Y-Neuadd, Talsarnau
Llwynderw Hotel, Llanwrtyd Wells
Llwyn Onn Hall Hotel, Wrexham
Llyndir Hall, Rossett
Palé Hall, Llanderfel
Penhelig Arms Hotel, Aberdovey
Porth Tocyn Hotel, Abersoch
Riverside Hotel, Abersoch
St Tudno Hotel, Llandudno
Soughton Hall, Northop
Tregynon Farmhouse, Pontfaen
Tyddyn Llan, Llandrillo
Ty Mawr, Brechfa
Ynyshir Hall, Machynlleth

## Channel Islands

Longueville Manor, St Saviour

701

# The Good Food Club 1989

Many thanks to all the following people who contributed, in one way or another, to this year's Guide...

Mary Abbey
Mrs J. Abbott
John Abel
Jean Aberdour
Mr and Mrs J. Able
Dr A.H. Abrahams
Dr Sidney
 Abrahams
Mr A.D. Abrams
J. Abramsky
Roy Acheson
E.P. and R.D. Adams
Miss M.E. Adams
Alissa Adams
Beverley Adams
Eric Adler
Mrs M.A. Adnams
Dr J.B. Ainscough
John R. Aird
Mrs E. Aitchison
Mrs C. Aitken
John Aitken
E.J.C. Album
Mrs P.E. Alconn
Hugh Aldersey-
 Williams
Mrs M. Alexander
Pauline Alexander
Montague
 Alexander
Minda and Stanley
 Alexander
Maria Alexander
Mrs Alford
Dr and Mrs A.A.
 Alibhai
Dr Margaret Alker
Mrs M. Allan
Stephen Allday
Dr A.J. Allen
Mr D.L. Allen
R.D. Allen
Mr E.M. Allen
W.J. Allen

Mrs Leslie Minturn
 Allison
Mrs J. Allom
Mrs G. Allwright
Sir Anthony Alment
Mike Alston
Lionel P. Altman
 CBE
Mr S. Amey
Mr J.K. Anderson
Lars Anderson
Mr R. Anderson
Prof. J.A. Andrews
Gwen and Peter
 Andrews
Mr E.I. Andrews
Mr and Mrs Kurt
 Angelrath
The Marquess of
 Anglesey
Michael R. Angus
Anthony Ansell
Mrs L.M. Anson
Johnny Apple
Michael and Betty
 Appleby
Liz Appleton
Mr and Mrs F.J.
 Apps
Simon C. Apps
Cynthia Archer
Dr J.R. Archibald
Mr B.J. Armstrong
Mr H.F. Armstrong
Leslie Arnett
G.J. Arnold
Mrs H.G. Ashburn
John Ashby
Kathy and Lawrence
 Ashe
Mr and Mrs Hubert
 Ashton
Mr and Mrs P.M.
 Ashwell

Mr and Mrs
 Ashworth
Mr and Mrs H.
 Ashworth
Helen Asquith
Mr M. Assouline
M.H.R. Astbury
Mr H.D. Astley
Mrs J.M. Aston
Adrian Aston
Mrs V. Atherton
Charles and Elaine
 Atkinson
John Atkinson
T.W. Atkinson
Shukor Attan
R.E.S. Attenborough
Mrs J. Atwell
Miss G. Avcott
Mrs P. Avison
Brigid Avison
J.L. Awty
Mr and Mrs Bruce
 Ayers
Freda Aykroyd
John and Sue
 Aylward
Jeff Bacall
John Bacharach
David R. Bache
Dr J.R. Backhurst
D.R. Bail
Sally Bailey
Lawrence F. Bailey
L. Bailey
R.R. Bailey
R. and J. Bailey
Ian C. Baillie
Gino Baio
Mrs Michael Baker
Valerie Baker
R. W. Baker
J.R. Baker
F.A.K. Baker

Julia Baker
Paul and Margaret
 Baker
Mr and Mrs I.
 Balaam
C. Baldock
Richard Balkwill
Peter Ball
Mr D.R. Ball
William Ballmann
Katrina Balmforth
Paul Bamborough
R. Bamforth
Mr D.D. Banfield
P. Bann
Roderick Banner
Diana Bannister
Mr K. Barber
Mr and Mrs M.
 Barbour
Dr M.C. Barchard
Mr and Mrs John F.
 Barclay
Jonathan Bard
Carmel Bardsley
Judith Barker
Dr and Mrs T.C.
 Barker
Revd J. Barker
John A. Barker
Mr and Mrs Barker
Anthony Barker
Chris Barker
Helen Barker
Jeremy Barlow
Dr C.J. Barlow
Tim Barlow
Mr C.A. Barnes
Mr and Mrs R.S.
 Barnes
Tony Barnett
Julian L. Barnett
Lord Barnett

Mr and Mrs L.M. Barnett
Anthony J. Barnett
Mr M.J.N. Barnett
Peter Barnsley
M.G. Baron
L.G. Barr
Penny Barr
Charlotte Barr
Mrs S.E. Barratt
Marie Barratt
Geoff Barratt
G.J. Barrett
Mr and Mrs Francis P. Barrett
Roger Q. Barrett
Michael Barsby
Mr F.E. Bartholomew
Mr C.R. Bartholomew
Tony Barton
Doreen Baskett
Mrs M.A. Batchelor
D.C.F. Bateman
Andrew Bates
Jean Bates
David Batten
Dr John R. Batty
Susi Batty
Jean Baugh
J.J. Bausor
Dr R. and S. Bawden
K. Baxter
Miss M.K. Baxter
Mr and Mrs T.A. Baxter
Muriel Baxter
A.J.M. Bayley
Conrad Bayliss
Valerie Bayliss
E.P. Bazalgette
C. Beadle
H.A. Beadnall
J.F.R. Beale
Wanda H. Bean
Miss M. Beardmore
J.P. Beardow
Mrs J. Beardsworth
Dr Alan Beaton
J. Beauchamp
Brian Beaumont
Phyllis Becherman
Mrs M. Beck
F.R. Beckett
H.H. Beckingsale
P. Bedford
Mr and Mrs Brian Bedwell
Elizabeth Begbie
Isabel Begg
Mr E.C.M. Begg

Moyra Beiny
Mrs D. Beiny
Richard Bell
C.J. Bell
Mr J.R. Belle
Mrs A. Bellerby
I.R. Bennet
Lt. Col. J.A. Bennett
P.A. Bennett
A.M. Bennett
Helen Bennett
John Bennett
Paul Bennett
Brian C. Bennett
Russell K. Bennett
Bruce Bennett
A. Bennett
G. Bennett
Mr J. Bennett
Mr and Mrs J.J. Bennis
Mr and Mrs P. Benny
Clare Benson
G.C. Benstead
Peter Bentley
M.A. Bentley
Mr R.G. Bentley
Anne and Martin Benton
Donna Beresford and Mr Hughes
K. Beresford
Mr and Mrs H.I. Berkeley
Gabriele Berneck
Graham Berown
A.I. Berry
R.R. and J. Berry
P.E. Berry
Mr W.J. Best
Joanne Bester
P.N.K. Beswick
Mr S.J. Betney
Mrs E.M.L. Betts
Bev Bevan
Stephen Bickford-Smith
J.T.S. Biddleston
Fred and Vera Biel
Dr and Mrs J. Biggs
Mr F. Binder
Geoffrey Bindman
John Binnie
Dr G.G. Birch
E.R. Birch
Prof. J.H. Bird
S.J. Bird
Mrs S.A. Bird
Keith William Bird
Dr D.I. Bird
George A.R. Bird

C.A.K. Bird
Michael D. Bird
Mr N. Birks
David J. Birn
Mr D. Bisbrown
J.W. Bishop
Mr and Mrs J. Bishop
Yvonne Black
Mrs V. Blackburn
Mr J. Blackburn
Mrs J. Blackmore
Mrs J.H. Blackwell
Mrs S. Blackwell
Mr P.R. Blair
Alan Blake
Diana Blake
Mrs M.M. Blakeley
Mrs H. Blakey
M.G. Blanchard
Mrs P.A. Blanchet
Roger Bland
Caroline and Alan Blandford
Mrs J.A. Blanks
Mr and Mr Blatch
S. Bliss
Mr C.E. Bloom
A.D. Blosfelds
Dr Kerry Bluglass
Mr R.K. Blumenau
Rachel Blumenstein
Dr S.M. Blunden
Gerald Blythe
Mrs M. Boatwright
S. Bobasch
J. Bobby
Mr A.J. and Mrs J.E. Boddrell
R.C.T. Boddye
Paul M. Bogaerts
Anne de Boisgelin
Jane Bolden
Mr C.T. Bolton
Lord Bonham-Carter
R. Boniface
F.A. Bonner
Mr L. Bonner
Mr E. Bonnor-Maurice
Mr M.T. Bonney
Ian Bonser
N. Bookbinder
Sajid Boota
G.H. Booth
Dr C. Booth
J.W. Booth
M.W. Booth
Ms C.I. Boothe
A.J. Boothroyd
Mr P.J. Bordiss
Mrs D. Borton

Mr C.J. Bosanquet
John S. Bottomley
L. Bottomley
Revd M.A. Bourdeaux
B.S. Bourne
R. Bourne
Mrs B. Bourne
Anne Boustred
A.R. Bowden
Lance Bowden
A.W. Bowden
Patricia Bowen
Mr A.J. Bowen
F. Bowles
Alistair K. Boyd
Alison Boyle
C.A. Boyle
C.P. Brabban
Heather Brace
David K. Bracken
David Bradbury
Kristin Bradbury
Dr J.A. Bradley
P.A. Bradley
Mr W.O. Bradley
Peter Bradshaw
Mrs B.J. Brady
Mr P. Braidford
Geoffrey Brain
P.M. Brash
A.R. Braunmuller
Dr A.M. Braverman
P.E. and N.N. Bray
N.P. Bray
D.W. Bray
Mr and Mrs S. Brett
P. Brewer
Mr and Mrs R.S.B. Brewer
Jeanne Brewis
Amanda Bridges
S. Bridwell
Mr D. Brief
Mr and Mrs D.J. Brine
Mr and Mrs C. Brining
Mr and Mrs Briscoe
Mr E. Brissco
Paul Brittain
Jill Brock
Roy Y. Bromell
Mr and Mrs B. Bromwich
Mrs H. Brooke
Rachel Brookes
Douglas Brooks
Harry Brooks
D. Brooksbank
Carol Broom-Smith

Major-General W.M. Broomhall
Miss V. Brown
Richard Brown
Carole Brown
Jennifer Brown
L.D. Brown
Katherine M. Brown
Mr D.C.A. Brown
R.C. Brown
Robin M. Brown
Ceridwen Brown
Norman Brown
Mr D. Brown
S.E. Browne
Mr C.J. Brownlie
Mrs I.M. Bruce
D.W.K. Bruce
M.G. Bruce-Squires
W.H. Bruton
David E.H. Bryan
John Bryant
Mr M. Bryant
A.E. Bryant
Mr J.M. Bryant
Mr and Mrs J. Buchanan
Mrs A.L. Buchanan
Jane Buchanan
Gerda Buckingham
Terry Buckland
R.W. Buckle
Mr M.I. Buckley
Miss G.D. Buckley
P.A. Buckley
Hans-Joachim Buldt
Dave Bullen
Peter Bullock
Mrs H.M. Bunch
Mrs M. Bunch
Nicholas Bunker
Mr D.J. Bunter
D.K. Bunting
Michael Burd
Roy Burden
A.J. Burgess
James P.C. Burgess
John Burke
M.J. Burke
J. Burke
Carol-Ann Burley
Tracey Burnett
David M. Burns
Fiona Burrell
Spencer Burrow
Mr D.C. Burrows
C.M. Burton
Dennis Burton
Ms A. Busby
Mr I.H.G. Busby
Mrs K.B. Bushen

Mr and Mrs Russell G. Butchart
Mr M. Butler
Mr and Mrs J. Butler
Paul and Christine Butler
Roy Butler
Jane Butler
John Butler
D. Butterfield
Noel Buxton
Mr and Mrs James Byrne
Mr and Mrs B.M. Byrne
Prof. Robert Cahn
Olive Cakkoll
Joyce Caldwell
Mrs G.C. Callaghan
D.M. Callow
Sue and Duncan Cameron
Anne Campbell
Mr N.K. Campbell
B.E. Campbell
Mrs E. Campbell
Ms C.J.B. Campbell
E.M. Campbell
Elspeth Campbell
Michael Camps
R.H. Carey
Mrs F. Carey
Mrs M. Carey
Mr and Mrs Carlisle
Mrs S.R. Carlisle
Mary Carmichael
Mrs A.E. Carnson
Mr R. Carpenter
M. Carpenter
Mr M.D. Carr
Patricia Carr
Anne Carr
John and Karen Carr
Mr D. Carr
Lt Cdr G. Carr
Mr and Mrs P. Carraro-Jost
Olive Carroll
Wing Cdr P.T.J. Carroll
P.J. Carruthers
Mr and Mrs K. Carruthers
Penelope Carter
Philip Carter
Mr and Mrs Carter
B.R. Carter
Mr P.E. Carter
Betty Carter
Pat Carter-Jones
Mrs S. Cartlidge

T. and M. Cartwright
Dr Neville Cartwright
Colette and Martyn Carus-Rattle
R.N. Carvalho
Mr G.J. Carwithen
Mr H.J. Case
Ian Case
Edward Casey
Louise Casey
John B. Cass
Mr A. Casson
R.J. Castle
R.E. Catlow
Leslie Caul
Gillian Cave
Mrs C.H. Cawley
Mr and Mrs T. Cerato
George C. Cernoch
N.R. Chadwick
H.J. Chadwick
Susan Chait
C.J. Chalkers
Mr C.J. Chalmers
Veronica Chamberlain
R. and M. Chamberlain
Mrs M. Chamberlain
J. A. Chambers
John Chambers
S. Chan
Thomas Y.K. Chan
M.S. Chance
J.M. Chandler
R.H.V. Chandler
D.E. Chapman
Nigel Chapman
Jane Chappelle
Barry Charles
Mr S. Charles
Mr J. Charles
Josephine Charlton
Mary Charnley
Mrs E. Chatten
Derek Cheesbrough
Steven Cheetham
F. Robert Cherry
H.P. Chicanot
Julian Chichester
K.V. Chin
Dr H.B.J. Chishick
Dr W.R. Chisholm-Batten
Ms C. M. Chisnall
Ian Churchill
J.E. Churchill
Mr D.M. Claisse

Stephen and June Clark
C.E. Clark
Martin Clark
Mrs W.M. Clark
Mrs P.M. Clark
Dr June R. Clark
Dave Clarke
Maggie Clarke
Paul E.C. Clarke
R. Clarke
Ms D. Clarke
Dr J.S. Clarke
A.F. Clarke
A.R. Clarksom
Lord Evans of Claughton
Malcolm Clay
Gill Clayton
Alan M. Clegg
Terence Clegg
Elizabeth Clegg
Gillian Clegg
Paul Cleland
C. Clement
Penny Cleminson
Mrs A.P. Cliff
L.A.J. Clifford
P. Clifford
H.C. Clifford
K.C. Clinch
W.A. Clode
David H. Close
Mr and Mrs J.G. Clothier
Robert G.M. Clow
Arthur Coates
P. Coatesworth
Peter Cockburn
Tony Cockcroft
Mrs A.F. Cockhill
E.G. Coe
Richard Coe
P.A. Coggle
W.F. Coghill
F.N. Cogswell
Howard Cohen
Alan Cohen
Mr and Mrs Cohen
Wing Cdr T.R. Cohu
G.B. Coisplan
Colbatch Clark
Mr I.G. Coldicott
Alison Cole
Ian D. Coleman
Mr and Mrs G. Coleman
Brenda Coles
N.G.T. Colfer
A.P. Collett
Simon C. Collett-Jones

Prof. Leslie Collier
G.L. Collier
Sylvia Collingwood
P.H. Collins
Paul Collins
Dr P.D. Collins
S.D. Collinson
Peter Collis
Mr and Mrs P. Collis
Mary Colmore
R.T. Combe
Mr M. Comninos
Mr M.A. Conboy
Dr J. Kai and Dr
A.E. Conway
Ronald R. Cook
Mr and Mrs A.W.
Cook
A.S. and L.A. Cook
T.N. Cook
Mr K.H. Cook
Lt. Col. C.P. Cooke
Mrs C. Cooke
Revd A. Cooke
D.J. Cooke
J.P.F. Cooke
D.A. Cookson
Mrs J. Cookson
Mrs P. Coolahan
Peter Coombs
G.V. Coombs
Montague
Thompson Coon
Neville and Linda
Cooper
B. Cooper
Jill Cooper
Mrs J.P. Cooper
P.J. Cooper
D.J. Cooper
Jane Cooper
R. Cooper
Marianne Cooper
Carolyn A. Cooper
Martyn Cooperman
B. Copleston
Mr J. Corbluth
Mary Corkery
Mr and Mrs L.
Cornelius
Mrs A.J. Cornick
Mrs K.I. Corteling
Mr A.L. Cotcher
Mr and Mrs A.N.
Cotter
Mr A.L. Cotterell
MBE
Mrs A.J.V. Cotton
MBE
P.W. Cotts
Isabel Coughlin

Walter Edwin
Coultrup
Mr A. Counsell
Norman Couper
M.R. Court
Mrs S. Court
P.L. Covell
Arthur Coverdale
Christopher and
Jean Cowan
Mrs M. Cowdy
Mr and Mrs H.L.
Cowdy
Mr C.E. Cowen
Teresa Cowherd
Mr and Mrs S.J.
Cowherd
Ms P. Cowley
Diane Cowling
Peter and Elizabeth
Cowsill
Dr. G.J. Cox
Elizabeth Cox
Mr and Mrs D. Cox
Miss H. Cox and Mr
T. Withers
A.P. Cox
A.E. Cox
Mr J.L. Cox
Mrs B.A. Cox
Mr D.M. Cox
Mrs A. Crabtree
R.D. Cramond
Mark Cran
R.A. Crane
Peter Crane
Philip Cranmer
Mr J.D. Cranston
T.J. Craven
Dr K.W.E. Craven
Lt. Col. R.C.F.
Craven
Clive Crayfourd
Muriel Crecraft
Richard Creed
P.I. Cresswell
J.W. van Crevel
Mrs R.M. Crichton
Mr and Mrs T.A.
Crisp
Dr G.S. Crockett
Mr T.E. Crompton
Ms R. Crook
Helen Crookston
Margaret J.N. Cross
Rodney Cross
W. Crossland
Mr and Mrs Steve
Crouch
His Hon. Thomas
Crowther QC
Mr J.D. Crowther

Mr and Mrs W.R.
Crozier
Dr S.N. Crutchley
D.M. Cryer
Mr B. Crymble
Prof. D. Crystal
Carolyn R.
Culbertson
Mrs J.A. Cullinane
Mr E. Cullingworth
John Culshaw
Mary Cumming
Frank Cummins
Mr and Mrs J.C.
Cummins
N.A. Cummins
Mrs Cupper
Dr James Stevens
Curl
Steve Currid
Caroline Currie
H.G. and B.A. Currie
Peter Curtis
Dr P.E.M. Curtis
R. Cussons
Mrs R.B. Custerson
Dr John Cuthbert
Ronald Cuttell
Peter Cutts
Dr P. D'Arcy Hart
Sarah Dacre
Sir William and
Lady Gloria Dale
Mr K.W. Daley
Dr N.L. Dallas
Mrs M. Dallisson
Gerald L. Daltry
T.D. Dampney
S.L. Dance
Mrs W.D. Dane
Dr V.J. Daniel
Mrs P. Danvers
P.R. Danzelman
L. and P. Darby
David Darley
Dr R.H. Davenport
Elizabeth Davey
D.V. Davey
Dr T.J. David
Alan Davidson
Captain J.L.
Davidson
Mr and Mrs A.W.
Davies
D. Davies
Mrs B. Davies
Ben Davies
D.D.G. Davies
G.J. Davies
Thelma Davies
Anne Davies

Dr R.J. and Mrs K.B.
Davies
Sydney G.C. Davies
Mr R.G. Davies
G. Davies
John Davies
Andrew Davis
Mrs H. Davis
Mr and Mrs Alex
Davis
Martin Davis
Mr and Mrs R. Davis
Mr A.M. Davis
Mrs M. Davison
Mrs V. Davison
Bill Davy
Dr and Mrs R.P.R.
Dawber
B.D. Dawkins
Mrs H.L. Dawson
J.M.T. Dawson
Helena Day
C. Day
Mr and Mrs A. Day
Mr and Mrs J. Day
J. de la Rue
W.P. de Winton
Brian Dean
Mr K.W. Dean
A. Dearing
N.C. Dee
N.F. Defrates
Mrs P.M. Dempsey
Mr J.A. Dennis
E.D. Dennis
Mr N. Denny
Sheila Devenish
C. Devereux
Dr M.R. Deveson
Mr and Mrs R.
Devine
Colm J. Devlin
Basil Devonshire
Mr G. Dewar
I.C. Dewey
V.H and B. Dewey
Charles Dewhurst
Mr and Mrs A.
Dexter
G.E.R. Dickes
Rita S. Dickie
Dr Ian Digby
Mr S. Dingle
S.B. Dingwall
G. Dinnage
Fiona Dinnis
Mrs B.M.C. Dixon
J.W. Dixon
Kay Dixon
Dave Dixon
Charles Dixon-
Vincent

Dr and Mrs Neville Dobie
Mrs Dobson
Mr A. Docherty
Anthony Docherty
M.P. Dodd
Peta Dollar
Dr W.F.G. Dolman
J. Donaldson
Diann Donne
Mr G. Donnelly
Judy and Allan Donner
Mr T.L. Donovan
A.N. Doody
Allan Dooley
Jayme Ribeiro dos Santos
James and Mary Douglas
Alan Downes
Colin Dowse
Mr Doyle
Kathleen Doyle
Stephen N. Dray
Stephen Drew
Mrs A. Drinkell
Garth Drinkwater
Mrs C.M. Drummond
Mr D. Drummond
Raymond du Bois
Mr and Mrs J. Duckworth
Marjory Dudgeon
Miss B.R. Dudkin
Mr A.A. Dudman
Mrs J. Duncan
Revd James Duncan
Mr Duncan-Jones and Ms Larsen
Mrs J. Dundas
Ann Dunn
Hugo and Alice Dunn-Meynell
Michael Dunne
Mr Dunstan
Chris Durbridge
Denis Durno
Mrs S.F. Durrell-Walsh
N.S. and J. Dury
Mr and Mrs N.R. Dutson
Dr F. Duvran
Paul Dwyer
Mr A.J. Dyer
Mr A.M. Dyer
Patricia Dyke
Dr and Mrs Dykes
Rodney Dykes
A.W. Dymond

Wendy Dymond
C.E. Dyos
R.S. Eades
Peter Earl
J. Earthy
Mr H. Easom
G.P. Easton
Dr and Mrs J.C. Easton
D.M. Easton
Mrs M. Easton
Miss V.J. Eastwood
Joyce A. Eastwood
Dr S. Eden
Dr W.M. Edgar
Mr T.D.J. Edge
Neil Edkins
Mr and Mrs S. Edridge
Mrs J.T. Edwards
R.W.L. Edwards
Elizabeth J. Edwards
R.J. Edwards
Anton Edwards
A.W. Edwards
Tom Edwards
K. Eglinton
Peter Eio
Nabeil El-Far
Dr J.W.H. Elder
Myra and Ray Elderfield
Judith Elders
Mr T.M. Eldrid
C. Eliot-Cohen
J. Elliah
Charles Ellingworth
E.J. Elliot
Mr L.C. Elliott
Chris Elliott
Claude Elliott
Barry Elliott
Dr M. Ellis
Mr D.R. Ellis
Mr and Mrs W. Ellis
Mrs A Ellis
I. Ellis
Mr T.D. Ellison
Lady Elmhirst
Judy Embleton and G. Dwyer Joyce
Mrs H. Embury
H. Emery
K. Emm
Mike and Anita Emmott
Roger Emmott
W.B. Emms
Prof and Mrs C.E. Engel

Mr and Mrs W.A. English
Revd Gerald Ennis
Robert Entwistle
Mr H. Errington
David Errington
Patricia Erskine-Hill
Mrs J. Erswell
Brian Escott
Ms J. Etchells
R.G. Etoe
Mr. and Mrs J. Ette
D. Anthony Evans QC
Mr and Mrs K.J. Evans
Mrs V.C. Davison Evans
Jonathon Evans
Howell Evans
Angela and Ray Evans
Mr and Mrs Antony Evans
John Evans
Lord Evans of Claughton
Mary Anne Evans
Lowri Evans
Gillian Evans
S. and R. Evans
Dr and Mrs R.R. Evans
Gina Evans
Elizabeth Evans
David D'Oyly Evans
J.S. Evans
Captain J.P. Evanson
W.R. Eyres
I. Fair
Mrs M. Fairall
Mr L. Fairbairn
John Fairweather
Mr F. Fallows
The Hon. Julian Fane
M. Farmer
R.G. Farmer
Mrs A. Farmer
Dr Niall Farnan
Rosalind Farnese
Mr R.S. Farrant
Angelique and Douglas Farrel
Lynne Farrell
Mr T.D. Farrell
Eric F. Farrer
Nicholas Farries
Ann Farrow
Mr Faruk
Mrs S. Faulkner

Caroline Faulkner
Mr and Mrs E.R. Faultless
Mr R. Fausset
Robert and Lesley Fawthrop
G.D. Fearnehough
G. Featherstone
W.P.Q. Feiner
Mr and Mrs R. Fell
Mr K.L. Fenner
Miss S. Fenton
Mr A.B. Fenwick
Mrs J. Ferguson
Robert Ferguson
R.J. Ferguson
Mr A. Ferns
Mrs J. Ferrett
Jon Ferrier
Bryan Ferriss
L. Ferrone
E.D. Field
P.A. Field
Mrs J. Finch Moyes
D.J. Firkin
Alan Firth
Chris Fisher
Jonathan Fisk
Mrs R.M. Fitton
Mrs B.A. Fitzpatrick
T.C. Flanagan
Mrs S. Fleming
D.J.R. Fletcher
Mr P.A.L. Fletcher
Dr Ben Fletcher
Dr R.F. Fletcher
Mr A.T.R. Fletcher
Marion J. Fletcher
E. Fletcher
Mr and Mrs J. Fletcher
Ron Fletcher
Prof. W.W. Fletcher
Susan Russell Flint
Mavis and Frank Florin
Andrea Fontaine
R.T. Fooks
A.G.M. Forbes
Mr and Mrs C.D. Forbes
Mrs I.A. Ford
Grahame Y. Ford
J.C. Ford
Bryan Ford
R.J. Foreman
Christopher Forman
P.J. Forrest
Alan J. Forrest
James W. Forrester
Mr B.W. Forster
J.M. Forster

Marie Forsyth
J. Forsythe
Roger Forward
A.L. Forward
Matthew Fosh
Mr R. Foss
M.D. Foster
Mrs G.M. Fothergill
J.C. Fowler
Mrs J.M. Fowler
Edmund Fox
Basil Fox and Jennifer Somerville
Dr Richard Fox
Dr and Mrs J. Fox
Mrs S.G. Fox
Alan Francis
Miss A. Francis
Mr D.D. Francis
Dr A. Frank
Mr R. Frankenburg
Mr and Mrs W. Frankland
Nigel Frankland
C.E. Franklin
I.R. Fraser
Richard and Catherine Fraser
R.H. Fraval
Mrs J. Frederic
John Freebairn
Jacqueline Freeman
B.A. Freeman
Mrs D. Friend
David Frise
G.L. Frost
Mr Froth
Mr G. Froyd
Mr and Mrs D. Fryer
Viola Fuller
R. and R. Furlong Brown
Mr G.J.U. Futcher
P.R. Fyson
Dr and Mrs Roger Gadsby
John Gagg
Bernard Gale
Selwyn Gale
R. Gallimore
Moira Gammell
Dr Robert Gandy
R.P. Gapper
Mrs Gardiner
Mr A. Gardner
C.M. Gardner
L. Gardner
Mr and Mrs E. Garford
Doron Garfunkel

Jill and Martin Garnett
Christine Garrett
Amanda Garrett
Hazel and Peter Garrod
Dr R.D. Gartside
Mr and Mrs F.H. Gateley
Mr L.T. Gates
Dr M.S. Gatley
Dr R.A.P. Gaubert
Dr Ian Gavin
Donald Mervyn Gay
Geoffrey Gay
R. Gaylard
Mrs V.M. Gaymer
Ann M. Geen
D.M. Gent
David Gent
E.J. George
Mr and Mrs David George
E. Gerard
Mrs D. Geyer
Mr and Mrs Austin Gibbons
Mr P. Gibbs
Richard J. Gibson
Kenneth Gilbert
Jenny Gilbert
Miss J. Gilbraith
Mrs A. Gilderslove
Christopher Giles
Dr J.J.H. Gilkes
Charles Gillams
Olga Gilleard
Austin and Audrey Gillham
Basil Gillinson
Susan Gillion
Peter Gillman
Mrs A.F. Gillon
Susan Gillotti
Mrs S.M. Gillotti
Meg Gilmore
M.N.B. Gilmour
Mr and Mrs A.J. Gladwin
Mrs J.R. Glanfield
Margaret Glassey
Gretel Glassman
B. Glastonbury
Joan Gledsdale
Prof. Duncan Glen
I.T. Glendenning
J.F. Glenister
Mr Glister
R.J.N. Glover
B.M. Glover
A.J. Goater
Peter Godber

G.K. Goddard
Mrs A.E. Godden
Peter Godden
Mrs J. Godfrey
Christine Godfrey
N. and P.A. Godley
R. Godrey-Wollin
Colin E. Goedecke
R. Goldblatt
Gill Golding
Joy and Raymond Goldman
C.M. Goldsmith
R.W. and Mrs M.E. Goldson
Mrs W. Gomes
Ms D.V. Gomez
Tom Gondris
M.E. Gooch
Michael Good
Mr R.M. Goodall
Norman Goodchild
Mr I. Goodfellow
Mrs T.A. Goodger
D. Goodger
Mr and Mrs B. Goodliffe
Mrs David Goodman
Linda Goodman
Miss F. Gordon
Lt. Col. R.P.D. Gordon
R.C.J. Gordon
Francis Gordon
Mr and Mrs J.J. Gordon
Michael Gordon-Gibson
M. Gordon-Russell
Dr S.M. Gore
Peter Gornall
D.M. Gostyn
Mrs M. Gough
Mr and Mrs A. Gough
Dr Gough
John Gough
Jean Gould
Mr and Mrs John Goulding
Mr R.J. Goundry
Mrs J.C. Goymour
Ms M.F. Grace
Mr A. Graham
Gavin and Tina Graham
S.E.F. Graham and J.S. Barron
Mr G. Graham
Olivia Graham
Alison Graham

Hugh Graham
Colin Graham
Michele Graham-Roe
Mrs J. Grain
Catherine Grale
Mr N. Grant
Mr A.G. Grau
M.R. Graves
David Gray
Mrs J. Gray
Peter Gray
Mrs M. Gray
Janet Greaves
Philip Green
J.B. Green
Jaci Green
John A. Green
Hughie Green
M.J. Greenan
H.I. Greenfield
N.D.A. Greenstone
J.R. Greenwood
Mr and Mrs K. Greenwood
Mr A. Greenwood
Eva Gregory
Derek Gregory
Mr and Mrs P.V. Gregory
Malcolm and Carolyn Greig
Celia Greig
W.P.L. Greville
John Gribbin
John Gridley
Paul Grier
Thomas A.L.L. Griffith
David Griffiths
G.G. Griffiths
Dr M.J. Griffiths
C. Martin Griffiths
David J. Griffiths
Nigel Grimshaw
Mr A.K. Grimwade
Shirley Grimwood
Don Grisbrook
Mrs R. Grogan
Elizabeth Grove
Mr R. Grover
A.D. Grumley-Grennan
Mr and Mrs B. Guard
Mr and Mrs R.K. Guelff
Naomi Guess
Mr A. Guest
Matthew Guest
Sally Gugen
A.W. Gulland

Jackie Gunn
Rosalind Gunning
D.B. Gurrey
Mary B. Guthrie
Mr R. Guy
Commander John
 W. Hackett
Prof. C.A. Hackett
Victor Haddad
Mr and Mrs M.E.
 Hadley
Marie and Hans
 Haenlein
Mr M.D. Hagan
Mr and Mrs D.W.
 Hague
Mrs A. Haig
Alan Haigh
Pamela Halasovski
Kevin Hales
Mrs W.T. Halford
Maureen Hall
Mr I. Hall
Dr and Mrs Hall
Mr P.K. Hall
Kate Hall
Mr D.W. Hall
Judith Hall
Ms J. Hall
Hazel Hall
R.A. Hall
Mr and Mrs Roy
 Hallam
Louise Hallett
W.J. Hallett
Linda and Martin
 Halliday
Mrs G. Hallsworth
Tom Halsall
Mr M.V. Hambling
Mrs A.E. Hambly
Emily Hamer
D. Hamilton
Dr J.R. Hamilton
Fiona Hamilton-
 Miller
Wendy Hammond
Elizabeth Hammond
John and Gloria
 Hammond
Mr H.J. Hamp
Jose Hampson
M.S. Hancock
A.M. Hancock
Alison Hancock
J. Hand
Lorraine M. Handley
Linden Handley
Dr Ruth A. Hanham
Walter Hanlon
Dorothy Hannan
Mrs G. Hansford

Dr A.E. Hall
J. Hardy
Mr C. Hardy
Mr and Mrs J. Hardy
Joan Hare
Joe Hare
Roger Hargreaves
Pamela Harman
J.E. Harmsworth
Corinne Jane Harper
R.J. Harper
M.J. Harper
Mr R.W. Harries
W.F. Harrigan
Miss N. Harrigan
Alan Harris
Mrs A. Harris
B.E. Harris
Dr James B. Harris
Mr F. Harris-Jones
Mr and Mrs Harris
Alan Harris
Jane Harris
A. Harris
J.A. Harris and A.
 Fuest
Rosemary Harris
James Harris
P.N. Harrison
Annette Harrison
P.R. Harrison
A. Harrison
Mr and Mrs Blair
 Harrison
D.J. Harrow
Sue Hart
Tim Hart
M.G. and V.A. Hart
Mr and Mrs D.J.
 Hart
Miss W. Hart
Mrs L. Hart
J.V. Hartley
J.V. Hartley
J.D. Hartley
Donald Hartog
Eleanor M. Harvey
Mrs P. Hase
George Hastings
Richard Haugwitz-
 Reventlow
E. Hatch
Dr Frank
 Haverkamp
Mr and Mrs S.K.
 Haviland
Mr J. Haviland
Mrs S. Haward
Mrs P.D. Hawker
D. Hawkes-Popham
Anne Hawkin
John F. Hawkins

Mr R.G.P. Hawkins
Mrs J. Hawkins
David Hawkins
A.A. Hawkins
S.J. Haworth
Mrs J.K. Hayes
R.N. Haygarth
Andy Hayler
Mr J.A. Hayles
Brian Hayman
Mr and Mrs R.M.
 Hayns
Dr and Mrs
 Hayward
Mrs J. Haywood
Miss C. Hazell
Mr and Mrs D.J.
 Heacock
Tim Heald
Revd Bruno Healy
Mr and Mrs J. Hearn
Dr and Mrs K.W.
 Heaton
S.M. Heaton
Penny Heaton
Revd N.C.
 Heavisides
Mrs R.V. Hebdon
Mr and Mrs Heber-
 Percy
Mr and Mrs M.
 Hedges
Amanda Heesom
R.E. Heffer
Colm Heffernon
Dr Hikka Helevuo
Mrs M. Helm
Mr W.S.D. Hendry
Dr Thomas
 Henninger
Peter Hensher
George W.
 Henshilwood
Hugh Heptonstall
Mr and Mrs Jack
 Herbert
Patricia Herrod
Craig Herron
Mr N.G.
 Hetherington
G. Heuman
Annette Heuser
John Heuston
Mrs John Hewer
Mr and Mrs B.
 Hewins
Mr A.J. Hewitt
Mrs M. Heywood
Ray Heyworth
E.V. Hibbert
Mr D.A. Hickling
Mrs K.A. Hickman

Michael S. Hicks
Mr and Mrs B.L.
 Higgins
Mr K. Higgins
G.A. Higham
Mr and Mrs G.
 Higson
J.G. Hill,
R.B. Hill
Joanna Hill
J.O.C. Hill
Mrs G. Hill
Philip Hill
Mr S.P. Hill
E. Hill
Mr H.A.O. Hill
J.M.M. Hill
Christine Hill
James and Anne Hill
Mrs M.M. Hill
H.T. Hill
Frank Hill
Wendy Hillary
Mr and Mrs Hillier
J.R. Hillman
Mrs M. Hilton
Ronald and
 Maureen Hinde
Gloria Hindhaugh
Michael J. Hindle
Stanley Hindle
Karen and Mark
 Hindle
Mr E. Hinds
C.E. Hinsley
Michael Hippisley
A.F. Hitch
Ophelia Ho
W.H. Hoade
I.M. Hoare
P. Hoare-Temple
J.H. Hobbs
K. Hobbs
Michael Hobsley
Ms J. Hobson
John Hobson
Mrs T. Hodge
Philip A.H. Hodgson
Mr and Mrs D.E.
 Hodgson
Mr A. Hodgson
Dr Michael J. Hoey
John Hogg
Mr R. Hogg
Mr.John Hogg
Mr Michael Hoggett
T. Holcroft
Derrick Holden
A.C. Holden
Dr and Mrs H.M.
 Holding
Mrs J. Hole

A.M. Holland
G. Hollas
G.T. Hollebine
Mark Holliday
Dr C.P. Hollis
Mr T. Hollis
David Hollister
Mr J.F. Holman
Steven Holmes
P. Holmes
Mrs A. Holmes
Mr and Mrs Mark
  Holmes
A.R.M. Holsey
D.A. Holt
Claire Holt
Peter Holt
L. Holt-Kentwell
F.J. Homer
S. Homer
Mr and Mrs I.J.
  Honder
Ian Honey
Paul Honney
Peter Hood
J.E. Hooker
Mr H.J. Hooper
N. Hooper
Mr and Mrs B. Hope
Mrs B.M. Hopewell
R.R. Hopkins
Lt. Col. and Mrs F.T.
  Hopkinson
R.C. Hopton
M. Hopton
Mr and Mrs R.H.
  Horncastle
J.A. Horne
Mr P.R. Hornsby
Rita Horridge
Susan Horwich
Sarah E. Hotchkiss
Dr Keith Hotten
H.J. Hough
Janet I. Housden
Mrs P.A. Houston
Mrs H.L. Howard
Francis Howard
E.N. Howard
S.F. Howarth
Mr and Mrs E.
  Howe
Guy Howel Jones
Geoffrey Howell
John Howell
Mr R.W.F and Dr
  P.J. Howell
Wendy M. Howes
Pippa Howes
Mrs G. Howey
R. Howgego
Jonathan Hoyle

Julia H. Hudson
R.E. Hudson
Marie Hudson
A.M. Hudson
Mrs J. Hudson
Joan and Peter
  Hudson
Mr C. Hughes
A.F. Hughes
Mr R.N. Hughes
Janice Hughes
Dr Louis Hughes
Mrs D. Hull
A.C. Hulse-Wright
P.W. Humphreys
Charles S. Hunt
Andrew Hunter
Dr James M. Hunter
Mr J. Hunter
Louise Hunter
Elizabeth Huntly
Mr C.J. Hurd
Mr M. Hurwitt
K.V. Hutchinson
Mike Hutton
W.E. Huxtable
L.M. Hyde
Mrs A. Hynes
Mr T.J. Hypher
Mrs V.A. Iddon
Ronald Ilian
Micheal Innes
Dr Richard Irons
Mr and Mrs Donald
  Irvine
Jane Isaac
Dr and Mrs D.H.
  Isaac
Mrs C. Isserlis
Mr and Mrs Jack
Dr H.R.S. Jack
Roberta Jackson
Mrs J.J. Jackson
Ann Jackson
C.R.A. Jackson
M.K. and C.V.
  Jackson
James Jackson
Paul Jackson
S. Jackson
Carl Jackson
Jill Jackson
Mrs L.M. Jackson
Susan B. Jackson
P.H. Jacobsen
Mrs N. Jacques
Eric Jaffe
Mr J. Jagdev
N. Jagota
J. Jakeman
Mrs T. Jalowiecki
F.S. James

Graham D. James
Mr B.G.W. Jamieson
Mr and Mrs A.A.
  Janes
Mr C.G. Jarman
Mr and Mrs D.
  Jarrett
Clare Jarrett
Moira Jarrett
Mrs R. Jarvis
Prof. Barrie Jay
Antony Jay
E.A. Jayashree
Mrs O. Jeacock
Col P.N.M. Jebb
Mrs P.M. Jefferis
Sue Jeffery and
  Edward
  Highmore
A.V. Jell
Mr D.L. Jelley
Mr and Mrs Michael
  Jellicoe
Margaret and
  Edward Jenkins
A.B. Jenkins
Mr C.R. Jenkinson
B.H. Jenkinson
J.C. Jennings
P.C. Jennings
Mrs M.M.G.
  Jennings
David Jervois
Michael Jobling
Brian Jobson
Ms V. Joel
Dr and Mrs R.T.
  John
C.M. John
D.G. John
H.A. and C. Johnson
Ruth and Roy
  Johnson
Michael H. Johnson
Mrs Johnson
Mrs J.K. Johnson
Chris Johnson
R.C. Johnston
Dr I.H.D. Johnston
R.C. Johnston
Andrew Johnston
John Johnston
Mr D. Johnston
Jane L. Johnston
Gina Jolliffe
Melanie Jones
Ian Jones
Mr W.C.M. Jones
Barbara Jones
Susan Jones
Heather Jones
Haydn Jones

Mr and Mrs K.
  Jones
E.S. Jones
Mrs R. Jones
G.L. Jones
Mrs E. Jones
Peter Jones
Simon M. Jones
Mr D. Jones and Mr
  P. Sayce
J.W.E. and P.R.
  Jones
Mr N.F. Jones
J.L. Jones
Peter Jones
Maurice Jones
Mandy Jones
Maureen Jones
D. Jones
Mr P.G. Jones
Canon Ronald Jones
Robin and Marion
  Jones
K.H. Jones
Clive Jones
Stephen Jones
N.P. Jones
Mr and Mrs J. Jones
S.R. Jones
P. Jonietz
C.B. Jonzen
Mr B. Jordan
P.M. Jordan
P. Jordan
Nathan and Sarah
  Joseph
Paul L. Joslin
Janet Joule
Peter J.R. Jowitt
Brian A. Joyce
Ann Juckes
M.R. Judd
Jane Julier
Mrs Justice
Dr A. Kabi
Ms J. Kaminski
Andrea Katerinas
Dr D. Katz
J.G. Kavanagh
L. Keeley
J.E.D. Keeling
R.E. Keen
Sheila Keene
Mr M. and Mrs S.
  Kellard
Kathleen Kelly
M.J. Kelly FRCS
Arthur S. Kelm
Dr C.J.H. Kelnar
Mr H.S. Kemp
Mr G. Kempton
Kenneth Kendall

J.G. Kendall
Michael Kenefick
J.O. Kennedy
Mrs Kennedy
Mrs G.M. Kennedy
Mr and Mrs S.
  Kennedy
Mr D. Kenrick
Christina Kent and
  Sean Egan
Michael Kent
Mr R.B. Kenyon
Dr David Kerr
D.F. Kerr
Simon Ketley
W.G. Ketteridge
Mr J.S. Kettle
Stephen F. Kew
Elizabeth Key
Dr J.W. Keyser
Simon M.
  Kibblewhite
Joan Kidd
J.H. Kilby
Mr and Mrs J.
  Kilner
Mr and Mrs Kimbel
Susan H. Kinber
Ronald James King
R.E. King
Mr E.B. King
C.F. King
P.J. King
Revd A.B. King
Mr and Mrs S. King
Jennifer and
  Stephen Kingsley
Susan Kingsley
Derek Kinsey
O.J.R. Kinsey
Mr and Mrs W.A.
  Kinsman
Lt Cdr and Mrs R.
  Kirby Harris
Mr R.J. Kirby Welch
Richard Kirker
Mr and Mrs
  Kirkman
A. and J. Kissack
Dr Paul A. Kitchener
Christopher Kite
Nicholas Kleiner
Mr R. Knapp
Robin Knapp
Sylvia Knapp
Mr A.B. Knapp
E.J. Knifton
Mrs C. Knight
R.A. Knight
Mrs B.A. Knowles
Mrs J. Knox

Mr and Mrs
  Alexander Korda
Mr R. Krawiec
Rasha Kudsi
Robert Kuehn
C.J. Kuhl
J.M. Kumarendran
Mr G. Kurt
Dr D.W. Kyle
Dorothy Kyne
Jean M. Lace
T. Laffin
Mr and Mrs C.E.
  Lake
Derek Lambert
Ralph Lambert
Elisabeth Lambert
  Ortiz
Gordon Lammie
Mr and Mrs
  Lancaster
Norman Land
A. Landsberg
Mrs S. Lanfranchi
Pamela J. Lang
Mr R.C. Lang
Jack Lang
Mr A.T. Langton
Lesley M. Langton
Eric Lansley
Mr and Mrs A. Lanzl
S.H. Large
Mr P. Larkin
Sheilagh Larner
Stephen Lashford
Dr R.D. Last
Andrew Lathwell
Anne Laurence
Barry Laver
Mr J.W. Lawes
Jane Lawrence
Mrs M.E. Lawrence
D. Lawrence
John H. Lawrence
Richard Lawrence
J. and M. Lawrence
Alan Le Chard
Ferrers Le Mesurier
P.V. Le Neve Foster
Valerie Lea
W.H. Lea
J.D. Leach
R.A.L. Leatherdale
Mr P.H. Ledger
Mrs B. Ledsome
Dr. Michael Ledson
A.J.N. Lee
K.R. Lee
David Lee
Geoffrey Lee
James Leek

Anne and James
  Leeming
K. Lees
Mrs W. Lees
Kevin Legrand
Michael Leitch
Mr R. Lennox
J. Leonard
A.J. Leonard
Hugh Leonard
P.L. Leonard
R.C. Leslie
Marjory Lester
Susana and Pierre
  Leval
Dr and Mrs J. Levi
A.S. Levitt
G.M. Levy
G.N. Levy
B.K. and R.S. Levy
Felix Levy
Mike Levy
Mr and Mrs Lewin
Mr and Mrs G.T.
  Lewis
Ms P.L. Lewis
Mr D.J.B. Lewis
Miss J. Lewis
Mr and Mrs E.
  Lewis
Janet Lewis
Denise Lievesley
W.I. Light
G. Light
Ms L. Lim
R.C. Limb
Rolf Lind and Turi
  Gilje
Mr M.M. Lindley
Donald C. Lindon
J.H. Ling
Mrs J. Lipman
Jeremy C.A. Little
Peter Little
Mrs E.M. Little
Penelope Lively
Mrs J.W. Lloyd
Mr D.M. Lloyd
Mrs S.C. Lloyd
S. Lloyd Jones
R.W. Lloyd-Davies
Charles Lockley
M. Lockwood
Mrs D. Loebl
Victoria Logue
Kevin Lonergan
Mrs J.A. Long
P.A. Long
E.I. Lonis
Mrs M.M. Lord
Mr S.J. Lott
Dr D. Lott

Prof. and Mrs R.
  Loudon
R.F. Lovelock
Mrs D.G. Loveluck
Mrs V. Low
Mrs M.S. Lowry
L. Lubett
Mrs P.A. Luckly
Mr F.G. Luff
Dr John Lunn
Philip Lusty
Frank Luxton
Lindsay Lynch
Patrick Lynch
M. Lynch
Thomas S. Lyon
Mr S. Lyons
Humphrey Lyttelton
T.C.H. Macafee
Dr Mac Carthy
B.E. MacDermott
Jean MacDonald
Gill Macey
Geralyn Macfadyen
R.B. MacGeachy
A.D. Macgillivray
  and R. Conn
Mr J.A. MacInnes
S. Mackay
Shirley A.
  Mackenzie
J.W. Mackley
Mr E.W.F. MacLeish
Patrick MacNamee
Isobel Macoun
Mrs S. Macpherson
Mr M. Madden
A.F. Maddocks
G.F. and J.
  Maddocks
P.J. Magee
Geoff Magnay
Daniel J. Maher
Peter Mair
Mrs J.W. Makinson
Mrs C.F. Malone
N.V. Malone
Jane Mann
David and Gina
  Mann
Dr Brian Manners
Mr John Graham
  Manning
Mr and Mrs J.
  Manning
Elisabeth Manning
Paul Manning
Mrs S.K. March
His Hon. Judge
  Bernard Marder
  QC
David Margetts

Michael J. Markey
Lewis Marks and
  Philippa Johnson
Christopher
  Marlowe
Rosemary Marsh
R.J.S. Marsh
Lady Caroline
  Marsh Smethurst
Mr A.J. Marshall
Roger Marshall
Jonathan Marshall
Drs Neil and Jean
  Marshall
Mr T. Marshall
Tony and Valerie
  Marshall
R.O. Marshall
Derek Marsland
Mr and Mrs Henry
  Martin
E.A. Martin
Jennifer Martin
Mrs J. Martin
Dr M. Martin-Jones
Mr B.N. Martin-
  Kaye
Peter and Alyson
  Martineau
J.R. Martyn
Janet Mascarenhas
Mr and Mrs M.V.G.
  Masefield
A. Mason
Dr S. Mason
Mrs H.S. Mason
D. Mate
Mrs C.M. Mather
K.G. Mather
A. Matheson
Dr and Mrs A.M.
  Mathewson
Mr and Mrs Mathias
Sally-Ann
  Mathieson
Mrs J.G. Mathieson
Mrs D. Matthew
Mr C.R. Matthews
Mrs Peter Matthey
Maurice Price
Michael Maxwell
Kenneth and
  Suzanne May
L.T. Mayes
Jack J. Mayl
Mr and Mrs D.G.
  McAdam
Mrs McAleen
Colin and Julie
  McAlinden
Andrew McAlpine
C. McAteer

Paul and Wendy
  McCallan
Harry McCann
Jane McCarten
E.J. McCarthy
Christina McComb
Walter McCrindle
Dr A.F. Scott and Dr
  C.F. McDonald
June McDonald
Dennis McDonnell
Brian McEvoy
Prof. and Mrs I.D.
  McFarlane
J.C. McGarvie
Alan McGee
Colin and Lilian
  McGhee
Malcolm McGreevy
Graham McGuire
Mrs K. McIntosh
Mrs C.E. McKay
T.A. McKee
Mr R.E.K. McKeith
Mr K.J. McKenna
Martha D. McKenna
Nancy McKenzie
C.E. McKerrell
C.W. McKerrow
J.A. McKinnell
Dr and Mrs J.G.
  McLaggan
Liz McLaughlin
E. McLoughlin
P.E.M. McLoughlin
Linda McLusky
Dr Ann McNeill
Ronald S. McNeill
  CBE
Anne McQuade
Dr and Mrs J.
  McRobert
Steven McTavish
Standish Meacham
Mr A.M. Meacock
D.R. Mead
David E. Mead
Ms M. Meah
Joan and Joe
  Mearns
M.R. Medcalf
Jean and Bob
  Meeson
Andrew and Pauline
  Meggy
Mr and Mrs T.
  Meldrum
Mr K.R. Mellin
Ms S. Melling
Mrs P.A. Mellor
J.A. Melrose
Carole Melvin

Malcolm C. Mentha
A.K. Mercer
Dr and Mrs A.P.
  Mercer
Major J.B. Merritt
David Mert
Mrs M.A.
  Messenger
Hilary Meth
C. Maill
Paul L. Michelson
Patricia Michelson
K. Micnes
Robin Middleton
R.T. Middleton
Mr J.R. Miele
Mr P.H. Miles
Miss G. Miles
W.G. and M.I. Miles
Hilarie Miles-Sharp
Barbara and Alan
  Millar
Duncan Miller
Keith Miller
G.S. Miller
J.L. Miller
John E. Miller
T.W. Miller-Jones
R.F. Millet
J.L. Millgate
M. Mills
Mr J.T. Mills
Mr H.G. Millward
Mrs F. Millward
S. Milne
Joe and Bett Milne
D.J. Milner
Mrs John Minter
G.B. Minter
K.J. Misch
Mr I.W. Mitchell
Simon Mitchell
John Mitchell
Hilary E. Mitchell
Miss J.E. Mitchell
Patricia Mitchell
Mr and Mrs K.
  Mitchell
John Mitchelmore
S. Mitchelmore
Sheila Miwyer
Mrs M. Mocsari
Dr J. Mollon
J.D. Mollor
John Molyneux
A.P. Monblat
C.J. Monk
Janet Monk
Mrs E. Moody
P. and J. Moody
T.L. Moody
R.D. Moon

Mr A.J.R. Moon
Mr and Mrs Mooney
Eric Moonman
Mr and Mrs M.
  Moorcock
Tania Moore
Mrs H. Moore
Mr A. Moore
Anthony Moore
Peter and Alison
  Moore
Mr K.C. Moore
Mrs P. Moorhouse
Mr and Mrs Patrick
  Morcas
R.N. Morgan
Colin Morgan
D.P. Morgan
Gwyn Morgan
Michael Morgan
Mrs H. Morgan
P.A. Morgan
Hazel Morgan
M. Gerard Morice
Mr F. Morrell
Mr G. Morrell
Peter Morrell
C.R.W. Morrell
David C. Morris
D. Morris
Mr L. Morris
Mr V.G.F. Morris
Mrs W. Morris-
  Jones
A.C. Morrison
T. and M.F.
  Morrison
David Mort
Mr and Mrs N.
  Morton
J.D. and L. Morton
Robin Morton-
  Smith
Jane Mosedale
T.J. Moseley
Alex and Mai Moss
Daniel Moss
Mrs A.D. Mould
Ms A. Mountfort
K.B. Mowle
Mr and Mrs W.A.
  Moxon
Stewart Muir
Mrs I.E. Muir
Mr J.P. Mullen
Richard Mullineaux
Kevin Mullins
D.W. Mullock
A. Mumford
Mrs Simon
  Mumford
Mr P. Munnoch

Mr A.H. Munro
John Munro
David Murdoch
Nicholas Murphy
Pat Murray
John Murray
Braham Murray
Mrs M.L. Murray Smith
A.A. Murray-Jones
Stephen and Kate Murray-Sykes
A.G. Mursell
D.M. Musitano
Mr M.J. Mylan
M. Naish
John Neal
Barbara Neale
Mrs S. Nee and Mr S. Taylor
Betty Netherton
Dr and Mrs H. Neubauer
Jenny Neubauer
Dr Peter Newbould
Robert de Newby
M.L.W. Newman
William Newman
Mr Nicholas
R.P. Nicholas
Mr D.J.B. Nicholls
David Nicholls
Roger and Jean Nicholls
M. Nicholson
M.C. Nicholson
Mrs P. Nixon
Mrs P.G. Nixon
Janet A. Nixon
Mrs M. Nixon
Revd Ronnie Noakes
Mrs D.A. Noble
Peter and Penny Noble
Dr John Nocton
Jean Nolan
Linda Nordenberg
J.A.G. Norman
Dr Remington Norman
D.L. Norman
Dr R. Norman
Geoff Normile and Pat Pavitt
Mr J.G. Norris
Dr Paul Norris
Carolyn Norris
Christopher North
Gerry Northam
Mr D. Norton
Mrs M. Norton

John H. Nugent
Trevor Nunn
David Nutt
G.H. Nuttall
John Nuttall
J.B. O'Connor
Peter O'Grady
T.P. O'Hare
Jane and Kevin O'Mahoney
Clara O'Neill
Rebecca O'Neill
W.B. O'Neill
Mr G.M. O'Reilly
Mr H.D. O'Reilly
Daniel O'Riordan
Ann O'Riordan
Mary O'Riordan
Peter O'Rorke
Mr K.J. O'Sullivan
Lesley Oakden
Peter Oakley
A. Oakley
Mr Oddey
John Oddey
Frank Oderkirk
R.T. Oerton
R.A.L. Ogston
A.I. Ogus
Mr and Mrs D.G. Old
H.N. Olden
David Oldfield
M.J. Oldfield
J.D. Oldroyde
L.S. Oliver
A.J. Oliver
Dr C.W. Oliver
T.N. Ondrey
A.M.F. Orange
Mr and Mrs S.J. Orford
Margaret N. Orme
Mrs A. Orton
J. Osborn Clarke
Norman Osborne
Mr and Mrs John Osborne
Kenneth Osborne
Isabel H. Oswald
Kirstie and Ian Oswald
T.R. Otley
Dr C.J. Otty
George Turner Overdale
Mr I.C. Overend
J.A.M. Overholt
Mr and Mrs D. Overton
Kenneth Owen

Melanie Owen-Smith
Linda Owens
Ann Owston
Mr and Mrs W. Pack
Mr T.J. Page
J.D. Page
R. Page
Dr S.D. Page
V.C. Page
Sue and Geoff Page
The Page family
Karen Pallister
N.J. Goddard Palmer
Dr A.C. Palmer
Mrs D. Palmer
Michael Y. Palmer
Andrew Parffrey
Mr G.D. Paris
Mr Richard Parish
Mr W.E. Parker
Mrs D.J. Parker
Mr and Mrs J.C. Parker
D.J. Parker
Mrs J. Parkes
Martin Parr
Andrew Parrish
Mrs J. Parry
Miss J. Parry
John E. Parsons
Dr C.J. Parsons
Christopher Parsons
David Parsons
T.G. Parsons
Alan Partington
Simon Parton
Prof and Mrs Keith Patchett
M.H.O. Paterson
Dr J.M.K. Paterson
Mrs D.S. Paterson-Fox
Mr B. Paton
John Paton
Mrs V. Patrick
Mr J.S. Patterson
Simon Pattisson
Dr R.A. Pauc
Dr Anne Paulett
Diana Paulson
Mr and Mrs R. Paxton
Murray S. Paxton
R.E.J. Payne
J.F. Peace
A. and R. Peace
H. Peach
B.I. Pearce
G.D.B. Pearse
Mrs R.J. Pearson

R. Pearson
David Pearson
Simon Peck
Rosemary Pegg
J.B. Penfold
Mr D.J. Penny
Alan Penson
Mrs C. Pepe
G. Perkins
K. Perry
George Perry-Smith
Helen Peston
B.A. Peters
Julia M. Petty
G.W. Petty
Mrs S.V. Phelps
Mr D.R. Philip
Mr R. Phillip
Beryl and John Phillip
Ms C. Phillips
Sally Phillips
Mrs A.J. Phillips
Dr and Mrs R.M. Phillips
Mr B.J.E. Phillips
Joan Phillipson
Mr J.M. Pickering
Dr and Mrs D.F. Pickering
A.M. Pickup
Mrs M.E. Piena
N.R. Pigott
T.J.D. Pigott
Ann Pilling
Josephine Pines
M. Edouard Pinich
Mr and Mrs L. Pipe
Michael Pitel
A.J. Pitkin
Hugh Pitt
Michael Pitts
V.J. Pizzey
G. Place
Elizabeth Plater
Michele Platman
Dr Jeremy Platt
Catherine Plummer
Nicola M.J.Y. Plummer
Richard Pocock
Mrs J. Pogue
Mrs John Pope
Mrs H. Pope
Mr W.D. Porter
David Potter
Mr S. Potter
Martin Potter
Dr J.M. Potter
Mr I.J. Poulton
Mr and Mrs A. Powell

I.R. Powell
Len Powell
Joan A. Powell
Mrs F.J. Powell
Mrs V.J. Power
Garry Pownall
Bruce Poynter
Martin Pratt
Dr J.M. Preece
Ms D. Pressly
J.B. Preston
F.S. Price
Dr M.J. Price
Neville Price
Derek J. Price
Mr and Mrs S.J. Prideaux
Mrs A. Prideaux
Rebecca Priestley
Edwin Prince
Capt. K. Pritchard
Dr Lindsay Pritchett
Mr S. Benjamin Pritchett-Brown
Mr L.F. Privett
Capt. E.F. Proctor
W.R. Proctor
Evlynne Provan
R. Pryce Jones
Ann and Brian Pudner
Dr G.P. Pullen
Leslie and Fiona Pulsford
Mr E. Punchard
Stephen J. Purse
E.J.D. Purse
Howard Pursey
Simon Pyle
Lord Quinton
Harry Rabinowitz
Dr Frank Rackow
Mrs V. Radcliffe
Ian and Daniele Radcliffe
E. Radcliffe
Jenny Raddish
Dr Stewart Rae
R.G. Rae
James Rae
Hilary Raeburn
Miss L. Raffell
R. Rainbird
G.E. Rainford
Daghni Rajasingam
Philip Rallison
B.G. Ralph
Mrs A. Ralphs
Mr D.S. Rampton
J.M. Rampton
Lucie Ramsden
Patrick Rance

Dr and Mrs D.G.S. Randall
Colin H. Randall
Dr A.M. Rankin
William Rankin
Mrs V. Ransome
Caroline Raphael
Mrs S. Raw
Dr and Mrs John Raw
Michael Rawling
Mary Rayner
Martin Rayner
Peter Rea
Dr and Mrs G.M. Read
Capt. P. Redman
A.P. Redmayne
D. Reed
Alec Reed
Jacqueline Reed
Dr A.I. Rees
Mrs K.M. Reeve
Roger H. Reeves
Mrs R.I. Reeves
David Regan
Geraldine Reid
W.B. Rhodes
T. Rhodes
Wendy Richard
Mrs D. Richards
Mr G.A. Richards
Peter Richards
S.G. Richards
Mr C.J. Richardson
G.B. Richardson
J.K. Richardson
Carol Riddick
J. Riddleston
Mrs J. Ridley-Thompson
Mr and Mrs A. Rieck
Mrs C.A. Rigg
Maggie Riley
N.R. Riley
Edwin P.C. Riley
Roger F. Rimmer
Danielle Rimmer
Gordon Ringrose
Norma J. Rink
W. Ritchie
Michelle and Mary Rivers
Ms S. Robb
His Hon. Judge Hywel ap Robert
Mr and Mrs J.R.L. Roberts
Mr D.E.G. Roberts
Dr and Mrs A.P. Roberts

Mr and Mrs J.W. Roberts
P.J. Roberts
Ruth Roberts
Mrs G.R. Roberts
Liz Roberts
Mr and Mrs K.P. Roberts
Dr A. John Robertson
Sarah Robertson
Claire Robertson
John Robertson
Mr and Mrs J.G. Robertson
R.H.C. Robins
J.V.H. Robins
Sophy Robinson
Sheila Robinson
M.V. Robinson
Peter Robinson
David Robinson and Ruth Hasty
Harry Robinson
W.G. Robinson
Ian Robinson
Rae Robinson
A.L. Roblin
Mr F. Rocca
Mr J. Rochelle
Mr and Mrs P.N. Rodgers
Mr E. Rodrigues
Paul M. Rogarris
Derek J. Rogers
Marie C. Rogers
Mr and Mrs H.F.N. Rogers
B. Rogers
Tim Rogers
Sir Frank Rogers
Miss E.L. Rogers
Mrs M.L. Rogers
M.O. Roland
David Roper
Mr and Mrs B.A. Rose
H.D. and A.L. Rose
Daniel Rose
Anthony Rosen
G. Rosenthal
Mr and Mrs Rosewell
Graham Ross
Mr Robert C. Ross-Lewin
P. Rossington
Mrs A. Rossiter
Mrs Rothenstein
Mrs E. Round
Lt. Col. D.P. Rowat
John Rowe

Sally Rowe
Ms E.B. Rowe
Sheila Rowell
Michael Rowland
Debra and Mike Rowlinson
Mr G. Rowntree
Mr W.S. Rowsell
Mr and Mrs Royle
Peter Rozee
Ms J.M. Ruane
Hilary Rubinstein
Peter Rudd
Carol A. Ruddick
Mr and Mrs D.E. Ruffell
Mr R.J. Ruffell
P.H. Ruffen
John Rumsey
John M. Rusk M.D.
A. Russell
Keith Russell
Philippa Russell
Denis N. Russell
Alexander B. Russell
P.M.G. Russell
A.N. Russell
M.P. Rutherford
Mr and Mrs Rutherford
Dr and Mrs L.D. Rutter
Duncan Rutter
Mr J.S. Rutter
R.S. Ryder
Miss M. Ruparelia
P.R. Sabin
Mr L. Saffron
A.J.H. Sale
Norman and Sheila Sales
Jasper and Celia Salisbury-Jones
Ron Salmon
Keith Salway
John Sambrook
D.E. Samuel
O.W. Samuel
Geoffrey J. Samuel
Mr S.D. Samuels
Barbara Samways
Mr M. Sanai
P.W. Sandes
Dr R.J. Sandry
Michael and Alison Sandy
Mr S. Sarcar
Dr Abigail Sargent
Ann Saunders
Mr and Mrs G. Saunders

M.V. Saunders
Vincent Saunders
Mr J.R. Saunders
Ruth Saunders
J.G. Savelli
S. Savertone
John W. Savery
Dean Saville
Mrs L. Savvides
Lt. Col. E.H. Sawbridge
George Sayer
J.F. and M. Sayers
Sally Saysell
Diane Scally
Mr J. Scarisbrick
Mrs F. Scarr
Alan Schachtman
Prof. P.J. Scheyer
Mr and Mrs E. Schmidt
Tony Schneider
N.D.S. Schofield
Theo Schofield
Mr and Mrs C.J. Schofield
Michael Schofield
Dr B.R. and Mrs P.M. Scholey
Craig Schorn
Alexander Schouvaloff
G. Shreiber
Mr and Mrs G. Schwab
Mr R. Schwarz
K.H. Scollay
Mr and Mrs Benson D. Scotch
Mr P.D. Scott
Prof. D.B. Scott
Revd P.L. Scott
Lady Scott
Stella Scott
Julian Scott
Mr D.A. and Mrs Gerda Scott
Mr and Mrs P.B. Scott
Mr J.D. Scott
C.G.P. Scott-Malden
Mr J. Scott-Smith
Tony Scull
Peter Seagroatt
K.A. Searle
Peter Searle
Dr A.H. Sears
Mr E.J. Seddon
J.R.E. Sedgwick
Gillian Seel
Harold E. Segelstad
Peter Seglow

P.S. Selby
Peggy Selby
Mr and Mrs Selby
Ms H.S. Self
G.C. Seller
Paul Sellers
Mr and Mrs D. Semmens
Maria Semper
Louise Semple
Chris Semprini
Guy Senior
B. Sessford
Linda Sewell
Mrs M. Seymour-Smith
S.A. Shamma
Mrs H. Sharman
Mr and Mrs R. Sharp
Jane Sharp
Dianne Sharp
John T.L. Sharpe
Dr J.T.R. Sharrock
Mr and Mrs P. Shattuck
Mr V.J. Shaw
Gabriele Shaw
L. Shaw
B.E. Shawcross
M.D. Shearman
George Shears
R.J. Sheen
Mrs Sheffield
Sylvia Sheinfield
Ailsa Shelley
F.L. Shepley
Peter and Priscilla Sherlock
Mr E.B.O. Sherlock
Miss J.C. Sherratt
J.N. Sherry
Marjorie Shilcof
David Shillitoe
Dr Wharton Shober
Mr and Mrs Shoosmith
D.G. Shrigley
Mr C. Shroff
J.G. Shurgold
Simon Shute
Major P.C.G. Shuter
B. Shutt
Mr C.B. Sibcy
Dr and Mrs T.E. Sicks
Mrs C. Sidhom
Mr G. Siggins
Harvey Silver
Mr and Mrs J.M. Silver

Dr and Mrs Silverstone
Mr R. Silverstone
Robert C. Sim
A. Sime
Peter Carr Simmonds
Mr B. Simmons
John Simmons
Mick Simmons
F.T. Simonds
R.F. Simons
Mr and Mrs J. Simpson
Andrew Simpson
Nigel Simpson
N.R. Simpson
Mrs P.M. Simpson
Mr P.S. Simpson
Mr and Mrs D. Simpson
Mrs J.A. Simpson
John Simpson
Paul Simpson
Dr I. Sims
Joseph Sinclair
Rivka Sinclair
Ian Sinclair
Mr and Mrs E. Sinclair
Mr R. Sinclair-Taylor
R. Sinclair
A.M. Singer
T. Singleton
Tony Sinnott
Marion Sitch
P.R. Skipper
Mr D.A. Slade
Mats Slunga
Dr Keith Smales
M.A.J. Smart
W.H. Smelt
Col. D. Smiley
D. Smiley
Ms F.J. Smith
Paul D. Smith
Mr and Mrs S.M. Smith
Mr and Mrs Gordon Smith
Mr and Mrs R. Smith
Dr S.J. and Mrs G.F. Smith
Mr G.J. Smith
A.J. Smith
Mr P. Smith
Kenneth E. Smith
Derek Smith
Mrs B.A. Smith
D.J. Smith

Janet Smith
William Smith
Mr D.C. Smith
Wynne Smith
Geoffrey Smith JP
Maureen A. Smith
Martin Smith
Stuart and Gina Smith
James A. Smith
Ms F.M.K. Smith
T.A. Smith
R. Smith
Prof. A.F.M. Smith
David Smith
Dr J.C. Smith
Barbara H. Smith
Pamela Smith
Richard Smith Wright
Mr G.C.K. Smith-Burnett
Dr G. Smyth
Mr R. Percy Smyth
Graham Snow
Sarah Solly
D.J. Solly
Tom Solomon
Dr B. Solomons
D. Solomons
Amin Somji
S.E. Sondergaard
Julia South
Mrs A. Southall
Mr J. Southern
Elwyn Soutter
Stephanie Sowerby
L.M. Spalton
Wing Cdr R.M. Sparkes
Nina Spear
Mr and Mrs Spiedel
Pauline Spence
Mr J. Spencely
C.A. Spencer
Becky Spencer
Mr F.E.V. Spencer
Mr P.G. Spencer
T. Spencer-Andrew
Jill Springbett
Nicholas Spruyt
E.P. Staff
Mr P.F. Stafford
Cynthia A. Stafford
Harry Stainton
Jacqueline Stanesby
Miss S.J. Stanley
S.J. Stanley
Mr J. Stanley-Smith
Rhoda Stanton
R.A.J. Starkey
Mrs G. Starling

John Stead
Philip Steadman
Mr and Mrs C.
  Steane
Adrian Stear
Bevis J. Steele
Genine Steele
W. Steer
F.M. Steiner
Mr and Mrs F.M.
  Steiner
R.J. Stephens
Simon Stephenson
L.J. Stephenson
M.V. Sternberg
Dr J. Stevens
Mr and Mrs P.N.
  Stevens
Mr and Mrs A.J.
  Stevens
Mark Stevens
Mr A.R. Stevens
R. Stevenson
John Stevenson
Capt. and Mrs J.S.
  Stewart
Dr R.H.M. Stewart
Catriona Stewart
I.G. Stewart-
  Fergusson
R.J.R. Stickland
Dr Mark Stocker
Mrs I. Stocks
Mrs J. Stockton
Christopher N.
  Stokes
Nicole Stolerman
Inga Stone
Mr and Mrs Stone
Malcolm Stone
Paul K. Stonebridge
C.M.R. Stoneham
Mr J.A.G.
  Stonehouse
C.B. Stones
Stephen Storey
T.L. Storrow
Laura Stout
David Strachan
Mrs P. Straight
Rosemary Stratford
Brian E. Strathie
Peter J. Strong
Hilary and Malcom
  Strong
Mr and Mrs J.
  Stroud
Julia Stuart
I.H. Stuart
Norman J. Stuart
Charles Stuart
S.R. Stubbins

Mrs Peter Stubbs
L.F. Stuckey
Silvio F. Stucklin
Warren Stupple
J.B. Stutter
H. Style
Mrs J.J. Styles
Helen E. Sugarman
Margaret Sugrue
Mr and Mrs C.
  Sultan
V. Summers
Michael Sumner
Mrs J. Sutton
Ms L. Sutton
Hugh Sutton
J.T. Sutton
Graham Sutton
Margaret Swain
R.A. Sweet
B. Swern
Andrew Swift
Brenda Symes
Neil and Kathy
  Symonds
J.W. Symonds
Mr and Mrs K.N.
  Symons
Mr and Mrs C.
  Synes
Dr Marian Tabutean
Mr Patrick Tailyour
Thomas T. Tait
Mr and Mrs P.
  Talbot
Mrs A.J. Talbot
Mr and Mrs J.W.
  Tallant
Mr E.E. Tallis
Ms Z.J. Tanvir
Nick Tarayan
Mr J.A. Tarrant
Mr D.W. Tate
Mrs J.E. Tate
Denis W. Tate
Mrs G.D. Tate
Dr P.F. Tatham
Dr P.H. Tattersall
John Tattersall
Dr D.M. Taub
Jack Taylor
Mr A. Taylor
Elizabeth Taylor
T.W. Taylor
Mrs A.C. Taylor
Mr and Mrs Bryan
  Taylor
Mr and Mrs J.
  Taylor
Mrs L.B. Taylor
Mrs A. Taylor
I. and O. Taylor

Mrs G.M. Taylor
A. Taylor
Kate Taylor
Chris and Anne
  Taylor
A.R. Taylor
Wendy Taylor
J.B.C. Taylor
A. Taylor
Mr C. Taylor
Mr and Mrs A.
  Taylor
Mr and Mrs P.
  Taylor
S. Taylor
Mrs G.J. Taylor
Jean Taylor
J. Teale
P. Teather
P.A. Temperton
Nigel Temple
Mrs G. Terry
Dr S.K. Tewari
Mr J.C. Thackray
Rebecca Thomas
Sophie Thomas
Alan Thomas
Anne Thomas
Mr and Mrs J.S.
  Thomas
Richard Thomas
R.E. Thomas
N.J. Thomas
A.I. Thomas
Fred Thomas
Dr J.S. Thomas
P.R. and D. Thomas
Jane Thomas
Ms M. Thomas
Mrs J.G. Thomas
R.B. Thomas
Dr M. Thomas
P. Thomas
B.G. Thomas
Carole Thomas
Rosemary Thomas-
  Peter
J.A. Thomason
Arthur and Mary
  Thomasson
Jacqueline
  Thompson
Joanne Thompson
H.J. Thompson
Jennifer Thompson
Dr Pat Thompson
Mr and Mrs M.
  Thompson
Ms A. Thompson
Diane Thomson
J.D.V. Thomson

Mrs A.W.B.
  Thomson
J.I. Thorn
Mrs E. Thornber
Mr D. Thornber
Christine
  Thornborrow
Dr S.D. Thornton
Roger Thornton
Dr Basil Thornton
P.A. Thorp
Michael Thrusfield
K. Thurstans
Mr G. Thwaites
P.L. Tikeman
T.J. Tilling
Mr Floyd Timms
Marjorie Tipton
Roberta Tish
Stephany Todd
P.J.M. Tollerson
Michael Tomlinson
Ann Toms
Dr C.M. Tonks
Ms P.A. Topping
Dr C.J. Torrance
Dr M. Townend
Mrs H. Towns
Michael Townson
Mr and Mrs A. Toy
Mr D.G. Toynbee
Mr G. Tragen
Mrs T. Trapani
Mr T. Tratalos
Ian Trelawny
Mrs B.J. Tremain
J.A. Trew
Mr and Mrs Ion
  Trewin
Sarah Tricks
C. and K. Trinder
Gordian Troeller
Mr and Mrs J.C.M.
  Troughton
Dr J.D.G. Troup
S.W. Tubbs
Nicholas Tubbs
Dr Gregory Tuck
Mr P. Tucker
Stephen K.
  Tuckwell
Keith Tudor
Patricia Tulip
Miss Tunstall and
  Mr Sullivan
Dr Simon Turley
L. Turnbull
Adrian Turner
Shirley Turner
David Turner and
  Ms J. Collier
Mr S.G. Turner

Simon Turner
Mr and Mrs G. Turner
R.K. Turner
Clare Turner
Mr and Mrs M. Turner
Mr and Mrs H.G.S. Turner
Mrs C.M. Turner
Stuart Turner
Simon Turner
David J. Turner
Mr B.W.B. Turner
Orren M. Turner
A.J. Turner
Mr J.S. Turpin
David Turvey
Mr R. and Mrs J. Turvil
Helen Tweedie
Stefani Twyford
Andy Tye and Sue Hill
Debbie Tyler
Mr I. Tysh
Gavin Udall
Mrs J. Ufland
M.P. Ullmann
Mr A. Underwood
Adrian Underwood
William Unway
Miss J.P. Urech
R.M. Usher
F.J. Usher
Patricia Valentine
Pamela Vandyke Price
Mr J.M. van Gurp
Nicholas van Zanten
Mr H.B. Vanstone
Stephen Vantreen
Mr D. Vardy
Mr J. Varley
Mr and Mrs K.J. Vaughan
Graham Venables
J.V. Verity
The Hon. Mrs A.M. Viney
Mrs M. Vink
Michael Volans
Mr D.H. Voller
H. Von Der Heyde
Alan Vose
D.C. Voysey
Michael Wace
W.C. Wade
Mr K. Wadsworth
Mrs J. Waggon
Mr P.H. Wainman
Mrs J. Wainwright

Loraine Waites
Mr A.H. Wakefield
A.C. Wale
Adam Walford
Dr P.H. Walker
H. Walker
Mrs G.F. Walker
Mrs D. Walker
Mr and Mrs E. Walker
Mr J.S. Walker
Mr J.D. Walker
Mr M.F. Walker
A.L. Walker
John Walker
Mrs V. Walker-Dendle
G.P. Wall
M. Wall
Dr M.V. Wallbank
Nick Waller and Barbara Gaskell
Mr and Mrs W. Waller
N.J. Wallis
M.A. Wallis
Mr and Mrs G.T. Walmsley
Trevor Walmsley
I.D. and M.F. Walsh
Mr A.J. Walsh
P.K. Walsh
Mrs G. Walthoe
H. Walton
Stuart Walton
Ms J.C. Ward
Pauline Ward
Pat and Tony Ward
Robert Ward
Ralph Ward-Jackson
Mr A.J. Wardrop
Mr and Mrs G. Ware-Owen
Alison Warner
Ruth B. Warner
Alen Warner
Ken Warner
Mrs Warnock
Stephen Warr and Dr Jane Lolley
Mr I. Warren
Pamela Warrington
E.B. and S.A. Warrington
Ian Warrington
G.M. Warrington
Mr R.A. Wartnaby
Mr J.F. Warwick
Eric Warwick
Mr and Mrs Ralph Waterhouse

Mrs P.M. Waterlow
Hazel K. Waters
C. Waters
L. Waters and P. Vanderweele
Mr M. Waterstone
Jenifer Wates
Mrs E. Watkins
W.L.G. Watkins
Robert M. Watkins
J.H. Watkins
Stephen Watson
Richard Watson
Aidan Watt
Mr and Mrs E.K. Watts
Cynthia Watts
Joan E. Way
R.A. Webb
Dr D.E. and Mrs E. Webster
Miss P.M. Webster
Tony Weekes
Al Weil
Mr and Mrs B. Weinreb
Peter Welbourn
Andrew Welch
Mrs J.B. Welch
Ruth Wellesley
Richard and Josephine Wells
Philip and Sarah Wells
Patrick Wellsbury
S. Wentworth
Michelle Werrett
M.J. West
Mr H.G. West
Virginia West
Mrs B.A. West
Mr J.F.M. West
I.E. West
Peggy Westall-Reece
Mr and Mrs Westlake
John Weston
Dr John Weston
Lynn Wetenhall
Susan Wharfe
Mrs J. Whatford
John E. Whatley
Mr G.C. Wheeler
C.M. Wheeler
J. Wheeler
Sacha Whelan
P.J. Whetton
E. Whitaker
S.N. Whitaker
E.H. Whitaker
Ben Whitaker
Dr D.R. Whitbread

Emilie Kate White
Caroline White
Mrs J. White
R.E. White
E. Clifford White
Mr and Mrs R. White
Mr W.G. White
Dr D.M.D. White
Linda White
Mrs V.P. White
Mr and Mrs R. White
N.H. White
Dr J.E.M. Whitehead
Mr and Mrs J.H. Whitehead
Sylvia A. Whitehead
Mrs R. Whitehouse
Jo Whiterod
Mr and Mrs Whiting
Richard O. Whiting
John Whiting
H. Whitney
Paul Whittaker
Pauline Whittaker
R.D. Whittaker
Stephen and Susan Whittle
Mr D.N. Whyte
Mrs R.M. Wickenden
Brian Wicks
B.M. Wicks
John Widdows
Mrs M.N. Wight
Miss A.J. Wilcock
C.B. Wilde
William Wildgoose
Jean Wilding
J. Wiley
Christopher Wilk
Regina C. Wilkinson
Dr R.J. Wilkinson
Anne Wilks
Simon Willbourn
Mr P. Willer
Pamela Williams
E.R. Williams
P.J. and Mrs J.L. Williams
Mrs O.M. Williams
Dr and J.M.W. Williams
Dr S. Williams
R.J. Williams
J.R. Williams
Mrs C. Williams
Mr P.A. Williams
Mr G.L. Williams
Janet Williams

Raymond J. Williams
Kieran Williams
Alan Peter Williams
Rona Williams
N.M. Williamson
J.R. Williamson
Gary Williamson
J.M. Williamson
Alison Williamson
Stephen Williamson
D.H. Williamson
Peter Williamson
Mr and Mrs J. Williamson
Peter Willis
R.V. Willoughby
D.M. Willoughby
A.J.T. Willoughby
Mr and Mrs G.M. Willsher
Kay Willy
Mr amd Mrs John Wilmshurst
A.P. Wilshaw
David F. Wilson
Ian T. Wilson
Janet Wilson
Mr and Mrs E. Wilson
Dr J.D. Wilson
Mr T.M. Wilson
Carol Wilson
Katherine Wilson
Prof. P.N. Wilson
Peter Wilson
Alan Wilson
J.B. Wilson

David G. Wilson
J. Wiltshire
Dr J. Winchester
Colin Wind
J. Winder
J.C. Window
Mr A.J. Wingate
Michael Winner
Mr and Mrs W.M. Winstanley
Dr R. Wise
Oliver and Judy Wiseman
Jean Wiseman
Alan Wiseman
G.M. Wisenfeld
Mr P.J. Witchell
Mr T. Withers and Miss H. Cox
Ruth Witny
Jean Wix
Jonathan J. Wix
Mr and Mrs A. Wolfe
David and Jennie Wolff
David Wolfson
Winnie Wong
David Wong
Mr and Mrs John Wood
Keith Porteous Wood
C.H. Wood
Pam Wood
Mrs M. Wood
Alan Wood
Mr and Mrs A. Wood

Harry Wood
J.M. Wood
William Kirkham Woodcraft
Jennifer Woodfine
Dr F. Peter Woodford
Caroline Woodford
K.W. Woodhall
Miss M.W. Woodhead
J. Woodhouse
Mrs A.D. Woodhouse
Mrs J. Woodman
W.C. Woodruff
Maurice B. Woods and P.M. Woods
Barbara M. Wooldridge
Keith Woolf
Mr C. Workman
Alan Worsdale
Paul Worsley
Sue and Julian Worth
G. Worth
Alvin Worthington
Dr and Mrs T.S. Worthy
Margaret Wragg
Veronica Wray
Judith R. Wren
Mr D.J. Wright
Dr P.W.G. Wright
Christine and Stephen Wright
Albert Wright

Jon Wright
Douglas Wright
Mr G.L. Wright
Mr and Mrs I. Wright
Ken Wright
Penny and Graham Wright
Alan Wright
Peter Wright
G. Wright
Fiona Wright
Steven Wrigley-Howe
David Wurtzel
Gary Wustig
Raymond and Ute Wyatt
Miss S. Wyatt
Richard Wyber
M. Wych
Mr B.D. Yates
Mr and Mrs R. Yates
Mr M. Savage and Ms R. Yeldham
Paul Yeoman
Richard Yorke
B. Youll
Phillip Young
P.T. Young
Miss K.A. Young
Philip Young
Mrs P.I. Young
Mrs L. Young
Paul Zaman
Robert Zara
Peter and Carola Zentner

# Alphabetical list of entries

# LIST OF ENTRIES

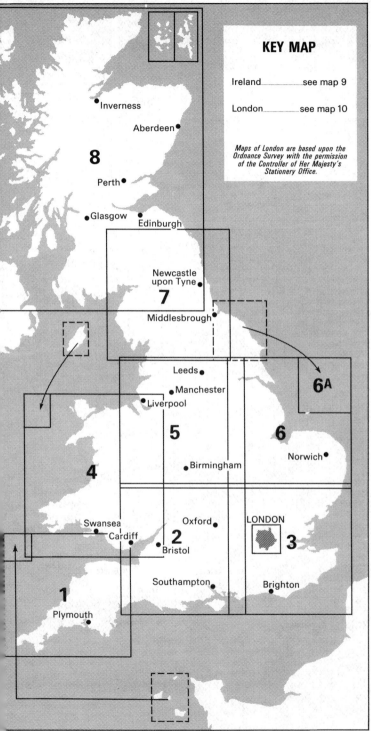

Inverness

Aberdeen

**8**

Perth

Glasgow
Edinburgh

Newcastle
upon Tyne

**7**

Middlesbrough

Leeds

Manchester

Liverpool

**5**

**6ᴬ**

**4**

Birmingham

**6**

Norwich

Swansea
Cardiff

Oxford

**2**

Bristol

LONDON

**3**

**1**

Southampton

Brighton

Plymouth

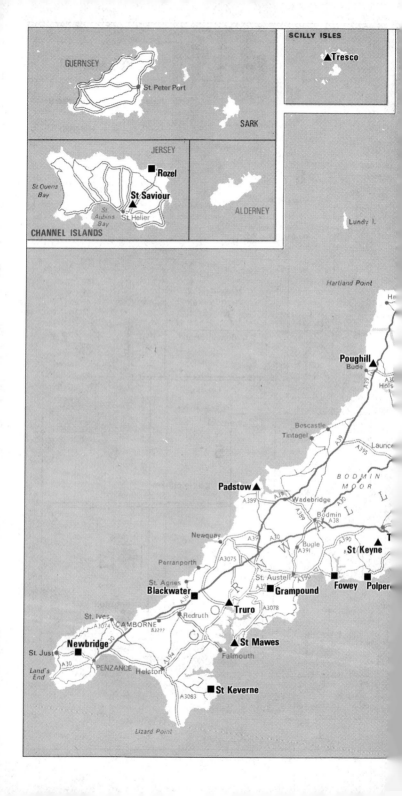

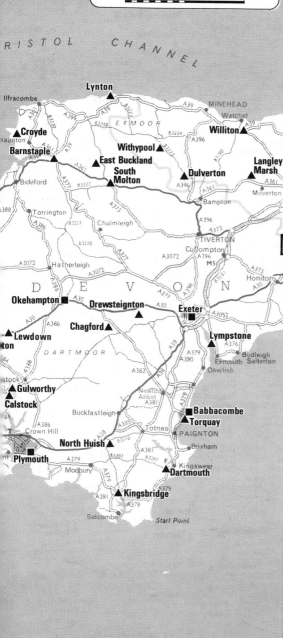

**1**

**DEVON and CORNWALL**

**CHANNEL ISLANDS**

Restaurant

Restaurant with accommodation

0 Miles   10   20

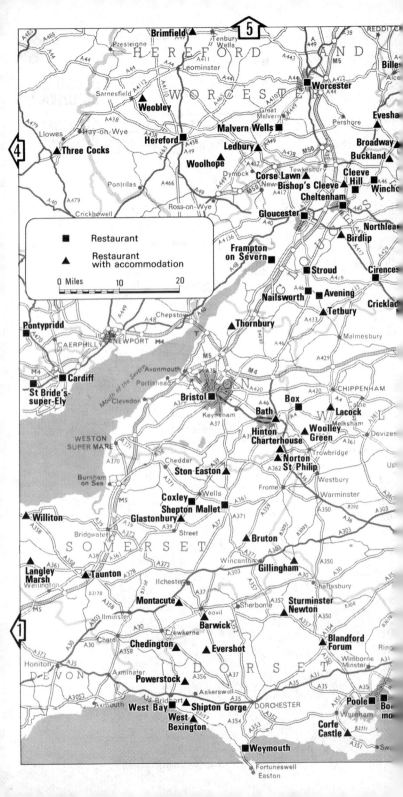

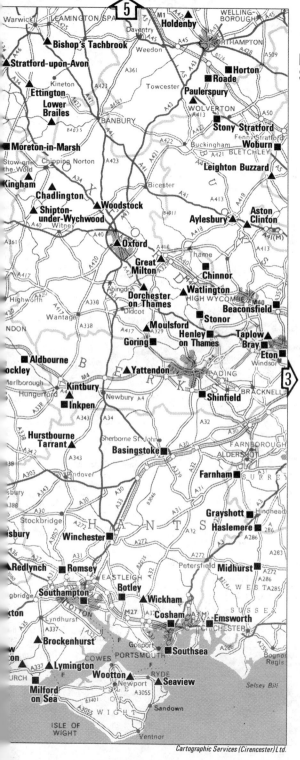

**2**

**ENGLAND:
SOUTH WEST**

Cartographic Services (Cirencester) Ltd.

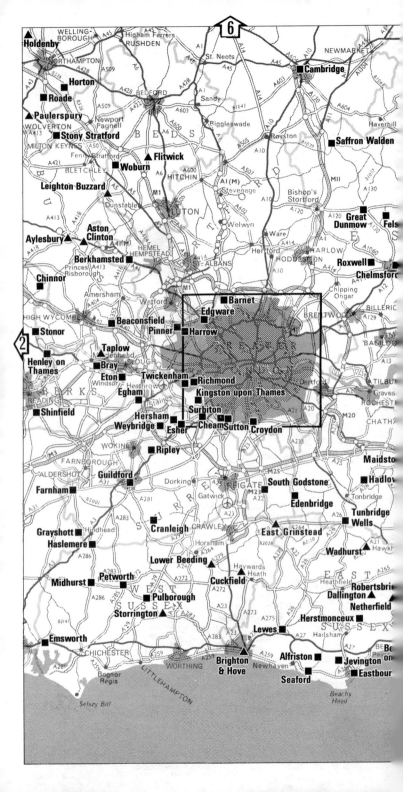

Bury St Edmunds
Saxmundham
Stowmarket
Leiston
Stonham
Aldeburgh
Campsea Ash
enham
Glemsford
Orford
Long Melford
Woodbridge
Orford Ness
Ipswich
Stoke-by-
Nayland
Hintlesham
East
Bergholt
FELIXSTOWE
Dedham
Harwich
Coggeshall
Colchester
The Naze
Walton-on-the-Naze
Frinton
Maldon
CLACTON-ON-SEA
West Mersea
Burnham-on-Crouch
Rochford
Southend-on-Sea
River Thames
SHEERNESS
Leysdown-on-Sea
MARGATE
North Foreland
Herne Bay
Whitstable
Ramsgate
SITTINGBOURNE
Faversham
Canterbury
Sandwich
Chilham
Deal
Barham
Walmer
Hastingleigh
St. Margaret's
at Cliffe
Ashford
DOVER
inghurst
FOLKESTONE
Hythe
STRAIT
Rye
OF DOVER
Lydd
Dungeness
STINGS
onard's

■ Restaurant

▲ Restaurant
with accommodation

0 Miles     10     20

*Cartographic Services (Cirencester) Ltd.*

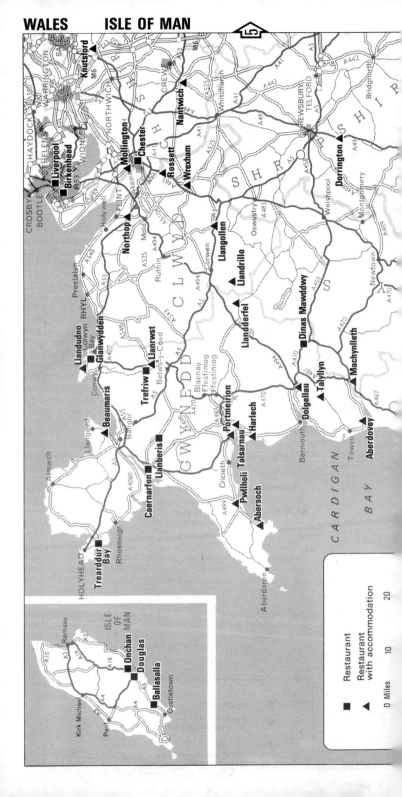

# WALES    ISLE OF MAN

5

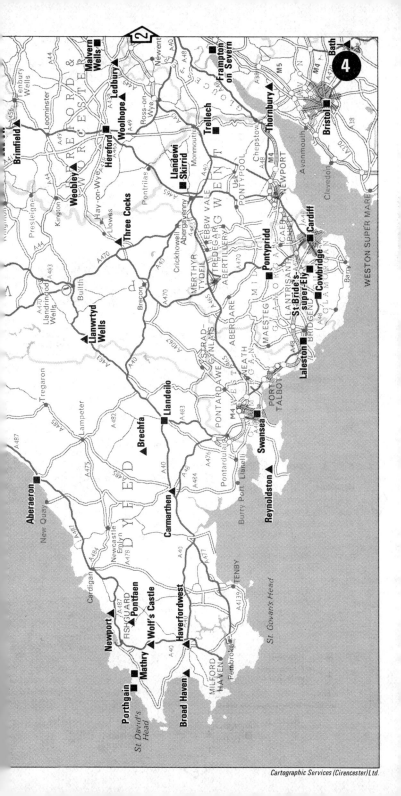

Cartographic Services (Cirencester) Ltd.

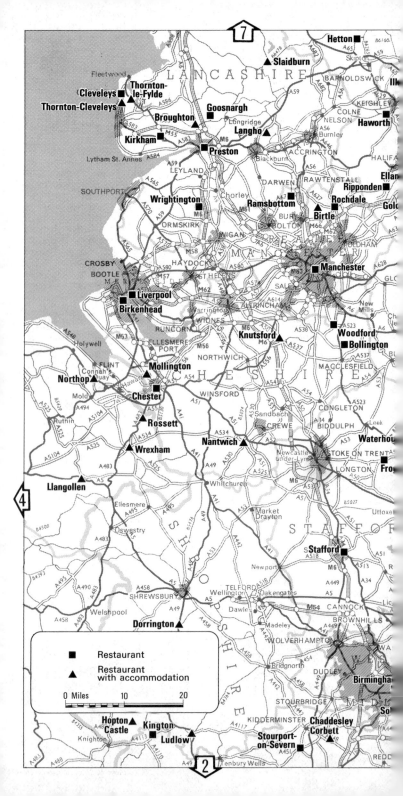

**Restaurant**

**Restaurant with accommodation**

0 Miles 10 20

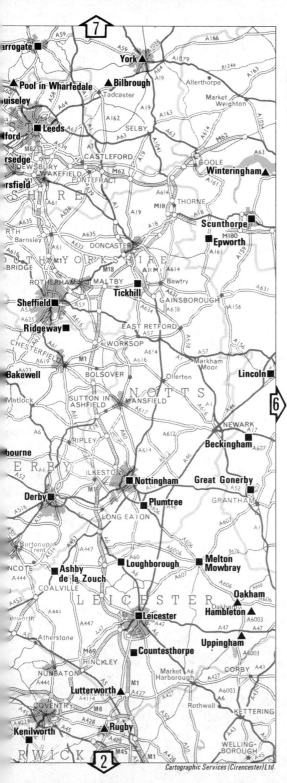

arrogate

York

Pool in Wharfedale

Bilbrough
Tadcaster

uiseley

Allerthorpe

Market Weighton

lford

Leeds

rsedge
DEWSBURY

CASTLEFORD

rsfield

SELBY

GOOLE

Winteringham

THORNE

Scunthorpe

Epworth

Barnsley

DONCASTER

Bawtry

Sheffield

ROTHERHAM  MALTBY

Tickhill

GAINSBOROUGH

Ridgeway

EAST RETFORD

Bakewell

BOLSOVER

WORKSOP

Markham Moor

Lincoln

Matlock

SUTTON IN ASHFIELD

MANSFIELD

Ollerton

bourne

RIPLEY

ILKESTON

NEWARK

Beckingham

Derby

Nottingham

Great Gonerby

Plumtree

GRANTHAM

LONG EATON

Burtonupon Trent

Loughborough

Melton Mowbray

Ashby de la Zouch

COALVILLE

LEICESTER

Oakham

Hambleton

Leicester

Uppingham

Countesthorpe

HINCKLEY

Market Harborough

CORBY

NUNEATON

Lutterworth

KETTERING

Kenilworth

Rugby

WELLING-BOROUGH

RWICK

*Cartographic Services (Cirencester) Ltd.*

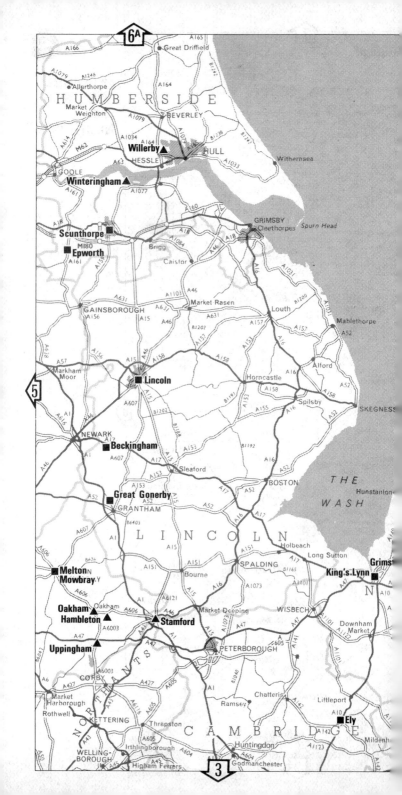

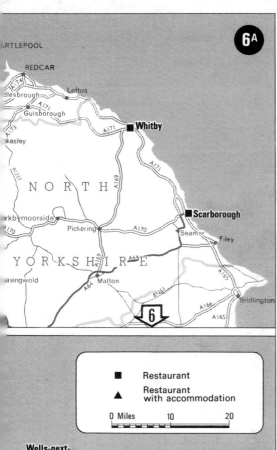

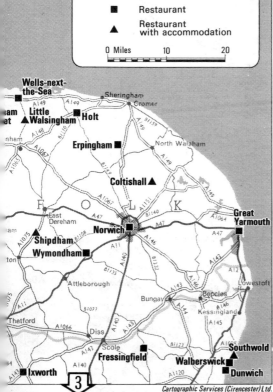

Cartographic Services (Cirencester) Ltd.

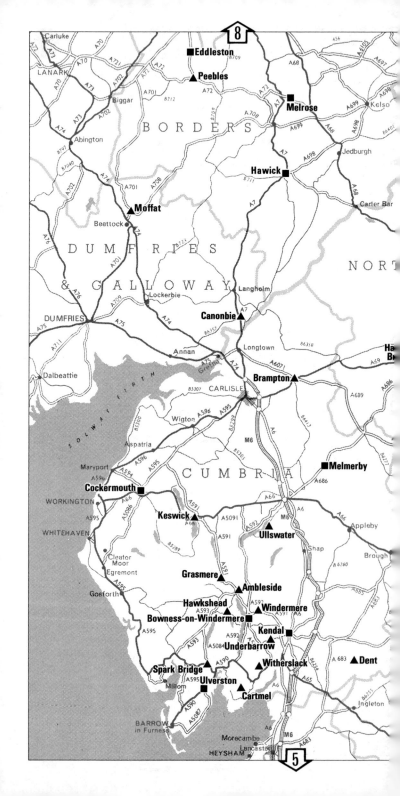

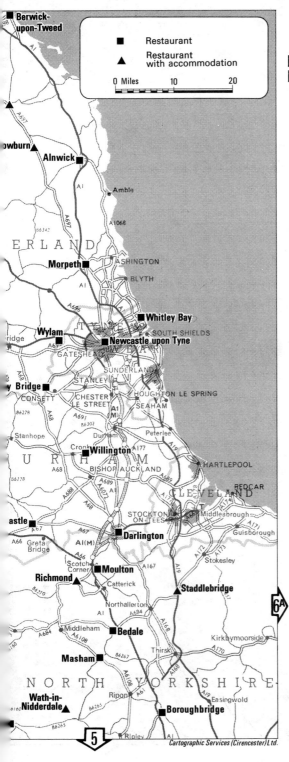

**7**

**ENGLAND: NORTH**

Restaurant

Restaurant with accommodation

0 Miles 10 20

Berwick-upon-Tweed

owburn ▲ Alnwick ■

Amble

A1068

ERLAND

Morpeth ■ ASHINGTON

BLYTH

Whitley Bay ■

Wylam ■ SOUTH SHIELDS

ridge Newcastle upon Tyne ■

GATESHEAD

SUNDERLAND

STANLEY

y Bridge ■ HOUGHTON LE SPRING

CONSETT CHESTER LE STREET

Stanhope SEAHAM

Durham Peterlee

Willington ■

BISHOP AUCKLAND HARTLEPOOL

REDCAR

CLEVELAND

STOCKTON ON TEES Middlesbrough

astle ■ Guisborough

Greta Bridge Darlington ■

Scotch Corner Stokesley

Moulton ■ A167

Richmond ▲ Catterick Staddlebridge ▲

Northallerton

Middleham Kirkbymoorside

Bedale ■ Thirsk

Masham ■

NORTH YORKSHIRE

Ripon Easingwold

Wath-in-Nidderdale ▲

Boroughbridge ■

Ripley

Cartographic Services (Cirencester) Ltd.

# SCOTLAND

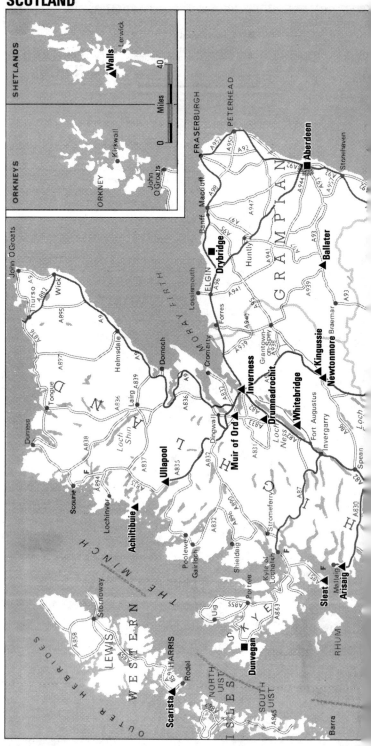

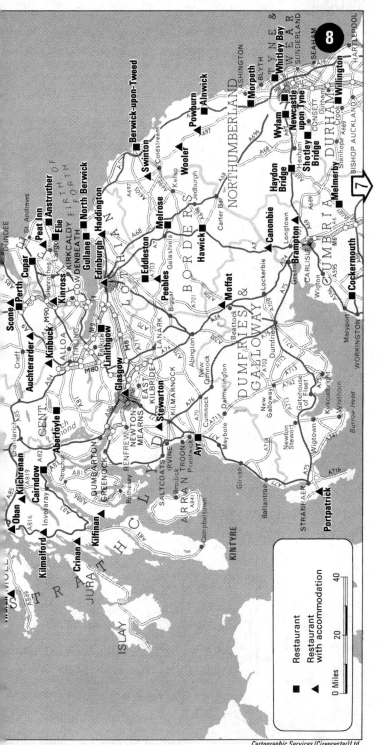

8

7

**Restaurant**

**Restaurant with accommodation**

0 Miles   20   40

Cartographic Services (Cirencester) Ltd.

# IRELAND

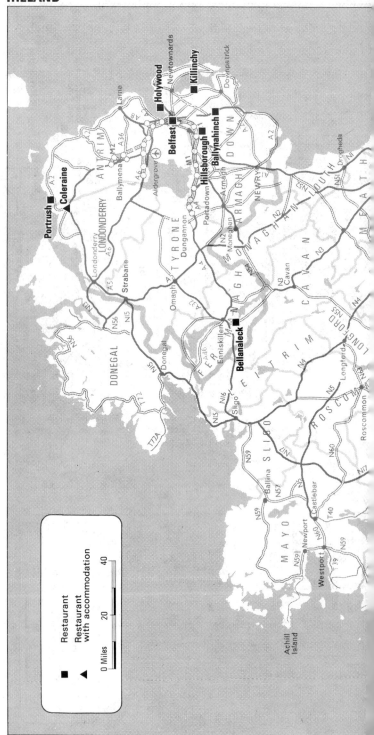

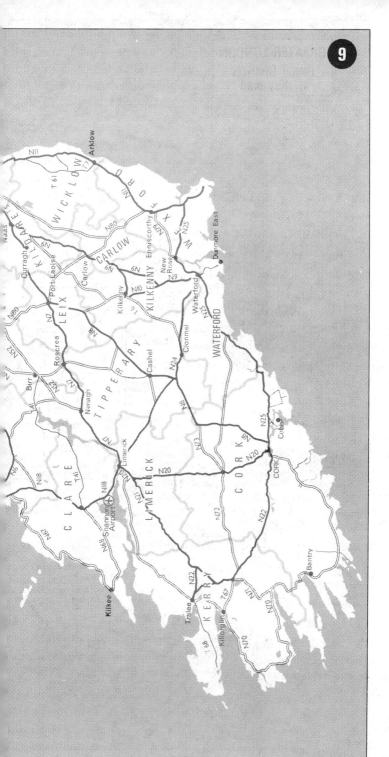

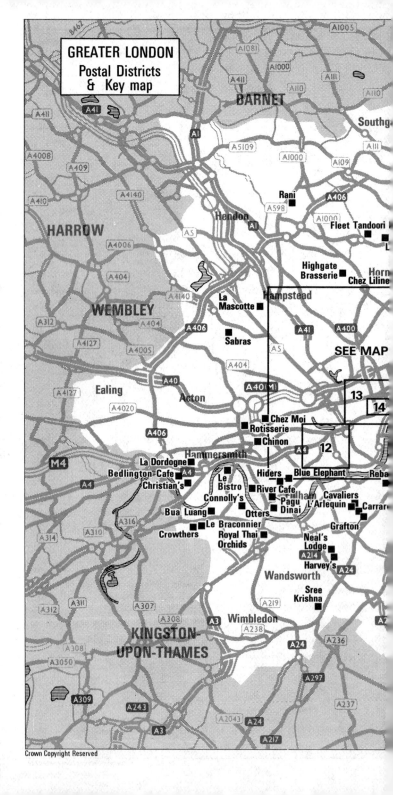

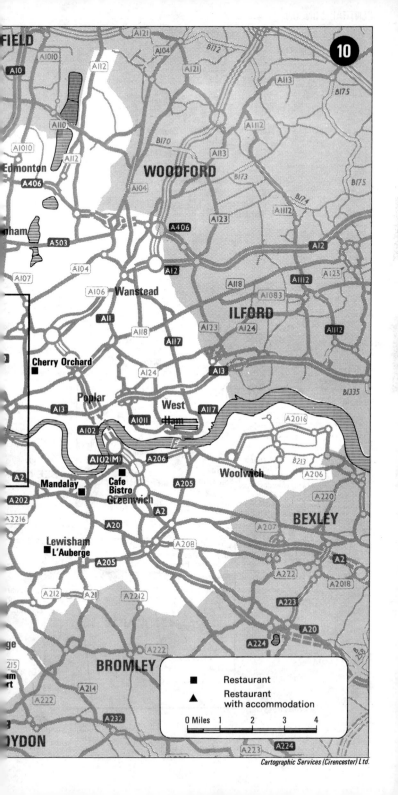

Child's Hill

A·598

Laurent

Fortune Green

Hampstead Heath

HEATH ST.

HIGH ST. POND ST.

FLEET RD.

HIGHGATE

GORDON HO. RD.

Soong Szechuan

Fleet Tandoori

Gospel Oak

FITZJOHNS AV.

Zen W3

Zamoyski's

ROSSLYN HILL

Cafe Flo

MANSFIELD RD.

MALDEN RD.

KENTISH TOWN RD. FORTESS

A502

B510

B511

FINCHLEY

FORTUNE GREEN RD.

MILL LA.

FOOT UP HILL

IVERSON RD.

W. END LA.

B510

B520

B507

HAMPSTEAD

Wakaba

ADELAIDE RD.

CHALK FARM

CAMDEN

Singapore Garden Rest.

Nichol's

Lemonia

Odette's

Primrose Hill

ST.

Nontas

A5

A4003

BRONDESBURY RD.

B451

B413

Kilburn

CAMBRIDGE RD.

414

ABBEY ROAD

BELSIZE

B509

B525

FINCHLEY ROAD A41

AVENUE

ALBERT RD.

Regents Park

PARK WAY

A400

A420I

HAMP

L'Aventure

Maida Vale

AVENUE

ABER CORN PL.

WELLINGTON RD.

Au Bois St. Jean

A52

A41

PARK RD.

A420I

WALTERTON RD.

B414

SHIRLAND

B413

ELGIN

CLIFTON GDNS.

EST. JOHNS WOOD RD.

LISSON GR.

A5205

Sta.

Canal Brasserie

Blue Nile

PADDINGTON

A404

EDGWARE

B507

Martin's

Galicia

A 40 (M)

A40

A5

MARYLEBONE ROAD

A501

ST. MARYLEBO

WESTBOURNE

CHEPSTOW RD.

BISHOPS BR.

PRAED ST.

Garbo's

OXFORD S

Limited

192

Leith's

Dragon Inn

Bayswater

Paddington Sta.

SUSSEX GDNS.

Los Remos

Maroush

SEE MAP

Mayfair

Mandarin Kitchen

Hung Toa

Kalamaras

Le Chef

A40

Hyde Park

PARK LANE

A420

PICCADILLY

Lilly's

NOTTING GATE HILL

PEMBRIDGE

Kensington Place

Boyd's

Clarke's

CHURCH ST.

Kensington Gardens

A4202

WE

Kingfisher Restaurant, Halcyon Hotel

Royal Roof Restaurant, Royal Garden Hotel

KNIGHTSBRIDGE

A4

A302

Auber Prov

KENSINGTON

Mon Petit Plaisir

KENSINGTON RD.

A315

SLOANE ST.

BELGRAVE SQ.

Santini

Mon Petit Plaisir

KENSINGTON HIGH ST.

A315

GLOUCESTER RD.

B325

BROMPTON

B319

EATON

Ciboure

ECCLESTON ST.

Le Maza

Phoenicia

Le Quai St Pierre

CROMWELL RD.

A3218

A308

SEE MAP 12

PIMLICO

NORTH

WARWICK RD.

EARL'S COURT

OLD BROMPTON RD.

Lou Pescadou

CHELSEA

SYDNEY ST.

B304

CHELSEA RD.

GROS

La Croisette

LILLIE RD.

A3218

B317

FULHAM RD.

Left Bank

A3217

CHEYNE

OAKLEY ST.

A3212

CHELSEA

A3216

B317

ROAD

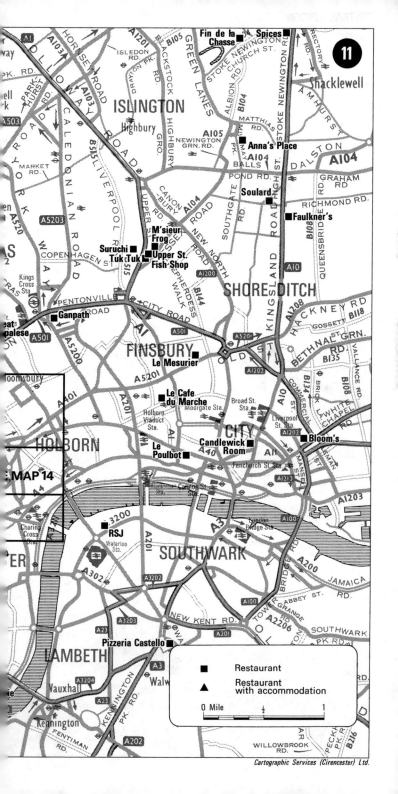

CENTRAL LONDON : South-West

Restaurant
Restaurant with accommodation

0 Mile    ¼

Crown Copyright Reserved

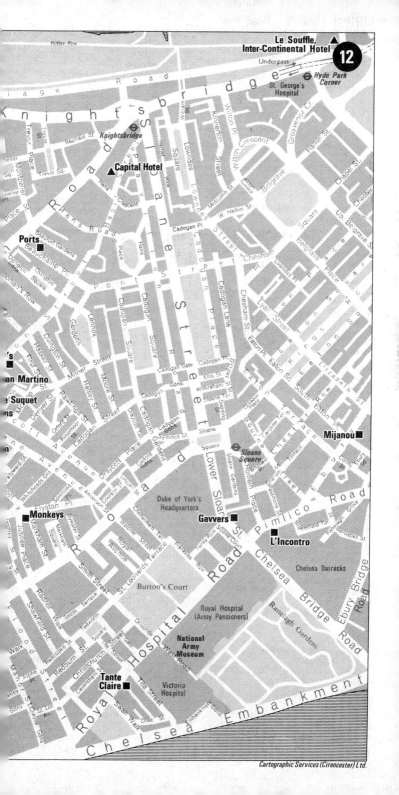

# CENTRAL LONDON : West End

Madame Tussaud's Exhibition

Royal Academy of Music

Regent's Park

Ninjin

Lal

Post Office Tower

Langan's Bistro

Rag

Guernica

Topkapi

Efes Kebab House

Nanten Yakitori Bar

Stephen Bull

Broadcasting House

All Souls Church

Wigmore Hall

Chez Nico

Jason's Court

Oxford Circus

Bond Street

Pizzeria Condotti

Le Gavroche

Connaught Hotel

Ninety Park Lane

Royal Academy of Arts

Wiltons

Zen Central

Langan's Brasserie

Miyama

Le Caprice

Al Hamra

Suntor

Dukes Hotel

Four Seasons, Inn on the Park

GREEN PARK

Crown Copyright Reserved

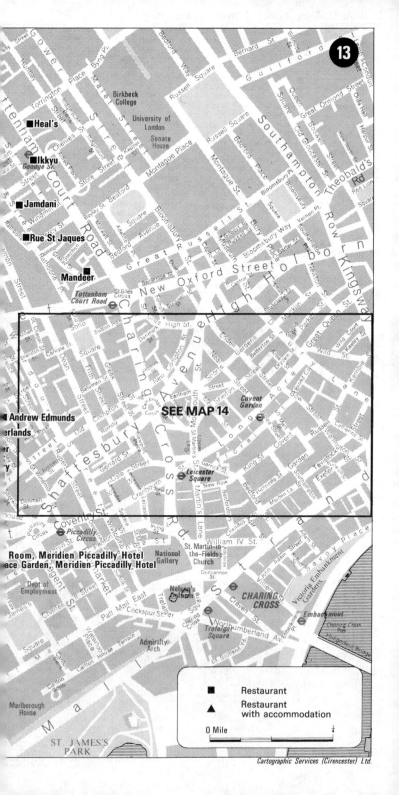

**13**

Birkbeck College

University of London

Senate House

■ **Heal's**

■ **Ikkyu**
*Goodge St.*

■ **Jamdani**

■ **Rue St Jaques**

**Mandeer**

*Tottenham Court Road*

New Oxford Street

**SEE MAP 14**

*Covent Garden*

◄ **Andrew Edmunds**

**erlands**

*Leicester Square*

*Piccadilly Circus*

**Room, Meridien Piccadilly Hotel**
**ace Garden, Meridien Piccadilly Hotel**

National Gallery

St. Martin-in-the-fields Church

Dept of Employment

Nelson's Column

*CHARING CROSS*

Victoria Embankment Gardens

Pall Mall East

Cockspur St.

Trafalgar Square

*Embankment*

*Charing Cross*

*Charing Cross Pier*

Admiralty Arch

Marlborough House

ST. JAMES'S PARK

| | |
|---|---|
| ■ | Restaurant |
| ▲ | Restaurant with accommodation |

0 Mile     ¼

*Cartographic Services (Cirencester) Ltd.*

**14**

Orso

Boulestin

Magno's

Neal Street
Restaurant

Mon
Plaisir

Inigo Jones

Beotys

Good Food

Cork and
Bottle

Ming   New World

China China

Fung Shing

Poon's

La Bastide

Gay Hussar

Frith's   Bahn
Thai

Burt's

Chuen-
Cheng-Ku

Wong Kei

Red Fort
Gopal's of Soho   Alastair Little
Chiang Mai

Si Chuen

Dragon's Nest

Melati

■ Restaurant
▲ Restaurant
   with accommodation

0 yards     110      220

Cartographic Services (Cirencest

# Report Form

To the Editor *The Good Food Guide*
FREEPOST, 2 Marylebone Road, London NW1 1YN

From my personal experience the following establishment
should/should not be included in the *Guide*.

_____

_____

Telephone_____

I had lunch/dinner/stayed there on _____ 19___

I would rate this establishment _____ out of five.

*please continue overleaf*

My meal for ____ people cost £ _____ *attach bill where possible*

☐ Please tick if you would like more report forms

I am not connected in any way with management or proprietors.
Name and address (BLOCK CAPITALS)

_____

_____

Signed _____

To the Editor *The Good Food Guide*
FREEPOST, 2 Marylebone Road, London NW1 1YN

From my personal experience the following establishment
should/should not be included in the *Guide*.

_____

_____

Telephone_____

I had lunch/dinner/stayed there on _____ 19____

I would rate this establishment _____ out of five.

*please continue overleaf*

My meal for ____ people cost £ _____ *attach bill where possible*

☐ Please tick if you would like more report forms

I am not connected in any way with management or proprietors.
Name and address (BLOCK CAPITALS )

_____

_____

Signed _____

To the Editor *The Good Food Guide*
FREEPOST, 2 Marylebone Road, London NW1 1YN

From my personal experience the following establishment
should/should not be included in the *Guide*.

_____

_____

                                        Telephone_____

I had lunch/dinner/stayed there on _____ 19____

I would rate this establishment _____ out of five.

*please continue overleaf*

My meal for ____ people cost £ _____ *attach bill where possible*

☐ Please tick if you would like more report forms

I am not connected in any way with management or proprietors.
Name and address (BLOCK CAPITALS )

_____

_____

Signed _____

To the Editor *The Good Food Guide*
FREEPOST, 2 Marylebone Road, London NW1 1YN

From my personal experience the following establishment
should/should not be included in the *Guide*.

_____

_____

Telephone_____

I had lunch/dinner/stayed there on _____ 19___

I would rate this establishment _____ out of five.

*please continue overleaf*

My meal for ____ people cost £ _____ *attach bill where possible*

☐ Please tick if you would like more report forms

I am not connected in any way with management or proprietors.
Name and address (BLOCK CAPITALS )

_____

_____

Signed _____

# Report Form

To the Editor *The Good Food Guide*
FREEPOST, 2 Marylebone Road, London NW1 1YN

From my personal experience the following establishment
should/should not be included in the *Guide*.

_____

_____

Telephone_____

I had lunch/dinner/stayed there on _____ 19____

I would rate this establishment _____ out of five.

*please continue overleaf*

My meal for ____ people cost £ _____ *attach bill where possible*

☐ Please tick if you would like more report forms

I am not connected in any way with management or proprietors.
Name and address (BLOCK CAPITALS )

_____

_____

Signed _____

# Report Form                                          90

To the Editor *The Good Food Guide*
FREEPOST, 2 Marylebone Road, London NW1 1YN

From my personal experience the following establishment
should/should not be included in the *Guide*.

_____

_____

Telephone_____

I had lunch/dinner/stayed there on  _____ 19____

I would rate this establishment _____ out of five.

*please continue overleaf*

My meal for _____ people cost £ _____ *attach bill where possible*

☐ Please tick if you would like more report forms

I am not connected in any way with management or proprietors.
Name and address (BLOCK CAPITALS )

_____

_____

Signed _____

# Report Form

To the Editor *The Good Food Guide*
FREEPOST, 2 Marylebone Road, London NW1 1YN

From my personal experience the following establishment
should/should not be included in the *Guide*.

_____

_____

Telephone_____

I had lunch/dinner/stayed there on _____ 19___

I would rate this establishment _____ out of five.

*please continue overleaf*

My meal for ____ people cost £ _____ *attach bill where possible*

☐ Please tick if you would like more report forms

I am not connected in any way with management or proprietors.
Name and address (BLOCK CAPITALS )

_____

_____

Signed _____